THE **NEW** ESSENTIAL
CHRONOLOGY

Text by Daniel Wallace, with Kevin J. Anderson
Illustrations by Mark Chiarello, Tommy Lee Edwards and
John Van Fleet

STAR WARS
THE **NEW** ESSENTIAL GUIDE TO
DROIDS

Text by Daniel Wallace
Illustrations by Ian Fullwood

STAR WARS
THE **NEW** ESSENTIAL GUIDE TO
ALIEN SPECIES

Text by Ann Margaret Lewis and Helen Keier
Illustrations by Chris Trevas and William O'Connor

LUCAS BOOKS

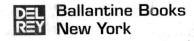
DEL REY Ballantine Books
New York

A Del Rey Book
Publish by the Random House Publishing Group

Originally published in three volumes as:
  Star Wars: The New Essential Chronology,
  Copyright © 2005 by Lucasfilm LTD & ® or ™ where indicated.
  All Rights Reserved. Used Under Authorization.
  Frontispiece art by Tommy Lee Edwards.
  Galaxy map created by Ian Fullwood.
  Interior design by Michaelis/Carpelis Design Associates Inc.

  Star Wars: The New Essential Guide to Droids,
  Copyright © by 2006 by Lucasfilm LTD & ® or ™ where indicated.
  All Rights Reserved. Used Under Authorization.
  Interior design by Michaelis/Carpelis Design Associates Inc.

  Star Wars: The New Essential Guide to Alien Species,
  Copyright © 2006 by Lucasfilm LTD & ® or ™ where indicated.
  All Rights Reserved. Used Under Authorization.
  Interior design by Foltz Design.

All rights reserved under International and Pan-American Copyright Conventions. Published in the United States by Del Rey Books, an imprint of the Random House Publishing Group, a division of Random House, Inc., New York.

Del Rey is a registered trademark and the Del Rey colophon is a trademark of Random House, Inc.
www.starwars.com
www.delreydigital.com

Library of Congress information available upon request.

ISBN 978-0-307-29212-4

Manufactured in China
9 8 7 6 5 4 3 2 1

The New Essential Chronology

STAR WARS®

The New Essential Chronology

TEXT BY DANIEL WALLACE
(WITH KEVIN J. ANDERSON)

ILLUSTRATIONS BY
MARK CHIARELLO
TOMMY LEE EDWARDS
JOHN VAN FLEET

LUCAS BOOKS

DEL REY

BALLANTINE BOOKS
NEW YORK

DANIEL WALLACE
To Grant

JOHN VAN FLEET
To Grace and Mae

TOMMY LEE EDWARDS
This one's for Iain Morris

MARK CHIARELLO
To John Van Fleet, my brother

Author's Acknowledgments

This book would not have been possible without the input and inspiration provided by others. Thanks to Steve Saffel, Keith Clayton, Erich Schoeneweiss, Colette Russen, Sylvain Michaelis, and Colleen Lindsay at Del Rey; Amy Gary, Jonathan Rinzler, Sue Rostoni, Leland Chee, and Pablo Hidalgo at Lucasfilm; Tommy Lee Edwards, Mark Chiarello, John Van Fleet, and Ian Fullwood for their amazing illustrations; and Jim Luceno, Haden Blackman, Abel Peña, Enrique Guerro, Jason Fry, Christopher McElroy, Michael Potts, and Bob Vitas for their advice and for the Star Wars resources they have written.

Finally, thanks to George Lucas for creating this universe, and for ending the movie saga in style with Revenge of the Sith. Lucas's imagination provided the backdrop for the other authors whose work is summarized in this volume, demonstrating that the *Star Wars* storytelling galaxy is a dynamic and welcoming place.

Contents

Introduction to Students of History

History survives only if it is recorded. This was true when Palpatine's Empire purged thousands of years of records from the galactic archives, and it is even more important today, in the wake of the Yuuzhan Vong invasion that saw the destruction of the great library of Obroa-skai. More than ever, it is vital that historians assemble a formal account for future generations.

Fortunately, new data caches have been uncovered since the HoloNet rel ease of the first edition of this chronicle. Holes have been plugged and gaps filled in as untold information on the Clone Wars, the extermination of the Jedi, and the nature of the ancient Republic has come to light. Often we have interviewed surviving eyewitnesses to history to gain a personal perspective on galactic events. And, of course, the recent events of the Yuuzhan Vong war and its aftermath have been recorded while the wounds are still fresh.

The resulting chronicle covers more than thirty millennia of history, from the Rakatan Infinite Empire to the rise of the Jedi Knights; from the Sith War to the Clone Wars; from the death of the Republic to the birth of the new Jedi order.

In this, the thirty-sixth year since the destruction of the first Death Star that marks our calendar's zero point, it is even more apparent that we study the rich and glorious tradition of our past, and also remember the many dark mistakes. We must learn from both.

Voren Na'al, Archivist Emeritus
Historical Council, Galactic Federation of Free Alliances

A NOTE ON DATING CONVENTIONS

The years in this document are marked according to the new standard convention, which uses the Battle of Yavin as its zero point. This event, which saw the destruction of the first Death Star and the dawning of a new hope for the people of the galaxy, represents the symbolic beginning of our current society. Events that precede this event are indicated B.B.Y., while those after are noted as A.B.Y.

For an extensive list of historical resources visit www.starwars.com.

The New Essential Chronology

PART ONE

Tales of the Ancient Republic

FORMATION OF THE REPUBLIC

THE PRE-REPUBLIC ERA
CIRCA 100,000–25,000 B.B.Y

Before its transformation into the Empire, the Old Republic stood for twenty-five thousand years. Its citizens liked to entertain the illusion that theirs was the only such civilization that had ever existed, but archaeologists have confirmed that this is certainly not true. Few details of the great powers of the pre-Republic era have survived, but what is known about the rise and fall of these societies provides us with the object lesson that no culture lives forever.

One of the earliest and most potent cultures can be identified only by the colossal objects it left behind. At some point that cannot be positively identified, these mysterious Architects created the Corellian Star system, tractoring its five planets into place around the star Corell, using the repulsorlift engine Centerpoint Station. The Architects may also have been responsible for the Maw, an unlikely cluster of black holes located near Kessel, and are believed to have frightened the advanced Sharu people of the Rafa system into adopting a forced culture of primitivism. The Architects populated the planets of the Corellian system with Dralls and Selonians, as well as humans—an ambitious species believed to have originated on the Core world of Coruscant.

Coruscant's humans may have come into dominance on their homeworld by defeating a near-human, gray-skinned species known as the Taungs in several series of legendary battles. The humans, who comprised the thirteen nations of the Battalions of Zhell, suffered an almost extinction-level defeat when a sudden volcanic eruption smothered their encampment. The towering plume of black ash loomed over the Taung army for two years, and the awed Taungs took the name Warriors of the Shadow—or, in the ancient tongue, *Dha Werda Verda*. The Battalions of Zhell recovered and claimed Coruscant for their own, while the Taungs may have become the Mandalorians, judging from what we have learned concerning similarities between the Mandalorian language and surviving Taung texts.

In the galactic Core, the big-brained Columi species achieved interstellar spaceflight approximately one hundred thousand years ago, and surveyed the "primitive" people of Coruscant and Duro before returning to a sheltered life on their homeworld of Columus. In the Outer Rim, the Gree civilization flourished, creating strange marvels of alien technology that have never been duplicated. The Gree reached their apex during the same era as the Columi, but modern Gree have been reduced to mere caretakers of decaying wonders. In opposition to the Gree empire, the reptilian Kwa constructed Infinity Gates, which allowed them to teleport between worlds. Unknown factors led to the decline of the Kwa, and their descendants eventually became the simpleminded Kwi lizards of Dathomir.

Approximately thirty thousand years B.B.Y., a species known as the Rakata achieved the highest extent of their own expansion. The Rakatan "Infinite Empire" stretched between worlds as far removed as Dantooine and Honoghr, but numbered few planets in total. The Rakatans used the

The Rakata urge their slaves to complete work on the Star Forge.
[ART BY TOMMY LEE EDWARDS]

Force to power much of their technology, and employed starship engines that allowed them to tunnel through hyperspace and reach other planets with Force-strong signatures. Some of the artifacts that the Rakata left on the worlds they visited triggered strange aftereffects, such as the stimulation of rampant plant and animal growth on Kashyyyk.

The Rakatans eventually became arrogant in their power. They forced entire populations of conquered worlds into slavery, including the Duros, the humans of Coruscant, and the trispecies mix of the Corellian system. Soon they had built a monument to their glory—the Star Forge, a living satellite that could build anything its creators desired using raw stellar material. The Star Forge fed off the aggression of its Rakata builders, amplifying the dark side in the vicinity of Rakata Prime and setting the species up for tragedy.

Three primary factors led to the implosion of the Infinite Empire, which occurred approximately 25,200 B.B.Y. A plague that affected only the Rakata spread to every corner of the kingdom, killing billions. The slaves, suddenly presented with an ideal opportunity, rose up and broke the Rakatan hold on the colonies. Finally, an apparent mutation of the plague virus stripped the surviving Rakatans of the ability to use the Force. Rakata Prime fell into civil war, then devolved into barbarism as its inhabitants forgot how to operate their technology. In orbit overhead, the mighty Star Forge sat empty.

No longer held under the yoke of the Rakatans, progress on Coruscant continued apace. The planet had birthed billions of humans, but so far its citizens had been unsuccessful in their bid to reach the stars. Limited to a single world, they dried up their planet's resources through generations of overuse. By the time the first "sleeper ships" (suspended animation vessels that took centuries to reach distant stars) came into use, impenetrable industry had choked every landmass and wreathed the planet in smoke and steam.

Aboard sleeper ships, Coruscant colonists spread to neighboring worlds such as Alsakan, Metellos, and Axum. On Alderaan (circa 27,500 B.B.Y.), another group of settlers discovered the empty spires of a vanished insectoid species, the Killiks, but nevertheless claimed the world for their own.

Improvements in hyperspatial theory led to the development of hyperspace cannons. Starships launched into hyperspace by a cannon could then induce a drag element and drop back into realspace, but needed a second hyperspace cannon to return to their origin point. A cannon network was developed to link the Core Worlds with the spacefaring Duros civilization.

Their experience with the Rakata had one positive effect on the people of the Core. Scientists on Corellia and Duro launched independent investigations into the Rakatan hyperdrive. If they could duplicate the technology, the Core would no longer consist of stagnant outposts separated by distance and expense.

First, however, the galaxy had to contend with Xim. Out in the Rim area now known as the Tion Cluster, a new power had arisen over the centuries, composed of alien castoffs and the human descendants of an ancient Core Worlds colony ship. Their hyperdrives fused bits of Rakatan technology with fixed-position hyperspace beacons, allowing for travel within a defined area but presenting potentially fatal dangers if they ventured outside the "lighthouse network." The Tionese, who had not yet discovered the length of the Perlemian superhighway hyperlane, remained isolated from the Core Worlds, but occasionally ran up against the sprawling borders of the young Hutt empire.

Xim, the "pirate prince," greatly expanded Tion space by raiding planets and enlisting governors to manage the new territory. Xim's father, himself a bloodthirsty raider, had carved out a corner of the Tion into the Kingdom of Cron during the Cronese sweeps a generation before. Xim soon came to be known as "the Despot." He plundered uncountable treasures from his father's holdings and housed them in a voluminous facility on Dellalt.

In the twenty-fifth year of Xim's rule, the Hutt empire demolished one of his fleets at Vontor in the Si'klaata Cluster. Two more battles followed, but by that point the Hutts had forged the Treaty of Vontor, which bound the Klatooinians, Vodrans, and Nikto to them as permanent slaves. In the Third Battle of Vontor (circa 25,100 B.B.Y.), the Hutt-allied conscripts vanquished Xim's war droids. Kossak the Hutt declared victory, and Xim died in shame as a prisoner in Kossak's dungeon. The Tion Cluster split into competing states.

The Republic Begins
25,000 B.B.Y.

At approximately twenty-five millennia before the current era, Corellian scientists succeeded in "perfecting" the Rakatan hyperdrive by implementing technology-based workarounds for the Force-attuned components. Starships could now travel among Corellia, Coruscant, Alderaan, and Duro in only a few days. The worlds of the Core linked themselves in a democratic union called the Galactic Republic, then tested their newfound freedom by exploring the uncharted expanses of hyperspace. The discovery of the Perlemian Trade Route linked Coruscant with distant Ossus, and the Jedi became the Republic's guardians.

Little is known of the genesis of the Jedi. The study of the Force—and the science behind the microscopic midichlorians that act as symbiotic Force carriers in most living things—had previously been practiced by the paladins of the Chatos Academy, the Followers of Palawa, and the mystic order of Dai Bendu, on planets as diverse as Had Abbadon and Ondos. The specific tenets of the Jedi Order, however, are believed to have been set down on the dawn world of Tython where many Force-users harnessed a positive energy called the Ashla. Those who hungered to wield the Force for personal power dragged the planet into an exhausting conflict known as the Force Wars. From the ashes of this conflict, the Force users of Tython established the Jedi as a society of monastic warriors who obeyed the precepts of harmony, knowledge, serenity, and peace. Traditions of the Tython Jedi included a "Jedi Forge" initiation ceremony, in which hopeful members of the order channeled Force energy into metal-bladed swords, honing the weapons to a supernatural degree of sharpness and strength. In time, the Jedi of Tython would face threats from beyond their world. Using advanced offworld technology, the Jedi forges were able to "freeze" a laser beam, resulting in a weapon that would eventually become the lightsaber. Taking it upon themselves to liberate other worlds from oppression, a proactive faction of Tython Jedi decided to go out into the galaxy. These warriors became known as the Jedi Knights.

In time, a school of Jedi philosophy took root on the planet Ossus. The Force came to be understood according to the "dark side" and "light side" alignments, both reflecting aspects of the living Force (the in-the-moment manifestation of life energy) and the unifying Force (the cosmic expression of prophecies and destinies). The Jedi faced their first true test since the Force Wars when followers of the Force's dark side (known in Tython lore as the Bogan) formed the Legions of Lettow and made war against the young Order.

The Jedi emerged victorious. Xendor, a general of the Lettow legions, lost his life to the Jedi, but his lover, Arden Lyn, fell into a mystic sleep, not to be broken until the time of the Empire. The war between the Jedi and the Legions of Lettow marked the first of many Great Schisms between the light and dark sides of the Force.

Soon, scouts had blazed a portion of the Corellian Run hyperlane, and the wedge defined by the Corellian Run and the Perlemian Trade Route became known as "the Slice." Since hyperspace, particularly the stretch to the galactic west of Coruscant, was anomaly-riddled and impassable to Republic technology, galactic expansion radiated eastward to fill in the Slice's pie wedge. The Core Worlds' tip of the Slice was dubbed the Arrowhead, and soon colony ships had uncovered habitable worlds farther out, establishing the Colonies region. Ossus and other outposts were considered Wild Space, and the vast majority of the galaxy bore the label Unknown Regions. Duro established settlements on Neimoidia and elsewhere, while the Jedi conferred with the gentle people of Caamas over the proper use of power.

While the Republic percolated in the Core and Colonies, Ossus became a fortress world—standing as a bulwark against the crumbling Tion and Hutt space and preventing the Perlemian from becoming an invasion corridor. With its enemies at bay, the Republic grew for a millennium, faster than Coruscant would have desired, mostly due to independent states that petitioned for membership in an effort to protect themselves from the Hutts.

GROWING PAINS
24,000–7000 B.B.Y.

Approximately twenty-four thousand years B.B.Y., war broke out between the Republic and the Tion. Armadas streamed up and down the Perlemian, exchanging volleys of pressure bombs on the respective capitals of Coruscant and Desevro. The Republic claimed victory when its agents stirred up trouble in Hutt space and steered the angry Hutts in the direction of their old foes in the Tion. Within a century, most of the Tion Cluster swore allegiance to Coruscant.

The borders of the Republic steadily expanded over the millennia but sometimes seemed to defy logic, incorporating odd juts, asymmetrical lumps, and lonely outposts surrounded by light-years of unexplored space. This was a function of hyperspace. Clear and stable paths through hyperspace, known as hyperroutes or hyperlanes, became the bedrock of travel, communication, and commerce, but trailblazing such paths was difficult. The Slice remained the heart of navigable territory as the Republic expanded radially toward galactic east. Gradually the Republic began to bleed past the northern and southern borders of the Slice, but most of the galaxy remained unknown, save for isolated outposts in the wilds such as Ord Mantell (established 12,000 B.B.Y.) and Malastare (established 8000 B.B.Y.).

The space due west of Coruscant resisted exploration. No analogues to the Perlemian or Corellian Run were discovered in that direction, and progress was limited to treacherous one- or two-light-year hops into a briar-patch stretch of hyperspace anomalies.

Coruscant, as the heart of the Republic, bore the coordinates 0–0–0 on hyperspace maps, where the first digit represented west–east, the second north–south, and the third up–down. Due to the unbalanced geography of early colonization, almost all colonized planets had a positive first digit, which they considered a mark of pride. Apart from the Republic, galactic colonization occurred among the Taung exiles, who settled a world that they named Mandalore, in honor of their leader Mandalore the First. Mandalore's warriors slaughtered the planet's mammoth Mythosaurs, modifying the creatures' skeletons into haunting cities of bone.

The Republic's Great Manifest period (20,000–17,000 B.B.Y.) marked an increased movement into the Rimward territories of the Slice, which became known as the Expansion Region. The Republic's boom collapsed due to internal scuffling, as the planet Alsakan attempted to usurp Coruscant as the rightful galactic capital. Dueling economic and political volleys eventually led to both sides firing shots. Though falling short of civil war—most fighting occurred between Coruscant's and Alsakan's holdings in the Expansion Region—Alsakan could not be brought fully to heel. Seventeen uprisings, collectively called the Alsakan Conflicts, would occur between 17,000 and 3000 B.B.Y.

While the Republic busied itself with the first Alsakan Conflict, the geneticists of Arkania began what would be the first of many experiments on sentient populations. They took a sampling of six-armed Xexto from their homeworld of Troiken and changed them into a new species, the Quermians, on another world.

At 15,500 B.B.Y., Rim scouts made contact with the Duinuogwuin, a species commonly known as Star Dragons. Not surprisingly, the scouts reacted with fear at the sight of fifty-meter creatures that soared through space breathing atomic fire. After a disastrous first encounter, hundreds of Duinuogwuin followed the scout ships back to Coruscant and waged war against the capital. Supreme Chancellor Fillorean brought an end to the Duinuogwuin Contention by forging a peace with Star Dragon philosopher Borz'Mat'oh. In the aftermath, the two helped found the University of Coruscant.

By this time, the Jedi had developed their signature lightsabers, but the weapons were unstable and power-hungry. Able to be operated for only short periods before overheating, lightsabers of this era often were simply ceremonial.

During the Pius Dea period (12,000–11,000 B.B.Y.), the Republic came under the influence of a theocratic sect. Over the next several centuries, Supreme Chancellor Contispex and his descendants sanctioned a number of crusades against rival alien sects. The fallout from this deepened tensions between the Core and the Rim that would ultimately be exploited during the Rise of the Empire era.

The Rianitus period (9000–8000 B.B.Y.) is notable for the 275-year reign of Blotus the Hutt, who defied traditional Hutt stereotypes by becoming one of the most distinguished personages to ever hold the chancellor's office.

EMERGENCE OF THE SITH

THE HUNDRED-YEAR DARKNESS
7000 B.B.Y.

The next Great Schism between the light and dark sides of the Force occurred approximately 7000 B.B.Y. By this time lightsabers had become more robust, although each required the use of a plug-in power pack attached to the user's belt. Among the Jedi Order, a cadre of dark-siders made a significant discovery—Force of sufficient intensity could bend life itself. They pioneered the twisted science of dark side mutations, and the century-long war that followed is known as the Hundred-Year Darkness.

The exiled Jedi raised an animalistic army—some of their soldiers monstrous, others merely pitiful. During the war's later years, their science birthed Leviathans, living superweapons that shambled across battlefields and drew life-essences into the blister-traps that speckled their broad backs. The dark lords made a last stand on Corbos, where Jedi hunters and evil rivals obliterated most of them, along with nearly all other life on the planet. The surviving dark lords fled beyond the Republic's borders, emerging in uncharted space, where they discovered the Sith species.

The Dark Jedi were treated as gods by these powerful yet malleable people. With unlimited resources and willing slaves, the Jedi exiles forged the Sith civilization into a new empire, bringing about a golden age of evil while separated from the Republic by the vastness of the galaxy. Over millennia, the dark rulers of the Sith Empire lost their charts and hyperspace maps, so that they no longer even knew how to locate the Republic.

The Manderon period lasted from 7000 to 5000 B.B.Y. At approximately 5500 B.B.Y., merchants in the Tapani sector established what would later become the Rimma Trade Route. This hyperlane, coupled with the recently blazed Corellian Trade Route, opened up new paths into the galactic southern quadrant. Dedicated explorers had tamed a significant portion of the galaxy, though many distant sectors remained uncharted.

THE GOLDEN AGE OF THE SITH
5000 B.B.Y.

It was a time of rugged frontiers. Pioneers established homes on harsh new colony worlds, and alien races encountered humans for the first time. Convoluted paths through the wilderness of hyperspace were still being mapped, which made long-distance travel treacherous and uncertain.

Gav and Jori Daragon, brother-and-sister hyperspace mappers, sought new trade routes in their ship *Starbreaker 12*. They used their "luck" and their blind faith to avoid collisions with stars or black holes, and hoped to blaze a new trail that would earn them a substantial fee from the Brotherhood of Navigators.

With nothing but creditors waiting for them, the two embarked on a random hyperspace hop, intending to map out a run farther than any that had been done before. They succeeded in skipping from the Koros system in the Deep Core all the way to Sith Space in the Outer Rim, an unlikely route known today as the Daragon Trail.

The Sith Empire—cut off from the Republic by vast distances and unexplored pathways—had grown powerful over the past two millennia, dabbling in its own brand of sorcery

Hyperspace explorers Gav and Jori Daragon
[Art by Mark Chiarello]

At the gravesite, the two strongest Sith opponents confronted each other: Naga Sadow, eager to expand Sith powers; and his rival Ludo Kressh, content with the existing borders and loath to risk a folly that could potentially cost them everything.

Sadow and Kressh engaged in a bloody duel that was interrupted by the unexpected arrival of *Starbreaker 12*. The Sith Lords seized Gav and Jori as alien spies and took them to the bleak planet Ziost for interrogation. The conservative Ludo Kressh saw the Daragons as precursors to an invasion, while his rival Naga Sadow viewed the unsuspecting Republic as a vast new field to conquer.

After a tribunal sentenced Gav and Jori to death, Naga Sadow sprang them from prison with help from his Massassi warriors, members of a specially bred soldier race. He took Gav and Jori to his own isolated fortress, but not before planting evidence indicating that agents of the Republic had freed the prisoners.

Playing innocent in the next Sith council meeting, Naga Sadow exploited doubts and fears regarding the Republic. He used the Daragons as scapegoats to galvanize the Sith Empire, convincing the other lords of an impending invasion. He insisted that they must strike first.

Back at his fortress, Sadow began to initiate Gav into the ways of Sith sorcery. Jori petitioned for the return of *Starbreaker 12*—because of the random route by which she and her brother had discovered the Sith Empire, the only safe path back to the Republic was stored in the ship's navicomputer.

Ludo Kressh discovered evidence that Sadow may have been behind the prisoners' escape, and gathered loyal Sith forces to assault Sadow's fortress and expose him as a traitor. Naga Sadow had planned for this and crushed his rival's "surprise" raid, declaring himself the Dark Lord of the Sith. Jori escaped during the attack in *Starbreaker 12*, leaving her brother behind in the Sith Empire under the promised pro-

and dark Force magic. But it had reached a time of crisis.

After a century of iron-handed rule, Dark Lord Marka Ragnos had died. The ensuing power vacuum sparked a great struggle, a brewing civil war that threatened to tear apart the Sith Empire. Hungry factions convened on the mausoleum planet of Korriban as Ragnos was laid to rest among the towering tombs. Even under the shadow-filled skies, the funeral was held with tremendous pomp and splendor, including sacrifices of Sith slaves, bonfires, and the completion of a spectacular new tomb.

tection of Naga Sadow. She vowed to come to his rescue as soon as she could, but she also knew that the Sith were gearing up for an attack on the Republic. Her top priority was to sound the alarm back home.

The Great Hyperspace War
5000 B.B.Y.

Jori Daragon was unaware that her ship carried a homing beacon that would lead Naga Sadow and his forces directly to the heart of the unsuspecting Republic. She arrived back in the Koros system, where the Empress Teta commanded a navy that was busy with pacifying the system's seven worlds, in the final stages of what is now known as the Unification Wars.

No one believed Jori's claims of an impending Sith invasion. Port officials arrested her on charges of fraud, felony, and starship theft. Eventually, she won an audience with Empress Teta herself, whose Jedi advisers—including Memit Nadill, Odan-Urr, and Odan-Urr's Master, Ooroo—recalled the stories of the outcast Dark Jedi who had long ago vanished into obscurity. The advisers convinced the empress to prepare for invasion. Empress Teta rallied support among other political leaders on Coruscant, while the Jedi Knights spread the word throughout the Republic.

Back in the Sith Empire, Naga Sadow continued training his pliable captive, Gav Daragon. Sadow had consolidated the remaining Sith forces, and set off on a surprise raid against the vulnerable Republic. His entire fleet arrived in Empress Teta's system, weapons blazing.

The conflict spread across the Republic like a storm: a succession of battles that pitted war fleets and loyal Jedi Knights against Sith sorcery and firepower. One of the young heroes of these battles was the alien Jedi Odan-Urr, who would become a pivotal figure in the Sith War a thousand years later.

Empress Teta proved to be a talented commander, but the Sith were relentless—and unpredictable, partly because Naga Sadow had only limited knowledge of this sector of the galaxy. The battles went poorly for the Republic.

Finally, the combined Republic fleet made a stand around the flare-active red giant star Primus Goluud, where Sadow duped Gav Daragon into facing the Republic forces alone. Gav ultimately redeemed himself, switching sides against the manipulative Naga Sadow just before the star went supernova. Sadow fled in his flagship as Empress Teta's forces hurled themselves after him.

With the changing tides of battle, the Republic rallied against the invaders, trouncing the Sith fleet. Memit Nadill and his team of Jedi Knights defeated enemy forces on Coruscant itself, while Odan-Urr won an important skirmish on the outlying planet of Kirrek, a victory that cost the life of the great Jedi Master Ooroo.

Naga Sadow called a retreat, taking his surviving warriors back to the Sith Empire. Limping home with tattered forces, Sadow returned only to discover that his old enemy Ludo Kressh was alive and well. Giving no quarter, Kressh mercilessly attacked Sadow's "traitors." At this point he had nothing to lose, and Naga Sadow fought back with wild abandon.

The pursuing Republic forces arrived in the middle of the fray to vanquish the Sith threat. They decimated the fleets of Sadow and Kressh in a hail of crossfire.

Naga Sadow took his most faithful followers and made a second getaway in his damaged flagship, sacrificing the rest of his forces. Republic ships again pursued him, but Sadow made one last sorcerous gambit. He flew his warship between a tight binary star, the Dena rii Nova, and used Sith powers to manipulate solar flares that destroyed the Republic ships in his wake.

Of all his former glory, Naga Sadow was left with merely a single ship and his Massassi crew. The Dark Lord went to ground on a little-known jungle moon around the gas giant Yavin. There on Yavin 4 he made his camp, entombed his warship, and left the Massassi behind as guardians. Using Sith technology and sorcery, he cocooned himself in a suspended animation chamber, hoping someone would pick up the dark teachings where he left off, and bring about the Sith

War beasts charge the Republic line during the Sith invasion of Coruscant. [Art by Tommy Lee Edwards]

Golden Age that the Dark Lord Marka Ragnos had foretold.

As he died on the battlefield of Kirrek, Master Ooroo had prophesied that his studious trainee Odan-Urr would found a great library, eventually dying among his beloved scrolls and books. Beginning with Master Ooroo's collection of arcane artifacts, as well as numerous items found among the wreckage of the Sith invasion fleet, Odan-Urr did indeed establish the greatest library of the Old Republic, the grand museum city on Ossus.

Following the Great Hyperspace War, the Jedi developed the modern lightsaber, which operated nearly indefinitely on a charge without the need of an external power pack.

These weapons came into use around the time of the Gank Massacres (4800 B.B.Y.), which coincided with the discovery of ryll spice on the half-burned, half-frozen Twi'lek homeworld of Ryloth. The Duros of Neimoidia, who had by this time evolved into a race distinctly different from their forebears, locked up distribution rights to ryll, but the drug whipped the Porporites, a newly discovered species, into a homicidal frenzy. Various factions hired the Gank mercenaries to protect them. After exterminating the Porporites, the Ganks embarked on a full-scale war until put down by the Jedi.

LEGACY OF THE SITH

The Sith Empire had crumbled, and victorious Republic observers could be forgiven their rosy optimism. New star systems were explored, and new races were taken into the fold as the galactic government slowly learned how to rule over many cultures and across vast distances.

Centuries passed with no further contact with the dark leaders or remnants of the Sith, but the evil influence would ultimately return in a different and more insidious form than before—a cancer from within.

THE SHADOW OF FREEDON NADD
4400 B.B.Y.

Six centuries after Naga Sadow had exiled himself on the jungle moon, an ambitious Jedi Knight, Freedon Nadd, followed rumors and his own intuition to the isolated Yavin system.

In the centuries since the defeated Dark Lord had sealed his essence beneath the focusing chamber of a primary temple, the Massassi refugees had degenerated into primitive but powerful savages. Nadd arrived and fought with them, and his use of the Force awed the Massassi into recalling their past. They showed him where the Dark Lord rested, waiting for someone like Freedon Nadd.

Nadd awakened the ancient Sith Lord, and Sadow in-

structed the Jedi in the dark twistings of the Force. Freedon Nadd then killed his mentor and set about making himself a king on the primitive world of Onderon, outside the boundaries of the Republic.

Centuries before, the peaceful people of Onderon had been beset by horrible creatures that crossed over from the erratic moon Dxun. The predators took a terrible toll on the population until the people constructed a walled city, Iziz, for their protection.

Freedon Nadd, with his knowledge of Sith magic, easily made himself the leader of these people. Over the decades the city grew, implacably driving back the jungle. One of the policies Nadd instituted was to banish criminals outside the walls of Iziz, where they would be devoured by the voracious predators. However, some of these exiles managed to band together and survive, even learning how to capture the beasts and domesticate them. Riding on the backs of flying beasts and carrying handmade weapons, the survivors struck back against the city that had exiled them, thus beginning centuries of unrest and rebellion—a scattered guerrilla war that even Freedon Nadd's powers could not crush.

After Nadd's death, the sarcophagus containing his body became a focus of dark side energy that was used by his descendants. Nadd's legacy passed from generation to generation, but the civil war continued, with a cost in blood nearly as high as the earliest attacks from the beasts of Dxun.

During the Vultar Cataclysm (4250 B.B.Y.), the Jedi Order experienced its Third Great Schism. Following a Jedi civil war on Coruscant, the dark side followers fell back to the Vultar system in the Core Worlds. There they discovered ancient technology indicating that the system's planets were artificial constructs, the likely creations of the alien Architects who had built the Corellian system. The dark-siders harnessed the machines (including the extraordinary Cosmic Turbine) but could not control them, and soon annihilated themselves along with the entire planetary system. Corellia's role as a similarly engineered system would remain unconfirmed until the Corellian insurrection, many millennia in the future.

TRIALS OF THE JEDI
4000 B.B.Y.

The survival of the Republic was predicated on two factors: wise governing from administrators and lawmakers, and a preservation of harmony by the Jedi Knights. This harmony was threatened during the Great Droid Revolution (4015 B.B.Y.), when thousands of droids—everything from sanitation to protocol to military models—rose up en masse against their owners. The Jedi destroyed the ringleader, the assassin droid HK-01, and put down the mutiny with a minimum of casualties. The Great Droid Revolution dealt a crippling blow to the budding "droids' rights" movement.

At the time, Jedi often became "watchmen" of new systems, overseeing their transition into the Republic and assisting with local difficulties. Jedi Master Arca Jeth of Arkania received the stewardship and responsibility for the Onderon system. Rather than becoming the watchman himself, he sent his three students—the brothers Ulic and Cay Qel-

Jedi Knight Ulic Qel-Droma
[ART BY MARK CHIARELLO]

Droma and the Twi'lek Tott Doneeta. Arriving on the war-torn world, the three Jedi Knights were greeted by Queen Amanoa. She explained about the depredations of the beast riders and requested help from the Jedi. In a bold move, the riders soon attacked the palace itself, kidnapping Queen Amanoa's daughter Galia.

The Qel-Droma brothers and Doneeta set out to rescue the queen's daughter, but discovered that all was not as they had been led to believe. Galia and the warlord leader Oron Kira had planned the abduction. They intended to marry and unify the two societies, ending centuries of bloodshed.

Queen Amanoa, however, had no interest in peace. For years she had been tapping into Freedon Nadd's power, and in her outrage she called upon the dark side to destroy Oron Kira's people. The Jedi fought back, but they were out-classed—in the struggle Cay Qel-Droma lost his arm, which he later replaced with a droid prosthesis.

Only Master Arca's arrival was enough to prevent a catastrophe. Arca used Jedi battle meditation to influence the forces on the battlefield and turn the tide of the conflict. Galia and Oron Kira then worked to restore their world to peace and to bestow the benefits of civilization.

Elsewhere, the Jedi Knight Nomi Sunrider would become one of the greatest leaders of her age. Nomi had taken up the lightsaber after her Jedi husband, Andur, had died dur-ing an ambush in the Stenness system. On the bleak world of Ambria, she began her formal training with Master Thon, an armor-plated Tchuukthai of savage countenance and significant wisdom. Nomi Sunrider became a master in the technique of battle meditation.

After training Nomi for some months, Master Thon brought her to the Jedi learning center on Ossus, where he turned her over to Master Vodo Siosk-Baas. There, with other Jedi trainees, Nomi Sunrider learned even more of the Force and finally built her own personal lightsaber.

The Naddist Revolt
3998 B.B.Y.

Following two years of relative peace on Onderon, unrest continued, sparked primarily by a grim sect that revered the memory of Freedon Nadd. In an attempt to remove the cancerous evil, Master Arca and his students prepared to move the sarcophagi containing Queen Amanoa's and Freedon Nadd's remains on the monster-filled moon of Dxun. During the funeral procession, followers of Freedon Nadd launched an unexpected attack from beneath the city

Queen Amanoa's funeral procession on Onderon
[Art by Tommy Lee Edwards]

of Iziz. The Naddist rebels captured the royal sarcophagi.

Arca then learned that Queen Galia's decrepit father, King Ommin, had been kept alive in a secret life-support facility. Suspicious, Arca, Galia, and Ulic Qel-Droma visited the dying old man, where they discovered that Ommin himself had been a follower of Freedon Nadd. The spirit-avatar of Nadd joined forces with Ommin, crippling Master Arca with blistering bolts of energy. Ommin fled with the paralyzed Arca to another dark side stronghold, where the stolen sarcophagi had been taken.

Hurt by his failure, Ulic Qel-Droma called for assistance from the Republic and the Jedi Knights. Republic military ships converged on the Onderon system, while another team of handpicked Jedi arrived from Ossus. Under fire, the Jedi reinforcements battled through the siege of Iziz to join Ulic and his companions.

In the midst of the chaos on Onderon, two other figures arrived: Satal Keto and his cousin Aleema, heirs to the now corrupt Empress Teta system (renamed from the Koros system following the Unification Wars). Spoiled, bored, and rich, Satal, Aleema, and their friends had dabbled in Sith magic, amusing themselves with artifacts recovered by the Jedi Odan-Urr during the Great Hyperspace War a thousand years earlier. These aristocrats dubbed themselves the Krath, after a fearsome childhood legend.

Satal Keto had stolen an ancient book of Sith secrets from a museum on Coruscant; egged on by the beautiful and ambitious Aleema, they departed for Onderon. Using freshly learned dark side skills as well as plain luck, the two made their way through the battle-ravaged city to the stronghold where King Ommin held Master Arca prisoner.

While a scribe diligently worked to reproduce the stolen Sith tome, the specter of Freedon Nadd appeared. With Republic troops pounding the city and the unified Jedi Knights on their way, Nadd knew that King Ommin would be defeated. Instead, Nadd threw in his lot with the two aristocrats, telling Satal Keto and Aleema that they alone held the key to the rebirth of the Sith Golden Age—and that he would guide them.

The Jedi Knights fought their way into Ommin's stronghold just as Master Arca was about to die in the grip of the dark side. Nadd withdrew his power and support from Ommin, and Ulic charged forward to kill the old man and rescue Arca.

Satal Keto and Aleema fled back to the Empress Teta system, bearing a wealth of Sith artifacts. Republic forces imposed order and martial law on devastated Iziz. The sarcophagus of Freedon Nadd was taken to an armored tomb on the moon of Dxun, sealed behind slabs of Mandalorian iron—which they hoped would last for millennia.

THE COMING RUIN
3997 B.B.Y.

With their Sith knowledge and artifacts, brash young Satal Keto and Aleema marshaled their Krath forces for a coup of the Empress Teta system. Killing old-guard aristocratic leaders proved far easier than actually subjugating the people, and the seven worlds revolted against the barbaric despots. However, Satal Keto and Aleema delighted in the chance to make use of their new Sith powers to crush the resistance.

Word of the revolt and the alarming use of Sith sorcery made its way to Onderon. Nomi Sunrider and Ulic Qel-Droma had grown close during the reconstruction of Iziz, and Master Arca decided to send them both to deal with the situation in the Empress Teta system.

Joining Republic military forces en route to the ferocious battles around the seven worlds, Ulic and Nomi assisted by using their Jedi abilities—but Aleema countered with her own powerful Sith illusions. In a suicide attack, one of the Krath ships nearly destroyed the bridge of the Republic flagship. Rebuffed, the Republic fleet retreated.

Around the same time, on distant Dantooine in Wild Space, Jedi Master Vodo Siosk-Baas trained three students: the Cathar mates Crado and Sylvar, and his most talented apprentice, Exar Kun. Kun easily defeated Crado in a lightsaber duel, then fought against Sylvar; as tensions escalated, she slashed him across the face with her claws. Master Vodo stepped in, and Kun met the challenge, defeating his own teacher.

Ambitious and curious, Kun had surreptitiously studied

the legends of the Golden Age of the Sith. He followed dark side clues to the tomb of Freedon Nadd on Dxun, and used his lightsaber to cut through the Mandalorian iron. When Kun cracked open the sarcophagus, he found a skeletal corpse clothed in black armor, but the ethereal form of Nadd's spirit shimmered to life.

The dark Jedi ghost revealed precious metal scrolls hidden in a compartment beneath his remains. He also told Kun that a great future awaited the young Jedi in the dark side. Continuing his explorations on the Sith tomb world of Korriban, Kun investigated a spectacular crypt, but the ceiling collapsed, crushing him.

As he cried out for help, the spirit of Freedon Nadd appeared, promising rescue only if Kun surrendered to the dark side. Kun made an empty promise to save his own life, but the vow sent him further down the slippery slope that he had already begun to walk. The flood of dark side power blasted away the rubble, knitted his broken bones, and left him lying naked on the dry clay of Korriban. Exar Kun let out a tremendous shriek that echoed across the galaxy, calling in despair upon Master Vodo, whom he had abandoned.

Master Vodo and all other Jedi had gathered on Deneba for a great convocation called to discuss the strife in the Empress Teta system. The historic meeting was called to order by Odan-Urr, who had spent the centuries after the Great Hyperspace War building Ossus into the foremost center of Jedi learning. In the audience were the premier Jedi of the period, including Master Arca, Master Thon, Nomi Sunrider, and Ulic Qel-Droma. Jedi witnesses spoke of the dangerous Sith sorcery unleashed by the Krath, and of the growing foothold of the dark side.

In the middle of the assembly, automated pods rained down through the atmosphere, unleashing hordes of Krath war droids that attacked the Jedi Knights. The Jedi defended themselves in a furious fight, but the battle left one tragic legacy—Master Arca died even as he saved the life of his student Ulic Qel-Droma. This became the pivotal event in Ulic's life, breaking his spirit and

Sith follower Aleema conjures an illusory herd of space grazers, menacing the Republic fleet. [Art by Tommy Lee Edwards]

leaving him open to the influences of the dark side.

As the Jedi Knights recovered from the onslaught, an anguished Ulic Qel-Droma vowed to go to the Empress Teta system, infiltrate the Krath despots, and destroy them from within. Master Thon warned him about the temptations of the dark side, but Ulic would not be swayed. His own pride did not allow Ulic to see the folly in his attempt to conquer the dark side by himself.

Disguised as a grim "fallen Jedi," Ulic infiltrated the iron-walled city of Cinnagar, where the Krath usurpers had crushed all dissent. He won acceptance into the Krath inner circle by killing an assassin who was gunning for Aleema. With innocent blood on his own hands, Ulic had taken another step on the road to his own damnation. Aleema intended to keep Ulic as her lover, though Satal Keto was jealous and highly suspicious. Keto interrogated and tortured Ulic, insisting that he was a Jedi spy. Finally, Keto injected Ulic with a Sith poison that affected the mind. Ulic became the Krath general in charge of military forces, and the personal pet of the evil Aleema.

As months passed with no word from Ulic, Nomi Sunrider joined Cay Qel-Droma and Tott Doneeta in an attempt to rescue the Jedi from the Krath. Nomi ended up as a prisoner inside the Cinnagar citadel, where Ulic—trying to maintain his cover—ordered her execution. When Nomi escaped, Satal Keto sent his men to kill Ulic, believing the Krath's new general to be a Jedi spy. Instead, Ulic killed Keto in a great duel, then took his place beside Aleema as the new ruler of the Krath.

On Korriban, Exar Kun had been healed and reborn in the dark side. The spirit of Freedon Nadd urged Kun to make his way to Yavin 4, the last resting place of Naga Sadow, who had instructed Nadd himself centuries before. On the jungle moon, Exar Kun discovered the degenerate descendants of the Massassi, who tried to sacrifice him to a gigantic monster beneath the main temple. Kun once again called upon the dark side in order to save himself.

Freedon Nadd reappeared, delighted with Kun's victory and claiming him as an ally and protégé—but Kun would hear none of it. Still simmering with the Sith powers he had mastered, Kun lashed out and obliterated Nadd for all time. Calling himself the Dark Lord of the Sith, Kun then subjugated the Massassi and had them construct huge structures based on Sith architecture, designed to focus dark forces. Beneath the sites of the ancient ruins, Kun uncovered Naga Sadow's Sith battleship and took it as his own.

An extremely powerful figure now, Kun dabbled in dark side alchemy, creating freakish two-headed avians and hulking terentateks that thirsted after Force-rich blood. He invented a glowing golden sphere that trapped the children of the Massassi and allowed him to feed off their energies. With his mind he reached across the galaxy and detected other users of Sith magic in the Empress Teta system. Knowing that his destiny was to bring about a new Sith Golden Age, Kun traveled to Cinnagar to destroy an unwanted rival, Ulic Qel-Droma.

The Jedi Knights Cay Qel-Droma, Nomi Sunrider, and Tott Doneeta executed a second rescue mission to drag Ulic away from the treachery of the Krath. Ulic responded to the Jedi attack with all of the military might at his disposal. Blind to his own delusions, he refused to join them, and the Jedi Knights withdrew in despair.

At that moment Exar Kun burst into the palace. He and Ulic fought with a blazing clash of Jedi blades—and during the conflict the Sith amulets both men wore began to shimmer. Before them appeared the image of the long-dead Dark Lord of the Sith Marka Ragnos—the Sith ruler whose death had triggered the civil war between Naga Sadow and Ludo Kressh a thousand years earlier. Ragnos commanded the two men to join forces, so that the alliance of Ulic Qel-Droma and Exar Kun could bring about the long-predicted return of Sith glory. Allies, not enemies, Kun and Qel-Droma clasped hands and vowed to do what was necessary to create such a future.

THE SITH WAR
3996 B.B.Y.

Exar Kun and Ulic Qel-Droma consolidated their forces. Kun worked to create Sith converts among the weaker-willed Jedi, spreading his insidious teachings on Ossus as if he were some sort of prophet. Among the believers was Kun's former training companion, the Cathar male Crado. Crado's mate, Sylvar, remained loyal to the Jedi.

From the Jedi library, Kun stole the original Sith Holocron used by Naga Sadow. Caretaker Odan-Urr was killed during the theft, fulfilling the prophesy by Master Ooroo that Odan-Urr would die among his books. Kun then took his converts back to the Massassi temples on Yavin 4, where he unleashed a powerful Sith spell that bound the Jedi to him. Kun appointed Crado his second in command.

Ulic Qel-Droma took control of the war's strategic side. He forged an alliance with the Mandalorian warrior clans, who had left their homeworld of Mandalore behind and now searched the galaxy hungering for conquest. Ulic defeated their leader, Mandalore, in open combat, and the Mandalorian Crusaders agreed to become an arm of the Krath military. The Mandalorians and their Basilisk war-mounts, augmented by Aleema's Sith illusions, executed lightning strikes to gather supplies and weaponry from outposts and shipyards. Exar Kun had also constructed a Sith superweapon, the Dark Reaper, that was capable of drawing in the life-energies of thousands of combatants. Ulic unleashed the Dark Reaper against hundreds of Republic troops on the outpost world of Raxus Prime.

Believing that the time was right, Ulic, Aleema, and Mandalore launched a brash, all-out assault on Coruscant itself. The capital's loyal Jedi force joined together against the invaders. Surrounded by light and the Force, Ulic was captured and the invaders were driven back, while Aleema escaped. A prisoner stripped of his power, Ulic was taken to face trial for his crimes against the Republic.

The trial took place in the great Senate Hall on Coruscant. For a Jedi Knight, betrayal of the Republic was an unforgivable crime. Ulic, however, displayed no repentance. Master Vodo attended the trial, suspecting that Ulic wasn't acting alone; Vodo sensed the dark hand of his lost student Exar Kun.

During Ulic's sentencing, the doors crashed open and Exar Kun strode in, flanked by bestial Massassi bodyguards. Before the whole assembly, the new Dark Lord of the Sith

Fallen Jedi Knight Exar Kun
[Art by Mark Chiarello]

mission to assassinate their own Masters. The bloodbath of slaughtered Jedi Masters shook the Republic. Kun's lieutenant, Crado, attempted to kill his former Master, but Thon defeated him and Crado fled.

Crado then teamed with Aleema to execute a military strike using Naga Sadow's Sith flagship. Armed with the vessel's star-destroying weapon, they intended to destroy the suns of the Cron Cluster, not realizing that their Masters had set them up for a fall. The chain reaction triggered by the weapon consumed them as well, thus punishing Crado for his incompetence and Aleema for her lack of loyalty; she had tried to take over Ulic's forces while he was imprisoned. The blazing shock wave from the exploding stars streaked toward Ossus—exactly as Kun had hoped.

THE DEVASTATION OF OSSUS
3996 B.B.Y.

During the frantic evacuation of Ossus, the Jedi scrambled to retrieve as many vital artifacts as possible. Amid this chaos, Exar Kun and Ulic brought their forces to the library world to raid anything that remained. A tree-like Neti Jedi, Master Ood Bnar, had taken on the mantle of librarian after Odan-Urr's death. Knowing that he could not protect every item from the oncoming shock wave, Ood buried a priceless collection of ancient lightsabers just before the arrival of Exar Kun and his Massassi warriors. To protect his treasure, Ood called upon the Force inside the soil of Ossus and transformed himself into a gigantic tree. Gathering up the remaining plunder, Exar Kun departed Ossus.

As the waves of supernova fire drew closer, Ulic Qel-Droma fought against the rallying Republic and Jedi forces.

used his powers to hypnotize the observers and manipulate the president of the Senate. Master Vodo Siosk-Baas stepped in to battle his former pupil. Exar Kun, now armed with a double-bladed lightsaber and the tricks of Sith magic, struck down and killed Master Vodo. Ulic and Kun left the Jedi and Senators behind, returning to their stronghold on Yavin 4.

Vodo wasn't the only Jedi to die that day. Exar Kun had dispatched his Sith-possessed disciples on an insidious

Cay Qel-Droma attempted to stop his brother, but Ulic unleashed his anger and, in a devastating fury, struck down Cay, killing him. Staring at the body of his brother and realizing what he had done, Ulic collapsed in horror.

Nomi Sunrider and Tott Doneeta arrived too late to help Cay, but a distraught Nomi unleashed a wild Force ability that blinded Ulic to the Force, effectively stripping him of his powers. Utterly crushed, no longer even a Jedi Knight, Ulic Qel-Droma finally saw how much pain he had caused. He had traveled the dark path with the intention of avenging Master Arca, but instead had grown worse than his very enemies.

Knowing how the Sith War must end, Ulic offered to take the remaining Jedi to the headquarters of Exar Kun on Yavin 4. Kun realized that the Jedi were coming. He gathered the remaining Massassi into the Great Temple, then chained himself to the focal point of the pyramids. As the Jedi forces in orbit generated a wall of light that bombarded the thick jungles, Exar Kun drained the power from his Massassi slaves, triggering a final wave of Sith sorcery that liberated his spirit but preserved it inside the giant structures. Kun found himself trapped, unable to escape the prison he had created for himself.

The Jedi attack resulted in an immense conflagration in the jungles, obliterating the trees and scorching the temple complex so completely that nothing could survive. The victorious Jedi Knights departed and worked to pick up the pieces of their damaged Republic. The Mandalorian Crusaders, defeated during a battle on Onderon, fled under the leadership of a new Mandalore. The Republic seized control of the Empress Teta system, scattering the Krath. Surviving Sith forces retreated to territory that had historically been considered Sith space in the Outer Rim near Korriban, Thule, and Yavin. The Dark Reaper superweapon lay smashed on Raxus Prime, though its power source, the Force Harvester, remained intact and overlooked beneath garbage strata.

With Ossus ruined, the Jedi relocated their headquarters to their existing Temple on Coruscant, expanding the struc-

---

Jedi Master Ood gathers up Ossus's treasures before the arrival of a supernova shockwave. [Art by Tommy Lee Edwards]

ture that already sat on the site of a Force wellspring. They also increased their ties to the office of Supreme Chancellor.

THE GREAT HUNT
3993 B.B.Y.

With the Sith seemingly extinguished, attention turned to cleanup. For three years following the Sith War, the Jedi Knights were sent on a "dragon quest." Terentateks, Exar Kun's alchemically birthed monstrosities that fed on Force-strong blood, still prowled the Rim worlds. Each stood about half the size of a rancor and was a match for an entire squad of Jedi, making the extermination of terentateks the Order's highest priority at the time.

Three renowned Jedi Knights shored up their remarkable legends during this Great Hunt. Duron Qel-Droma, cousin of Ulic and Cay, joined with his lover, Shaela Nuur, and the hard-bitten brawler Guun Han Saresh to slay the mightiest terentateks. In the final days of the Great Hunt, Guun Han perished in the teeth of a terentatek in the shadow-lands of Kashyyyk. Duron Qel-Droma and Shaela Nuur were slain while fighting an-other of the killer beasts in the tombs of Kor-riban. Qel-Droma's Force-imbued robe, once worn by Cay Qel-Droma, would be found by Darth Revan decades later.

Jedi Knight Nomi Sunrider
[ART BY MARK CHIARELLO]

THE REDEMPTION OF ULIC QEL-DROMA
3986 B.B.Y

Ulic Qel-Droma, a disgraced war criminal, never regained his Jedi powers. A ruined man, he wandered from world to world and hid from history, haunted by the ghosts of his own guilt. Ten years after the Sith War, he went to the frozen world of Rhen Var to make his final home in the ruins of an abandoned fortress.

Nomi Sunrider, too, was scarred by the loss of Ulic, the second man she had ever loved. She devoted much of her life to politics and to rebuilding the Order of the Jedi Knights. Intensely focused on her duties, Nomi failed to pay sufficient attention to her impressionable daughter. Young Vima Sun-rider did not receive adequate training as a Jedi—until she ran away from a Jedi Convocation at Exis Station and set out to find Ulic Qel-Droma, convinced that the legendary man would take her as an apprentice.

On Rhen Var, Vima persuaded the bitter Ulic to teach her what he knew of the Force. Even without the use of his powers, Ulic taught Vima about honor and duty, and his heart softened toward the girl; Vima came to love him like the father she'd never known.

Sylvar, the Cathar Jedi, had never overcome her anger at the death of her mate, Crado, during the Sith War. Placing much of the blame on Ulic, Sylvar vowed to find Vima—and to make Ulic pay for his crimes. Enlisting the aid of a scavenger pilot named Hoggon, Sylvar tracked her quarry to Rhen Var.

Sylvar and Nomi Sunrider confronted Ulic, but with assistance from Vima, overcame their anger and pain, and managed to forgive the man who had already paid so much for his crimes. But Hoggon—eager to make his own mark on history—shot Ulic in the back and killed him. To everyone's astonishment, though he had been blinded to the Force, Ulic Qel-Droma vanished into the light, a technique known only to a true Jedi Master.

With such a beginning to her career as a Jedi Knight, Vima Sunrider learned much and eventually became one of the greatest Jedi of her age.

The Mandalorian Wars
3995–3961 B.B.Y.

The Mandalorian Crusaders had gained strength during the Sith War, but their leader Mandalore had died on the jungle moon of Dxun. Following tradition, a new soldier took up the name and identity of Mandalore, and this warrior led his "Neo-Crusaders" to triumphs that would be forever celebrated in the refrains of Mandalore skirmishsongs. Slowly at first, Mandalore conquered fringe worlds left defenseless in the Sith War's aftermath. Joining their war matériel to his own, within a decade Mandalore had accumulated a swath of "clan territory" that dwarfed Hutt space. Republic efforts to halt Mandalore's advance were halfhearted, until the warlord took advantage of his enemy's apathy and poured into Republic space.

Mandalore's top strategist, Cassus Fett, decided to punish the planet Cathar for opposing the Mandalorian clans in clashes long since silenced. Fett's Basilisk war-mounts decimated Cathar's primitive settlements, nearly driving the proud feline species into extinction. After the Cathar incident, the Jedi joined with the Republic fleet in head-to-head confrontations against Mandalore's armies, but the ineffectual Jedi Council called for caution, hobbling the war effort.

A pair of charismatic Jedi, Revan and Malak, turned the tide of the war through sheer force of will. Revan openly defied the Jedi Council and drove back Mandalore by co-opting his enemy's own tactics. Revan was willing to sacrifice the populations of some planets in order to win key victories elsewhere. This earned Revan the grudging respect of the Mandalorians and the contempt of the Jedi Council—but even they reluctantly admitted that the coldhearted strategy was successful. Revan and Malak liberated Taris, sparred with Cassus Fett at Jaga's Cluster, and annihilated a large portion of the Mandalorian army at Althir. At Malachor V, Revan drew Mandalore into a direct fight and killed him in hand-to-hand combat.

At last defeated by a worthy opponent, the Mandalorians destroyed their armor and war-mounts under the eyes of Revan and Malak. Some survivors returned to the planet Mandalore; others became guns-for-hire and were to be known informally as the "Mandalorian Mercs."

The Second Sith War
3958–3956 B.B.Y.

During their string of victories in the Mandalorian Wars, Revan and Malak had acquired a taste for rebellion. In the spirit of seeking out what the Jedi Council would deny them, the two discovered artifacts created by the pre-Republic Rakata civilization on Dantooine, Kashyyyk, Tatooine, Manaan, and Korriban. Knowledge gained on Korriban, the Sith tomb world, may have proved too tempting for war commanders steeped in blood. They abruptly

Darth Malak, with his dark side apprentice, Bastila Shan
[ART BY TOMMY LEE EDWARDS]

announced themselves to the galaxy as the *new* Dark Lords of the Sith—Darth Revan and Darth Malak.

Many of the Republic crewers and Jedi Knights who had fought with Revan and Malak in the Mandalorian Wars joined their cause, eager for the chance to again serve the two great champions. At the shipyards of Foerost, Revan and his accomplices seized control of the bulk of the Republic fleet. This brash action initiated the Second Sith War.

Revan's fleet commander, Admiral Saul Karath, intimidated hundreds of key military worlds by threatening to slag their cities through orbital bombardment. Revan and Malak took up Sith holdings left dormant after the First Sith War, establishing a link between their ideology and that of Exar Kun, despite their lack of a connection to the Sith species itself. Many citizens admired this take-charge mentality, and much of the Sith territorial expansion was the result of Republic defections. Revan revitalized an existing Sith training academy on Korriban, ensuring that a corps of Dark Jedi would be ready to defend the new Sith Empire.

Revan and Malak, on the trail of the Rakatan clues they had uncovered, located a colony of surviving Rakatans on the species' original birthworld of Rakata Prime. Though the Rakata had fallen into relative primitivism since their golden age many millennia in the past, their Star Forge remained in orbit and possessed the power to create fully formed machines at the flip of a lever. Bolstered with ships of Rakatan design, the Sith forces drove the Republic to its knees. Absolute victory seemed within Revan's grasp.

The Jedi Knight Bastila Shan, a master of Battle Meditation, helped prevent the Republic's defeat, and soon the Jedi arranged a trap for Darth Revan. In the midst of a pitched fleet battle, Bastila and a strike team boarded Revan's flagship and subdued the Sith Lord. Darth Malak treacherously opened fire on his own Master's ship, but Bastila escaped with her captive in tow.

The Jedi Council chose not to imprison or execute Revan. Instead they Force-scoured the memories from the fallen Jedi's brain, placing Bastila in charge of a powerful warrior who was now little more than a blank slate. The Council

hoped that an amnesiac Revan might lead them to the Star Forge without presenting a threat to the Republic.

Malak, now the reigning Sith Lord, took Darth Bandon as his apprentice and pushed ahead in the war. A major engagement over Taris nearly netted him Bastila as well as the combatant who had once been Revan. In Malak's efforts to capture them, he leveled Taris and destroyed the Jedi academy on Dantooine.

Bastila, working with Revan and a number of hangers-on including Mandalorian clansman Canderous Ordo and Revan's former assassin droid HK-47, found the location of the Star Forge and launched an assault to shut it down. Aided by the full Republic fleet, Revan—now in possession of the memories the Council had erased—killed Darth Malak and destroyed the Star Forge above Rakata Prime.

THE SITH CIVIL WAR
3951 B.B.Y.

Revan's fate following the Battle of Rakata Prime is unclear, but the Sith Empire that had sworn fealty to Revan (and later Malak) now found itself rudderless. Darth Bandon had also perished during the recent fighting, and so a host of potential Sith Lords rose up to fill the void. Darth Sion, Darth Kreia, Darth Traya, and Darth Nihilus were among the many to take advantage of the Republic's inability to safeguard its holdings after the Second Sith War.

As the Outer Rim descended into chaos and the Sith once again took hold, the surviving Jedi publicly disbanded. By going underground, they hoped to escape assassins that had been dispatched by Darth Sion. Working to uncover the Sith in secret, salvation came instead from a former Jedi who had been excommunicated for assisting Revan during the Mandalorian Wars. This hero—aided in part by Canderous Ordo, the new Mandalore heading the reemerging Mandalorian clans—uncovered the origin of the Sith plot to wipe out the Jedi. Eventually, the Sith destroyed themselves in a bloody civil war, decimating the ranks of the evil cult. At least one Sith Lord survived, however, ensuring the perpetuation of the "Darth" line for centuries to come.

Darth Sion
[Art by Mark Chiarello]

REPERCUSSIONS THROUGH THE REPUBLIC
3900–3000 B.B.Y.

Years of consolidation and recovery followed the two Sith Wars. At approximately 3900 B.B.Y., Queen Tasia of Grizmallt sponsored one of the last of her world's colonization missions. The three ships—*Beneficent Tasia, Constant,* and *Mother Vima*—departed Grizmallt and vanished from sight. Much later it was learned that they had reached the planet

Naboo in the Wild Space of the southern galactic quadrant, where the colonists became embroiled in a war with the planet's native Gungans.

In the Kanz sector on the Republic's frontier, Provisional Governor Myrial of Argazda used the recent chaos to cover her attempts at establishing a military dictatorship. Myrial's armies bombed recalcitrant planets, including Lorrd, and sold their inhabitants into slavery. The Lorrdians, forbidden from speaking aloud by their slave masters, developed into geniuses at nonverbal communication, a trait still seen today. The Kanz sector eventually seceded from the Republic and existed as a totalitarian state for three centuries, until Jedi efforts toppled the regime at 3670 B.B.Y. More than five billion lives were lost during the Kanz Disorders.

Concurrent with the Sith War was the rise of the matriarchy in the Hapes Consortium. A few decades before Ulic Qel-Droma and Exar Kun nearly toppled the Republic, a band of Jedi Knights—including Master Arca Jeth—traveled into the densely-packed Hapan worlds and eliminated the barbaric Lorell Raiders who had preyed on Republic shipping for generations. The women of the Hapes Consortium, freed from their servitude to the Raiders, established a female-dominated society and placed all power in a single monarch, the Queen Mother. The Hapan Queen Mother sealed the borders to the star cluster centuries later (circa 3100 B.B.Y.), and the Consortium developed in near-total isolation for millennia until Princess Leia Organa broke down the barriers in a historic diplomatic achievement for the New Republic.

At 3000 B.B.Y., the legendary pioneer woman Freia Kallea blazed a remarkable new hyperspace route—the Hydian Way, which spanned nearly the entire north–south width of the galaxy. The Hydian finally opened up the galaxy to widespread colonization beyond the narrow wedge of the Slice and fundamentally altered the scale of galactic civilization.

The Hydian Way and the discovery of other super-hyperroutes including the Corellian Trade Spine helped spur the second great colonization of the galaxy. The Republic exploded into the galactic northern and southern quadrants, and simultaneously expanded out into new settlers' regions dubbed the Mid Rim and the Outer Rim Territories.

THE NEW SITH
2000–1000 B.B.Y.

Two thousand years before the rise of the Empire, a rogue Jedi Knight broke away from the teachings of the Council and founded a new order of the Sith, marking another Great Schism. Over time, more Jedi Knights joined the renegade, and soon the Republic once again found itself threatened. The followers of the Sith grew in power and eventually made war against the Republic.

These centuries of strife, known as the Draggulch period (2000–1000 B.B.Y.), saw a consistent decline in Republic power as mineral mines ran dry and thousands of mega-corporations went bankrupt. The Republic borders began to shrink for the first time in millennia, as colony worlds dried up and were abandoned. Hardship bred lawlessness, and the overextended Jedi took a more active role in government. In a move of desperation, several Jedi even served as Republic Supreme Chancellor. Scandal continued to plague the Jedi, most notably following the military strike against the Ubese that left the Ubese homeworld inhospitable and forced its survivors to live the rest of their lives beneath filtration helmets.

The Battle of Mizra (1466 B.B.Y.) saw the victory of a massive Sith army over the Jedi. It was immortalized by the poet Felloux, who described scores of Sith speeders bearing scores of Sith Lords, each vehicle bearing the name of a predatory creature—*Ng'ok, Hssiss, Sleeth*—that embodied the character of its rider. The Sith Lords' drawn lightsabers illumi-

nated the ash-blackened sky, and their whining repulsorlift chariots drowned out the screams of the dying.

The final hundred years of the Draggulch period are sometimes called the Republic's "dark age." The Republic could no longer afford to maintain its communications network, dropping all settlements outside the Core off the grid and forcing them to rely on hyperspace courier ships. At the same time, an outbreak of the Candorian plague killed off as much as two-thirds of the citizens of some major population centers.

The Sith grew exponentially during the dark age, ravaging entire star systems while under the squabbling leadership of a host of Sith Lords, including Kaan, Bane, Qordis, Seviss Vaa, and Kaox Krul.

The Jedi, shaken out of their complacency by the galactic crisis, raised their own champions, such as the stalwart Lord Hoth and his Army of Light, the charismatic Kiel Charny, and Lord Farfalla, a foppish alien whose retinue and wooden-hulled battleship looked like elements of a forgotten fairy tale. Jedi casualties grew so common that the Order sanctioned recruiters to seek out able-bodied Republic citizens with any hint of Force sensitivity. Many of those recruited into the war were children.

Lord Hoth's Army of Light clashed with the Sith on countless worlds, and the Sith leaders clashed with one another. Lord Kaan eventually raised his own army, the Brotherhood of Darkness, numbering twenty thousand warriors and dedicated to the principle of "rule by the strong." Fearful that Bane would usurp his position as head of the Brotherhood of Darkness, Kaan poisoned his rival and left him for dead.

THE BATTLE OF RUUSAN
1000 B.B.Y.

Jedi and Sith ultimately squared off on the planet Ruusan, where they fought seven blood-soaked ground battles that left both sides demoralized. The Brotherhood of Darkness lost all but two of the battles, reducing their once fearsome army to a tenth of its original size.

Into this morass came Bane. He chose not to take revenge on Kaan for the failed attempt at poisoning, instead focusing his attention on the annihilation of Lord Hoth's forces. Gathering all the Sith Lords on a mountaintop, Bane sharpened their dark energies into a Force storm that aged the lush Ruusan landscape into dust and ash. Kaan used the opportunity to attack the reeling Jedi. Then the most devastating blow came from one of the Jedi army's own recruits, an untrained boy named Tomcat. He killed Kiel Charny with Charny's own lightsaber, then defected to the Sith side.

Unfortunately for the Sith, it was apparent that the power of the dark side had driven Lord Kaan mad. Kaan and his disciples hunkered in their underground chambers and used their powers to create a "thought bomb"—a volatile cauldron of seething Force energy.

The following morning, Lord Hoth and the Army of Light marched into the enemy encampment, past the severed heads and dangling corpses of Jedi. The Lord of Darkness and the Defender of Light confronted one another, and Kaan triggered the thought bomb. A furious explosion of energy annihilated nearly every member of both armies, sucking their disembodied spirits into an unbreakable state of equilibrium.

Bane was one of the few to survive the blast. Afterward, he sensed the latent power of a young girl named Rain, Tomcat's sister who had slipped into darkness while she was lost in the Ruusan wilderness. Bane approached her as a potential apprentice, telling her to find her way to Onderon if she wished to continue in her journey as a Sith.

Bane departed for Onderon's dark side–saturated moon, Dxun. In the tomb of Freedon Nadd, he meditated on Sith power as barnacle-like orbalisks covered him in a permanent suit of living armor. Bane believed that he had discovered the secret to the Sith's continued survival. Too many Sith Lords spread the energy of the dark side too thin, while also inviting power struggles. By establishing a strict dictate of only one Master and one apprentice at any time, the Sith could dwell in the shadows until they had consolidated more power than ever before. Darth Bane retrieved Rain from Onderon, and she became his apprentice—Darth Zannah.

Meanwhile, the Jedi could not free the spirits from the valley that encircled the Ruusan battle site. Lord Hoth's former apprentice petitioned the Senate to erect a memorial on the grounds, and the Valley of the Jedi soon boasted towering statuary and memorial inscriptions. But the Jedi Order wished to forget its failure, and deleted most mentions of the battle from their archives. The passage of time did the rest. Ruusan would be all but forgotten within a few centuries, save for an enigmatic prophecy made by Ruusan's natives: "A Knight shall come, a battle will be fought, and the prisoners go free." That prophecy would remain unfulfilled until a year after the Battle of Endor.

THE RUUSAN REFORMATIONS
1000 B.B.Y.

Ruusan went down as a Republic victory—Kaan's Brotherhood of Darkness was no more, and all the Sith Lords had either died or disappeared. But the ranks of the Jedi had suffered terribly during the war, and without their unifying police-like presence, more than two dozen self-contained kingdoms announced their intentions to follow the lead of the Hapes Consortium two thousand years earlier and withdraw from the Republic.

The chancellor at the time, Tarsus Valorum, knew that radical steps had to be taken to prevent the splintering of the once proud Republic. Proclaiming that the Republic as its citizens knew it no longer existed, Valorum ushered in a new era with the passage of the Ruusan Reformations. The act diminished the governmental authority of the chancellor and gave greater control to planetary systems and sectors, thereby giving the Senate unprecedented levels of power. The Republic vowed to dismantle its standing army (already decimated by the last Sith conflict) and assist territories in raising their own defense forces. Finally, the Reformations codified the Jedi Order as a branch of the Judicial Department, answerable to the Senate. Valorum even

The armies of the Jedi clash with the Sith Brotherhood of Darkness in the climactic Battle of Ruusan. [ART BY TOMMY LEE EDWARDS]

began a new calendar, with years starting over at 1.

The Ruusan Reformations may have saved the Republic, but by giving every Senator a powerful voice, Tarsus Valorum had invited gridlock and greed. Frustration with the system would continue to grow among the populace throughout the following centuries.

JEDI VALIANCY
1000 B.B.Y.

Over the next thousand years, the Sith Brotherhood remained in hiding. They meditated on the dark side and systemitized their teachings. Choosing not to recruit widely, they continued by the system of each Master training only one apprentice. Like monks in a hermitage, the Sith waited in isolation for a chance to strike at the Jedi. Yoda, born in 896 B.B.Y., would shape the Jedi Order during this era.

Even without the influence of the Sith, some Jedi were occasionally seduced by evil. The Council rarely executed these fallen Jedi Knights, preferring instead to banish the offenders, in the hope that in primitive isolation the outcasts might focus on their Masters' teachings and return to the light. Approximately 600 B.B.Y., a fallen Jedi named Allya was exiled to the savage forests of Dathomir, a rugged planet that had long served as a prison colony for some of the Republic's worst criminals. Allya used the Force to subjugate the other prisoners and to tame Dathomir's feral rancors. Over time Allya had many daughters, all of whom she taught to use the Force. A female-dominant society eventually took shape, led by "Witches" who viewed the Force as a form of atavistic magic.

Economic forces continued to shape the Republic. In 490 B.B.Y., the Corporate Sector was established in the fringes of the galaxy's Tingel Arm, where companies could buy and manage star systems in an early attempt at founding a free trade zone. In 470 B.B.Y., the Corellian sector invoked the ancient constitutional clause of *Contemplanys Hermi,* which allowed them to temporarily withdraw from the Republic in a short-lived bid at territorial independence. In 350 B.B.Y., the Trade Federation came into existence to represent the needs of major shipping corporations. The Trade Federation, dominated by Neimoidians, became known for its greed.

Other Jedi, continuing their work across the Republic, laid the foundations for events that would have an impact centuries later. Approximately 400 B.B.Y., a Hutt Jedi hopeful, Beldorion the Splendid, traveled to Nam Chorios and discovered that the planet's crystal energy magnified his Force powers. Beldorion set himself up as a petty local dictator. Elsewhere, a tiny Kushiban named Ikrit journeyed to Yavin 4 and discovered the golden sphere that Exar Kun had created thousands of years earlier. Realizing that he was incapable of freeing the Massassi spirits trapped within the orb, Ikrit placed himself in stasis to await the arrival of one who could break the curse, even if it would take centuries. In 380 B.B.Y., the Corellian Jedi Keiran Halcyon defeated the *Afarathu* terrorists, a radical group of Selonians who wanted to eliminate humans from within the Corellian system's borders.

Dathomir's Witches came to the Republic's attention in 340 B.B.Y. when the massive Jedi training vessel *Chu'unthor* crashed on the planet's surface. A triumvirate of famous Jedi Masters—Gra'aton, Vulatan, and Yoda—along with many Jedi Knights and acolytes attempted to rescue the *Chu'unthor*'s passengers by battling the native spellcasters. On a return visit, Master Yoda used his insight to negotiate a peaceful settlement with the leader of the Witches.

The Mandalorian warrior clans committed the greatest crime of this era. Having defeated the Ithullans in a war over a narcolethe distillery in 200 B.B.Y., the Mandalorians then went on to exterminate the entire Ithullan species. Unfortunately, the Jedi Council did nothing in response to the genocide, and several rogue Jedi allied with the Bounty Hunters' Guild to take down the ruling Mandalore.

PART TWO

The Fall of the Republic

Approximately two hundred years before the Battle of Yavin, the shape of the Force abruptly seemed to flux. The greatest Jedi Masters, those most in touch with the unifying Force, studied this puzzle in quiet meditation. All of them reported the same thing—the murkiness, the uncertainty, the looming sense of dread all pointed to the growing power of the dark side. At first, some proposed that the Sith had returned, but when no Dark Lords made an appearance, an alternate explanation gained credence. Under this theory, one championed by Master Yoda, the gathering darkness indicated the coming fulfillment of an obscure, millennia-old prophecy that a Chosen One would one day destroy the Sith and bring balance to the Force. Yoda believed that the dark side could not be fully defeated by anyone save the Chosen One, and Yoda knew that he was not that person. The Chosen One would be a vessel of pure Force, more powerful than any Jedi in the history of the Order.

Not every Jedi agreed with Yoda's interpretation of the Chosen One prophecy. Some even disputed that the dark side was mustering strength. Seventy years after the first discovery of the flux (approximately 130 B.B.Y.), a group of Jedi formed a breakaway sect called the Potentium. Their creed stated that the dark side didn't truly exist and that the Jedi should embrace the Force's benevolence without regard for the strictures laid down by the Jedi Council. Yoda led the campaign to expel the Potentium from the Jedi Order.

Under the gathering darkness, Jedi victories seemed to be offset by setbacks of injustice or self-indulgence. In 124 B.B.Y., the Wol Cabasshite Jedi Master Omo Bouri orchestrated the famed Treaty of Trammis, but later that same year the Republic Senate declared the Outer Rim a free trade zone. This permitted the Trade Federation to represent planets that chose to align with it, giving corporations voting power in the Senate.

THE MAKING OF DOOKU
89–53 B.B.Y.

Count Dooku, heir to the aristocracy of Serenno, became a ward of the Jedi at a very early age and spent years training with Yoda in the Jedi Temple on Coruscant. In 89 B.B.Y., at the age of thirteen, Dooku was chosen as the Padawan of Master Thame Cerulian. Scandal marred his ascension, however, when Dooku was caught up in a fellow student's plot to steal a Sith Holocron from the Jedi archives. Though the Council cleared Dooku of any wrongdoing, they expelled student Lorian Nod from the Order. The experience left Dooku wary of friendship, and inordinately curious about the teachings of the Sith.

In his early twenties, Dooku took on his own Padawan learner, Qui-Gon Jinn—an at-times rebellious pupil with a deep connection to the living Force. On one early mission, Dooku and Qui-Gon fought Dooku's former friend Lorian Nod, who had become a pirate following his banishment from the Jedi Order.

Qui-Gon eventually became a Jedi Knight, but his kindness stood in stark contrast to the severity of his Master. Qui-Gon would endure his own troubles, however. He took on an apprentice of his own named Xanatos, but the boy never fully appreciated the teachings of the Jedi. In 53 B.B.Y., Master Yoda asked Qui-Gon and Xanatos to mediate a dispute on Telos.

This was intended to be Xanatos's final test before Jedi Knighthood. Telos, however, had been Xanatos's home before his induction into the Jedi Order, and his father Crion now ruled the planet with an iron grip. Rather than aiding the rebels, Xanatos took command of his father's army. Qui-Gon brought an end to the civil war by killing Crion. Xanatos, vowing revenge against his Master for his father's murder, vanished.

Dooku considered the incident a natural outgrowth of Qui-Gon's reliance on the living Force—Qui-Gon's "feelings" had failed him, and Dooku knew that, in the end, everyone was capable of betrayal.

FAILING REPUBLIC, THRIVING SITH
52–46 B.B.Y.

The Republic had grown stagnant. As a sprawling representative government hobbled by numerous sets of checks and balances, even simple decision making had turned impossible. Many Senators and planetary governors began to take the view that the existing system of government would continue through sheer force of inertia. Laziness and complacency became the rule, and with this apathy came corruption.

The crafty Senator Palpatine studied the government's decay with a practiced eye and a knowing smile. Elected in 52 B.B.Y. to represent the citizens of Naboo, he knew the time was drawing near when the citizenry would cry out for strong leadership. Palpatine set wheels in motion behind the scenes.

It is unclear how Palpatine fell under the mentorship of the Sith Lord Darth Plagueis, and little is known of Plagueis's own career. A mystic obsessed with eternal life, Plagueis is believed to have possessed knowledge that could sustain those who were dying, and perhaps had even gained the ability to use midi-chlorians to draw new life directly from the wellspring of the Force. Palpatine—under the Sith name Darth Sidious—learned dark side traditions from Plagueis, but grew concerned over his Master's stated intentions to create life from nothing. The child that resulted from this Force miracle, Plagueis insisted, would be the living embodiment of the Force itself—and at that moment, Sidious knew that his Master was discussing Sidious's *replacement*. Soon after, Sidious killed Darth Plagueis in his sleep. The work necessary to create a Force-conceived child continued, however. It is unclear whether Plagueis had initiated the process before his death, or whether Sidious instead implemented his former Master's scheme for his own dark purposes.

In keeping with the Sith rule, Sidious accelerated the training of his own pet project, the Zabrak child called Maul. Unknown to Plagueis, Sidious had taken the Zabrak from his homeworld of Iridonia and, in a dark reflection of the Jedi Order's own training methods, began tutoring Maul in the art of cruelty and manipulation. Droids did most of the day-to-day work, for Sidious needed to maintain his role as Senator of Naboo. But whenever Sidious returned to his secret Coruscant lair, he gave Maul lessons in how to take a blow without flinching and how to kill lesser creatures without mercy.

On Tatooine, the slave Shmi Skywalker had given birth to a child more powerful in the Force than any other in history—the apparent product of forbidden research initiated by Darth Plagueis and taken up by Darth Sidious. This boy, Anakin Skywalker, had seemingly not been conceived by a human father, but by the midi-chlorians themselves. Palpatine kept a close watch on Anakin as the boy grew. If trained as a Sith apprentice, such a child could be vastly more powerful than Maul.

Local uprisings began to afflict the Republic during these years, the first being the Arkanian Revolution in 50 B.B.Y. Centered on Arkanian space in the Colonies region, the incident pitted a noninterventionist faction of Arkanians against the hard-line geneticists of the Arkanian Dominion. The geneticists, who had forcibly reengineered a number of species over the millennia including the Quermians and the Yakas, now stood helpless in the face of a spliced-together army.

The revolutionaries had created fierce mercenary cyborgs, who slaughtered thousands until the Dominion appealed for help from the Jedi. The revolutionaries perished, but a few of their creations survived. One of them, the patchwork bounty hunter Gorm the Dissolver, would later battle a rising star in the Jedi ranks named Mace Windu.

In 47 B.B.Y., the Jedi lost one of their greatest warriors—Sharad Hett, "the Howlrunner." Hett vanished after discovering the murder of his birth parents, and was presumed dead. In truth he had fallen in with the Tusken Raiders on Tatooine, where he became the leader of a Tusken tribe.

In the Republic Senate, officials continued to throw money away on grandiose projects. One example was the *Katana* fleet, an armada of two hundred slave-rigged Dreadnaughts completed in 46 B.B.Y. Tragically, a hive virus caused the crew of the flagship *Katana* to go mad. They jumped their ship into hyperspace using random coordinates, and the slave rig brought the other 199 vessels along for the ride. The *Katana* fleet would remain undiscovered for more than half a century, and the fiasco further eroded public confidence in the Republic's leadership.

FATEFUL APPRENTICESHIP
44 B.B.Y.

Qui-Gon Jinn took his second Padawan this year, following his failure with his apprentice Xanatos. Thirteen-year old Obi-Wan Kenobi had originally been slated for a career in the Jedi Agricultural Corps, but earned his place alongside Qui-Gon following a crisis on Bandomeer.

Clues behind the Bandomeer mission indicated that Xanatos had reemerged, now reigning as the corrupt kingpin of the Offworld Mining Corporation and the new ruler of Telos. The ex-Padawan attempted to assassinate Yoda and destroy the Jedi Temple, but Qui-Gon and Obi-Wan caught up with him on Telos. In a final confrontation with his former Master, Xanatos killed himself in a pool of acid rather than surrender. His son, under the name Granta Omega, would make trouble for Obi-Wan nearly twenty years in the future.

THE STARK HYPERSPACE CONFLICT
44 B.B.Y.

Though its battles took place only on a single planet, the so-called Stark Hyperspace Conflict intensified calls for a Grand Army of the Republic and raised the fortunes of two key historical players—Senator Finis Valorum

of Coruscant and Minister Nute Gunray of the Trade Federation.

The incident began with a bacta supply crisis. Iaco Stark, a charismatic Outer Rim pirate and head of the Stark Commercial Combine, raided cargo ships carrying bacta and sold the stolen goods at a huge markup. Senator Valorum proposed that the Trade Federation, the Republic, and the Stark Commercial Combine air their issues at a diplomatic summit on the Xexto homeworld of Troiken.

Jedi negotiators assigned to the Troiken summit included Tyvokka—a Wookiee Master serving on the Jedi Council—as well as Plo Koon, Qui-Gon Jinn, and Qui-Gon's new Padawan Obi-Wan Kenobi. Plans for a peaceful meeting, however, were doomed from the start. Senator Ranulph Tarkin of Eriadu, a devout militarist, had assembled his own armada. He was already en route to Troiken to crush Stark's pirate fleet and win himself glory.

Stark, knowing an attack was imminent, unleashed a computer virus that affected all Republic navicomputers. No longer able to plot courses through hyperspace, most of Tarkin's vessels collided with mass shadows or disappeared into black holes. Stark attempted to hold the delegates hostage, but they escaped and regrouped in the caverns of Troiken's Mount Avos.

Tyvokka succumbed to injuries, and Plo Koon—who had once been Tyvokka's Padawan—used the crisis to make himself a legend. In a series of punishing ground battles against Stark's troops, Koon rallied the Republic soldiers under his command and drove back the enemy despite overwhelming odds.

The Republic finally assembled reinforcements, but at this point Stark had decided that he couldn't win. In exchange for immunity, he supplied the patch to eliminate the navicomputer virus. But no one informed Ranulph Tarkin, who was determined to go out as a hero. Tarkin detonated an explosive charge at Mount Avos, killing himself and freeing millions of flesh-eating insects from the inner caverns that devoured the remainder of Stark's army.

The resolution of the crisis made Valorum a political star. Nute Gunray earned a promotion to viceroy. And Plo Koon honored his former Master's dying wish by taking Tyvokka's seat on the Jedi Council.

Months after the Stark incident, the Republic experienced the Kol Huro Unrest, in which a local despot used the Kol Huro factories to turn out an army of battle droids. The Jedi squashed the minor rebellion, but the use of droids in combat would become an increasingly hot topic as the Trade Federation moved to grow the size of its own automated "security force."

THE BATTLE OF GALIDRAAN
40 B.B.Y.

The Battle of Galidraan marked the end of the Mandalorian Civil War, a conflict between the True Mandalorians and the Mandalorian Death Watch that had been sizzling for over a quarter century. Following the Mandalorians' extinction of the Ithullans a century and a half earlier, some clan members had expressed a desire to shed the amoral ways of the "Mandalorian Mercs." Eventually, the charismatic Jaster Mereel came to lead the clans as Mandalore, and set down an idealistic code of conduct in the Supercommando Codex. A Mandalorian named Vizsla attracted followers fond of the old ways, who formed the Death Watch faction. Armed conflict broke out approximately 60 B.B.Y.

Vizsla succeeded in killing Jaster Mereel, but Mereel's role as head of the True Mandalorians was filled by Jango Fett. After decades of infighting, Galidraan was to be the end of the Death Watch—but instead it proved to be the end of four thousand years of Mandalorian dominance.

The governor of Galidraan informed Jango Fett that he would give up Vizsla's location if Jango's troops terminated a group of local rebels. They did so, only to learn that the governor and the Death Watch had set Jango up. Protesting to the Republic that the True Mandalorians had slaughtered innocents, the governor called in a Jedi peacekeeping force led by Master Dooku and his Padawan, Komari Vosa. The Mandalorian army fought to the last man; only their commander Jango survived, to become the prisoner of slavers.

The once great Mandalorian power had been forever gutted. Besides Jango, only Vizsla and a few surviving Death Watch members remained active in the galaxy, while a small regiment of troopers remained on the planet Mandalore as a home guard.

MOVING INTO ALIGNMENT
40–36 B.B.Y.

In 40 B.B.Y., Finis Valorum began the first of two terms as Supreme Chancellor of the Republic. The influential Tarkin family helped push the election through, on the condition that Valorum posthumously decorate Senator Ranulph Tarkin for his role in ending the Stark Hyperspace Conflict.

Obi-Wan Kenobi continued to grow in his apprenticeship to Qui-Gon Jinn. The two found themselves running missions on behalf of Supreme Chancellor Valorum, who was a fan of the Jedi Order. Their assignments frequently paired them with Adi Gallia and her Padawan Siri Tachi. Obi-Wan grew fond of Siri, as both a colleague and . . . something more. In this, he was following the lead of his impulsive Master Qui-Gon, who held his own feelings for a fellow Jedi Master named Tahl. In 39 B.B.Y., Tahl died on a mission to New Apsolon, spurring Qui-Gon to vengeance—but he managed to pull himself back from the brink of rage.

Qui-Gon and Obi-Wan also helped Attichitcuk, leader of a Wookiee colony, establish a new settlement on Alaris Prime despite opposition from the Trade Federation. Attichitcuk's son Chewbacca would later become one of the greatest heroes of the Rebel Alliance.

In 36 B.B.Y., Finis Valorum won a second four-year term as Supreme Chancellor, though by this time many Senators were beginning to have doubts about his leadership. Opposition parties began considering possible replacements, a list that always seemed to include Naboo's Senator Palpatine.

THE YINCHORRI UPRISING
33 B.B.Y.

The Jedi Order numbered more than ten thousand members and could have vanquished any foe if permitted to attack en masse, but Judicial Department bureaucracy tied the hands of the Jedi and often left them shockingly

Padawans Anakin Skywalker and Siri Tachi, with their Masters, Obi-Wan Kenobi and Adi Gallia [Art by Tommy Lee Edwards]

ineffectual. No incident better captured this paralysis than the Yinchorri Uprising.

The reptilian Yinchorri controlled several worlds in their star system, including their home planet Yinchorr and the colony moons of Yitheeth, Yibikkoror, and Uhanayih. Stirrings of aggression against neighboring planets prompted Chancellor Valorum to dispatch a Jedi team to assess the situation. The Yinchorri dumped the bodies of the Jedi investigators on Valorum's doorstep.

Mace Windu sent only three Republic cruisers to put down the uprising. Though the cruisers carried some of the best Jedi in the order—including Windu, Adi Gallia, Eeth Koth, Plo Koon, Micah Giiett, Qui-Gon Jinn, and Qui-Gon's Padawan Obi-Wan Kenobi—the Yinchorri possessed cortosis-weave armor that could resist lightsaber cuts. They also had the advice and silent backing of Darth Sidious.

Yoda stopped a Yinchorri assault against the Jedi Temple on Coruscant, but Mace Windu's team walked into a bloodbath on the worlds of the Yinchorr system. The Jedi casualties included Micah Giiett, who sacrificed himself to slow the advance of Yinchorri troops. Ultimately, Valorum won Senate approval of an emergency measure to blockade the system, forcing the Yinchorri to surrender in the face of overwhelming power.

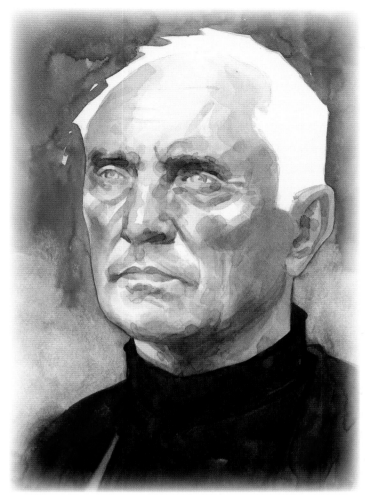

Supreme Chancellor Finis Valorum
[Art by Mark Chiarello]

The Jedi Council failed to apply any learnings from the debacle, passing over the iconoclastic Qui-Gon Jinn for Micah Giiett's Jedi Council seat in favor of the by-the-book Cerean Jedi Ki-Adi-Mundi. Chancellor Valorum looked more ineffectual than ever, and political observers declared Valorum's career to be on life support.

Before Ki-Adi-Mundi accepted the Jedi Council's offer to serve as one of their members, he returned to his homeworld of Cerea. Unlike other Jedi of the time, Ki-Adi-Mundi had children and several wives, a unique dispensation given

Mace Windu whirls to face a charging Yinchorri warrior.
[Art by Tommy Lee Edwards]

to Cerean Jedi due to the species' low birthrate. Ki-Adi-Mundi became involved in a dispute between the Cerean preservationists, who wished to outlaw technology, and the young people of his world, who were enamored with the high-speed swoopbikes imported by offworlders.

THE ERIADU SUMMIT
32.5 B.B.Y.

Darth Sidious had shaped Maul into a razor-honed weapon. The Zabrak apprentice, now a Dark Lord of the Sith, wielded a double-bladed lightsaber (patterned after the one used by Exar Kun during the Sith War) and wore a jagged red-and-black tattoo over his entire body. Sidious wasted no time sending his agent out on missions. At a lommite-mining colony on Dorvalla, Maul used stealth to pit two rival mining operations against each other, leaving the planet ripe for takeover by the Trade Federation.

The event solidified the hold that Darth Sidious had over Nute Gunray of the Trade Federation. Sidious also had contacts among the Nebula Front, a band of pirates and terrorists who fought the Trade Federation in the outlying systems. The violence between the Trade Federation and the Nebula Front had become a political hot button in the Republic Senate. From his darkened sanctum, Darth Sidious saw this as the perfect wedge. By pushing it, he could crush Chancellor Valorum and eventually split the Republic.

Sidious set things in motion with a second incident at Dorvalla. Space pirate Arwen Cohl, working on behalf of a radical arm of the Nebula Front, raided the Trade Federation freighter *Revenue* and made off with a stash of aurodium ingots worth two billion credits.

In response to the theft, Sidious—in his role as Senator Palpatine—convinced Chancellor Valorum to propose a tax on the Outer Rim trade routes, effectively abolishing the free trade zone that had made the Trade Federation so wealthy. Senator Lott Dod of the Trade Federation objected to this obvious check to its power, and demanded that his conglomerate be allowed to expand its droid armies to defend against the Nebula Front. To allow both sides to voice their concerns, Palpatine suggested that a summit be held on Eriadu, the Outer Rim home of the powerful Tarkin family.

On Coruscant, a Nebula Front assassin shot and wounded Valorum. In response, a Jedi task force

Darth Maul makes short work of Black Sun's defenders on Ralltiir. [Art by Tommy Lee Edwards]

smashed a Nebula Front base on Asmeru in the Senex sector, uncovering enough clues for Qui-Gon Jinn and Obi-Wan Kenobi to learn of a second assassination plot against Valorum, this time on Eriadu. Qui-Gon received unexpected help from pirate Arwen Cohl, who had had a falling-out with his Nebula Front confederates.

Valorum survived the Eriadu summit without a scratch. The true targets of the assassination proved to be the ruling members of the Trade Federation directorate, who were gunned down by their own security droids. This left Sidious's puppet Nute Gunray as the Trade Federation's ruling viceroy.

On Naboo, the corrupt King Veruna chose this moment to abdicate the throne. Padmé Naberrie, a fourteen-year-old girl currently serving as Princess of Theed under the "name of state" of Amidala, became Naboo's new monarch. Veruna, who was known to have had close ties with Senator Palpatine, later died under mysterious circumstances.

Showing little sympathy for the Trade Federation after the Eriadu disaster, the Republic Senate passed Valorum's taxation proposal. Sidious suggested to Nute Gunray that he retaliate in symbolic fashion by blockading a planet, preferably Senator Palpatine's homeworld of Naboo.

Chancellor Valorum suffered yet another blow when evidence, planted by Sidious, suggested that he had arranged for the two billion in stolen aurodium to be transferred to a small family company, Valorum Shipping, on Eriadu. Though formally cleared of charges, Valorum privately admitted that his rule had been crippled. Rumors swirled that he might be forced from office before the completion of his term.

FINAL PREPARATIONS
32 B.B.Y.

With his plans now inevitable, Darth Sidious moved to tie up loose ends. Darth Maul traveled to the Core world of Ralltiir in his newly acquired Sith Infiltrator starship *Scimitar*, aiming to kill the assembled mob bosses of the Black Sun syndicate. Maul buzz-sawed his way through the stronghold, eviscerating Black Sun leader Alexi Garyn and scores of underlings. The loss of Black Sun's entire command structure left the organization in disarray for many years. Following an intense power struggle, the Falleen prince Xizor assumed authority over the consortium.

Nute Gunray and the other Neimoidians were vital to Darth Sidious's plans, but they carried with them a huge risk—as a rule, Neimoidians had difficulty keeping their mouths shut. Sidious had revealed his plans for the invasion of Naboo to only three top-level Neimoidians besides Gunray, but one of them, Hath Monchar, decided that selling the information could make him very rich.

By the time Sidious realized the risk, Monchar had already fled to Coruscant with a holocron that contained full details on the Sith plot. Darth Maul set off in search of Monchar and the intelligence he carried.

The Neimoidian soon lost his head to Maul's dual-bladed lightsaber, but other people had already been exposed to the information, including Jedi Padawan Darsha Assant and data broker Lorn Pavan. Maul chased them through the undercity past cannibalistic Cthons and a train-sized taozin worm, and eventually killed the Padawan. Lorn Pavan foolishly tried to get the drop on Maul aboard an orbital space station, but received critical injuries during the fight. Before he died, Pavan gave Monchar's information to Senator Palpatine, never knowing that he had only brought it full circle, back to the original mastermind.

One month before the event now known as the Battle of Naboo, the Trade Federation carried through on its threat and blockaded Naboo in defiance of the taxation of the Outer Rim trade routes. Valorum realized he had to do something radical to shore up his crumbling support base. Exploiting his friendship with Jedi Master Adi Gallia, Valorum went directly to the Jedi Council to request mediators, breaking protocol by neglecting to inform the Senate of his decision. Mace Windu sent Qui-Gon Jinn and Obi-Wan Kenobi to Naboo to apply direct pressure on the Trade Federation viceroy and to force Gunray's vessels to stand down.

THE BATTLE OF NABOO
32 B.B.Y.

Qui-Gon and Obi-Wan received a poor welcome aboard the Trade Federation flagship. Viceroy Nute Gunray destroyed their landing ship and attempted to eliminate them with poison gas and droidekas. The two Jedi escaped to the planet's surface with the knowledge that the Trade Federation was planning a full-scale invasion of Naboo using a vast battle droid army.

In Naboo's capital city of Theed, Queen Padmé Amidala waited with a heavy heart for the Trade Federation's army. She had been Naboo's monarch for only six months, and for the past several weeks she had worked in vain to end the blockade. Columns of battle tanks approached the Palace, and Queen Amidala became the prisoner of battle droids.

In the Naboo swamps, Qui-Gon and Obi-Wan met a native Gungan named Jar Jar Binks, who introduced them to Boss Nass, ruler of the underwater city of Otoh Gunga. The trio borrowed a submersible to take them to Theed, where the Jedi freed Queen Amidala and her military aides. The group escaped Naboo aboard the Royal Starship, bound for Coruscant.

Unfortunately, a hyperdrive malfunction forced the ship to drop into realspace before it could begin its jaunt down the Corellian Run. In need of discreet repairs, the group had no choice but to touch down on the desert planet Tatooine.

Qui-Gon took it upon himself to obtain a replacement hyperdrive generator. In Mos Espa he found a Toydarian dealer with the parts Qui-Gon needed. The Toydarian also owned a nine-year-old slave, Anakin Skywalker. Anakin's mother, Shmi, confirmed in her own words what Qui-Gon had already suspected—the boy was immeasurably strong in the Force. Neither knew of Darth Plagueis's suspected involvement in inducing midi-chlorians to create life, though Shmi informed Qui-Gon that Anakin had no natural father.

Queen Padmé Amidala of Naboo
[ART BY MARK CHIARELLO]

By wagering that Anakin would win Mos Espa's Boonta Eve Podrace, Qui-Gon obtained the hyperdrive parts, and he secured Anakin's freedom. Tearfully, the boy bid farewell to his mother, promising to return one day to free her. He also left behind C-3PO, a protocol droid he had built from spare parts.

Darth Sidious learned of his enemies' arrival on Tatooine. He dispatched his apprentice Darth Maul in order to prevent the Jedi from meddling with Anakin Skywalker's fate. Maul engaged Qui-Gon in a frenzied lightsaber attack, but failed to prevent the Jedi from bringing both Anakin and Queen Amidala to Coruscant.

Qui-Gon brought Anakin before the Jedi Council. Yoda and Mace Windu remained unconvinced that the boy could be the Chosen One of prophecy who would restore balance to the Force. In the Republic Senate, Queen Amidala begged for help on behalf of her conquered homeworld. When her pleas failed to move anyone to action, she gave in to Senator Palpatine's advice and called for a vote of no confidence in Chancellor Valorum.

Rather than wait for the Senate to determine Valorum's successor, Amidala decided to return to Naboo and stand beside the people she had sworn to represent. Qui-Gon, Obi-Wan, and Anakin accompanied her with the blessing of the Jedi Council. The Queen enlisted the help of Boss Nass's Gungan army to provide a diversion on the great grass plains so that Amidala's group could sneak into the Palace and capture Nute Gunray.

A strike team captured the Theed hangar and seized its N-1 starfighters, taking off to attack the Trade Federation's orbiting Droid Control Ship. Anakin Skywalker inadvertently joined this group along with the astromech droid R2-D2, and Anakin's natural skill with the Force led to the destruction of the Droid Control Ship with a pair of proton torpedoes. The explosion of the vessel triggered the collapse of the Trade Federation's droid army, saving Boss Nass's Gungans from annihilation in the ground battle below.

Queen Amidala scaled the Palace walls and forced the surrender of Viceroy Nute Gunray, while Qui-Gon and Obi-Wan battled Darth Maul above the bottomless abyss of the Theed power generator. During the fighting, impenetrable electron walls closed to separate Obi-Wan from his Master. Obi-Wan watched in helpless shock as Maul stabbed Qui-Gon through the chest with his double-edged light-saber.

As soon as the electron walls dropped, Obi-Wan attacked in a haze of grief and sliced Darth Maul in half. Later, in the Palace turret room, Yoda promoted Obi-Wan to the rank of Jedi Knight. He also passed along the Council's recommendation that Anakin be trained as Obi-Wan's new apprentice. The Jedi Order realized that Darth Maul had been a Sith, and Yoda began the search for the second Sith—the one who would have trained Maul and possibly even orchestrated the Naboo invasion. The reemergence of the Sith also seemed to confirm Yoda's interpretation of the prophecy of the Chosen One.

In a final celebration on the Palace steps, Queen Amidala and Boss Nass presided over the long-overdue unification of their two civilizations. Behind them, Palpatine, the newly elected Supreme Chancellor of the Republic following Valorum's forced ouster, looked on with satisfaction.

At this time, Nute Gunray, viceroy of the Trade Federation, began the first of what would be four trials in the Supreme Court for his actions in the invasion of Naboo. Exonerated time and again by his timid prosecutors, who didn't want to upset the Trade Federation economic engine, Gunray held on to his title and status. Eventually, the Republic announced the public disarmament of the Trade Federation's battle fleet and droid army, but no significant reductions followed.

THE LOST TWENTY
32 B.B.Y.

Master Dooku, hero of the Battle of Galidraan, had become a thorn in the side of the Jedi Order. Dooku's first Padawan, Qui-Gon Jinn, had died at Naboo, while his second, Komari Vosa, had disappeared after Galidraan. Dooku had since become a very public critic of the Republic's corruption and the Jedi Order's complicity in

propping up a broken system. His protestations disturbed the Jedi Council, but none of its members were aware that Dooku had already fallen under the sway of Darth Sidious.

One of Dooku's close friends within the Order, Master Sifo-Dyas, perceived the events surrounding the reappearance of the Sith and believed that the Republic could not survive without additional defenders. Without the knowledge of his Jedi colleagues, Sifo-Dyas placed an order for a massive clone army with the geneticists of Kamino. Darth Sidious learned of the plan and moved to secure the army for his own purposes. As a final test of loyalty for his would-be apprentice, he ordered Dooku to kill Sifo-Dyas.

After the clandestine murder, Dooku erased all traces of Kamino from the Jedi archives and announced his intention to leave the Order. Now a true Sith Lord, Dooku took the secret name of Darth Tyranus. He returned to his native Serenno, taking up the title and holdings due to him as the planet's hereditary Count, then disappeared from public view. Dooku became the newest Jedi Master to leave the Order, making the Lost Nineteen into the Lost Twenty.

THE PRIME CLONE
32 B.B.Y.

Dooku knew that the Kaminoan clone army had to be flawless if it hoped to stand a chance against the forces of industry he would soon marshal on the opposite side. For the genetic template that would become the Prime Clone, Dooku had his eye on Jango Fett, the greatest (and one of the last) of the Mandalorians. Jango had escaped from two years spent as a slave, following his capture in the Battle of Galidraan—a battle that Dooku had orchestrated. After once again donning the armor of the Mandalorians, Jango reinvented himself, this time as a

Jango Fett
[Art by Mark Chiarello]

bounty hunter. Having heard that Jango had also tracked down and killed Vizsla of the Mandalorian Death Watch, it was clear to Dooku that slavery had done nothing to dull Jango's edge.

Dooku chose to test Jango and the galaxy's other top bounty hunters by posting a five-million-credit bounty on the head of his former Padawan Komari Vosa, who had become the leader of the Bando Gora cult. Jango's quest took him to the penitentiary on Oovo IV, where he fought his way through a jailbreak alongside fellow hunter Zam Wesell, who revealed herself as a shape-shifting Clawdite. Jango escaped by stealing a prototype *Firespray*-class police interceptor, which replaced his former vessel, *Jaster's*

The Gungan Grand Army prepares to engage Trade Federation forces on Naboo. [Art by Tommy Lee Edwards]

Legacy. Jango christened his new ship *Slave I.*

Jango tracked Komari Vosa to Kohlma, one of the Bogden moons. There he defeated an old Mandalorian rival named Montross to claim the five-million-credit bounty. Although Jango got the drop on Komari Vosa, it was Dooku who delivered the killing blow.

Now confident of Jango's skills, Count Dooku summoned the bounty hunter to his retreat on one of the moons of Bogden, engaging him in a test of wits involving mutual poisonings. At last satisfied with each other's sincerity, Jango agreed to Dooku's offer and accepted a lucrative and low-effort contract as the Kaminoan Prime Clone. Jango made one special request—he wanted an unaltered clone to raise as his own. He would name this clone Boba Fett.

The Kaminoans set to work growing soldiers based on the Fett genetic template. Within ten years, the Republic would have the finest army in the galaxy. As leader of the Republic, Chancellor Palpatine would control the clones, while Dooku would raise an opposing army of corporate droids. The two sides, each under the control of a Sith Lord, would then fight a sham war that would decimate the Jedi and make the public hunger for a centralized government.

As a final step, Sidious ensured that every clone received special training for even the most extreme eventualities. When Sidious felt the time was right, he would activate this contingency plan by issuing "Order Sixty-Six."

DUTIES OF THE JEDI COUNCIL
32–30 B.B.Y.

To some, the Naboo crisis appeared to represent a new culture of lawlessness. The members of the Jedi Council had their hands full over the next year, putting down emergencies large and small.

Ki-Adi-Mundi returned to Tatooine to investigate reports that the legendary Jedi Knight Sharad "Howlrunner" Hett had reappeared after a fifteen-year absence. Sharad had apparently gone native and now controlled a tribe of Tusken Raiders. His young son, A'Sharad Hett, wore the mask and wrappings of a Tusken but wielded the lightsaber of a Jedi.

The mission was complicated by a local Hutt gang war between Gardulla and Jabba, as well as the appearance of Aurra Sing—a failed Padawan who had become a bounty hunter and assassin, collecting the lightsabers of the Jedi she murdered. Sing killed Sharad Hett, and Ki-Adi-Mundi took A'Sharad back to Coruscant as his new apprentice.

Months later, Mace Windu led a mission to Malastare to help mediate a dispute between the government of Lannik and a Lannik terrorist organization, the Red Iaro. The Jedi prevented the terrorists from feeding the Lannik prince to akk dogs, ravenous beasts hailing from Windu's homeworld of Haruun Kal. Mace Windu and Depa Billaba later smashed the illegal Nar Shaddaa operation that had been trafficking in akk dogs.

Aurra Sing made a reappearance in 30 B.B.Y., slaying Jedi Knights in the Coruscant undercity. Adi Gallia, along with Ki-Adi-Mundi and his new Padawan A'Sharad Hett, received the assignment to track Sing down. On a tropical planet buffeted by meteorites, A'Sharad tried and failed to take his revenge on the woman who had murdered his father. Even the arrival of the Dark Woman, Aurra Sing's former Master, was not enough to eliminate this dire threat to the Jedi.

QUINLAN VOS'S ROAD BACK
32–30 B.B.Y.

Jedi Knight Quinlan Vos had served the Order with honor. Former Padawan of Master Tholme, Quinlan possessed the Kiffu talent of psychometrics, allowing him to read memories and impressions directly off the surface of objects. He had recently taken the Twi'lek Aayla Secura as his Padawan.

Aurra Sing fights for her life against Jedi Padawan A'Sharad Hett.
[Art by Tommy Lee Edwards]

On a mission to investigate a new spice drug called glitteryll, Quinlan Vos and Aayla found themselves too close to a glitteryll-processing operation on Ryloth. Aayla's uncle, Pol Secura, wiped the memories of both Jedi and took Aayla as a house slave. Quinlan Vos awoke on Nar Shaddaa with no memory of who he was or how he had arrived there.

The Devaronian scoundrel Vilmarh "Villie" Grahrk helped Quinlan recover bits and pieces of his life history. Burning with rage, and no longer bound by the forgotten rules of his Jedi training, Quinlan would have murdered the Twi'lek Senator behind the glitteryll plot if not for Mace Windu's intervention. Quinlan agreed to return to the Jedi Temple for retraining.

In a field test of his reemerging abilities, Quinlan Vos executed a solo mission to Dathomir. Six hundred years after the arrival of Allya, the Witches of Dathomir had developed into primitive, Force-wielding clans. One of their more malevolent members, the Witch Zalem, had discovered a teleportational Infinity Gate buried in the heart of the planet by the pre-Republic Kwa species. Zalem triggered the Gate and unleashed a wave of energy directed at Coruscant, but Quinlan engineered the machine's destruction.

Aayla Secura, still tormented by her damaged memories, accidentally became stranded on the prison world of Kiffex. She freed the fallen Anzati Jedi Volfe Karkko from a stasis field, and Karkko rallied an army of his fellow Anzati vampires that overran Kiffex and terrorized the prisoners. Quinlan Vos, with help from his former Master Tholme, killed Karkko and freed Aayla Secura from his Anzati spell. Master Tholme agreed to train Aayla during her long path to recovery.

Nearly two years after the glitteryll incident, Aayla's homeworld of Ryloth became a trouble spot once more. Lon Secura, another of Aayla's uncles and ruler of Clan Secura, invited his niece and Master Tholme to mediate a clan dispute. Soon after their arrival, Kh'aris Fenn, an ambitious Twi'lek in league with Count Dooku, hired two Nikto of the Morgukai warrior tradition to kidnap Lon Secura's son Nat. In the lava fields of Kintan, Quinlan Vos and Aayla Secura defeated the two Morgukai and freed the young heir. For their roles in the rescue, the two Jedi received promotions—Quinlan Vos became a Jedi Master, while Aayla Secura graduated to Jedi Knight.

MISSION TO ZONAMA SEKOT
29 B.B.Y.

The Tarkin family of Eriadu played a critical, but mostly offstage, role in shaping galactic politics. Wilhuff Tarkin had once been a commander in the Republic Outland Regions Security Force and had recently served as the lieutenant governor of Eriadu. Like his cousin Ranulph—who had kick-started the Stark Hyperspace Conflict fifteen years earlier—Wilhuff Tarkin was an instigator.

Tarkin had already been contacted by Darth Sidious and was seduced by the Sith Lord's vision of a Human High Culture in which aliens would be pushed from power and forced to grovel as slaves. Tarkin enlisted his friend Raith Sienar, the genius starship engineer behind Republic Sienar Systems. Raith Sienar had designed Darth Maul's ship *Scimitar* and had already begun conceptual work on a moon-sized battle station, but Tarkin believed he could locate an even greater weapon.

Tarkin learned that the Jedi Council had dispatched Obi-Wan Kenobi and his Padawan Anakin Skywalker to the far-flung Gardaji Rift, the rumored location of the mythical "living planet" Zonama Sekot. A Jedi Knight named Vergere had vanished on a mission to Zonama Sekot one year prior. Obi-Wan and Anakin hoped to find Vergere, while Tarkin wanted to exploit Zonama Sekot's strange ability to fuse organic and high tech into starfighters faster than anything else in the galaxy. Sienar and Tarkin followed the two Jedi to Zonama Sekot with a Trade Federation armada.

The number and variety of living things in the jungles of Zonama Sekot left Anakin and Obi-Wan speechless. The planet's colonists, many descended from the expelled Jedi sect known as the Potentium, sold organic "seed-partners" that bonded to their hosts, allowing the living planet to grow ships personalized for each customer. Anakin attracted twelve seed-partners, more than anyone in history, and named his living starship *Jabitha* after the daughter of Zonama Sekot's ruling Magister.

By the time Tarkin arrived with a force sufficient to subjugate the planet, Obi-Wan and Anakin had learned that Zonama Sekot possessed a sentient consciousness. The planet revealed to them that a year earlier, Vergere had given herself up to scouts from an extragalactic species called the "Far Outsiders" (known to modern historians as the Yuuzhan Vong) in order to prevent them from attacking Zonama Sekot. Anakin and Obi-Wan's original mission could no longer be carried out, but they suddenly had a more pressing problem—halting Tarkin's attack and making it off the planet alive.

Anakin killed Sienar's Blood Carver bodyguard in a fit of rage, telekinetically burning the alien from the inside out. Anakin also met Wilhuff Tarkin for the first time, as a prisoner aboard his flagship. Obi-Wan Kenobi destroyed Tarkin's vessel, and the fighting gave Zonama Sekot sufficient time to initiate its planetary hyperspace engines. The entire planet vanished in a blink, presumably bound for the safety of the Unknown Regions.

Anakin did not get to keep *Jabitha*. Away from her creator-planet, the organic starfighter sickened and died. Sienar and Tarkin both returned to Republic space, winning forgiveness for the debacle by presenting the plans for Sienar's moon-sized Expeditionary Battle Planetoid to Supreme Chancellor Palpatine. When the battle station project shifted from conceptual stage to architectural planning, work moved to the planet Geonosis. There, engineer Bevel Lemelisk teamed with the hive-minded Geonosians to hammer out structural and power supply issues.

EDUCATION OF THE CHOSEN ONE
29–27 B.B.Y.

At this point in his apprenticeship, Anakin had progressed enough in his training to construct his own lightsaber, which he did inside the sacred crystal caves on the snow-wrapped planet of Ilum. He also notched his second kill in anger, following his execution of the Blood Carver on Zonama Sekot. On a mission to take down Krayn, the infamous pirate and slaver, Anakin allowed the pain and humiliation he had experienced in his former life as a slave to overtake his propriety as a Jedi. Though Krayn could have been apprehended, Anakin used his new lightsaber to burn a hole through the slaver's chest.

As Anakin grew further into his training, he struggled with the issue of mentorship. He had never known a father, and Qui-Gon Jinn had died mere days after taking Anakin from his mother. Obi-Wan was now his master—though Anakin suspected that Obi-Wan had agreed to the training only out of obligation to Qui-Gon's dying wish—and Supreme Chancellor Palpatine had become another influence, dispensing advice and veiled flattery to the Chosen One. Among his peers, Anakin found a friend in Padawan Tru Veld and a rival in Ferus Olin, the apprentice of Obi-Wan's close companion Siri Tachi.

THE OUTBOUND FLIGHT PROJECT
27 B.B.Y.

Two years after the Zonama Sekot catastrophe, Jedi Master Jorus C'baoth brought a new exploratory proposal before Supreme Chancellor Palpatine. C'baoth's project, named Outbound Flight, would send almost 45,000 colonists on a swing through the Unknown Regions, with the ultimate goal of reaching a nearby galaxy.

Extra-galactic travel had long been thought impossible due to the intersecting ripples formed in hyperspace by galactic masses. C'baoth believed that the Jedi could use the Force to smooth this zone of turbulence. He tested his theory on the briarpatch border of the Unknown Regions, then recommended that he, with seventeen other Jedi Knights and Masters, accompany the Outbound colonists on their journey.

Palpatine remained cool on the concept, but intrigued with the possibility of sabotaging the project and causing the deaths of a number of prominent Jedi, he allowed C'baoth to move forward.

The Outbound Flight project—six dreadnaughts linked in a ring around a central fuel tank—launched from Yaga Minor.

Among the Jedi aboard were Obi-Wan Kenobi and Anakin Skywalker, but Palpatine—who knew that Anakin would play a critical role in events yet to come—arranged for them to disembark after the first leg of the trip. Outbound Flight continued on under the command of Jorus C'baoth until it reached the Unknown Regions, where it ran head-on into the Chiss Ascendancy, and the brilliant alien mastermind who would someday become Grand Admiral Thrawn.

As far as the rest of the galaxy was concerned, Outbound Flight mysteriously disappeared somewhere in the Unknown Regions. Not until decades later, when its remains were found by the Chiss and returned to the New Republic, would its true fate be discovered.

DEATHS ON THE JEDI COUNCIL
27–26 B.B.Y.

The Jedi Council lost one of its members when the Quermian Jedi Master Yarael Poof tracked down a rogue Annoo-dat general, who had hoped to use the ener-gies of an alien religious idol to destroy Coruscant. Deep in the heart of the capital planet near the core power relays, bounty hunters Jango Fett and Zam Wesell stopped the doomsday plot, but could not prevent the death of Master Poof. Master Coleman Trebor assumed a post on the Council to fill the vacancy.

As their Master–Padawan bond deepened, Obi-Wan and Anakin made a powerful enemy of Granta Omega, the son of Qui-Gon's fallen apprentice Xanatos. Omega lacked any connection to the Force, but his extreme wealth had allowed him to become an expert in Sith lore. By killing the Jedi heroes, Omega hoped to attract the attention of the Sith Lord Darth Sidious. Obi-Wan and Anakin clashed with Omega several times over the years, but the would-be Sith committed his greatest crime on the war-torn world of Mawan. There, Jedi Council member Yaddle sacrificed her life to prevent Omega from poisoning the population with dihexalon gas. Shaak Ti, a red-and-white striped Togruta, took Yaddle's place on the Council.

THE SEPARATIST MOVEMENT
24 B.B.Y.

After eight years out of the limelight, Count Dooku made his first public reappearance on the industrial powerhouse of Raxus Prime. Decrying the corruption that consumed the Republic like a Raxan garbage-worm, Dooku rallied star systems to join his new government, the Confederacy of Independent Systems, or CIS.

In public, he swayed planets and commercial concerns to his side. In private he trained a number of Force-sensitive individuals in the ways of the dark side, and recruited high-powered killers to silence his enemies. Among Dooku's dark side minions was Asajj Ventress, a pale-skinned native of Rattatak who had learned a heavily distorted version of the Jedi way from a shipwrecked Jedi Knight. Others included Sev'rance Tann, a Chiss who had been brought into civilized space with her lover Vandalor by Darth Sidious, and Saato, a Witch from Dathomir with a fearsome tattooed face.

The soldiers in Dooku's employ included Durge, an armored Gen'Dai who had recently awakened from a century-long hibernation following a battle with Mandalorians, and Cydon Prax, a reptilian Chistori who concealed his identity behind a battle suit. But the greatest among them was Grievous, an alien battlefield commander who had been critically injured in a shuttle crash arranged by San Hill of the Inter-Galactic Banking Clan. Hill then had Grievous rebuilt as a cyborg. Dooku, who taught the half-machine killer to wield four blades at once, would eventually name Grievous the supreme general of the Separatist droid armies.

Not coincidentally, Dooku's reemergence corresponded with the end of Chancellor Palpatine's eight years in office. To lead the Republic through the crisis of Separatism, Palpatine won an indefinite extension of his term—despite the measure's clear unconstitutionality. Most observers hoped that Palpatine would bring about a swift end to what looked like the foolhardy act of a political dreamer.

Obi-Wan and Anakin battle Granta Omega on Mawan.
[Art by Tommy Lee Edwards]

THE DEATH OF GRANTA OMEGA
24 B.B.Y.

Obi-Wan Kenobi and Anakin Skywalker eventually caught up with their enemy Granta Omega on the Sith world of Korriban. Following an incident in which the Senate chamber had nearly been poisoned by Separatist scientist Jenna Zan Arbor, both Zan Arbor and Granta Omega had arrived on Korriban to receive new assignments from their secret commander, Count Dooku.

A Jedi task force led by Obi-Wan Kenobi moved in to capture the plotters. Dooku and Zan Arbor escaped, but Obi-Wan killed Granta Omega in a final showdown. Jedi Padawan Tru Veld inadvertently caused the death of a fellow Jedi when his lightsaber malfunctioned in the heat of battle. Ferus Olin and Anakin Skywalker had both known about the lightsaber malfunction beforehand, but neither had told their Masters. Anakin remained silent, but Olin stepped forward to take the blame for the incident. He voluntarily resigned from the Jedi Order.

Elsewhere, on Maramere, the Trade Federation contended with a new threat as the Feeorin mercenary Nym joined forces with pirate Sol Sixxa to drive all traces of Nute Gunray's conglomerate out of the system. Since Maramere had become a repository for invisibility-generating stygium crystals from Aeten II, the Trade Federation tied up many of its assets in the recapturing of Maramere in order to ensure the future of cloaking technology.

THE CONFEDERACY TAKES SHAPE
23 B.B.Y.

In one year, Count Dooku's Separatist movement had grown significantly more powerful. Every day saw news of another planet joining the Confederacy of Independent Systems. Many Senators thought the chancellor should simply let them go, allowing the Confederacy to exist side by side with the Republic. Others pushed for the passage of a Military Creation Act that would create a Grand Army of the Republic to bolster the meager Judicial security forces.

Dooku had made great strides in soliciting the help of the galaxy's six major industrial powers. Though none of them had yet signed on as official members of the CIS, their financial assistance had proven invaluable to Dooku. The Baktoid Armor Workshop's foundries on Geonosis produced thousands upon thousands of battle droids. The InterGalactic Banking Clan of Muunilinst was both a financial hub and a manufacturer of hailfire and IG-style droids. The Commerce Guild controlled raw materials under the leadership of Gossam magistrate Shu Mai. Wat Tambor of the Techno Union provided dozens of "mechworlds" dominated by smoke, fire, and machinery. The Corporate Alliance, which regulated the distribution of retail products, remained a quiet backer. Nute Gunray of the Trade Federation insisted that Dooku deliver Padmé Amidala's "head on his desk" before he would sign on with the CIS.

Palpatine claimed that he would not allow the Republic to be split in two, but did not publicly advocate the creation of the Grand Army. The Senate chamber on Coruscant rang with the shouts of angry legislators debating the pros and cons of the movement and complaining about the endless delays in bringing the issue to a vote. Beginning with the Battle of Antar 4, events quickly snowballed and left the chancellor with no options besides armed conflict.

THE BATTLE OF ANTAR 4
22.5 B.B.Y.

Over a thousand worlds had already joined the CIS, but violence had thus far been limited to the wounded pride of spurned diplomats. The blood spilled on the moon Antar 4 changed that and cast the conflict in a new and deadly light.

Home to the furry, flat-faced Gotals, Antar 4 had given rise to the Roshu Sune, a militant splinter branch of the Gotal Assembly for Separation. During New Year Fete week, Roshu Sune terrorists activated the undercover agents that they had infiltrated into Antarian Ranger chapter houses across the moon, decimating the Jedi-allied Rangers and throwing Antar 4 into chaos. The Roshu Sune then issued a declaration of secession.

The Republic refused to honor terrorist proclamations. Antarian Rangers from across the galaxy descended on the moon, eager for revenge against those who had desecrated the chapter houses where their order had originated. Following close on their heels came battalions of Jedi Knights led by Masters Coleman Trebor and Saesee Tiin.

The first assault proved disastrous, resulting in heavy casualties to both Jedi and civilians. The second assault used an electromagnetic pulse to overwhelm the Gotals' sensitive head cones. This tactic eventually succeeded, but at the cost of the goodwill of the people of Antar 4, who were incapacitated by the pulse and blamed the Jedi for sloppy tactics.

Separatist-leaning planets across the galaxy looked at Antar 4 and realized that the Republic wasn't omnipotent. The Jedi Council, however, refused to trace any direct link between the Roshu Sune and Count Dooku. The Council's denials persisted even as random terrorist bombings began striking Coruscant, despite Dooku's failure to condemn the killings being done in his name.

SPLINTERING OF THE REPUBLIC
22.5–22 B.B.Y.

The final months leading up to the Clone Wars were a chaotic dance of shuffling alliances and desperate overtures. When war eventually broke out, it almost came as a relief.

The secession of the planets Ando and Sy Myrth three months prior to the Battle of Geonosis marked a sort of tipping point. The two worlds and their sector fiefdoms brought the total of Separatist planets to more than six thousand. The Refugee Relief Movement struggled to contain displaced citizens, leading to civil unrest. Angry showdowns occurred throughout the galaxy, such as the one on Naboo, where kassoti-spice miners on one of the planet's moons refused to give up their landing slip to accommodate refugee freighters.

Ando in particular became a microcosm of the greater galactic conflict when the Aqualish of the Andoan Free Colonies refused to acknowledge the secession ordered by their walrus-faced brethren on the homeworld. The always belligerent Aqualish now looked as if they might tear themselves apart regardless of what happened outside their borders.

Weeks later, Senator Garm Bel Iblis of the Corellian sector announced that his sector had closed its borders and would no longer participate in future discussion. With a cry of "Corellia for Corellians," the Republic lost the support of one of its founding Core Worlds.

Chancellor Palpatine responded to Corellia's withdrawal with an offer to Count Dooku to negotiate a peaceful solution to their differences. Dooku didn't show and the Republic shook from a rapid-fire string of prominent secessions.

The Elrood, Danjar, Tantra, and Sluis sectors all joined the CIS, making the entire Rimward leg of the Rimma Trade Route inaccessible to Republic shipping. The Lahara sector followed suit, bringing with it the planets of Agamar and Oorn Tchis and the Mirgoshir hyperspace crossroads. The Abrion sector gave the CIS more than two hundred farming planets when it seceded. The Expansion Region planet of Tynna joined the Separatists following an outbreak on their world of building-eating insects called stone mites, believed to be a biologically engineered terrorist weapon. The mathematical Givin of Yag'Dhul left when their ruling Body Calculus determined that the risks of staying with the Republic were "greater than or equal to" the risks of seceding.

Not everyone on the Republic side was content to sit and watch. On board the Republic Judicial Department corvette *Scarlet Thranta,* Captain Zozridor Slayke and his crew withdrew from Republic service to wage their own private war against Separatist forces in the Sluis sector. Slayke's army soon became known as Freedom's Sons.

Two weeks after Slayke's resignation, the Republic dispatched a Jedi-led task force to reign in the rogue captain. Mas-ter Nejaa Halcyon, a Corellian Jedi and descendant of early Jedi hero Keiran Halcyon, commanded the cruiser *Plooriod Bodkin* on its mission to the Sluis sector. It took weeks, but Halcyon eventually pinned down Slayke—who promptly turned the tables on the Jedi Master and stole the *Plooriod Bodkin.*

Mission to Ansion
22 B.B.Y.

Not every development was disadvantageous for the Republic. The simple world of Ansion in the Mid Rim responded favorably to a Jedi diplomatic mission and elected to remain a member of the Republic, rejecting a Separatist invitation extended by Commerce Guild magistrate Shu Mai. The Jedi team of Anakin Skywalker, Obi-Wan Kenobi, Luminara Unduli, and Bariss Offee received credit for the outcome. Though Ansion had little to offer in the way of natural resources, its involvement in a number of ancient treaties including the Malarian Alliance and the Keitumite Mutual Military Treaty meant that Ansion's defection would have pulled an entire web of planets into the Separatist fold.

But a closer look at the Ansion victory revealed an unpleasant truth—if the Republic's successes occurred only when it managed to *prevent* a defection, the Confederacy could not help but gain in power. Calls for the passage of the Military Creation Act increased in volume. Terrorist bombings on Coruscant continued.

Diplomacy could not stanch a bleeding artery. Unless the Republic wanted to concede victory already, war appeared inevitable.

THE CLONE WARS

The Battle of Geonosis
22 B.B.Y.

Formerly the planet's Queen, Padmé Amidala had become Naboo's representative to the Republic Senate after the ascension of Queen Jamillia. Padmé had also become one of the most vocal opponents of the Military Creation Act. Upon arriving on Coruscant to vote on the measure, her starship exploded on the landing pad. Padmé survived the assassination attempt, which had been ordered by Count Dooku on behalf of Nute Gunray and contracted out to Jango Fett—who had enlisted his own subcontractor, Zam Wesell. The Jedi Council assigned Obi-Wan Kenobi and

Count Dooku
[ART BY MARK CHIARELLO]

locate anything about the planet in the Jedi archives—thanks to Dooku's erasure of the information ten years prior—and so decided to travel to Kamino himself.

The Kaminoans were happy to host a representative from the Jedi, still believing that their growth-accelerated army, now nearly one million strong, belonged to Jedi Master Sifo-Dyas. During his tour of the Tipoca City facilities, Obi-Wan met Jango Fett, the army's Prime Clone, and his son Boba Fett. Convinced that Jango had been behind the attacks on Padmé, Obi-Wan tried to bring the bounty hunter to Coruscant for questioning. Jango bested Obi-Wan in combat and escaped with Boba in *Slave I*.

Anakin had recently been disturbed by vague and disturbing nightmares of his mother's torture. He left Naboo with Padmé and traveled to Tatooine, where he learned that Shmi Skywalker had been freed from slavery years ago, to become the wife of local moisture farmer Cliegg Lars. At the Lars homestead, Anakin met Cliegg's son Owen Lars and Owen's girlfriend Beru, and enjoyed a reunion with C-3PO, Anakin's home-built protocol droid. But Shmi was not there. She had been kidnapped by a tribe of Tusken Raiders weeks before.

Anakin tracked down his mother, who had been tortured and was near death, in a Tusken camp. When she died in his arms, Anakin welcomed the liberating fury of the dark side. He slaughtered the entire Tusken clan, including the children.

After burying Shmi, Anakin intercepted an urgent message from Obi-Wan, who had tracked Jango Fett to the droid foundries on Geonosis. Obi-Wan had learned of Count Dooku's involvement with the galaxy's major commerce factions. With the Trade Federation, Techno Union, Commerce Guild, Corporate Alliance, and InterGalactic Banking Clan officially joining the Separatist cause, the Republic faced grave danger. Obi-Wan would not escape to deliver his news,

Anakin Skywalker to protect the Senator.

A second attempt on Padmé's life, involving poisonous kouhuns, also failed, but this time the Jedi apprehended Zam Wesell. Before the Clawdite shapeshifter could reveal the identity of the other plotters, Jango Fett killed her with a toxic dart.

In light of the violence, the Council decided that Padmé would be safer on her homeworld. Anakin accompanied her to Naboo, where he found himself struggling with his increasingly powerful feelings of infatuation. Padmé tried to resist her own attraction to Anakin, but the two soon fell in love.

On Coruscant, Obi-Wan investigated Jango Fett's dart and connected it to the cloners of Kamino. He could not

Clone troopers and gunships take out Geonosian defenses during the Battle of Geonosis [ART BY TOMMY LEE EDWARDS]

however—a squad of droidekas had captured him and locked him in the Geonosian dungeons. Anakin and Padmé rushed to free their friend, but became prisoners themselves.

Back on Coruscant, Chancellor Palpatine, Mace Windu, and Master Yoda agreed that war was the only way to stop the Separatists. Representative Jar Jar Binks put forth a motion that gave emergency war powers to Palpatine, who then announced the creation of the Grand Army of the Republic.

Yoda departed for Kamino. While the Jedi still weren't sure who had orchestrated the clone army's creation, they could not afford to wait for volunteers and conscripts to build up a standard army. And if the Separatists were involved in creating the clone army (as Jango Fett's dual role seemed to indicate), the Jedi wanted to prevent Dooku's forces from claiming the clones for themselves. The Kaminoans gladly turned over the first two hundred thousand clones to Yoda, and he led them to Geonosis at top speed.

Obi-Wan, Anakin, and Padmé received death sentences from Dooku, to be carried out by the teeth and claws of wild beasts in the Geonosian execution arena. Meanwhile, two hundred Jedi Knights, led by Mace Windu, arrived outside the arena in their Jedi starfighters. They failed to force a surrender from Count Dooku, and the arena exploded in violence as Dooku unleashed his super battle droids. Mace Windu beheaded Jango Fett, yet Dooku's forces held the upper hand until Yoda's armies arrived aboard laser-spewing Republic gunships.

The battle quickly moved to the dust plains of Geonosis, where both sides' heavy equipment clashed with stunning might. Geonosian starfighters sparred with clone gunships. Commerce Guild spider droids blasted beetle-like AT-TEs. Huge SPHA-T cannons carved up Trade Federation core ships. Elsewhere on the battlefield, trained acklays and nexus devoured clone troopers, and Count Dooku's lowest-ranking dark acolytes lost their lives in a tank battle with Mace Windu.

Dooku himself escaped to a secret hangar, where he was confronted by Obi-Wan and Anakin. The count left Obi-Wan beaten and Anakin without his right arm, and may have killed them both if not for Yoda, who arrived and launched a whirlwind attack. Dooku barely escaped with his life.

By the battle's conclusion, only Republic soldiers remained. Though considered a victory, the cost to the Republic was high—thousands of clone trooper deaths and scores of fallen Jedi. Most of the Confederacy's battle droids and heavy equipment escaped into space aboard core ships.

Geonosian leader Poggle the Lesser was nowhere to be found, although his second in command, Sun Fac, had been assassinated by a squad of clone commandos during the fighting. The Geonosian workers retreated into the catacombs far beneath the spire-hives, where they resisted every effort to dislodge them.

War had been joined, and the Republic's new clones would give a name to the conflict that had begun. Before the next round of attacks, Anakin escorted Padmé back to Naboo, where they were secretly married. The only witnesses, besides the Naboo holy man who presided over the ceremony, were C-3PO and R2-D2.

THE SHAPE OF WAR
22 B.B.Y.

Had the Republic pressed the advantage, they most likely could have overrun Confederacy space before the CIS had time to fortify its positions. The Republic had one glaring problem, however—it wasn't ready for war. Until all the clones could be activated and new warships launched, the Republic didn't have enough assets to fight on a galactic scale.

Meanwhile, the Confederacy deployed along the major hyperspace lanes into Separatist space, solidifying its defenses. The Republic had no choice but to rely on harassment tactics for the time being, guaranteeing that the war would not have a swift end.

Victories did not always come only on the battlefield. On isolationist Corellia, the Twi'lek Jedi Aayla Secura and the Caamasi Jedi Ylenic It'kla helped take a defecting Techno Union researcher into Republic custody. Unexpected assistance came from the Corellian Jedi Master Nejaa Halcyon, recently returned from his failed mission to stop the Freedom's Sons vigilantism in the Sluis sector.

The dead had just been recovered from the red sands of Geonosis when the Clone Wars exploded to life on new worlds. Atraken, a tiny mining planet of great strategic value, became one of the brightest-burning flashpoints.

A Confederacy world, Atraken had both the blessing and curse of being rich in the rare metal doonium. Republic assault ships touched down on Atraken's crust, unloading clones who besieged the doonium mines. Digging out the enemy on Atraken would consume most of the year, with the seeming futility of the efforts proving to many Jedi that they should not fight in a war this nihilistic.

The green-scaled Trandoshans, inhabitants of a planet orbiting the same sun as the Wookiee homeworld of Kashy-yyk, had long exploited the Wookiees as slave labor. Now the Trandoshans had allied themselves with the Confederacy of Independent Systems. Armed with the latest in Separatist weaponry, rowdy bands of Trandoshan brawlers roamed the spaceways and stirred up trouble for Republic ships.

The Republic sent units of clone commandos to Kashy-yyk to prepare for a possible invasion. Upon their arrival, the clones discovered that Trandoshan slavers had already set up containment camps for Wookiee captives, and the full force of the Separatist army soon followed. Though the clone troopers beat back the first incursion, Kashyyyk would be a contested world for the remainder of the war.

THE JEDI AS GENERALS
22 B.B.Y.

At Geonosis, Atraken, and Mirgoshir, the Jedi and the clone troopers fell into a natural battlefield hierarchy— Jedi Masters, Jedi Knights, and Jedi Padawans command- ing the clone ranks of commanders, captains, lieutenants, sergeants, and troopers. Jedi, regardless of their experience, always outranked clones.

One month into the war, Supreme Chancellor Palpatine made the role of the Jedi official. Most Jedi Knights and Masters would henceforth be given the rank of general in the Grand Army of the Republic; most Padawans, the rank of commander.

This clarified the military command process, but it also had the effect of *requiring* that all Jedi take an active role in the war. For many reasons—frustration with Republic corruption, devotion to the ideal of peaceful contemplation—some Jedi refused to obey the Council's order to return to Coruscant and receive their promotions. Although most Jedi accepted their assignments and left to defend Ossus and retake Excarga, the dissident Jedi remained a mounting problem.

THE HUNT FOR THE DECIMATOR
21.95 B.B.Y. (1 month after the Battle of Geonosis)

Only one Confederacy general held more sway than Grievous during the war's first month—the Chiss Force user Sev'rance Tann. General Tann saw her first true battlefield test on sunbaked Tatooine, where Separatist spies had learned of a new Republic weapon known only as "the Decimator."

On Eredenn Prime, Tann captured several Decimators for herself. The weapons—tanks with giant turbolaser cannons mounted atop—proved stunningly destructive. She raided the Wookiee colony of Alaris Prime (which had just recovered from the attack during the Dark Reaper crisis), and made a bold strike against the Core world of Sarapin.

A crucible of flame and magma, Sarapin generated enough geothermal energy to supply a significant fraction of the power for the Core Worlds. Scaling the slopes of Mount Corvast, Tann's captured Devastators vaporized the Republic's geother- mal generators. Dozens of Core Worlds plunged into darkness.

General Echuu Shen-Jon, Sev'rance Tann's counterpart on the Republic side, held a personal grudge against the enemy commander, for Tann had murdered Echuu's Padawan during the Battle of Geonosis. Echuu led a massive Republic coun- terattack to recapture Sarapin, then ultimately caught up with his quarry on the snow-dusted tundra of Krant. Calling on the power of the dark side, Echuu Shen-Jon cut Sev'rance Tann in half with a mighty sweep of his energy blade.

Although the Separatists had lost their stolen Decimators, Echuu Shen-Jon had also crossed a line. Telling his surviving troops to return to the Republic, he vanished into the wilderness of Krant to wander and forever contemplate his moral failure.

THE DARK REAPER PROJECT
21.9 B.B.Y. (1 month after the Battle of Geonosis)

Buried for thousands of years on Raxus Prime lay the Force Harvester, an artifact of Sith technology capable of sucking the life from every living thing within a number of kilometers. During the First Sith War, the Force Harvester had been used as a power device for an even greater monstrosity—the Dark Reaper.

The Dark Reaper had not been seen in millennia, but Count Dooku knew that some Force spirits persisted even after death. Dooku sent a Trade Federation fleet to frozen Rhen Var to secure Ulic Qel-Droma's crypt. Guided by the ancient Jedi ghost, Dooku began excavating for the buried Force Harvester on Raxus Prime.

The Jedi Council mobilized an attack. Marching through a forest of rusted girders, the Republic's new AT-XT scout walkers blasted Separatist mortar tanks, while nimble Jedi hovertanks cleared out gun turrets. When Dooku made an appearance, Anakin chased him aboard a starship, which then blasted into orbit. Left behind, Obi-Wan defeated the Count's going-away present: a giant, crablike siege weapon called a protodeka.

On board Dooku's vessel Anakin sat in a holding cell, having fallen victim to a sneak attack by Dooku's mercenary Cydon Prax. Soon the ship reached the Wookiee colony of Alaris Prime, where Dooku tested his Force Harvester. Anakin escaped only centimeters ahead of the weapon's shock wave, and sent an SOS to the Republic. By the time a clone legion arrived, Anakin had Alaris Prime well on its way to freedom.

Meanwhile, Count Dooku unleashed the Force Harvester on Mon Calamari, Bakura, and Agamar. The Republic counterattacked on Thule, a crumbling planet that had once been part of the glorious Sith Empire. The Republic army advanced on the old Sith city of Kesiak, but the deadliest weapon in their arsenal proved to be Anakin Skywalker. When Cydon Prax destroyed Mace Windu's vehicle in a tank-versus-tank showdown, Anakin killed Prax in a fusillade of energy darts. Anakin

The ancient Dark Reaper superweapon
[ART BY TOMMY LEE EDWARDS]

then penetrated the Dark Reaper and destroyed the alchemical monstrosity with old-fashioned Republic ordnance.

Though counted as a victory, the Republic's preoccupation with the Dark Reaper allowed the Separatists to seize Bespin's Tibanna gas refineries as well as the historic Jedi stronghold of Ossus.

THE BATTLE OF KAMINO
21.83 B.B.Y. (2 months after the Battle of Geonosis)

Jedi Master Quinlan Vos had gone deep undercover on the seedy gambling station known as the Wheel. Among the Jedi, Quinlan Vos had acquired a reputation for undisciplined behavior, but this time his intelligence coup was of epic proportions. A decrypted data disk revealed a Separatist plan to assault the Republic cloning laboratories on Kamino.

Count Dooku appointed Corporate Alliance Magister Passel Argente as the ranking Confederacy officer for the attack, though Argente's military experience was nonexistent. Mon Calamari Commander Merai joined the CIS navy following the attack on his homeworld by the Force Harvester, and received the honor of leading the assault. Outfitted with submersible starfighters, Commander Merai believed his expertise in amphibious warfare would carry the day.

Republic forces on Kamino were keenly aware of the threat—only a few weeks earlier, a traitor among the Kaminoans had attempted to murder the clones by releasing a nanovirus. The Jedi hoped to defend Kamino with a three-pronged battle plan. Obi-Wan Kenobi and Anakin Skywalker would shoot down landing ships with a squadron of Jedi starfighters, Master Shaak Ti would defend Tipoca City itself, and Oppo Rancisis and a Republic armada would wait for their cue to leap into the system and squeeze the Separatists in a vise.

The day of battle dawned, rainy as always on storm-rocked Kamino. Commander Merai sent down his landing ships accompanied by a thick droid starfighter escort. Obi-Wan and Anakin could not stop them all, and dozens of fully stocked transports landed on Tipoca City.

Shaak Ti activated Kamino's "secret weapon"—a special batch of clone troopers who had been bred for greater autonomy. These ARC (Advanced Reconnaissance Commando) troopers had been trained by Jango Fett himself. The ARC troopers and Shaak Ti mowed through the advancing super battle droids, scattering body fragments like metallic sawdust.

Commander Merai personally piloted his custom submersible *Shark* in an attempt to destroy the city's shield generator. When he discovered that no generator existed, Merai began to suspect that someone had tampered with Separatist intelligence. In a last act of defiance, Merai rammed his vessel into the Jedi starfighter hyperspace rings, a spectacular but ultimately futile gesture. Passel Argente executed a full Separatist retreat.

What neither side had realized was that the Battle of Kamino had been an intentional stalemate in the larger game being orchestrated by Darth Sidious. Count Dooku had ensured that the Separatists would attack Kamino, and had also guaranteed that the assault would prove a failure. The war would now drag out for years, consuming billions of lives and trillions of credits as the people cried out for firm, decisive leadership.

Within a few weeks, Kamino's million battle-ready clones went out to join the two hundred thousand already in service. The Republic began investigating alternate cloning methods (with Spaarti Creations coming into prominence within the next year). Conscription, however, was a necessary reality. Countless beings of every species became draftees into the Grand Army of the Republic.

Meanwhile, ARC troopers bolstered the Republic's ground forces. Clad in modified clone trooper armor, they boasted a touch of Jango Fett's dry wit, and often questioned their superiors' orders if they conflicted with their own tactical training. One ARC trooper, assigned to General Obi-Wan Kenobi, received the nickname "Alpha" from Anakin Skywalker.

THE DEFENSE OF NABOO
21.8 B.B.Y. (2.5 months after the Battle of Geonosis)

The destruction of the Dark Reaper only made the Separatists strive to develop even deadlier weapons. On the Techno Union mechworld of Queyta, Separatist researcher Dr. Jenna Zan Arbor succeeded in bottling a virulent aerosol poison. Nicknamed "swamp gas," the green mist raised blisters on the skin and caused shuddering death in most humanoid species. Commander Asajj Ventress decided to test this toxin on the Gungan settlers of Ohma-D'un, one of the inhabited moons orbiting Naboo.

All of the Gungans died instantly. A Jedi investigative team soon followed. Amid the corpses they found super battle droids outfitted with swamp gas sprayers, accompanied by Dooku's welcoming committee—Asajj Ventress and the bounty hunter Durge.

The two Separatist warriors laid into their enemies with glee. Several Jedi perished, but Anakin Skywalker and Obi-Wan Kenobi managed to keep Durge at bay. Asajj Ventress retreated, satisfied with the deaths she had caused. Meanwhile, the ARC trooper Alpha destroyed the Separatist landing ships that would have carried the swamp gas to the planet Naboo.

THE BATTLES OF LIANNA AND TEYR
21.77 B.B.Y. (3 months after the Battle of Geonosis)

Lianna, in the Tion Cluster, was a vital Republic manufacturing world home to a Sienar starfighter facility. Raith Sienar and his engineers had been enlisted by the Republic to develop new starfighters for the clone troopers, and the Lianna facility held all the secrets to Sienar's Twin Ion Engine project. Jedi Master Cei Vookto led the campaign to preserve Lianna, using his powers of elemental summoning to cleanse the planet with twin pillars of fire and water. The strain cost Vookto his life.

On Teyr, the Whiphid Jedi Master K'Kruhk led an army of clone troopers against a Trade Federation battleship that had made a hard landing on the planet's surface and was now serving as a Separatist bunker. Trudging on foot through Teyr's Great Canyon, K'Kruhk watched as spider tanks shredded his clone troopers with laser barrages. Master K'Kruhk managed to lead his army to the lip of the canyon, where they destroyed the great battleship, but only K'Kruhk survived the final assault. Shell-shocked, he fled Teyr without telling the Council that he still lived, and joined other dissident Jedi opposed to the war.

JEDI SCHISM
21.75 B.B.Y. (3 months after the Battle of Geonosis)

Hundreds of Jedi had refused to honor Chancellor Palpatine's decree that made them generals, and had formed a growing movement of dissidents. Few of them had actively joined the Separatists, but their refusal to fight for their Commander in Chief threatened to divide the Jedi Order.

Mace Windu decided to meet with the defectors on the Weequay moon of Ruul. Sora Bulq, leader of the dissidents, had earned respect in Mace's eyes for his devotion to Form VII ("Vaapad") lightsaber combat—an aggressive style that took its user to the edge of the dark side. Bulq, however, had secretly joined Count Dooku, and Ruul was a trap.

Asajj Ventress raided the Ruul gathering, hoping to kill some of the dissidents and blame their deaths on the Jedi Council. But Mace had deduced Sora Bulq's true nature, and forced Bulq and Ventress to flee offworld. Despite the incident, the dissident Jedi remained split. While shocked at Master Bulq's betrayal, many still had hostile feelings toward a Republic that they considered irredeemably corrupt. K'Kruhk, however, returned to Coruscant to resume his role as a Jedi general.

RAID ON PENGALAN IV
21.75 B.B.Y. (3 months after the Battle of Geonosis)

From Pengalan IV, a dry, sparsely populated world in the Inner Rim, came word of a Separatist military breakthrough—diamond boron missiles designed to punch through the shielding of most Republic starfighters. But the Republic's attack against the "secret factory" proved to be a trap. Gun emplacements and droid starfighters opened up on the invaders, destroying a wave of gunships and sending the survivors limping away in defeat.

One gunship, carrying republic observer Joram Kithe and a crew of clone troopers, crashed in a canyon near the tiny village of Tur Lonkin. On foot, this small band infiltrated Tur Lonkin and discovered that the Confederacy's *real* missile factory lay deep underground in a shielded bunker. The clone troopers destroyed the facility at a great cost of lives within their own ranks. Upon returning to Coruscant, Kithe

reported that the Republic had purchased an army that was nothing short of remarkable.

In the hostile wilderness of Qiilura, a group of clone commandos provided further support for Kithe's glowing assessment. In a mission to capture a Separatist scientist and destroy a bioweapons facility, the commandos, with help from an untested Jedi Padawan, dealt with the proliferation of an anti-clone nanovirus.

MISSION TO QUEYTA
21.7 B.B.Y. (4 months after the Battle of Geonosis)

Following the "swamp gas" outbreak on the Gungan moon, four Jedi Masters united in a strike against the guilty laboratory on Queyta before the Separatists could target a second world. Obi-Wan Kenobi earned a fifth spot alongside this dream team due to his familiarity with the toxin. The Queyta chemical plant floated atop a lava river, and its Skakoan workers exploded like proton bombs when their pressurized armor shells were ruptured. Asajj Ventress and Durge lay in wait for the team, and killed all four Jedi Masters. Only Obi-Wan Kenobi survived, and he returned with the plague's antidote.

Unknown to the Republic, a second laboratory on the far side of Queyta had installed its equipment aboard the science vessel *Gahenna,* and then abandoned the compromised world. For the next two years *Gahenna* would cruise the Outer Rim, perfecting a new strain of toxin.

THE STORM FLEET DESTROYERS
21.67 B.B.Y. (4 months after the Battle of Geonosis)

The heavily armed bulk freighters of Count Dooku's Storm Fleet had been produced by the shipbuilding conglomerate Kuat Drive Yards. Once a member of the Techno Union, KDY had broken ranks with the Separatist organization at the start of the war so that it could continue producing assault ships for the Republic Navy. Yet KDY's new Storm

Sith hopeful Asajj Ventress and bounty hunter Durge
[ART BY TOMMY LEE EDWARDS]

Fleet went straight to the Confederacy—grounds for treason, but Palpatine's investigators chalked it up to mistaken corporate connections, and KDY escaped repercussions.

Of course, that didn't help the Republic vessels no w terrorized by the Storm Fleet. Up and down the Perlemian Trade Route, the Storm Fleet intercepted convoys of medicine and munitions, opening their victims' hulls to the cold vacuum of space.

Anakin Skywalker and Obi-Wan Kenobi, at the Llon Nebula's Kronex spaceport during a mission layover, encountered the Storm Fleet as it came in for refueling. Against the wishes of his master, Anakin followed the Storm Fleet as it left Kronex and flew his Jedi starfighter between the larger ships like a flitnat among banthas. When the bridges of the two vessels crumpled under asteroid impacts, the Storm Fleet limped back to Kronex for repairs.

The encounter delayed the Storm Fleet's mission just long enough for a Republic fleet to arrive at their target of Cyphar. In the Battle of Cyphar, the Storm Fleet lost nearly half of its vessels, and Cyphar remained an open port.

THE FORTRESS OF AXION
21.67 B.B.Y. (4 months after the Battle of Geonosis)

At the Battle of Geonosis, Master Yoda had proven himself a superior battlefield commander. Since then, Chancellor Palpatine had requested that the centuries-old sage be kept far from the front lines.

Master Yoda still found ways to insert himself into strategic combat. One such situation presented itself on Axion. Once inhabited by humans, the planet had been bought out by the cannibalistic Colicoid insects and now served as a Separatist research and development center. One Colicoid engineer, responsible for the design of the protodekas used during the Dark Reaper crisis, had been sealed away in Axion's corporate fortress by his brethren. He made a tempting target for a Republic extradition mission.

Several companies of clone troopers, along with their

Jedi Master Kit Fisto, who led clone scuba troopers in the Battle of Mon Calamari [ART BY TOMMY LEE EDWARDS]

heavy equipment, made planetfall on Axion, led by Commander Brolis—one of the outside military advisers hired by the Kaminoans to fine-tune the clones into fighting shape. Within two days, the small force had penetrated the fortress through a hole in its foundation. Two days, however, was all the time that the Colicoids needed to call in the Separatist army.

Super battle droids flushed the clones from the fortress and killed every last clone in vicious house-to-house fighting. Soon only Commander Brolis remained, holed up in the bombed-out shell of a residential apartment, his call for reinforcements apparently ignored by Republic High Command.

He awoke to the sight of Master Yoda—his single reinforcement. Armed with only a lightsaber, Yoda reduced the advancing battle droid line to scrap, and engaged a hoop-wheeled hailfire droid tank in a strangely elegant duel. Finally, Yoda tricked the robot into burying itself beneath twelve tons of collapsing rock. Yoda escaped with Brolis, but the overall mission to Axion had failed.

THE BATTLE OF MUUNILINST
21.66 B.B.Y. (4 months after the Battle of Geonosis)

San Hill, the arrogant chairman of the InterGalactic Banking Clan, had worked to make his homeworld of Muunilinst an unassailable castle keep. The Republic countered with sheer numbers, sending hundreds of assault ships, each one groaning from the weight of troopers and war machines. Many vessels reached the surface only as smoldering hulks; others found themselves cut off from their drop zones, forced to make landings behind enemy lines. General Obi-Wan Kenobi took command of the ground assault, while Anakin Skywalker fought for control of space in his Jedi starfighter.

Panicked, San Hill turned to Count Dooku's "special reinforcements"—the mercenary Durge and his droid team of IG-series lancers. Armed with laser lances and mounted on speeder bikes, the killers roared forth to decimate the Republic's field headquarters.

Like dark knights from the tales of the pre-Republic, Durge's crew rode into the camp. Obi-Wan Kenobi mounted his own speeder bike and led a squad of Republic lancers in a classic joust that ended with Durge's defeat. Obi-Wan capitalized on his success by hooking up with some lost ARC troopers and staging a final offensive against the IBC command center.

In space, Asajj Ventress toyed with Anakin Skywalker, leading her prey into hyperspace. They emerged at the jungle world of Yavin 4, and were soon joined by a company of clone troopers whom Obi-Wan had dispatched as backup. Anakin led the troopers through the sticky Massassi rain forest, watching helplessly as Ventress eliminated his men one by one.

Finally, the two crossed blades atop a vine-blanketed ziggurat. Neither fighter could gain an advantage in a contest where they seemed to be evenly matched, but Anakin found his edge by tapping into his own rage. Knocked from the pyramid, Ventress vanished into the jungle below.

On Dantooine, Master Mace Windu used his martial arts talents and the invisible punch of the Force to defeat a Separatist droid battalion, then carved up a hovering seismic charge minelayer. Master Yoda, Luminara Unduli, and Bariss Offee prevented cloaked "chameleon droids" from destroying the crystal caverns of the sacred Jedi planet Ilum. On Mon Calamari, Kit Fisto led a regiment of clone scuba troopers against the Quarren Isolationist League, defeating the Separatist-allied faction with help from the ancient order of Mon Calamari Knights.

On Hypori, a factory world, General Grievous chose a key moment to attack Republic forces and nearly killed the Jedi Masters Ki-Adi-Mundi, K'Kruhk, Shaak Ti, and Aayla Secura. A squad of ARC troopers burst in before the Jedi could be slaughtered.

Grievous's sudden appearance on Hypori stunned the Jedi Council. While they had been aware of the existence of the Separatist general—Republic commandos had fought him in the catacombs during the Battle of Geonosis—none of them was prepared for the ease with which he took apart a knot of fully trained Jedi.

THE BATTLE OF BRENTAAL
21.6 B.B.Y. (5 months after the Battle of Geonosis)

It would be difficult to overstate the importance Brentaal IV had to the Republic. An ancient Core world home to noble families and trade guilds, it sat at the crossroads of the Perlemian Trade Route and the Hydian Way—two of the galaxy's most vital hyperroutes. At the time, no one realized that the population ached for a new life under the leadership of the Confederacy of Independent Systems.

Brentaal clan leader Shogar Tok incited his people to riot. The Republic moved to secure their hyperspace junction, but by then Shogar Tok already held the triggers of Brentaal IV's formidable magna-guns. Republic strategists assembled an invasion force led by Jedi generals Shaak Ti, Plo Koon, the Zabrak Agen Kolar, and Shon Kon Ray.

General Plo Koon commanded the fleet, while the other three led the invasion armies. Things began to go wrong almost immediately. General Shon Kon Ray perished aboard an exploding gunship. General Kolar became a captive of the enemy. General Shaak Ti survived long enough to make it to a prison facility, where she recruited a few allies, including Lyshaa, the murderer of Shaak Ti's former Padawan. Lyshaa betrayed her rescuer to Shogar Tok at the earliest opportunity. Fortunately for the Republic, the rest of Shaak Ti's prison recruits sabotaged Brentaal's shield generator and wrecked its magna-guns. Plo Koon's fleet landed inside the hour, pacifying the planet and disposing of Shogar Tok's body.

Meanwhile, a similar situation had occurred on the neighboring Core world of Esseles. When a Separatist-funded government faction declared that Esseles had joined the Confederacy, a resistance movement of Republic loyalists forced the faction out in a bloody five-day battle.

DEFECTION ON NAR SHADDAA
21.52 B.B.Y. (6 months after the Battle of Geonosis)

Jedi Master Quinlan Vos had always played in the moral "gray zone" of the Jedi Code. But after faulty intelligence surrounding the Battle of Brentaal IV became associated with him, some Jedi thought that Quinlan might be a traitor.

The Jedi Council still trusted their agent, but saw the suspicion opening up an opportunity for enemy infiltration. Delib-

Korunnai warrior Kar Vastor holds an akk dog as Republic war machines attempt to pacify Haruun Kal. [ART BY TOMMY LEE EDWARDS]

erately giving Quinlan the latest military codes, they allowed him to return to his undercover life as an information broker. Days later, the Council sent Master Agen Kolar to capture Quinlan, telling the Zabrak that Vos had stolen the codes.

The two Jedi had their showdown on the Smugglers' Moon, Nar Shaddaa, in neutral Hutt space. Fully convinced of the rightness of his mission, in his zeal Agen Kolar nearly killed his target. But, as planned, Quinlan eluded capture, and now possessed the perfect reputation of "Jedi fugitive" to ease his penetration of Count Dooku's inner circle.

THE HARUUN KAL CRISIS
21.51 B.B.Y. (6 months after the Battle of Geonosis)

With their Force-given powers, Jedi Knights could be supernatural in battle. But even with the clone troopers at their disposal, the Jedi could not win the war on their own.

Local militias became the unsung heroes of many conflicts. Clone troopers had been trained to recruit native forces and set up independent chains of command, making it pos-

sible for a handful of clones to trigger a planetwide uprising. After seeing the success of the "militia model" on Malastare and Giju, the Jedi Council decided to try an extreme version of the model on the Separatist-controlled jungle world of Haruun Kal. This time, they sent Jedi Council member Depa Billaba to rally the locals.

Other than the fact that Haruun Kal sat at a hyperspace crossroads called the Gevarno Loop, the planet had little to recommend itself. Its "cloudsea" of toxic volcanic gases made colonization possible only on the highest mountain peaks. Nevertheless, two distinct societies had arisen on Haruun Kal—the Korunnai (Mace Windu's people), Force-sensitive jungle dwellers descended from shipwrecked Jedi, and the Balawai, more recent settlers concentrated in the capital city of Pelek Baw. The two sides had fought one another for generations in a bitter conflict known as the Summertime War.

Haruun Kal supported a heavy Separatist presence, but Depa Billaba formed a guerrilla force called the Upland Liberation Front. Shortly after her arrival, the Separatist force

withdrew. But just when Depa should have returned to Coruscant, the Jedi Council received the disturbing news that she had gone native, massacring Balawai settlers and refusing to answer the Council's inquiries. Mace Windu went to Haruun Kal to bring back his former Padawan.

The reality of the Summertime War proved to be more brutal than Mace had believed possible. The Balawai and Korunnai loathed one another with such ferocity that atrocities of war were commonplace. Mace eventually located Depa deep in the jungle, protected by the Korunnai shaman Kar Vastor. A primal warrior, Vastor defeated Mace in a one-on-one brawl by turning the living jungle against his opponent. Depa had completely lost focus, insisting that the Jedi would have to become creatures like Kar Vastor if they hoped to survive the Clone Wars.

Meanwhile, the Balawai military commander, Colonel Geptun, launched an all-out attack against the Korunnai hideout with help from Separatist droid starfighters. Mace responded by taking the battle to Pelek Baw, where he smashed Geptun's defenses and forced a surrender from the colonel. The Republic took control of Haruun Kal and forced both the Balawai and Korunnai to disarm.

Depa Billaba was sent back to the Temple on Coruscant, where she remained in a near-catatonic state. Jedi healers saw no hope for improvement.

ASSASSINATION ON NULL
21.5 B.B.Y. (6 months after the Battle of Geonosis)

Count Dooku liked to use the term *old friend* in conversations with his business associates, but most suspected that the aloof aristocrat had no real understanding of the concept. During his years as a student in the Jedi Temple, Dooku had formed a friendship with fellow trainee Lorian Nod, a relationship that had ended with finger-pointing and betrayal over the theft of a Sith Holocron. Dooku's past connection to Lorian Nod would come back to haunt the Count in an encounter on the planet Null.

Set amid the stars of the Mid Rim, the planet Junction V and its sister systems of Bezim and Vicondor sat at the nexus of several hyperspace lanes. Bound together by ages-

old treaties, the rulers of the three worlds and the Delaluna moon vowed to move as one when choosing sides between the Republic and the Separatists (similar to the prewar diplomatic dance that had centered on the planet Ansion). The four entities also controlled the Station 88 spaceport, the "gateway to the Mid Rim." The loss of one system would mean the loss of all, with Station 88 thrown in to boot—potentially an eviscerating blow to the Republic.

Dooku arranged a conference with the leaders of the worlds on the neutral planet of Null. Lorian Nod was now the ruler of Junction V. The ensuing decades had further poisoned the bad blood between them. Nod decided to pay lip service to Dooku's overtures, while secretly working with the Jedi Council to bring his fellow delegates in on the side of the Republic.

In Dooku's private cliffside villa on Null, the Count prepared to host the Mid Rim delegates. Dooku tried to assassinate one of the delegates in order to swing the vote in his favor, but the hit failed, and Lorian Nod reaffirmed his Republic loyalties. Station 88 and its systems would now support the Republic.

Count Dooku did not take his defeat well. Locking the doors to the meeting room, he ordered a squad of super battle droids to murder everyone inside. Obi-Wan Kenobi and Anakin Skywalker helped mangle the machines, while Lorian Nod followed Dooku to his escape ship. Nod hoped to force Dooku into a final reckoning for his crimes, but Dooku stabbed his "old friend" through the heart with his crimson lightsaber.

Anakin remained haunted by the thought that *he* could have stopped Dooku had he not been constrained by Obi-Wan's orders. First on Raxus Prime and now on Null, Anakin had squandered two chances to end the war by killing the Separatist leader. Soon, Anakin vowed, Dooku would feel the bite of his lightsaber blade.

THE DEVARON RUSE
21.41 B.B.Y. (6 months, 1 week after the Battle of Geonosis)

Aurra Sing, Jedi killer and professional assassin, accepted a contract from Senator Vien'sai'Malloc of Devaron. Behind the backs of her constituents, the Senator had started a smuggling operation that waylaid Republic freighters traveling near Devaron and stole their cargo. Aurra Sing's role was to eliminate anyone who came too close to discovering the truth.

The attacks had already hobbled the Republic's resupply efforts at Bestine as well as points beyond. A Jedi task force consisting of Kit Fisto, Aayla Secura, the Dark Woman, Master Tholme, and the Neti Jedi T'ra Saa arrived at Devaron with orders to find the smuggler base and crush it. They soon uncovered Senator Vien'sai'Malloc's treachery and moved against her hired raiders at their hideout in Devaron's mountains. But Aurra Sing lay in wait. Incapacitating Tholme and her own former Master, the Dark Woman, Aurra Sing then used her captives as bait to lure Aayla Secura into a trap.

Aayla, however, proved more resourceful than Aurra Sing had anticipated. In a lightsaber duel that became a test of wills, Aayla defeated the notorious mercenary and rescued the wounded Jedi. Kit Fisto's subsequent destruction of the pirate hideout ensured that Devaron space would remain safe for the time being.

Aurra Sing arrived at the Oovo IV asteroid prison under heavy guard. Within a few months she would be free again, beneficiary of an early release—in exchange for vital intelligence regarding a bounty that had recently been posted by an anonymous party on the heads of Jedi Knights.

THE DESCENT OF QUINLAN VOS
21.38 B.B.Y. (7.5 months after the Battle of Geonosis)

The Gotal moon of Antar 4, site of one of the pre–Clone Wars uprisings, had become a battlefield once more, as Separatist loyalists struck back against the militant Antarian Rangers who now kept order. Count Dooku's orbital bombardment decimated the Rangers, and the Count set up a new command HQ on Antar's surface, notching himself another triumph.

It was here that Quinlan Vos grew into his role as one of Dooku's Dark Jedi. Dooku, who knew the truth behind Quinlan's undercover mission, allowed the spy to sink into the part. The Count could see that Quinlan already walked close

to the dark side. It would not take much to make the deception a reality.

Quinlan worked with three of Dooku's other Dark Jedi—Kadrian Sey, Tol Skorr, and Master Sora Bulq—on missions including the Separatist conquest of the planet Tibrin. To the cheers of thousands of liberated Ishi Tib, Dooku executed the cruel dictator Suribran Tu, and hung Tu's corpse out for public display.

Quinlan's undercover assignment came to a head on his homeworld of Kiffu. There Dooku hoped to construct a secret Separatist base with the cooperation of Sheyf Tinté, the ruler of Kiffu and Quinlan's great-aunt. When the arrogant Tinté spurned Dooku's offer, the Count ordered her death. Quinlan, caught in a crisis of conscience, cut down Kadrian Sey in order to save his aunt's life.

Dooku, however, had his pawn right where he wanted him. After the Count hinted to Quinlan that Sheyf Tinté held a secret, Quinlan used his own psychometric power to read past events hidden in his aunt's mind. What he saw sent him into a blood rage. Years earlier, Sheyf Tinté had sacrificed Quinlan's parents to Anzati vampires as part of an unholy business deal. With a surge of dark side power, Quinlan butchered his terrified aunt.

Satisfied, Count Dooku welcomed Quinlan Vos to the Separatist side, knowing that this time, the conversion was no act.

THE BASSADRO MASSACRE
21.25 B.B.Y. (9 months after the Battle of Geonosis)

For a Republic that had enjoyed total control over the media through government seizure of the HoloNet, the emergence of a Confederacy pirate "shadowfeed" broadcast became a vexing problem. Now the public had dueling propaganda to choose from. A case in point was the so-called Bassadro Massacre.

A volcanic mining planet, Bassadro became the nucleus of a twelve-day battle when Jedi Knight Empatojayos Brand led a clone force to dislodge entrenched Separatists in the Agao Ranges. Brand's decision to fire concussion missiles at the overhanging ridge filled the air with millions of glassy shards, shredding the Separatist troops—along with a village of four hundred unaffiliated miners. Both sides put their own spin on the story, and the Republic could not manage to shut down the shadowfeed.

The propaganda streams further polarized segments of the population, turning some Republic citizens rabidly loyal. One outgrowth of this was the Commission for the Protection of the Republic (COMPOR), a primarily human group of civilians given to marches and rallies.

In other war theaters, Jedi died in the ongoing Aqualish conflicts between the Republic's Andoan Free Colonies and the Separatist planet of Ando. The Republic also lost the world of Ord Canfre to the Separatists. Good news, however, came in for the Republic from Balamak in the Mid Rim, where Anakin Skywalker again proved his stratospheric talent by firing missiles that destroyed a Droid Control Ship—a ship that happened to be carrying a prototype communications jammer that could have taken out an entire HoloNet node.

RISE OF THE CORTOSIS BATTLE DROIDS
21.17 B.B.Y. (10 months after the Battle of Geonosis)

On the Techno Union mechworld of Metalorn, Wat Tambor's engineers invented battle droids that incorporated cortosis into their chassis, making them resistant to lightsaber blades.

Tambor had obtained his cortosis through Jabba the Hutt. Anakin Skywalker, dispatched to investigate Jabba's operations, killed Dooku's Sith witch Saato. Bounty Hunter Aurra Sing also tried to kill Anakin, although she escaped with her head still attached to her shoulders.

The first of the cortosis droids then attacked Coruscant and overran the Jedi Temple. Anakin chased off the rest of Dooku's droid raiding party, but the damage had been done. With the Sarapin blackout and now this latest attack, Coruscant's citizens no longer felt safe from the war's ravages.

The Jedi Council ordered Anakin to destroy the cortosis droid factory on Metalorn. While planting detonators, Anakin encountered and killed three more of Dooku's second-tier lieutenants: the dark side brothers Vinoc and Karoc, and the Chiss bounty hunter Vandalor. Enraged by the indiscriminate slaughter of his staff, Count Dooku confronted Skywalker himself. Their lightsaber battle was brutal and short. Prodded to berserker fury through the Count's taunts, Anakin struck his opponent down, though he later learned that this Dooku may have only been a clone doppelgänger.

Anakin returned to Coruscant with Techno Union leader Wat Tambor as his prisoner, leaving behind a radioactive crater where Metalorn's cortosis droid plant had stood.

THE DEATH OF ATRAKEN
21.1 B.B.Y. (11 months after the Battle of Geonosis)

On Atraken, fighting had persisted for a year in a murderous string of stalemates. At last the Republic gained the upper hand with Operation Katabatic, but the Separatists viewed their own impending defeat as an excuse to spit in their enemy's victory cup. A virulent biochemical toxin was released into Atraken's water table. By the time a triumphant clone trooper raised the Republic banner over the capital city, Atraken was already a dead planet.

If the first months of the Atraken campaign had convinced the dissident Jedi that the Clone Wars were futile, the final days assured them that the war was morally repugnant. Atraken proved that it was impossible for the Republic to wage a "clean" war. Republic High Command admitted that victory might have to come by any means necessary.

Anakin Skywalker's capture of Wat Tambor during the Metalorn mission had caught Darth Sidious by surprise. The move could have potentially destabilized the war, and so Sidious, as Chancellor Palpatine, ordered that Wat Tambor be relocated to a prison on distant Delrian.

Tambor received a visit from two legal deputies, both pressure-suited Skakoans like himself. The two Skakoans proceeded to breach their pressure suits, and the release of their compressed methane atmospheres detonated like twin bombs. In the chaos, a third member of their party—a Clawdite shapeshifter known as Nuri—slipped in to free the Techno Union foreman. With the Techno Union again active, the balance of power between the Separatists and the Republic tipped back into a dead heat.

The Spaarti Incident
21 B.B.Y. (12 months after the Battle of Geonosis)

Cartao, trading hub of the Prackla sector, had remained unaligned in the war thus far. But Cartao sheltered Spaarti Creations, one of the most remarkable (and least known) factories in the galaxy. By using a "fluid retooling" process unique to their species, the native Cransoc could adjust the Spaarti factory overnight to produce virtually any product, and the results were almost always superior to similar items on the market. Darth Sidious saw in Cartao an opportunity to turn Spaarti Creations to his own ends, while discrediting his enemies in the process.

Kinman Doriana, Chancellor Palpatine's aide, became the agent of Cartao's ruin. Doriana had been double-dealing since the outset of the war, believing that he had successfully created *two* lives—one to serve Chancellor Palpatine and the other to serve Darth Sidious. On Sidious's orders, Doriana used his credentials to seize Spaarti Creations in the name of the Republic. Immediately, the factory began churning out cloning cylinders that could grow battle-ready soldiers in less than a tenth of the time it took the Kaminoans to do the same.

But the Separatists had a similar idea, intending to use Spaarti to produce a new variety of battle droid. Their invasion force seized the facility. Since no one wanted to wreck the factory in a careless crossfire, the two sides fought a very precise battle; the factory changed hands several times over the next few weeks. Finally, one of Darth Sidious's agents remote-steered a Republic gunship into the roof of the Spaarti complex, sparking a fire that melted the priceless Cransoc technology.

Darth Sidious had achieved what he wanted. The Jedi, implicated in the gunship crash through false evidence, suffered another blow to their credibility. Spaarti Creations could no longer be used by potential rivals. And the Republic took a delivery of thousands of Spaarti cloning cylinders. These cylinders saw heavy use following their installation on Wayland and other planets. Spaarti clones became increasingly common during the war's final year.

The Bio-Droid Threat
21 B.B.Y. (1 year after the Battle of Geonosis)

Ord Cestus, a relatively forgotten planet in the far reaches of the Outer Rim, had established a booming economy based on the manufacture of bio-droids—robots with a unique living circuit composed of a sleeping Dashta eel. These eels, found only in a single underground lake beneath Ord Cestus's mountains, had a powerful connection to the Force. When wedded to a security droid's circuitry through a secret Cestian procedure, the resulting biological–mechanical gestalt could seemingly react to threats before they happened. This slight precognitive ability made bio-droids the only battle droids that could efficiently stand up to a Jedi in one-on-one combat, giving them the nickname "Jedi Killers."

Dooku's lieutenant Asajj Ventress soon approached Ord Cestus's leaders with an offer they couldn't refuse—an order for hundreds of thousands of bio-droids, and the machinery and tissue-cloning tanks needed to fulfill that order. The huge influx of credits would be enough to ensure Ord Cestus's survival in the uncertain postwar future.

Word of the deal soon reached the Jedi Council. They could not let the bio-droid army reach completion, but neither did the Council wish to antagonize neutral planets by bullying Ord Cestus into submission. Obi-Wan Kenobi, Kit Fisto, and a squad of clone troopers received the Ord Cestus assignment. The clones would follow the textbook "militia model" by organizing the planet's low-caste workers into a fighting force. If negotiations failed, sabotage would follow. If *both* options failed, a Republic assault ship stood ready to bombard the bio-droid factories into oblivion.

Out in the planet's countryside, the clone troopers created their ragtag militia. Obi-Wan and Kit Fisto soon joined them, and the small army began to strike the high-end bio-droid factories. The Cestian government scrambled the bio-droids to fight the insurgents. Hundreds died under the guns of the unstoppable automatons.

The two sides reached a stalemate. A Republic orbital bombardment—and the complete destruction of Ord Cestus society—seemed inevitable. But something remarkable and unprecedented had happened to the clone captain. During the recruitment of the local militia, he had fallen in love with a transport pilot, who had awakened a need in him that went beyond the imprinted loyalty he had to his corps. In the end, the clone captain sacrificed himself to destroy the control center for the bio-droid production line. With his death, the specter of a vast bio-droid army evaporated.

MASSING THUNDERHEADS
20.9–20.8 B.B.Y. (1 year, 1–2 months after the Battle of Geonosis)

Eriadu in the Seswenna sector held a strategic Republic position, straddling both the Rimma Trade Route and the Hydian Way. The Rimward end of the Rimma had turned unfriendly since before the Battle of Geonosis, with major worlds such as Sluis Van and Clak'dor VII defecting to the Separatist side. The nearby planet Sullust, a major manufacturing center, had remained in the Republic stable. For more than a year Eriadu and Sullust had served as bastions, stemming the tide of Separatist incursion. That is, until Sullust's secession.

The Republic was quick to respond lest they lose control of the Hydian. Eriadu had by now become the preeminent Republic staging point for all battles in that quadrant, boasting a full fleet under the command of Brigadier Gideon Tarkin—Wilhuff Tarkin's brother—and numerous wings of Jedi starfighters. Brigadier Tarkin merged various planetary navies into "priority theaters" and launched t hem from Eriadu.

Ultimately, a betrayal in the Republic ranks led to their defeat in the Battle of Sullust, yet the overall campaign eventually resulted in the Republic's partial recapture of the Sluis sector.

Violence across the galaxy continued to build as if heating to a boiling point. Kuat and Neimoidia—key members of the Republic and Confederacy, respectively—escalated their military standoff by saturating the space around their sectors with mines, effectively shutting down a crucial leg of the Hydian Way. In another part of the galaxy, Anakin and Obi-Wan helped bring peace to the embattled planet of Skye. Along the Rimma Trade Route, Mace Windu foiled a Separatist plot to mine the route, chasing a battle droid

army from the Squib homeworld of Skor II.

Elsewhere on the Rimma, in the Separatist-aligned Sluis sector and neighboring space, Freedom's Sons continued to score victories under the leadership of Captain Zozridor Slayke. Hoping to take control of the situation, the Republic sent diplomats to negotiate with the Sluis sector rulers, but both sides' negotiators were killed when the space station hosting the meeting exploded.

THE BATTLE OF JABIIM
20.79–20.67 B.B.Y. (1 year, 2–4 months after the Battle of Geonosis)

Republic negotiations again fell apart over the fate of Jabiim, a soggy ball in the Outer Rim rich in minerals. The charismatic Alto Stratus, who had recently seized control of Jabiim in a coup, had allied his majority government with the Separatists, despite the presence of Republic loyalists on his world. Chancellor Palpatine authorized the use of force to protect the loyalists from Stratus's aggression, though unofficially the Republic was more concerned about going after Jabiim's ore.

Rain fell around the clock on Jabiim. The world was a mess, too stormy for atmospheric flight and too muddy for most heavy equipment. Nevertheless, the Republic chose Jabiim to be a field test for its newest walker, the All Terrain Armored Transport, or AT-AT. These four-legged behemoths packed enough firepower to decimate any Separatist AAT or spider droid. Combined with six-legged AT-TEs and two-legged AT-XTs, the Republic battle line appeared unstoppable.

Unfortunately, the Republic ran into trouble almost immediately, and it wasn't the mud. Alto Stratus and his elite Nimbus commandos employed native technology like repulsor boots to skate above the quagmire that passed for a surface. It took weeks for the Republic to score a major victory at Camp Aurek. After that, their successes seemed to come quickly—Point Down and Outpost Shear fell within days. But the Republic's forward march was taking them farther and farther from their main HQ, Shelter Base, precisely as Alto Stratus had intended.

In a brutal raid, Stratus's hailfire droids pummeled Shelter

Base and killed hundreds. General Obi-Wan Kenobi and the ARC trooper Alpha were believed to be among the dead. Unknown to their fellow soldiers, the two survived, only to become prisoners of Commander Asajj Ventress.

Now Masterless, Anakin received a transfer to the "Padawan Pack," a group of orphaned apprentices bunched together in the hope that several Padawans would be equal to one Jedi Knight. With Obi-Wan's disappearance, the Jabiim campaign fell to General Leska, who moved her surviving troops to the Razor Coast in an effort to kill Alto Stratus.

The Battle of Jabiim dragged into its second month. Alto Stratus had a new target in mind—reinforced with fresh battle droids, he marched against the Republic's Cobalt Station with an army ten thousand strong.

General Leska perished in the offensive, and Republic High Command had no choice but to order a full evacuation of Jabiim. The Padawan Pack agreed to delay Stratus's troops long enough for a full evacuation. Staging from Cobalt Station, they fell one by one in a last stand against overwhelming odds. Anakin, however, wasn't with them. Ordered by Chancellor Palpatine to assist with the evacuation, the Chosen One was kept safely away from the grinder that soon claimed the lives of every member of the pack.

The evac transports didn't have room to carry the native Jabiimi loyalist fighters. They were left behind to face certain execution at the hands of Stratus's conquerors. Any Jedi wounded in the Battle of Jabiim went to the medical planet New Holstice for treatment, while Anakin received temporary orders to pair with Jedi Knight A'Sharad Hett on a mission to Aargonar.

The Dragon of Aargonar
20.67 B.B.Y. (16 months after the Battle of Geonosis)

The desert planet Aargonar had little value save its location, which at this point in the war happened to be directly on the border between Republic and Confederacy space. To beat back Separatist encroachment, the Council sent Jedi Master Ki-Adi-Mundi and Jedi Knight Bultar Swan to lead an Aargonar attack. Also contributing were A'Sharad Hett and Anakin Skywalker.

Early in the battle, the gunship carrying A'Sharad and Anakin crashed behind enemy lines. Though the two Jedi had much in common, having both come late to the Temple following Tatooine childhoods, A'Sharad remained steeped in the Tusken Raider culture of his upbringing. Anakin hated him. Unable to forget his mother's murder at the hands of Tuskens, Anakin slipped into a nightmare in the Aargonar heat and screamed out the secret that he had kept from everyone—that in his fury following his mother's death, he had slaughtered an entire Tusken village.

A'Sharad chose not to reveal Anakin's secret, calling it a burden that the Padawan must bear alone. The two Jedi made it back to the Republic line, where Ki-Adi-Mundi and Bultar Swan held a rapidly crumbling position in the Vondar Canyon. By luring a hovertrain-sized gouka dragon onto the battlefield, Anakin managed to break up the Separatist offensive and allow for a Republic evacuation of Aargonar.

Anakin refused to give up hope regarding Obi-Wan's survival on Jabiim, but the Council did not share his optimism. Recognizing the need to keep Padawans paired with more experienced Jedi following the deaths in the Padawan Pack, the Council reassigned Anakin to Jedi Master Ki-Adi-Mundi. Though Master Mundi was hardly a typical Jedi—he had once married and raised a family—Anakin found it difficult to open up to him. Ki-Adi-Mundi was a dour man with other things on his mind than training a Padawan.

The two spent much of their time away from the war's front lines. Pirates, the perennial scourges of the spaceways, had become emboldened by preoccupation of the Republic security forces. To send an unmistakable message to these criminals, the Republic dispatched special task forces to cut the strongest pirate fleets to ribbons.

Escape from Rattatak
20.66 B.B.Y. (1 year, 4 months after the Battle of Geonosis)

Obi-Wan Kenobi and the ARC trooper Alpha were now prisoners of war, imprisoned in Asajj Ventress's citadel on Rattatak. Ventress tormented Obi-Wan with muscle maggots and a Sith torture mask, hoping to prove to Dooku that the Jedi was unworthy of his attention as a potential apprentice.

Obi-Wan sprang himself and Alpha from their holding cell and tore through Ventress's guards. Ventress intercepted him on the landing pad, but couldn't prevent Obi-Wan from stealing her own ship and flying himself and Alpha back to civilization.

Separatist starfighters perforated the hyperdrive of Obi-Wan and Alpha's escape vessel, however, and it crashed on a forgotten planetoid. Their Separatist pursuers followed them

down, but fell in a shower of blasterfire, the victims of bounty hunters eager to claim the price on the heads of Jedi posted by Asajj Ventress. Yoda and Mace Windu had an open bounty posting of 1,250,000 credits each, and Anakin Skywalker, still a Padawan, fetched 225,000 credits, dead or alive.

Anakin Skywalker and Ki-Adi-Mundi rescued Obi-Wan from the hunters. Obi-Wan Kenobi returned to the Republic as a war hero. With his master's safe return, Anakin's brief apprenticeship to Ki-Adi-Mundi came to a close.

Alpha, meanwhile, returned to Kamino to train new clones. Obi-Wan joked that Alpha should give the clones *real* names, and Alpha took him at his word. The next batch of commanders to arrive from Kamino bore simple one-word names in addition to their numeric designations. The new commander assigned to Obi-Wan called himself Cody.

DEATH OF A CHANCELLOR
20.65 B.B.Y. (1 year, 4 months after the Battle of Geonosis)

On Coruscant, Chancellor Palpatine took advantage of every development in the war, both setbacks and victories, to acquire more power for himself. The passage of the so-called Reflex Amendment gave him authority over planetary and sector matters. Critics speculated that it was only a matter of time before Coruscant-appointed territorial governors stripped all control from local governments.

Bail Organa, Senator of Alderaan, was one of a growing number of politicians who mistrusted Palpatine's expanding power base. In the eleven years since he had replaced Chancellor Valorum, Palpatine had far outlasted his eight-year term limit, as well as taken on emergency powers.

The Republic's latest failures became more fod-

A Republic clone commando
[ART BY MARK CHIARELLO]

der for Bail Organa's Senate colleagues. Agora in the Sluis sector had fallen to the Separatists, despite last-minute resistance by Freedom's Sons. On Cerea, Commerce Guild spider droids befouled the paradise world in a monthlong battle that ended when Gossam commandos assassinated Cerea's President Bo-Ro-Tara. Pirates had even attacked Bail Organa's ship. In response to the news, Palpatine called for even more draconian security measures. When Senator Seti Ashgad argued against the installation of new surveillance cams in the Senate Building, he suddenly disappeared. Much later it emerged that he had been exiled to the prison planet Nam Chorios.

Organa had already formed an alliance with the like-minded senator Mon Mothma of Chandrila. Now he received a surprising visit from Finis Valorum. Over the past decade, the ex-chancellor had collected reams of stories concerning Palpatine, including the fact that, as with Seti Ashgad, his critics often mysteriously vanished. Initially, Organa couldn't be sure that Valorum's words weren't the bitter griping of a man forced from power, but two facts changed Organa's mind. The first was the suspicious explosion of Valorum's transport as it lifted off from a Coruscant starport, killing Finis Valorum and everyone else aboard. The second was Palpatine's exploitation of the incident to pass another security bill, which gave him unprecedented central power.

Clearly, aboveboard politicking was not enough. Over

the next several months, Bail Organa and Mon Mothma, with the occasional help of other Senators including Garm Bel Iblis of isolationist Corellia, began laying the groundwork for a political alliance opposed to Palpatine's rule.

CORUSCANT ASSASSINATION
20.63 B.B.Y. (1 year, 4 months after the Battle of Geonosis)

Dooku wasted no time sending his new agent, Quinlan Vos, on missions. On the Sith tomb world of Korriban, Quinlan retrieved a holocron once belonging to the Sith Lord Darth Andeddu from a booby-trapped catacomb. On Coruscant, Quinlan assassinated a double-dealing Senator who had displeased Dooku. While escaping from Coruscant, he ran afoul of the Whiphid Jedi Master K'Kruhk, hero of Teyr and former dissident Jedi. K'Kruhk nearly died in his pursuit of Quinlan through the vertical city. Even those in the Order who knew of Quinlan's undercover mission became convinced that his cover story could no longer explain his deeds. Quinlan continued to delude himself, believing any actions to be justified if they ingratiated him with Dooku and got him closer to uncovering the identity of Dooku's Master, the "second Sith."

THE HERO WITH NO FEAR
20.3 B.B.Y. (1 year, 10 months after the Battle of Geonosis)

Though some segments of the population continued to distrust the Jedi, planets liberated from Separatist control often viewed the Jedi as heroes. Anakin Skywalker had already received more than his share of the glory. Following his exploits at Jabiim and Aargonar, the news-net media had dubbed him "the hero with no fear." Entire worlds began expecting Anakin to free them single-handedly. In a surprising number of cases, they weren't disappointed.

On Virujansi, Anakin defeated a Separatist occupation force by taking command of the planet's Rarefied Air Cavalry and luring the enemy's vulture fighters into a treacherous warren of mountain caverns. The grateful Virujansi named Anakin their "warrior of the infinite."

At Togoria, the Republic suffered a total defeat. The planet, homeworld of the fierce feline Togorians, became a flashpoint when General Grievous's troops arrived in force—apparently menacing Togoria's small shipyard. The Republic dispatched General Bridger to the rescue, only to realize that Togoria had voluntarily gone over to the enemy. Togorian warriors tore General Bridger's landing party to shreds with their claws. Grievous spared Bridger and challenged him to a duel. The fight lasted less than twenty seconds, and Grievous left the body on the dirt to feed the mosgoths.

THE BATTLE OF DREIGHTON
20.2 B.B.Y. (1 year, 10 months after the Battle of Geonosis)

Cloaking technology had been one of the greatest break-throughs of the last five millennia, yet it was rarely used in the Clone Wars. Making a starship invisible could only be done with stygium crystals, and the stygium mines had gone dry years earlier on the planet Aeten II. The space pirate Nym's stygium cache on Maramere had likewise run empty.

Both the Republic and the Confederacy hoped to locate undiscovered caches of stygium on Aeten II. Dreaming of invisible fleets, they clashed in the monthlong Battle of Dreighton, named for the nebula that shrouded Aeten II from outside eyes. The Republic received support from an independent army known as the Pendarran Warriors, but it proved to be of little use. The conflict cost the lives of more than a hundred Jedi, many of them killed when Hutt and Black Sun forces moved in to rout the weakened combatants.

There was no victor at the Battle of Dreighton. Aeten II was declared barren of military resources and soon forgotten, again emerging into importance decades later in the middle of the Galactic Civil War.

Closer to home, General Grievous personally led the Confederacy's boldest push yet—an assault on the Core world of Duro, one of the founding members of the Republic and home to key corporate and shipbuilding concerns. Separatist naval forces hammered the Republic *Acclamator*-class warships tasked with Duro's defense, and captured a key orbital city after less than a week of fighting. Using the city's command codes to drop Duro's planetary shields, Grievous unleashed an orbital bombardment followed by a mass landing of his droid troops on the planet's polluted surface.

BREAKING THE FOEROST SIEGE
20.1 B.B.Y. (1 year, 11 months after the Battle of Geonosis)

The shipyards of Foerost lay practically in Coruscant's backyard. During the Great Sith War they had been used as a military staging area, and in more recent centuries they had been purchased by the Techno Union. At the start of the Clone Wars, the Republic had simply blockaded Foerost space. Without access to Separatist supply lines, the Republic hoped the shipyards would wither into decay.

For nearly two years the standoff continued, until the besieged Techno Union engineers exploded from Foerost with warships that no one had imagined. The engineers called the design the Bulwark Mark I—a kilometer-long behemoth with turbolasers, ion cannons, and enough armor to ram small ships with impunity. With the old Sullustan Dua Ningo in charge of the armada, the Bulwark Fleet broke through the Republic's blockade and proceeded to smash military outposts throughout Coruscant's Sector Zero. To stop Ningo, the Republic launched its newest warship—the *Victory*-class Star Destroyer—nearly six months early.

These arrowhead-shaped craft measured nine hundred meters from stem to stern, boasting ten tractor beam projectors and 80 concussion missile launchers. Born of the Victor Initiative Project between Kuat Drive Yards and Rendili StarDrive, they performed with distinction in a shakedown cruise that became a naval slugging match for the heart of Core space. Captains Terrinald Screed and Jan Dodonna led the two task forces that made up the Victory Fleet, surviving clashes with Ningo at Ixtlar, Alsakan, and Basilisk.

The final showdown came in the skies above Anaxes. Dodonna, under heavy fire with dead wrecks from his task force plunging planetward, held out long enough for Screed to pop in from hyperspace and disintegrate Ningo's flagship with a broadside fusillade. Screed required cybernetic reconstruction to survive the injuries he received in the Battle of Anaxes, but both men returned to Coruscant as heroes.

THE CASUALTIES OF DRONGAR
20 B.B.Y. (2 years after the Battle of Geonosis)

War is hell, goes the saying, and no one knows it better than field surgeons. Battlefield medics experience a near-continuous parade of severed limbs, exploded torsos, and gushing arteries. During the Clone Wars, giant MedStar frigates accompanied most Republic fleets into battle, deploying mobile field hospitals known as Republic Mobile Surgical Units or RMSUs—"Rimsoos." On contested Drongar, one Rimsoo had to choose sides over the fate of the planet.

Drongar was a young world of steam fissures and lightning strikes with no plant life more advanced than fungus. Bota, an ugly native mold, had the curious quality of being useful to nearly every species as an antibiotic, painkiller, or intoxicant. Since bota, once picked, deteriorated quickly, both the Republic and the Confederacy maintained harvesting operations on-planet and fielded armies to fight for control of the bota fields.

The planet's atmospheric spores contaminated airspeeder engines and made airborne warfare impossible, so battle on Drongar came down to face-to-face shootouts. Hundreds of bleeding clone troopers arrived every week at the Rimsoos, only to be patched up and sent back into the fray.

The war on Drongar had been burning for more than a year when Padawan Barriss Offee, who had participated in such earlier conflicts as the mission to Ansion and the Battle of Ilum, arrived to practice her skills as a Jedi healer. At Rimsoo Seven in the Jasserak Lowlands she encountered Dr. Jos Vondar, a young surgeon whose cynicism covered his idealistic hope that he could save the lives of every clone to come under his laser scalpel. The Rimsoo personnel aided in uncovering evidence that Admiral Bleyd, commander of the Drongar MedStar, had masterminded a bota-skimming ring to line his own pockets.

Bleyd's scheme ended with his death, but the Drongar operation continued to be plagued by Separatist spies and saboteurs who attacked the bota fields. Barriss Offee discovered that the bota acted as a Force magnifier for her Jedi perceptions, and briefly flirted with an addiction to the medicinal mold. The Republic used Drongar to test its own superlaser project, using an enhancement of the weaponry employed by SPHA-T heavy cannons. After much refinement, the superlaser ultimately would see use aboard the first Death Star following the rise of the Empire.

Eventually, the fighting resulted in the destruction of the Drongar operation, as most settlements were bombed out of existence. Dr. Vondar went on to other assignments, and Barriss Offee returned to Coruscant, secure in her new status as a Jedi Knight.

DISASTER ON HONOGHR
20 B.B.Y. (2 years after the Battle of Geonosis)

At this point in the war, the Republic believed that it had blunted the threat of Separatist biological warfare. By enlisting the experts of the Lurrian Genetic Enclave to study the "swamp gas" antidote recovered from Queyta, the Republic had cracked the enemy's bioweapon signature.

Across the galaxy, however, one Separatist commander struggled to create a toxin that could *never* be cured. The lab aboard his scientific vessel *Gahenna* had been rescued two years earlier from Queyta. The *Gahenna* developed a poisonous defoliant, TriHexalophine1138, and headed back toward Naboo to complete the planned mission that had seen the devastation of Ohma-D'un. But a Republic cruiser got wind of the plan and drove the *Gahenna* to ground above a forgotten world called Honoghr.

The Scientific Information Packet aboard the ship contained all the details on the TriHexalophine plot, and both the Republic and the Separatists scrambled to secure it. The planet's native Noghri, however, had already taken the SIP to the heart of a sacred temple built there thirty millennia

Jedi Knight Aayla Secura and Jedi Master Quinlan Vos
[ART BY MARK CHIARELLO]

before by the ancient Rakata.

Quinlan Vos headed into the temple to retrieve the SIP for Dooku. Opposing him were Aayla Secura and Commander Bly, one of the newest clone commanders to come from Kamino. The two sides teamed up to defeat the temple's booby traps, but Quinlan betrayed his former Padawan and tried to make off with the SIP for himself. By forcing Quinlan into a position where he might have to kill her, Aayla made him realize that his obsession with rooting out the "second Sith" might not be worth the choices he had made. Doubting himself for the first time in months, Quinlan escaped Honoghr empty-handed.

Honoghr suffered mortal damage as the *Gahenna's* toxins leaked from the cracked laboratories and devastated the ecosystem, leaving almost no plant life, save for dry plains of kholm-grass. Forgotten by the Republic, the Noghri bore their misery in stoic silence.

TARGET: GRIEVOUS
20 B.B.Y. (2 years after the Battle of Geonosis)

General Grievous energized the Separatist armies during this phase of the war, chewing through Republic territory like a logger droid felling deadwood. On Vantos, Nadiem, and dozens of other worlds, Grievous slaughtered clone troopers and civilians alike, collecting lightsaber trophies from the Jedi Knights whom he beheaded.

Grievous's atrocities led to the rise of a splinter faction within the Jedi Order, whose members advocated the general's assassination. Master Yoda opposed this radicalism, fearing that the actions of Jedi assassins could drive them to the dark side, but a few risked excommunication to dish out what they perceived as frontier justice.

One Padawan, Flynn Kybo, joined up with the Coway Jedi Master B'dard Tone and several others to track down Grievous in the Ison Corridor. The general's droid armies had conquered the Ugnaught homeworld of Gentes, strip-mining the landscape and massacring thousands of Ugnaughts after the species showed little value as slaves. Grievous also imprisoned a group of young Padawans on Gentes, planning to lobotomize them and turn them into cyborgs like himself. Kybo and Master Tone freed the Padawans, but both died before they could take out Grievous.

STONE MITES OF ORLEON
19.9 B.B.Y. (2 years, 1 month after the Battle of Geonosis)

Stone mites, bioengineered insects that could devour building foundations, had ruined many worlds since their introduction in the months prior to the Battle of Geonosis. The Separatist scientist Jenna Zan Arbor had created the stone mites with help from Arkanian geneticists,

but the Republic had been looking for a chance to turn the creatures to its own ends.

An opportunity presented itself when the freighter *Spinner,* on approach to Coruscant's busy Westport, fell like a rock into Kishi. The *Spinner* had been crawling with stone mites, and the creatures quickly overtook the Kishi. The stone mite outbreak resulted in the total collapse of the Pillar Zone before Jedi healers skilled in the art of *Morichro* snuffed out the lives of every last mite.

Armand Isard, head of the Senate Bureau for Intelligence, labeled the incident an act of terrorism. Isard's agents traced the *Spinner* back to a previous stopover on Orleon, a small Mid Rim planet of little note. Believing that Orleon held Separatist bioweapons facilities, Isard authorized the release of Republic-altered, mutant stone mites onto the world. Carbonite canisters fired from high orbit thawed on impact and released thousands of hibernating mites.

But Isard was wrong—Orleon had no biolabs, and might have escaped the Clone Wars untouched had it not been for the unlucky *Spinner.* Nothing could stop Isard's mites. Structures that had stood for thirteen thousand years crumbled into powder within a week. Orleon's entire population of eight hundred million fled offworld, and hordes of breeding stone mites set to work devouring the planet's crust.

BPFASSH UPRISING
19.75 B.B.Y. (2 years, 3 months after the Battle of Geonosis)

The Sluis sector continued to boil. Assailed by relentless internal raids from Captain Slayke's Freedom's Sons and pressured from the outside by the Republic fortress at Eriadu, the sector had known nearly continual fighting since the outset of the war.

Bpfassh, one of the Sluis sector's lesser lights, boasted a satellite Jedi training facility similar to the one on Kamparas. Due to its remoteness, the Jedi Council had always had trouble with the Bpfassh enclave, putting down minor insurrections from time to time when inexperienced students unwisely decided to flex their power. At the start of the Clone Wars, the Bpfasshi academy joined the dissident Jedi movement.

The ongoing stress of the Sluis sector battles is believed to have triggered an outbreak of fanatical militarism among the Bpfasshi Jedi. Fully in the grip of the dark side, and quite mad, the Bpfasshi Dark Jedi set themselves against Freedom's Sons and slaughtered everyone who got in their way. Soon opposed in battle by loyal Coruscant Jedi, the Bpfasshi Jedi fell one by one, until their leader ultimately perished in an epic Force clash with Master Yoda.

ATTACK ON AZURE
19.59 B.B.Y. (2 years, 5 months after the Battle of Geonosis)

Obi-Wan Kenobi and Anakin Skywalker, accompanied by fellow Jedi Siri Tachi, acquired a foolproof code-breaker developed by technical genius Talesan Fry. When they delivered the codebreaker to the Republic-controlled spaceport of Azure, the Separatists launched a massive attack in an attempt to seize the gadget for themselves.

Though the Republic repelled the assault, Siri Tachi died from wounds sustained in battle. Obi-Wan, who had always allowed a part of him to love Siri despite the Jedi principles of nonattachment, now allowed himself to feel the pain of loss.

THE PRAESITLYN CONQUEST
19.5 B.B.Y. (2 years, 6 months after the Battle of Geonosis)

The first strike in the Battle of Praesitlyn came without warning. Recently recaptured from Separatists, the planet held a cutting-edge communications complex that linked datafeeds throughout the galactic quadrant. Praesitlyn itself had few defenses. Concerned that the planet could again become a Separatist target, the Republic hoped to dispatch a fleet from the nearby Sluis Van shipyards.

Dooku's lieutenant Asajj Ventress soon revealed the flaw in the Republic's strategy. She dispatched a fleet under the command of InterGalactic Banking Clan bigwig Pors Tonith,

while also blockading the Sluis Van system. With Sluis Van's warships stuck in stardock, the bulk of Tonith's fleet zipped to Praesitlyn and landed an invasion force tens of thousands strong. The Separatists soon held Praesitlyn, and—thanks to a system-blanketing jamming field thrown out by Tonith's fleet—no one in the Republic had any idea of the problem.

Fortunately for the Republic, they had a local ally—Captain Zozridor Slayke of Freedom's Sons. His fleet had been operating in the area when the Praesitlyn invasion occurred. Slayke dispatched a message to Chancellor Palpatine, who agreed to send a relief force of clone troopers and Jedi. But Slayke, who viewed himself as a charmed figure, landed his entire volunteer army without waiting for the Republic's reinforcements. This time, Slayke badly miscalculated. Though hundreds of droids fell, the ground oozed red with the blood of Slayke's soldiers.

But the Republic reinforcements were soon on their way, streaking through hyperspace under the command of Master Nejaa Halcyon and Padawan Anakin Skywalker. For Halcyon, this was another opportunity to prove himself against the pirate who had shamed him two and a half years earlier by stealing his starship *Plooriod Bodkin*. For Anakin, it was another chance to show the Council that no enemy could stand against the Chosen One.

With twenty thousand clone troopers under their command, Anakin and Master Halcyon made planetfall on Praesitlyn and linked up with Slayke's harried forces. Anakin seized the communications complex with a company of clone troopers, but his sense of triumph on rescuing the hostages turned to boiling fury when a second force of droids murdered most of the hostages in an indiscriminate crossfire.

Hate had fully enveloped him now, weighing on his shoulders like a heavy robe. Anakin didn't bother to wait for support from Halcyon's or Slayke's lines; he pushed deeper into the encampment, penetrating Tonith's fortified HQ. When Tonith presented himself for surrender, Anakin nearly cut him in half before forcing himself back from the raw edge of fury.

Nejaa Halcyon focused his attention on mopping up the enemy fleet in orbit. Once in space, Anakin made a suicidal run on the enemy flagship's bridge, and he vanished in the explosion that followed. Anakin soon reappeared, revealing that he had made a risky, last-instant hyperspace hop. On the ground and in space, with little regard for his own life, Anakin had won the Battle of Praesitlyn.

Shortly after, on Susevfi, Nejaa Halcyon lost his life in a duel against the Anzati Dark Jedi Nikkos Tyris. The Anzati also perished in the battle, turning his Force-using followers, the Jensaarai, against the Jedi Order. The Jensaarai would develop their teachings in secret until being discovered by Luke Skywalker decades later.

LURE AT VJUN
19.49 B.B.Y. (2 years, 6 months after the Battle of Geonosis)

As an ex-member of the Jedi Order, Count Dooku stood alone among the Separatist leaders as a former friend to those he now fought. The Count had a special connection to Yoda, having learned much at the Jedi Master's side in the years before Dooku's apprenticeship to Thame Cerulian. Dooku believed that he could exploit this bond, tempt Yoda into a private meeting, and kill him.

Dooku drew Yoda to his new base on Vjun with the hint that he, Dooku, was willing to discuss the terms of his defection. Yoda suspected treachery, but didn't want to throw away the possibility of bringing a lost Jedi back into the fold. In a bit of misdirection arranged by Republic Intelligence, an actor famous for playing Yoda on the stage made a public departure from Coruscant in a Jedi starfighter. The real Yoda, concealed within the shell of an R2 unit, boarded a passenger liner with a quartet of Jedi guardians, bound for Vjun.

The Jedi Masters Jai Maruk and the Gran female Maks Leem, with their respective Padawans, Scout and Whie, made up Yoda's escort. Scout, a rebellious girl with low Force sensitivity, was embarking on her first mission outside the Temple walls. Whie had been heir to the House Malreaux on Vjun before the Jedi had brought him to the Temple as a child. Vjun itself had fallen into utter madness in subsequent years, brought on by generations of interbreeding to pro-

duce Force-strong traits in the populace.

Commander Asajj Ventress, eager to please Dooku, tracked down the Yoda decoy and blasted his ship to shards, taking the actor prisoner. Once she realized her error, Ventress caught up with the real Yoda at the Phindar Spaceport. As her assassin droids tore up the concourse, Ventress killed both Jai Maruk and Master Leem in a test of lightsabers. The two Masterless Padawans located Yoda and continued to Vjun under his protection.

The final confrontation within Vjun's Château Malreaux ended in a draw. Whie and Scout, aided by Whie's family droid, Fidelis, survived an inconclusive battle with Asajj Ventress. Dooku failed in his attempt to sway Yoda to the dark side with words; nor could he deliver a killing blow with a lightsaber. Dooku fled Vjun to regroup and plan the war's final stage.

For his heroism in the war to date, the Jedi Council inducted Obi-Wan Kenobi into their ranks, and he received a promotion to Jedi Master as dictated by tradition. Obi-Wan also used the opportunity to construct a new lightsaber.

In a related move, the Council agreed to grant Anakin Skywalker the rank of Jedi Knight. Anakin had accomplished great things and was no longer dependent on the guiding influence of his Master. In a small, private ceremony inside the darkened Council chamber, Yoda and the other members ignited their light-sabers in a ritualistic display of honor for the Chosen One. Yoda gently admonished Anakin, telling him that proper Jedi trials could not be conducted with a war on, and that his greatest test was still to come.

DREADNAUGHTS OF RENDILI
19.48 B.B.Y. (2 years, 6 months after the Battle of Geonosis)

The planet Rendili, home to a critical shipbuilding operation, voluntarily joined the Separatists. Rendili's home defense fleet consisted of state-of-the-art Dreadnaughts that could bolster the CIS—but the commander of the fleet had not yet decided where his allegiances lay. The Republic Navy, led by Saesee Tiin and Plo Koon, arrived in full force in the Rendili system. If the Dreadnaughts did not agree to join the Republic, Master Tiin had orders to destroy them.

During negotiations, Plo Koon and Republic Captain Jan Dodonna (a rising naval star who had participated in both the Stark Hyperspace Conflict and the Foerost Siege) became prisoners of the younger, Separatist-leaning officers in the Rendili fleet. With hostages, these officers hoped to break the Republic blockade. Saesee Tiin refused to back down from his ultimatum.

During the standoff, Obi-Wan Kenobi and Jedi renegade Quinlan Vos arrived together, having rescued each other from Asajj Ventress's trap aboard a derelict spacecraft. Quinlan claimed that his role as a double agent was over, since Count Dooku wanted Quinlan dead for his failure to recover the SIP from Honoghr. Both Obi-Wan and Quinlan helped rescue the hostages from the Rendili fleet, then joined the fight against the Separatist starfighters. Anakin Skywalker disabled the Rendili Dreadnaughts to prevent their escape to hyperspace.

The captured vessels were refitted to serve as prisoner transports. Chancellor Palpatine issued an order that immediately nationalized all similar, planetary-level defense fleets.

Quinlan Vos appeared before the Jedi Council, admitting that he had fallen into the shadows during his undercover mission and presenting himself for sentencing. The Council agreed to accept him back into the Order after he went through a period of meditation and repentance. Quinlan, however, was still working for Dooku as part of an elaborate triple cross—by maintaining his "dark" role, he felt that he could earn Dooku's complete trust and uncover the identity of the second Sith.

Burning with hatred toward Obi-Wan Kenobi for escaping her on Rattatak, Asajj Ventress slipped undetected onto Coruscant. She resolved to kill Obi-Wan's Padawan. In a battle on an industrial catwalk high above the city canyons, Ventress scarred Anakin Skywalker's face with her lightsaber. Anakin soon turned the tables, holding Ventress in a Force grip above an abyss and then letting her drop. Believed killed, Ventress barely survived by riding a thermal updraft. She escaped Coruscant soon after.

THE OUTER RIM SIEGES
19.48 B.B.Y. (2 years, 6 months after the Battle of Geonosis)

For the first time since the war began, it appeared that the Republic had momentum on its side. Battles on Duro, Commenor, and Balmorra cleared the CIS from key holdings in the Core and Colonies, forcing much of the Separatist navy to retreat to the Mid and Outer Rims.

Sora Bulq, the fallen Weequay Jedi, established a base on Saleucami, where he continued to serve the interests of Count Dooku. Bulq hired teachers from the elite Anzati assassin school to train his own clone soldiers, grown from the genetic material of Nikto Morgukai warriors. Jedi Master Tholme helped put an end to Bulq's plans. Months later, during the Siege of Saleucami, General Quinlan Vos led a brutal ground assault intended to drive home the horrors of war to the Separatist combatants.

The Confederacy reinforced its positions within the Rim territories, particularly its vast holdings on either side of the Slice. Confident that steady pressure would crumble the Separatist bulwarks and trigger a Confederacy surrender, nearly every fleet element and troop carrier pushed to the Rim borders to assail CIS bases on Ord Radama, Ossus, Ryloth, and elsewhere. Thus began the Outer Rim Sieges.

BETRAYAL AT BOZ PITY
19.43 B.B.Y. (2 years, 7 months after the Battle of Geonosis)

The Outer Rim Sieges marked the final stage of the Clone Wars. Fittingly, the battles saw the end of several of the Confederacy's top commanders. Obi-Wan Kenobi, still burning with shame over the torture that he had endured while a prisoner in Asajj Ventress's citadel, had requested of the Jedi Council that he be allowed to find and neutralize Ventress. Obi-Wan's single-minded fixation on his target violated the Jedi Code's rules against passion and emotion, but Yoda and Mace Windu hoped that Kenobi's solo quest would free up troops needed on the front lines.

Obi-Wan recruited the assistance of Anakin Skywalker,

though the two no longer held the connection of Master and Padawan. A tip from a crimelord led them to believe that Ventress would attack a space yacht, but when the Jedi investigated the ship, they discovered a trap set by Durge.

Anakin battled Durge as explosive charges burst and the vessel disintegrated around them. The hulking Gen'Dai put up a brutal fight, but Anakin succeeded where other Jedi had failed by mainlining the power of the dark side. Forcing the beaten Durge into an escape pod, Anakin sent the pod into the burning arms of a nearby sun.

That left Commander Ventress. The ship's logs indicated that she could be found at a major Confederacy base on Boz Pity. Obi-Wan put aside his pride and called in a full Republic assault force. Bail Organa, one of the mission commanders, hoped that the combined effort could eliminate Ventress, Grievous, and Dooku in one motion.

The attack went better than planned. In short order, Republic troops had secured most of Boz Pity's surface installations, allowing the Jedi to raid the HQ. Obi-Wan caught up with Ventress, but refrained from striking a killing blow. He believed that what he had learned of Ventress's history during his imprisonment on Rattatak painted the picture of a woman who could yet be saved from the lure of the Sith. He tried to reach her with words, but the battlefield actions of her "allies" proved more persuasive. Dooku fled Boz Pity with General Grievous, leaving Ventress behind to face capture or death. Stung by Dooku's betrayal, Ventress apparently perished in her final duel with Kenobi. Her dying words, "Defend Coruscant," provided a hint to the Separatists' future plans and indicated a deathbed change of heart. Obi-Wan ordered that Ventress's corpse be shuttled back to Coruscant for a Jedi cremation.

A curious footnote to the proceedings came with the word that the ship bearing Asajj Ventress's body had never arrived at its destination. Investigators later learned that she had merely muffled her life functions on Boz Pity to achieve a state of near-death stasis.

Commandeering the shuttle, she had leapt into hyperspace, bound for parts unknown.

THE XAGOBAH CITADEL
19.42 B.B.Y. (2 years, 7 months after the Battle of Geonosis)

Almost forgotten in the larger sweep of events, Boba Fett had survived the death of his father, Jango, in the Battle of Geonosis, and now moved to secure his status as the best bounty hunter in the galaxy. After signing on with Jabba the Hutt as a freelance agent—and acquitting himself against Dooku's Gen'Dai mercenary Durge—Boba accepted a Republic bounty on Techno Union foreman Wat Tambor.

Supreme Chancellor Palpatine
[ART BY MARK CHIARELLO]

Knowing his enemies would besiege him, Tambor had taken refuge in a fortress on the Outer Rim planet of Xagobah. Although Boba Fett succeeded in penetrating Tambor's citadel, General Grievous humiliated Boba in combat and ensured the escape of the Separatist leader.

During the Xagobah incident, Boba Fett ran into Anakin Skywalker, who helped Boba repair his damaged starship *Slave I*. Anakin assisted in arranging a meeting between Boba and Chancellor Palpatine, who was singularly unimpressed by Boba's revelation that Count Dooku and the "Tyranus" who had recruited Jango as a clone template were one and the same. Boba departed Coruscant, though it would not be the last time that he would attract the attentions of either Palpatine or Anakin Skywalker.

Elsewhere, the Mandalorians staged an unlikely resurrection following their decimation in the Battle of Galidraan. Alpha-02, an aberrant Kaminoan clone of Jango Fett, became obsessed with rebuilding the clans, and recruited two hundred soldiers from police units on the planet Mandalore, along with former members of the Death Watch. These new Supercommandos comprised the Mandalorian Protectors, and they struck against the Republic at Null, Kamino, and New Bornalex. Following many bloody battles, only two recruits remained—Tobbi Dala and Fenn Shysa, both of whom returned to Mandalore.

THE HUNT FOR DARTH SIDIOUS
19.1–19 B.B.Y. (2 years, 11 months–3 years after the Battle of Geonosis)

A series of strikes led by Obi-Wan Kenobi and Anakin Skywalker eliminated the remaining Separatist bases on the Neimoidian colonial purse worlds of Cato Neimoidia, Deko Neimoidia, and Koru Neimoidia. The final assault on the Neimoidian homeworld pitted AT-ATs and juggernaut tanks against the delicate Trade Federation citadels. The planet suffered greatly in the onslaught that followed, and the destruction of the grub-hatcheries spelled bad news for the future viability of the Neimoidian species.

But Viceroy Nute Gunray's greed burned so brightly that he risked capture and death by returning to Cato Neimoidia, hoping to salvage his treasures. Republic Captain Jan Dodonna led an assault that failed to capture the viceroy, but in his haste to escape, Gunray left behind his walking throne. This custom-crafted piece of furniture contained a holoprojector that broadcast on an encrypted channel, allowing Gunray to communicate directly with Darth Sidious. If the Republic could crack the code, it would take a giant step forward on learning the whereabouts of the elusive second Sith.

Like Gunray, Corporate Alliance Magistrate Shu Mai couldn't resist returning to her headquarters on Felucia to make arrangements regarding the disposition of her holdings. Jedi Knight Bariss Offee tried to move against Shu Mai, but Offee wound up a prisoner, requiring a rescue by Aayla Secura and her top clone, Commander Bly. Shu Mai then escaped, but not before unleashing a poisonous biological agent that spread through Felucia's water distribution infrastructure.

General Grievous, on orders from Darth Sidious, collected Gunray, Shu Mai, and the other bickering members of the Separatist Council and looked for a secure place to stash them. His first choice, the Outer Rim planet Belderone, became known to the Republic after a transmission was intercepted via Gunray's mechno-chair. Republic battleships lay in wait at Belderone, led by Anakin Skywalker and Obi-Wan Kenobi. Skywalker again added to his legend by flying through a screen of turbolaser fire and taking repeated potshots at the bridge of Grievous's flagship, *Invisible Hand*. Grievous escaped the trap by opening his ship's cannons on a refugee convoy, killing ten thousand innocents.

By ambushing Grievous at Belderone, the Republic had revealed its advantage regarding its receipt of the mechno-chair messages. But Gunray's throne would still be useful in other ways. Reverse-engineering the device revealed hints regarding its manufacture, and soon Republic Intelligence had discovered Darth Sidious's secret lair—an abandoned industrial building in the heart of The Works, Coruscant's decaying factory sector.

Darth Sidious may have sensed that his disguise could

not hold for much longer. As Supreme Chancellor Palpatine, he delivered a State of the Republic address that identified three targets in the Outer Rim Sieges—Saleucami, Mygeeto, and Felucia, which he called a "triad of evil"—and committed more than half of Coruscant's defense fleet to the continued pacification of those worlds. At the same time, he ordered General Grievous to initiate an assault on Coruscant, using secret hyperlanes that cut through the Deep Core. It was to be the opening act of Sidious's endgame.

Anakin Skywalker was preoccupied with events on the Outer Rim planet of Nelvaan. After slaying a gargantuan monster in the thicket of the alien jungle, Anakin earned the admiration of the Nelvaan natives. They took his arrival as a sign that the gods had delivered a champion to eradicate the evil presence that stained their land.

His face smeared with ceremonial warpaint, Anakin set off to restore the spiritual balance on Nelvaan. After experiencing a vision quest in the darkness of an ill-omened cavern, Anakin uncovered a Separatist research facility where CIS scientists had been experimenting on captured Nelvaan warriors. Anakin shut down the facility, but, more importantly, he touched the minds of the mutated natives and convinced them to return to their village, demonstrating his fitness as a Jedi.

General Grievous
[Art by Mark Chiarello]

Anakin Turns to the Dark Side
19 B.B.Y. (3 years after the Battle of Geonosis)

General Grievous executed an attack against the capital world that stretched on for a week and struck terror into the hearts of all Coruscantis. The planet had suffered wounds in the past, such as the invasion of the cortosis battle droids ten months into the war—but never before had an enemy battle fleet slugged it out with home defense forces in the skies above the Senate District, for all to see. And never before had a Coruscant strike been orchestrated directly by General Grievous, butcher of a thousand worlds.

As smoking wrecks fell from orbit and turned into bombs on impact, Grievous and a squad of his IG 100-series Magna-Guards slipped through the orbital scrum and flew to Chancellor Palpatine's apartment in 500 Republica. Palpatine's Jedi defenders, including Mace Windu, Kit Fisto, Stass Allie, and Shaak Ti, hustled the chancellor to a hovertrain, and then a hardened command bunker, but none of them could stop Grievous. The Separatist general captured Palpatine and then spirited him to the waiting *Invisible Hand.* No one knew, of course, that Palpatine had wanted to be abducted, and had in fact arranged it as a test for Anakin Skywalker.

Both Anakin and Obi-Wan had been occupied elsewhere per Sidious's design, pursuing Count Dooku on the ruined world of Tythe. They leapt to Coruscant's defense in their Jedi starfighters. Punching through a thicket of buzz droids and droid tri-fighters, they landed aboard *Invisible Hand* to stage an against-the-odds rescue of the Supreme Chancellor.

Palpatine was their object of rescue; Grievous, their anticipated opposition. Neither Jedi expected Count Dooku to confront them in the General's quarters, but he swiftly became a target of opportunity. Palpatine, bound in a chair, urged Anakin to bloodlust, and Dooku fought for his life. Dooku may have expected to be taken into custody by the Jedi after putting on a good show for his Master, to later assume a role in the new government when Palpatine made their intentions clear to the galaxy. Dooku never guessed that Palpatine would order his death. Anakin beheaded the Count and fled with the chancellor.

General Grievous failed to prevent their escape, and he abandoned *Invisible Hand* in an emergency pod as the ship disintegrated. Anakin amazingly crash-landed the remains of the unflyable wreck of the *Hand* on Coruscant, further bolstering his legend.

Palpatine then insisted that Anakin receive a position on the Jedi Council as his personal representative. Yoda and Mace Windu obeyed the chancellor's wishes, but refused to grant Anakin the rank or privileges of a Jedi Master. Anakin, whose ego had been growing throughout the Clone Wars, now had targets for his arrogant scorn.

Based on Republic Intelligence's investigation of the Sith hideout in The Works and the discovery of a tunnel leading to the apartment building 500 Republica, the Jedi Council concluded that Darth Sidious was an agent in Palpatine's inner circle of advisers. With this knowledge, they at last confirmed that the Clone Wars had been a Sith plot all along. Sidious had controlled one side, his apprentice Dooku the other, both with the intention of bleeding the Jedi dry. The Council decided to force Sidious's hand by capturing or killing General Grievous. If the war continued, even after such a decisive move, the Jedi would arrest Palpatine as a pawn of the Sith.

Obi-Wan Kenobi drew the Grievous assignment, and caught up with the general on the sunken planet Utapau. Grievous dueled Kenobi using four lightsabers, and then led the Jedi on a wild chase along the sinkhole walls. But it was not enough. Obi-Wan shot Grievous in the gut with a blaster, killing him.

With news of Grievous's death, Mace Windu prepared to confront Palpatine—but he soon learned the stunning truth from Anakin Skywalker. Anakin had recently learned that Padmé was pregnant, and had been haunted by visions of his wife dying during childbirth. Palpatine had carefully cultivated Anakin's hopes for preventing this dire premonition, and had revealed everything to Anakin: Palpatine's secret identity as Darth Sidious. His murder of his own Master, Darth Plagueis. The role that the Sith had played in creating Anakin by manipulating the midi-chlorians. And the hint that by studying the ways of the Sith, Anakin could learn to conquer death.

Upon Anakin's confirmation that Palpatine was a Sith Lord, Mace Windu assembled the Jedi Masters Saesee Tiin, Kit Fisto, and Agen Kolar to confront Palpatine in his chambers. Palpatine at last dropped the façade and unleashed his full fury, killing the three lesser Jedi. As Anakin arrived on the scene, Master Windu appeared to have gotten the drop on Palpatine, but Anakin—panicked that the knowledge to save Padmé would be lost with Palpatine's death—hacked off Mace's arm. Palpatine then charred Master Windu with Force lightning, sending Mace out the window to his death.

By giving in to his darkest nature, Anakin Skywalker had become Darth Vader. At Palpatine's command, he led a clone assault on the Jedi Temple, slaughtering hundreds, including even the youngest students. He then left for the volcano world of Mustafar, current hiding place of the Separatist Council, and executed Nute Gunray, Wat Tambor, San Hill, Shu Mai, and all the other corporate tycoons whom Palpatine no longer had any use for. Palpatine also prepared to shut down every battle droid in the galaxy using a master control signal, knowing that the Clone Wars had fulfilled their objective.

Anakin Skywalker and Obi-Wan Kenobi duel on Mustafar.
[Art by Tommy Lee Edwards]

But while the droids no longer served a purpose, Palpatine had a final task for his clone troopers. He commanded his soldiers to execute "Order Sixty-Six." The instructions were one of several contigency plans to deal with varying threats to the Republic, both internal and external. On Felucia, Commander Bly and other clone troopers abandoned the effort to reverse the poisoning of the water supply, and killed Aayla Secura and Barriss Offee. On Mygeeto, Ki-Adi-Mundi died when his clones turned on him during an assault on Confederacy forces. Plo Koon was shot down by clones in the skies of Cato Neimoidia. Saleucami became a death trap for Stass Allie when clone troopers destroyed her speederbike. Obi-Wan Kenobi barely survived an attack by Commander Cody on Utapau, while Yoda escaped from his clone troopers when they turned traitor on Kashyyyk.

Palpatine moved to secure his public standing on Coruscant. Claiming that he had been the victim of a Jedi assassination attempt, he instituted martial law, making a speech before the Senate where he proposed a new society, an "Empire that will stand for a thousand years." As the new dictator-for-life, Palpatine looked out over a cheering Senate, declaring that day as the first Empire Day.

Not all Senators joined in the jubilation. Days earlier, Bail Organa and Padmé Amidala had joined with others, including Mon Mothma, Fang Zar, and Giddean Danu, in opposition to Palpatine's Sector Governance Decree, which placed the chancellor's lackeys as governors to oversee every planet in the Republic. The opposers had presented Palpatine with the dissenting Petition of the Two Thousand, but now many of the two thousand senators who had signed the document had been arrested. Bail Organa decided that he could do more to undermine Palpatine's rule if he appeared to support him in public, while plotting to overthrow him in secret.

Obi-Wan Kenobi and Yoda were the only Jedi left in a position to do something about the disaster. Yoda went after Palpatine in the empty Senate chamber, but could not defeat the most powerful Sith Lord in history. Yoda barely escaped offworld. Obi-Wan Kenobi stowed away on Padmé's ship, confronting Anakin Skywalker on Mustafar. Anakin, assuming that Padmé had betrayed him, locked her in a Force choke that left her near death. Obi-Wan faced his former apprentice in battle.

The contest left both combatants bruised and exhausted, but in the end Obi-Wan maimed Anakin, cutting off his legs and his left arm. Anakin, beaten, lay at the edge of a lake of lava, his head and torso igniting.

Emperor Palpatine's surgical droids rebuilt Darth Vader, and his ebony skull mask reflected the darkness of the spirit within. Encased forever in a walking coffin, his every wheezing breath pure agony, Darth Vader was doomed to live with Palpatine's revelation that Padmé had died from her injuries. He, Vader, had killed the only thing he had loved.

Palpatine, however, didn't know the whole truth. At a secret location in the Polis Massa asteroid belt, Padmé had given birth to twins before her death. The girl, Leia, would be raised by Bail Organa and his wife on Alderaan. The boy, Luke, would be placed with Anakin's stepbrother Owen at the Lars moisture farm on Tatooine, where Obi-Wan would watch over the child's development as the hermit "Ben Kenobi." The overly talkative droid C-3PO received a memory wipe, and he and R2-D2 received new assignments in the service of Captain Raymus Antilles of Alderaan.

Yoda planned to go into hiding on the swamp planet of Dagobah. When Anakin's children reached the appropriate age, Yoda believed that the Force would bring one or both of them to him. At that time, he would craft them into weapons that would spear the heart of Palpatine's dark Empire.

Darth Vader on an early mission, flying an Eta-2 starfighter [Art by Tommy Lee Edwards]

PART THREE

The Empire and the New Order

THE DARK TIMES

JEDI SURVIVORS
19–0 B.B.Y.

A few Jedi, such as the blind archaeologist Jerec, embraced the dark side to save their own lives. Other Jedi survivors went underground. Among these were the Whipid master K'kruhk, who took a young Padawan under his wing and followed clues to the mysterious "Hidden Temple," a rumored place of refuge for harried Jedi to hide from the Emperor's hunters. A'Sharad Hett returned to live among the Tusken Raiders of Tatooine where he planned his own war of revenge. Jeisel, a female Devaronian, found herself forced into the life of a fugitive, pursued by bounty hunters and agents of Darth Vader. It seemed impossible, but the 25,000 year-old Jedi Order had vanished. The Sith had finally exacted their revenge.

Still adjusting to life inside his armored suit, Darth Vader constructed a new lightsaber containing a crimson Sith crystal provided by Palpatine. The Emperor, wishing to test the extent of his apprentice's diminished powers, sent Vader on a series

of missions to give him focus and prevent him from wallowing in self-pity. These took him in search of Jedi who had escaped Order 66, and led to the enslavement of the Wookiees on Kashyyyk. With the help of the Trandoshans, the Empire took control of the entire planet, and the wookiees were assigned to work gangs, forced to labor on Imperial construction projects.

Obi-Wan Kenobi soon learned the awful secret of the Emperor's new apprentice —that the black-armored cyborg suit concealed the burned, limbless body of Anakin Skywalker. Other than Obi-Wan's allies (Yoda, Bail Organa, Owen and Beru Lars, and Artoo-Detoo), the galaxy's citizens did not know of Vader's true origin.

As Emperor Palpatine instituted his New Order across the civilized galaxy, Vader recruited his own cadre of bodyguards by visiting the Noghri of Honoghr and promising to restore their poisoned world in exchange for their unquestioning loyalty. The Emperor's agents also enlisted the help of Mitth'raw'nuruodo, the Chiss commander who had crippled the Outbound Flight mission in the Unknown Regions. Thrawn had since become an exile from his people, and came to the Empire to study at their finest military academies.

In his hovel on Tatooine, Obi-Wan tried to settle into his new life as Ben Kenobi. Yoda had helped him connect with the Force spirit of his former Master Qui-Gon Jinn, and Obi-Wan entered a second apprenticeship under Qui-Gon's ethereal guidance. He found himself compelled to leave Tatooine for short missions to aid the few surviving Jedi, or to protect the identities of Anakin's twins..

During the first year of his exile, Obi-Wan crossed paths repeatedly with former Jedi Knight Ferus Olin. The Emperor, who had established a corps of Jedi hunters and "truth officers" called the Inquisitors, sent many of his agents after Olin, trying to thwart Olin's plans to create a Jedi shelter. Tragically, many Jedi fell to the Inquisitors, while others turned traitor and joined their ranks. Palpatine encouraged these defections—which swelled the ranks of his "Dark Side Adepts"—despite the public's continued ignorance of the Sith. From these, Palpatine secretly hoped to train an apprentice to replace Vader, whom he viewed as a disappointment due

to the crippling accident on Mustafar. Vader began looking for his own apprentice, knowing he lacked the power to overthrow Palpatine on his own.

The Emperor's Inquisitors also awoke Arden Lyn of the Legions of Lettow after a sleep of twenty-five millennia. Lyn killed one Inquisitor, but lost her arm to another. Palpatine recognized her power and, after outfitting her with a prosthetic limb from a war droid, invited her to become part of a new cadre of elite, Force-using agents called the Emperor's Hands. The Hands answered only to Palpatine, and included top assassins and experts in physical and psychological combat. Each of them labored under the delusion that he or she was the only Emperor's Hand.

A separate branch of Palpatine's agents, the Secret Order, consisted mostly of spies. Identified by their hooded cloaks and the Sith tattoos on their forearms, the members of the Secret Order skulked around the bridges of Star Destroyers, giving special assignments to those who had won the Emperor's favor. The Prophets of the Dark Side, mystics who could tell the future by reading the unifying Force, composed a distinct subgroup of the Secret Order.

One Imperial warship, a gargantuan, asteroid-shaped battlemoon called *Eye of Palpatine,* existed only to crush hidden Jedi enclaves on distant worlds. The *Eye* targeted a small enclave on Belsavis that sheltered youngling survivors from the Jedi Temple massacre, but two Jedi Knights—Callista and Geith—sabotaged the death-engine before it could attack. The Belsavis refugees fled to parts unknown.

Birth of the Empire
19–0 B.B.Y.

Emperor Palpatine's hold on the galaxy tightened. The power of the Senate waned as Palpatine erected his own system. Planetary governors soon were overseen by Moffs, who possessed power over entire sectors. Moffs who reached for too much power, like Flirry Vorru of the Corellian sector, found themselves imprisoned in the Kessel spice mines. Entities such as the Trade Federation and the Commerce Guild were absorbed, their interests reflected through Imperial-friendly entities such as the Mining Guild.

Grand Moff Wilhuff Tarkin
[ART BY MARK CHIARELLO]

Emperor Palpatine's New Order took root and thrived, particularly in the Core Worlds. Coruscant became Imperial Center. Civilians received only restricted access to the HoloNet communications system, stifling any news that wasn't Imperial propaganda. Under the guidance of Ishin-Il-Raz, COMPOR became COMPNOR, the Committee for the Preservation of the New Order, and rapidly became a humans-only organ of Imperial propaganda. Disdain for alien species became the norm under the New Order principle of Human High Culture. It wasn't long before entire species—including the proud Wookiees and the dauntless Mon Calamari—became officially sanctioned slave labor.

Nonhuman population centers in the Core found them-selves marginalized—or worse. Caamas, a member of the Republic since its earliest days, protested the destruction of Republic principles and advocated "peace through moral strength" as an alternative. The beloved Caamasi soon found themselves under attack and their world ruined by an outbreak of firestorms, triggered when Bothan saboteurs brought down the shield generators and left the planet defenseless against assault. Other alien species quickly learned to keep their mouths shut.

The most visible expression of Emperor Palpatine's New Order became the military. New clone hosts and new cloning facilities swelled the ranks of the stormtrooper corps, as did the forced conscription of young humans from occupied planets. With a few exceptions (such as the Khommites and the Lurrians), the Emperor banned the science of cloning for non-Imperial projects. Palpatine greatly expanded the army and navy, instituting new tools of war including the *Imperial*-class Star Destroyer and the TIE fighter, a nimble attack craft born from Raith Sienar's advances in Twin Ion Engine technology.

Under the guiding hand of Wilhuff Tarkin, the moon-sized battle station first proposed by Sienar began to take shape in the Outer Rim. The project bore the code name *Death Star*. When completed, the weapon would be able to destroy entire planets with its hypermatter-fueled superlaser.

DAWN OF DISSENT
19–0 B.B.Y.

Eventually, both Palpatine and Vader ceased to view the scattered Jedi holdouts as a threat, and made no concerted effort to root them out. The Jedi, in turn, lived their fugitive lives as quietly as possible. The flame of rebellion endured in the hearts of some politicians, such as Bail Organa, Mon Mothma, and Garm Bel Iblis. Small resistance cells sabotaged Imperial efforts, including numerous strikes against the Death Star construction project. Isolated groups of Separatist fighters, who had fought against Palpatine dur-

ing the Clone Wars for ideological reasons, became unexpected allies.

The Ghorman Massacre finally proved that the Emperor's excesses could not be reined in by a bureaucratic system of checks and balances. In the Sern sector near the Core Worlds, the citizens of Ghorman massed in the capital square to protest a new Imperial tax. When a warship arrived under the command of Wilhuff Tarkin, it landed on *top* of the protestors and killed hundreds. The Ghorman Massacre horrified many, but the Emperor wasn't among them. In response to the incident, he gave Tarkin a promotion.

After the rise of the Empire, Captain Jan Dodonna had resigned from the navy rather than serve what he considered a corrupt regime. When the Empire decided it could not retrain or convert Dodonna, a secret order was issued for his execution. Mon Mothma warned him, trying to sway him to her cause, but Dodonna initially refused—according to his rigid outlook, the Rebellion represented treason against the lawful government, though he himself had come to hate what the Emperor stood for. When Imperial assassins charged in and tried to kill him in cold blood, Dodonna fled in his nightshirt, fighting his way out. Dodonna became a staunch ally of the budding revolution. Elsewhere, an insurgent leader named Cody Sun-Childe briefly became the charismatic face of the opposition, but he soon vanished, and resistance carried on in secret.

Bail Organa and Mon Mothma, sometimes accompanied by Corellian Senator Garm Bel Iblis, began holding regular meetings in Organa's Cantham House residence on Coruscant to discuss organized rebellion. Mon Mothma was far more outspoken in her opposition. After many years of secret plotting, the firebrand Senator was accused of treason. Mon Mothma went underground to escape a certain death sentence, visiting oppressed planets and speaking to fledgling guerrilla movements. Sedition spread from world to world, though it was still disorganized and unfocused.

The X-wing prototypes blast away from the Incom design facility.
[Art by Tommy Lee Edwards]

Senators Mon Mothma and Bail Organa
[Art by Mark Chiarello]

Less than two years before the Battle of Yavin, the Corellian Treaty was signed—a landmark moment in the history of the revolution. The Corellian Treaty merged the three largest revolutionary groups into a single unified party—the Alliance to Restore the Republic. The document was signed by Bail Organa, Mon Mothma, and Garm Bel Iblis.

The Alliance to Restore the Republic, more commonly known as the Rebel Alliance, had a clear command hierarchy with Mon Mothma at its head. It also possessed an enthusiastic and growing military. Mon Mothma negotiated a secret arrangement with the Mon Calamari shipyards that gave the Rebels access to top-of-the-line capital ships, while a team of defectors from the Incom Corporation provided the Alliance with prototypes and blueprints for a new precision attack craft—the T-65 X-wing starfighter.

Though the Alliance had countless cells on thousands of planets, a single command headquarters was necessary for the Rebel leadership to rest and plan strategy. The first of these top-secret bases was established on a tiny planetoid in the Chrellis system, though the HQ was designed for continual relocation. From Chrellis the base moved to Briggia, Orion IV, and several other worlds before relocating to Dantooine, which had a connection with the great Jedi Knights of the past.

Alarmed at the growing opposition, the Emperor initiated Operation Strike Fear to crush Mon Mothma and her followers. However, the Alliance fleet distinguished itself with hard-fought victories, including the capture of the frigate *Priam* and the demolition of the Star Destroyer *Invincible.* More and more planets joined the revolution with each passing day.

The Rebel Alliance had begun.

PART FOUR

Profiles in History

Galactic history is more than the epic sweep of battles and conquerors, of grand armies and dread discoveries. On its most basic level, history is the story of individual people. Emperor Palpatine and Mon Mothma are so revered and reviled by various segments of the population that they appear as archetypes in the modern consciousness, not as human beings at all. Nevertheless, it is important to remember that even the highest heroes have humble beginnings, and that the actions of a single person can affect billions of lives.

Outcasts and fringe characters are not often given their due in historical memoirs, but their heroism deserves as much note as any Senator, monarch, or admiral. Without the contributions of "scoundrels" such as Han Solo and Lando Calrissian, as well as the youthful heroism of Luke Skywalker, then Princess Leia Organa would have died in Imperial captivity, and the second Death Star would have destroyed the Alliance fleet at Endor. As a service to future historians, we have interviewed these personages, chronicling their elusive early careers to better understand what made them into the heroes they are today.

HAN SOLO

Han Solo never knew his parents. His earliest memory was of being lost and alone on Corellia, until a venal con man named Garris Shrike took the abandoned child under his wing. Solo spent his youth aboard the ancient troopship *Trader's Luck* as a member of Shrike's well-organized "trading clan," a group who earned their keep through begging, pickpocketing, and grand larceny. If the children failed, they were beaten to near death. The only bright spot in Han's early life was a kindly female Wookiee named Dewlanna, who worked for Shrike as a cook and acted as the human boy's surrogate mother. She taught Han to speak and understand Shyriiwook.

Han desperately wanted to learn more about his parents, but that door remained closed to him. The only "Solo" relative he located was his cousin Thrackan Sal-Solo. After an unpleasant encounter, Sal-Solo disappeared from sight, and eventually rose to a leadership position with an anti-alien organization called the Human League. More than three de-

cades would pass before Sal-Solo tormented the New Republic during the Corellian insurrection.

Over the years, Han Solo became an expert thief and street fighter. His skill at piloting swoop racers earned plenty of prize money for Shrike, and his mastery of alien languages served him well when *Trader's Luck* traveled from system to system on moneymaking scams. At seventeen, Han was captured by law enforcement officials and forced to fight in the Regional Sector Four's All-Human Free-for-All on Jubilar. He won the contest by defeating four much larger opponents, but Shrike mercilessly beat him for insubordination when he returned to *Trader's Luck*.

YLESIA
10 B.B.Y.

At nineteen, Han escaped from *Trader's Luck* by stowing away in a robotic cargo freighter. The freighter deposited its passenger on Ylesia, a tropical world located

Han Solo, newly-commissioned Imperial officer
[Art by Mark Chiarello]

and their t'landa Til underlings. Though the pay was good, the attentions of a beautiful woman shook Solo from his complacency. He fell in love with Pilgrim 921, also known as Bria Tharen, and vowed to rescue her from slavery. During the escape, Han and Bria destroyed the primary glitterstim factory and plundered the t'landa Til High Priest's priceless art collection. They fled Ylesia aboard a stolen yacht, after staging a daring rope-ladder rescue of a Togorian prisoner from a neighboring colony.

THE ACADEMY
10–5 B.B.Y.

The Besadii Hutts placed a bounty on Han Solo's head, but they knew him only under the alias of "Vyyk Drago." Han planned to sell the Ylesian loot and enroll in the Imperial Academy to start a new life as a naval officer. He suffered a devastating blow when a suspicious Imperial Bank manager placed a freeze on his account—and another when Bria Tharen left him.

within the lawless borders of Hutt space. Though Ylesia advertised itself to the galaxy as a religious retreat, it was actually a brutal spice-processing planet controlled by the Besadii Hutt crime family. Weak-minded converts, attracted by the empty promises of a pseudo-religion, were shipped to Ylesia and put to work toiling in the glitterstim and ryll factories.

Han Solo ended up piloting spice cargoes for the Hutts

Bankrupt and despairing, Han scraped together his last few credits to obtain a forged set of ID papers and have his retinas surgically altered. Since the Besadii clan was looking for him under an alias, he used his true identity on an application to the Imperial Academy. His final night before enrollment was spoiled by an ugly figure from the past—Garris Shrike, who had been lured by

Chewbacca
[ART BY MARK CHIARELLO]

Vyyk Drago was dead.

Free and clear for the first time in his life, Cadet Solo boarded a troop transport for Carida, the most respected military academy in the Empire. Over the next four years, Han proved to be extremely talented, but not a model Imperial student. During one infamous exercise, he landed a malfunctioning U-33 orbital loadlifter with suicidal flair, earning himself the nickname "Slick" from Lieutenant Badure, his piloting instructor. In another incident, Han's classmate Mako Spince destroyed Carida's mascot moon with a gram of antimatter. Despite the misadventures, Han graduated at the top of his class, beating out Cadet Soontir Fel for the title of valedictorian.

Graduation was followed by eight months of commissioned service in the Imperial Navy. A promising career in the Corellian sector fleet was cut short when Han rescued a Wookiee slave from ill treatment at the hands of a superior officer. This earned him a dishonorable discharge, which prevented Han from obtaining any civilian piloting job. However, the Wookiee—Chewbacca—swore a life debt to Han and promised to follow him everywhere. Han initially tried to discourage Chewie, but gradually realized that a two-and-a-half-meter, fanged Wookiee wasn't a bad thing to have at one's side during cantina brawls. With no hope of lawful employment, Han and Chewbacca headed into Hutt space to work for the criminal syndicates.

the Hutt bounty. Unlike the other bounty hunters on the trail, Shrike was the only person in the galaxy who knew Han's alias. Fortunately, a rival bounty hunter shot Shrike down, and Han killed the second man in a brutal bare-knuckled brawl. He then switched clothes and ID and shot the corpse in the face—destroying all possibility of forensic identification. As far as the Besadii Hutts would know,

The Life of a Smuggler
5–2 B.B.Y.

Hutt politics seethed with intrigue. On Nal Hutta, the two most powerful clans—Besadii, headed by Aruk and his offspring Durga, and Desilijic, led by Jiliac and his nephew Jabba—vied for dominance. The Besadii clan controlled the spice operation on Ylesia, but Desilijic possessed important holdings on Tatooine and elsewhere. Their discreet maneuverings would inevitably be replaced by deadly conflict.

On Nar Shaddaa, the Smugglers' Moon, Han Solo and Chewbacca were introduced to illicit Hutt activities by Mako Spince, Han's old friend from the Academy. As the months passed, the new partners met dozens of offbeat individuals, such as Shug Ninx, Salla Zend, and Xaverri. They visited hideaways and hellholes like Smuggler's Run and Kessel, and Han learned how to fly the dangerous Kessel Run cargo route by skirting the Maw black-hole cluster. Han's piloting skills caught the attention of Jabba the Hutt, and soon Han was making regular smuggling runs for the Desilijic clan.

Rubbing elbows with high-level Hutts was a risky game, especially since Han still had a price on his head from the rival Besadii clan. On Ylesia, the colony's High Priest uncovered astonishing evidence that Vyyk Drago—reported dead five years earlier—had resurfaced under the name "Han Solo." The galaxy's best bounty hunter was hired to bring in Solo's hide.

Boba Fett tracked Han to Nar Shaddaa, but his capture was spoiled with an impromptu rescue by a charming stranger: Lando Calrissian, pilot of a banged-up YT-1300 freighter called *Millennium Falcon,* which he had won in a recent sabacc game. Han taught his rescuer the basics of flying, and Calrissian soon headed off in the *Falcon* for the Rafa system and some adventuring of his own.

Han began working as a magician's assistant on Xaverri's six-month illusionist tour. Upon his return, he purchased a shoddy, cut-rate SoroSuub Starmite, which he christened the *Bria,* after his lost love Bria Tharen.

Sudden scrutiny from the Empire brought normal life on Nar Shaddaa to a screeching halt. Moff Sarn Shild proclaimed that the Hutts' lawless territory would greatly benefit from stricter Imperial control. As a public relations stunt, Shild was authorized to blockade Nal Hutta and turn the Smugglers' Moon into molten slag.

The Hutts responded in typical fashion—they sent a messenger to Shild's offices in an attempt to bribe him. When the Moff refused to bend, the Hutts shifted their attentions to Admiral Greelanx, the officer in charge of executing the assault. Greelanx proved to be considerably more accommodating, agreeing to sell his battle plan. The Hutts organized a defense and placed their ships in precise locations dictated by the admiral's plan, hoping to inflict enough damage on the Imperial fleet to force a strategic withdrawal.

The scheme worked perfectly. The Battle of Nar Shaddaa was a localized conflict involving no ship larger than a Dreadnaught, and today is considered little more than a historical footnote. But for the desperate smugglers who banded together to protect their adopted home from annihilation, it was a life-or-death struggle against staggering odds. Though he did not realize it at the time, Han Solo was pitted against his former Academy classmate Soontir Fel, who was then serving as captain of the Dreadnaught *Pride of the Senate.* The battle came to a premature end when one of Greelanx's three Dreadnaughts was destroyed. Unable to justify further losses, the admiral retreated into hyperspace.

After distinguishing himself in the Battle of Nar Shaddaa, Han Solo lost the *Bria* in a mishap. To raise funds for a new starship, Han entered the annual championship sabacc tournament, held that year in Cloud City's Yarith Bespin casino. Lando Calrissian, freshly returned from his adventures in the ThonBoka, was one of Han's many opponents. The roster of players steadily dwindled, until the two men faced each other alone across a card-strewn table. Han took the final hand, winning the sabacc championship and earning his pick of any vessel on Calrissian's used-starship lot. Han chose *Millennium Falcon*.

Celebrating the acquisition of their new ship, Han and Chewbacca visited Kashyyyk, the Wookiee homeworld, where Chewbacca was married in a formal ceremony to his love Mallatobuck. Han became involved in a serious relationship with fellow smuggler Salla Zend, but, spooked by commitment phobia, he abandoned Zend and fled Hutt space entirely, heading out with Chewbacca for the Corporate Sector in the hope of striking it rich.

CORPORATE SECTOR BLUES
2–1 B.B.Y.

The semi-independent Corporate Sector Authority was, in many ways, worse than the Empire. The ruling CSA cared little for ideology and ruthlessly rolled over individuals who stood in the way of pure profit. Prior to Han's arrival, the CSA completed construction on the Stars' End prison complex located on the desolate rock Mytus VII. Dissidents, agitators, smugglers, and other troublemakers were quietly rounded up and imprisoned in stasis cells.

Han accepted small-time smuggling commissions for Big Bunji and Ploovo Two-For-One, but he also fell in with a covert team of independent dissidents investigating the recent disappearances. Team members included Bollux, a labor droid, and Blue Max, a positronic processor hidden in Bollux's chest cavity. When Chewbacca was captured, Han became more determined than ever to scuttle the CSA's top-secret prison. Posing as a troupe of entertainers, Han and his team landed on the airless planetoid and were escorted to the dagger-shaped prison tower.

On Han's orders, Blue Max triggered an overload in the prison's reactor core. As the team tried to free their friends and escape, Stars' End's power plant exploded—much more than the simple distraction Han had hoped for. The blast, contained by the prison's anticoncussion field, was funneled downward against the surface of the planet. With negligible gravity and no atmospheric friction, the entire tower rocketed into near orbit.

The structure reached the top of its arc and fell back to-ward the rocky face of Mytus VII. It was a race against time as the *Falcon* docked against the tower so that Chewbacca and other prisoners could be rescued, and then detached just as Stars' End smashed back into the surface. According to unconfirmed reports, the CSA salvaged the molecularly bonded structure and erected it on a different world, a rumor that soured later negotiations between the New Republic and the Corporate Sector Authority.

Han and Chewbacca continued their association with Bollux and Blue Max. They inspired the "Cult of Varn" on the arid planet Kamar by showing the holofeature *Varn, World of Water* to the desert-dwelling native insectoids. When Han replaced the bland documentary with a toe-tapping musical comedy, the water-worshiping Kamarians angrily chased away the false prophet and his great flying chariot. Over the last twenty years, Varn cultists have established evangelical religious orders on Mon Calamari, Bengat, and Varn itself, much to the consternation of the locals.

Heading back to the Corporate Sector, Han Solo was promised ten thousand credits to make a pickup on Lur. When he learned that the pickup consisted of slaves, he turned the tables on the slavers and freed their captives. Han stubbornly insisted that *somebody* still owed him ten thousand credits, and he doggedly followed the slavers' trail to Bonadan, where Fiolla, an assistant auditor-general of the CSA, enlisted Han's help. When the slavers tried to jump them, Han hopped aboard a swoopbike and used the racing skills that Garris Shrike had taught him to throw off pursuit.

The next link in the slaving chain was the planet Ammuud. Han and Fiolla booked passage aboard a luxury liner, while Chewbacca and the droids took the *Falcon* along with the CSA territorial manager, Odumin. Odumin was working to crack the slaving ring on his own and had an agent already in place on Ammuud: the legendary gunman Gallandro. After Han and Gallandro wound up facing each other over a duel, the ruling clan of Ammuud turned over all records they had relating to the slaving ring and its operations. Han and Fiolla fought against the vengeful slavers, and were rescued by the timely arrival of a CSA *Victory*-class Star Destroyer.

Territorial Manager Odumin, while grateful to the two smugglers for their help, fully intended to prosecute them to the fullest extent of the law for their numerous violations of the CSA legal code. With a fast maneuver, Han managed to take both Odumin and Fiolla hostage; then he successfully negotiated his unconditional release—and managed to have his ten thousand credits thrown in to boot.

DESTITUTE IN THE TION
1–0 B.B.Y.

All CSA naval patrols now received holographs of *Millennium Falcon* and orders to "destroy on sight." Realizing that their days in the Corporate Sector were over, Han, Chewbacca, and the droids Bollux and Blue Max hopped through the Outer Rim for months, squandering their ten thousand credits on repairs, celebrations, and far-fetched, disastrous schemes. Bankrupt, they eventually ended up in the backwater Tion Hegemony, working as starship mechanics for Grigmin's Traveling Airshow.

Han parlayed this embarrassing vocation into a slightly better job running cargo for the University of Rudrig. While there, he bumped into his old friend "Trooper" Badure, formerly a respected piloting instructor on Carida but now a desperate fortune hunter looking for the fabled lost ship *Queen of Ranroon*. Built during the glory days of Xim the Despot, *Queen of Ranroon* had once hauled the plunder of a thousand conquered worlds. Xim had constructed a vault on Dellalt to house the treasure, but, according to legend, the ship had vanished, along with all her wealth.

Accompanied by Badure and Skynx, a multilegged Ruurian academic, Han landed on primitive Dellalt. The *Falcon* was promptly stolen by rivals of Badure's, who left it on the opposite side of a mountain range. With no other ships available for hire on the uncivilized world, they were forced to head over the mountains on foot. During one fight for survival, Han was slashed across the chin with a primitive

hunting knife. The wound never healed properly, and left a scar that is noticeable to this day.

Marching through the snowy highlands, they were captured by a strange cult called the Survivors. The inbred, backwards descendants of *Queen of Ranroon*'s honor guard, the Survivors had existed on Dellalt for over a thousand generations, maintaining Xim the Despot's war droid army in their secure mountain keep. Han and the others escaped the Survivors and located *Millennium Falcon* at a contract-labor mining camp. The fast-gun mercenary Gallandro, pining for a rematch with Han after Ammuud, was waiting for him.

Before either party could make a move, the war droids of Xim marched into the clearing, rank on rank. Despite their antiquity, the droids followed their orders and razed the camp with ruthless efficiency. Bollux and Blue Max saved the day by transmitting a rhythmic frequency to the automation army as it paraded over a rickety suspension bridge. The signal caused the droids to march in a pounding lockstep. Beneath their shaking, vibrating footfalls, the bridge bounced, swayed—and collapsed.

Gallandro, one of the few survivors, claimed that he would forget his enmity with Han in exchange for a full share of Xim's treasure. The *Falcon*'s quad guns made short work of the vault gates. When Han discovered the hidden treasure chambers beneath empty decoy chambers, Gallandro showed his true, traitorous stripes. In a one-on-one blaster duel, Gallandro outdrew Han and incapacitated the Corellian with a blaster wound to the shoulder. He then strode down the vault corridor to burn down the fleeing Skynx, but the multilegged Ruurian tricked the gunman into a lethal no-weapons zone. Dozens of laser bolts fried Gallandro to cinders. It was the end of the gunman's legendary career, though he was survived by his infant daughter Anja on the colony world of Anobis. Anja Gallandro would cause new problems in Han Solo's life more than a quarter century in the future.

Han didn't even catch a lucky break on Xim the Despot's treasure. Instead of the priceless jewels Han had expected, he found only kiirium and mytag crystals—valuable war matériel in Xim's day, but worthless in the modern era. Skynx stayed behind on Dellalt to translate and catalog the vault's many historical artifacts, and Bollux and Blue Max remained with the Ruurian rather than accompany Han and Chewbacca back to Hutt space.

Skynx eventually became the lead researcher on the Dellalt Project, as it came to be known in archaeological circles. After ten years of study, Skynx succumbed to the life cycle of his species and metamorphosed into a mindless chroma-wing, but his offspring Amisus grew up to become the leader of the Unified Ruurian Colonies. Amisus pledged the Ruurians' loyalty to Grand Admiral Thrawn during the Hand of Thrawn incident fifteen years after the Battle of Endor.

RETURN TO YLESIA
0 B.B.Y., months before the Battle of Yavin

The devious intrigues of the Hutts had not remained static during Han's absence. Two years earlier, the Desilijic clan had surreptitiously poisoned Aruk the Hutt, ancient leader of the Besadii clan. In that time, Aruk's offspring

Durga had assumed control of Besadii with under-the-table help from Prince Xizor and the Black Sun criminal syndicate. When Durga uncovered the truth about his father's death, he slithered over to the Desilijic palace and challenged clan leader Jiliac to single combat under the Old Law . The two Hutts crashed into each other with their mammoth bodies, swinging their tails as massive bludgeons. After an exhausting contest, Durga emerged victorious.

The death of Jiliac made Jabba the ruler of the Desilijic clan. Jabba immediately began to implement a scheme that would devastate the Besadii clan by eliminating their primary source of income—the spice-processing facilities on Ylesia. To do this, Jabba contacted Han Solo's ex-love Bria Tharen.

Over the past decade, Tharen had become an undercover operative in the growing resistance movement opposed to Emperor Palpatine. She had helped lay the groundwork for Mon Mothma's orchestration of the Corellian Treaty, which merged various dissident groups into a unified Rebel Alliance. Jabba agreed to help Tharen fund a full-scale Ylesian assault that would destroy the spice factories and leave the Besadii with nothing. The Rebels would then be free to sell the spice on the open market to fund their growing insurgency.

On Nar Shaddaa, Han Solo and Bria Tharen fell in love all over again. Accompanied by Lando Calrissian, Han agreed to join in the Ylesian assault with his fellow smugglers for half of the spice profits. While Jabba's assassins killed the Ylesian priests, the smugglers and Rebels assaulted the colonies on foot. Casualties were high, but before long the invaders had eliminated all opposition, and secured the spice factories. In the aftermath, however, Commander Tharen and the Rebel troops double-crossed their smuggler allies and took all the spice for themselves.

The betrayal was a double blow for Han. He and Tharen parted on the worst of terms, and Han's comrades assumed he'd been in on the whole operation from the beginning.

Han soon caught up with Bria again, this time as part of a Hutt-sponsored, galaxywide treasure hunt for the Yavin Vassilika statue. His competitors included the bounty hunters Bossk, Dengar, Zuckuss, 4-LOM, Boba Fett, and an inexperienced Greedo (who won the respect of his peers only at his own funeral, following a deadly confrontation with Han weeks later). After surviving treacherous turnabouts from his rivals, Han saw Bria take possession of the Vassilika on Yavin 4. Once again, she took the prize for the

Rebel Alliance and left him with nothing. Lando Calrissian proclaimed that he never wanted to see Han's face again as long as he lived.

THE LAST SPICE RUN
0 B.B.Y., immediately prior to the Battle of Yavin

Hurt and dejected, Han and Chewbacca agreed to make a Kessel Run for Jabba on their way back to Nar Shaddaa. While pursued by Imperial customs vessels that had been tipped off by the spice supplier Moruth Doole, *Millennium Falcon* skimmed closer to the Maw blackhole cluster than anyone had thought possible. The result was a new distance record of less than twelve parsecs. Unfortunately, Han was forced to dump his load of spice to avoid detection; the loss of such a valuable shipment angered Jabba greatly.

Since none of his former friends would loan money to a man they considered a traitor, Han was forced to go to Tatooine in the hope of finding enough credits to pay

The galaxy's most notorious bounty hunters assemble for the funeral of Greedo. [Art by John Van Fleet]

off Jabba. There, a bounty hunter from the past made an unexpected reappearance. Boba Fett wasn't interested in Han's head this time—instead, he wished only to relay a message. Fett had once crossed paths with Bria Tharen and had agreed to notify the woman's father in the event of her death. Fett's sources had confirmed Tharen's demise as a member of the Rebel Alliance's Operation Skyhook on Toprawa, which had relayed the Death Star plans. Han passed on the information to Tharen's surviving family.

With his first love dead, one chapter of Han Solo's life closed forever. But a new one was about to begin. The Corellian smuggler strode into the smoky darkness of the Mos Eisley cantina for a fateful rendezvous with two local desert dwellers who needed passage to Alderaan.

LANDO CALRISSIAN

Unlike most reluctant heroes, Lando Calrissian is extremely forthcoming with details about his early entrepreneurial career. Unfortunately, every one of the stories is more outlandish than the last, and few agree. As a result, Calrissian is a riddle. One can only guess at the environment that spawned this ambitious man and the forces that shaped him into a charming gambler who always places his biggest bet on the underdog.

Luckily, Lando entered a high-profile career phase in his late twenties, allowing his stories to be verified through independent eyewitnesses, historical accounts, and interviews with contemporaries such as Han Solo. Approximately four years prior to the Battle of Yavin, Lando was already separating fools from their money as a professional sabacc gambler and con artist. Lando lost quite often, but when he won, he won big. His profits were enough to indulge his tastes in clothing, fine cuisine, and members of the opposite sex.

He hopped around the galaxy in style aboard luxurious pleasure liners such as *Star of Empire,* and so when he won a dilapidated Corellian freighter, *Millennium Falcon,* from a sabacc player on Bespin who couldn't cover his debt, Lando had mixed feelings. It would be an expensive and time-consuming process to learn how to fly, but having his own mode of transportation would come in handy whenever he needed to make a quick getaway. Besides, the ship could always be sold for ready cash if funds ran low.

But first he needed to learn the art of piloting, so Lando Calrissian hired a tutor—Han Solo, a smuggler, a fair sabacc player, and one of the best star jockeys in all of Hutt space. He caught up with Han at just the right time. The bounty hunter Boba Fett had Han at gunpoint, but Lando intercepted the pair and turned the tables on Fett. He injected the bounty hunter with an obedience drug and ordered him to fly off to the Rim of the galaxy. A grateful Han offered to teach Lando how to pilot, at no charge.

THE SHARU AWAKEN
4 B.B.Y.

Lando was a quick study, but learning to single-pilot a freighter was a tricky proposition. He was still an abysmal aviator when he decided to pack up and leave Hutt space for someplace—anyplace—else. Boba Fett would be back looking for revenge, and Nar Shaddaa was not an easy place for a con man to find gullible marks. His next stop was the wealthy asteroid field in the Oseon system, stuck in the outback Centrality region. Normally the Oseon was a gambler's paradise, but Lando had poor luck at the tables. From a pretentious academic, he did win ownership of a droid, which remained in storage on Rafa IV.

Every planet in the Rafa system was covered with colossal plastic pyramids built by the ancient Sharu. At the time of Calrissian's visit, the Sharu were considered a long-vanished aboriginal species; their impregnable pyramids had never been opened or explored. The present natives of the system were referred to as the Toka, or "Broken People." To all appearances the Toka were primitive and

Lando Calrissian scouts his new acquisition, the Millennium Falcon
[ART BY JOHN VAN FLEET]

this monumental event, making him a hero to legions of archaeologists and anthropologists.

Initially, though, the gambler had no intentions in the Rafa system beyond picking u p his newly won droid. The robot turned out to be a strange, starfish-shaped construction named Vuffi Raa, boasting five detachable limbs and a perky personality; Lando sensed there was more to this unusual droid than he could see.

When Lando was arrested on trumped-up charges issued by the colonial governor, he and his new droid were forcibly enlisted in the hunt for the Mindharp on behalf of Rokur Gepta, the Sorcerer of Tund. The mysterious gray-cloaked wizard was a disciple of ancient Sith teachings, eager to get his hands on the artifact for his own purposes.

On Rafa V, Lando and Vuffi Raa unlocked the largest Sharu pyramid with a transdimensional key. There, they discovered the Mindharp—a strange object that constantly changed form as it shifted through dimensions—and removed it from its eons-old place of rest.

Rafa IV's colonial governor greedily took the Mindharp, sentencing the gambler to a lifetime sentence of hard labor in a penal colony. Vuffi Raa freed Lando, but the planet then began to rock with violent quakes and tremors. The colonial governor had activated the Mindharp, and the artifact's subharmonic emanations stimulated a complete reversal of the social order throughout the entire planetary system. The pyramids crumbled, and bizarre new cities emerged from the dust. Intelligence and memories were restored to the primitive Toka, making them into the legendary Sharu once again.

For weeks the Rafa system was completely blockaded, and when the inexplicable interdiction field suddenly vanished, the first visitors beheld an utterly changed society. The new cities were frighteningly alien, and the Sharu appeared to care little for the concerns of "lesser" sentients. Many of the human cities had been damaged beyond

simpleminded, and they were exploited by the human colonists as cheap slave labor.

As Lando eventually discovered, the ancient Sharu had been threatened by an unimaginably powerful alien entity. To ensure their own survival, the Sharu went underground—hiding their cities beneath the plastic pyramids and using crystalline "life-orchards" to temporarily drain their intelligence. Then they spread rumors of a fabulous treasure—the Mindharp of Sharu. When another civilization was advanced enough to reactivate the Mindharp, the Sharu would know that it was safe to come out of hiding. In the course of his adventures, Lando Calrissian was responsible for triggering

repair in the quakes, and the surviving colonists chose not to remain behind in a place where they were the objects of scorn. Trade with the Rafa system dried up virtually overnight.

On the other hand, the event was a boon to scientists, who descended on Rafa in droves. While the Sharu did not shoo the researchers away, neither did they cooperate. Detailed information on Sharu history and technology is still an elusive unknown. Apparently, Emperor Palpatine felt threatened enough by the Sharu to post a permanent picket on the system's outer fringes, though he never made a military move against the advanced race. The New Republic largely ignored the Sharu, with the exception of a five-hundred-member, government-funded research team staffed by the Obroan Institute.

THE BATTLE OF NAR SHADDAA
3 B.B.Y.

Calrissian and Vuffi Raa fled the Rafa system mere hours after the Mindharp's activation, escaping to the safety of hyperspace with a full cargo of rare "life crystals" in the *Falcon's* hold. When worn around the neck, life crystals were rumored to increase a person's life span. Lando possessed the last load of life crystals before the Sharu locked down all trade—which meant that he could set his own price. The gambler cleared nearly a quarter of a million credits on the crystals.

He returned to Nar Shaddaa and, with a portion of his credits, purchased a used-starship lot from a dissatisfied Duros salesman. But running the business was more difficult and expensive than he had anticipated; despite the able assistance of Vuffi Raa, Lando was considering cutting his losses—when the Empire invaded the system. Along with hundreds of other smugglers, Lando took to the sky and successfully blunted the Imperial offensive in the Battle of Nar Shaddaa. Vuffi Raa piloted *Millennium Falcon* through the blaster barrages like a born maestro.

But the Battle of Nar Shaddaa signaled the end of the used-starship lot. Lando, feeling a sense of obligation to his fellow outlaws, donated his entire inventory for the space skir-

mish. When the dust cleared, less than a tenth of his stock remained spaceworthy. Privately, Lando sold his old friend Roa 90 percent ownership in the lot at a considerable loss, then puzzled over how to salvage his once promising career.

In six months, Cloud City's Yarith Bespin casino would be hosting the regional sabacc championships—the perfect opportunity for Lando to recoup his losses. Unfortunately, the entry fee was ten thousand credits. After paying off his creditors, Lando didn't even have a tenth that amount. Discouraged, he decided to return to the Centrality with Vuffi Raa.

There, Calrissian used the *Falcon* for its original cargo-hauling purpose, but he was a washout as an interstellar trader. Tariffs, import fees, and sales licenses sucked his credit account dry. Thus, when he received an invitation to play sabacc in the Oseon system, Lando jumped at the chance.

BACK TO THE OSEON
3 B.B.Y.

Calrissian and Vuffi Raa arrived just in time for the annual Flamewind. For three weeks each year, stellar flares interact with ionized vapors to create a stunning visual feast in brilliant pulsing hues of green, yellow, blue, orange, and every color between. The Oseon asteroid belts are infamous playgrounds for the wealthy and powerful, but things get even more decadent during the Flamewind: since it is impossible to navigate during the event, guests are stuck in the system until the breathtaking light show subsides.

Lando was apprehended by the administrator senior of the Oseon system and forced to participate in a dangerous drug bust. The trillionaire industrialist Bohhuah Mutdah, drug addict and sole owner of Asteroid 5792, had made some powerful enemies in the upper echelons of the Imperial law enforcement community. The administrator was authorized to arrest him in a sting operation. Posing as Mutdah's drug dealer, Lando ferried two drug enforcement agents to Asteroid 5792, through the heart of the Flamewind. As Lando made the drug exchange, the two agents burst in to place Mutdah under arrest. Ten seconds later, both agents were dead.

As Lando looked on in astonishment, Mutdah set down

his blaster and began to shimmer and fold in a mind-bending display. The disguise melted away, revealing a familiar figure—Rokur Gepta, the Sorcerer of Tund, whom Lando had outwitted with the Mindharp of Sharu.

In hindsight, the fact that Gepta took the time to insinuate himself into this affair is remarkable, given that his only motive was a deep-seated hatred of Lando Calrissian. Gepta blamed the rogue gambler for the loss of the Sharu artifact, and he was spiteful enough to carry a grudge across light-years. He also enjoyed an amicable relationship with Emperor Palpatine, who had given the Sorcerer a decommissioned Republic cruiser and granted him near-total autonomy within the confines of the Centrality. Gepta could command Imperial naval units and call in TIE bomber air strikes on recalcitrant worlds. It is a testament to Lando's notoriety that this power was completely subverted toward making the gambler's life miserable.

Lando was saved from Rokur Gepta when a squadron of starfighters bearing Renatasian markings appeared outside the asteroid's canopy, lasers blazing. The transparisteel dome shattered, and Lando reached his ship through the swirling air and debris. The *Falcon* escaped just as the Renatasians hurled a towed Dreadnaught engine straight into the asteroid, destroying it utterly.

The timely intervention was a lucky coincidence—the starfighters had not been gunning for either Lando or Rokur Gepta, but rather for the harmless but mysterious droid Vuffi Raa. In 13 B.B.Y., Renatasia, one of many "lost" human colonies founded by ancient Grizmallt settlers, had been rediscovered in a seldom-visited pocket of the Centrality. Obeying his programming, Vuffi Raa had landed on Renatasia and paved the way for an Imperial takeover. A group of hand-picked natives had commandeered twelve aging starfighters and vowed to kill the "Butcher of Renatasia."

Lando Calrissian, while sympathetic to the Renatasians' motives, was unwilling to help them annihilate his closest friend. He left them behind in the Oseon. The Renatasians soon teamed up with Rokur Gepta, who had escaped the destruction of Asteroid 5792, and continued their search for Vuffi Raa.

FORTUNE WON, FORTUNE LOST
3 B.B.Y.

The aftermath of the Mutdah drug bust was the most fortuitous turn of fortune Lando Calrissian had *ever* experienced. During the chaos of his escape, Lando lifted the case containing Mutdah's drug payment. In one day, he went from insolvency to being a millionaire twenty times over.

Like all things with Lando, though, it didn't last. He deposited the money in small lump sums across numerous bank accounts to reduce suspicion and the risk of a financial audit. Fifty thousand credits—more than enough to cover the sabacc tournament entry fee—went into the bank first, and was then electronically transferred to another numbered account on Aargau. Lando then departed in *Millennium Falcon* for Dela, the Centrality's financial hub, to deposit the rest of his money. Through sheer dumb luck, he arrived at Dela during the middle of a pirate attack by Drea Renthal's gang. Renthal, the infamous "pirate queen," possessed one of the largest freebooter fleets in the galaxy and had fought against the Imperials in the Battle of Nar Shaddaa.

The *Falcon* was captured and boarded. When the pirate raiders discovered the astonishing sum stashed in Mutdah's lockbox, Lando was brought before Renthal. The queen was an attractive woman, and Lando turned his charm up to maximum wattage in the hope of convincing her to leave him at least a token portion of the cash. He failed, but it was not the last time Lando and Renthal would cross paths.

TO SAVE THE THONBOKA
3–2.5 B.B.Y.

With the sabacc tournament mere months away, Lando and Vuffi Raa made a new friend—Lehesu of the Oswaft. The Oswaft, an extremely reclusive species of gigantic vacuum breathers who resemble a cross between a Corellian sea ray and an Arkanian jellyfish, can instinctively make natural hyperspace jumps.

The Centrality had known of the Oswafts' existence for generations, but the aliens did not come to the attention of the Emperor until just before Lando's debacle at Dela.

Mistrustful of an intelligent species that could traverse hyperspace at will, Palpatine issued orders to exterminate the Oswaft. Five hundred capital ships blockaded the "mouth" of the creatures' home, a sack-shaped nebula known as the StarCave or the ThonBoka. All *Carrack*-class cruisers were modified to emit electrical charges to contaminate the interstellar plankton that drifted inside the nebula. With their sole source of nutrients poisoned, the Oswaft began to starve.

Lehesu's desperate pleas spurred Lando and Vuffi Raa to action. *Millennium Falcon* ran the Imperial blockade, and Lando met with the besieged Oswaft elders—each colossal creature nearly a kilometer in diameter. As the Oswaft had no conception of warfare, Lando was forced to improvise a plan of survival. The alien defenders synthesized Oswaft-shaped excretions through their pores, so that the Imperial gunners shot at false targets and inflicted friendly fire on their own ships. Also, many Oswaft "shouted" at the warships in their information-dense language; their powerful voice-streams were sufficient to destroy many enemy vessels.

The fighting abruptly ceased when a vengeful Rokur Gepta arrived in his battleship and ordered the fleet to stand down. He delivered a startlingly bitter ultimatum: he would fight Lando Calrissian, one on one, in the zero-gravity vacuum between the ships. If Lando refused, he would fire an electromagnetic torpedo and lethally irradiate everything in the nebula.

The holographic log recorder aboard the Star Destroyer *Eminence* recorded the single combat, much to the gratitude of future historians. Zipped up in spacesuits, Lando and the Sorcerer of Tund faced off in the middle of the watching fleet. They shot at one another while maneuvering for position with jet packs. One of Lando's wild shots caught Gepta in the ankle. With a shriek, the Sorcerer's form withered and disappeared.

It is unknown whether Emperor Palpatine was aware that Rokur Gepta was actually a Croke, a tiny snail-like creature from the Unknown Regions. The Emperor had long been interested in the Sorcerers of Tund, since their religious teachings were based on an archaic interpretation of original Sith doctrine. Gepta had used his Croke powers of illusion to infiltrate that secret society, co-opt its Sith teachings, and then annihilate it—Tund is now an uninhabited, irradiated wasteland, and the death of Gepta marked an end to the Sorcerers of Tund.

The Imperial fleet responded to Gepta's demise with a hail of laserfire. Immediately, a booming cry burst across all comm channels: *"Cease fire or be destroyed!"* Thousands of gargantuan, fifty-kilometer-wide metallic spheres suddenly surrounded the armada on all sides. The new arrivals were self-aware droids, hailing from deep in the Unknown Regions. They had come for Vuffi Raa, their "child."

Vuffi Raa had been constructed by the mechanical beings for the purpose of recording new experiences throughout the galaxy. Now that his purpose had been fulfilled, Vuffi Raa departed with his progenitors. The Imperial fleet quietly withdrew when confronted with this unknown variable and never returned to complete their mission of Oswaft genocide.

The massive, mysterious droids disappeared into the vastness of the Unknown Regions, and have not reappeared since—or have they? Numerous eyewitness reports of massive objects roughly matching the droids' appearance were later compiled from all over the New Republic, including a hundred-thousand-person mass sighting during the Priole Danna festival on Lamuir IV.

ENTREPRENEURISM
2.5–0 B.B.Y.

Lando was sorry to see his companion go, but he had learned a great deal about starship piloting through the strange droid's tutelage. Furthermore, the grateful Oswaft had given him a full cargo hold of precious gemstones as a generous farewell gift. He invested the gemstones into a berubium mine in the Borgo asteroid belt, and then lost the fortune again when the mine proved to be worthless. Once again down to nothing, Lando withdrew the fifty thousand credits from his numbered account and waited for the sabacc tournament.

Two things made the waiting easier. The first was his old used-spaceship lot on Nar Shaddaa. Lando picked up the pieces of the struggling business and hired several new managers. The second was Drea Renthal, the pirate queen. Though he had good reason to carry a grudge against her, Lando realized that he and Renthal shared a similar outlook on life. Against all odds, the two became an item—at least for a few weeks.

The sabacc tournament on Cloud City was a crushing disappointment for Lando, however. The gambler made it to the final championship round and found himself facing his old friend Han Solo—a fair sabacc player, but far from a master of the game. When the final chip-cards were played, though, Solo had won an impressive stack of credits and sole ownership of Lando's ship, *Millennium Falcon.*

After the match, Lando was so impoverished that he was forced to swallow his pride and ask Solo for a fifteen-hundred-credit loan. Over the next year he turned the small sum into hundreds of thousands of credits by gambling with the galaxy's high rollers. He also carried out several masterful con jobs against the Imperials, including a scam on Pesmenben IV similar to the berubium mine that had previously ruined him.

Lando's second run-in with Boba Fett occurred aboard a luxury liner, where Fett had come to capture Rebel Alliance Commander Bria Tharen. He picked up Lando for use as an expendable hostage, but fortunately, a chance attack by Drea Renthal's star pirates saved both their lives. Renthal put up a substantial sum to buy Lando's and Bria's freedom.

Bria Tharen eventually joined forces with the Desilijic Hutts to coordinate a massive attack on the spice-processing planet Ylesia. Lando Calrissian participated in the assault, fighting alongside Han Solo. But when the combined Rebel—smuggler armies had wiped out all resistance, Bria Tharen swindled her allies. The Rebels departed with all the spice, leaving the smugglers with nothing.

Lando, like many others, blamed Solo for the double cross. A few days later, Lando briefly crossed paths with Han again, when both men became pawns in a Hutt wager involving the priceless Yavin Vassilika statue. Watching Bria Tharen claim the Vassilika on behalf of the Rebellion only embittered Lando further. He *knew* that Han must have had something to do with the swindle. When Solo came to Calrissian to ask for a loan to pay off Jabba the Hutt, Calrissian threw him against the wall and declared their friendship to be a thing of the past.

"THE RESPECTABLE ONE"
0–3 A.B.Y.

The Rebels won the Battle of Yavin not long afterward, but Lando Calrissian was busy with larger and larger escapades, including his single-handed decimation of the Norulac pirates in the notorious Battle of Taanab. He briefly investigated Hologram Fun World as a possible investment opportunity and got caught up in the Imperials' Project Starscream.

Lando's greatest coup, however, was in a sabacc game held in the Trest casino on Bespin. His opponent was Dominic Raynor, Cloud City's Baron Administrator. By the time Raynor folded his cards in frustration, Lando had won the title of Baron Administrator—and all the power that went with it.

To his credit, Lando took his new political assignment very seriously. He charmed the citizenry of Cloud City and won over the Exex business administration board. He established an excellent working relationship with the city's computer coordinator, a cyborg named Lobot. He staved off the advances of the Mining Guild and deflected the attention of the Empire, allowing business to continue as usual despite the growing Rebellion. He hired a squadron of commando-pilots to protect the city from pirate raids. When the droid EV-9D9 went psychotic and dismantled a quarter of the city's droid population, he salvaged the situation and enacted new security procedures. He increased net Tibanna-mining profits by more than 35 percent and turned Cloud City into a stable, prosperous center of industry. Millions of citizens looked to him for their well-being.

Which is why the arrival of twin intruders—Han Solo and Darth Vader—along with a third unwelcome interloper, Boba Fett, threw Lando Calrissian into a moral quandary. He balanced the life of Solo against the welfare of an entire city, and found his friend wanting. But Lando was not so foolish that he would keep on playing when the Empire had stacked the deck.

Fortunately for the fate of the galaxy, the gambler made the right decision in the end.

THE SKYWALKERS

The Skywalker twins emerged from one of the galaxy's most turbulent periods to reverse a generation of injustice and genocide. They were destined for great things from the moment of their birth. Though their early lives are not as colorful as those of Han Solo or Lando Calrissian, Luke Skywalker and Leia Organa have arguably influenced modern history more than any other duo.

Luke Skywalker, Jedi Master, brought the Jedi order back from extinction and presided over a new generation of Force-strong galactic guardians. Leia Organa, the second Chief of State of the New Republic, helped overthrow the Empire and shepherded the civilized galaxy through some of its bleakest years.

The lineage of the Skywalker twins is, quite simply, epic. Their father was Anakin Skywalker, one of the most powerful Jedi Knights in history, whose dark actions under the name Darth Vader nearly brought an end to that order. Their mother was Queen Amidala, elected monarch of Naboo. The two grew up in different foster homes on opposite sides of the civilized galaxy.

Both infants were amazingly strong in the Force. Because Emperor Palpatine feared rival Force users so much, he had overseen the Jedi Purge, and Obi-Wan Kenobi and Yoda helped hide the newborns, both from the Emperor and from their own father. In the care of others, the twins would develop into finely honed weapons that could

eventually be turned against the Emperor.

Kenobi placed Luke with Owen and Beru Lars, hardworking moisture farmers on the sun-seared planet of Tatooine. Owen and Beru told their neighbors that they gave the baby the name *Skywalker* after Owen's stepmother Shmi, whom he had loved. Yoda and Obi-Wan soon learned that Vader had survived the fiery confrontation on Mustafar, but they decided to rely on the fact that since the planet held such

Luke Skywalker
[Art by Mark Chiarello]

Princess Leia Organa
[Art by Mark Chiarello]

Raised on the pacifist planet Alderaan by Senator Bail Prestor Organa, Leia lived a life of privilege and responsibility. House Organa was the royal family of Alderaan, and Leia was accorded all the prerogatives due a Princess. Like her mother, Leia became a confident, poised young woman and a quick political thinker. In the ruling city of Aldera, Leia studied diplomacy, government, and languages, and played in the palace corridors with her best friend, Winter. Senator Organa often brought his adopted daughter on trips to other worlds, including Coruscant, and attended to her physical development by hiring weapons master Giles Durane to instruct Leia in the arts of self-defense and marksmanship. While still in her teens, Leia became the youngest representative ever elected to the Imperial Senate.

The general public did not learn of Luke and Leia's sinister lineage until years after the Battle of Endor. In fact, due to their having been raised apart, the two siblings did not even realize they were brother and sister until four years after Leia's rescue from the Death Star battle station. In the wake of the revelation regarding Darth Vader's ancestry, some partisan politicians accused Leia Organa of following in her father's footsteps. However, most citizens have been surprisingly conciliatory toward the offspring of Vader, holding the view that children should not be punished for the transgressions of their parents. The good that Luke and Leia have accomplished over the decades weighs heavier than any shadow legacy.

painful memories for Anakin following Shmi's death, Vader could never again set foot there. The Larses were low-profile isolationists, and Kenobi remained behind on Tatooine as added insurance. From his sparse hermitage in the Jundland Wastes, "Old Ben" Kenobi hid from Emperor Palpatine and simultaneously watched over young Luke, waiting for the day when the Force would provide a sign and fulfill a destiny.

Leia's upbringing was the polar opposite of her brother's.

PART FIVE

The Galactic Civil War

ARMED REBELLION BEGINS

THE DEATH STAR'S COMPLETION
3–0 B.B.Y.

The Death Star project continued despite scattered efforts at sabotage. The massive skeleton of the battle station moved from location to location in continual response to intelligence leaks. As the years stretched on, doubts emerged as to the viability of its planet-shattering superlaser—the Death Star's entire reason for being.

Wilhuff Tarkin, who secretly harbored his own doubts, decided to create a proof-of-concept model. In the exact center of the Maw black-hole cluster near Kessel lay a hidden island of gravitational stability. Tarkin chose this place, the universe's own fortress, as the site for his own top-secret weapons installation.

Construction slaves and droid-controlled equipment hauled a cluster of small asteroids inside and joined them together. Buildings and vacuum facilities were erected, laboratories stocked, and personnel assigned permanently—their records indicated that they had died in the line of duty. Next, Tarkin gathered the best researchers from across the Empire. Some of these came willingly, such as the great Dr. Ohran Keldor, and the driven and partially insane weapons designer Umak Leth. Other captive scientists were snatched unsuspecting, including Qwi Xux, an Omwati female. She was the only survivor of a large group of Omwati students put through rigorous tests by Tarkin himself.

The austere research station, Maw Installation, was run by the Twi'lek administrator Tol Sivron and guarded by four Star Destroyers under the command of Daala, Tarkin's former lover. Upon giving her this assignment, Tarkin had increased her rank to admiral. Daala remained isolated, never questioning her orders; her job was to ensure that the scientists in the research station continued to work without interruption.

The Maw Installation scientists refined the original plans of Raith Sienar and Bevel Lemelisk, discovering flaws in the Geonosis blueprints that were still being carried out in the current construction. Lemelisk himself worked on the Maw project under Tarkin's orders. Finally, Tarkin—now carrying the rank of Grand Moff—returned to the Emperor with a revised recommendation. Pleased, the Emperor approved the plans for a prototype to test the concept.

Inside Maw Installation, work crews of Wookiee slaves assembled a scaled-down version of the core superlaser mounted inside a stripped-down superstructure, an armillary sphere similar to the skeleton of the final design. When the superlaser proved effective, construction restarted on the stalled Death Star, in orbit around the penitentiary planet Despayre in the Horuz system.

Bevel Lemelisk received the title of chief engineer, and Darth Vader became an unofficial, and often unwelcome, supervisor. The labor force again consisted largely of Wookiee slaves, as well as exiles from the Despayre prison. Grand Moff Tarkin hoped to use the Death Star to enforce his Tarkin Doctrine throughout the Outer Rim territories, which he now controlled. The key precept of Tarkin's philosophy was

"Rule through the fear of force, rather than by force itself." The Grand Moff's personal slave, the Mon Calamari called Ackbar, took careful notes on both the superweapon and Imperial military strategy, waiting for the opportunity to escape back to his people.

Despite the intense security surrounding the project, shortages and sabotage continued to plague the construction site. When Tarkin and his engineer began to lose control of the schedule, Darth Vader came to Despayre and executed several workers and supervisors in order to encourage greater attention to detail. Soon thereafter, the Death Star was back on track.

Darth Vader's grim methods of discipline inspired rebellion within the ranks. Shortly before the Battle of Yavin, several Moffs, including Grand Moff Trachta, banded together and arranged for the assassinations of both Vader and Emperor Palpatine. Trachta's stormtroopers planted a bomb on the Emperor's shuttle and tried to kill Vader aboard his Star Destroyer, but both attempts failed. The treacherous Moffs all met with appropriately lethal ends.

Just after the completion of the battle station, but before it could be tested, a Rebel assassination attempt nearly took Grand Moff Tarkin's life. Tarkin avoided death, but his Mon Calamari slave Ackbar escaped to the Rebel Alliance. Ackbar recruited several of his people and aided the Rebellion, directing such victories as the Battle of Turkana aboard a Mon Calamari star cruiser.

The Rebel Alliance received fresh confirmation of the Death Star project from an informant on Ralltiir; the information was later verified by the Empire's own Lord Tion. Knowing that the Alliance's only chance lay in obtaining a copy of the station's blueprints and analyzing them for vulnerabilities, Bail Organa and Mon Mothma set up multiple plans for the capture operation. Toprawan rebels, in a raid on a space convoy, stole most of the technical information before it could be transferred to the Imperial Information Center. On Danuta, an untested Alliance agent named Kyle Katarn broke into an Imperial facility and made off with another set of plans. When combined, the two readouts formed a complete schematic of the Death Star from pole to pole.

The Rebel cell on Toprawa now had complete data, but Imperial Intelligence had learned of the leak. Star Destroyers blockaded the Toprawa system while stormtroopers moved in to crush the Rebels and recover the plans. The Alliance's only hope lay in a risky in-system data transmission. Princess Leia Organa, adopted daughter of Bail Organa and heir to the legacy of Anakin Skywalker, arrived in the Toprawa system under cover of diplomatic immunity. Her consular ship *Tantive IV*, commanded by Captain Antilles, intercepted the Death Star plans and immediately jumped to hyperspace. The Rebels on Toprawa—led by Commander Bria Tharen and Red Hand Squadron—were killed shortly after Leia's receipt of their transmission.

With the Empire's ultimate weapon compromised, Darth Vader pursued the fleeing Princess in the Imperial Star Destroyer *Devastator*. He vowed to retrieve the stolen information at any cost.

PREPARATIONS FOR BATTLE
0 B.B.Y.

Just before the Toprawan capture of the Death Star plans, Mon Mothma grew alarmed at the number of Imperial Intelligence agents digging for any Rebel activity. She wisely instructed Jan Dodonna—now a Rebel Alliance general in charge of the Dantooine headquarters—to move his operations to the Massassi ruins on the jungle moon of Yavin 4.

Mon Mothma's suspicions were proven correct when the Dantooine Rebels discovered an Imperial tracking device in a cargo shipment. General Dodonna stripped and abandoned the base and moved all personnel to the Yavin system. There, he and his troops waited for battle.

Several months earlier, as an inevitable outgrowth of the Corellian Treaty, Mon Mothma had issued a strongly worded Declaration of Rebellion against Palpatine and his policies. In response to this widely disseminated Declaration, the Emperor formally disbanded the Imperial Senate, sweeping away the final vestiges of the Republic. Palpatine placed regional governors, ruthless Grand Moffs like Tarkin, in direct control over the oversectors.

If it hadn't been apparent before, it was blindingly obvious now: the conflict between Rebellion and Empire could never be settled through political means. The Rebel Alliance prepared for full-scale war.

THE CAPTURE OF PRINCESS LEIA
0 B.B.Y.

Leia Organa disseminated much of the propaganda that helped to bind the Alliance together. Because of her outgoing nature, she traveled from world to world on well-publicized "mercy missions," which were often a cover for her Rebel activities. Darth Vader and the Emperor suspected Organa's involvement, but could not prove it.

Leia had been the perfect agent to intercept the Death Star plans from the Toprawan rebels. She immediately set course for Tatooine, where she hoped to recruit Obi-Wan Kenobi and bring him and the blueprints to Bail Organa on Alderaan. If the Death Star became operational, the Empire could use the battle station to launch an unparalleled reign of terror across the galaxy.

Vader's Star Destroyer *Devastator* caught up with *Tantive IV* near Tatooine. In the ensuing firefight, Leia managed to plant the Death Star readouts inside R2-D2. The little droid escaped the battle in a tiny life pod and, along with his counterpart C-3PO, landed on Tatooine. R2 attempted to deliver Leia's urgent message to Obi-Wan Kenobi, who was still living in a hovel at the edge of the planet's desert wasteland.

Captain Antilles of *Tantive IV* died at the hands of Darth Vader. Leia was brought as a prisoner to Grand Moff Tarkin's newly completed Death Star. She resisted Vader's rigorous interrogations in order to conceal the location of the new Rebel headquarters on Yavin 4. Tarkin, anxious to test his Death Star and to reinforce the Emperor's iron grip, found

General Jan Dodonna
[ART BY MARK CHIARELLO]

another way to coerce her: he threatened to destroy Leia's peaceful homeworld unless she divulged the information he demanded.

Knowing full well the capabilities of the superweapon, and Tarkin's own prior record of ruthlessness, Leia understood that he was not bluffing. Reluctantly, she announced the location of the Dantooine base, hoping that it had already been abandoned as planned. Tarkin, however, needed to make Alderaan a brutal example for the Rebels and the entire galaxy.

In the darkest act of the Galactic Civil War, the Death Star destroyed Alderaan and its billions of inhabitants. Bail Organa numbered among the dead. Leia Organa was returned to her detention block and scheduled for execution.

A NEW HOPE
0 B.B.Y.

At the same time, seemingly insignificant events unfolded on the desert world of Tatooine to set the stage for the Emperor's downfall. R2-D2 and C-3PO were captured by Jawa traders and sold to an out-of-the-way moisture farm, which happened to be the same homestead where Anakin Skywalker's son, Luke, had been raised since infancy. While cleaning his new droids, Luke accidentally discovered the holographic message encoded by his sister, Leia. Not knowing of their brother–sister relationship, but recognizing that the "Obi-Wan Kenobi" in her recording might be the local hermit Ben Kenobi, Luke resolved to pass on the droids to Old Ben.

R2-D2 went searching for Kenobi on his own, and Luke survived a brush with Tusken Raiders in order to retrieve him. When they finally encountered Kenobi and replayed the message, Obi-Wan agreed to break his long exile and escort the Death Star plans to Bail Organa on Alderaan. Obi-Wan believed that the Force was guiding Luke toward a larger destiny, which was what he and Yoda had hoped for when they agreed to raise Anakin Skywalker's children in secret. In Luke's absence, Owen and Beru Lars had been killed and their homestead razed by Imperial stormtroopers, and this revelation only seemed to confirm the presence of a guiding hand. Luke, of course, had no choice but to go along on the Alderaan mission, and Obi-Wan resolved to begin the formal training that would turn Luke into a fitting opponent for the Emperor.

In Tatooine's Mos Eisley spaceport, Obi-Wan commissioned the smuggling duo of Han Solo and Chewbacca to take them to Alderaan. As the Imperial net tightened around the escaped droids, Han Solo's ship, *Millennium Falcon,* blasted away from Tatooine and slipped through a Star Destroyer blockade. En route to Alderaan, Obi-Wan showed Luke the basics of lightsaber combat and the notion that using the Force was a matter of instincts, not intellect. As Obi-Wan had

hoped, Luke possessed an astonishing natural talent, indicating that he had inherited the bloodline of the Chosen One.

When *Millennium Falcon* arrived in the Alderaan system, they found only a spinning asteroid cloud. The entire planet had been destroyed by the Death Star, and they became the battle station's next target. Swallowed up by one of the Death Star's tractor beams, Luke and Han disguised themselves as stormtroopers and seized the docking bay's control room. Obi-Wan headed off alone to shut down the tractor beam controls. When Luke learned that Princess Leia was being held prisoner on the battle station, he convinced Han to help spring her by appealing to the Corellian's boundless sense of greed. In an unorthodox rescue that took them through the guts of the Death Star's garbage system, the group escaped the detention block and headed back for their rendezvous point.

Obi-Wan Kenobi sabotaged the tractor beam generator that would have prevented the *Falcon* from fleeing. But before he could return to the docking bay, Obi-Wan encountered his nemesis and former friend, Darth Vader. In a refined, classical duel, far different from the punishing battle that they had engaged in on Mustafar, Master and Padawan parried with lightsabers and words. Obi-Wan called Anakin "Darth," an indication that Kenobi saw little in the black armor that reminded him of the boy who had once been a surrogate son. Luke, Princess Leia, and the rest returned to the *Falcon,* ready to fight their way out, and Obi-Wan realized he could accomplish more with sacrifice than combat. Remembering the teachings of Qui-Gon Jinn, who had maintained his spirit form after entering the netherworld, Obi-Wan Kenobi let Vader cut him down. The *Falcon*'s passengers used the opportunity to flee the station.

Bearing the precious Death Star plans, the *Falcon* blasted through a TIE fighter picket line and jumped to hyperspace, emerging at the new Rebel base on Yavin 4. Han Solo realized too late that the Imperials had placed a tracer on his ship. General Dodonna and his team of experts frantically studied the blueprints to find a flaw, even as the Death Star arrived in the Yavin system to destroy the Rebel base.

The Rebels had only one chance. If a small ship were to fly into a surface trench and launch a proton torpedo into a tiny thermal exhaust port, the torpedo could reach the hyper-matter core and annihilate the battle station in a catastrophic chain reaction.

As the Death Star orbited into a firing position to destroy the jungle moon, swarms of Rebel X-wings and Y-wings attacked like stinging insects. Many Rebels died in the Battle of Yavin, but one pilot—Luke Skywalker, using his newfound skills with the Force—scored a direct hit. The Death Star exploded, killing Grand Moff Tarkin and eliminating the Empire's ultimate weapon that had taken nearly twenty years to build. It was an enormous victory for the Rebel Alliance.

Impact and Consequences
0–0.5 A.B.Y.

In his modified TIE fighter, Darth Vader escaped the destruction of the Death Star. Alone in space and calling on the power of the dark side of the Force, he limped to a nearby Imperial outpost on Vaal.

During the battle, he had sensed that the pilot who destroyed the station had shown unusual strength in the Force. Already suspecting the pilot's possible heritage, Vader chose not to report back to Palpatine in person. Instead, the Dark Lord spent many weeks on a private mission, running down hints about the newest Rebel hero. A Rebel deserter named Tyler Lucian promised to reveal the truth of the pilot's identity, but he committed suicide on Centares before either Vader

or the bounty hunter Valance could extract a confession. Through the torture of another informant, Vader finally got the confirmation he sought—the Death Star's destroyer was Luke Skywalker, Vader's own son.

Back on Coruscant, the Emperor was greatly displeased with the design flaw that had allowed the Rebels to annihilate his Death Star. He summoned Bevel Lemelisk, the

Obi-Wan "Ben" Kenobi
[Art by Mark Chiarello]

original designer of the superweapon, and executed him in the most horrific manner possible. But the genius and imagination of such a brilliant man as Lemelisk would not be wasted by the Emperor. Resurrected through dark alchemy in a cloned body, vividly remembering the agony of his own execution, Lemelisk had no choice but to work even harder on a second Death Star design.

Some questioned the Emperor's wisdom in building a second Death Star, but the superweapon *worked*, as the destruction of Alderaan had proved. No one in the Empire could simply scrap such an expensive creation when a flaw like a carelessly uncovered thermal exhaust port could so easily be rectified.

Vader and the Emperor briefly focused their attentions away from the Rebels and onto the Bounty Hunters' Guild, at the urging of Prince Xizor, the criminal godfather of the Black Sun syndicate. Palpatine approved Xizor's plan to eliminate the guild, over Vader's objections. Boba Fett, now the most notorious bounty hunter in the galaxy, was hired to be the agent of the guild's destruction. In a bloody conflict known as the Bounty Hunter Wars, Fett succeeded in fragmenting the organization into innumerable splinter groups and free agents. Over the next few years, Vader frequently employed these rogue bounty hunters for his own purposes.

REBEL TRAP
0–0.5 A.B.Y.

Immediately after celebrating their victory, the Alliance prepared to abandon their base on Yavin 4. The destruction of the Death Star had been a miracle, and the Rebels knew that they wouldn't stand a chance against the full Imperial armada. Much of the Rebel fleet, including a group of huge Mon Calamari cruisers commanded by Ackbar, as well as refugee vessels containing the government-in-exile led by Mon Mothma, had not been present at Yavin, and were scattered across space to form a mobile task force. General Dodonna orchestrated the Yavin base's evacuation.

The blockade had been ordered by Darth Vader, who did not want the base ground into dust—at least not yet. At the starship yards of Fondor, the first Super Star Destroyer, christened *Executor*, was nearing completion. It was to be Vader's new flagship, carrying as much military might as an entire fleet of smaller ships. As payback for his humiliation at the Death Star, Vader wanted to use the *Executor* as his personal sword of vengeance against the Rebel insurgents.

Han Solo and Chewbacca had left almost immediately, before the implementation of the blockade, hoping to pay off Jabba the Hutt with the reward that they had received from the Rebellion. They had a few adventures on their own, including an encounter with a Sith monster on Aduba III, but events soon conspired to put them back into the Alliance's service. Han also lost his reward money, thanks to the larcenous pirate Crimson Jack. None of Han's subsequent attempts to erase his debt would meet with success.

Luke Skywalker and Leia Organa proved adept at using small ships to slip through the blockade. Hooking back up with Han Solo, the group ran into trouble on the Wheel casino station, but continued to vex Darth Vader, bringing the permeability of the Yavin barricade to light. During the early weeks following the Death Star's destruction, responsibility for the blockade had fallen to the House of Tagge, one of the most influential merchant families in the Empire. The Tagges—brothers Silas, Orman, and Ulric, and sister Domina—were fierce rivals of Vader's, and hoped to gain the Emperor's favor at the Dark Lord's expense. The Tagge presence in the Yavin system collapsed after Luke Skywalker destroyed their base, which had been comprised of a giant turbine suspended in the clouds of Yavin Prime. Admiral Griff, Darth Vader's direct agent, then assumed control of the blockade, directing his efforts from the nearby Jovan Station.

Other high-ranking Imperials derided Vader's choice of military strategy, viewing the *Executor*'s construction as little more than grandstanding in light of the ineffective blockade. Several admirals secretly plotted to sabotage Vader's Super Star Destroyer as it lay in Fondor's shipbuilding docks.

TIE bombers harass the Rebel base on Yavin 4 during the Imperial blockade. [ART BY TOMMY LEE EDWARDS]

Admiral Griff, pretending to have turned traitor, provided key information about the *Executor*'s construction to the Rebel Alliance. Luke Skywalker ran the blockade and infiltrated the construction yards at Fondor, but Griff's "treachery" was a ruse, and Skywalker barely escaped. Luke had done little damage, but managed to return to the Rebels with a great deal of information on the huge battleship.

Not long after, while returning from a different mission, Skywalker eluded Imperial pursuit by plunging his ship into the slipstream of a passing hypercomet in an isolated system. Following the comet's trajectory along an asteroid-filled orbit, Skywalker crashed on a forgotten, frozen planet named Hoth. There, he encountered an exiled Imperial governor who had made a primitive home in the ice fields. Skywalker killed the treacherous governor in self-defense, and then reported to the Alliance, suggesting Hoth as a possible location for their next headquarters stronghold.

The Rebellion desperately needed to relocate, and fast—if the *Executor* managed to wipe out the Yavin base, they would lose their emerging nucleus of top star pilots. Luke Skywalker had teamed with Wedge Antilles, a fellow veteran of the Death Star battle, to form a group of X-wing fliers that would ultimately become Rogue Squadron. The existence of the Rogues helped offset the loss that the Alliance had suffered on the same day as the Battle of Yavin, when several starfighter squadrons were lost in the Battle of Ord Biniir.

Darth Vader
[Art by Mark Chiarello]

IMPERIAL COUNTERSTRIKE
0.5–2 A.B.Y.

The blockade situation began to enrage local fleet commanders, who impressed upon Vader the need for a quick and decisive strike. Consequently, the *Executor*'s construction was stepped up. General Dodonna grew concerned—while small ships like the *Falcon* could run the blockade, larger vessels would surely be captured. Dodonna contacted Mon Mothma and Admiral Ackbar aboard the Alliance fleet and arranged for a diversionary assault.

The Empire's attack finally came, six months after the Battle of Yavin. While Ackbar staged a feint in the Vallusk Cluster to draw off most Imperial forces, the mighty *Executor* arrived to decimate the Yavin base. Dodonna scrambled all of the base's fighters and transports, but stubbornly refused to evacuate until the others were away. The old general set off a series of concussion charges that wiped out an entire squadron of attacking TIE bombers. Dodonna was believed killed in the explosion, but in reality he was taken, critically wounded, to the dark Imperial prison *Lusankya*.

The evacuating Rebels rendezvoused with the main Alliance fleet, intending to establish a new base on icy Hoth. Instead, they were forced to put their plans on hold until they could replenish their equipment stores, medical supplies, and foodstuffs. In a dangerous gamble, the Alliance negotiated with Imperial Overlord Ghorin of the Greater Plooriod Cluster for several shipments of badly needed grain, but then turned the tables on Ghorin when they discovered the grain was poisoned.

Alliance agent Kyle Katarn, who had helped capture the Death Star plans, was pressed into service again when Mon Mothma learned of the Empire's Dark Trooper Project, launched to create mechanized super stormtroopers. Katarn scuttled the operation by destroying the Dark Troopers' spacegoing construction site, and also rescued Crix Madine from an Imperial prison. Madine was an elite Imperial—the ex-leader of the Storm Commandos—who had decided to defect to the Rebels after being forced to release an incurable plague on the planet Dentaal.

En route to the Alliance, Madine was nearly recaptured by the Empire during a layover on Corellia, but was rescued by the pilots of the newly formed Rogue Squadron. Mon Mothma welcomed Madine into the Rebel Alliance and made him a general. Madine would work closely with Rogue Squadron for several years.

The stress took its toll on Rebel leadership. Bail Organa had been killed in the destruction of Alderaan, leaving Mon Mothma and Garm Bel Iblis as the highest-ranking Alliance representatives. The two rarely saw eye-to-eye, and when Mon Mothma ordered an attack on Milvayne that Bel Iblis viewed as suicidal, he took his loyal forces and seceded from the Rebellion. His private army would score many independent victories over the next nine years.

The loss of Bel Iblis was offset when the Bothan politician Borsk Fey'lya and his sizable faction joined the Alliance. Fey'lya had been impressed by the Rebel victory at Yavin and made the move not for ideological reasons, but to gain more status and power.

Leia Organa met up with a survivor of the old Jedi Order after her vessel was shot down above the planet Krant. Echuu Shen-Jon, the general who had led the Republic's effort to recover its Decimators during the Clone Wars, still lived on Krant, serving out a sentence of exile for his brush with the dark side of the Force. Echuu helped Leia destroy a Jedi artifact known as the Vor'Na'Tu before dying under the blade of Darth Vader, yet another Jedi casualty attributable to the Dark Lord.

Approximately one year after the Battle of Yavin, Leia learned that a top-secret list containing names of Rebel sympathizers who were embedded within the Imperial government had been left in a place that was accessible to the Empire. Leia tasked two agents—Dusque Mistflier and Finn Darktrin—with the responsibility of capturing the data holocron from the ruins of a Jedi temple on Dantooine. Though the pair recovered the item, Darktrin revealed himself as an Imperial agent and attempted to transmit the file's contents to Darth Vader. Luckily for the Rebellion's leaders, the data stream was incomplete, protecting the identities of most of their top contacts.

The Rebellion staged a series of guerrilla-style strikes against the Empire over the next year, including the Ram's Head mission, which demolished four Star Destroyers in dry dock. But the Alliance fleet remained scattered and on the run as it searched for another central base. The jungle planet Thila was briefly used, but abandoned when it was suggested that the Empire would expect the Rebels to move to another jungle world like Yavin 4. Alliance engineering teams went to a number of possible worlds to begin excavation, including

Borsk Fey'lya
[Art by Mark Chiarello]

Hoth, but Mon Mothma wanted to keep her options open.

The Imperials, too, sent out fleets to search space for the hiding places of their enemies, launching thousands of automated probe droids. But the sheer number of uncharted settlements and smuggler encampments created hundreds of false alarms.

Circarpous Joins the Resistance
2 A.B.Y.

As the business hub of the Expansion Region, Circarpous IV was home to many of the galaxy's financial leaders. Disgusted by the astronomical tariffs and self-destructive spending so common in Palpatine's Empire, these ruling financiers agreed to covertly fund the Rebel Alliance, pending a face-to-face meeting with Leia Organa.

Organa and her protocol droid traveled to the rendezvous on Circarpous IV, escorted by Luke Skywalker. An engine malfunction caused both Alliance ships to crash on Circarpous V—a drenched, strategically worthless swamp planet known locally as Mimban—where the Empire had established an illegal dolovite mine. Leia and Luke became prisoners of the mining colony's governor. Darth Vader headed for the system as soon as he received word about their capture, but by the time he arrived on Mimban the two Rebels had escaped.

Vader caught up with his quarry at the vine-encrusted Temple of Pomojema, deep in the swamps of Mimban. The temple held the fabled Kaiburr Crystal, a luminous shard capable of magnifying the Force a thousandfold. Luke Skywalker took up his lightsaber and faced Vader in a one-on-one duel.

It is interesting to note that Skywalker, still an untrained Jedi, held his own against his much more experienced opponent. Possibly, the Kaiburr Crystal provided an edge, but Luke later admitted that the spirit of Obi-Wan Kenobi appeared to have inhabited his body, guiding his actions as a puppeteer directs a marionette. Obi-Wan's energy drove Luke to sever the Dark Lord's sword arm in a furious drive, but the effort seemed to exhaust Luke's intangible benefactor. Darth Vader shrugged off his injury, and only Vader's chance misstep into a crumbling well allowed Luke and Leia to escape.

When they rejoined the Alliance fleet, Leia notified the Circarpousians of the Imperial mine on Mimban. Outraged by the subterfuge, the Circarpous business underground went ahead with the plans to open a covert supply line to the Rebels. The flow of credits was a critical factor in strengthening the Alliance military, and resulted in the purchase of a KDY Planet Defender ion cannon for installation at their next base.

The recovered Kaiburr Crystal did not perform to ex-

Darth Vader confronts Luke Skywalker in the jungles of Mimban.
[Art by Tommy Lee Edwards]

pectations. Mimban, like Nam Chorios and Dathomir, appeared to be a planet with a biosphere that magnified the Force. Luke discovered that the power of the Kaiburr Crystal decreased in direct proportion to its distance from Mimban and, more specifically, from the Temple of Pomojema itself.

Little more than a curiosity, the trinket remained in Luke's possession for years. Eventually he used it as a teaching aid and even experimented by installing it as a focusing crystal in a lightsaber. He found the resulting blade to be remarkably strong and energy-efficient.

HOME IN THE ICE
2–3 A.B.Y.

Mon Mothma eventually agreed to establish the new Rebel command headquarters on the frozen world of Hoth. Alliance engineers completed the work that had been started months earlier, constructing an installation that took advantage of the climate. "Echo Base" was commanded by General Carlist Rieekan, a survivor of Alderaan who had watched his own world destroyed by the Death Star. Princess Leia Organa also took up residence in the ice tunnels, choosing safety over physical comfort.

The Rebels made every effort to keep their headquarters a secret, minimizing the number of ship arrivals and departures. Han Solo had several run-ins with bounty hunters while offworld on Ord Mantell, but none of the mercenaries learned the location of Echo Base.

Meanwhile, Mon Mothma continued to gather forces at the main Rebel fleet, preparing for another strike. Before she could take action, the Alliance suffered a stunning defeat in the Battle of Derra IV. A badly needed supply convoy and its starfighter escort were blasted to bits in an attack executed by Darth Vader himself. The death of the squadron's flight leader elevated Luke Skywalker to the rank of commander, but nothing could replace the loss of the critical munitions shipment.

It had been years since their major victory on Yavin, and the Empire continued to hound them. It was a dark time for the Rebellion.

THE BATTLE OF HOTH
3 A.B.Y.

One of the Imperial probe droids dispersed to search for the Rebel headquarters picked up faint transmissions in the Hoth system. Upon inspecting the planet, the probot discovered evidence of a military installation and sent a signal to Darth Vader's flagship. Vader deployed his personal Star Destroyer fleet, the Death Squadron, to attack the base.

General Rieekan's team discovered the probot but could not silence it before it broadcast their location. Rieekan realized that Hoth was sure to be the target of an Imperial attack. Having seen firsthand the destruction of Alderaan, he ordered an immediate evacuation. It would be a desperate race.

Vader's fleet arrived before the first transport could be launched, but a surprise blast from the Rebel's new ion cannon cleared an escape corridor for the Alliance ship. While Imperial AT-AT walkers hammered the base at ground level, Rebel snowspeeders harried them in a losing battle. Many defenders sacrificed themselves to buy time for the remaining forces to get away. Echo Base fell after a great loss of life on both sides. Just as Vader strode into the ruined command center, Leia Organa and C-3PO escaped with Han Solo and Chewbacca in *Millennium Falcon*.

Vader launched his fleet into full pursuit. At the time, though he understood Luke Skywalker was his son, he did not suspect that Leia Organa was his daughter. Nevertheless, Leia was a powerful figure in the Rebellion, and Luke was known to never stray too far from his friends in the *Falcon*, so capturing the vessel became a priority for Vader. Han Solo proved a remarkable pilot, eluding pursuit by flying directly through the heart of the Hoth asteroid belt, but faulty equipment prevented his ship from jumping to hyperspace.

To assist in the hunt, Vader called in a rogue's gallery of bounty hunters, most of them independent agents after the destruction of the Bounty Hunters' Guild. Among the hunters was Boba Fett, who had known Vader during the Clone Wars, back when he was Anakin Skywalker. In recent years, the two had established a working relationship and professional rivalry. Before the Battle of Yavin, Fett had recovered the severed head of an Icarii prophetess on the Dark Lord's behalf, a contest in which each player had exhibited his full depth of skill.

Believing that *Millennium Falcon* had escaped Imperial capture, Han Solo limped across the Ison Corridor with a patched-together backup hyperdrive to reach the gas world of Bespin. On Cloud City, he met up again with Lando Calrissian, former owner of the *Falcon* and now a respectable businessman. Though they had had their disagreements in the past, most notably over the aftermath of Ylesia, Han still considered Lando a friend and requested his assistance in getting repairs for his ship.

Unknown to Han or his passengers, Boba Fett had tracked the *Falcon* to Cloud City and betrayed the ship's location to Vader. Darth Vader coerced Lando into setting a trap for Han and Leia, and the two Rebel fugitives became prisoners in Cloud City's detention cells. Vader ordered the torture of Han Solo and Chewbacca, to no apparent purpose. In truth, he meant to stir the Force with the agony of Luke Skywalker's friends, and lure his true prize to Cloud City.

A NEW JEDI
3 A.B.Y.

After flying a snowspeeder alongside Wedge Antilles during the Battle of Hoth, Luke escaped the ice planet to follow a vision he had received from Obi-Wan Kenobi. Days earlier, while lost in a Hoth blizzard and bleeding from a wampa attack, Luke had been told to go to the Dagobah system and learn from a Jedi Master named Yoda. Luke flew his X-wing to the coordinates laid out by R2-D2, crashlanding his starfighter in a swampy bog.

AT-ATs overrun Rebel trenches in the Battle of Hoth.
[ART BY TOMMY LEE EDWARDS]

Jedi Master Yoda
[ART BY MARK CHIARELLO]

and discouraging days testing himself in the Force, attempting to meet the strange and seemingly impossible challenges that Yoda gave him. He learned to face his fears and to trust his instincts.

As he opened his mind and explored his Jedi abilities, Luke saw another vision: Han Solo and Leia Organa held in brutal captivity on Bespin. He could no longer focus on his training with the knowledge that his friends were in pain. Luke ignored the dire warnings of Yoda and the spirit of Obi-Wan Kenobi, both of whom told him it was a trap. He boarded his X-wing and followed his heart to Cloud City, just as Darth Vader had hoped.

Now finished with Han Solo, Vader had the smuggler frozen in a block of carbonite and delivered to Boba Fett. Vader intended to use the same freezing process on Luke, in order to capture the novice Jedi. Fett left Cloud City with the preserved Solo in *Slave I,* heading for Tatooine and Jabba the Hutt, who still had a price on Solo's head for unpaid debts.

After Vader's trap was sprung, Lando had a change of heart. His guards freed Leia, Chewbacca, and C-3PO, and the four of them tried and failed to rescue Han. Knowing the Empire would heap retribution on Cloud City and its people, Lando called for an evacuation. In the resulting chaos, their small group escaped aboard *Millennium Falcon.*

Luke made it to Cloud City, but could not rescue any of his friends. Instead, Vader herded him into the carbonite chamber. Luke and Vader fought one another in a clash of

Luke could not believe that the unassuming and gnomish creature who greeted him could possibly be a great warrior. Yoda, who had always believed that the Force would one day guide the offspring of Anakin Skywalker to him, had been waiting for this moment for more than two decades. He agreed to train the doubting youth in the ways of the Jedi, and to forge him into a weapon that could at last destroy the Sith. Yoda warned his pupil that upcoming decisions would be difficult, and that he must be strong. Luke spent many long

lightsabers, and their angry duel spilled over onto a platform overlooking Cloud City's wind core. Darth Vader mercilessly hacked off Luke's right hand.

Vader then revealed the terrible secret that he was Luke's father. He beseeched his son to join him in overthrowing the Emperor and ruling the galaxy together. Reeling from physical and emotional pain, Luke instead stepped into the seemingly bottomless core shaft. He slipped into an airshaft that dumped him out through Cloud City's ventral side, where he desperately clung to a weather vane. *Millennium Falcon* picked him up and fled the system, its hyperdrive repaired. The *Falcon* soon rendezvoused with the remainder of the Alliance fleet.

It had been a devastating defeat for the Rebellion. The base on Hoth was destroyed, Han Solo had been lost, Luke Skywalker had discovered the truth of his dark past, and the scattered fleet seemed to have no chance of victory over the Empire.

IMPERIAL INTRIGUE
3–3.5 A.B.Y.

Against all odds, the Alliance pressed on. Mon Mothma heard rumors of a second, even larger Death Star under construction around the Sanctuary Moon of Endor. Gathering concrete information on the battle station became a top priority.

The Empire continued to implement grand schemes, including the *Tarkin* superweapon and the Phantom TIE project. The *Tarkin,* a scaled-down version of the Death Star similar in principle to the one created inside Maw Installation, was capable of shattering worlds. Grand Admiral Batch had been tasked by the Emperor with developing a working cloaking device, and he used the *Tarkin* to demolish the burned-out planet Aeten II—blasting loose millions of rare stygium crystals. Boasting stygium invisibility screens, Batch's "Phantom TIEs" would have proved invincible in dogfights had Rebel saboteurs not scuttled the project. The *Tarkin* suffered a similar fate, blowing itself apart when Leia Organa and a small team infiltrated the station and disrupted its workings. Years later, one of Grand Admi-

ral Batch's discarded cloaking designs (which suffered from the flaw of not letting its users see *out*) would be used during Grand Admiral Thrawn's military campaign.

Darth Vader employed a subtle stratagem to get closer to the Rebels, and to Luke Skywalker in particular. Shira Brie, one of Palpatine's elite Emperor's Hands, became an undercover agent within the Alliance starfighter corps. Luke respected her as a squadron mate and soon grew close to her as a romantic interest, but during a heated space battle he shot her down—the Force having told him that the pilot of the other ship was an enemy. Shira survived the ordeal, and Vader rebuilt her body with cybernetic parts. Shira Brie became the Dark Lady Lumiya, disciple of the Sith.

These months also saw the long-awaited return of the Mandalorians. Leia Organa visited the Mandalorian homeworld during the search for Han Solo's carbonized body and encountered Mandalorian Supercommandos Fenn Shysa and Tobbi Dala, who had been keeping a low profile since the Clone Wars. Tobbi Dala died in a fight against Imperial slavers, but Fenn Shysa rallied several of his Mandalorian warriors to aid the Rebel Alliance.

PRINCE XIZOR AND BLACK SUN
3.5 A.B.Y.

The unstable political situation fostered by the Rebellion caused certain parties to cast their eyes on the Imperial throne. One was Xizor, a reptilian prince from Falleen and the head of Black Sun, the Empire's largest criminal syndicate. Xizor had masterminded the Bounty Hunter Wars a few years earlier and was now said to be the third most powerful person in the galaxy, behind Palpatine and Vader. Xizor decided to increase his rank by eliminating Vader, his longtime rival.

Prince Xizor was one of the few who knew of the blood ties between Darth Vader and Luke Skywalker. Palpatine wanted Skywalker alive in order to turn him to the dark side of the Force, and had entrusted Vader with the task of capturing the boy unharmed. To make Vader look incompetent in the eyes of the Emperor, Xizor decided that he wanted Skywalker *dead*.

Black Sun criminal operatives began hatching assassina-

Arden Lyn and Grand Admiral Zaarin
[Art by Mark Chiarello]

tion plots against Skywalker, who was busy tracking down Boba Fett and the carbonized body of Han Solo. Distressed by this latest turn of events, Leia Organa ironically turned to Black Sun, hoping the syndicate's underground spy network could uncover the identity of the assassins.

Luke returned to Tatooine, where he constructed a new lightsaber to replace the weapon he had lost on Cloud City. When he received a message from the Bothan homeworld of Bothawui, Luke Skywalker and the smuggler Dash Rendar went there to assist in the capture of the Imperial freighter *Suprosa,* which was carrying plans for the Empire's second Death Star.

Luke and a squadron of Bothan pilots intercepted the Imperial freighter and disabled it, though the cost in Bothan

lives was high. They then brought the freighter's computer core to the nearby planet Kothlis, where a crack team of data slicers decrypted the blueprints and construction schedules. Though the Rebels congratulated themselves on their victory, it was later learned that Palpatine had allowed the freighter to be captured in order to lure the Alliance fleet into a trap at Endor.

On Kothlis, bounty hunters captured Luke Skywalker; fortunately, the Imperial computer core was spirited away by Bothan technicians and eventually made its way into the hands of Mon Mothma. As Vader rushed to Kothlis to collect his son, Luke managed to escape.

On Coruscant, Leia Organa and Chewbacca disguised themselves as bounty hunters to gain access to Prince Xizor's opulent fortress. At first, the Falleen crimelord was polite and gracious toward his guests, but then he imprisoned Leia. Chewbacca escaped, as part of Xizor's master plan: the Wookiee would notify Skywalker, and when Skywalker arrived, he would be killed.

Luke and his companions came to Organa's rescue. They broke into Xizor's castle, found the Princess, and then set off a time-delay thermal detonator to cover their escape. When Xizor realized he had less than five minutes before the thermal detonator destroyed his fortress, he fled to his orbiting skyhook, *Falleen's Fist.* The resulting implosion of Xizor's castle left a gaping hole in the Coruscant cityscape.

Aboard *Falleen's Fist,* Xizor ordered his personal navy to destroy the escaping *Millennium Falcon.* Han Solo's ship fought valiantly, although it was quickly overwhelmed. But then the entire group was overtaken by a vast flotilla of Imperial warships led by the Super Star Destroyer *Executor.* The *Executor* and its TIE squadrons, however, ignored the *Falcon* and opened fire on Xizor's vessels instead.

Darth Vader, never a subtle or patient man, had been driven over the edge by Xizor's brazen attempt to eliminate Skywalker. The Dark Lord delivered an ultimatum: if Xizor did not immediately recall his navy and surrender himself into Imperial custody, the *Executor* would destroy his skyhook. Xizor refused to respond, and Vader's gunners blasted *Falleen's Fist* into flaming debris.

Xizor's death created a power vacuum within Black Sun. His second in command, the human replica droid known as Guri, dropped out of sight, and Xizor's various lieutenants began squabbling. The body count climbed as the struggles escalated into open warfare.

While Vader was preoccupied with Black Sun, one of the Emperor's Grand Admirals finalized his plans for a daring, but ultimately doomed, coup d'état. Immediately after Xizor's death, Grand Admiral Zaarin attacked Vader's fleet in the Ottega system, and captured the Emperor's private shuttlecraft at Coruscant. To catch Palpatine unaware, Zaarin enlisted the assistance of Arden Lyn, one of the Emperor's Hands. The coup failed thanks to the appearance of loyal Imperial forces, and Zaarin soon died in a confrontation with Grand Admiral Thrawn. Palpatine later took revenge on the twenty-five-thousand-year old Lyn, killing her at last.

The computer core captured aboard the *Suprosa* revealed the existence of a second Death Star at Endor, but the Rebellion wanted to confirm the data. Rebel spy Tay Vanis had supposedly captured similar information, but had not been heard from for weeks. Luke Skywalker, Leia

Prince Xizor, head of Black Sun.
[ART BY MARK CHIARELLO]

Organa, and Lando Calrissian ran down clues to Tay Vanis's whereabouts, discovering that he was now a broken man, the victim of Imperial torture.

ALLIANCE TRIUMPHANT

THE REBELLION REGROUPS
4 A.B.Y.

Learning that Han Solo's carbonite slab now hung inside Jabba the Hutt's palace, Luke Skywalker helped organize a complex and desperate plan to free his friend. Leia Organa and Lando Calrissian gained entry to the palace in disguise, Chewbacca masqueraded as a prisoner,

C-3PO and R2-D2 were given to Jabba as gifts, and Luke Skywalker simply walked in the front door. All Luke's preparations seemed to fall apart when the group was discovered and sentenced to die in the Great Pit of Carkoon, but the rookie Jedi Knight decimated the Hutt's entourage with ease. Leia strangled Jabba, leading to the collapse of the Desilijic crime family.

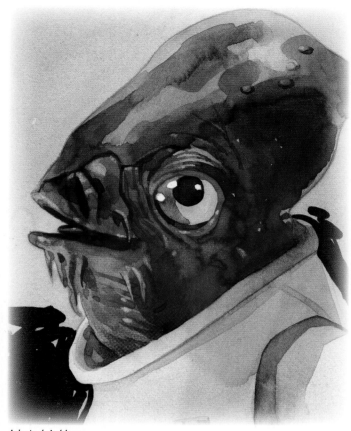

Admiral Ackbar
[ART BY MARK CHIARELLO]

decrypted computer core from Kothlis, containing the details of the second Death Star's construction site around the green moon of Endor. As Mon Mothma and Admiral Ackbar planned their attack, another piece of data galvanized them even more: Emperor Palpatine himself would be at the station on an inspection tour. If they could strike quickly and succeed in destroying the new battle station, they would eradicate the Empire's superweapon, as well as the evil despot himself.

THE BATTLE OF ENDOR
4 A.B.Y.

After gathering in the Sullust system and executing a feint attack, Rebel commandos slipped through the Imperial security net around Endor. A team led by Leia Organa, Luke Skywalker, and Han Solo (newly promoted to general) crept through Endor's dense forest in an effort to destroy the shield generator that was protecting the Death Star's orbital construction site. Unfortunately, the team encountered numerous difficulties, first when a squad of Imperial speeder bike scouts threatened to expose their location, and again when Endor's native Ewoks mistook the Rebels for invaders and nearly roasted them in a cooking fire.

Luke felt conflicted by his dual role as a Jedi and as Anakin Skywalker's son, and voluntarily gave himself up to the local Imperial commander. He became a prisoner aboard the Death Star, Luke's words of compassion failing to penetrate the shell that Darth Vader had constructed around his own emotions. As the Rebel Alliance's attack fleet swept through hyperspace to strike at the Death Star, the shield generator continued to protect their target.

In the Death Star's throne room, Vader presented Luke Skywalker to Emperor Palpatine. When the Rebel fleet arrived in the Endor system and launched its assault, Luke learned of the web of deceit that had been spun by Palpatine

Leia, Lando, and a thawed Han Solo rejoined the Rebel fleet in preparation for a major strike against the Empire. Luke Skywalker returned to Dagobah to continue his training under Yoda. When he arrived, however, he found the nine-hundred-year-old Jedi Master near death. Yoda said his farewells, and at last confirmed the truth that Darth Vader was indeed Luke's father. The spirit of Obi-Wan Kenobi revealed another startling fact, telling Luke that Princess Leia Organa was his sister. Obi-Wan urged him to destroy Vader, calling the Dark Lord "more machine than man," but Luke couldn't entertain the thought of killing the man who had once been Anakin Skywalker, his father. Reeling from the information and from the death of Yoda, Luke returned to the fleet.

On the Rebel flagship out in open space, Alliance leader Mon Mothma addressed the troop leaders and explained the Rebellion's latest plan. Bothan spies had delivered the

The Super Star Destroyer Executor collides with the second Death Star during the Battle of Endor. [ART BY TOMMY LEE EDWARDS]

himself—the whole thing was a trap. An enormous Imperial battle fleet, led by the Super Star Destroyer *Executor,* emerged from the far side of Endor and began hammering the Alliance armada. Luke appealed to the lost sentiments of his father, trying to touch Vader's heart and turn him back to the light side of the Force. Darth Vader remained unconvinced.

The Rebel forces continued to be decimated, both by the Imperial fleet and by the Death Star's operational superlaser, which targeted capital ships and blasted them to powder. Lando Calrissian, leading the starfighter attack in *Millennium Falcon,* encouraged Admiral Ackbar to press the attack against the enemy battleships at point-blank range. Lando's move was risky, but it was the only tactic that could buy time until the team on the ground brought down the Death Star's shield projector.

The Emperor goaded Luke into snatching up his lightsaber, and father and son battled one another in a rematch of the duel they had fought on Cloud City. During the struggle, Vader's resolve began to flicker as he saw the good in his son. Through the Force, he also read in Luke's thoughts and learned of the existence of his daughter, the second of Padmé's twins. When Vader speculated that his daughter might make for a fitting dark side apprentice, a frantic Luke unleashed his pent-up rage. His fury gave him the strength to severely wound his father and cut off Vader's sword hand. Seeing Skywalker's raw emotion, the Emperor applauded, pleased to see him take the first steps toward the dark side.

But Luke surprised Palpatine by surrendering, refusing to continue the fight that would have resulted in his father's death and made him the Emperor's new Sith apprentice. A livid Palpatine then used his own dark powers to attack, searing Luke with blasts of blue lightning. As he watched the agony of his son and the Emperor's glee, Vader finally broke the hold of evil that had suffocated him for so long. Vader grabbed the energy-seething Palpatine and hurled him into the Death Star reactor shaft, where the evil leader was disintegrated. The shock waves of dark power mortally wounded Vader. Luke Skywalker could do nothing for his dying father, the terrible enemy who had saved him in the end.

On the surface of Endor, General Solo's mission had gone critically off course when stormtroopers and AT-ST scout walkers had ambushed the Rebel strike against the shield generator bunker. The Rebellion might have perished there had it not been for the Ewoks, who sprang from the forest to assail the Imperials with slings, arrows, and log traps. Han Solo planted explosive charges inside the bunker, and the giant projector dish vanished in a riot of fire. The energy shield surrounding the Death Star sputtered and died.

Rebel starfighters led by Lando Calrissian and Wedge Antilles raced into the Death Star's superstructure to drop a warhead directly into the central reactor core and trigger a chain reaction similar to the one that had destroyed the Death Star at Yavin. Outside, Admiral Ackbar's fleet continued the battle against enemy commander Admiral Piett's Star Destroyers. Rebel pilot Arvel Crynyd, his doomed A-wing disintegrating, steered his fighter into the bridge of Piett's flagship, the *Executor.* The grand Super Star Destroyer crashed into the hull of the Death Star and was completely annihilated. Lando and Wedge dropped their charge in the battle station's reactor and raced back out to space, one step ahead of the detonation wave.

Luke Skywalker dragged his dying father to a shuttle bay, but Vader died before they could escape. Skywalker took the black-clad body with him as he flew away, seconds before the Death Star detonated.

All around the galaxy, freedom-loving citizens celebrated the end of the New Order and the death of Emperor Palpatine. Though the Empire was far from vanquished, the Battle of Endor signified a crucial and decisive victory for the Rebellion.

At last, a New Republic could be born.

THE TRUCE AT BAKURA
4 A.B.Y.

After the remaining Imperial fleet's retreat from Endor, the Rebel Alliance had no time to savor their victory. The following day, an Imperial drone ship arrived at the site of the Death Star's cooling wreckage, with a message addressed to Emperor Palpatine. "Bakura is under attack from an alien invasion force from outside your domain. We have lost half our defense force and all outersystem out-

posts. Urgent, repeat urgent, send stormtroopers."

Mon Mothma gathered a small task force to go to the remote planet's defense. Luke Skywalker, still suffering from his injuries at the hands of the Emperor, received a visit from the Force spirit of Obi-Wan Kenobi. Kenobi urged his former protégé to attend to the Bakura matter personally, and Luke agreed to lead five Corellian gunships, one corvette, and *Millennium Falcon* to Bakura, at the edge of known space.

Bakura's peril came at the hands of the Ssi-ruuk, a species of warm-blooded saurians who had embarked on a campaign of conquest. Their "entenchment" technology could transfer a human prisoner's life-energy into the circuits of a battle droid, giving the Ssi-ruuk a cheap and expendable fighting force. If they succeeded in entenching the population of Bakura, the Ssi-ruuk would have enough mechanical warriors to pose a threat to the entire galaxy.

The beleaguered Imperials of Bakura welcomed the small Alliance fleet. Eager to discuss a formal truce, Leia Organa met with Imperial Governor Wilek Nereus in the capital city of Salis D'aar. Governor Nereus, along with Prime Minister Yeorg Captison and his beautiful niece Gaeriel Captison, listened to the Alliance's offer. Nereus agreed to a cease-fire. With a handshake, the first-ever truce between Rebel and Imperial forces took effect.

Later that evening, Leia Organa received a visitation by an unwelcome presence—the spirit-form of Anakin Skywalker, her true father. The man who was once Darth Vader begged his daughter for her forgiveness. Leia, who had learned of her parentage only days earlier, was unable to forget the fact that Vader had tortured her aboard the Death Star and blasted her homeworld of Alderaan into cinders. The apparition vanished, and did not appear to his daughter again.

On board the mighty flagship *Shriwirr,* the Ssi-ruuk's Admiral Ivpikkis readied his battle droids for a single, overwhelming assault against Bakura. One of Ivpikkis's subor-

Ssi-ruuk armies run riot over a Bakuran plaza.
[ART BY TOMMY LEE EDWARDS]

dinates owned a brainwashed human "pet" who had been raised by the Ssi-ruuk since he was a young boy. This human collaborator, Dev Sibwarra, sensed the presence of Luke Skywalker through the Force and alerted his masters. The Ssi-ruuk hoped this powerful Jedi would be capable of entenching victims from great distances, sucking their life-energies from afar. Sibwarra secretly contacted Governor Nereus with an offer. If the governor would turn over Skywalker, the Ssi-ruuvi fleet would leave Bakura in peace.

Nereus was far too shrewd to take the aliens at their word, but he saw a devious way to eliminate *both* threats—Skywalker and the Ssi-ruuk—with a single thrust. He placed three Olabrian trichoid egg pods into Skywalker's food. The bloodsucking, highly contagious larvae would hatch in Skywalker's body once he was safely aboard the Ssi-ruuik flagship, killing him in gruesome fashion and infecting the aliens with a lethal parasite to which they had no natural immunity.

Nereus felt confident of victory, and arrested Leia Organa on charges of sedition. Many of Bakura's citizens saw the action as a clear abuse of authority, and rioting broke out in Salis D'aar.

Luke, captured by the Ssi-ruuk, was hooked into the *Shriwirr*'s entenchment rig. Dev Sibwarra, impressed by the Jedi's heroism, shrugged off his masters' brainwashing and helped Luke escape. Ivpikkis and the Ssi-ruuvi crew escaped the *Shriwirr* in life pods.

In orbit above Bakura, the Rebel and Imperial fleets formed a united front against the invaders, shelling the Ssi-ruuvi armada. In order to live and fight on, the saurians began a full retreat. Every Ssi-ruuvi vessel (except for the abandoned flagship *Shriwirr*) vanished into hyperspace toward the Unknown Regions.

But Nereus turned traitor yet again. With the Ssi-ruuk gone, he ordered his fleet to open fire on their ostensible allies. The Rebel flagship and many other ships were destroyed by Nereus's treachery. The surviving Rebel fighters were caught in a bottleneck with no hope of escape. General Solo grimly lined up a suicidal "carom shot" in which the *Falcon* would ram a small Imperial patrol craft, ricocheting the patrol craft into the Imperial command ship's main generator. Success meant escape for the Rebel fleet, but death for everyone aboard the *Falcon*.

The enemy craft, however, broke formation to strike at the *Shriwirr*. The *Falcon* aborted its carom shot, and instead rescued Luke Skywalker and Dev Sibwarra from the damaged *Shriwirr*. Luke had already sensed the presence of the Olabrian larval parasites in his bronchial tubes and used the Force to eliminate the threat.

The Rebel fleet rallied from near disaster. Commander Pter Thanas, leader of the Imperial defense force, surrendered. On Bakura, Governor Nereus was captured by resistance fighters, and killed in a mishap not long afterward.

It was a welcome victory. Prime Minister Captison assumed control of Bakura and joined the Rebels' fledgling Alliance of Free Planets. Commander Thanas oversaw the Imperial withdrawal from Bakura and then defected, agreeing to lead the Bakuran home defense force. Senator Gaeriel Captison had grown quite close to Luke Skywalker over the course of the incident, but she loved her homeworld even more. Gaeriel married Commander Thanas, and was eventually elected Prime Minister of Bakura. One of her first actions was to commission new, powerful defensive warships in case the Ssi-ruuk should ever return.

Despite all the medical attention Luke Skywalker could provide, Dev Sibwarra succumbed to injuries sustained during the battle aboard the *Shriwirr*. But Luke vowed to find more Force-sensitive candidates and eventually restore the order of Jedi Knights.

ONWARD TO SSI-RUUVI SPACE
4–5 A.B.Y.

A footnote to the Ssi-ruuvi incident, the invasion of Ssi-ruuvi space stretched on for a year and involved a dozen Nebulon-B frigates and smaller vessels accompanying the refitted Ssi-ruuvi flagship. This latter vessel had since been renamed *Sibwarra,* but its crew commonly called it the *Flutie*—a derisive nickname for the Ssi-ruuk, derived from their musical speech patterns.

Life aboard the *Sibwarra* was exceedingly odd. Throughout their tour of duty, the crew struggled with the ship's baffling onboard equipment. Several crewers were injured or killed by the confusing alien devices.

The Empire declined to join in on the attack. It was quite a surprise, then, when the *Sibwarra* arrived at the Ssi-ruuvi star cluster and discovered a half-beaten foe. The Chiss, striking from deep in the Unknown Regions, had already attacked the Ssi-ruuvi Imperium on the opposite front. It is believed that Grand Admiral Thrawn, newly returned to the Unknown Regions following his defeat of Grand Admiral Zaarin, had orchestrated the attack, combining his Imperial warships with renegade Chiss craft in what he was already calling his "Empire of the Hand."

The *Sibwarra* strike force engaged Admiral Ivpikkis of the Ssi-ruuvi fleet as they battled their way to Lwhekk, the Ssi-ruuvi homeworld. Eventually the two sides reached a standstill. Satisfied that the Ssi-ruuvi could not mount another invasion, Mon Mothma ordered the Alliance vessels to fall back and assist in the liberation of Clak'dor VII.

In the aftermath of the defeat, a Ssi-ruu called the Keeramak, whose multicolored scales were believed to be a sign of his near divinity, helped rally the P'w'eck slave species and overthrow what was left of the Ssi-ruuvi social order.

PART SIX

Birth of the New Republic

While Leia Organa, Han Solo, and Luke Skywalker defended Bakura from the Ssi-ruuk, Mon Mothma made preparations to establish a new galactic government. Clearly, it could take years, even decades, to eradicate the Empire, but the victory at Endor was a symbolic starting point for marking a new era.

THE ALLIANCE OF FREE PLANETS
4 A.B.Y.

Within days of the Battle of Endor, the Rebel Alliance became the Alliance of Free Planets, an interim stage until the details of the government could be worked out. Already, key star systems, including the Fondor shipyards in the Tapani sector, were announcing their defections from Imperial rule. From a temporary headquarters on Endor, the new government—which had just closed the books on the Ssi-ruuvi incident—suddenly had to deal with an invasion from a different quarter.

The Nagai, chalk-skinned humanoids who specialized in emotionless cruelty, launched an assault on the galactic southern quadrant. Believed to hail from one of the dwarf galaxies that orbit tightly around the known galaxy, the Nagai had allied with Shira Brie, now the Dark Lady Lumiya, to crush the fledgling government in its infancy. The Nagai forced the Alliance from its Endor base and attacked worlds from Iskalon to Zeltros.

The Nagai invasion ended as quickly as it began. The Tofs, a robust, boastful species from the same dwarf galaxy and the traditional enemies of the Nagai, followed their prey to the new killing grounds. In a final confrontation on Saijo, the Alliance wound up fighting alongside the Nagai to force a surrender from the Tof crown prince. The Nagai survivors returned home. Lumiya fled the battle and retreated to the ancient Sith worlds, where she trained her first apprentice, Flint, and later the Royal Guardsman Carnor Jax.

Dark Lady Lumiya, formerly known as Shira Brie.
[ART BY MARK CHIARELLO]

DECLARATION OF A NEW REPUBLIC
4 A.B.Y.

One month after the formation of the Alliance of Free Planets, Mon Mothma formally issued the "Declaration of a New Republic" on the public HoloNet channels. Though the Battle of Endor is viewed as the beginning of the New Republic era, Mon Mothma's pronouncement marked the official establishment of the true government. The document was signed by Mon Mothma, Leia Organa, Borsk Fey'lya, and Admiral Ackbar, as well as officials from Corellia, Duro, Kashyyyk, Sullust, and Elom. Under the New Republic's first charter, these nine individuals comprised the New Republic Provisional Council. Mon Mothma was elected Chief Councilor.

For several months, the New Republic made no large-scale military invasions into Imperial territory. Instead, they consolidated their holdings and won over hundreds of planets through diplomacy. News of the Emperor's death caused countless worlds to join the New Republic's fold, most of them in the Rim territories. Captain Wedge Antilles and the X-wing pilots of Rogue Squadron acted as scouts, escorts, and negotiators during this period.

Disappointingly, a promising opportunity to bolster the New Republic Fleet fell apart when Kuat Drive Yards (KDY), the Empire's leading shipbuilder, failed to switch allegiances. During the Battle of Endor, KDY's former CEO had committed suicide and destroyed a portion of the Kuat shipyards rather than see his independent corporation nationalized by the Empire. The New Republic hoped that his successor would be an ally, but she quickly repaired the damaged dry docks and cozied up to Sate Pestage, the new Imperial leader.

IMPERIAL FRAGMENTATION
4–4.5 A.B.Y.

One reason the New Republic saw no need for an immediate strike against the Empire was that the Empire was doing a fine job of tearing itself apart.

Without Palpatine's commanding presence, the Imperial war machine seemed unfocused. After the destruction of the second Death Star, the Imperial fleet had continued to fight for four hours under the command of Grand Admiral Teshik—but were systematically beaten back by their numerically inferior foe. When Rebel forces disabled Teshik's ship, Captain Gilad Pellaeon of the Star Destroyer *Chimaera* ordered the fleet to retreat and regroup at Annaj, where the first signs of stress began to show.

Admiral Harrsk, commander of one task force within the Endor fleet, saw the death of the Emperor as a great opportunity, and was unwilling to take orders from Pellaeon, a mere captain. Harrsk took his segment of the fleet and jumped to the restricted Deep Core at the very center of the galaxy. There, among the secure Imperial safeworlds, Harrsk began building up his own pocket empire.

Though Harrsk was the Empire's first breakaway warlord, he wouldn't be the last. The Empire had long rewarded ambition over cooperation—only cruel and intimidating leaders, such as Palpatine and Vader, had kept their subordinates in line. Suddenly, post-Endor, everyone wanted to rule the Empire, or at least create their own kingdoms. More than any other factor, warlordism was responsible for the decline of the Empire.

Many other warlords broke away in the first few months. Admiral Teradoc followed Harrsk's lead and established a miniature empire in the Mid Rim just days after Endor. Admiral Gaen Drommel became the dictator of his home sector using the Super Star Destroyer *Guardian*. Grand Moff Ardus Kaine, Tarkin's successor, walled off a large chunk of the Outer Rim Territories and dubbed it the Pentastar Alignment. "Superior General" Delvardus laid claim to most of the worlds near the Rimma Trade Route, until battles forced him into the Deep Core. Grand Admirals Grunger and Pitta locked themselves into a struggle over the Corellian sector. Admiral Zsinj, ruler of the Quelii sector, would later prove to be one of the New Republic's most formidable foes.

To add to the confusion, Palpatine had not been truly destroyed at Endor. As with Obi-Wan Kenobi, the Emperor's spirit-form had survived when his body died. Palpatine's life-essence made a tortuous journey to his hidden throneworld of Byss in the Deep Core, where it inhabited the body of a fresh young clone. Palpatine's clone began to consolidate his own forces, though it would be years before he made his presence known to the galaxy.

It was obvious that Sate Pestage, the Emperor's former Grand Vizier and the man responsible for keeping the Empire intact, was failing miserably. Pestage had been cunning enough to assume the Imperial throne upon learning of his master's death. But the Grand Vizier lacked the charisma and influence to lead the Empire, and he had a host of enemies within the Imperial Palace. Pestage's chief rivals were Palpatine's former advisory staff, who had formed a tribunal known as the Ruling Circle. As they schemed to overthrow the new Emperor, Pestage plotted to keep the Ruling Circle in check. Ysanne Isard, head of Imperial Intelligence, acted as a neutral intermediary between the two parties.

Neither faction realized Isard's true goal until it was too late. Isard was secretly pitting each side against the other so she could rise from their ashes and rule as Empress.

Black Nebula
4–4.5 A.B.Y.

The Black Sun criminal syndicate could not recover from the death of its leader, Prince Xizor. The various lieutenants, or vigos, began to fight over what remained. One of Black Sun's lesser operatives, a Jeodu named Dequc, tried to revive the organization under the name Black Nebula, with himself as its head. Palpatine had ordered Dequc eliminated; mere days before Endor, Mara Jade, one of the Emperor's Hands, had executed him on Svivren. Mara later learned that the victim on Svivren had been a decoy. Dequc continued to expand Black Nebula in the post-Palpatine Empire, until Mara tracked him down and killed him on Qiaxx several months later.

Ysanne Isard and Sate Pestage discuss who will inherit the Emperor's throne. [Art by Tommy Lee Edwards]

At the same time, Savan, Prince Xizor's niece, attempted to piece together the remaining factions of Black Sun. The key to Savan's plot was the human replica droid known as Guri, who had formerly been Xizor's second in command and knew all the syndicate's secrets. Savan located Guri on Hurd's Moon, where she was undergoing synaptic rewiring to erase her memory and her assassin droid programming.

Councilor Leia Organa and generals Han Solo and Lando Calrissian also journeyed to Hurd's Moon, attempting to prevent the rise of another destructive criminal empire. After a shootout, they took Savan into custody. Guri, her criminal programming purged, was allowed to go free.

Black Nebula crumbled without Dequc, and Xizor's vigos murdered each other in an internecine bloodbath. Black Sun was dead, and it would remain defunct until the New Republic inadvertently resurrected the syndicate during the liberation of Coruscant three years later.

ISARD'S ASCENSION
4.5–5 A.B.Y.

Ysanne Isard's conspiracy began to bear fruit when the New Republic threatened Brentaal, a wealthy and influential Core world not far from Ralltiir, which had fallen to the New Republic only days before. As the New Republic military geared up for an all-out assault from their base on nearby Recopia, Sate Pestage vowed that Brentaal would not fall.

Under Isard's advice, Pestage allowed the incompetent Admiral Isoto to defend Brentaal. Baron Soontir Fel and the legendary 181st Imperial fighter wing did what they could, but Isoto's bumblings allowed the New Republic to capture the world. During the final battle, Baron Fel was taken prisoner by the New Republic. Fel would later fly with the X-wing pilots of Rogue Squadron, until his disappearance into the Unknown Regions.

To all appearances, Pestage had been responsible for the loss of Brentaal, and the Ruling Circle screamed for his head. Knowing that Isard had sold him out, Pestage

Mara Jade, former Imperial assassin.
[ART BY JOHN VAN FLEET]

made preparations to defect.

On Axxila, Pestage held a secret meeting with Councilor Leia Organa to discuss the terms of his surrender. In exchange for leaving Coruscant undefended against a New Republic assault, he asked for twenty-five planets that he could rule as he pleased. Realizing that Coruscant was the key to the war effort, Leia agreed to Pestage's offer, despite her misgivings. Isard learned of the Axxila talks and informed the Ruling Circle of Pestage's treachery. An order was issued for his arrest, and the Ruling Circle set itself up as the new governing power in the Empire.

Sate Pestage fled to Ciutric, but was apprehended by the local Imperial governor. Though the Axxila deal was obviously dead, the New Republic felt it had to take action. If Pestage were rescued by the New Republic, it would serve as an example to other high-ranking Imperials and encourage further defections. Rogue Squadron and a commando team were sent to Ciutric to retrieve Pestage.

The rescue operation failed. Pestage was murdered by Imperial Admiral Krennel, who then seized Pestage's personal territory—the Ciutric Hegemony—and set himself up as the Empire's latest breakaway warlord. On Coruscant, Ysanne Isard ruthlessly exterminated the Ruling Circle and assumed the throne in their place. Isard would succeed where the others had failed, holding the crumbling Empire together for more than two years.

Eight months after the Battle of Endor, Admiral Ackbar and the New Republic Fleet made another aggressive push into Imperial territory. Ackbar defeated Grand Admiral Syn at Kashyyyk and scored other victories in the Mid and Inner Rims. Concerned that the campaign might presage a siege of Coruscant, Isard recalled hundreds of Star Destroyers to defend the capital planet and other key Core Worlds.

One of the Imperial armadas that received the order was the Black Sword Command in the Koornacht Cluster, a little-known patch of territory at the fringes of the Deep Core. As the Black Fleet prepared to evacuate the central shipbuilding planet of N'zoth, the shipyards' Yevethan dockworkers erupted in a shocking uprising. Led by underground commando Nil Spaar, the Yevetha murdered thousands of Imperials, captured hundreds more, and seized every Star Destroyer in the Black Fleet armada—including the Super Star Destroyer *Intimidator*.

The Yevetha covered up the incident. The New Republic never heard a word about it, and Isard—operating on inaccurate intelligence data—believed that the Black Fleet had perished in a debacle at Cal-Seti, several sectors over. The Koornacht Cluster would remain a closed-border curiosity until the frantic events of the Black Fleet Crisis, twelve years in the future.

General Skywalker challenges Lord Shadowspawn's troops on Mindor.
[ART BY TOMMY LEE EDWARDS]

One year after the Emperor's death, the Central Committee of Grand Moffs decided to increase their own power base by moving against Isard. They proclaimed their own candidate—Trioculus, a former Kessel slave lord—as Imperial leader, and attempted to rally the fleet behind him, eliminating such possible rivals as Grand Admiral Takel. Some followed their lead, but the bulk of the fleet, including Captain Pellaeon of the Star Destroyer *Chimaera,* remained loyal to Isard.

The New Republic moved against the Grand Moffs under the auspices of the Senate Planetary Intelligence Network (SPIN), a newly formed analysis and infiltration task force. Isard, meanwhile, freed Jabba the Hutt's father, Zorba, from

prison and sent him into the fray as her unwitting agent. Zorba seized Cloud City from Lando Calrissian, who had only recently rescued the city from the clutches of the Empire. In the end, the matter was settled without a fleet battle. Trioculus, Zorba, and a shadowy group of mystics called the Prophets of the Dark Side wiped each other out in an internal struggle. Those Grand Moffs who had been involved in the conspiracy were executed, and Isard's position at the head of the Empire was more secure than ever.

Several months later, Ysanne Isard was instrumental in foiling a New Republic espionage mission to Coruscant. Pilot Tycho Celchu, a member of Rogue Squadron, took a TIE fighter that had been captured during the truce at Bakura and infiltrated the Imperial capital. Isard, however, uncovered the spy and imprisoned him in the hellish prison known only as *Lusankya*. Celchu eventually escaped to the New Republic, but was viewed with suspicion by many, who suspected that he had been brainwashed into becoming a sleeper agent.

GENERAL SKYWALKER
5–5.5 A.B.Y.

Throughout the Trioculus affair, the New Republic was engaged in a protracted military campaign for possession of Milagro, a world at a key hyperspace junction.

The Empire was prepared to lay waste to Milagro rather than allow the Rebels access to its manufacturing facilities. Following three months of exhausting clashes between AT-AT walkers and the New Republic Army, the defeated Imperials slagged the planet's surface with a withering orbital bombardment, then fled.

The New Republic remained in the system, using the Dreadnaught *New Hope* as an orbital HQ. Soon after the disbanding of SPIN, a damaged Imperial Star Destroyer leapt into the Milagro system, hoping to effect repairs. Instead, they stumbled into a brawl with the *New Hope*. General Solo led the fighter attack, while Mon Mothma coordinated the battle from the bridge of *New Hope*. Finally, Luke Skywalker's superior X-wing tactics forced the Imperials' surrender. The captured Star Destroyer was renamed *Crynyd* in honor of the A-wing pilot whose self-sacrifice at the Battle of Endor took down the Super Star Destroyer *Executor*. For his heroism at Milagro, Commander Skywalker was at last promoted to the rank of general.

General Skywalker was quickly saddled with the responsibilities of command, a burden he loathed. Ever since his experience at Bakura, Skywalker had grown less interested in military conquest and more interested in the spiritual understanding of the Force. Skywalker's views were reinforced when he witnessed the heroic deeds of Kyle Katarn—a Force-sensitive individual who, five years earlier, had helped recover the Death Star plans and sabotaged the Empire's Dark Trooper program. Now Katarn was realizing his own potential as a Jedi.

Several of the Emperor's Dark Side Adepts, led by the Dark Jedi Jerec, had attracted corporate backers to form a warlord cabal. Their influence was limited, but Jerec had discovered the Valley of the Jedi on Ruusan, where the spirits of the Brotherhood of Darkness and Army of Light had been trapped in limbo for a thousand years. Jerec planned to use the valley's power to topple Isard and rule a vast new Empire. Katarn single-handedly defeated Jerec and his minions before the Dark Jedi's grandiose plans could come to fruition.

Skywalker, impressed, offered to train Katarn as a Jedi apprentice, but the other man declined. Soon afterward, the New Republic became bogged down in a brutal military campaign in the Inner Rim. Skywalker led his troops onto the battlefields of Mindor, digging out entrenched pockets of Imperial resistance. Stormtroopers, under the command of Lord Shadowspawn, fought to the last man. Though Fenn Shysa and his new Mandalorian Protectors helped deliver the deciding blow against Shadowspawn, Skywalker grew dismayed at the bloodshed and unnecessary loss of life.

Less than six months after receiving his general's commission, Luke Skywalker resigned from the New Republic military.

THE LAST GRAND ADMIRAL?
6 A.B.Y.

Emperor Palpatine frequently rewarded his most capable servants with grandiose titles, further encouraging the notorious Imperial culture of greed and ambition. The best stormtroopers were molded into Royal Guards, and there were rumors that the best Royal Guards became Imperial Sovereign Protectors on Byss. Initially, the highest possible rank in the Imperial Navy was admiral, until two years before the Battle of Yavin, when Palpatine created the elite rank of Grand Admiral. There could never be more than twelve Grand Admirals at one time.

The twelve Grand Admirals, easily recognizable by their stark white uniforms and braided gold epaulets, were the best of the best—unparalleled geniuses at military strategy. Only Admiral Ackbar could be considered their equal in the New Republic Navy. In the aftermath of Endor, had the surviving Grand Admirals united against their common enemy, the New Republic could have been wiped out while still in its infancy.

Fortunately, that threat never materialized. The first Grand Admiral to fall was Zaarin, whose coup d'état had ended in disaster just before Endor. Grand Admiral Declann perished with the second Death Star. Grand Admiral Teshik, captured at Endor, was executed by the New Republic. Grand Admiral Syn was outfought by Ackbar during the liberation of Kashyyyk, his flagship vaporized. Grand Admirals Grunger and Pitta turned warlord and annihilated each other in a bitter and ultimately futile fight for control of the Corellian sector. Grand Admiral Takel was executed by Trioculus, while the Central Committee of Grand Moffs did away with Grand Admiral Tigellinus for perceived disloyalty. The fanatical Grand Admiral Il-Raz committed suicide by plunging his flagship into the heart of the Denarii Nova, shortly before the events that eliminated Grand Admiral Makati. Grand Admiral Batch was assassinated by his second in command, who then took the ships in Batch's task force and joined Warlord Harrsk in the Deep Core.

Grand Admiral Grant, the so-called last Grand Admiral, defected to the New Republic on the condition that he be granted immunity from prosecution for war crimes and allowed to retire on Rathalay. The defection took place two years after Endor. The New Republic closed the books on the Emperor's Grand Admirals, believing that they had finally all been accounted for.

No one realized that one Grand Admiral remained at large, possibly the most dangerous of all. Blue-skinned Thrawn, the "thirteenth Grand Admiral," had been promoted by Palpatine in a secret ceremony following the treason of Grand Admiral Zaarin. Soon afterward, Thrawn had been sent to the Unknown Regions to continue his exploration near Chiss space, accounting for the New Republic's oversight. Years would pass before Thrawn's return, when the New Republic would once again learn to fear the title of Grand Admiral.

THE BATTLE FOR CORUSCANT
6.5–7 A.B.Y.

Two and a half years after the birth of the New Republic, the Empire was still the galaxy's dominant government. Despite the rise of rogue warlords, Imperials held a majority of settled planets and had a stranglehold on the important Core Worlds. Without an aggressive military push, the New Republic would never bring about an end to the Galactic Civil War.

The most effective way to destroy the Empire would be to capture Coruscant, the universal symbol of governmental power and authority. The New Republic began seizing planets in Imperial territory as "stepping-stones" to a strike at Coruscant. As part of the mobilization, Wedge Antilles was recalled from a propaganda tour and restored to active duty. Antilles's legendary X-wing unit, Rogue Squadron, was reformed with a roster of new pilots.

The New Republic captured Borleias, in the Colonies region, after two costly attacks. Borleias was perfectly situated as a forward base for a Coruscant assault. Admiral Ackbar, however, knew that the capital's defensive energy shield would negate any orbital bombardment. Before any attack could begin, Coruscant's shield must fall.

Antilles and Rogue Squadron were sent undercover into Imperial City to sabotage the planet's shield generator. At the same time, sixteen of the galaxy's worst criminals were freed from the spice mines of Kessel and let loose on Coruscant, in the hope that they would foster chaos. The latter decision was unusual for the New Republic, and opposed by many members of the Ruling Council, who were proven correct in the end. The freed criminals, led by Y'ull Acib, resurrected the defunct Black Sun criminal cartel, which would plague the New Republic in later years.

Rogue Squadron's operatives gambled that if they could condense a large amount of water vapor and create a massive storm, they could knock out Coruscant's shields with lightning strikes. The Rogues commandeered a forty-story construction droid to take them to a command building, and then took remote control of one of the planet's orbiting solar mirrors. The tightly focused light beam from the mirror flash-boiled one of Imperial City's artificial reservoirs. The steam cloud coalesced into an angry cloudburst, and soon the shields collapsed.

With Coruscant vulnerable, Ackbar leapt into the system with a full armada. The battle was intense, but victory came surprisingly easily—Ysanne Isard had kept only a handful

of Star Destroyers to defend the capital. Ackbar wiped out all resistance, and at last Coruscant was in the hands of the New Republic.

THE KRYTOS VIRUS
7–7.5 A.B.Y.

When the New Republic secured the Imperial Palace, they discovered that Isard had vanished. Worse, she had left behind a sick and dying world.

After years of work on an isolated biological research asteroid, Isard's chief scientist, Evir Derricote, had engineered an artificial plague—the Krytos virus. Within days of transmission, Krytos turned healthy flesh into a bloody soup. Isard had seeded Coruscant's water reservoirs with the plague before the Rebels arrival, and millions of citizens had already contracted the disease. However, Derricote had carefully tailored the Krytos virus to affect only specific nonhuman species—Sullustans, Gamorreans, and others. The fact that Coruscant's human population was immune drove a wedge between the New Republic's member species.

The Krytos plague spoiled the New Republic's triumph and made it look ineffectual and weak. Thus, governing the civilian population of Coruscant was nearly impossible. Furthermore, Mon Mothma was forced to spend millions of credits on voluminous amounts of bacta to treat the infected and research a vaccine—credits that the near-bankrupt government didn't have.

Diverting the public's attention during this difficult time was the trial of Tycho Celchu. Celchu, a member of Rogue Squadron, had been arrested for treason and the murder of his fellow pilot Corran Horn immediately following the liberation of Coruscant. No one had forgotten that two years earlier, Celchu had been captured on an undercover mission and incarcerated in the Empire's *Lusankya* prison. Prosecuting attorneys at his trial claimed Celchu had been operating as a brainwashed Imperial agent ever since.

Victorious troopers raise the New Republic banner on Coruscant.
[ART BY TOMMY LEE EDWARDS]

The truth was even more shocking—not only was Celchu innocent, but Corran Horn was alive. Horn had been secretly captured by Isard and himself imprisoned in *Lusankya*, where he was forced to undergo regular torture and indoctrination sessions. His only relief came in conversation with his fellow prisoners, one of whom was the famed Alliance leader Jan Dodonna, who had been captured during the evacuation of Yavin 4 seven years earlier.

Horn escaped, forcing Isard to abandon her hiding place. As the members of Rogue Squadron flew a mission above Imperial City, a panicked call suddenly came from the Manarai Mountain district. Antilles saw a massive object rising from the subterranean depths, obliterating vast tracts of homes and businesses as it came to the surface—a Super Star Destroyer that answered to the name *Lusankya*. Despite the efforts of Rogue Squadron to stop it, the *Lusankya* tore a gaping hole out of Imperial City's heart, killing millions in its effort to free itself. It then vanished into hyperspace.

The presence of Corran Horn, alive, cleared Celchu of the murder charge. Luke Skywalker investigated Horn's background and discovered that the pilot was actually the grandson of the great Jedi Nejaa Halcyon, who had fought with honor at Praesitlyn during the Clone Wars. Horn refused Skywalker's offer to train him as a Jedi, but he reconsidered his decision years later.

New Republic scientists developed a cure for the Krytos virus by mixing bacta with the spice ryll kor. The resulting vaccine, rylca, was administered to Coruscant's alien population and prevented further loss of life.

THE BACTA WAR
7.5 A.B.Y.

Ysanne Isard fled Coruscant aboard the *Lusankya* and quickly acted to hold her power base. At Thyferra, the bacta-manufacturing planet, she supported a coup and was elected Head of State by the victorious faction. The New Republic was unhappy with the development, but it was against their principles to depose a duly elected planetary leader. Since the Thyferran government refused to move against Isard, Antilles and Rogue Squadron resigned from the New Republic Fleet. As civilians, they answered to no one, and were free to move against Isard on their own.

But the bacta planet was defended by four capital ships: the *Lusankya*, two Imperial Star Destroyers, and a Victory Star Destroyer. A direct, frontal assault would be a quick way to commit suicide. Instead, Antilles flitted around like a Sacorrian grain fly—stinging Isard, then retreating to a safe distance before she could swat back. The Rogues occupied an abandoned space station near Yag'Dhul as a base of operations, and hired smuggler Booster Terrik to manage the station. Terrik obtained weapons from the smuggling kingpin

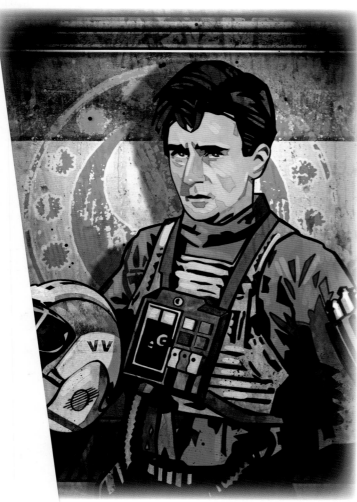

edge Antilles
ᴛ]

Talon Karrde, and Rogue Squadron began harassing Isard's bacta convoys.

Rogue Squadron destroyed one capital ship in a fight near the rubble of the Alderaan Graveyard, and convinced the captain of another ship to defect. With half of her defensive force suddenly gone, Isard ordered the *Lusankya* and her remaining Star Destroyer to blast the Rogues' Yag'Dhul space station into atoms.

Antilles and the other Rogues seized the opportunity and jumped into hyperspace to attack the now undefended Thyferra. At Yag'Dhul, the *Lusankya* closed to firing range, but the space station suddenly locked on to the Super Star Destroyer with more than three hundred proton torpedoes. Knowing that no vessel's shields could withstand such a volley, the *Lusankya* fled to Thyferra, and the remaining outgunned Star Destroyer surrendered.

It was all a bluff perpetuated by Antilles. The Yag'Dhul space station didn't have *any* torpedoes, just three hundred targeting locks. The torpedoes were aboard the small armada of freighters and X-wings heading for Thyferra.

At the bacta planet, the Rogues and the *Lusankya* both emerged from hyperspace and fell upon one another with a vengeance. More than eighty proton torpedoes impacted against the Super Star Destroyer, collapsing its shields and ripping its guts open. When Booster Terrik arrived aboard the newly captured Star Destroyer and joined the fight, the ailing *Lusankya* surrendered. The *Lusankya* was towed to a secret shipyard for extensive repairs. Sadly, Jan Dodonna and the rest of the prisoners had been transferred off the ship weeks earlier. Their rescue would happen another day.

Ysanne Isard was smart enough to know when she was beaten, and attempted to escape Thyferra. Her shuttle was destroyed while trying to make the jump to hyperspace, and Isard was believed killed. Isard, however, had engineered the incident to cover her tracks. She spent the following years putting herself back together mentally, and would plague the New Republic again in the wake of the Thrawn incident.

Antilles and Rogue Squadron were welcomed back as heroes. After much wrangling, New Republic Intelligence allowed Booster Terrik to keep his captured Star Destroyer, which he renamed the *Errant Venture*. The ship became a movable trading bazaar, famous for eclectic merchandise.

In the aftermath of the Bacta War, the New Republic captured another Star Destroyer, the *Tyrant*, from an underdefended Imperial fueling outpost. This ship had been a member of Vader's Death Squadron and had assisted in the decimation of Echo Base on Hoth. Impressed by the symbolism, Councilor Organa renamed the vessel *Rebel Dream* and made it her personal flagship.

The Hunt for Zsinj
7.5–8 A.B.Y.

The New Republic had been right about one thing: controlling Coruscant was the key to the Galactic Civil War. As soon as Isard lost control of the capital world, the fragmentation of the Empire grew more severe as officers lost faith in their leaders. A coalition of Moffs and Imperial advisers replaced Isard, but found their power slipping away in favor of warlords like Zsinj.

Zsinj was now the most powerful Imperial warlord, having gained many new officers, ships, and planets during the post-Isard defections. He was also arrogant enough to fight his war on two fronts, both against the New Republic and against his former comrades in the Empire, whom he viewed as weak-willed and ineffectual. Furthermore, he possessed the mighty Super Star Destroyer *Iron Fist*, which could take on an entire armada by itself. The New Republic made the liberation of Zsinj's dominion a top priority and put together a task force under the command of General Solo to hunt down the warlord. The task force departed on its mission just prior to the events of the Bacta War.

Aboard the Mon Calamari flagship *Mon Remonda*, Solo probed the borders of Zsinj-controlled territory and witnessed firsthand the horrors that the warlord perpetrated on worlds that resisted his will. Solo was supplemented by the best military units the New Republic had to offer, including the legendary Rogue Squadron—but another group of X-wing pilots would provide the key to toppling Warlord Zsinj.

Commander Wedge Antilles, following his reinstatement in the New Republic military, chose not to join *Mon Remonda*. Instead, Antilles assembled a new group of pilots, dubbed Wraith Squadron, composed of commandos, snipers, spies, and infiltrators to whom piloting a starfighter was of only secondary importance. Soon after their formation, the Wraiths captured a Corellian corvette belonging to Zsinj and decided to pose as the corvette's crew. The ruse allowed them to infiltrate Zsinj's fleet and learn of an ambush planned against the New Republic on Ession in the Corporate Sector. The Battle of Ession was a victory for the New Republic, which demolished one of Zsinj's Star Destroyers and bombed a key manufacturing plant into oblivion.

The subterfuge with the captured corvette would not work a second time, so the commandos of Wraith Squadron changed tactics. They posed as a pirate band in order to work their way into Zsinj's loose organization of freelance raiders. The warlord hired the disguised Wraiths as mercenaries for his strike on the vast shipbuilding facilities in the Kuat system. Kuat Drive Yards, still allied with the Empire, had nearly completed a new Super Star Destroyer. Zsinj planned to steal the colossal vessel and pair it with *Iron Fist* to deliver a double hammer blow to his enemies. New Republic saboteurs foiled Zsinj's plans by destroying both of the new vessel's topside shield generator domes, and *Mon Remonda* blasted the unprotected warship to scrap. *Iron Fist* escaped into hyperspace.

Solo headed back out to hunt down Zsinj. The warlord, however, had a more devious plot afoot. Several of Zsinj's pet scientists had developed a method of rapid, forced brainwashing that could turn even the most placid citizen into a raving murderer, and the technique was tailored to work only with specific species—Twi'leks, Gotals, Sullustans, and others. Much as Ysanne Isard had attempted to do with the "aliens only" Krytos virus, Zsinj preyed on the suspicions and resentment that many species felt toward humans. "Project Minefield," as it was known in Zsinj's organization, resulted in hundreds of deaths, including several high-profile assassination attempts. A brainwashed Twi'lek tried to kill Ackbar, while Mon Mothma's loyal Gotal bodyguard suddenly turned on her, but died before he could injure the Chief Councilor. Aboard *Mon Remonda,* a Twi'lek A-wing pilot shot out the bridge viewport and nearly killed Han Solo through explosive decompression. New Republic Intelligence cracked the pattern behind the attacks and shut down Project Minefield before it could cause further havoc.

In an unprecedented move, the New Republic formed a loose alliance with the Empire to wipe out Zsinj. The Imperial fleet had its own anti-Zsinj task force, led by Admiral Rogriss. A New Republic representative held a secret meeting with Rogriss aboard his flagship, and the two sides hammered out an uneasy agreement—each side would exchange all intelligence data it had gathered on Zsinj's organization, no strings attached. The Empire and the New Republic now viewed Zsinj as their common foe.

Growing frustrated at the length of the campaign and the paucity of his victories, Han Solo authorized a number of lures to draw out Zsinj and force a confrontation. Since the warlord increasingly regarded the conflict as a personal showdown between himself and Solo, a mock-up of *Millennium Falcon* was constructed and flown to worlds deep in Zsinj's territory. This vessel was later fitted with a bomb and used to destroy an enemy Dreadnaught.

Zsinj, however, did not take the bait. He realized the Imperial–Republic collaboration was crippling his ability to hold his kingdom together, and devised a secret stratagem of survival. Since his enemies seemed fixated on the destruction of *Iron Fist,* Zsinj resolved to give them the illusion of what they craved. His agents gathered up the wreckage of the Super Star Destroyer ruined at Kuat and pieced it back together in a hodgepodge of structural beams and hull plates. On the bow of the makeshift vessel they printed the words IRON FIST, then waited for the warlord's orders.

Solo and Rogriss collaborated on an assault in the Va-

haba asteroid belt that severely damaged the real *Iron Fist.* The wounded Super Star Destroyer jumped to the nearby system of Selaggis, but Solo followed with his full fleet, intent on blasting Zsinj into vapor. As *Mon Remonda* closed to firing range, the crippled *Iron Fist* disappeared into a black cube of nothingness.

Warlord Zsinj had obtained an orbital nightcloak—a string of satellites that absorb all visible light. By deploying the nightcloak in a cube pattern, he had created a small hideaway that his enemy's sensors couldn't penetrate. The decoy Star Destroyer was already in position inside the nightcloak, and Zsinj triggered its destruction. Then *Iron Fist* jumped to hyperspace.

When the nightcloak collapsed, Solo saw the wreckage of a Super Star Destroyer that clearly bore the markings of *Iron Fist.* Confident that Zsinj's fleet had been crippled beyond recovery, Solo ordered a triumphant return to Coruscant.

THE HAPANS AND THE DATHOMIR NIGHTSISTERS
8 A.B.Y.

General Han Solo and *Mon Remonda* returned to Coruscant after their seeming victory over Warlord Zsinj. The arduous, five-month campaign had exhausted everyone in the task force, and Han planned to put his crew in for some much-needed downtime. When he arrived at the capital world, however, he was startled to see dozens of saucer-shaped Battle Dragons in orbit. The mysterious Hapans had made a social call.

Any description of the Hapes Consortium requires superlatives—it is the most powerful, wealthy, cultured, and standoffish political federation in its region of space. Three thousand years earlier, the Hapan Queen Mother had sealed the borders of the star cluster, and as Hapes developed in isolation behind the Transitory Mists, legends of its fantastic riches continued to grow.

Several months earlier, Councilor Leia Organa's diplomatic visit to the sixty-three Hapan worlds had convinced the Queen Mother Ta'a Chume to consider the possibility of a union with the New Republic. The Hapan honor fleet

circling Coruscant was a remarkable sight, the first time in millennia that the reclusive society had made significant outside contact.

In Coruscant's Grand Reception Hall the Hapan delegation presented Councilor Organa with many extravagant gifts, including several Imperial Star Destroyers captured by the Hapans during recent border skirmishes. But the final gift was the biggest surprise of all. Prince Isolder, the Queen Mother's son and heir, presented himself to Leia as a marriage suitor.

Leia was shocked, but politically savvy enough to realize the benefits of an arranged marriage between two political factions. Knowing that the Hapan navy and treasury could help greatly in ending the Galactic Civil War, Mon Mothma urged her friend to accept Isolder's offer.

General Solo, however, grew deeply jealous of the attention showered on his longtime love interest. Hoping to secure Leia's affection, he won a habitable planet, Dathomir, worth 2.4 billion credits, in an outrageously high-stakes sabacc game. Han hoped the planet could house the homeless refugees of Alderaan. Unfortunately, Dathomir was deep in the heart of Zsinj's territory. Disappointed that his gamble had failed and desperate to get Leia's attention, Solo impulsively resigned his general's commission and kidnapped her.

Millennium Falcon emerged from hyperspace near the blue-green world of Dathomir. There, Solo discovered that Zsinj had built an orbital stardock above the planet, where the Super Star Destroyer *Iron Fist* was undergoing reconstruction. The *Falcon* fell under attack and barely managed to touch down on Dathomir's forested surface.

The group headed off on foot through the woods, but they were soon intercepted by a patrol of female warriors belonging to the Singing Mountain Clan. These Witches of Dathomir rode trained rancors and could cast "magic spells" by tapping into the Force. They were the descendents of

The Nightsisters—Sith witches of Dathomir
[Art by Tommy Lee Edwards]

Warlord Zsinj
[ART BY JOHN VAN FLEET]

Isolder of Hapes on a rescue mission to Dathomir. The two men discovered the rusting wreck of the *Chu'unthor* and met Teneniel Djo, a beautiful witch of the Singing Mountain Clan. She reunited them with Han and Leia.

But their problems were far from over. The Nightsister clan launched an attack on the Singing Mountain Clan in an effort to steal the *Falcon*. The Nightsisters wielded dark side powers, and had an army of Imperial slaves at their disposal. Eight years earlier, the Emperor had constructed a prison on Dathomir, but when he'd learned of the Nightsisters, he had destroyed all of the prison's starships from orbit—better to lose a prison than to let rival Force users loose upon the galaxy. The Nightsisters were desperate to escape their planet, and directed their prison army in a fierce but ultimately futile attack on the Singing Mountain stronghold.

THE DEATH OF ZSINJ
8 A.B.Y.

Warlord Zsinj was well aware of the existence of the Nightsisters and the depth of their power. He opened negotiations with Gethzerion, leader of the Nightsisters, and delivered an ultimatum. Gethzerion would give him Han Solo, or he would activate his orbital nightcloak—the light-absorbing device used at the Battle of Selaggis. A full array of nightcloak satellites in position around Dathomir would turn the planet into an ice ball within days.

When he learned that the Nightsisters' attack on the Singing Mountain Clan had failed, Zsinj activated the nightcloak to encourage Gethzerion's immediate compliance. The skies grew dark and the temperature plunged as the shrewd Witch made her counteroffer. Gethzerion agreed to provide Han Solo, but also asked for a ship to escape her dying planet. Zsinj agreed to send two ves-

Allya, the fallen Jedi Knight who had been exiled to the planet more than six centuries in the past, and they had been largely ignored since Quinlan Vos's investigation into the Infinity Gate incident prior to the Clone Wars.

Luke Skywalker, meanwhile, had been scouring the galaxy for lost secrets of the Jedi Order. On Toola he discovered data cards telling the story of Master Yoda's efforts to recover the Jedi training ship *Chu'unthor* from Dathomir. Skywalker returned to Coruscant and learned of his sister's kidnapping; before long he had agreed to team up with Prince

sels—an armed craft for transporting Solo, and a defense-less, stripped-down model for the Nightsisters to use as they pleased.

Han Solo was brought to the Imperial prison, where Zsinj's twin shuttles were landing. Gethzerion turned traitor, killing all the Imperial guards—including Zsinj's longtime aide, General Melvar—with a crushing blow of Force energy. Solo was saved from certain death by the timely arrival of the *Falcon,* but Gethzerion and her followers escaped on the armed shuttle. Two of the warlord's Star Destroyers intercepted the Nightsisters just outside the planet's atmosphere. After a brief but withering crossfire, all that remained of the shuttle was a cloud of glowing metal.

The Nightsisters were gone, but Zsinj's fleet still barricaded Dathomir. *Millennium Falcon* knocked out the orbital nightcloak, and the full battle fleet of the Hapes Consortium arrived to take on *Iron Fist* and dozens of Zsinj's smaller warships. During the chaos, Solo flew the *Falcon* straight at the bridge of *Iron Fist* and released a pair of concussion missiles at point-blank range. Warlord Zsinj was vaporized in an instant. The Battle of Dathomir was over.

In the aftermath, Singing Mountain Clan Mother Augwynne united the Witch clans of Dathomir and petitioned for planetary membership in the New Republic. Luke Skywalker was given a box filled with log recorder disks from the *Chu'unthor* wreckage, which would prove invaluable when he established the Jedi academy three years later.

Prince Isolder of Hapes had fallen madly in love with Teneniel Djo of the Singing Mountain Clan, an arrangement that outraged Queen Mother Ta'a Chume. Nevertheless, Isolder soon married Djo, making her the heir apparent to the throne of the Hapes Consortium. Isolder and Djo soon had a daughter, Tenel Ka, who proved to be very strong in the Force.

The adventure on Dathomir had resulted in Han Solo and Leia Organa growing even closer to each other, and they agreed to be married upon their return to Coruscant. The wedding was held in the Alderaanian consulate building on Coruscant, attended by hundreds of friends and dignitaries, and watched on holovid by billions across the galaxy. The two honeymooned on the scenic Corphelion asteroid resort.

PICKING UP THE PIECES
8.5 A.B.Y.

With such a promising start, the prospect of full cooperation between the Hapes Consortium and the New Republic had a disappointing denouement. Prince Isolder had vowed to join the New Republic after the Dathomir incident, a pledge that did not sit well with the Hapan Royal Court and the individual planetary potentates. Queen Mother Ta'a Chume was only too willing to bend to the court's will in the interest of preserving internal stability. Hapes promised to commit their full Battle Dragon armada "in due time." Mon Mothma's hoped-for strategic alliance never materialized.

The sudden implosion of Warlord Zsinj's domain emboldened the Imperial fleet. The coalition of advisers that had supplanted Isard had worked just as furiously as the New Republic in an effort to eliminate Zsinj. Now that that goal had been achieved, Admiral Rogriss and other fleet commanders moved to seize the newly liberated territory, all pretense of former partnership abandoned.

One benefit of the Hapan incident was the New Republic's acquisition of the several new Star Destroyers presented to Leia Organa during the Coruscant reception. These warships, added to the Star Destroyers that the New Republic had already captured, gave the fleet some formidable muscle. Admiral Ackbar led the New Republic ships to the Outer Rim to fight over the scraps of Zsinj's empire.

Ackbar and Rogriss ran directly into a *third* fleet—that of Warlord Teradoc, the self-appointed High Admiral of the Mid Rim. The New Republic Star Destroyers were thrown into the worst of the fighting, and consequently took the brunt of the punishment. Most of the Hapan ships, as well as the Star Destroyer *Crynyd,* were destroyed. The *Emancipator* and *Liberator* suffered severe damage and were recalled to undergo extensive repairs at the Hast shipyards. At the Battle of

Storinal, Princess Leia's flagship *Rebel Dream* was mercilessly shelled by the Imperial Star Destroyer *Peremptory* and recaptured by the Empire, its crew of thirty-seven thousand taken prisoner. Luckily, Organa Solo was on Coruscant at the time of the incident.

But for every hit the New Republic took, they gave it back to the Empire threefold. Admiral Rogriss lost the majority of the engagements. Bloodied, Rogriss ordered a retreat. Warlord Teradoc, whose hit-and-run strikes had made him an exasperating gadfly, also scurried back to his own territory. Admiral Ackbar charged into the region and fortified his newest gains.

The New Republic at last captured Kuat, giving access to the system's unparalleled shipbuilding docks, though damage to the yards was so extensive that new construction was delayed indefinitely. Unfortunately, the Kuat Drive Yards design team escaped to the Deep Core aboard the half-completed warship *Eclipse*. But with the seizure of Kuat and its subsidiary systems, the New Republic now controlled three-quarters of the settled galaxy.

During the relentless battles, the Republic and Empire had both suffered grave fleet losses. The construction and acquisition of new warships became a top priority for both sides.

RETURN TO TATOOINE
8.5 A.B.Y.

As Han and Leia settled into their marriage, the question of children reverberated among the HoloNet news outlets. Would two of the Rebel Alliance's greatest heroes give rise to a new generation of champions? For Leia, the answer was emphatically no. All too aware of the legacy of her biological father, a part of her saw too much risk in continuing the bloodline.

Although the Force spirit of Anakin Skywalker had appeared to Leia during the truce at Bakura, she still knew almost nothing about the man whose genes she carried. Leia got the chance to connect with the forgotten branch of the Skywalker family tree on a visit to Tatooine. Auction-

Han Solo and Leia Organa Solo gain clues to the past in Tatooine's Tusken Raider "ghost oasis." [ART BY TOMMY LEE EDWARDS]

eers in the city of Mos Espa had announced the impending sale of the Alderaanian moss-painting *Killik Twilight,* which depicted the insectile species that had inhabited Alderaan before human colonization. Leia was one of the few who knew that the lost masterpiece concealed an encrypted Shadowcast key containing codes once in use by the Rebel Alliance. If the Imperials bought the painting at auction and decrypted its contents, it could imperil dozens of New Republic deep-cover operations.

Arriving at Tatooine in *Millennium Falcon,* Han and Leia tried to bid on the *Killik Twilight,* but couldn't match the sum offered by Commander Quenton of the Star Destroyer *Chimaera.* Determined to destroy the painting rather than let the enemy take possession, Leia tried to incinerate it with a grenade. One of the attendees, a local man named Kitster Banai, saved the painting and fled on a swoopbike.

In their efforts to recover the *Killik Twilight,* Leia and Han met many people who had known Anakin Skywalker when he was only a nine-year-old slave and a gifted Podracer. Kitster Banai had been one such associate. Others willing to share their stories included the Rodian trader Wald (now running Watto's junk shop in Mos Espa) and the younger sister of Beru Whitesun, the woman who had raised Luke as his "Aunt Beru," and been present when Anakin Skywalker had buried his mother, Shmi. At the moisture farm where Luke had grown up, the new owners, the Darklighters, welcomed Leia and gave her a video diary that had once belonged to Shmi. Watching Shmi narrate the entries, Leia became acquainted with her grandmother, and learned what had transpired in the ten years between Anakin joining the Jedi and Shmi's death at the hands of Tusken Raiders.

Leia and Han—intermittently assisted by a trio of furry Squib con artists—caught up with Kitster and the *Killik Twilight* at a sacred Tusken oasis. It was here that Anakin Skywalker had slaughtered an entire village in retaliation for the torture and murder of his mother. Through the Force,

Leia could sense the pain, rage, and blood that permeated the sand as a psychic stain. The Sand People would have sacrificed Kitster Banai to the vicious "ghost" they believed still haunted the oasis, but Han and Leia rescued him and escaped offworld. The *Killik Twilight,* its Shadowcast key destroyed, ended up in the greedy paws of the Squibs.

Although the crimes of Vader were unforgivable, Leia's time on Tatooine had given her an understanding of the choices that had led Anakin Skywalker down the path of evil and, in his final moments, allowed him a last shot at redemption. No longer worried that her children might carry a dark mark of destiny, Leia made plans with Han to start a family. Soon afterward, she learned that she was pregnant—with twins.

PART SEVEN

Empire Resurgent

The Imperial dominion had been reduced to a mere quarter of what Palpatine had once called his own, most of it in out-lying sectors along the Rim. The surviving Moffs were forced to fight the Republic on one front, while simultaneously keeping their beloved Empire from splitting into ideological factions under squabbling warlords.

Since Imperial forces had suffered decisive defeats at Endor and Coruscant, overconfident New Republic prog-nosticators predicted the imminent end to all Imperial resis-tance—but the wheels of the Empire continued to turn, even in secret. The next two years very nearly saw the death of the New Republic.

THE DEPREDATIONS OF GRAND ADMIRAL THRAWN
9 A.B.Y.

The ailing Empire needed a miracle. It got one when a brilliant military commander emerged from the Unknown Regions—Thrawn, the last of the Emperor's Grand Admirals, who had been in isolation since before the Battle of Endor. Upon his return, Grand Admiral Thrawn picked the Imperial Star Destroyer *Chimaera* as his flagship, making Captain Pellaeon his de facto second in command. This fur-ther elevated Pellaeon in the eyes of the Moffs.

For six months, Thrawn reorganized the fleet and ex-ecuted strategic raids along the Republic–Imperial border. It had been Thrawn who had led the efforts to recover the *Killik Twilight* from Tatooine. While these incursions were not sufficient to panic the New Republic, they deeply impressed the Moffs, governors, and other political leaders. Thrawn was effectively handed the reins of the Empire.

Thrawn consolidated loyal Imperial forces and margin-alized warlord fiefdoms such as Admiral Krennel's domain and Grand Moff Kaine's Pentastar Alignment. Before long, he made his first overt strike against the New Republic, capturing key information from the library world of Obroa-skai. Analysis of the data led him to Wayland, site of the Emperor's secret Mount Tantiss storehouse. On Wayland, Thrawn collected three items that would soon devastate the New Republic.

The first was a functional cloaking device, an offshoot of the Project Vorknkx research conducted before the Em-peror's demise. The second was an array of Spaarti cloning cylinders stored deep in the bowels of Mount Tantiss—tech-nology that the Emperor had adapted for his own uses in the Deep Core. The third item was the mad Jedi Joruus C'baoth, apparently a clone of the Jorus C'baoth who had led the Outbound Flight mission. C'baoth had been stranded on Wayland for years and had gone completely insane. Grand Admiral Thrawn, protected by the Force-blocking abilities of ysalamiri lizards, secured C'baoth's cooperation by promising him that he could deliver Luke Skywalker and Leia Organa Solo, as well as Leia's unborn twins. The lunatic Jedi Master wanted to mold them into his evil, twisted apprentices.

Joruus C'baoth held up his end of the bargain, Force-linking the ships of Thrawn's fleet into a supernatural fight-ing force. Grand Admiral Thrawn was determined to fulfill his part of the deal. Twice, he dispatched teams of Noghri death

Grand Admiral Thrawn, with an ysalamiri, plots the defeat of the New Republic from the bridge of the Chimaera. [ART BY TOMMY LEE EDWARDS]

commandos to kidnap Luke Skywalker and Leia Organa Solo, but both attempts failed.

Thrawn activated the cloning complex and produced thousands of clone soldiers; he also sent a Spaarti cylinder to his secret base on Nirauan in the Unknown Regions to produce a clone of himself. The use of Force-blocking ysalamiri allowed him to grow clones in mere days, instead of the years that the process had taken during the Clone Wars. However, though he had an endless supply of loyal vat-grown troopers, he did not have the military infrastructure to outfit and transport them to the battlefield. In the aftermath of the post-Zsinj campaign, both the Empire and New Republic were desperate for starships.

Thrawn developed a novel way to restock his fleet and simultaneously rob the New Republic of much of its own. Mole miners, compact burrowing vehicles, could drill through a starship's hull. The Grand Admiral planned to steal dozens of mole miners, then use them to dispatch armed boarding parties onto every New Republic warship stationed at the Sluis Van shipyards.

Unfortunately for the galaxy's unluckiest entrepreneur, Thrawn chose the planet Nkllon for his mole miner raid. Lando Calrissian had invested millions of credits into the construction of Nomad City, a mobile mining complex that remained on the cool shadow side of the planet throughout Nkllon's ninety-day rotation. Nomad City had just begun to turn a profit when one of Thrawn's Star Destroyers arrived, stealing fifty-one of the expensive mole miners.

After the calamity, Calrissian accompanied Han Solo to Myrkr, the base of operations for smuggling kingpin Talon Karrde. Solo hoped to convince Karrde to ship cargo for the New Republic. Neither man realized, however, that Talon Karrde had a very familiar figure locked up in a storage silo.

Several days prior, Luke Skywalker's X-wing had been yanked out of hyperspace by an Interdictor cruiser and severely damaged by Thrawn's flagship. When Skywalker was picked up by Karrde's personal freighter, the smuggling chief remembered the sizable Imperial bounty on his captive's head and imprisoned Luke at his base.

Shortly after the arrival of Solo and Calrissian, Luke es-caped and stole a Skipray blastboat, but Mara Jade, Karrde's second in command, pursued in a second blastboat. The high-speed chase ended when the two ships collided and crashed, and Luke and Mara were forced to hike through Myrkr's dense forest for three days. Mara revealed that she had once been an Emperor's Hand in the service of Palpatine, and since Luke was indirectly responsible for the Emperor's death, she had vowed to kill him. But Mara put aside her homicidal impulses until they reached Hyllyard City at the edge of the forest, where Karrde's men rescued them from an Imperial scout patrol. Karrde's actions placed him squarely on the side of the New Republic.

Luke, Lando, and Han Solo departed Myrkr and headed for Sluis Van. Coincidentally, they arrived just as Grand Admiral Thrawn unleashed his fleet on the shipyards, using his new cloaking device to increase the element of surprise. Commander Wedge Antilles and Rogue Squadron fought against the enemy starfighters, but Lando realized that his stolen Nkllon mole miners had drilled into the docked vessels. Once inside, commando teams leapt out and seized control of the bridges. Within minutes, dozens of hijacked capital ships pulled out of their berths and headed toward a hyperspace jump point on the fringe of the system. Lando transmitted a master control code that reactivated all the mole miners simultaneously. The machines began to drill again, grinding through the navigation and propulsion controls. Thrawn was forced to retreat without his prize.

THE NOGHRI SWITCH SIDES
9 A.B.Y.

Leia Organa Solo had sat out the Battle of Sluis Van on the Wookiee homeworld of Kashyyyk, in order to protect herself from Thrawn's Noghri kidnapping teams. The Noghri attacked a third time, but the Wookiees took one of them captive. From this solider, Khabarakh, Leia learned that the Noghri revered Darth Vader for his help in restoring their homeworld of Honoghr after its poisoning during the Clone Wars. The Noghri had served Vader, and later Thrawn, as death commandos. What the Noghri did not realize was that the Imperial restoration teams had deliberately *kept* Honoghr in a state of ruin, thus ensuring that the Noghri remained in the Empire's thrall indefinitely.

As the daughter of Darth Vader, Leia suspected she might be able to bring the aliens around through diplomacy. Bringing Chewbacca and C-3PO, she traveled with the captured Noghri, and surveyed Honoghr's endless plains of scorched grass. Before long, Leia uncovered the Empire's trickery and demonstrated the proof to a square filled with angry Noghri, dramatically winning them over to her side.

Immediately, word was sent to all Noghri death commandos out on missions for the Empire. They either secretly abandoned their assignments and returned to Honoghr, or attempted to sabotage the Empire's aims before being killed. News of the Imperial treachery even reached the Star Destroyer *Chimaera,* where the Noghri warrior Rukh worked as Grand Admiral Thrawn's bodyguard. Rukh chose to bide his time, waiting for the appropriate moment to take revenge on the deceivers of his people.

The Katana Fleet and the Clone Troopers
9 A.B.Y.

Thrawn's machinations were not limited to military maneuvers; he also manipulated financial records and banking transactions to make it appear that Admiral Ackbar, the commander of the New Republic fleet, was guilty of treason. At the urging of the Bothan Councilor Borsk Fey'lya, Ackbar was placed under house arrest until the matter could be resolved.

Solo and Calrissian decided to investigate, and they ended up encountering three vintage Dreadnaughts under the command of General Garm Bel Iblis. In the nine years since he had quit the Rebel Alliance, the legendary Corellian Senator had built up a private army. His hit-and-run strikes against the Empire were successful, but limited in scope. His stubborn pride, and simmering anger toward Mon Mothma, had prevented Bel Iblis from joining the New Republic.

Bel Iblis's Dreadnaughts came from the *Katana* fleet. The two hundred *Katana* Dreadnaughts had been the object of countless "lost treasure" hunts for generations, but now, with both sides in the Galactic Civil War desperately in need of warships, the acquisition of the lost armada could easily tip the scales. While Bel Iblis did not know the location of the fleet, he had a contact who did; unfortunately, before Solo and Calrissian could meet with him, Grand Admiral Thrawn apprehended the man.

Fortunately, the smuggling chief Talon Karrde also had discovered the location of the *Katana* fleet. The New Republic hastily threw together a strike team and arrived at the point in space where the forgotten Dreadnaughts had been drifting battle broke out as Luke Skywalker and Han Solo boarded the

Smuggling kingpin Talon Karrde
[Art by John Van Fleet]

flagship *Katana*. Unexpected reinforcements—General Garm Bel Iblis and his Dreadnaughts, along with members of Talon Karrde's smuggling organization—briefly bolstered the New Republic, but the Imperials called in their own reserves.

Aboard the flagship, Han Solo remembered that the *Katana* fleet had been primarily slave-rigged. The slave controls in the *Katana's* bridge allowed Solo to reactivate one of the idle Dreadnaughts and remote-steer it straight into the nose of the Star Destroyer *Peremptory*. Both ships exploded in a spectacular fireball, and Thrawn's Imperials fled.

The New Republic's victory was dampened by two pieces of sobering news. Out of the original two hundred Dreadnaughts, only fifteen remained—the others were already in Imperial hands. The second grim reality came to light after examining the bodies of the dead stormtroopers aboard the *Katana*. Each corpse shared the same face.

In the five years since the Empire's defeat at Endor, the cloning technology that had once produced legions of stormtroopers had vanished, made useless by dwindling resources or destroyed outright in accordance with Emperor Palpatine's posthumous orders. The surviving clone stormtroopers perished through attrition, and, for years prior to the Thrawn incident, the stormtrooper corps had been composed almost exclusively of conscripts and recruits. The idea that Grand Admiral Thrawn had resurrected this lost science terrified the New Republic, particularly the news that he had found a way to grow fresh clones in a matter of days. Mon Mothma and the others envisioned a new round of Clone Wars, this time with Coruscant on the losing side, and made the uncovering of Thrawn's cloning complex their top priority.

Admiral Ackbar was reinstated as fleet commander, the financial scandal having been revealed as an Imperial setup. On Coruscant, Leia Organa Solo gave birth to twins, a boy and a girl—Jacen and Jaina—who were to join the new generation of Jedi Knights.

Because she had been an Emperor's Hand, Mara Jade had known many of Palpatine's secrets—including the location of the Mount Tantiss cloning facility on Wayland. Mara led Luke Skywalker, Han Solo, Chewbacca, Lando Calrissian, and their

droids to Wayland to destroy Thrawn's ready-made soldier factory. Upon reaching Mount Tantiss, Luke and Mara headed for the Emperor's throne room. Waiting for them on the throne, like an arachnid at the center of its web, was Joruus C'baoth.

The demented Jedi Master was easily a match for both Skywalker and Jade combined. While he toyed with them, he unleashed a shocking surprise: C'baoth had grown a special clone from Skywalker's own genetic material, taken from the hand Luke had lost at Cloud City. The mindless drone, Luuke Skywalker, was his exact duplicate.

The clone had a lightsaber as well—the blue-bladed saber that had once belonged to Anakin Skywalker, a weapon that had been considered lost since the tragic events in Cloud City. The doubles squared off in a frenzied duel. Though she had often expressed her desire to murder the man who had brought about the Emperor's death, Mara Jade ended the combat by killing the Luuke clone. C'baoth, in a fit of rage, collapsed the chamber's ceiling, but Mara skewered him cleanly through the torso.

Deep in the lower levels, Lando Calrissian and Chewbacca sabotaged the central equipment column of the cloning complex, triggering an irreversible overload spiral. The infiltration team escaped just as Mount Tantiss exploded spectacularly.

The laboratory's destruction meant the loss of priceless artworks and historical artifacts stored in the Emperor's private vaults. It also seemed to bury forever all evidence of Bothan involvement in the devastation of Caamas, much to Councilor Borsk Fey'lya's relief. More than a decade would pass before a data card plucked from the rubble would stir up old animosities and touch off a galaxywide search for the Caamas Document.

THRAWN'S FALL
9 A.B.Y.

Grand Admiral Thrawn seemed infallible in his military strategy. While the Emperor had used cloaking devices for the straightforward purpose of disguising warcraft (as in the experimental "Phantom TIE" project), Thrawn relished devising ingenious, nonstandard uses for the invisibility screen. One ruse was to cloak a number of cruisers and slip them beneath a planet's energy shield. When an attacking

Star Destroyer fired at the shield, its lasers dissipated harmlessly. But the cloaked cruisers waiting beneath the shield at precise, predetermined locations would fire their own lasers simultaneously, creating the illusion that the Star Destroyer's lasers could punch through energy barriers. This trick worked so well that dozens of planets surrendered to the Empire without a fight.

Thrawn also used cloaking technology to create an innovative siege weapon. After fitting twenty-two asteroids with cloaking devices, Thrawn's Star Destroyers carried them to Coruscant, then dumped the invisible asteroids into close planetary orbit. The New Republic couldn't risk dropping Coruscant's energy shield lest one of the asteroids impact the heavily populated surface. Until they could find a way to eliminate the unseen obstacles, Coruscant was thoroughly blockaded.

Following this incident, Ackbar planned a retaliatory raid that would severely damage Thrawn's shipbuilding capability, as well as simultaneously net them a sophisticated gravfield detector that could pinpoint the asteroids' mass shadows. Thrawn learned of the raid, and was waiting for the New Republic armada when it emerged from hyperspace at Bilbringi.

Commander Wedge Antilles and Rogue Squadron led the fighter attack, while Ackbar launched withering cannonades from his capital ships. Talon Karrde's smuggling associates executed quick hit-and-fade strikes against the Imperial defense platforms, forcing Thrawn to split his forces. Nevertheless, it seemed only a matter of time before the Imperial noose drew tight.

The New Republic was handed a victory through chance. Thrawn's Noghri bodyguard Rukh, burning with anger toward the Empire ever since Leia Organa Solo's revelations on Honoghr, fatally stabbed his master through the heart. Rukh fled the scene and tried to reach a shuttlecraft, but was intercepted and executed by a stormtrooper squad under the command of Major Grodin Tierce.

Captain Pellaeon took command of the beleaguered Imperial fleet, but was smart enough to realize that he had no hope of winning the battle. Pellaeon ordered a full retreat, to live and fight again another day.

The Imperial fleet regrouped near the Unknown Regions while Pellaeon assessed the situation. Thrawn had captured an astonishing amount of territory, nearly doubling the size of the Empire, but it had been held together by his authority alone. Without a similarly charismatic leader, the union would splinter yet again. Pellaeon, while respected, was not such a leader. The Empire again reverted to warlordism, and the New Republic began recapturing its lost territory, planet by planet.

THE RETURN OF ISARD
9–10 A.B.Y.

While the New Republic reveled in the victory, ominous developments bubbled just beneath the surface. On Byss, in the Deep Core, Emperor Palpatine's spirit had finally recuperated from its difficult transition into a new clone body. Palpatine knew the New Republic had little interest in the Deep Core, since hyperlanes into the star-choked region were practically nonexistent. Protected from prying eyes, the resurrected Emperor secretly began contacting specific fleet commanders, warlords, and Moffs. Those who pledged fealty to their former master were rewarded; those who resisted were slaughtered. The secret Imperial war fleet swelled in size as new ships arrived daily.

The Deep Core warlords, particularly Harrsk and Delvardus, were among the first to join Palpatine's cause. Ysanne Isard also learned of the Emperor's return. Isard, who had been lying low since her "death" at Thyferra, was terrified of being executed for losing Coruscant to the enemy, and devised a strategy to win a place of honor for herself in Palpatine's new Empire. Her peace offering would be the Super Star Destroyer *Lusankya,* undergoing reconstruction in a New Republic dry dock.

New Republic forces were amazed at the ease with which they swept up small pieces of the Empire, as if the Imperial fleet had gone into hiding. The New Republic Provisional Council made its next goal the liberation of the Ciutric Hegemony, a region dominated by Imperial Admiral Krennel. According to New Republic Intelligence, the prisoners who had once suffered aboard the *Lusankya* were likely to be found within the borders of the Ciutric Hegemony. The New Republic leadership placed a high priority on recovering the *Lusankya* inmates, particularly General Jan Dodonna, Rebel hero of the Battle of Yavin.

A raid by Rogue Squadron ended in failure, but surprisingly, the Rogues were rescued by TIE defender pilots in the service of Ysanne Isard. Isard met with her old enemies and explained that she had as much stake in bringing down Krennel as they did—the warlord had betrayed her years

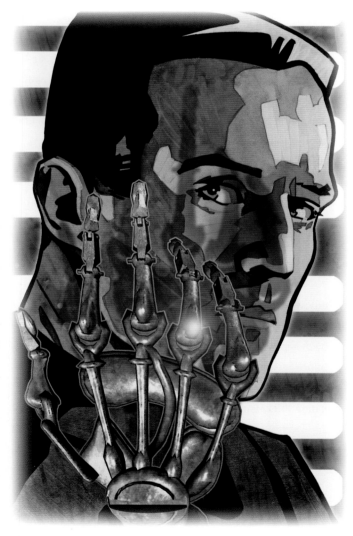

Admiral Delak Krennel
[Art by John Van Fleet]

before, and had stolen the *Lusankya* prisoners from under her nose. Worse, Krennel was in league with a clone of Isard, grown through unknown means years before Grand Admiral Thrawn had activated the Mount Tantiss cloning facility. In exchange for the destruction of her clone and the humiliation of Krennel, Isard agreed to assist Rogue Squadron members in their mission.

The Rogues posed as TIE pilots hoping to defect to Krennel's empire, while a New Republic commando team prepared to spring Dodonna and the other prisoners. Admiral Ackbar also commanded a substantial force of New Republic capital ships and support craft, drawn from the defenses around the Bilbringi Shipyards. All three groups coordinated their actions in a single, unified assault on Krennel's heavily defended throneworld of Ciutric.

Isard did not participate in the mission; instead, she treacherously struck the weakened defenses of the shipyards containing the *Lusankya*. Isard's handpicked infiltration team quickly seized the Super Star Destroyer's bridge and prepared to steer the monstrous vessel toward the nearest hyperspace jump point. Isard's treachery had not taken New Republic Intelligence entirely by surprise, though. Agent Iella Wessiri had prepared for a possible hijack and already had a team in place to prevent the theft. In a confrontation inside Isard's former quarters, Wessiri shot and killed the deranged Imperial. The *Lusankya* was recovered immediately afterward.

The attack on Krennel's base succeeded. The admiral and the Isard clone both died. The *Lusankya* prisoners were rescued and brought back to the New Republic for disease treatment and psychological evaluations. General Dodonna, however, adamantly refused all testing and insisted on an immediate meeting with Mon Mothma to discuss the current state of the Galactic Civil War. Dodonna formed a body of aged advisers called the Gray Cadre, which included such luminaries as Adar Tallon and Vanden Willard, and reassumed the role of senior military adviser as if he had never been gone.

Krennel's dominion crumbled without his leadership,

and the New Republic Navy pushed farther forward. In only a short time since the death of Thrawn, the Empire had lost nearly all of its recently won territory. Tasting victory, the New Republic Fleet advanced outward into the Imperially held sections of the Rim, leaving Coruscant and the Core Worlds relatively unprotected. Which was exactly how Emperor Palpatine wanted it.

THE RESURRECTION OF EMPEROR PALPATINE
10 A.B.Y.

In the six years following the Emperor's death at Endor, the New Republic had established itself as a governing force as well as a military power. But without the thousands of Jedi Knights who formed the backbone of the Old Republic, the political confederation remained a precarious one. At no point was that deficiency more obvious than during Palpatine's ghastly return—a nightmarish year of horror, calamity, and ruin.

Immediately after the defeat of Admiral Krennel, the Imperial fleet commanders joined with surviving members of the Emperor's ruling council, a development no one had predicted. The unified Imperial force launched from the Deep Core with stunning violence, surprising the New Republic, whose own fleet was hopelessly out of position in the Rim. Within days, the Imperials had conquered several key systems, forcing Mon Mothma to consider a last-ditch plan for the defense of Coruscant itself. She didn't get the chance.

An Imperial armada began a merciless bombardment of Coruscant's energy shield, waiting for the shield to buckle and break. Rather than see the civilian population decimated, Mon Mothma evacuated the capital world. Ralltiir, Chandrila, Esseles, and other key Core Worlds soon fell to the Imperials, and the leaders of the beleaguered New Republic returned to guerrilla fighting to battle their old enemy.

The resurrected Palpatine had done a better job of reuniting the Imperial factions than anyone before him, including Thrawn—only the Emperor could rule the Empire. Surviving warlords such as Harrsk, Delvardus, and Teradoc swore obedience to the same master and fought under the same banner, and even forces that did not yet know of Palpatine's return (such as the mainline Imperial forces under Pellaeon) fought alongside the warlords. The New Republic remained unaware of the identity of the mastermind behind the sudden unification.

Then suddenly, everything appeared to fall apart. Now that Coruscant was theirs, the factions of the Empire fell upon each other like nek battle dogs in a civil war to grasp control. The brief but bloody struggle, known as the Imperial Mutiny, involved the ruling council, the Moffs, the fleet, the Inquisitorius, COMPNOR, and the Imperial Security Bureau, each trying to claim the whole sabacc pot at the expense of the others. The New Republic seized this chance to create confusion among the feuding Imperials, using two captured Star Destroyers to conduct hit-and-run sorties into the war zones. Longtime Alliance hero Wedge Antilles was promoted to general, while other old warriors, including Han Solo and Lando Calrissian, reactivated their commissions and returned to the military. In one such raid over the battleground of Coruscant, the Alliance Star Destroyer *Liberator*, commanded by Luke Skywalker, Wedge Antilles, and Lando Calrissian, crashed into the planet's surface. Leia Organa Solo and her husband led a mission to rescue their comrades.

Taking *Millennium Falcon* into the heart of the battle zone, they found Antilles and Calrissian barricaded in and fighting for their lives. Then, with a swirl of Force, Jedi Luke Skywalker strode into the fray and single-handedly defeated an AT-AT walker. Luke had sensed an evil power reaching out to him, and warned his companions to stay back. A Force storm opened a hole in space, dragging Luke and R2-D2 into it.

Luke became a prisoner on Byss at the heart of the Deep Core. Eager to meet his captor, Luke learned that the dark side nexus he had sensed was none other than the cloned reincarnation of Emperor Palpatine himself. The Emperor, who had been unable to fully implement Darth Plagueis's teachings and cheat death through the Force, had settled for a lesser solution that required cloning technology to create host bodies.

Palpatine was allowing the Imperial Mutiny to rage on, considering it the culling of the weak from his forces, while

he prepared his own attack on the water world of Mon Calamari. Luke believed the only way he could ultimately defeat Palpatine was to use the Emperor's own knowledge of the dark side against him. Believing that he could destroy the dark side from within, Luke agreed to join Palpatine as the Emperor's new apprentice.

The government-in-exile of the New Republic had established a secret "Pinnacle Base" on the isolated moon of Da Soocha V at the heart of Hutt space. Here, Ackbar and Dodonna discussed the ongoing assault against Mon Calamari, which involved new superweapons called World Devastators. Designed by Umak Leth, one of the engineers involved with the Death Star project, these weapons consumed everything in their path, feeding automated manufacturing plants that then spewed out war machines. The combined military might of the ragtag New Republic rushed out to fight the World Devastators, and suffered terrible losses. The Alliance Star Destroyer *Emancipator* crashed into the resource-hungry Maw and became scrap.

Sensing that Luke had slipped into terrible danger, Leia set out to rescue her brother, despite being pregnant with her third child. Leia and Han first made a stop at the Smugglers' Moon of Nar Shaddaa. They hooked up with Solo's former girlfriend, Salla Zend, and an old smuggling buddy, Shug Ninx. Leia also came across a decrepit crone named Vima-Da-Boda, who had once been a Jedi.

Leia and Han won their way to Byss aboard Salla Zend's freighter, which was licensed to haul military cargo to the Deep Core. Once in port, Leia used the Force to guide them to the citadel where her brother reigned as the Emperor's protégé, but then they became Imperial captives. The Emperor visited Leia in her cell, revealing that he knew of Luke's plans to trick him, but was confident that he would win in the end. Playing on her emotions, Palpatine also said that his aging body would soon burn out from the dark forces he wielded—and that he wanted to shift his consciousness into

Rebel commandos lead an amphibious assault on the reborn Emperor's World Devastators. [ART BY TOMMY LEE EDWARDS]

the new baby that Leia carried in her womb. Revolted, Leia attacked the Emperor and escaped.

Salla Zend helped rescue them, but Luke claimed he had more work to do on Byss. He had, however, already loaded the override codes for the World Devastators into R2's memory circuits. New Republic forces used the data to complete their victory at Mon Calamari.

Before the decrepit Palpatine could use his sorcery to switch into one of his new clones, a grim Luke Skywalker marched into the laboratory chamber and smashed tank after tank. But Palpatine succeeded in transferring his consciousness to one of the last remaining clones, a strong and agile fifteen-year-old. Filled with dark side power, the reborn Emperor engaged Skywalker in a ferocious lightsaber duel—and forced the Jedi Knight into submission.

Broken and lost, Skywalker accompanied the victorious Emperor in his enormous flagship *Eclipse* to the New Republic stronghold on Pinnacle Base. There, the Emperor issued an ultimatum—he would destroy all the Rebels, unless the pregnant Leia Organa Solo agreed to come aboard his ship.

Leia boarded the *Eclipse,* but defied the Emperor and tried to bring Luke back to the light side. Her efforts allowed Luke to break the hold of evil, and they both turned against Palpatine. The desperate Emperor summoned up a huge Force storm, but he could no longer control what he had unleashed. As brother and sister fled, the conflagration consumed the gigantic black ship and, presumably, all that remained of the Emperor.

OPERATION SHADOW HAND
10 A.B.Y.

The Rebel triumph was to be short-lived. Palpatine had anticipated even this worst-case scenario and had hidden another of his clones in a secret location on Byss. His loyal forces already had a plan—Operation Shadow Hand—designed to subjugate the galaxy in a series of unstoppable assaults. Palpatine's military executor, Sedriss, led the operation, assisted by seven of the Emperor's most skilled Dark Side Adepts, a group he called his "Dark Jedi."

Executor Sedriss consolidated the forces remaining in the newly subjugated Core and Colonies regions. First, he targeted the weapons factories on Balmorra, which had turned against Imperial domination. But when Sedriss attacked the weapons world, massive new combat droids rebuffed his forces.

Upon returning to Byss, Sedriss found that two of the Emperor's Dark Side Adepts had turned traitor and completed destroying the clone laboratory, so they could control the Empire themselves without worrying about Palpatine's return. Fiercely loyal even in his master's absence, Sedriss killed the saboteurs and turned at last to see the Emperor reborn, in his only remaining clone body. Rewarded for his faith, Sedriss received the mission to track down Luke Skywalker and bring him back to the Emperor—alive.

Palpatine's traitorous adepts had not been working alone. Carnor Jax, one of the Emperor's crimson-armored Royal Guardsmen, had secretly trained in the Force under the Dark Lady Lumiya and had paid the Byss clonemaster to damage the genetic structure of all Palpatine's clones, knowing it would trigger a premature aging cycle and a quick death for the resurrected Emperor. Jax escaped Sedriss's notice, and quietly waited for his own chance to ascend the throne.

Meanwhile, Luke traveled to the abandoned space city of Nespis VIII, where he found Kam Solusar, a hard-bitten survivor of Darth Vader's Jedi Purge. Initially angry and reclusive, Solusar faced Skywalker in an ancient and risky Jedi game called lightsider. After Skywalker bested him, Solusar agreed to join the Jedi. Skywalker and Solusar proceeded to the ruined library world of Ossus, which had been obliterated by the Cron Cluster explosion during the Sith War. Amid the blasted rubble on Ossus, Skywalker and Kam Solusar found a group of primitive shamans, the Ysanna, who exhibited a weak and untrained ability to use the Force.

Before the two could complete their search for information, Executor Sedriss tracked them down. The Jedi and Ysanna warriors drove back the Imperial shock troops. Desperate, Sedriss took a young Ysanna woman, Jem, as a hostage, and backed up against a twisted tree. When the tree began to move, it revealed itself as Master Ood Bnar, who had clung to life since the firestorm had swept Ossus millennia ago. Ood destroyed both himself and Sedriss in a final confrontation.

Beneath the ruins of the dead Jedi, Luke uncovered a precious stockpile of ancient lightsabers. Taking this discovery as an omen, Luke allowed two of the young Ysanna—Jem and her brother Rayf—to accompany him and Solusar. Also intent on finding other Jedi Knights, Leia Organa Solo went to the underworld of Nar Shaddaa and tracked down the fallen Jedi Vima-Da-Boda, despite the intervention of Boba Fett. Along the way they also found another Jedi warrior, Empatojayos Brand, who had lost much of his body during an earlier battle with Darth Vader.

In the previous few months, Palpatine's weapons designer Umak Leth had completed a terrible new armament, the Galaxy Gun. In orbit around Byss, this weapon could fire hyperspace projectiles to any part of the galaxy and destroy any target. Palpatine launched the first projectile toward Pinnacle Base, hoping to destroy the Rebels with a single blow.

The projectile annihilated the hidden moon just as Luke returned from Ossus. The Rebel base exploded, but Mon Mothma and the core of the resistance had evacuated in time. The Emperor continued to launch his deadly projectiles, destroying unruly worlds and bringing the resistance to its knees. Within a short time, Palpatine had regained key territories in the Inner and Outer Rim. The future of the New Republic looked bleak.

Luke and his companions went to the secret world of New Alderaan, where the Solo twins Jacen and Jaina had been taken for protection. But the Emperor's commando forces struck there, too, killing Jem Ysanna. The survivors fled to the derelict space city of Nespis VIII, where Leia gave birth to her third child, named Anakin after her father.

When he discovered the location of the latest Rebel hideout, the Emperor launched yet another projectile from the Galaxy Gun. The surviving New Republic forces barely escaped before the ancient space city exploded. The ragged remnants of the cowed Alliance scattered across the galaxy, fleeing in separate small groups.

PALPATINE VANQUISHED
11 A.B.Y.

Though Palpatine seemed to be winning his war of conquest, his final cloned body had begun to fail him, aging at a rapid rate and eaten from the inside by the sabotage of Carnor Jax. He tried to clone other bodies so that he could resurrect himself again, but Jax's manipulations had tainted even the genetic source material. Palpatine's scientists and physicians could offer no solutions.

Attempting to find an answer, Palpatine journeyed to the Sith tomb world of Korriban, where the spirits of fallen dark lords informed him that he needed to find a Jedi body. They told him where to locate the newborn Anakin Solo, a child powerfully strong in the Force.

The Emperor brought his latest flagship, *Eclipse II*, to Onderon, where the Solos had taken their three children. While New Republic defenders attacked the Imperial juggernaut in orbit, Luke Skywalker and his Jedi companions sought out Palpatine himself. During the space battle, Lando Calrissian infiltrated the flagship and, using R2-D2's computer specialization, sabotaged the hyperdrive engines. *Eclipse II* took off into hyperspace, toward coordinates set to match the location of Umak Leth's Galaxy Gun. The out-of-control Imperial flagship crashed into the huge weapon, destroying both in a titanic collision. The Galaxy Gun's final projectile, pulled by the gravity of Byss itself, turned the central world of the Deep Core into space debris.

A final battle was fought on the surface of Onderon. Very sick and barely able to walk in his festering body, Palpatine demanded Anakin Solo as the new repository for his spirit. Luke Skywalker and the other Jedi joined the battle. Rayf Ysanna and Empatojayos Brand were both mortally wounded in the confrontation. Luke tried to take Palpatine alive—but Han Solo shot the old man with his blaster.

As the Emperor fell toward death yet again, he attempted to send his spirit into the baby Anakin—but Empatojayos

Brand intercepted the dark essence. Clasping himself to the light, Brand held the Emperor's presence within his body as they both succumbed to death.

With all of his clones destroyed, Emperor Palpatine was finally defeated. Without orders, the confused Imperial fleet went into retreat, abandoning Coruscant and other Core planets. Mon Mothma spread the news that the New Republic had once again regained control. To cement the victory, the leaders reestablished their capital on devastated Coruscant.

This fresh start allowed them to establish a new system of government. The Provisional Council and position of Chief Councilor had worked effectively in the past, but that system was now viewed as the government that had lost Coruscant to Palpatine. A new, more powerful single leader was desired, as well as a more clearly defined governmental hierarchy. Mon Mothma was elected Chief of State and President of the Senate. Leia Organa Solo was elected her second in command, the Minister of State.

JAX, KANOS, AND THE INTERIM COUNCIL
11 A.B.Y.

The Empire forged by Thrawn and expanded by Palpatine's clones collapsed at last, its death presided over by a former Royal Guardsman named Carnor Jax. Palpatine's scarlet-robed bodyguards had been trained on the harsh planet Yinchorr to show unswerving loyalty, but Jax's dreams of power had overcome his devotion. Jax had arranged for the insidious sabotage of Palpatine's clones, a shortsighted and selfish move. When the last clone finally succumbed on Onderon, the Empire was left without the iron ruler who had conceived and guided it. Jax, though, preferred to rule over a dying Empire than to serve in a thriving one.

The speed with which the Empire crumbled after Palpatine's final death was amazing, surpassing the mass confusion that had occurred following the Battle of Endor. Jax manipulated the creation of a thirteen-member Interim Council to succeed Palpatine, with himself a senior member.

Powerful alien leaders—including a Devaronian, a Whiphid, a Givin, and a Defel—were granted membership in the Interim Council, a remarkable move for the historically anti-alien Empire. Carnor Jax felt that alien strength might give new life to the dying Imperial military. Unfortunately, it was too little, too late.

Many fleets refused to follow the dictates of the council. Admiral Harrsk returned to his power base in the Deep Core and other warlords followed suit, realizing that the protected Deep Core offered an opportunity for them to regroup and plan their next course of action.

Carnor Jax and the Interim Council held the Empire proper, a narrow band stretching from the Outer Rim to the Colonies. But even this would not remain intact. The last of the Emperor's Royal Guardsmen, Kir Kanos, was everything Jax was not in terms of loyalty and devotion. Kanos had learned of Jax's culpability in Palpatine's death, and had survived the Jax-ordered massacre of the remaining Royal Guards on Yinchorr. Kir Kanos vowed to track down his former comrade-in-arms and execute him as a traitor.

On Phaeda, an Imperial holding in the Outer Rim, Jax's Star Destroyers attempted to capture Kanos, but he escaped to Yinchorr. Jax followed, leaving one of his ships at Phaeda, where it was surprised by General Wedge Antilles and the New Republic Super Star Destroyer *Lusankya*. After years of time-consuming repairs, the *Lusankya* had finally been launched in the wake of Operation Shadow Hand, and was still such a secret that many Imperials were unaware of its existence. Antilles, aided by Rogue Squadron, captured Jax's Star Destroyer and liberated Phaeda.

At Yinchorr, Kir Kanos used a booby-trapped assault bomber to annihilate Jax's flagship. On the surface of the barren world, Kanos and Jax faced off inside the abandoned Royal Guard training compound, a place of dark memories for both. On an elevated platform suspended above a bottomless pit, Kanos killed his rival, then vowed to avenge his master further by destroying every member of the sham Interim Council.

While Kanos began moving against his enemies, another

group was also trying to sabotage the council—the criminal organization Black Sun. The syndicate arranged to have several of the council members replaced with clones. After several assassinations had already thinned out the ranks of the council, the ranking member, Xandel Carivus, decided to disband the organization and rule alone as the new Emperor. Carivus was operating on the instructions of Nom Anor, an advance agent for the extra-galactic Yuuzhan Vong who was careful to keep his true allegiances a secret.

Carivus's actions angered Baron D'Asta, a pro-Imperial business leader who controlled the largest privately owned fleet in the galaxy. Baron D'Asta's fleet attacked the council headquarters on Ord Cantrell, forcing "Emperor" Carivus to sue for peace. In a confrontation on the planet's surface, Kir

Kanos executed the spurious Emperor.

With the Interim Council gone and most of the Imperial fleet disappearing into the Deep Core to form warlord allegiances, die-hard Imperial planets like the Academy world Carida were left with no significant defensive forces. Carida and many other worlds throughout the former Imperial jurisdiction drew in upon themselves, fortifying their planetary defenses to make any New Republic invasion difficult and costly. The New Republic chose to leave most of these "fortress worlds" alone, hoping that a lack of trade would eventually force them to open up their borders.

Pellaeon, now a vice admiral, reluctantly joined in with the Deep Core warlords as well. The Star Destroyer *Chimaera* had been severely damaged and abandoned in the capture

Royal Guardsman Kir Kanos fights Imperial troops on Phaeda.
[Art by Tommy Lee Edwards]

of Duro during Operation Shadow Hand; many of Pellaeon's most loyal and skilled officers had been killed. Lacking his core power base and his flagship, Pellaeon cast his lot with High Admiral Teradoc, who had lost his Mid Rim holdings, but now carved out a kingdom in the Deep Core. Teradoc possessed the largest intact military, and Pellaeon felt that this would provide a safe haven for his surviving fleet until the post-Palpatine confusion could be sorted out. Teradoc placed Pellaeon in charge of his Crimson Command, a huge flotilla of red-hulled *Victory*-class Star Destroyers.

Immediately following the resurrected Emperor's brutal assaults, the New Republic had ordered a sweeping new warship development program—the "New Class." During the days of the Rebellion, most of the Rebel warships were secondhand Corellian models, captured Imperial craft, or heavily modified noncombat vessels (such as Mon Calamari cruisers, originally built as pleasure liners). The ease with which Palpatine's clone was able to rout the New Republic fleet highlighted the need to replace these aging and outdated craft with dedicated combat vessels.

The New Class consisted of eight basic designs—the *Agave*-class picket ship, the *Warrior*-class gunship, the *Sacheen*-class light escort, the *Hajen*-class fleet tender, the *Majestic*-class heavy cruiser, the *Defender*-class assault carrier, the *Endurance*-class fleet carrier, and the *Nebula*-class New Republic Star Destroyer. The first finished ship of the New Class was the *Sacheen,* but it would be years before all eight designs were engineered and manufactured.

PART EIGHT

The Return of the Jedi Knights

SKYWALKER'S JEDI ACADEMY
11 A.B.Y.

After the final defeat of the resurrected Emperor, the New Republic understood the need to consolidate its political hold on the worlds of the New Republic. Luke Skywalker spoke before Mon Mothma and the Senate on the oratory floor of the former Imperial Palace. He voiced his dream to re-create the Jedi Knights, a beacon of hope in the old times, once nearly wiped out by Palpatine.

Though his own training had not been completed by Obi-Wan Kenobi or Yoda, Luke asked permission from the Chief of State to train others in the use of the Force. He knew that his sister Leia, her three children, Kam Solusar, the Witches of Dathomir, Kyle Katarn, and Mara Jade had all exhibited an aptitude for the Force. Surely, there must be others across the galaxy who showed similar, latent abilities.

Luke went to the volcanic planet Eol Sha, where he found a fiery-tempered leader named Gantoris. Next, he tracked down the cloud prospector Streen, living as a hermit in an abandoned floating city on Bespin. Later, he found Tionne, a woman with only a minor talent in the Force, but a great interest in the history of the Jedi.

He located other candidates, including the clone Dorsk 81, the warrior woman Kirana Ti from Dathomir, and Corran Horn from Rogue Squadron. New Republic Commander Kyle Katarn also joined the first batch of students, having spent the previous year battling Palpatine's Imperials and investigating a Sith temple on Dromund Kaas with Mara Jade, where he nearly fell to the dark side. Luke chose the abandoned Rebel base on Yavin 4 for his "praxeum," a place for the learning of action. In the temple ruins left by the ancient Massassi, Luke began to instruct his candidates in the ways of the Force.

MAW INSTALLATION
11 A.B.Y.

In an attempt to open a diplomatic dialogue with the glitterstim spice miners of Kessel, General Han Solo and Chewbacca visited the planet in *Millennium Falcon*. Since the fall of the Empire, freed inmates from Kessel's Imperial correctional facility had been running the operations; Solo hoped to convince the planet to join the New Republic.

Moruth Doole, a fat Rybet who had set himself up as Kessel's planetary governor, took Han and his Wookiee copilot prisoner. Doole sent his two captives to work in the spice mines, where they met fellow prisoner Kyp Durron. The young man had a strong affinity for the Force, having been trained by Vima-Da-Boda during her stay in the mines. Durron helped the two escape from Kessel, under hot pursuit by Doole's space navy.

In a desperate move, their vessel plunged into the navigational nightmare of the Maw black-hole cluster, where enormous gravity wells made a maze of hyperspace paths. Only Kyp's intuitive use of the Force allowed them to reach the gravitational stability at the center—a site that housed Maw Installation, Grand Moff Tarkin's secret weapons research facility. The skeleton of the Empire's prototype Death

Luke Skywalker and several members of his starting class at the Yavin 4 Jedi academy. [ART BY TOMMY LEE EDWARDS]

Star still orbited the asteroid laboratories, guarded by four Imperial Star Destroyers under the command of Tarkin's former lover, Admiral Daala.

Han Solo and his companions found themselves captured again, this time by an Imperial commander who had no inkling that the war was over and the Emperor dead. Admiral Daala refused to believe what her new captives told her. In prison, Han met Qwi Xux, a brilliant Omwati scientist who had helped develop the Death Star's workings along with Bevel Lemelisk and Umak Leth. Qwi Xux had recently developed an even deadlier weapon—the Sun Crusher—that could set up a supernova chain reaction in the core of a star.

Eventually, Han convinced Qwi Xux to turn against the Imperials and help them escape. Together, they stole the Sun Crusher and headed out of the black-hole cluster, protected from Daala's Star Destroyers by the vessel's quantum armor.

The Sun Crusher streaked out of the Maw cluster, running right into Moruth Doole's space navy. Doole's fleet collided with Daala's four Star Destroyers in a titanic and unexpected space battle, which destroyed one of Daala's vessels and most of the Kessel warships. Now unleashed from her confinement, Daala decided to make up for lost time. With her three Star Destroyers, she vowed to fight a guerrilla war against the New Republic.

POLITICAL TROUBLES
11 A.B.Y.

During a seemingly minor spat at a Coruscant diplomatic reception, Ambassador Furgan from the Imperial Academy world of Carida hurled his drink in Mon Mothma's face. It wasn't clear until later that Furgan had contaminated Mon Mothma with a slow-acting, specially tailored toxin that debilitated the Chief of State. As Mon Mothma grew gravely ill from the poison, rumors spread that she was dying.

A short time earlier, on a diplomatic mission to Vortex, Admiral Ackbar had made a piloting error and crashed into the Cathedral of Winds, killing hundreds of Vors. In disgrace, Ackbar had resigned from his duties and retired to his watery homeworld of Mon Calamari. Leia Organa Solo went to Mon

Calamari to talk to the retired admiral, hoping to convince him to return to his post in light of Mon Mothma's illness.

Admiral Daala's Star Destroyers began to prey on star systems, causing death and devastation. The renegade Imperial fleet struck Mon Calamari during Leia Organa Solo's search for Ackbar, bombarding the planet's floating cities from orbit. Ackbar was forced to take charge to defend his people, destroying another of Daala's Star Destroyers.

The ordeal had given a reticent Ackbar his catharsis, but he refused to return to Coruscant. His main duty was on his homeworld, helping his people rebuild. He would not take the place of the Chief of State, though Mon Mothma grew weaker every day.

EXAR KUN'S REVENGE
11 A.B.Y.

The continuing threats to the New Republic reinforced Luke Skywalker's need to reestablish the Jedi Knights. The training of candidates on Yavin 4 was, however, a process of trial and error. Kyp Durron joined the Jedi trainees, though Luke found a disturbing shadow in Kyp's personality.

Gantoris soon began to receive guidance from a grim spirit that haunted his dreams. Gantoris built his own lightsaber and challenged Master Skywalker to a duel. That night, Gantoris was found burned to a crisp, consumed by a black fire within himself.

Kyp Durron proved to be a phenomenal student who rapidly surpassed the other trainees. In the privacy of his quarters, Kyp encountered the same presence that had corrupted Gantoris: the spirit of Exar Kun, the long-dead Dark Lord of the Sith. Trapped within the Massassi temples for four thousand years, Exar Kun had been awakened by the new Jedi and their explorations of the Force. Restricted to his ethereal form, Kun increased Kyp's hatred of the Empire, brainwashing him to believe that he was the best hope for the salvation of the New Republic. Kyp took it upon himself to wipe out Admiral Daala's renegade fleet. Still manipulated by Exar Kun, Durron stole a ship and flew off alone.

The New Republic Senate had agreed to destroy the Sun

Crusher superweapon that they had recovered from Maw Installation. Their plan called for someone to deposit the quantum-armored ship in the high-pressure heart of the gas giant Yavin. Wedge Antilles and Qwi Xux sent the Sun Crusher into the swirling maelstrom, leaving Qwi as the only person alive with knowledge of the Sun Crusher's workings. But Kyp Durron tracked down Xux on Ithor, using his newfound dark side powers to wipe clean the weapons knowledge from her memory.

Now set on his course of action, Kyp returned to Yavin 4. Standing alone atop the academy's Great Temple, he summoned the Sun Crusher from the mists of Yavin. Luke Skywalker confronted him in a titanic duel of Jedi powers, but the spirit of Exar Kun joined with Kyp to overwhelm Master Skywalker, leaving him for dead. The Jedi students found their Master's motionless body, showing no breathing, no heartbeat, and no response.

Fleeing the scene, Kyp Durron piloted the Sun Crusher to the Cauldron Nebula, where Admiral Daala's fleet had hidden inside an ocean of coalescing gas. When Kyp triggered the superweapon, a cluster of stars went supernova, obliterating the third ship from Daala's original quartet of Star Destroyers. Kyp then reached Carida, the stormtrooper training center represented by Ambassador Furgan. Kyp issued an ultimatum: renounce the Empire or face complete destruction. When the planetary defenses mobilized instead of capitulating, Durron fired at Carida's sun, starting a chain reaction. The sun exploded, and its shock wave wiped out every living thing in the system. Ambassador Furgan escaped the destruction but was later killed in an abortive attempt to kidnap the youngest Solo child, Anakin, on the isolated world of Anoth.

At the Jedi academy, Luke Skywalker remained trapped in stasis for a month, neither dead nor alive. In fact, Luke had been freed from his body and was aware of his surroundings, though no one else could see him. Exar Kun's malevolent spirit possessed other Jedi students in failed at-

Admiral Daala
[ART BY JOHN VAN FLEET]

tempts to destroy Skywalker's physical form.

Once the true nature of Exar Kun's existence became known to the trainees, Skywalker's students pooled their newfound powers. In a final battle, fighting alongside the spirit-forms of Luke Skywalker and even the long-dead Jedi Master Vodo Siosk-Baas, the students vanquished Exar Kun for all time. Luke Skywalker returned to full health.

Kyle Katarn left the academy after the Exar Kun incident. His brush with the dark side on Dromund Kaas still fresh in his mind, he set aside his lightsaber and allowed his Force skills to atrophy. He would advise Luke in a military capacity only, until the Desann incident nearly two years later.

The Recapture of Maw Installation
11 A.B.Y.

Han Solo and Lando Calrissian tracked down Kyp Durron, urging him to cease his Sun Crusher rampage. Kyp attempted to destroy *Millennium Falcon,* but at the peak of his fury, the anger faded from him. The manipulative spirit of Exar Kun had been destroyed.

Realizing the magnitude of what he had done, he surrendered and agreed to return to Coruscant. After a hearing in which many voices were raised in opposition, an ailing Mon Mothma wielded her veto power. "You have the blood of billions on your hands, Jedi Knight, but I am not the one to judge you. Go to Yavin Four. Let the Jedi Master decide your punishment."

A repentant Kyp Durron asked Master Skywalker how he could find forgiveness. Luke announced that the Sun Crusher needed to be utterly obliterated, and that Kyp Durron must do it himself as an act of contrition. Together, they would go to the Maw cluster and plunge the superweapon into one of the black-hole singularities.

The New Republic assembled a force to return to Maw Installation, to liberate and take control of the weapons outpost. Joining the troops were Chewbacca, who wished to free the remaining Wookiee slaves at the research facility, and ex-researcher Qwi Xux. The occupation force picked its way through the black-hole cluster. Upon seeing the arrival of his enemies, the flustered Maw administrator Tol Sivron commandeered the Death Star prototype and escaped.

New Republic soldiers scoured through the unfinished work of Installation scientists, taking what they could. Before the New Republic forces could secure the station, a battered Star Destroyer appeared inside the Maw—the sole remaining ship of Daala's guardian fleet. Admiral Daala intended to take back Maw Installation, or die in the attempt.

Unlike Grand Admiral Thrawn, throughout her reign of terror Daala had never claimed to be a great military leader or strategist. She had no interest in ruling the Empire or governing conquered worlds—she knew that she couldn't win. Like a nek battle dog, she was willing to attempt even

suicidal plans. With all her remaining weapons, she fired upon the Installation as the occupation soldiers scrambled to protect themselves.

At the same time, Tol Sivron took the Death Star prototype out of the black-hole cluster to the adjacent Kessel system. He used the battle station's superlaser to wipe out some of the massed New Republic battleships, as well as to destroy Kessel's moon. Unbeknownst to Tol Sivron, Han Solo had managed to hide *Millennium Falcon* inside the Death Star's tangled superstructure. With Lando Calrissian and Mara Jade, Han sabotaged the Death Star's superlaser before Sivron could fire on Maw Installation.

Kyp Durron and Luke Skywalker arrived at the Maw cluster on their mission to destroy the Sun Crusher. Wanting to make up for the destruction he had caused, Kyp flew the Sun Crusher, leading the prototype Death Star in a moog-and-rancor game through the gravitational quicksand of the black-hole cluster. The Sun Crusher and the Death Star both plunged into the event horizon of a black hole, and both craft fell to their doom—though Kyp escaped the gravitational pull inside a tiny message pod.

Chewbacca led the offensive against Daala's remaining Star Destroyer. As the occupation force evacuated the Installation, Daala came in on a suicide run, firing on the facility's main power reactor. It exploded in a blinding flash, presumably destroying the Imperial ship, but Daala used the blinded sensors to make good her escape to the Deep Core territory of the major Imperial warlords.

On Coruscant, Mon Mothma's condition had grown progressively worse. In an unlikely gambit, the Force-strong Mon Calamari ambassador Cilghal worked for hours at Mon Mothma's deathbed. Focusing her powers, Cilghal was able to remove the insidious poison one molecule at a time. Though healed, Mon Mothma did not wish to continue as Chief of State, and nominated Leia Organa Solo as her successor.

Soon ratified by a popular vote, Leia assumed her role as leader of the New Republic. General Carlist Rieekan took up Leia Organa Solo's former post as Minister of State. Admiral Ackbar had regained his confidence as a military leader and offered his assistance to the new Chief of State. After years of turmoil, the New Republic looked forward to a time of recovery.

THE EMPEROR'S HAND AND THE SENEX LORDS
12 A.B.Y.

Following Admiral Daala's defeat and the destruction of the Sun Crusher, nearly a full year elapsed with few overt conflicts. Corran Horn, one of the Jedi trainees who had helped defeat the spirit of Exar Kun, left the academy in the middle of the Daala conflict to rescue his wife from Leonia Tavira, a pirate leader and former Imperial who coordinated her destructive raids from her flagship Star Destroyer *Invidious*. Over several months, Horn infiltrated the "Invid" pirates, where he fell afoul of Tavira's Jedi advisers. The presence of new Jedi intrigued Master Skywalker, and he teamed up with Horn on a successful rescue mission to Tavira's headquarters. The strange, reclusive Jedi sect called themselves the Jensaarai, and they traced their origin back several decades to the tutelage of Nikkos Tyris, an Anzati Dark Jedi. Despite their evil influence, the Jensaarai were not sinister, and Skywalker resolved to continue studying their unique approach to the Force.

Centralized Imperial authority had collapsed utterly. The warlords in the Deep Core engaged in open warfare among one another, entire battle fleets clashing amid the dense backdrop of stars. The New Republic adopted a wait-and-see attitude, hoping that the Imperials would eventually burn themselves out.

One warlord, Admiral Harrsk, began shuttling troops out of the Deep Core and amassing a force in the Atravis sector in the Outer Rim, where he was supported by several Imperial fortress worlds. While New Republic Intelligence kept a close eye on this development, they completely missed the ominous stirrings in the Senex and Juvex sectors of the Mid Rim.

Both the Senex and Juvex sectors are ancient aristocracies ruled by a multitude of houses. Emperor Palpatine kept only a token military force in the region, and the New Republic had no success in persuading the Senex Lords to take a more active role in galactic affairs. Their arrogance and sense of noblesse oblige prompted the Senex Lords to forge an alliance with Roganda Ismaren. The woman did not have a blue-blooded pedigree, but she answered to the title by which Palpatine had called her—Emperor's Hand.

Palpatine, of course, had employed many Hands. Arden Lyn had been among the first, and Mara Jade was arguably the best. Others had included Maarek Stele, Sarcev Quest, Blackhole, and Roganda Ismaren. Following the death of her Master, Roganda had gone to ground on the sleepy world of Belsavis. As the years passed, she trained her son Irek in the ways of the Force.

Irek was rumored to be the offspring of Palpatine himself, and had been implanted with a subelectronic converter allowing him to control any machine with a mere thought. Roganda also located a long-dormant Imperial battlemoon—*Eye of Palpatine*—and ordered her son to call the distant ship to Belsavis. The *Eye* was her bargaining chip with the Senex and Juvex Lords, and they had no choice but to listen.

Chief of State Leia Organa Solo made a goodwill visit to the Ceremony of the Great Meet on Ithor. A wild-eyed psychotic shattered the festivities, raving about "the children of the Jedi." Research into the subject revealed that Force-strong children had lived on Belsavis during the dark times, following the establishment of the Empire. Under cover of a diplomatic visit, Leia, Han, Chewbacca, and R2-D2 headed there to investigate, learning that eighteen years prior to the Battle of Yavin, dozens of Jedi younglings had been sheltered on Belsavis by Plett, a Ho'Din Jedi Master. The Emperor had sent the battlemoon to destroy them, but when *Eye of Palpatine* miraculously failed to arrive and carry out its assigned massacre of the settlement, Plett and the children had fled to parts unknown.

In Belsavis's Plawal rift domed city, Leia ran into Roganda Ismaren, whom she recognized from Palpatine's court. Roganda stunned Leia and took her prisoner, locking her in a room near the lip of the rift dome. Leia learned the details of the Ismaren plot, including *Eye of Palpatine*, the Senex and Juvex financial backers, and Irek's ability to scramble the electronics of attacking New Republic fighter craft. But when *Eye of Palpatine* finally emerged from hyperspace in the Belsavis system, Irek Ismaren found that he could no longer control it. Without guidance, the ship reverted to its original mission of complete planetary annihilation.

By the time things had settled down, the Ismarens had vanished to seek asylum within the Senex sector, and they eventually made their way to a laboratory on Coruscant, where Roganda subjected her son to further experiments. Irek Ismaren would not reemerge until the new Jedi order era.

EYE OF PALPATINE
12 A.B.Y.

The colossal, asteroid-shaped *Eye of Palpatine* had been constructed in an era when Palpatine had still found it necessary to hide the extent of his cruelty. His abominable action of wiping out every inhabitant in the Plawal rift—most of them children—would have caused untold outrage in the Senate had it become known. Instead, Palpatine had diverted governmental funds to construct the *Eye,* and ordered the ship's contingent of stormtroopers to await pickup on scattered worlds throughout the Outer Rim.

Luckily, Palpatine's plan never came to fruition. Thanks to the sabotage efforts of the Jedi Knights Geith and Callista, *Eye of Palpatine* had remained dormant in the Moonflower Nebula. The inhabitants of Belsavis escaped, and the waiting stormtroopers grew old and died. The *Eye* slept for thirty years until Roganda Ismaren found it. While Irek Ismaren used his subelectronic converter to summon the ship, Jedi Master Luke Skywalker boarded the *Eye* in the Moonflower Nebula and was inadvertently carried along for the ride.

Two of Luke's Jedi students—Cray Mingla and Nichos Marr—accompanied him. Both had recently joined the Yavin 4 praxeum: Mingla was a brilliant computer programmer and showed much promise as a Jedi, but her lover Nichos Marr had been diagnosed with fatal Quannot's syndrome. In order to preserve Marr's

life, Mingla had transferred his consciousness into the body of an amazingly life-like droid. She had hoped to parallel the Ssi-ruuvi "entechment" method of harnessing life-energy, but instead it appeared that she had accomplished little more than programming a droid with a false set of memories.

Trapped aboard the *Eye,* Luke and Cray Mingla were forcibly brainwashed by the ship's automated indoctrination equipment. Skywalker had the strength of mind to overcome the imprinting, but the other prisoners did not. *Eye of Palpatine* had attempted to fulfill its programming by picking up its stormtrooper contingent—but after three decades, the *Eye* had settled for whatever warm bodies it found in the appropriate places.

Callista
[ART BY JOHN VAN FLEET]

Two tribes of Gamorreans engaged in a full-scale clan war aboard the automated vessel. Talz, Kitonaks, Tusken Raiders, Affytechans, and other aliens aimlessly roamed the halls, waiting for orders. Jawas began ripping out wires, and a tribe of Tusken Raiders nearly killed Luke. While Luke pondered how to destroy the battlemoon before it could wipe out all life in the Plawal rift, a Jawa gave him a strange object they had found on board: a lightsaber.

Luke soon discovered that the saber's owner, Callista, had transferred her life-essence into the *Eye*'s central computer during her sabotage mission thirty years prior. Though they could communicate only through a computer screen, Skywalker soon realized that Callista—someone whose strength in the Force was as great as his own—was a woman with whom he could spend the rest of his life. The decision to destroy the *Eye* now meant that he would have to destroy Callista as well.

As time ran out, Luke managed to get the aliens loaded aboard escape shuttles. He steeled himself to trigger the *Eye*'s self-destruct, but Cray Mingla unexpectedly dropped him to the floor with a stun blast. Luke woke up on one of the fleeing lifeboats just in time to see *Eye of Palpatine* explode with a soundless roar.

During recovery operations above Belsavis, a team of workers discovered a life pod containing Cray's hibernating body. But the woman who opened Cray's eyes was *not* Cray Mingla. In the *Eye*'s final moments, Cray had voluntarily left her body and allowed Callista to step inside, using the same form of Jedi spirit transference that had allowed Emperor Palpatine to inhabit a succession of fresh clones.

An unexpected side effect of the transfer was Callista's sudden inability to touch the Force. For the moment, though, Luke and Callista were together in body as well as spirit.

THE DARKSABER THREAT
12 A.B.Y.

By this time, several of the Jedi had built their own lightsabers and become Knights of the Republic. New Jedi student Dorsk 81, an alien clone from Khomm, accom-panied Kyp Durron on a mission to Khomm. The planet lay at the fringes of the Deep Core, and Kyp wanted to check in on the current activities of the Imperial warlords.

Inside the Deep Core, Admiral Daala had been trying to unify the squabbling warlords into a full-fledged attack force. Not until she allied herself with Vice Admiral Pellaeon—Thrawn's former second in command—did she make any headway. Prepared to do anything necessary in the name of the Empire, Daala murdered thirteen of the strongest Imperial warlords, including Harrsk, Teradoc, Yzu, and Delvardus, and gathered their forces under her own banner. Before his death, Superior General Delvardus had constructed a Super Star Destroyer, *Night Hammer,* which Daala took as her own flagship. Aware of the battles that she would have to fight against the Jedi Knights, she renamed it *Knight Hammer.* Finally, having learned from mistakes of her first depredations, Daala coordinated her massive space fleet and prepared to launch against the New Republic.

At the same time, the Besadii Hutt clan—which had grown to dominate all the other Hutt clans over the previous decade—and the reborn Black Sun criminal syndicate had embarked upon a scheme of their own. The leader of both groups, Durga the Hutt, had established a secret construction base in the Hoth asteroid belt. Armed with the blueprints to the original Death Star and the expertise of engineer Bevel Lemelisk, Durga intended to build his very own superweapon.

The weapon, code-named Darksaber, was a bare-bones version of the Death Star's planet-destroying superlaser, similar in principle to the Empire's experimental *Tarkin* battle station. Small, simian taurill composed the construction force, using their hive mind to work as a single entity. But the taurill were easily distracted, and the Darksaber Project was beset by hundreds of small, but potentially catastrophic, design errors. Once the taurill had finished the Darksaber, Durga planned to extort protection money from star systems wherever he went.

Suspicious of Durga's activities, Chief of State Leia Or-

gana Solo arranged a diplomatic visit to the central Hutt world of Nal Hutta. A two-pronged military fleet accompanied her (ostensibly engaged in "war gaming exercises"), commanded by General Wedge Antilles and Admiral Ackbar. General Crix Madine, New Republic chief of covert operations, also slipped onto Nal Hutta. He used his espionage skills to plant a tracker beacon on Durga's ship.

Madine soon uncovered the Hutt hideout in the Hoth system. With a group of handpicked commandos, Madine went into the asteroid field to infiltrate the industrial assembly, and the team breached the Darksaber laser housing. Before he could sabotage the works, Madine became a prisoner; his team members died trying to buy his escape. Madine sent out an alarm via an implanted transmitter as the guards hauled off him to face Durga the Hutt.

On the command bridge, Durga ordered his crew to power up the Darksaber. Then, as a christening for his new weapon, Durga ordered the execution of General Crix Madine, who died a hero to the New Republic.

As the Darksaber lumbered into motion, military fleets arrived in the asteroid field in response to Madine's distress signal. Wedge Antilles issued an ultimatum to Durga. Bevel Lemelisk was appalled to see his Hutt boss push the engines to maximum and warm up the superlaser. Sensing disaster, Lemelisk slipped away and jumped ship in a small shuttle. Durga, arrogant and confident, flew the Darksaber into a danger zone of colliding asteroids. He intended to use his superlaser to blast a path through the rubble, but the weapon fizzled without igniting even a spark. Asteroids obliterated the Darksaber weapon and Durga the Hutt in a shattering space collision.

Bevel Lemelisk's shuttle was intercepted by New Republic forces. Later, Lemelisk was incarcerated on Orinackra—ironically, a prison where General Madine himself had once been held—and tried for his crimes of genocide. He became one of the few Imperial criminals to receive the death penalty. The sentence was carried out four years later, and Lemelisk's only comment was "At least make sure you do it right this time."

ADMIRAL DAALA RETURNS
12 A.B.Y.

In the Deep Core, Admiral Daala served as the spokesperson for the reunited Imperial forces. She had caused a dramatic attitude shift in the Imperial military by allowing aliens and women to participate; previously, with the exception of Carnor Jax's Interim Council, they had been largely excluded because of Palpatine's prejudice. In closed consultations, Daala and Pellaeon chose their first strike—they would attack the Jedi academy on Yavin 4. This was a battle they could certainly win, Daala concluded, and it would cost them few casualties and minimum damage.

During these preparations, Kyp Durron and Dorsk 81 had infiltrated the Deep Core. Upon learning of Daala's plans, the two Jedi spies fled, sounding the alarm. Vice Admiral Pellaeon arrived at Yavin 4 with a vanguard fleet of twelve Star Destroyers. The Imperial ships sent down assault forces, armored scout walkers, and ground assault machinery, with orders to crush the Jedi training center to dust. Only hours behind the vanguard force, Daala followed in her Super Star Destroyer, the *Knight Hammer.*

Luke Skywalker, occupied elsewhere with Callista, was not on hand to lead his trainees, but the Jedi candidates defended their academy using everything they had learned of the Force. Durron, Dorsk 81, Kam Solusar, Tionne, Kirana Ti, Streen, Kyle Katarn, and others fought against the Empire's forces. But in the face of such massive military strength, they had no chance. Gathered for a last stand at the stronghold of the Great Temple, Dorsk 81 suggested combining all the Force abilities of the Jedi into a single dramatic effort. He cited

Yoda's famous adage, "Size matters not," and suggested that they could strike directly against the Imperial battleships.

The Jedi channeled their unified push through the conduit of Dorsk 81—a blast strong enough to shove Pellaeon's entire Star Destroyer fleet to the fringes of the Yavin system. The surge of power was too great for Dorsk 81's physical body, and he died, incinerated from within. When Admiral Daala arrived in her *Knight Hammer* for the second wave of the assault, she could not find Pellaeon or his ships. She bitterly launched a renewed attack on the small green moon, blasting the jungles from orbit.

The *Millennium Falcon* arrived during the fighting, carrying Luke Skywalker, Callista, Han Solo, Chewbacca, and Leia Organa Solo. Luke and Callista landed to assist the Jedi trainees against the ground attacks. Callista had been unable to reconnect with the Force following her ordeal on *Eye of Palpatine,* but chose to fight in other ways. Stealing an Imperial ship, she piloted it alone to *Knight Hammer* and planted explosive charges near the rear engine bank.

As Callista had hoped, the exploding charges set off a chain reaction that ripped out *Knight Hammer's* engine chambers. Within moments, the Super Star Destroyer, with no engines and no guidance control, plunged toward the gas giant Yavin. Daala ordered an immediate evacuation and rushed to the executive command pods to make her own escape. Callista confronted her there, her lightsaber drawn.

At last Callista sensed the potential for using the Force again, but her anger only allowed her to feel the cold tendrils of the dark side. Daala tricked her, however, blasting Callista with a stunner and fleeing as the gas giant Yavin dragged *Knight Hammer* down forever.

Luke later learned that Callista had managed to climb aboard one of the last escape pods and make her way to safety, but after her brush with the dark side, she swore not to return to him until she learned how to control her anger. Luke would not see Callista again for nearly a year.

At the far edge of the Yavin system, Pellaeon had regrouped his damaged Star Destroyers and retrieved as many of *Knight Hammer's* escape pods as possible, including Ad-

miral Daala's. Once again, Daala's grand plans had fallen to rubble. She relinquished full command of all Imperial forces to Pellaeon in the hopes that he could lead the Empire better than she had. This transfer of power had enormous implications for the eventual settlement of hostilities between Imperial and Republic forces, seven years later.

At the Jedi academy, Luke Skywalker and his students mourned the passing of Dorsk 81. Within months, however, Dorsk 81's clone successor, Dorsk 82, had arrived from Khomm to pick up where his predecessor had left off. On his first official mission, Dorsk 82 teamed with Kyp Durron to investigate the mining planet Corbos. They ran across two monstrous Leviathans, still alive after the devastation of Corbos during the Hundred-Year Darkness, and freed dozens of trapped spirits.

DESANN'S REBORN
12 A.B.Y.

Now working as a New Republic–affiliated mercenary, Kyle Katarn no longer felt a connection to the Force. Late in the year, he accepted Mon Mothma's request to investigate the activities of Galak Fyyar, an Imperial admiral who had allied himself with an ex-Jedi student named Desann. Prior to the *Eye of Palpatine* incident, Desann had killed a fellow Jedi trainee and fled Yavin 4. Now the reptilian Chistori had used Sith alchemy and artusian crystals to artificially imbue a legion of followers with the Force.

After reenergizing himself with a trip to Ruusan's Valley of the Jedi, Katarn proved to be more than a match for Desann's "Reborn" warriors. With help from Luke Skywalker and Lando Calrissian, Katarn defeated Admiral Fyyar and destroyed Desann's flagship *Doomgiver* in the skies above Yavin 4. In a lightsaber duel on the jungle moon's surface, Katarn killed the power-mad Chistori. This time, Kyle Katarn agreed to stay on as an academy instructor and permanent

Luke Skywalker's Jedi academy students take down a Juggernaut.
[ART BY TOMMY LEE EDWARDS]

member of Luke's emerging order of Jedi Knights.

THE EMPIRE REGROUPS
12–13 A.B.Y.

Thanks to Daala's unification efforts, the Empire was stable, though still only a shadow of its former self. If anyone could restore the Empire, or at least slow its inexorable decline, Pellaeon appeared to be the one.

Daala had already pulled all the warlord fleets out of the Deep Core, so Pellaeon abandoned that region as a staging area. The Outer Rim and Mid Rim offered much more favorable opportunities for harassing New Republic shipping. These systems also had more resources, better-traveled hyperspace lanes, and hundreds of thousands of worlds ripe for conquest. Pellaeon hooked up with the existing Imperial fortress worlds, and used his considerable fleet to carve out a well-defined territory for the Empire stretching from Wild Space to the Mid Rim, with a few scattered holdings in the other regions of the galaxy.

The Moffs of the former Imperial fortress worlds threw support behind their new commander, donating carefully hoarded stores of munitions and war matériel. The most impressive acquisition was the Super Star Destroyer *Reaper*. The colossal vessel had once been the flagship of Grand Moff Ardus Kaine's mini Empire, the Pentastar Alignment, before Kaine's death during Operation Shadow Hand. Pellaeon absorbed the remnants of the Pentastar Alignment and made the *Reaper* his personal command vessel.

Six months after Daala relinquished her command, Pellaeon made an aggressive lunge at the New Republic by seizing the small planet Orinda. By the time General Antilles mounted a counterattack, Pellaeon had already captured six neighboring systems. In a monthlong campaign, the New Republic pushed Pellaeon back, but suffered a grave defeat in the Battle of Orinda. There, the *Reaper* destroyed most of Antilles's starfighters by annihilating the fleet carrier *Endurance*. Rogue Squadron, stationed aboard the *Lusankya*, covered the fleet's retreat. The New Republic chose to leave Orinda in Imperial hands, and instead fortified the surrounding systems.

Admiral Daala had no role in Pellaeon's effort. She had voluntarily withdrawn from the Empire and was now the president of an independent settlers' group on Pedducis Chorios. Daala remained disgusted by the overall composition of the Empire—various pockets were still under the sway of petty governors and greedy Moffs. One such pocket was the Antemeridian sector under the rule of Moff Getelles.

MISSION TO ADUMAR
13 A.B.Y.

The New Republic saw the remote planet of Adumar as a way to threaten the Empire on two fronts. Located on the fringe of Wild Space, Adumar was maniacally militaristic, possessing a rigid duel-oriented culture and a worshipful reverence toward starfighter pilots. The first side to bring it into their fold would gain a military powerhouse.

Adumari culture eschewed diplomats in favor of military heroes. Consequently, General Wedge Antilles was sent to the city of Cartann to negotiate with the leadership. His ambassadorial counterpart on the Imperial side, Turr Phennir, had assumed command of the legendary Imperial 181st fighter wing following Baron Fel's defection to the New Republic years before. Antilles witnessed firsthand the locals' love of bloodsport and their ritualized death duels. Appalled by the unnecessary loss of life, Antilles made his feelings known, prompting the Cartann monarchy to lean toward an alliance with the Empire.

Unlike most civilized planets, Adumar did not possess a single worldwide government. Though Cartann's nation was the most powerful, dozens of smaller states existed. Representatives of the other nations contacted Antilles, who agreed to lead their combined militaries in a major offensive that broke Cartann's rule. Adumar reverted to a coalition government with representatives from every nation. After

due deliberation, the planet agreed to join the New Republic.

THE DEATH SEED PLAGUE
13 A.B.Y.

One month after the Battle of Orinda, eight months after the destruction of *Knight Hammer,* Chief of State Organa Solo and a small fleet traveled to the backwater Meridian sector, which ran up against the Antemeridian sector and was thus situated directly on the contentious Republic–Imperial border. Organa Solo was there to meet with Seti Ashgad of Nam Chorios, who had requested New Republic intervention on his planet. Ashgad claimed to be the son of the original Seti Ashgad, who had been exiled to Nam Chorios by Chancellor Palpatine during the Clone Wars.

Seven hundred years earlier, Nam Chorios had been a prison colony. The prisoners' descendants had grown into a tough, independent group called the Oldtimers, who were in direct conflict with the more recent colonists, the Newcomers. Ashgad asked that Organa Solo force the Oldtimers to open up their planet to outside trade, but this request was only a stalling tactic. Aboard Leia's ship, Ashgad's synthdroid bodyguards released thousands of squirming droch beetles that carried the Death Seed plague. Ashgad knocked Leia out

The pilots of Rogue Squadron:
Derek "Hobbie" Klivian,
Wedge Antilles, Wes Janson, and
Tycho Celchu
[ART BY MARK CHIARELLO]

and had spent the past eight months tracking her down. He arrived on Nam Chorios, and Seti Ashgad's men destroyed the Bleak Point gun station. Without the anti-orbital cannon in place, Ashgad would escape the planet and join Moff Getelles's fleet.

Luke and Leia rushed back to Ashgad's fortress. While Luke pursued Ashgad's vessel, Leia faced off against Beldorian. Beldorian, at nine meters, was staggeringly large even for a Hutt, and possessed none of the corpulent rolls that immobilized lazy Hutts like Jabba. All muscle and fire, he slithered toward Leia like a snake, but a long, swift side cut with her lightsaber messily ended the career of Beldorian the Splendid.

In the atmosphere, Luke used the Force to convince the crystals of Nam Chorios of the danger the galaxy would face if Ashgad's plan succeeded. As Ashgad's ship neared a Star Destroyer, several of Moff Getelles's needle fighters—powered by Chorian crystals—suddenly broke formation and destroyed the craft.

In the Battle of Nam Chorios, Getelles's fleet battled a makeshift armada thrown together by Han Solo and Lando Calrissian, as well as Admiral Daala, fighting on the New Republic's side. Daala had nothing but contempt for an Imperial who would ally himself with a schemer and a madman like Ashgad. Commanding her own warships, she defeated Getelles in the name of Imperial honor.

In the aftermath, Skywalker completed negotiations with the Chorian crystal mind. It agreed to send hundreds of crystals offplanet to destroy every plague-carrying droch in the Meridian sector, in exchange for the eventual return of every crystal that had been installed in a Loronar product. The New Republic forced Loronar to comply with the decree, and

and brought her to his fortress on Nam Chorios.

Leia soon learned that the man who captured her was the *original* Ashgad, kept young and vital through stomach-turning "renewal treatments" administered by Dzym, a grossly mutated humanoid droch beetle. Ashgad had allied with Moff Getelles of the Antemeridian sector, who hoped to cripple the Meridian sector through the spread of the Death Seed. The Moff's sector navy would then invade, armed with automated "needle fighters" from the Loronar Corporation. Loronar's CEO had pledged to arm the plotters in return for the rights to strip-mine Nam Chorios's minerals. The crystals of Nam Chorios were more than just programmable matrices for synthdroids or needle fighters. They were intelligent, silicon-based life-forms.

Leia escaped Ashgad's fortress, crossing paths with the Hutt Beldorian the Splendid, a former Jedi Knight who had been living on the world for centuries. Leia fled across the rocky wasteland to the planetary gun station at Bleak Point, where she saw a familiar face among the Oldtimer settlers: her brother's lost love, Callista.

Luke Skywalker had been devastated by Callista's decision to abandon him following the *Knight Hammer* incident,

also canceled a government contract for *Strike*-class cruisers. The move nearly sent Loronar into bankruptcy.

Luke Skywalker's reunion with Callista was bittersweet. Luke had slowly come to realize that his life lay along a different path than his lover's. They did not even exchange words—merely a warm look and a wave, and then Luke boarded a shuttle and left Callista behind.

Back on Coruscant, Leia had to accept more elaborate security precautions. She was assigned a pair of bodyguards, whom she nicknamed "the Sniffer" and "the Shooter." Also during the Nam Chorios crisis, Minister of State Rieekan had been incapacitated by poison. One of the culprits, Senator Q-Varx, was arrested and tried for treason. Rieekan's recovery was the only thing that saved Q-Varx from a death sentence, though Rieekan chose not to return to his former post. Mokka Falanthas became Minister of State in his stead.

The New Republic pressed its advantage and entered Moff Getelles's Antemeridian sector with two full fleets. Getelles was powerless to stop them, and the sector (along with a huge chunk of neighboring space) became New Republic territory. Admiral Pellaeon, initially preoccupied with a protracted campaign against Adumar, eventually stopped his enemy from advancing into the heart of the Empire, though the effort cost him the Super Star Destroyer *Reaper*.

Admiral Daala's history following the battle was the most curious of all. While surveying the combat wreckage on Nam Chorios, Daala caught sight of Ashgad's pilot, Liegeus Vorn. Vorn had once had a romance with Daala, and the two rekindled their connection and departed for Pedducis Chorios. The couple then dropped out of sight for nearly a year, during which time Daala reclaimed a leadership position with the new warlords of the Deep Core. Successors to Harrsk, Delvardus, and the others now held power within the Deep Core kingdoms, and while warlords such as Foga Brill and Moff Tethys lacked military muscle, they made up for it in base cruelty. Still trying to impose order, Daala united the squabbling factions to make preparations for a unified strike against the New Republic.

PART NINE

Uprisings and Insurgencies

Following the previous year's crisis in the Meridian sector, the New Republic settled into a period of relative stability. Luke's new Jedi Knights now served as active peacekeepers and powerful symbols of the restored Republic. Chief of State Organa Solo marked the occasion by embarking on a peaceful tour of remote member worlds with her three children. Tragically, the tour indicated just how fragile that peace actually was. The "Empire Reborn" was the first of several localized movements that would cause substantial regional troubles over the next four years.

THE EMPIRE REBORN MOVEMENT
14 A.B.Y.

As Organa Solo visited the provincial planet Munto Codru, her children were kidnapped while at play. Chairman Iyon tried to reassure the Chief of State by speculating that the incident was a "coup abduction"—in Codru-Ji society, children of royal birth were routinely kidnapped and ransomed by rival political factions. The truth was much more complicated.

The children had been kidnapped by Lord Hethrir, a near-human Firrerreo. During the Empire's reign, Hethrir and his mate, Rillao, had been trained by Darth Vader in the ways of the Dark Jedi. Palpatine was so impressed with Hethrir's abilities that he promoted him to Procurator of Justice—an unprecedented appointment for a nonhuman in the New Order. The Procurator of Justice was responsible for carrying out Imperial death sentences against both individuals and entire worlds. As

a sign of his loyalty, Hethrir condemned his own homeworld, Firrerre, to death. But the position was so shadowy that the Rebel Alliance was never able to uncover the Procurator's name. Hethrir lost his power and position in the aftermath of

Hethrir, leader of the Empire Reborn, contemplates grand schemes.
[ART BY JOHN VAN FLEET]

Endor. He fled to the Outer Rim aboard an artificial planetoid given to him by the Emperor, and began attracting wealthy backers to fund his fledgling "Empire Reborn" movement.

His skills with the dark side of the Force, while minor compared to those of Vader or Palpatine, were enough to win over any doubters. Hethrir's core financing came through the sale of slaves. While serving as Procurator, he had dispatched dozens of passenger freighters into deep space, each loaded with prisoners kept in suspended animation. Since he was the only one who knew the location of the freighters, Hethrir could visit them whenever funds were running low, and select potential slaves at his leisure.

At the time of their kidnapping, Jacen and Jaina Solo were five, Anakin only three and a half. Hethrir locked them in individual rooms aboard his worldcraft and placed them under the control of older, uniformed proctors. It was Hethrir's hope that all the captive children would be purchased by his wealthy sponsors.

Hethrir had also forged an alliance with an enigmatic being called Waru on the floating bazaar of Crseih Station. He planned to sacrifice the Force-strong Anakin Solo to Waru in exchange for the creature's help.

Back on Munto Codru, the Chief of State took immediate action to rescue her children, breaking all protocols. She told no one of her intentions—she simply dropped out of sight. Minister of State Falanthas stepped in to keep the government running smoothly. A curious public was told that Organa Solo had fallen ill, and the truth did not become known until months after the actual incident.

Organa Solo, accompanied by Chewbacca, followed the kidnappers' trail in her personal yacht *Alderaan*. Eventually, she crossed paths with Rillao, Hethrir's proud ex-mate. Rillao pointed them on the trail of Crseih Station.

On the way, Organa Solo stumbled across Hethrir's worldcraft. After ensuring the safety of everyone on the tiny planetoid, Organa Solo loaded her other two

children aboard the *Alderaan* and raced for Crseih Station to save Anakin's life.

THE POWER OF WARU
14 A.B.Y.

Hethrir's sudden decision to kidnap the children of the Chief of State was shockingly brash. But Hethrir would not have taken such action without feeling confident about his payoff—specifically, the extra-dimensional anomaly called Waru.

During the height of the Empire, Crseih Station been an Imperial research center where Hethrir had authorized

New Republic agent Kyle Katarn
[Art by John Van Fleet]

experiments that tested the limits of realspace, hyperspace, and the theoretical realm of otherspace. In the sinkholes near a black hole and a crystallizing white dwarf star, Hethrir's scientists breached the walls between dimensions and brought into existence a massive slab of meat covered with shining golden scales. Though this entity, Waru, lacked discernible sensory organs, it was highly intelligent and could communicate in a deep resonating voice. Waru could heal any disease and could open up other beings to the limits of the Force, but it also consumed life-essences to gain enough power to return to its own dimension.

Waru had gained fame as a healer, curing the sick at the Altar of Waru. Luke Skywalker and Han Solo investigated the goings-on at Crseih, running across Han's old flame Xaverri, who had helped Han's smugglers seventeen years earlier at the Battle of Nar Shaddaa. Before long, Hethrir arrived with a retinue of wealthy supporters, bearing Anakin Solo for a sacrifice. In exchange for Anakin's life-essence, Hethrir hoped that Waru would bestow omnipotent Force powers upon him.

Han, Luke, and Leia rescued Anakin, but Luke let himself be drawn inside Waru's golden essence. He nearly fell into the dark vortex that led to Waru's home dimension, but broke the seductive spell and swam away from the swirling mass. An enraged Waru consumed Hethrir instead, and both of them vanished from the known universe.

Outside Crseih Station, the white dwarf star had reached the final stages of compression into an unstable quantum crystal. The heroes helped fire up Crseih's long-dormant hyperdrive to escape the catastrophic fragmentation of the crystal star. The movable space bazaar arrived at Munto Codru and then relocated to the neighboring Pakuuni system, where it remained.

The most tangible benefit of the Empire Reborn incident was the acquisition of Hethrir's worldcraft. This astonishing structure—a movable planetoid with a forested surface and a blue sky—was scoured by teams of researchers including Death Star designer Bevel Lemelisk (before his execution). The New Republic had no interest in replicating the ridiculously expensive design, but gained insights into engineering and energy management issues, which aided the rollout of the "New Class" warship program.

The eight new starship designs of the New Class had been commissioned following the victory over the resurrected Emperor. The last of the ships, the *Nebula*-class New Republic Star Destroyer, was christened eleven years after Endor. One year later, enough of the New Class had been produced at the Kuat yards to make an entire armada, the New Republic's Fifth Fleet. Some Senators began to question the Chief of State, even going so far as to compare the Fifth Fleet to the sweeping military expansions of Emperor Palpatine.

Later the same year—three years after the defeat of Exar Kun's spirit on Yavin 4—Luke Skywalker's academy students endured another brush with the ancient Sith. Trainee Jaden Korr, who had studied under Kyle Katarn, uncovered traces of a new Sith cult. Inside Vjun's Bast Castle, Jaden Korr confronted fellow student Rosh Penin, who had fallen to the dark side under the cult's influence.

In their efforts to root out the Sith cult, Jaden Korr and Kyle Katarn learned that the spirit of long-dead Sith Lord Marka Ragnos had survived for five millennia in the tombs of Korriban, and was largely responsible for this latest dark side outbreak. Jaden Korr's heroics brought an end to the crisis, as well as pride to his teacher.

THE BLACK FLEET CRISIS
16–17 A.B.Y.

The Black Fleet Crisis had its genesis eight months after the Battle of Endor, during the Imperial Black Sword Command's retreat from the Koornacht Cluster. Yevethan dockworkers at N'zoth rose up, murdered their captors, and seized the Black Fleet armada for themselves. Over the next twelve years, the Yevetha learned to operate their captured warships, including the Super Star Destroyer *Intimidator*. Nil Spaar, chief commando behind the uprising, became the leader of the Yevetha and head of the Duskhan League, a political federation of pure Yevethan colony worlds.

Twelve years after the fall of the Empire, the New Republic was in a tranquil state of relative peace. Other than Hethrir's kidnapping of the Solo children, the galaxy had experienced no serious crisis since the power struggle in the Meridian sector. Leia Organa Solo engaged in a series of peaceable talks with Nil Spaar. Admiral Hiram Drayson, head of a covert New Republic intelligence agency, suspected Spaar was hiding something, and arranged for an unarmed scout ship to make a reconnaissance run deep into the Koornacht Cluster. The ship was promptly blown to bits. Spaar seized upon the incident as proof of Organa Solo's "warmongering," and milked the tragedy for all it was worth to a citizenry weary of war. Several member worlds went so far as to submit articles of withdrawal from the New Republic.

It was the perfect time for the Yevetha to make their move. In a series of lightning raids, they used stolen Black Fleet warships to strike at all non-Yevethan colonies within the Koornacht Cluster. To the Yevetha, this act of genocide was merely the extermination of "alien vermin." They proudly labeled their bloody crusade the Great Purge.

Leia faced a political disaster. Unlike the high-profile strikes of Thrawn and Daala, the Yevetha's Great Purge failed to agitate the electorate. Koornacht was too isolated—most citizens were unwilling to risk New Republic lives to defend worlds they'd never visited. Leia delivered an ultimatum to Nil Spaar, ordering the Yevethan leader to surrender the planets he had seized through immoral force. Spaar called her bluff.

At the cluster colony world Doornik-319, the Yevethan fleet and the Republic armada clashed. But as K-wing bombers lined up for strafing runs against enemy thrustships, the Yevetha broadcast a signal across all wavelengths—the pleading cries of recently seized hostages who begged for Republic restraint lest they be killed along with their captors. Enough K-wings hesitated, and the carefully planned attack runs failed. The New Republic retreated in shameful defeat.

Nil Spaar of the Yevetha rallies his people while thrustships launch behind him. [ART BY TOMMY LEE EDWARDS]

Leia Organa Solo wasn't willing to back down. Several recon flights revealed that every warship in the "lost" Black Fleet was now in the hands of the Duskhan League, including the Super Star Destroyer, now rechristened *Pride of Yevetha*. Han Solo, given the temporary rank of commodore, was placed in charge of a massive New Republic force sent to patrol the cluster's borders. On his way to take command, Han's shuttle was yanked from hyperspace and captured. Han was taken as a prize to N'zoth and brought before a gloating Nil Spaar.

With her husband a prisoner of Nil Spaar, some believed that Leia might risk the lives of New Republic soldiers in an ill-advised attempt to free him. Many Senators thought she should be replaced with someone "less involved" and started drafting a recall petition. Leia continued the fight, ordering an attack that demolished the Yevetha's Black Nine shipyards. Nil Spaar was livid. He transmitted a private hologram to the Chief of State in which he savagely beat and kicked a trussed-up Han Solo for an excruciating twenty minutes. Only three words were spoken throughout the whole stomach-turning display: "Leave Koornacht now."

By revealing his naked cruelty, the hologram was the worst tactical mistake Spaar could have made. With righteous fire in her heart, the Chief of State addressed the Senate regarding the petition of no confidence. She calmly announced that, mere hours before, the New Republic had declared war on the Duskhan League.

Several Wookiees, including Chewbacca and his young son, organized a rescue of Han Solo, exhibiting typical Wookiee subtlety by charging at *Pride of Yevetha* with all guns blazing. *Millennium Falcon* attached itself to the Super Star Destroyer and cut through its hull, allowing Chewbacca and his son to rescue Han Solo from his cell.

With Spaar's bargaining chip eliminated, it was time for a decisive strike against the Duskhan League. The New Republic fleet leapt into the heart of the Koornacht Cluster and squared off against the enemy. The clash grew into a savage brawl, but the Republic received an unexpected gift from a surprising source.

Every ship in the Black Fleet was partially crewed by Imperial prisoners of war, captured years earlier during the shipyard uprising at N'zoth. While the Imperials had no love for the Rebels, they despised their Yevethan captors even more. The human captives activated a hidden slave circuit web that they had installed piecemeal in the Black Fleet's control boards over the previous decade. The Imperials stopped the warships dead, brought them about, and jumped every last Star Destroyer in the direction of Byss in the Deep Core. Nil Spaar, aboard the *Pride of Yevetha,* disappeared along with them.

Many Yevethan thrustships remained, but the battle was essentially over. Even so, the Yevetha fought to the bitter end. The Battle of N'zoth was a victory, but a costly one.

When the Black Fleet finally arrived at Byss, it found a scorched asteroid field expanding in Byss's orbit after the planet's destruction by the Galaxy Gun. Within a month, the vast majority of the Black Fleet had accepted the reality of their situation and defected to the New Republic. Four *Victory*-class Star Destroyers hooked up with Daala's warlords in the Deep Core, and two of the most advanced Star Destroyers, as well as the experimental weapons test bed *EX-F,* chose to join Admiral Pellaeon's shrinking Empire in the Outer Rim. *Pride of Yevetha* vanished entirely. The Super Star Destroyer was discovered four years later, drifting near the Unknown Regions and damaged beyond repair.

MASTER SKYWALKER AND THE FALLANASSI
16–17 A.B.Y.

The resolution to the Black Fleet Crisis would not have been possible without the intervention of a mysterious group of women known as the Fallanassi. The members of this reclusive religious order practiced pacifism and followed the "White Current." Similar to the Witches of Dathomir or the disciples of Ta-Ree, the Fallanassi used the White Current in much the same way that Jedi Knights manipulate the Force. As Luke Skywalker has said, "The Force is a river from which many can drink, and the training of the Jedi is not the only cup which can catch it."

Just prior to the crisis, Luke had been visited by Akanah Norand Pell, a member of the Fallanassi. As a child, Akanah had been forced to leave her people and was embarking on a search to pick up their trail. To secure Luke's help, she told him that his mother, "Nashira," had once been a Fallanassi herself. Everything about Akanah's story turned out to be counterfeit, including the name *Nashira,* but at the time Luke was unaware of the identity of his true mother, Padmé Amidala.

The trail of the Fallanassi led to J't'p'tan in the heart of the Koornacht Cluster. There, the Fallanassi had hidden from the Yevetha by projecting the illusion of a bombed-out ruin over their thriving temple settlement.

Luke convinced the Fallanassi to lend assistance to the New Republic by creating an illusory "phantom fleet" at the Battle of N'zoth. The phantom fleet did not frighten the Yevetha, but it did split their fire and allow the New Republic to take out the thrustship armada with fewer casualties than expected. Following the battle, the Fallanassi departed on their private starliner and remained out of public view for nearly two decades, until Jacen Solo ran into them during the events of the Killik expansion.

THE TELJKON VAGABOND
16–17 A.B.Y.

Lando Calrissian spent his time during the Black Fleet Crisis chasing a "ghost ship" code-named the Teljkon vagabond. Lando and Lobot, accompanied by R2-D2 and C-3PO, spent weeks trapped aboard the vagabond before discovering that the organic vessel had been built by the Qella species, just prior to a catastrophic ice age that had befallen their homeworld. The vagabond was a "tool kit" for melting a frozen planet. Beneath the kilometer-thick ice, thousands of Qella lay in hibernation, waiting for the thaw.

The vagabond took up position in orbit and began melting the ice. It eventually completed its work in the middle of the Yuuzhan Vong invasion, when no New Republic scientists could be spared to oversee the reveal. When an overdue team finally arrived at the planet, the Qella and their

strange starship had vanished. The Teljkon vagabond still ranks as one of the most significant archaeological discoveries of the past century, alongside the Corellian repulsors, the cities of the Sharu, and the Jedi library on Ossus.

UPRISING AT ALMANIA
17 A.B.Y.

The Black Fleet Crisis had serious repercussions for galactic peace. The Yevetha were an isolated and numerically insignificant foe, yet they had caused the New Republic more grief than anyone since Admiral Daala. Other groups, including the remnants of Pellaeon's Empire and the Deep Core warlords, began to reconsider armed conflict against their old foe. To add more fuel to the fire, the Senate passed a measure allowing former Imperial officials to hold elective office.

The measure's most vocal opponents predicted that admitting unrepentant Imperial loyalists into the Senate would cause the government to dissolve into partisan gridlock. The ex-Imperial Senators delighted in opposing Organa Solo at every turn. On the fifty-first day of the new term, when Organa Solo stepped into the Senate Hall to address the body, a tremendous explosion knocked her off her feet.

The Chief of State survived with minor injuries, while dozens of Senators died instantly. Senate Hall was a ruin, closed off to visitors as construction began on its replacement, the Grand Convocation Chamber.

The bombing had been executed by Brakiss, a former Imperial spy who, years before, had unsuccessfully tried to infiltrate Luke Skywalker's Jedi academy on Yavin 4. Brakiss was in league with Dolph, a fallen Jedi trainee. Dolph had abandoned his training in order to fight the despotic Je'har regime on remote Almania. He rose to prominence among the resistance, assuming the name Kueller and hiding his identity behind a formfitting death's-head mask. Over several years, Kueller employed dark side skills to exterminate the Je'har and become Almania's undisputed leader.

Brakiss had fled the Jedi academy when Skywalker had forced Brakiss to confront the darkness in his soul. Kueller had helped put him back together, and Brakiss served the powerful man out of gratitude and fear. For two years, Brakiss had been the sole operator of the Telti droid factories, and had secretly rigged his droids with explosive detonators. This was Kueller's secret weapon—unexpected, unseen, and completely devastating.

In addition to the Senate bombing, Kueller used rigged droids to obliterate the populations of Pydyr and Auyemesh, two of the three inhabited moons orbiting Almania. Despite the fact that Almania had never been a member of the New Republic, many pro-Imperial observers dubbed this struggle between mismatched opponents "the new Rebellion."

Luke Skywalker investigated Brakiss's droid-manufactur-ing plant on Telti and set out for Almania. Luke's sabotaged X-wing fighter exploded, however, and he became a captive of Kueller's, imprisoned on Almania to serve as bait for his headstrong Jedi sister.

Back on Coruscant, Leia presided over the political equivalent of a ticking thermal detonator. The opposition Senators now held a majority, and a petition of no confidence—the second in less than two years—was entered into the record. When Kueller threatened to kill Luke unless Leia turned the reins of the New Republic over to him, Leia resigned her position as Chief of State. This nullified the no-confidence vote and freed her to go after Kueller on her own. Mon Mothma returned to lead the New Republic in a temporary role, until new elections could be held.

Mon Mothma sent a small fleet under the command of General Wedge Antilles to provide firepower for the rescue mission. Leia Organa Solo left for Almania in her personal ship, accompanied by Antilles in a Mon Calamari star cruiser and a number of smaller warships.

When they arrived in the Almania system, three *Victory*-class Star Destroyers rose from the planet, unleashing scores of deadly TIE fighters. Antilles streaked into pitched battle with Kueller's armada, while Organa Solo slipped through the fighter screen and landed on Almania's surface. General Antilles soon realized the reason for the enemy ships' oddly precise maneuvers—they were crewed entirely by droids.

Brakiss (foreground) and Kueller
[Art by John Van Fleet]

With this knowledge, Wedge exploited the tactical flaws of artificial intelligence and crippled the Star Destroyers with turbolaser hits.

On Almania, Leia rescued her brother, but found Kueller standing between them and freedom. Kueller ignited his energy blade and joined battle with Luke, who realized that his aggression was only making Kueller stronger. Recognizing the Master–student parallels with Kenobi and Vader's showdown aboard the Death Star, Skywalker prepared to sacrifice his own life. If Kueller struck him down, he would return in spirit-form and guide Leia to victory.

But as Luke raised his lightsaber in a passive salute, a native thernbee animal—carrying Force-repelling ysalamiri in its belly—nullified Kueller's Force advantage. In a blind rage, Kueller pulled out a master detonator that could trigger the explosion of every droid manufactured on Telti. Before anyone could stop him, he stabbed his finger on the button.

Light-years away, on Telti, C-3PO and R2-D2 had infiltrated Brakiss's droid factories and, with help from the mechanic Cole Fardreamer and an army of astromechs, had broken into the control room. Jacking into a computer terminal, R2 intercepted Kueller's master control signal and deactivated the remote detonators at the last instant.

Leia had no way of knowing whether Kueller's bombs had been discharged, so she took the quickest possible route to prevent further trickery. Drawing a blaster, she shot Kueller cleanly in the head. Was her deed—a violent killing committed in anger—an act born from the dark side? At that moment, she didn't care.

Leia, Luke, and Wedge Antilles returned to Coruscant as heroes. Mon Mothma gladly stepped down, and Leia returned to her former position, which was ratified without dissent. The Chief of State addressed the congress in the temporary Senate Hall, vowing to make this new term one of unity and strength.

In the wake of his failure on Telti, Brakiss fled the droid-manufacturing moon. He disappeared for several years, and was later discovered serving as a neutral intermediary between the warlords of the Deep Core. Eventually Brakiss rose to a leadership position with the Second Imperium, a group that caused significant headaches for the New Republic during the later years of Imperial–Republic peace. He founded a training center for dark Jedi, the Shadow Academy, with the intention of creating evil Force warriors for the continuing battle.

IMPERIAL SKIRMISHES
17–18 A.B.Y.

Hot on the heels of the Almanian uprising, both the Deep Core warlords and Pellaeon's Empire attempted to reclaim some formerly held sectors. They gambled that the New Republic wouldn't put a full effort behind stopping them, for fear of inspiring another public relations debacle like the Yevethan conflict at Doornik-319. They were mistaken.

The New Republic added the Super Star Destroyer *Guardian,* captured during the previous year from the rogue Imperial Admiral Drommel, to the third fleet, then sent both the Third and Fifth fleets out to engage Pellaeon in several major brawls. The most notable were the Battle of Champala and the Battle of Anx Minor. In the latter climactic conflict, Admiral Ackbar scored a last-minute victory by focusing a hail of concentrated fire on the engines of the experimental vessel *EX-F* (also known as *Glory of Yevetha*). The ship exploded, igniting its volatile antimatter reservoir and annihilating six nearby Star Destroyers. When the dust from the conflicts finally settled, Pellaeon's Empire had been pushed back into a mere eight sectors of a strategically barren section in the Outer Rim.

The Deep Core warlords fought on the opposite edge of space, but did not present a unified front. Therefore, they crumpled under a series of deadly perimeter assaults from the Republic's Fourth Fleet. In one of the final assaults, General Bel Iblis attempted to capture Admiral Daala in a pincer move with a pair of CC-7700 gravity-well frigates. In a shocking move, Daala's lead frigate rammed one of the CC-7700s, destroying it, and eliminating its projected mass shadow.

Admiral Gilad Pellaeon
[Art by John Van Fleet]

The Corellian Insurrection
18 A.B.Y.

During the lull, Chief of State Leia Organa Solo visited a major trade conference on Corellia. The system itself contained five inhabited planets—Corellia, Drall, Selonia, and the double worlds of Talus and Tralus—which had been transported into their orbits by an unknown pre-Republic power. As the home of major conglomerates including Corellian Engineering and the birthplace of famous Republic heroes such as Han Solo and Wedge Antilles, the Corellian sector was respected throughout the galaxy.

In the post-Palpatine era, however, the sector had surrounded itself in airtight isolation. The ruling Corellian diktat vanished, and the sector became inward looking and inward thinking. Lucrative trade routes dried up, and businesses relocated elsewhere. The New Republic installed a Frozian named Micamberlecto as Corellia's governor-general, but he was little more than a figurehead attempting to control a discontented populace. The Chief of State hoped this trade conference would be the first step in bringing the sector more fully into the fold.

Lando Calrissian, meanwhile, had decided to turn over regular operation of the Kessel mines to Nien Nunb, his Sullustan copilot during the destruction of the second Death Star at Endor. Calrissian invested his funds in an underground housing project on Coruscant called Dometown, but when that didn't satisfy the gambler's yearning for a quick score, he decided on the easiest and oldest method of getting rich quickly—marrying into money. Lando and Luke embarked on an outlandish "wife hunt," which unexpectedly bore fruit when Lando met Tendra Risant on the Corellian sector world of Sacorria. Both men found themselves expelled from Sacorria, however, when they offended the planet's repressive government, the Triad.

Neither Luke nor Lando realized that the masterminds of an imminent Corellian insurrection were lying right under their noses. The Triad of Sacorria had orchestrated a plot to

Daala's badly damaged flagship then vanished into hyperspace, and has not been encountered since. New Republic Intelligence was tempted to declare Daala killed in action, but it had learned from past experience never to presume an enemy's death—especially not hers.

The New Republic's enemies were in retreat, their navies spent. No further galactic conflicts loomed on the immediate horizon. Ackbar took advantage of the temporary respite to order most warships into dry dock for repairs and upgrades. Those fleet vessels not affected by the recall were put to work patrolling the borders of the Empire and the Deep Core.

The Battle of Centerpoint Station, the final conflict of the Corellian Insurrection. [Art by Tommy Lee Edwards]

break away from the New Republic and have the Corellian sector recognized as an independent state. The key to their scheme was Centerpoint Station, a pre-Republic space depot located between the twin worlds of Talus and Tralus. Millions of citizens lived inside the alien artifact, both in its labyrinthine corridors and along the spherical walls of its hollow interior. After more than thirty thousand years, the Triad had at last uncovered Centerpoint's purpose.

As a massive hyperspace tractor-repulsor, Centerpoint Station had been used by alien architects to pull the Corellian planets through hyperspace. Vast repulsor chambers buried beneath the crust of each world then nudged the planets into stable orbits around the star Corell. The Triad realized that Centerpoint, and the individual planetary repulsors, could be turned into superweapons. They backed various insurgent groups on each planet—the Human League on Corellia, the Overden on Selonia, and the Drallists on Drall—and ordered them to find their respective planetary repulsors, thus preventing the devices from being used against the Triad. They also learned how to make Centerpoint Station fire hyperspace repulsor bursts and trigger supernovas in distant stars. Finally, the Triad used Centerpoint to generate an interdiction field that encompassed the entire star system, making hyperspace travel impossible within its sphere of influence. With Chief of State Organa Solo trapped by the interdiction field, and a supernova countdown as their non-negotiable ultimatum, the Triad planned to create a breakaway "mini Empire" with themselves at the head.

Unfortunately for them, the Triad made a fatal mistake by approaching Thrackan Sal-Solo, the treacherous leader of Corel lia's anti-alien Human League. When Leia arrived at the trade conference, the Triad triggered the interdiction field. Sal-Solo, however, double-crossed his masters and also activated Centerpoint's jamming field, preventing the Triad from negotiating with the Chief of State. Sal-Solo declared himself diktat, figuring that he could grab most of the Corellian sys-

tem for himself before the Triad could move against him.

What was supposed to have been a quiet trade conference had turned into a catastrophe. The Chief of State was held captive by Human League troops. Chewbacca and the three Solo children, along with their Drallish tutor Ebrihim, had escaped Corellia on *Millennium Falcon,* but were trapped in-system by the interdiction field. Han Solo had been captured by Thrackan Sal-Solo, and in the underground head-

quarters of the Human League, the two men confronted each other. Solo's worst fears were confirmed—Thrackan was indeed his cousin, returned to make trouble after a thirty-year absence.

Han Solo's cellmate was Dracmus, a furred Selonian. The Selonians follow an insect-like hive structure, and each den controls a patch of territory. Dracmus's people were struggling for dominance against the Triad-backed Overden. After

escaping from jail with Dracmus, Han became a prisoner on Selonia, to be used as a bargaining chip in the ongoing negotiations with the Overden.

Leia Organa Solo escaped from house arrest with help from fellow prisoner Mara Jade. Chewbacca piloted the *Falcon* to Drall, where he and the children were taken in by Ebrihim's stubborn but levelheaded Aunt Marcha. Jacen, Jaina, and Anakin Solo soon located Drall's planetary repulsor, a vast shining chamber more than a kilometer deep. Anakin activated the ancient device through an unconscious manipulation of the Force.

On Coruscant, the top New Republic strategists were debating how best to deal with an utterly baffling situation. Because of the interdiction field, they could send a task force in only at sublight speeds, a mind-numbingly slow journey that would take more than two months. Mon Mothma had a better solution. She knew that the Bakurans had succeeded in developing a countermeasure for an interdiction field, and asked Luke Skywalker to visit Bakura and request that the New Republic "borrow" their fleet.

It had been fourteen years since the historic truce at Bakura, but the planet's inhabitants hadn't lowered their guard against a possible Ssi-ruuvi return. They had built four powerful cruisers, each equipped with an experimental device allowing it to escape from an interdiction field. Luke met with Gaeriel Captison, now a councilor and retired politician, who agreed to help. With Gaeriel along as a Bakuran representative, the four war cruisers planned to break through the Corellian interdiction field, stage a diversionary assault at Selonia, then move on to Centerpoint Station to shut it down.

The small armada leapt blindly into the system's heart. One ship, heavily damaged during realspace reentry, was evacuated and used as a remote-decoy as they slowly approached Selonia. When they neared the planet, an invisible blow from the Selonian planetary repulsor slammed into the decoy vessel, turning it into a loose jumble of bolts, rivets, and hull plates.

The remaining three ships retreated from Selonia and proceeded to their true target: Centerpoint Station. The colossal structure was now abandoned, save for its chief operations officer. All residents of Centerpoint's inhabited interior had been evacuated to Talus and Tralus following the two recent "flare-ups." During these incidents, Centerpoint's artificial interior sun had swelled with such intensity that the city's lakes had burned away and its buildings had been charred to ash.

The flare-ups were actually a byproduct of Centerpoint's "starbuster" firing process. The Triad had already destroyed two stars—an unnamed, uninhabited test system and Thanta Zilbra, a colony system that had once held thousands of inhabitants. The third solar system on Centerpoint's automated countdown list was Bovo Yagen, inhabited by billions. Now in a race against the clock, the Bakuran forces deduced that in order to stop Centerpoint, they needed to take control of one of the planetary repulsors.

On Selonia, Han Solo was trying to do just that. Solo had been reunited with his wife, and the two of them tried to aid Dracmus's den in seizing the planetary repulsor from the Overden, without success. On Drall, Thrackan Sal-Solo seized control of the local repulsor from Chewbacca and the Solo children, taking them prisoner. They escaped in the *Falcon,* leading Thrackan Sal-Solo on a chase that ended with Sal-Solo a prisoner aboard one of the Bakuran vessels.

The entire New Republic contingent prepared for imminent battle. The Triad had at last decided to show its face. The systemwide interdiction field suddenly dropped, and moments later, a massive war fleet leapt into the Corellian system to crush the New Republic interlopers and chastise the Triad's renegade underling, Sal-Solo.

The New Republic's greatest heroes went into battle against the Triad armada. The Triad fleet quickly gained the upper hand through the use of robot ramships—solid metal bullets built for suicide runs. Four of the ramships plowed into the Bakuran flagship, crippling it beyond repair. Gaeriel Captison and Admiral Ossilege were in the flagship's bridge at the time, and realized they would not make it to the escape pods. In a heroic act of self-sacrifice, Gaeriel triggered the ship's self-destruct, tearing a hole into the heart of the Triad formation. Minutes later, Admiral Ackbar plowed into the fray with a host of last-minute New Republic reinforcements to mop up the stragglers.

The enemy fleet was smashed, but Centerpoint still geared up for its unavoidable shot at Bovo Yagen. On the surface of Drall, at the last possible instant, young Anakin Solo fired an invisible repulsor burst that splashed into Centerpoint and disrupted the station's firing process. The star-shattering shot dissipated harmlessly.

The aftermath of the Corellian insurrection was choked with thorny issues. Corellians had always been a self-reliant lot, and, while most disapproved of the Triad's extreme methods, many sympathized with the reasoning behind it. Once again, the New Republic was criticized for butting in where it wasn't welcome, and the Chief of State was roundly vilified for letting the situation progress as far as it did. With no-confidence motions filed against her during the Black Fleet Crisis and the uprising at Almania, this latest round of faultfinding was the branch that broke the bantha's back.

Leia insisted on, and was granted, an indefinite leave of absence. Interim elections were held, and the Calibop senator Ponc Gavrisom was elected the new Chief of State and President of the Senate.

The Corellian sector was given a new governor-general, Marcha of Drall. As a native of one of the Corellian worlds, Marcha was widely accepted by the Corellian populace. Luke Skywalker agreed to become the sponsor of Gaeriel Captison's orphaned daughter, Malinza, on Bakura. As Malinza grew, she fell in with the isolationist Freedom terrorists, becoming a leader of that faction by the time of the Yuuzhan Vong invasion.

PART TEN

A Lasting Peace

At its peak, Palpatine's Empire had been an awe-inspiring example of omnipotence. But fifteen years after the death of its ruler, the Empire was scarcely more than a pitiable curiosity. Pushed into the wild fringes of the Outer Rim, consisting of eight small sectors and only a thousand inhabited systems, Imperial dominion was little threat to anyone—certainly not to the prosperous worlds of the ever-growing New Republic. Admiral Pellaeon, commander of the Imperial Fleet, was smart enough to realize that he'd been beaten.

THE CAAMAS DOCUMENT
19 A.B.Y.

After Admiral Daala had promoted him to his current position following the disastrous attack on Yavin 4, Pellaeon had put his best efforts into halting the erosion of the Empire's borders. But despite a few scattered victories, including the Battle of Orinda and the reacquisition of his former flagship *Chimaera* in the Battle of Gravlex Med, he had been unable to stop the march of history. Pellaeon met with the remaining Moffs on the capital world of Bastion and broached the unthinkable: an Imperial surrender. The Moffs met his plan with understandable resistance, but eventually agreed that a conditional capitulation to their hated enemies was the only way to guarantee the Empire's continued survival.

One of the Moffs, however, had other plans. Ambitious and amoral, Moff Disra was a political genius, and he was just one member of a secret triumvirate determined to scuttle Pellaeon's submission strategy and restore the Empire to its former grandeur. Disra's aide, Major Tierce, was an expert on

military tactics and claimed to be one of Palpatine's former Royal Guardsmen (Tierce had executed Rukh following the Noghri traitor's assassination of Grand Admiral Thrawn). But the third member—a simple con man named Flim—was the key to Disra's plan. Flim bore an uncanny resemblance to the late Thrawn, and with blue makeup and glowing corneal inserts, the likeness was nothing short of astonishing. Flim—or, rather, "Thrawn"—would be an inspirational figurehead, a badly needed propaganda tool that would breathe flame into the dying embers of the Empire.

Disra's first step was to intercept Pellaeon's envoy before the man could deliver the offer of peace. One of Disra's Star Destroyers captured the envoy's corvette at Morishim. Pellaeon remained unaware of Disra's treachery; he assumed that his enemies had received the Empire's offer and were contemplating its implications. Pellaeon headed off to his chosen rendezvous point and waited fruitlessly for a New Republic delegation that wasn't coming.

Disra's second step was more devious. A private performance by "Grand Admiral Thrawn" was enough to convince several Imperial fleet captains that their beloved leader had returned from the grave. On Thrawn's orders, three Star Destroyers were fitted with cloaking devices and sent into the Bothawui system. There, high above the Bothan homeworld, the invisible ships anchored themselves to a passing comet and waited patiently for the signal to attack.

Disra's target of Bothawui had not been a random selection. A few weeks earlier, Leia Organa Solo—now holding the position of councilor—had been visiting a Noghri relocation settlement on Wayland, when a Devaronian treasure hunter uncovered a shocking item from the ruins of Palpatine's storehouse inside Mount Tantiss. The item was an unremarkable black data card, but its scandalous contents gave full historical details on the decades-old devastation of Caamas. For years, no one had been sure who had been behind the vicious and indiscriminate slaughter. Now the painful truth was laid bare—the aggressors had included a group of Bothan saboteurs.

Many galactic citizens already resented the Bothans for their devious politics, and now those citizens had a lightning rod on which to focus their fury. Angry denunciations of the Bothans began in the New Republic Senate. Battle lines had been drawn, and the divisive issue threatened to tear the New Republic apart. The only solution appeared to be placing the actual Bothans who had participated in the incident on trial for war crimes. But a list of those participants—designated the Caamas Document—was nowhere to be found in the current databases. A call went out to all top New Republic officials: *Find a copy of the Caamas Document.*

Leia Organa Solo and her husband, recovered from a recent confrontation with Boba Fett on Jubilar, hoped to prevent the Bothan incident from boiling over into violence. The two visited Bothawui to inspect governmental financial records, but were swept up in an anti-Bothan riot. Just when things looked like they couldn't get much worse, Lando Calrissian, taking a break from his latest mining operation on Varn (the water world around which Han Solo had started a religion during his early smuggling career), encountered Disra's convincing Thrawn facsimile and concluded that the rumors of Thrawn's death had been greatly exaggerated. The news of a possible Imperial military resurgence only deepened the agitation over the Bothan incident, and the New Republic came to the brink of civil war.

Far from the galactic hubs of information, Admiral Pellaeon began to suspect that the New Republic had never received his overtures of peace. When Disra tried to eliminate Pellaeon with a pirate fleet painted with New Republic

insignia, Pellaeon realized that someone in his Empire had tried to set him up.

In all other respects, the grand scheme hatched by Moff Disra, Major Tierce, and Flim was working to perfection. "Thrawn" made numerous appearances. With the New Republic dissolving into fratricidal squabbling over the Bothan incident, the newly animated Empire looked powerful and attractive. Soon, dozens of systems were clamoring for voluntary readmittance into the Empire.

In a seemingly unrelated incident on Pakrik Minor, Han Solo and his wife encountered a group of Imperial clones. This small sleeper cell, grown from the legendary Baron Fel fighter pilot template, had been deployed a decade earlier by the real Thrawn. But after ten long years waiting for orders, the clones were no longer interested in serving their Imperial masters. One of their number supplied the top-secret coordinates for the Imperial capital world of Bastion. Solo, Calrissian, and Lobot headed into the fortified heart of the Empire to secure the Caamas Document from Bastion's information libraries. They failed.

Fortunately, the New Republic had a backup plan. Yaga Minor, the shipbuilding center and intelligence base, was one of the last jewels in the Empire's crown. An assault there would be perilous and costly, but it appeared to be the only place that might still possess a duplicate of the Caamas Document. Admiral Ackbar and General Garm Bel Iblis drew up plans for a raid using Booster Terrik's Star Destroyer *Errant Venture*, which had been captured more than a decade earlier at the conclusion of the Bacta War and operated by the smuggling captain as a floating bazaar ever since.

Around Bothawui, passions over the Bothan incident had reached a boiling point. Ragtag battleships from dozens of pro- and anti-Bothan factions finally exploded into armed conflict, triggered by the sudden destruction of the Bothawui planetary shield generator by Imperial saboteurs. As ships fired on the planet's surface and on each other, Leia struggled to impose order.

Han Solo inadvertently found the solution. Investigating a suspicious comet on close approach to Bothawui, Han yelped in surprise as *Millennium Falcon* dipped beneath the invisibility screen of a cloaked Imperial Star Destroyer. Their ambush spoiled, the three Star Destroyers that Disra had sent many months before abruptly dropped their cloaks and charged forward to decimate the survivors of the New Republic's fratricidal bloodbath. Unfortunately for them, the appearance of an external threat was sufficient to unite the squabbling fleets against their common foe. Lando Calrissian led the assembled armadas to victory.

At Yaga Minor, Booster Terrik's vessel prepared for its information raid on the data libraries. The disguised Star Destroyer successfully cleared the outer planetary defensive ring, but was trapped by dozens of heavy industrial tractor beams as soon as it passed the point of no return. Moff Disra, Major Tierce, and Flim, all at Yaga Minor at the time of the failed attack, demanded Terrik's unconditional surrender.

But an uninvited guest crashed the trio's private party. Admiral Pellaeon strode onto the bridge of the false Thrawn's command ship in front of the vessel's crew. Of all those present, Pellaeon had known Thrawn best, and he dropped the explosive news that the glorious return of Grand Admiral Thrawn had been nothing more than a parlor trick pulled by a small-time swindler named Flim.

Major Tierce attempted to deny the facts, but Pellaeon had an even more startling revelation regarding the former Royal Guardsman. Far from being the last of Palpatine's original bodyguards, Tierce was in fact a clone of the *real* Grodin Tierce, grown during Thrawn's original military campaign. Enraged and embarrassed by the truth, Tierce attempted to attack Pellaeon and died instantly. Their coup an utter failure, Flim and Disra were taken into Imperial custody.

Luke Skywalker secured a copy of the Caamas Document. The guilty Bothans were brought to trial, bringing an end to most New Republic discord. And with the threat of a resurrected Thrawn drained away overnight, no obstacle remained to forestall an official treaty between the Empire and the New Republic. Within weeks, the historic peace accords were signed aboard the *Chimaera* by Admiral Pellaeon and Chief of State Ponc Gavrisom. After more than two decades, the galaxy's most devastating war ended with the muted scratch of a writing stylus.

THE HAND OF THRAWN
19 A.B.Y.

Just prior to the hunt for the Caamas Document, Luke Skywalker had left his Yavin academy to investigate a disturbing trend—increasing numbers of cloned crewmen had been appearing aboard outlaw pirate vessels. The presence of new clones indicated that someone had found a way to activate Thrawn's sleeper cells of clone soldiers.

While scouting out a pirates' nest in the Kauron asteroid field, Luke and Mara Jade noticed a strange alien craft. Tracking the vessel back to its origin point—the distant planet Nirauan on the fringes of the Unknown Regions—Mara investigated a cave and encountered a thick swarm of tiny winged creatures who were half bat, half mynock. Luke and R2-D2 followed Mara to Nirauan, where the native "bats" revealed themselves as intelligent creatures. The cave dwellers called themselves the Qom Jha, while the bats in the outside cliffs were known as the Qom Qae. Both races requested the humans' assistance in eliminating the menace that lurked in the High Tower, a foreboding black castle atop a nearby promontory.

The safest path to the Tower lay beneath hundreds of meters of rock. Skywalker and Jade picked their way through dripping underground tunnels, using their lightsabers to clear stalagmites and foil predators. Eventually they reached their destination and discovered the High Tower's true purpose.

Nirauan's High Tower, also known as the Hand of Thrawn, had been Grand Admiral Thrawn's base of power back when he had been sent by Emperor Palpatine to scout the Unknown Regions. Thrawn had succeeded beyond the Emperor's wildest dreams: an immense new swath of previously undiscovered territory had been meticulously mapped and cataloged, representing a bottomless new source of resources that could turn the Empire from victim to vanquisher in a single day. And the Hand of Thrawn's occupants had

every intention of turning their closely guarded prize over to the current Imperial leadership on Bastion.

Admiral Voss Parck—a longtime associate of Thrawn's from the Empire's early days—operated the stronghold, along with many blue-skinned, red-eyed Chiss. They had been waiting on Nirauan for a decade, for Thrawn had always promised his followers that if he should ever be killed, he would come back to them in ten years' time. Parck, Baron Soontir Fel, and other former Imperials now lived in the Unknown Regions, where they worked alongside Chiss soldiers in a kingdom called the Empire of the Hand. Their realm did not answer to either the Empire or the Chiss Ascendancy.

Skywalker and Jade realized that they couldn't allow Parck to contact Bastion. The two Jedi escaped the castle, and Mara used the beckon call installed aboard *Jade's Fire* to rouse her cherished ship and guide it directly into the Hand of Thrawn's docking bay, destroying every craft on the launching pad.

But that was not enough, and they both knew it. Luke and Mara returned to the enemy citadel, this time arriving at a series of chambers far beneath the structure's foundation. There, in a room so protected that not even Parck knew of it, they found a Spaarti cloning cylinder. And floating inside the cylinder was a fully grown clone of Grand Admiral Thrawn.

Their difficult moral choice—to execute a helpless being or to stand aside and allow a new Thrawn to possibly resubjugate the galaxy—was decided for them. The room's automated defensive systems focused hot blasterfire on the intruders, weakening the chamber's rock wall. With an angry gurgle, thousands of gallons of icy lake water flooded the room and drowned the Thrawn clone before it could be born. Luke and Mara escaped, waterlogged but very much alive.

Over the past decade, Luke and Mara had progressed from enemies to friends to fellow Jedi. But their experiences on Nirauan marked a turning point in their relationship. They both realized that no two people in the universe were

A clone of Grand Admiral Thrawn nears completion in the fortress on Nirauan. [ART BY TOMMY LEE EDWARDS]

so perfectly matched in ability and in attitude, in strength and in spirit. Though they didn't always see eye-to-eye, their differences complemented one another perfectly, meshing together peak-to-valley in a hold that was far stronger than either standing alone. Luke Skywalker proposed marriage. Mara Jade accepted.

The two lovers left Nirauan behind in a stolen alien starship and headed back to the New Republic with a copy of the Caamas Document gleaned from Thrawn's personal library.

THE MARRIAGE OF LUKE AND MARA
19 A.B.Y.

Symbolically, the union of Luke Skywalker and Mara Jade held even more value than the signing of the peace treaty. The marriage of the Rebel Alliance's iconic hero to the woman who had once been Emperor Palpatine's top assassin drew attention from all corners of the galaxy, including the embittered residents of the shrunken Empire, now called the "Imperial Remnant" on New Republic maps.

To those who had once claimed near-total dominion over known space, their territory, no matter how small, would always be known as the Empire. On snowy Dolis 3, a band of Imperial partisans viewed the looming nuptials with contempt. Believing the event to be more proof that the Empire had been watered down like weak caf, the loyalists made plans to slip into Coruscant and sabotage the ceremony.

One of their number claimed to be a former Royal Guardsman, and though his experience was likely a mere boast, his attempt to kill Mara Jade during her dress fitting gave a murderous edge to the plot. The other Imperials focused on infiltrating the event site and hiring a gang of swoopbikers to harass the wedding guests.

Despite the scheming, the wedding went off with minimum mayhem. Following Luke's raucous bachelor party in Coruscant's lower levels, the happy couple joined together in a private Jedi ceremony officiated by Kam Solusar in the renovated Jedi Temple. The public ceremony, held in Coruscant's Reflection Gardens, remained peaceful thanks to extra muscle provided by Booster Terrik and others, who kept the swoopbikers at bay. When the final Imperial plotter crashed the ceremony and threatened to release a crippling computer virus, Luke persuaded him to give himself up and join the party. With that quiet denouncement, a generation of hostilities suddenly seemed as dead as Palpatine himself. Weeks later, Lando Calrissian wed Tendra Risant, the woman he had met during the events of the Corellian insurrection.

After his wedding, Luke Skywalker decided to alter the instruction schedule of his Yavin academy, devoting more time to the training of younger pupils. Some of the more advanced trainees left Yavin 4 to engage in one-on-one Master–apprentice relationships throughout the galaxy. Tionne took over many of the historical chores, enriching the legacy of the Jedi Knights. Mara Jade insisted that she was no teacher and spent little time on the jungle moon, even when her husband returned to the praxeum to address his students.

Generations of Jedi Knights

The armistice brought about by the Pellaeon–Gavrisom treaty was a durable peace. Three long, quiet years passed, blissfully uninterrupted by Imperial schemes, mad Jedi, local brushfires, or unexpected alien invasions.

After more than a decade of labor, Luke Skywalker had many successes in his Jedi praxeum on Yavin 4. He had found many new trainees, some human and some exotic. However, because Skywalker was frequently called away on his own adventures and also to spend time with Mara Jade, one of his first trainees—the scholar and minstrel Tionne— took over Luke's duties. Interplanetary squabbles and trade conflicts were as much a constant as always. At the urging of her friends in the government, Leia Organa Solo ran again for the post of New Republic Chief of State, and was elected back into that office in 21 A.B.Y. Organa Solo's three children, the twins Jacen and Jaina and her younger son Anakin, all had a strong talent in the Force. The three youths spent much time at the Jedi academy.

THE GOLDEN GLOBE AND KENOBI'S LIGHTSABER
22 A.B.Y.

Though there had been a few lessons in historic Jedi Holocrons regarding the training of extremely young children, Luke Skywalker was unaware of any specific rule for the age at which a talented person could begin to learn the ways of the Force. Anakin Solo came to the Jedi academy when he was midway through his eleventh year. Different from his outgoing twin siblings, Anakin was studious and reserved, often a loner. He liked puzzles, mysteries, mental challenges, and brainteasers. On Yavin 4 he

befriended a young girl named Tahiri Veila, who had grown up with the Tusken Raiders of Tatooine, keeping her face fully bandaged and breathing through metal filters until discovered by the Jedi instructor Tionne.

Anakin and Tahiri crossed the nearby jungle river to the Palace of the Woolamander, a crumbling ruin abandoned ages before. Both young trainees had been drawn there by identical dreams. As they explored the dim ruins, they broke into a sealed chamber that contained a glowing sphere of golden light. Curled up at its base lay a mysterious furry creature, deep in sleep; it had large eyes, floppy ears, and simian features. The furry being identified himself as Ikrit, a Kushiban Jedi Master who had come to the jungle moon to study the Massassi temples four centuries earlier. He had discovered the golden globe, but could not break its curse, and he had been hibernating ever since.

After journeying to the nearby moon of Yavin 8, they learned that the golden globe contained the trapped spirits of young Massassi victims of Exar Kun's experimentations. Anakin and Tahiri broke past the barricades erected long before by Exar Kun, and freed the trapped Massassi spirits. When the two emerged, they found Luke Skywalker waiting for them, standing beside Ikrit.

Anakin remained troubled by dreams of himself as a Dark Jedi, by his heritage as the grandson—and original namesake—of Darth Vader. When Leia Organa Solo was pregnant with Anakin, the resurrected Emperor had touched her and tried to take over the unborn child. To be sure that he didn't have the potential for evil inside him, young Anakin asked if he could go to the cave on Dagobah, as Luke Skywalker had done, and face himself.

Before arrangements could be made, a stowaway teenager was found on one of the supply ships to the Jedi academy. The young man, Uldir Lochett, begged Skywalker to train him as a Jedi—though when tested, Uldir showed no Force potential whatsoever. When Anakin, Tahiri, and Ikrit traveled to Dagobah, Uldir stowed away again and fell into trouble with some swamp creatures. The group finally reached the cave where Skywalker had faced his own dark side during his training with Yoda; there, Anakin faced down the manifestations of his own doubts and fears and emerged with confidence.

Back on Yavin 4, the Jedi historian Tionne had learned that Darth Vader had saved Obi-Wan Kenobi's lightsaber after their fight aboard the Death Star. It had been sent to Vader's stronghold, Bast Castle, on Vjun. Tionne, Ikrit, Anakin, Tahiri, and Uldir made the journey to Vjun, but as soon as they had retrieved the artifact, a group of mercenaries and pirates stormed into the room. Their leader, Orloc, claimed to be a Mage with great powers. In a brief confrontation, Orloc tempted Uldir, promising the powerless boy that Orloc could grant him all the Jedi skills that Uldir wished. But Tionne, Ikrit, and the others rescued him and retrieved the lightsaber, as well as a Holocron filled with Jedi knowledge.

Uldir remained obsessed with what the Mage had told him. He stole both artifacts and a ship and fled to find Orloc. Anakin, Tahiri, Tionne, and Ikrit pursued him to an ancient ghost city in space, Exis Station, where Tionne herself had met Luke Skywalker in her search for relics. There, Mage Orloc had set up his base and taken Uldir as a new recruit. Orloc actually had no Force talent himself, but used high-tech gimmicks to fool others with demonstrations of "power."

In a battle of Force versus fake technomagic, Uldir saw true Jedi power in action. He helped to defeat Orloc and left Exis Station with the Holocron and Kenobi's lightsaber. The students returned to the Jedi academy, knowing they still had much to learn—and many years yet in which to do so.

THE RETURN OF OUTBOUND FLIGHT
22 A.B.Y.

The Outbound Flight Project had been one of the curiosities of the Old Republic, nearly forgotten in the rush of the Clone Wars and the Jedi Purge that followed. Certainly, no one had expected to hear from the Outbound Flight Dreadnaughts after their disappearance a half century earlier. Luke Skywalker and Mara Jade believed that Grand Admiral Thrawn had destroyed the vessels during his early career as a Chiss military renegade.

Now, however, Luke and Mara received word that their assumptions about Outbound Flight may have been faulty. Through Admiral Parck at Nirauan's Hand of Thrawn base, the two Jedi learned that the Chiss had located the remains of the Outbound Flight vessels in an inaccessible pocket of the Unknown Regions known as the Redoubt. As official representatives of the New Republic, Luke and Mara boarded the Chiss Diplomatic Vessel *Chaf Envoy* for the long journey into the heart of the Redoubt.

The ship's other passengers appeared to be evenly split between politicians and pilgrims. Aristocra Formbi, the head Chiss aboard *Chaf Envoy,* welcomed guests that included Commander Chak Fel (one of the sons of Baron Soontir Fel) of the Empire of the Hand; Dean Jinzler of the New Republic, who wanted to see Outbound Flight to honor his Jedi sister; and a mass of timid Geroons who wished to pay their respects to the Outbound Flight Jedi who had freed them from their "Vagaari enslavers."

Eventually reaching a planetoid inside the Redoubt, the passengers of *Chaf Envoy* discovered that, while the Outbound Flight Dreadnaughts still hung together in their original hexagonal-linked configuration, only the topmost Dreadnaught protruded above the loose shale that passed for a surface on the irradiated world. Within the junk-strewn corridors of the vessel, they soon made two shocking discoveries: a band of crash survivors had established a colony and

The final resting place of the Outbound Flight Project.
[ART BY TOMMY LEE EDWARDS]

remained alive for the last five decades, and the Geroon penitents were not the innocents they had claimed to be. Rather, the Geroon *were* the Vagaari slavers, come to take revenge on the Chiss for defeating them long ago.

As Vagaari troopers fanned out to assume control of the Outbound Flight complex, Luke and Mara worked with Commander Fel's stormtroopers and several of the colonists to minimize the bedlam. Most of the Vagaari packed aboard the uppermost Dreadnaught, freed it from its sister ships with explosive charges, and escaped into space. Pursuit seemed impossible until one of the colonists revealed the existence of a mothballed starfighter. Luke and Mara activated the craft, caught up to the Dreadnaught, and eliminated the threat posed by the Vagaari renegades.

In the aftermath, Aristocra Formbi revealed that the Chiss had known the nature of the Geroon/Vagaari ruse all along. Since the Chiss had a moral principle against making first strikes, Formbi had hoped the Vagaari would take advantage of the Outbound Flight bait and make an aggressive move. Now that they had, war had been declared between the Chiss Ascendancy and the Vagaari.

Dean Jinzler found closure, realizing that his sister had done everything she could to protect Outbound Flight, and had died with honor during Thrawn's attack. The Outbound Flight colonists left the Redoubt, the only home they'd known for decades. Most of them began new lives in the Empire of the Hand.

THE SHADOW ACADEMY AND THE SECOND IMPERIUM
23 A.B.Y.

The Solo twins—Jacen with his quirky sense of humor and rapport with animals, and Jaina with her aptitude for mechanics—became two of the most talented of the new generation of Jedi Knights. Together with their companions Tenel Ka, warrior daughter of Prince Isolder of Hapes and Teneniel Djo of Dathomir, and Lowbacca, the Wookiee nephew of Chewbacca, they fought for the New Republic with as much bravery as the legendary Jedi Knights of old.

During a training exercise in the jungles of Yavin 4, the young Jedi Knights discovered the wreckage of a TIE fighter—an Imperial ship that had crashed there years before, during the Rebel battle against the first Death Star. The Jedi Knights were unaware that the original pilot, a grizzled old man named Qorl, had survived the crash and had been eking out a living in the wilderness. Qorl forced the Jedi students to complete the final repairs so that he could flee the jungle moon, and then flew off to rejoin the Empire . . . wherever he could find it.

Months later, as the Jedi continued their training, Jacen, Jaina, and Lowbacca accompanied Lando Calrissian to his new Corusca gem mining facility, *GemDiver Station,* in the atmosphere of the gas giant Yavin. While Calrissian showed them his operations, the station came under attack by a frightening black-clad woman, Tamith Kai, one of the Nightsisters of Dathomir. Jacen, Jaina, and Lowbacca were stunned and taken prisoner.

They awoke aboard the Shadow Academy, a cloaked space station that acted as a dark counterpart to Skywalker's Jedi academy. Brakiss, the former academy student who had assisted in the Almanian Uprising six years earlier, now headed the Shadow Academy on behalf of the Second Imperium, a radical Imperial group that did not recognize the "sham" peace accords signed by Pellaeon. The Nightsister Tamith Kai, along with the former TIE pilot Qorl, planned to use Jacen, Jaina, and Lowbacca as recruits for Imperial brainwashing.

The captives resisted all attempts to convert them to the dark side. They escaped, with some surprising assistance from the troubled TIE pilot Qorl.

Returning to Coruscant to spend time with Han Solo and Leia Organa Solo, the young Jedi Knights recovered from their ordeals. They explored the lower levels of the huge planetary city with Zekk, an orphaned street urchin the twins had known for years. Soon, however, Zekk—along with the members of the Lost Ones street gang—became a new recruit for the Shadow Academy.

Aboard the Shadow Academy, Brakiss showed Zekk how

Jacen Solo and Tenel Ka
[ART BY JOHN VAN FLEET]

Republic military forces. The Shadow Academy vanished into hyperspace, once again foiling pursuit.

With the known threat of the Shadow Academy and the Second Imperium, Luke Skywalker decided that his students must build their own lightsabers. When finished, the students trained against remotes and then each other—but in a tragic accident during a sparring match against Jacen Solo, Tenel Ka lost her arm when her weapon failed.

Recuperating, Tenel Ka went home to be pampered on the wealthy world of Hapes, home of her father, Isolder. She refused to be fitted with an artificial arm. While on Hapes, Tenel Ka and her Jedi friends foiled an assassination attempt designed to overthrow Tenel Ka's grandmother Ta'a Chume.

Agents of the Second Imperium struck next on Kashyyyk, with the intention of raiding New Republic stores of powerful new computer units. Zekk led the Imperial commando team. Jacen, Jaina, Tenel Ka, and Lowbacca defeated most of the Imperial troops, and Jaina faced off against her former friend Zekk in the deep jungle. Zekk could not bring himself to hurt her, but he warned her to stay away from Yavin 4.

On the Shadow Academy itself, Brakiss had learned the astonishing news that Emperor Palpatine himself was coming to the cloaked station. Brought aboard in a giant isolation tank on repulsorlifts, "Palpatine" gave no explanations as to how he had survived the destruction of all his clones years earlier. The Emperor's red-armored Royal Guards, who blocked all of Brakiss's inquiries, were former stormtroopers promoted to guardsman status during Admiral Daala's rule, as a symbolic display of power.

to tap into unsuspected Jedi potential. Suddenly, Zekk found himself in control of great powers he had never dreamed of—and became an easy mark for Imperial brainwashing. He turned into one of the most exceptional of the new Dark Jedi.

Jacen, Jaina, and their friends discovered that Zekk had been taken captive—and that the Imperial station was secretly in orbit around Coruscant itself. Using giant solar mirrors in space, they burned out the Shadow Academy's cloaking systems and exposed the station to rallying New

(The last true Royal Guard had been Kir Kanos; Major Tierce had been a simple clone.)

On Yavin 4, the young Jedi Knights braced for an attack by the Shadow Academy. Imperial assault teams dropped to the surface: TIE fighters, stormtroopers, and swarms of Dark Jedi Knights led by Zekk and the Nightsister Tamith Kai. Tenel Ka sabotaged Tamith Kai's floating battle platform and the structure crashed into the river, killing the Nightsister.

When the tides of battle turned against him, Brakiss demanded to see the Emperor. Two Imperial guards blocked his way, but Brakiss cut them down with his lightsaber, then chopped through the door of Palpatine's isolation chamber. Inside, he found a third guard working a bank of controls, computer screens, and hologrammic generators, maintaining the illusion that Palpatine had returned to lead the Second Imperium. The last guard escaped before using the override controls to trigger the Shadow Academy's self-destruct systems. The giant station turned into a fireball.

On Yavin 4, an Imperial soldier planted a bomb inside the Great Temple, but Zekk prevented the Jedi from entering, saving all their lives. He was a broken young man now, realizing what damage he had caused and how he had betrayed his friends. The bomb's explosion destroyed much of the Great Temple.

The Second Imperium had been quashed in a single major confrontation, the Shadow Academy destroyed, and the remaining Imperials and Dark Jedi taken prisoner. Qorl, the castaway TIE pilot, returned to his former life in the jungle.

THE DIVERSITY ALLIANCE
23–24 A.B.Y.

Skywalker's trainees set to work rebuilding the academy. While Zekk recovered from his injuries, he was haunted by nightmares stemming from his deep involvement with the dark side. Zekk never wanted to use the Force again. He left Yavin 4 in search of his home, in search of peace, and eventually decided to use his talents to become a bounty hunter.

During the repairs, Han Solo arrived with a grim message for Jedi student Raynar Thul, a prince of the surviving highborn family that had escaped Alderaan. Raynar's father, Bornan Thul, a wealthy merchant and shipping magnate, had disappeared while en route to an important trade meeting with the Twi'lek Nolaa Tarkona, leader of the radical Diversity Alliance, an "aliens first" political movement.

Nolaa Tarkona was the embittered half sister of the dancing girl Oola whom Jabba the Hutt had fed to his pet rancor. By being both vicious and skillful, Nolaa had succeeded in becoming the first female leader of her race. She held many charismatic and enthusiastic rallies, whipping up support for her all-alien Diversity Alliance, whose ultimate goal was to punish humans for the horrors of the Empire and past excesses. From the Twi'lek world of Ryloth, she offered a huge reward for Thul, and most especially for the mysterious cargo he carried.

Ailyn Vel, believed to be the daughter of bounty hunter Boba Fett, assumed the identity of her renowned father and took up the Thul bounty. The Fett impersonator tried to capture the Solo children near the remains of Alderaan, but Zekk drove the bounty hunter off. Jaina tried to convince Zekk to come back with them, but now he was even more determined to make his own life. Later he, too, decided to search for Bornan Thul.

Hoping to track down Thul themselves, the young Jedi Knights searched the man's last known locations, from ancient ruined worlds to the droid factories of Mechis III. They found a female Wookiee named Raaba who had joined the Diversity Alliance. Raaba recruited Lowbacca to leave his friends and come with her to Ryloth, so that he could learn more about the antihuman organization.

On Thul's trail, Zekk learned that Thul had stumbled upon the location of a secret asteroid laboratory that held stockpiles of horrific plagues. This research center had been the scientific headquarters of the Imperial scientist Evir Derricote, who had unleashed the devastating Krytos plague in the early days of the New Republic. Though Derricote was long dead, his legacy of disease and death remained sealed on the asteroid. In her political fervor, Nolaa Tarkona wanted to exterminate humanity, and needed Thul so that she could uncover the Emperor's plague storehouse.

Terrorist acts against humans escalated, including several assassination attempts. The young Jedi Knights journeyed to Ryloth to bring Lowbacca back, and barely escaped from a sentence of slavery in the ryll spice caverns. Master Skywalker requested an inspection tour be sent to Ryloth, and Nolaa Tarkona frantically covered her tracks.

The Fett impersonator had also succeeded in tracking down the location of the plague storehouse and, per contract, reported it to the Diversity Alliance. Nolaa Tarkona set off with her forces to obtain the Emperor's human-killing pestilence. Zekk and his Jedi friends set to work planting explosive charges throughout the asteroid depot in a race against time.

Summoned by the young Jedi Knights, the New Republic emergency fleet arrived, led by Han Solo. The fleet engaged the Diversity Alliance ships in orbit, while commandos below set off explosions to wreck the Imperial weapons depot. Bornan Thul sealed himself inside the central containment chamber that held the disease solution, trapped with Nolaa Tarkona. When they fired upon him, the plague cylinders cracked. Thul died, hoping he had succeeded in denying the Diversity Alliance access to the bioweapon. Nolaa Tarkona escaped, but didn't realize that she had been infected by one of the alternate strains of Derricote's plagues. She died alone in quarantine on an asteroid not long afterward.

Jaina Solo and Zekk
[ART BY JOHN VAN FLEET]

THE RETURN OF BLACK SUN
24 A.B.Y.

Finally, after confronting his dark past, Zekk agreed to stay at the Jedi praxeum to learn to control his anger. Zekk later won the Blockade Runners Derby at Ord Mantell, a classic race judged by Han Solo, one of its previous champions. Czethros, a race sponsor, had once been an enemy of Solo's, but now claimed to be a respectable businessman.

A mysterious young woman, Anja, helped Han drive off some chameleon creatures in the hangar bay. Anja had her own lightsaber, but no Jedi training, relying instead on doses of spice to enhance her senses. She revealed that she was the daughter of Gallandro, the gunslinger whom Han Solo had battled in his early smuggling days. Anja, who believed that Han had murdered her father, had vowed revenge.

Anja worked for Czethros, who was in reality a leader of the Black Sun criminal organization. Black Sun had kept a low profile for years, but continued to work behind the scenes, infiltrating agents into positions of political and economic power throughout the New Republic. Czethros had addicted Anja to spice in order to keep her under his thumb.

Han promised to show Anja his good side by helping in the civil war that had ravaged Anja's planet Anobis for so long. When *Millennium Falcon* arrived on Anobis, Solo met with the two factions and brokered an uneasy peace. Anja began to wonder if her hatred might have been misplaced. She agreed to join Jacen, Jaina, and the others back at the Jedi academy to see what she could learn from Master Skywalker.

Lando Calrissian, who still owned *GemDiver Station* around Yavin, had repurchased a controlling interest in the spice mines of Kessel several years earlier with dividends from a mining operation on Varn. He had invested the profits in his new commercial venture, SkyCenter Galleria, an amusement park on Cloud City. He and his business partner Cojahn wanted the Solo twins and their friends to be "test subjects" for the new attraction.

When they arrived at Cloud City, Calrissian learned that his partner Cojahn was dead. The Jedi investigated, and discovered that Czethros had tried to extort cooperation from Cojahn in order to control the casinos for Black Sun. When Cojahn refused, Czethros had murdered him.

New Republic investigation teams searched the galaxy for Czethros, but he had gone to ground, hoping to set in motion the final stage of his plot for a government takeover. But Anja realized that without Czethros around, she had no supplier for the spice that fed her addiction. Desperate, she slipped away from the academy, stole Zekk's ship, and flew off to retrieve a spice stash hidden under the polar ice cap of Mon Calamari.

The Sullustan Nien Nunb, Calrissian's longtime manager of the Kessel mines, barely survived an "accident" in the carbon-freezing sections of the processing facility. Black Sun had infiltrated even here, and Nien Nunb felt he was in great danger. His own workers were turning against him.

Jaina and Lowbacca agreed to help Nien Nunb on Kessel, while Jacen, Zekk, and Tenel Ka raced off to Mon Calamari to catch up with Anja. At the floating resort city of Crystal Reef, they confronted her as she tried to lease a mini sub to explore the ice cap. By now Anja had admitted her addiction to spice, and she meant to get her revenge on Czethros by destroying his Mon Calamari stockpile.

The Jedi trainees followed her to the ice cap, where she destroyed the drug stash. During their escape through the ice from a sea creature, the Jedi used healing techniques to free Anja of her chemical addiction to spice—though she would have to deal with the mental part herself.

On Kessel, Czethros had landed with an army of mercenaries. Black Sun took over the planet's spice mines. Nien Nunb became a prisoner, but Jaina and Lowbacca hid in the tunnels and learned that Black Sun had established infiltrators in the government, in the military, and on numerous allied planets and industrial stations. From his new HQ on Kessel, Czethros planned to send a signal that would call them to arms.

However, Czethros did not count on the sabotage work of Jaina and Lowbacca, who destroyed the transmitter before Black Sun could send its signal. They also freed the prisoners in the spice mines and drove back the mercenaries who had taken over Kessel. Rather than allow himself to be captured, Czethros fell into a vat of carbonite. Later, Chief of State Leia Organa Solo supervised his unthawing and interrogation and uncovered the names of the Black Sun infiltrators who remained.

After their numerous successes, Master Luke Skywalker declared that his group of young trainees could now consider themselves full Jedi Knights—a new generation of defenders for the New Republic.

PART TWELVE

The New Jedi Order

It was a time for transitions. Mon Mothma, the Rebellion's guiding spirit, died peacefully in her sleep. Borsk Fey'lya, also a longtime member of the Rebellion, but about as different from Mon Mothma as it was possible to be, ascended to the office of Chief of State after Leia's voluntary retirement, despite several dark scandals in his past.

Luke Skywalker's new Jedi order found itself at a crossroads. Since the dawn of the Jedi, tension had existed between the meditative Jedi consulars and the more militaristic Jedi guardians. Now, with the first true peace the galaxy had known in decades, Luke's Jedi showed signs of philosophical fracture.

Luke, dividing his time between Coruscant and Yavin 4, considered reestablishing the concept of a ruling Jedi council. Other, more proactive Jedi Knights followed the lead of Kyp Durron and found new targets for their aggression. Durron and his former apprentice Miko Reglia formed a freelance starfighter squadron called the Dozen-and-Two Avengers to harass smugglers in the Outer Rim. Jaina Solo found herself increasingly attracted to Kyp's aggressive faction; Anakin Solo remained loyal to his Uncle Luke. Jacen Solo found himself wondering if he could follow the Force without having to pick sides.

Mara Jade, now a Jedi Master, supported her husband's efforts to keep the Jedi order focused, but grew weaker and weaker, victim of a mysterious ailment she had contracted during a diplomatic meeting on Monor II, a meeting at which professional firebrand Nom Anor had been present. Years before, Anor had manipulated Carnor Jax's Interim Council; now he was stirring up trouble between the planets of Rhommamool and Osarian. Soon, Anor would drop his façade and reveal his true identity as an advance agent.

Nom Anor, and Mara's disease, were harbingers of a much greater threat. All of the galaxy's major powers—the New Republic, the Empire, the Hutts, and the Chiss—would soon be pushed to the brink of extinction by invaders from outside.

THE INVASION BEGINS
25 A.B.Y.

The Yuuzhan Vong came from another galaxy. In their legends, they had once fought against a machine-based civilization that solidified their hatred of high technology. The Yuuzhan Vong had developed a society in which everything was grown, cloned, or otherwise bioengineered, from handcuffs to worldships the size of moons. Their love for organic grafting extended to themselves, and ritual mutilation and the replacement of body parts came to signify veneration of the gods.

The gods of the Yuuzhan Vong, who all stood beneath Yun-Yuuzhan the Creator, were closely aligned with their rigid caste system. Yun-Yammka the Slayer was the patron god of warriors. Yun-Harla the Trickster was often associated with priests. Yun-Ne'Shel the Modeler was invoked by shapers, the members of the bioengineering caste. Members of the intendant and worker castes could call any god their own, including Yun-Txiin and Yun-Q'aah, the Lovers. Yun-Shuno the Pardoner was the patron god of the Shamed Ones—those Yuuzhan Vong from every caste whose bodies had rejected biological implants of rank. Curiously, all

Yuuzhan Vong seemed to be unable to use, or even register within, the universal energy field of the Force.

The Yuuzhan Vong had embarked on a nomadic lifestyle following the ancient Cremlevian War, in which Supreme Overlord Yo'gand defeated Warmaster Steng by dropping a moon on his encampment. With many of their colony planets destroyed, including their homeworld of Yuuzhan'tar, their warrior society continued its program of aggressive religious fanaticism. After thousands of years, they had bled dry their home galaxy. The Yuuzhan Vong eventually found themselves aboard a fleet of worldships, wandering the void between galaxies in search of a new home.

Our galaxy was first scouted long ago, first by Yuuzhan Vong–engineered slivilith creatures and, starting during the Clone Wars, by advance bands of scouts and political infiltrators. At 29 B.B.Y., Supreme Overlord Quoreal, leader of the worldship fleet, received word of his scouts' encounter with the living planet Zonama Sekot. Quoreal recognized that Zonama Sekot held some connection to his home galaxy, but didn't realize it was actually a seed of Yuuzhan'tar, grown to full size after the destruction of its "parent" world. Nevertheless, Quoreal believed the legends that said such a planet could bring about the end of his species, and declared that the Yuuzhan Vong would leave this galaxy in peace and continue their wanderings.

The news made Quoreal suddenly unpopular, and a rival named Shimrra chose that moment to usurp the throne. Shimrra covered up the evidence of Zonama Sekot's existence. He distracted his people with the announcement that the gods had declared this galaxy to be the rightful home of the Yuuzhan Vong—once it had been purified of infidels. Now the time had come to strike.

The first invasion ship breached the galactic disk in the northern fringe, far from any major population centers. The vessel, easily mistaken for an asteroid or comet, carried legions of Yuuzhan Vong warriors belonging to the advance force known as the Praetorite Vong.

Two embedded Yuuzhan Vong infiltrators helped prepare the way for the Praetorite Vong. On Belkadan, site of a New Republic research outpost, agent Yomin Carr killed most of the outpost's staff and released a plague into the atmosphere that would reshape the planet into a biofactory. On Rhommamool, Nom Anor had touched off war between that planet and its sister world, Osarian. Both actions helped distract the New Republic long enough for the Praetorite Vong worldship to reach the ice world Helska 4 and unload its "war coordinator"—a colossal, tentacled brain known as a yammosk.

Several scientists from the Belkadan outpost had been offplanet at the time of Yomin Carr's sabotage. They stumbled across the new Yuuzhan Vong headquarters at Helska, as did the Dozen-and-Two Avengers under Kyp Durron's command. The Yuuzhan Vong's acid-secreting grutchin insects made short work of both groups. Only Kyp Durron escaped. The Yuuzhan Vong captured the scientist Danni Quee and Kyp's Jedi lieutenant Miko Reglia.

Pieces of the puzzle started to come together when Luke and Mara arrived at ruined Belkadan. Defeating an enraged Yomin Carr and witnessing the speed of the planet's environmental reprogramming, they realized the face of their enemy and the breathtaking extent of their foes' biology-based powers.

THE DEATH OF CHEWBACCA
25 A.B.Y.

Altering the atmosphere of a planet paled next to what the Yuuzhan Vong did then, at the Outer Rim world of Sernpidal. Using the tactic they called "Yo'gand's Core," the Yuuzhan Vong used a gravity-altering dovin basal creature to pull the planet's moon Dobido down to a shattering collision. Han Solo, Anakin Solo, and Chewbacca, all present on Sernpidal during a supply run for Lando Calrissian, did all they could to save the doomed world, but not even the Force could slow the moon once it had slipped into a terminal orbit.

Loading *Millennium Falcon* with refugees as Dobido loomed overhead, Chewbacca paused to help Anakin, who

Chewbacca dies a hero's death on Sernpidal.
[ART BY TOMMY LEE EDWARDS]

had fallen. Chewie threw Anakin aboard the *Falcon,* but his actions had cost him precious seconds. Anakin believed that the *Falcon* and its passengers would not survive if they remained in the area to make a pickup for Chewbacca, and he rocketed the ship away from Sernpidal at full speed. Han, watching from the boarding ramp, saw Chewbacca receding in the distance, his fists raised in defiance at the sinking moon as the atmosphere superheated around him.

After the Sernpidal atrocity, the Yuuzhan Vong could no longer operate in secret. The warships of the Praetorite Vong attacked Dubrillion—site of Lando Calrissian's latest moneymaking venture—and massed for more assaults. Borsk Fey'lya and the New Republic leaders on Coruscant remained skeptical of the threat. The only battleship Leia could recruit for a counterattack on the Yuuzhan Vong forward base was the Star Destroyer *Rejuvenator.*

This inadequate force moved against the Yuuzhan Vong at Helska 4 and failed spectacularly, victim of the New Republic's ignorance of the enemy's technology. Though Jacen Solo rescued Danni Quee from imprisonment, the Yuuzhan Vong yammosk coordinated a swarm of coralskipper starfighters, who used their shield-stripping dovin basals to annihilate the *Rejuvenator.* Jedi Knight Miko Reglia also died during the fighting.

The crushed New Republic forces withdrew, but returned for a second Battle of Helska 4. This time, they came with a small fleet of umbrella-shaped shieldships. Using the shieldships to accelerate the plant's natural evaporation, they froze the world and killed the real threat—the yammosk embedded under the ice. The entire planet of Helska shattered under the strain.

The victory at Helska provided some breathing room. Two months passed while the main Yuuzhan Vong force assembled its own invasion fleet. On Coruscant, Borsk Fey'lya claimed the lull was proof that no threat was imminent. Some elements of the New Republic military, including Bothan Admiral Kre'fey of the assault carrier *Ralroost* and Colonel Gavin Darklighter of Rogue Squadron, knew better. They risked insubordination and court-martial by remaining on high alert.

The death of Chewbacca had deep repercussions for the Solo family. Han sank into a deep depression, blaming Lando for sending him on the Sernpidal mission and Anakin for choosing to fly away when he did. Leia found herself unable to connect with her husband. Anakin, wondering if he'd done the right thing, recommitted himself to the fight against the Yuuzhan Vong. C-3PO and R2-D2 used the time to compile an oral history of Chewbacca from those who had known him best. Among those interviewed was Chewie's father Attichitcuk, who sighed, "No father should ever outlive his own son."

DANTOOINE ONSLAUGHT
25.2 A.B.Y.

On Yavin 4, Luke Skywalker assembled all his Jedi Knights for a council of war. Though Kyp Durron ached for a bloodier role, most Jedi departed on scouting missions to ascertain the extent of the danger.

Corran Horn and Ganner Rhysode went to sand-swept Bimmiel in the Outer Rim, where an archaeological team had uncovered the remains of a Yuuzhan Vong warrior, mummified after fifty years in the desert. They discovered that the Yuuzhan Vong had already beat them to Bimmiel, and Corran and Ganner enlisted the planet's native slashrats to help them wipe out the enemy's slave colony. Yuuzhan Vong commander Shedao Shai arrived in the aftermath of the battle, and saw that the hated *Jeedai* Knights had disturbed the body of his ancestor Mongei Shai. Enraged, he vowed to kill Corran Horn and taste his blood.

Luke and Jacen arrived at Belkadan, discovering that the Yuuzhan Vong–terraformed planet now served as a "farm" for growing new coralskipper starfighters. The slaves toiling in the jungle fields remained docile due to chunks of surge-coral implanted in their faces. Jacen recklessly tried to rescue them and became a prisoner himself, but Luke fought for Jacen's freedom and both Jedi escaped Belkadan.

Mara Jade and Anakin Solo traveled to Dantooine, where Mara hoped to halt the progress of her disease in the un-

Corran Horn battles Shedao Shai for the fate of Ithor.
[ART BY TOMMY LEE EDWARDS]

spoiled expanses of the gentle grasslands. Yet the Yuuzhan Vong invaders had already reached Dantooine, and what should have been a peaceful convalescence turned into a gritty struggle to stay alive.

As it turned out, Mara and Anakin soon had plenty of company. Lando Calrissian had decided to evacuate the citizens of Dubrillion before the Yuuzhan Vong could finish the job they'd begun two months prior. Thousands of Dubrillion refugees arrived on Dantooine, and the Yuuzhan Vong soon followed.

The Battle of Dantooine began as a slaughter. The Yuuzhan Vong used the opportunity to test new ground tactics against their prey, unveiling beetle-like crawlers and throngs of reptilian Chazrach slaves from their home galaxy. The Jedi staged delaying actions, allowing most of the surviv-

ing refugees to pack up and head for space, where Rogue Squadron (including its newest member, Jaina Solo) and Admiral Kre'fey of the *Ralroost* helped them escape to hyperspace. Dantooine remained in the hands of the enemy.

THE RUIN OF ITHOR
25.3 A.B.Y.

Commander Shedao Shai hadn't forgotten his vow to kill Corran Horn. During this, the first phase of the invasion, Shai had been tasked with paving the way for the arrival of the Yuuzhan Vong's warmaster, Tsavong Lah. No fan of Lah's, Shai hoped to consolidate his own power by eliminating the hated *Jeedai*.

New Republic Senator Elegos A'Kla, under a flag of am-

bassadorial truce, met with Shedao Shai at the new Yuuzhan Vong headquarters on Dubrillion. At first amused by the weakling Caamasi, Commander Shai eventually grew tired of A'Kla and murdered him. Knowing that A'Kla and Corran Horn had been friends, Shai believed he could use the act as a challenge to Horn's honor.

Corran Horn had been busy with a mission to Yuuzhan Vong–occupied Garqi, where his forces rescued several slaves and accidentally discovered a critical secret—the pollen of the bafforr tree reacted violently with the vonduun crab armor worn by all Yuuzhan Vong warriors. Bafforr trees were native to Ithor, the unspoiled homeworld of the "Hammerhead" Ithorian pacifists. Ithor had unwittingly become a target in the war.

Forces began to gather above Ithor. Admiral Pellaeon of the Empire arrived to lend a hand. A squadron of enigmatic Chiss aliens from the Unknown Regions also made an appearance, led by Jagged Fel, the eighteen-year-old son of Baron Soontir Fel and Syal Antilles (the sister of Wedge Antilles). Anakin Solo also showed up, fresh from an adventure where he had helped stop two rogue Jedi from reactivating old Imperial superweapons for use against the Yuuzhan Vong.

Shedao Shai dispatched a shuttle to Ithor. It contained the bejeweled skeleton of Elegos A'Kla, bearing a message to Corran Horn explaining that *this* was the proper way to venerate the dead. Shortly after, Shai's cruiser, *Legacy of Torment,* arrived at Ithor, its holds filled with murderous warriors.

The Yuuzhan Vong combatants attacked the floating herd ship *Tafanda Bay* and Ithor's virgin surface, until Corran Horn forestalled further attacks with an appeal to Shai's pride. According to the terms of Horn's challenge, if he defeated Shai in a one-on-one duel, the Yuuzhan Vong would leave Ithor alone. If he lost, Shai would win back the body of his ancestor Mongei Shai.

Corran won the duel, killing Shedao Shai. But Shai's second in command refused to honor the terms of the pact, loosing bioweapons that turned the rain forests of Ithor into oozing swamps of black ash. The New Republic managed to destroy *Legacy of Torment,* but the death of Ithor horrified the public.

Many were quick to blame Corran Horn for arranging the duel in the first place. In response, Horn placed himself in exile on his homeworld of Corellia. As anti-Jedi sentiment grew, Borsk Fey'lya gained even more power over the New Republic.

THE PEACE BRIGADE
25.5 A.B.Y.

The Yuuzhan Vong had broken their pact at Ithor, and the aliens apparently felt there was little use in pursuing further treaties. Instead, warships led by Supreme Commander Nas Choka captured a swath of worlds lying in the northern invasion corridor over the next four months, including the library planet Obroa-skai. Choka also sponsored uprisings on Atzerri and other isolated pockets along the galaxy's southeastern face.

This new aggression frightened many groups, which approached the Yuuzhan Vong with their own entreaties. The Hutts proposed an alliance with the Yuuzhan Vong based on information sharing, while a despicable gaggle of humans calling themselves the "Peace Brigade" offered to sell out their fellow citizens in exchange for favorable treatment in the postwar galaxy.

Nom Anor, now working with the priest Harrar, had a new scheme—poisoning the Jedi by infecting them with fatal bo'tous spores. The priestess Elan agreed to pose as a defector. Once she had arranged a meeting with the Jedi, she would exhale the virulent spores that nested in her lungs. Elan was accompanied by her pet, a bird-like alien called Vergere. None of the Yuuzhan Vong realized that Vergere was a Jedi of the old Order, lost after her mission to Zonama Sekot nearly a decade before the Clone Wars.

Chewbacca's family held a belated memorial service for him on Kashyyyk. Han Solo chose that moment to embark on his own quest. Hooking up with Roa, his companion on the caper to pilfer Xim's treasure vaults decades before, Han set off for Ord Mantell, gunning for the Peace Brigade traitors. More old faces resurfaced on Ord Mantell, including the bounty hunter Bossk and Han's old employer Big Bunji, but

Droma
[Art by John Van Fleet]

inexplicably left a vial of her tears with Han before departing. To everyone's surprise, the dosage of Vergere's tears sent Mara Jade's disease into temporary remission.

THE BATTLE OF FONDOR
25.7 A.B.Y.

The Yuuzhan Vong had now moved halfway across the galaxy and had penetrated the Expansion Region. Jedi Knight Wurth Skidder allowed himself to become a prisoner during the Battle of Gyndine, and found himself assigned to a yammosk-nurturing vessel called the *Crèche.* Alongside his fellow prisoner Roa, Skidder toiled at menial tasks designed to stimulate the growing, telepathic brain.

The alliance between the Hutts and the Yuuzhan Vong remained one in name only, as neither side held one atom of trust for the other. The Yuuzhan Vong carefully leaked information to the Hutts concerning their supposed battle plans, and this information soon found its way into the New Republic's possession. Yet another world, lake-dappled Tynna, fell to the Yuuzhan Vong and became a breeding ground for organic communications villips.

Han and Droma, on the hunt for Roa and any sign of Droma's relatives, followed the refugee trail to Ruan, where they met a droid who acted curiously like Bollux, Han's droid companion from his early adventures. Once they realized that Ruan was a dead end, the two followed further clues to the starship yards of Fondor.

Leia Organa Solo had been spending her time in the isolated Hapes Consortium, trying to convince Isolder's people to join the fight. Isolder defeated a political challenger in a combat duel to ensure the Consortium's compliance, and agreed to commit his fleet to the aid of the New Republic. The Hapans' first test would come at Fondor.

Jacen and Anakin Solo, with unwelcome help from Thrackan Sal-Solo, had succeeded in reactivating Centerpoint Station in the Corellian system. The famed "starbuster"

a Yuuzhan Vong attack force crashed the reunion party. The enemy fleet ravaged Ord Mantell's orbital station and captured thousands, including Roa.

To get his friend back, Han joined forces with Droma, a member of the furry, gypsy-like Ryn species. Aboard the starliner *Queen of Empire,* the two crossed paths with Yuuzhan Vong "defector" Elan and her companion Vergere, just as Peace Brigade raiders attacked the vessel and a Yuuzhan Vong fleet jumped in-system.

Han soon realized that the Yuuzhan Vong acted a bit *too* nonchalant about recapturing their defector. Her ruse revealed, Elan fell victim to her own poison, while Vergere

had been dormant since the Corellian insurrection, but New Republic Intelligence hoped to use its awesome destructive energies against the enemy. Now, with reports coming in that the Yuuzhan Vong had arrived at Fondor, the time for action had come. Jacen advised against taking rash action, and Anakin hesitated—long enough for Thrackan to seize the controls and fire the superweapon himself.

Centerpoint's poorly aimed energy pulse shot through the Fondor system just as Isolder's Hapan armada began taking up positions. The shaft of white light took out three-quarters of Isolder's fleet and nearly half of the Yuuzhan Vong forces.

Though considered a victory (Thrackan Sal-Solo won election to the post of Corellian governor-general for his part in the incident), the Battle of Fondor cost the New Republic dearly. The Hapan fleet limped on in tatters, Wurth Skidder had died during a rescue attempt on the *Crèche,* and Centerpoint Station switched off again, this time for good.

THE FALL OF DURO
26 A.B.Y.

Over the following four months, more critical planets fell. The Yuuzhan Vong moved against their former allies in Hutt space, annihilating Nal Hutta and forcing the Hutts from territory that had been theirs for more than twenty-five thousand years. The Yuuzhan Vong attacked Rodia, Druckenwell, Falleen, and Kalarba in an attempt to cut off the Corellian Run. In the assault against Kalarba, the Yuuzhan Vong used a copy of the Sernpidal tactic, drawing in Kalarba's moon Hosk and destroying both spheres. Lieutenant Jaina Solo, flying with Rogue Squadron, suffered injuries that temporarily blinded her. She received a medical leave transfer to the planet Duro, home of the famed pre-Republic spacefarers.

Duro had been chosen as a refugee relocation site for citizens displaced by the invasion. Though Duro's surface had long ago been rendered inhos-

pitable to life, Leia Organa Solo and other New Republic personnel worked to erect atmosph eric shelters and begin long-term terraforming. Despite the Yuuzhan Vong's stab at Fondor, New Republic Intelligence believed the enemy lacked the resources to mount a serious campaign against a major Core world.

But Warmaster Tsavong Lah, second only to Supreme Overlord Shimrra in the Yuuzhan Vong hierarchy, had at last settled in the galaxy. With his arrival, the war had assumed a more belligerent face. The invasion corridor took a sharp right turn toward the galactic center, with Duro squarely in its sights.

Jacen Solo, on Duro with his family to help settle the ref-

Warmaster Tsavong Lah
[ART BY JOHN VAN FLEET]

ugees, received a Force-induced vision of a galaxy in danger of tilting out of balance. Believing that withdrawal from the Force might mark the path to peace, Jacen began taking on more and more of the trappings of a Jedi hermit. Han and Leia used this time to repair a relationship that had been strained since the death of Chewbacca.

Nom Anor, hoping to make up for his failure with the bo'tous spores, had already set up shop on Duro, using an ooglith masquer disguise to impersonate a Duros scientist. He created a beetle swarm that chewed up the refugee shelters before Mara Jade and Jaina Solo uncovered his identity. Anor eluded capture long enough for Warmaster Tsavong Lah's fleet to arrive, giving the New Republic much bigger things to worry about.

Jacen had been using his time to investigate suspicious dealings of the CorDuro Shipping corporation on one of the many orbital cities that ringed the poisoned world. His discovery that CorDuro had hoped to offer up the refugees as sacrifices in exchange for amnesty came too late to make a difference. Tsavong Lah had only contempt for CorDuro's cowardice, and his warships attacked refugees and orbital cities alike.

On Duro's surface, Yuuzhan Vong warriors captured Leia Organa Solo and brought her before the warmaster. Slashed across the knees when she tried to resist, Leia was rescued by her son Jacen, who abandoned his doubt in this critical moment and opened himself fully to the Force. The telekinetic storm summoned by Jacen picked up everything in the room and sent Tsavong Lah flying out a window.

The Solo family escaped the Battle of Duro, but most combatants did not. Every orbital city save one died in spectacular fashion, pulled to the surface by dovin basals. Warmaster Tsavong Lah now had his foothold in the Core Worlds, and used the occasion to make a galaxywide broadcast. The Yuuzhan Vong invasion would end here, he stated, if the New Republic would surrender its Jedi.

Now viewed with suspicion and greed by a fearful populace, the Jedi had little to cheer. Luke Skywalker, however, found some solace in the news that his wife was expecting a child—a boy. Luke vowed to win peace for the next generation, or die trying.

TREACHERY IN THE SENATE
26.2 A.B.Y.

Han Solo took Leia to a medcenter on Corellia, knowing that she could lose her legs without immediate bacta treatments. But Peace Brigade thugs attacked there, and the newly elected Governor-General Thrackan Sal-Solo made it clear that neither his cousin nor his cousin's wife was welcome in the Corellian system. While finding a new spot to recuperate, Han and Leia ran into a former Jedi student of Luke's named Eelysa, who, along with her maverick Jedi pupils, had formed a rogue starfighter squadron called the Wild Knights.

Leia recovered in time to act against Viqi Shesh, the New Republic Senator from Kuat. Shesh, in response to Tsavong Lah's decree, had sponsored an "appeasement bill" that would outlaw the Jedi order. Leia was nearly killed by mines on her way to Coruscant, but could not prove that Shesh had arranged for her murder. The Senator placed all blame on her aide, and while the appeasement bill went on to defeat, Shesh continued to hold secret talks with Nom Anor. If the New Republic lost the war, a possibility that looked increasingly likely, Shesh wanted to head the collaborationist government.

After fortifying their prize conquest of Duro, the Yuuzhan Vong made an experimental thrust at the Corellian sector, capturing the Nosaurian homeworld of New Plympto. The occupation quickly became a headache, with the Twi'lek Jedi sisters Alema and Numa Rar leading a resistance army of guerrillas. The Yuuzhan Vong ultimately sterilized the troublesome planet, killing nearly seven million.

BIRTH OF THE HERETIC MOVEMENT
26.2 A.B.Y.

Cowed by Tsavong Lah's ultimatum, worlds such as Ando and Devaron began offering up their Jedi protectors to prevent further bloodshed. Dorsk 81 was among the Jedi sacrificed. Witnessing the way such citizens had been so easily turned, Luke Skywalker called for the evacuation

of the Yavin 4 academy, currently home to only the youngest
Jedi initiates. Information kingpin Talon Karrde agreed to assist
in the evacuation, and Anakin
Solo also flew to Yavin 4 to help
his friend Tahiri Veila.

Anakin arrived to find the
base already under siege by the
Peace Brigade. Master Ikrit, the
tiny Kushiban who had advised
Anakin during his own time
at the academy, died in battle
against the brigadiers. Tahiri became a prisoner.

With help from Qorl, the
TIE pilot who lived in Yavin 4's
jungles, Anakin set off to rescue
Tahiri. Fortunately, by this time
Talon Karrde had evacuated the
rest of the academy students,
for the arriving Yuuzhan Vong
forces cared little for what had
come before. The Yuuzhan Vong
obliterated the five-thousand-
year old Massassi temples, erecting damuteks that served as
vivisection laboratories for the
members of the shaper caste.

Luke Skywalker and Mara Jade Skywalker, with newborn baby Ben
[ART BY JOHN VAN FLEET]

The shapers had already created monstrosities such as the
crab-legged Vagh Rodiek slave species on conquered Rodia.
On Yavin 4, head shaper Mezhan Kwaad and her apprentice
Nen Yim began brainwashing Tahiri, replacing her personality with that of "Riina Kwaad," an identity formed out of
memories copied from Nen Yim's own childhood. Mezhan
Kwaad had a secret she kept carefully guarded from the rank
and file—she had no reverence for the gods. Nen Yim, who
loved only science, shared her heresy.

In the jungle, Anakin encountered Vua Rapuung, a former Yuuzhan Vong warrior now relegated to the caste of
Shamed Ones after a failed bio-implant condemned him to
the lowest possible status in Yuuzhan Vong society. Rapuung
knew that his ex-lover Mezhan Kwaad had engineered his
humiliation, and was willing to fight alongside a *Jeedai* if it
brought him closer to revenge.

Infiltrating the shaper compound, Anakin and Vua
Rapuung fought their way to a shuttle that carried Mezhan

Kwaad, Nen Yim, and Tahiri. In front of hundreds of Yuuzhan Vong, Kwaad revealed her heresy and her part in Vua Rapuung's Shaming, then died at Tahiri's hands.

Rapuung also perished, but a movement had been born. The story of Vua Rapuung, the Shamed One who had earned redemption fighting alongside a Jedi Knight, was endlessly whispered within the ranks of the Shamed Ones. Among this ignored caste of Yuuzhan Vong, the Jedi began to be seen not as enemies, but as saviors.

THE GREAT RIVER
26.5 A.B.Y.

Seeds of change among the Shamed Ones did little to soften the hearts of some New Republic citizens, who now viewed the Jedi as their enemies. Luke Skywalker enlisted many of his most trusted operatives to establish a "Great River"—a secure network by which Jedi could be moved out of hostile areas and into safe houses, including a secure base set up in the Maw cluster near Kessel. Uldir Lochett, the failed Jedi student who had adventured with Anakin Solo years ago, acted as a key link in the Great River. Uldir and his crew crossed paths with a Jedi calling herself Klin-Fa Gi, who led them to Wayland to uncover evidence of a Yuuzhan Vong plot to poison the galaxy's bacta supply. On the bacta planet of Thyferra, Uldir uncovered a Jedi traitor and stopped the scheme before it could trigger a new Bacta War.

THE BATTLE OF YAG'DHUL
26.5 A.B.Y.

Even on Coruscant, the Jedi had become pariahs. Certain members of the Senate issued a warrant for Luke Skywalker's arrest. Jaina decided to take the fight to the *real* enemy, and joined Kyp Durron's vigilante Jedi faction in the Outer Rim. Durron, who knew that the Yuuzhan Vong were building a new worldship from the broken fragments of Sernpidal, deceived Jaina into believing that the construction site housed a new Yuuzhan Vong superweapon. The Jedi squadron attacked and destroyed the worldship, killing thousands of enemy noncombatants. Jaina felt sick over her part in it.

Anakin Solo and the recovering Tahiri, safeguarding the Jedi students aboard Booster Terrik's Star Destroyer *Errant Venture*, decided to join Corran Horn on a supply run to Eriadu. Horn had emerged from his voluntary exile following the debacle at Ithor, and felt confident that his small group would encounter little trouble on Eriadu.

A brush with Peace Brigaders, however, tipped them off that a Yuuzhan Vong invasion of Yag'Dhul was imminent. They rushed to the Givin homeworld to warn the skeletal mathematicians of the danger. During the Battle of Yag'Dhul, the three Jedi faced down Nom Anor, and Anakin and Tahiri shared a tentative kiss while sealed in a storage locker. The advanced ships of the Givin fleet helped beat back the Yuuzhan Vong attackers.

Luke and Mara arrived at *Errant Venture* after their departure from unfriendly Coruscant. There, a disease-weakened Mara went into labor, knowing that the effort would probably kill her. Through the Force, Luke joined minds with his son, using their shared energies to scour every trace of contagion from the cells in Mara's body. Mara and Luke named their newborn baby Ben, in honor of Ben Kenobi.

Elsewhere, the heretical shaper Nen Yim struggled with her punitive assignment to the dying worldship *Baanu Miir*. Soon, aboard the vessel, a master shaper who had spent weeks tormenting Nen Yim revealed himself as Onimi, the misshapen court jester who served at the side of Supreme Overlord Shimrra. It seemed that Shimrra had great need for someone with Nen Yim's scientific talents.

THE DEATH OF ANAKIN SOLO
27 A.B.Y.

By this point the Great River network had moved most Jedi out of harm's way, and Luke Skywalker reestablished a fixed Jedi headquarters, this time on a secret Deep Core planet code-named Eclipse.

The Yuuzhan Vong shaper caste had also kept busy.

Jacen, Jaina, and Anakin Solo face off against a ring of voxyn while infiltrating the worldship at Myrkr. [Art by Tommy Lee Edwards]

Realizing that many Jedi still remained at large, they had fashioned a horde of six-legged monsters called voxyn. Flawless Jedi-killers, the voxyn contained genetic material taken from Myrkr's Force-hunting vornskrs, and used this sensitivity to compensate for their masters' Force blindness. Numa and Alema Rar, the Twi'lek sisters who had led New Plympto's failed resistance, were the first Jedi to battle a voxyn. Numa died, a victim of the creature's razor claws and acid-spitting glands. Alema barely escaped with her life.

This new threat finally united the Jedi order. Kyp Durron and other renegades, including the "Wild Knights" Jedi squadron that had appeared after the Battle of Duro, closed ranks behind Luke Skywalker. To prevent the Yuuzhan Vong from cloning more voxyn, Anakin Solo agreed to lead a strike team behind enemy lines, to destroy the genetic template aboard the worldship *Baanu Rass,* orbiting Myrkr.

Anakin's squad included his brother and sister, along with many of their old academy classmates such as Lowbacca, Tenel Ka, Raynar Thul, and Tahiri. Ganner Rhysode stood out in their ranks as the oldest adult. Despite their youth, the team landed on *Baanu Rass* and systematically fought their way to the heart of the cloning center.

Along the way they liberated two prisoners, Lomi Plo and Welk, who had been captured during the Yuuzhan Vong conquest of Dathomir. Both were disciples of the new Nightsister philosophy taught by Brakiss's now-defunct Second Imperium. True to their nature, they stole a ship and deserted Anakin's group at the earliest opportunity, dragging Raynar with them to face an unknown fate.

Anakin Solo had been widely considered the logical choice to succeed Luke Skywalker as head of the Jedi order. His actions on *Baanu Rass* only deepened his legend. He fought against hordes of enemies without ego or fear, and in the end sacrificed himself so that the other members of his team could live. Cut down by a rain of Yuuzhan Vong amphistaffs while buying time for the others to destroy the queen voxyn, Anakin passed into the Force with a shudder felt halfway across the galaxy.

The death of her younger brother sharpened the edge of Jaina Solo's rage. Now bathing in the violence of the dark side, she burned several Yuuzhan Vong with Force lightning to retrieve Anakin's body. When the fierce fighting separated her from Jacen, she left her twin behind on *Baanu Rass* and escaped with the surviving members of the strike team aboard the Yuuzhan Vong frigate *Ksstar.*

Jacen Solo became a trophy captive. Ever since he had defeated Tsavong Lah on Duro, he had become the most-wanted enemy combatant on the Yuuzhan Vong rolls. Vergere, the former Jedi and current Yuuzhan Vong pet, warned Jacen that his true education was about to begin.

The Fall of Coruscant
27 A.B.Y.

On Coruscant, Chief of State Borsk Fey'lya had pulled a 180-degree attitude change from his former hostility toward the Jedi. When Nom Anor came to address the Senate, Fey'lya denounced him as a coward and rallied the fractured New Republic. Fey'lya's refusal to negotiate meant that the Yuuzhan Vong would probably execute the hostages whom they held aboard a refugee colony in the Talfaglio system—unless the Jedi got there first.

In a frenzied assault on Talfaglio, Jedi and New Republic forces broke the Yuuzhan Vong cordon and liberated the hostages. Fuming over the effrontery of his opponents, Warmaster Tsavong Lah gave the order to all his warriors to initiate Battle Plan Coruscant. Nearly every vessel in the Yuuzhan Vong fleet assembled into two pincers: one based at Reecee and one at Borleias, and both pointed squarely at the galactic capital.

The New Republic's defense of Coruscant was noble, but futile. No force could stand against the power that Tsavong Lah had assembled. Even Coruscant's planetary shields, the strongest in the galaxy, warped and ruptured when the Yuuzhan Vong hit them with wave after wave of powerless refugee vessels. The tactics of old warhorses like General Rieekan, Garm Bel Iblis, and Lando Calrissian delayed the conquest long enough for many evacuation transports to reach orbit. Ben Skywalker was one of those who escaped the Coruscant battle zone, despite attempts by Viqi Shesh to kill the newborn and curry favor with her new masters.

Borsk Fey'lya made no attempt to leave. He remained in his executive office, watching Yuuzhan Vong landing ships descend on the world that had once been his. When warriors burst in, he demanded to speak to Tsavong Lah face-to-face, but the warmaster could not be drawn into Fey'lya's trap. With a sigh of finality, Fey'lya triggered the proton bomb hidden beneath his desk. Twenty-five thousand Yuuzhan Vong died in a white-hot blast radius that stretched for kilometers.

It is doubtful that the Yuuzhan Vong appreciated the symbolic value of Coruscant's capture, but the galaxy's citizens could feel it in their bones. For years the New Republic and the Empire had fought over Coruscant as a way to give their reigns legitimacy. The latest conquest was more than another tally in the enemy's column. It meant that the Yuuzhan Vong were not just a nightmare that would disappear with the dawn.

Coruscant held a different symbolic meaning for the Yuuzhan Vong. Using a tremendous allocation of resources, they set out to transform the world into a mirror of Yuuzhan'tar, the forgotten home of their ancestors. Dovin basals pulled Coruscant closer to its sun and jump-started a tropical climate. More dovin basals pulverized one of Coruscant's moons, allowing the planet to wear a flat disk of spectacular rings. Green vegetation began to cover gray durasteel, in preparation for the arrival of a seedship that would complete the metamorphosis.

INTRIGUE ON HAPES
27.2 A.B.Y.

Jaina Solo, piloting the Yuuzhan Vong frigate *Ksstar* after her escape from Myrkr, flew the vessel back to where she believed she could find safe harbor. Instead, she emerged in the middle of the battle for Coruscant. Barely escaping intact, she rendezvoused at the Hapes Consortium with her parents, who wished to commiserate over Anakin's death and Jacen's capture. But Jaina's guilt and rage ran too

hot. Rather than seek the support of family or friends, she desired only to inflict pain on the Yuuzhan Vong.

Tsavong Lah warranted most of her hatred, but the warmaster remained untouchable. Closer enemies included the priest Harrar and Khalee Lah, the warmaster's son. These two Yuuzhan Vong had tracked the *Ksstar* to Hapes, but Jaina's uncanny ability to elude and confound her enemies elicited comparisons between her and Yun-Harla, the Yuuzhan Vong goddess of trickery.

On Hapes, three personalities circled around Jaina like satellites. The first, Jagged Fel, agreed to fly with Jaina, accompanied by his Chiss wingmate Shawnkyr. Jag believed he might have a future with Jaina, but viewed Kyp Durron as a rival for her attentions.

Kyp had arrived on Hapes shell-shocked, having lost his newest squadron mates during the Battle of Coruscant. Though he and Jaina had parted on bad terms following the raid on the Sernpidal worldship, her recent ordeal with the dark side meant that they had more in common than ever. Jaina spurned her childhood friend Zekk in order to consider Kyp's offer of apprenticeship.

Finally, Ta'a Chume had lost none of her malevolence in the nearly two decades since she had been deposed as Queen Mother of the Hapes Consortium. Teneniel Djo, the current Queen Mother and Isolder's wife, had been rendered nearly comatose by psychic pain when the Hapan fleet had been devastated at the Battle of Fondor. Ta'a Chume wanted a new Queen Mother that she could manipulate, and she set her sights on Jaina to become Isolder's new bride.

Anakin Solo's body at last received a proper Jedi burning on Hapes. While Luke Skywalker, Kyp Durron, Han Solo, Tahiri Veila, and others read a eulogy, the flames of the funeral pyre consigned Anakin's body to ash and his spirit to the Force.

Harrar and Khalee Lah massed their war fleet around Hapes, but Jaina hatched her most devious plan yet. By manipulating the gravitic signatures of vessels within the Yuuzhan Vong fleet, she could trick them into mistaking friend for foe. Her tactic worked brilliantly, with dozens of Yuuzhan

Vong warships destroyed by friendly fire. The Yuuzhan Vong withdrew, earning Jaina even more comparisons to Yun-Harla. In honor of her new status, Jaina gave the *Ksstar* a new name—the *Trickster*.

The palace machinations of Ta'a Chume had become murderous. She arranged for the fatal poisoning of the invalid Teneniel Djo. Tenel Ka, daughter of Teneniel and Jedi veteran of the Myrkr mission, stepped in to restore order by assuming her rightful place as the next Queen Mother of Hapes.

The Struggle for Borleias
27.3 A.B.Y.

The New Republic responded to the loss of Coruscant by striking back while they knew their enemy was overextended. A small task force under the command of General Wedge Antilles reclaimed Borleias from its outgunned Vong occupiers, establishing a foothold on the world that had traditionally been seen as the "stepping-stone to the Core."

The surviving members of the New Republic Advisory Council regrouped on Borleias. One of their number, the Quarren Senator Pwoe, had named himself Fey'lya's successor as Chief of State in absence of a proper vote. No one could yet make a claim to challenge Pwoe, and the Quarren made it clear to General Antilles that no additional forces would be spared to defend Borleias against counterattack. Later, he grudgingly requested that the Super Star Destroyer *Lusankya* bolster Borleias's defensive line, but it became clear that Pwoe was organizing a stalling tactic in order to buy time for a New Republic surrender.

Wedge and the others vowed not to let that happen, advocating a return to the guerrilla tactics of the Rebel Alliance of old. But Warmaster Tsavong Lah, on conquered Coruscant, had already fixed his gaze on Borleias. He entrusted the counterattack to his father, Czulkang Lah, who had once held the title of warmaster and now spent his days as a tactics instructor. Once New Republic forces at Borleias used a "Starlancer" to fire a laser beam through hyperspace and damage Tsavong Lah's worldship at Coruscant, Lah gave the reconquest his highest priority. In truth, the Starlancer had been more of a light show than a true superweapon, but the Yuuzhan Vong retaliatory strike proved to be real enough.

Czulkang Lah's attack on Borleias involved thousands of starfighters and ground assault crawlers. Jaina Solo, leading Twin Suns Squadron, did what she could with assistance from Jagged Fel, but Yuuzhan Vong troops continued to advance on the New Republic base. In desperation, the Super Star Destroyer *Lusankya* responded with a tactic not seen since the days of the Empire—it initiated an orbital bombardment, annihilating every Yuuzhan Vong on the ground and turning several square kilometers of jungle into blackened glass.

Behind Enemy Lines
27.5 A.B.Y.

Luke Skywalker missed out on the fighting, having volunteered to lead a team of infiltrators to enemy-held Coruscant. Accompanied by Mara Jade, Tahiri, Danni Quee, and several members of Wraith Squadron, the team roamed the transformed city-planet while wearing Yuuzhan Vong disguises. From local survivors they learned that, more than twenty years after the death of Vader, a Dark Jedi strode Coruscant once more. The survivors called the marauder "Lord Nyax" after a terrifying figure from Corellian legend.

After days of searching, Luke's team learned the truth behind Nyax. After the *Eye of Palpatine* incident on Belsavis fifteen years prior, Roganda Ismaren and her son Irek Ismaren had come to Coruscant. Roganda had placed her son in a laboratory, where scientists held him in suspended animation, adding muscle and bone mass to his frame and implanting lightsaber blades into his wrists, elbows, and knees. Irek had awoken during the Yuuzhan Vong invasion and, suffering from brain damage, had killed his mother. Now he roamed Coruscant as Lord Nyax, trying to breach a Force wellspring hidden at the site of the old Jedi Temple.

The Super Star Destroyer Lusankya sacrifices itself in the Battle of Borleias. [Art by Tommy Lee Edwards]

Luke, Mara, and Tahiri faced off against Nyax, who by this time had tapped into the Force repository and could toss debris around in a whirlwind of power. Their combined efforts were enough to fell the Dark Jedi.

Ex-Senator Viqi Shesh also met her end on Coruscant. Far from being named the head of a collaborationist government as she had hoped, Shesh had been marked for death by Warmaster Tsavong Lah. Wraith Squadron foiled her efforts to escape offworld. In the end, Shesh stepped out a window to her death rather than face a life without power.

Warmaster Tsavong Lah had been busy dealing with internal problems, including a plot initiated against him by the shaper caste, who had tainted Lah's recently grafted arm in a manner that would seem to indicate the gods' disfavor. Lah took his revenge by feeding the disloyal shapers to hungry rancors, then turned his attention to Borleias.

His father, Czulkang Lah, organized another onslaught to recapture the world, this time using so much firepower that the New Republic could not hope to win. At first his tactics seemed to work—the New Republic evacuated Borleias, surrendering possession of the planet to the Yuuzhan Vong—but the situation was rapidly reversed. The Super Star Destroyer *Lusankya* rammed Czulkang Lah's worldship, destroying both vessels, while the priest Harrar's efforts to capture Jaina Solo were also met with shameful failure.

In the Belly of the Beast
27–27.9 A.B.Y.

After his capture by Yuuzhan Vong forces on the worldship *Baanu Rass,* Jacen Solo became the victim of unrelenting torment. Shaved bald and locked into a torture rack called the Embrace of Pain, he suffered for unknowable stretches of time while being visited by Vergere, who spoke only in riddles. Though Vergere had once been a Jedi and now lived with the Yuuzhan Vong, it became clear that she answered only to herself. She promised to be Jacen's guide through a painful spiritual journey which she likened to the rebirth of a shadowmoth emerging from its cocoon. The one truth that Jacen could count on, she told him, was that "everything I tell you is a lie."

Nom Anor and Warmaster Tsavong Lah approved of Vergere's actions. Both believed that Jacen could be broken

and made to accept the True Way of Yuuzhan Vong worship and sacrifice.

Jacen spent weeks aboard a seedship, a gigantic repository for Yuuzhan Vong genetic specimens. The seedship nurtured a number of growing dhuryams, telepathic blobs related to the yammosks that were used as battle coordinators. The dhuryam that displayed the most promise would become the "World Brain" to oversee the terraforming of Coruscant. Like children playing with toys, the dhuryams forced slaves into meaningless tasks as they honed their mind-controlling powers.

One of the dhuryams formed a special bond with Jacen, who convinced the developing brain that he was a friend to be trusted. When the seedship arrived at Coruscant, Jacen made his move, slaughtering the competing dhuryams and killing scores of Yuuzhan Vong warriors as the seedship prepared to implant itself on Coruscant.

Vergere knocked Jacen out and arranged for his safe passage out of the seedship. When Jacen awoke on the planet's surface, the vessel had already done its work. Moss now dripped from towers, and rivers roared through right-angled canyons. Beneath the "rainbow bridge" formed by Coruscant's new planetary rings, almost every centimeter of the cityscape wore a thick carpet of vegetation. Only the lower levels remained more or less intact, and down there, frightening examples of wildlife from the Yuuzhan Vong home galaxy hunted the desperate survivors.

Yuuzhan Vong warriors pursued Jacen through the transformed landscape in an effort to recapture him. The chase took Jacen to the former site of the Jedi Temple and into the gullet of a building-sized monster before he arrived at the Solo family apartment, where the spirit of his brother, Anakin, seemingly appeared to him. No longer willing to fight, Jacen allowed Nom Anor to take him prisoner, claiming to have become a convert to the truth of the True Way.

Alone among the Jedi, Ganner Rhysode believed that

Vergere
[Art by John Van Fleet]

Jacen had survived the mission to Myrkr. He pursued clues, but wound up a prisoner on Coruscant. Nom Anor proposed that Jacen prove his new faith by killing Ganner at the Well of the World Brain, where the dhuryam nested in a fluid-filled pit at the bottom of the former Galactic Senate's Great Rotunda. In full view of thousands of assembled Yuuzhan Vong, Jacen and Ganner marched to the Well, where Jacen opened his mind to the dhuryam and gave it a special message. Ganner bought time by guarding the building entrance, massacring hundreds of Yuuzhan Vong with a flashing lightsaber and the battle cry, "None shall pass." Ganner eventually perished under the weight of the assault, but earned the respect of the awestruck Yuuzhan Vong.

Jacen escaped Coruscant with Vergere, who shared with her new pupil a radical understanding of the Force. To Vergere and Jacen, the Force had no light side and no dark side—the Force was simply what one made of it. Jacen revealed that his instructions to the World Brain would cause little things to go wrong with the ongoing terraforming. This subtle sabotage might teach the Yuuzhan Vong how to live with compromise.

VICTORY AT EBAQ 9
28 A.B.Y.

The loss of Coruscant, then of Borleias, forced the New Republic Advisory Council to hop back to the water world of Mon Calamari, a planet far from the front lines. Despite Mon Calamari's strategic importance as a military shipyard, it had remained relatively isolated after the severing of the Perlemian Trade Route. For the moment, Mon Calamari provided a welcome opportunity to regroup and formalize a new government.

Senator Pwoe's power grab at Borleias was ignored in favor of new elections. Alderaanian Senator Cal Omas, a friend of the Jedi, received sufficient votes to become the next Chief of State. Omas approved Luke Skywalker's suggestion of a Jedi council composed of both Jedi and "regular" members. Those with seats on the new council included Skywalker, Kyp Durron, and the Barabel Saba Sebatyne, as well as politicians including Omas, the Wookiee Senator Triebakk, and Caamasi Minister of State Releqy A'Kla, the daughter of Elegos A'Kla.

Omas's new position made him a target for Yuuzhan Vong assassins, but New Republic forces were already taking the fight to the enemy. Above occupied Obroa-skai, Jaina Solo worked with Queen Mother Tenel Ka and Jedi General Keyan Farlander to destroy the flagship of Supreme Overlord Shimrra, though Shimrra was not aboard. At Mon Calamari, the arrival of Jacen Solo and Vergere brought cheers from those who had thought Jacen dead at *Baanu Rass.*

Supreme Overlord Shimrra, accompanied by his jester Onimi, had arrived at Coruscant to take a direct hand in the galaxy's subjugation. Chief among Shimrra's concerns were the planet's malfunctioning World Brain and the growing heresy of Jedi worship among the lowly caste of Shamed Ones.

The galaxy's lesser political factions had reacted in wildly differing fashion to the news of Coruscant's fall. The Empire had maintained a policy of noninterference since Ithor, while the Bothans—stirred by the noble death of Borsk Fey'lya— had initiated ar'krai, a condition of genocidal war that would end only when the Yuuzhan Vong had been utterly exterminated. The notion of ar'krai appealed to the black ops Alpha Blue division of New Republic Intelligence. Working in conjunction with Chiss scientists, Alpha Blue had developed a biological weapon keyed to Yuuzhan Vong DNA. If unleashed, this "Alpha Red" virus would exterminate every Yuuzhan Vong and Yuuzhan Vong creation in the galaxy.

Luke Skywalker opposed such indiscriminate slaughter, believing it to be against the will of the Force. The debate was rendered moot, however, when Vergere used the healing properties of her tears to render Alpha Red inert.

Admiral Ackbar, slowed by his advancing years but still sharp of mind, helped the New Republic plan a trap for Warmaster Tsavong Lah. In the Deep Core, where gravitic anomalies warped hyperspace into a near-impassable morass, New Republic forces would set an ambush near the ninth moon of Ebaq, at a former Imperial base called Tarkin's Fang. When the Yuuzhan Vong fleet arrived, the New Republic would blockade the only hyperroute leading into or out of Ebaq and pin the enemy under a blistering crossfire.

The first stage of the Ebaq 9 trap unfolded according to plan. With his fleet in ruins, Tsavong Lah ordered his remaining troops to the surface of the moon to capture the Tarkin's Fang installation. Knowing that at this point he would be unlikely to secure a victory, Lah wished instead to disembowel the *Jeedai* who had caused him so much pain.

Vergere sacrificed her life, thinning the enemy ranks by crashing an A-wing into the vacuum-sealed base. Tsavong Lah survived the explosive decompression, eventually facing

Tahiri Veila
[Art by John Van Fleet]

Galactic Federation of Free Alliances. Under a new constitution, the Galactic Alliance incorporated a new federalism that defined the boundaries between the Senate and planetary governments, as well as strengthening the judiciary in order to check the power of the Senate.

More good news came in from the planet Ylesia in Hutt space, where New Republic forces had driven the Yuuzhan Vong away from the Ylesian spice factories. They had also captured Thrackan Sal-Solo, who had been forced by the Yuuzhan Vong to give up his governor-general position in the Corellian system in order to become the head of the Ylesian Peace Brigade.

Across the Stars
28.2–28.7 A.B.Y.

The Yuuzhan Vong's defeat at Ebaq was intended to result in them pulling inward to consolidate the rest of their hard-won territory. Instead, like krakanas maddened by a blood-boil, they continued to send their surviving warships against new targets. Among the newest worlds to fall were Barab I, Rutan, and Belderone.

The latest attacks—and the sudden loss of Holo-Net communications with scores of worlds—prompted Han and Leia to take *Millennium Falcon* on a mission to reestablish the broken information chain. Tahiri came with them, still haunted by the brainwashing she had received on Yavin 4, and by the Yuuzhan Vong personality of "Riina Kwaad" that tried to take over her dreams.

At their first stop, Galantos, they learned that the native Fia had struck a deal with the Yuuzhan Vong—capitulation in exchange for the elimination of their enemies, the Yevetha. The Yuuzhan Vong, it seemed, had accomplished what the New Republic chose not to do during the Black Fleet Crisis. The Yevetha had been bombed to the point of extinction.

The *Falcon*'s next trip took it to Bakura, where recent events appeared to have ushered in a new age of coopera-

off against Jaina Solo in a one-on-one duel—the warmaster against the so-called Sword of the Jedi. Living up to her reputation as the living incarnation of Yun-Harla, Jaina outmaneuvered Lah and speared her lightsaber through his throat.

The Battle of Ebaq 9 was a rousing success for the New Republic, by far its most significant victory since the start of the war. Many began to believe in the New Republic's ability to turn the tables on its overextended enemy, but Cal Omas disagreed. That is, Omas could not see the *New Republic* winning the war—but a rebuilt, streamlined government might have a fighting chance. He used the current political shake-ups as an opportunity to restructure the New Republic as the

tion between the Bakurans and the P'w'eck Emancipation Movement, a group composed of the Ssi-ruuk's traditional slave species. Unknown to any of the players at hand, the Yuuzhan Vong had already infiltrated Ssi-ruuvi society. Chaos soon enveloped Bakura, with Prime Minister Cundertol revealed as a human replica droid and Malinza Thanas—daughter of Gaeriel Captison and leader of the Freedom revolutionaries—arrested for kidnapping. The various plots collapsed when the Keeramak, the current head of the Ssi-ruuvi Imperium, attempted to claim Bakura for his own, renaming it "Xwhee." But fighting again broke out between the Ssi-ruuk and their P'w'eck slaves, sparing Bakura from enemy conquest.

The *Falcon*'s third mission involved the planet Esfandia. Han's Ryn friend Droma, who had emerged as the head of a Ryn intelligence network, emphasized the importance of maintaining Esfandia's HoloNet relay station, which the Yuuzhan Vong were already threatening to smash. Esfandia was blanketed by a soup-thick atmosphere populated by starfish-like Brrbrlpp, who helped the Galactic Alliance shatter the Yuuzhan Vong strike force. By the conclusion of her adventures, Tahiri had established a balance between her dueling personalities. She now viewed herself as half human, half Yuuzhan Vong.

Military campaigns seemed to be unraveling for the Yuuzhan Vong, and their internal problems were even more severe. Nom Anor had gone underground on Coruscant, afraid of Shimrra's wrath in the wake of the Ebaq 9 disaster. There he had hooked up with Shamed Ones preaching the Jedi heresy that had begun on Yavin 4. Ever willing to exploit any opportunity for power, Nom Anor reinvented himself as "Yu'shaa the Prophet" and attracted thousands of heretic followers to his banner. Shimrra dispatched warriors to crush this newest threat to his rule, but Nom Anor kept abreast of court developments thanks to a spy in Shimrra's confidence.

Nom Anor, as Yu'shaa the Prophet, overlooks the greening of Coruscant. [Art by Tommy Lee Edwards]

INTO THE UNKNOWN REGIONS
28.2–28.8 A.B.Y.

Following the Yuuzhan Vong's defeat at Ebaq 9, Luke Skywalker decided to press the advantage in the face of the enemy's weakness. Before her death, Vergere had told him the story of the living planet Zonama Sekot and how it had repelled a squad of Yuuzhan Vong scouts decades before. Now Luke assembled a small team, including Jacen, Mara, Saba Sebatyne, and Danni Quee, to seek out Zonama Sekot in the Unknown Regions, with the hope that it could help put an end to the war.

Aboard Mara's ship *Jade Shadow,* they made an initial stop at the Empire to obtain maps of the hyperroutes through the Unknown Regions. But they were unprepared for the sight that greeted them at the Imperial capital of Bastion. The Yuuzhan Vong had thoroughly routed the Empire there, forcing Admiral Pellaeon to retreat to Yaga Minor. Recognizing that his enemy's success had been due to surprise only, Pellaeon soon ordered his Star Destroyers to strike back in the Battle of Borosk, snapping the spine of the Yuuzhan Vong fleet.

Luke Skywalker and his companions proceeded into the Unknown Regions, where they established contact with the reclusive Chiss Ascendancy. Baron Soontir Fel and his wife, Syal Antilles, provided familiar faces on the icy capital of Csilla, but rogue elements within the Chiss Expansionary Defense Fleet tried to kill the visitors. After helping to quell the uprising, Jacen scoured the Chiss data library to learn Zonama Sekot's current location—an unknown system called Klasse Ephemora.

Penetrating even deeper into the Unknown Regions, *Jade Shadow*'s crew landed on Zonama Sekot and received a welcome from the Magister, Jabitha. Decades of time and half a galaxy of distance had passed since Jabitha had welcomed Obi-Wan Kenobi and Anakin Skywalker to her world, yet she retained a primal connection to the planet's green consciousness.

The hyperjumps that Zonama Sekot had taken in order to reach the Klasse Ephemora system had scarred the world and killed many of its Ferroan settlers. Several angry Ferroans now kidnapped Jabitha, but the actions of the Jedi in rescuing the Magister convinced Zonama Sekot of the rightness of the visitors' cause.

Luke and his Jedi were not the only ones seeking more information on the living planet. Supreme Overlord Shimrra had always believed that Zonama Sekot would be a threat to his rule. Now, working with master shaper Nen Yim, he developed plagues that could exterminate Sekot's biosphere. Nen Yim, convinced that Shimrra had lost his mind, established a secret alliance with the priest Harrar. When Corran Horn and Tahiri Veila arrived on Coruscant, the two Yuuzhan Vong escaped aboard the Jedi vessel, accompanied by Nom Anor in his guise as Yu'shaa the Prophet. Though none of the five trusted one another, they entered the Unknown Regions and soon reached Zonama Sekot. The Yuuzhan Vong members immediately remarked on how "right" the world felt, and Nom Anor realized that he could gain great power in Shimrra's eyes if he could poison this powerful world.

Corran and Tahiri tried to establish contact with Luke's team. The two groups eventually hooked up, but by then Nom Anor had made his move—bashing in Nen Yim's head with a rock, he stole her collection of tailored plagues. Anor released a virus into Sekot's neural interface, then escaped offworld while the pained planet shuddered with groundquakes. As Anor watched aboard his vessel, Zonama Sekot and its passengers fled into hyperspace.

Back in known space, the Galactic Alliance struggled with a separate problem—the near-total collapse of the HoloNet communications system due to enemy sabotage. During a mission to liberate the Bilbringi Shipyards, General Wedge Antilles found himself unable to contact reinforcements. Han Solo and Leia Organa Solo prevented the battle from becoming a rout by using the *Falcon* as a courier. Most Galactic Alliance troops escaped Bilbringi, but other soldiers, including lifelong military men Pash Cracken and Judder Page, became prisoners of war.

THE DEFENSE OF MON CALAMARI
29 A.B.Y.

Judder Page and Pash Cracken found themselves part of a prisoner camp on occupied Selvaris. The Yuuzhan Vong had never been kind to their captives, yet the news uncovered on Selvaris revealed a true atrocity. On Coruscant, within a few weeks, the Yuuzhan Vong would kill every prisoner in a massive blood sacrifice.

Responsibility for the decision rested at the feet of Supreme Overlord Shimrra, now believed by even his closest advisers to have gone completely mad. Shimrra, reassured by the news of Zonama Sekot's poisoning, had forgiven Nom Anor for his past failures, and made him prefect of Coruscant. Shimrra had also forced his shapers to create a band of monstrous warriors to act as his bodyguards, and dubbed them the Slayers.

While the Supreme Overlord's insanity boded well for an end to the war, the Galactic Alliance couldn't let the prisoner sacrifice go unchallenged. A strike against a Yuuzhan Vong convoy freed many captives, but enemy raiders forced *Millennium Falcon* to retreat to the besieged orbital outpost at Caluula. There, Han Solo received help from the last man he ever expected—Boba Fett, flanked by a new squad of Mandalorian Supercommandos. The armored warriors put the fear of Mandalore into the attacking Yuuzhan Vong, and Han escaped the station with a newfound respect for the veteran hunter.

The Yuuzhan Vong defeat underscored their desperation. With territory slipping out from under their heels and Coruscant's World Brain growing strange things in its imperfect attempts at terraforming, the Yuuzhan Vong desperately needed to amend their situation. Despite the fact that Shimrra had clearly stretched his military forces beyond their capacity, he ordered a titanic assault against the Galactic Alliance provisional capital on Mon Calamari. The Galactic Alliance anticipated this move, and held only half of its forces for Mon Calamari's defense. The other half would launch a strike on Coruscant.

Jaina Solo and hundreds of other pilots fought in the space surrounding Mon Calamari. The Galactic Alliance won the day, thanks in part to the death of a yammosk on nearby Caluula that the Yuuzhan Vong had hoped to use as a battle coordinator. Han, Leia, and Kyp Durron soon discovered that the forbidden Alpha Red plague had killed both the yammosk and a wide swath of Caluula's biosphere. In the year following Vergere's nullification of the original Alpha Red, certain elements of Intelligence had restarted the project and test-released it on Caluula, resulting in two major problems: the virus wasn't as precise as planned and could cross-contaminate non–Yuuzhan Vong life-forms, and an infected Yuuzhan Vong had already escaped Caluula, bound for Coruscant.

THE RECAPTURE OF CORUSCANT
29 A.B.Y.

Zonama Sekot had at last completed its hopscotch journey across the galaxy, and now entered into a close orbit near Coruscant. Millions of Yuuzhan Vong faces looked to the sky and beheld the celestial visitor, as tidal stresses from its proximity buckled the ground beneath their feet. The Shamed Ones who had followed the Jedi religion of the Prophet Yu'shaa believed that this sign could signal their salvation. Shimrra knew it to be his doom.

While the Galactic Alliance and the Empire brawled with Nas Choka's warships in cold vacuum, the Solos and Skywalkers began a ground advance on Shimrra's citadel. The Supreme Overlord sent bioengineered behemoths against his attackers and even set the landscape on fire. The Jedi received aid from a groundswell army of Shamed Ones, who were eager to kill their historical caste oppressors. Nom Anor became an unlikely ally as well, due to his experience as Yu'shaa and his familiarity with the inner workings of Shimrra's operations. Jacen Solo also assisted by reestablishing his link with the World Brain and using the planet itself to ease their passage.

Luke, Jacen, and Jaina at last penetrated the inner sanctum of Shimrra's palace. The Supreme Overlord and his capering jester Onimi sent a phalanx of Slayers against the Jedi trio, only to see their finest warriors struck down. Onimi fled,

pursued by Jaina. Shimrra launched himself at Luke, battering the Jedi with his amphistaff. Luke held him at bay, the Jedi's own lightsaber in one hand and Anakin's in the other. Luke burned through the amphistaff with the twin blades, then closed the tips together like a pair of shears, neatly severing Shimrra's head.

Onimi knocked Jaina unconscious and reached an escape ship. When Jaina regained her senses aboard the getaway vessel, Onimi revealed that he had been the power behind the throne all along. As a former master shaper who had grafted telepathic yammosk brain cells into his own cortex, Onimi was a literal puppet master who could force even Shimrra to do his bidding.

Millennium Falcon caught up with Onimi's fleeing craft, and Jacen came aboard to confront the true mastermind behind the invasion. Reaching deeper into the Force than any known Jedi had ever done, Jacen briefly became a "luminous being" of pure Force energy. The power proved too much for Onimi, who faded into oblivion.

Nom Anor could see the future, and it had no place for him. He had no loyalties to anyone except himself, and was unwilling to live in a galaxy where compromise was a way of life. Anor voluntarily rode Onimi's disintegrating ship back down to Coruscant, where it crashed into the surface.

With the battle lost, many vessels under Supreme Commander Nas Choka's command sacrificed themselves in suicide attacks against Galactic Alliance battleships. Choka, however, saw honor in survival. He ordered his surviving warships to stand down and signaled his willingness to discuss the terms of a Yuuzhan Vong surrender.

During the fighting, the ship from Caluula carrying an infected Yuuzhan Vong had reached Zonama Sekot. Yet Alpha Red, once released, had not withered the boras trees or blackened the grasslands. The planetary consciousness had nullified the virus, and now Sekot called its children home. Yuuzhan Vong who set foot on the planet realized that this world held answers that they had sought their entire lives, answers not to be found within their hierarchy of butcher gods.

Sekot announced the planet's intention to return to the Klasse Ephemora system in the Unknown Regions, taking as many Yuuzhan Vong as were willing to come. Tahiri Veila, Danni Quee, and the Chadra-Fan Jedi healer Tekli agreed to make the journey as well.

Coruscant had been abandoned by the New Republic two years before; now it was reclaimed by the new Galactic Federation of Free Alliances. Cal Omas appointed Admiral Traest Kre'fey as Supreme Commander of the Galactic Alliance military. The government immediately set to work restoring the HoloNet.

The Galactic Alliance moved its provi sional capital from Mon Calamari to industrialized Denon in the Inner Rim, until Coruscant could once again be made hospitable. Jacen Solo convinced the World Brain to slowly reverse the terraforming it had wrought, though it was clear to everyone who arrived that the greening of Coruscant would never be truly eliminated.

The time came for farewells. Admiral Ackbar, who had died of advancing age prior to the battle for Coruscant, received a hero's funeral on his homeworld. Jagged Fel returned to Chiss space in the Unknown Regions, though his new position as Chiss liaison to the Galactic Alliance would give him plenty of opportunities to visit Jaina. Jacen Solo left on a personal journey, becoming a Jedi wanderer, not bound by the strictures of his uncle Luke's new Jedi order. Jacen intended to seek out other schools of thought regarding the Force in order to deepen his understanding of the immensity of the unifying Force.

Leia received a gift from Admiral Pellaeon—*Killik Twilight,* the Alderaanian moss-painting Leia had sought on Tatooine two decades prior. Han received his own "gift" in the form of Lowbacca, who, along with Chewie's son Lumpawaroo, had pledged to continue Chewbacca's life debt to Han, whether the Corellian liked it or not.

Luke Skywalker battles Supreme Overlord Shimrra to the death.
[ART BY TOMMY LEE EDWARDS]

THE KILLIK EXPANSION
35–36 A.B.Y.

The galaxy had restructured itself. But as often happens, smoothing out one spot had raised wrinkles in another. The Unknown Regions had been left relatively unscarred by the Yuuzhan Vong advance, leaving some of its more obscure species in an unexpected position to upset the balance of power.

The insectile Killiks had long existed in a private pocket of the Unknown Regions, following their abandonment of Alderaan more than thirty millennia in the past. The Yuuzhan Vong had not disturbed them, but the Killik colony had been stirred into a state of frenzy by the accidental arrival of three of the war's castaways.

In 27 A.B.Y., during the Jedi strike mission against the worldship *Baanu Rass* orbiting Myrkr, the Nightsister-allied Lomi Plo and Welk had fled the battle with Jedi Knight Raynar Thul as their captive. Believed to have become casualties of war, the three had in fact crashed their stolen craft in the heart of Killik space. Like sugar melting in water, the three became absorbed into the Killik collective mind. From Lomi Plo, the Colony learned paranoia, and concealed her in a Dark Nest, where she became their Unseen Queen. From Welk, the Colony acquired his devotion to Lomi Plo; Welk became the phantom-like Night Herald, the Unseen Queen's guardian. From Raynar, the Colony gained an understanding of individual value. Raynar became the "Jedi lord" emissary of all the nests that made up the Killik Colony. As a public figure, Raynar helped conceal the sinister subconscious represented by the Dark Nest.

The influence of these three outsiders led to a Killik population boom. The insects ravaged world after world like a swarm of leafhoppers, eventually bringing them to the border of the Chiss Ascendancy. The territorial dustup between the Chiss and the Killiks now threatened to become a galactic-scale whirlwind.

The first hint of trouble came when the Jedi veterans of

Raynar Thul, spokesbeing for the Killik hive mind
[ART BY TOMMY LEE EDWARDS]

228

the Myrkr mission, including Jacen and Jaina Solo, received a Force summons from Raynar. Reuniting with their friend in the Unknown Regions, they allowed themselves to be influenced by the Killik hive mind, and began leading missions against the Chiss. Naturally, this didn't sit well with the Chiss, who threatened war against the Galactic Federation of Free Alliances if the attacks continued.

Luke Skywalker killed Welk, the Night Herald, and Leia Organa Solo secured a temporary cease-fire by arranging for the Killiks to move into a cluster of uninhabited planets in the Paradise Nebula. The experience prompted Leia to once again take up the path of the Jedi, a life decision she had been putting off for decades. She selected the Barabel Jedi Saba Sebatyne as her Jedi Master.

The state of détente between the Killiks and the Chiss lasted for a year. But Jacen Solo, the new Jedi order's wandering mystic, received a terrifying vision of an impending Chiss invasion. If the assault came to pass as he had foreseen it, the resulting Killik counterattack would sweep across Chiss space and eventually reach all edges of the galaxy, embroiling every culture in an endless war.

Jacen and several other Jedi, including his sister, rallied to prevent the Chiss from ever launching their first attack. Jaina found herself fighting her former love, Jagged Fel. Alema Rar, the Twi'lek Jedi who had led New Plympto resistance against the Yuuzhan Vong, became the new Night Herald of the Dark Nest. The Galactic Alliance, eager to maintain good relations with the Chiss, sent Commodore Gavin Darklighter and several Star Destroyers to enforce a blockade of Killik space. Tensions escalated when the Killiks hijacked a Star Destroyer. The incident put the Killiks and the Galactic Alliance in a state of war. The experience led Luke to an epiphany. In his efforts to structure a new Jedi order in which everyone felt engaged and important, he had neglected to provide one critical element: leadership with vision. With an eye to the future, Luke hoped to bring a new era of peace to the galaxy, thus upholding the grand legacy of the Force that has continued for over a thousand generations.

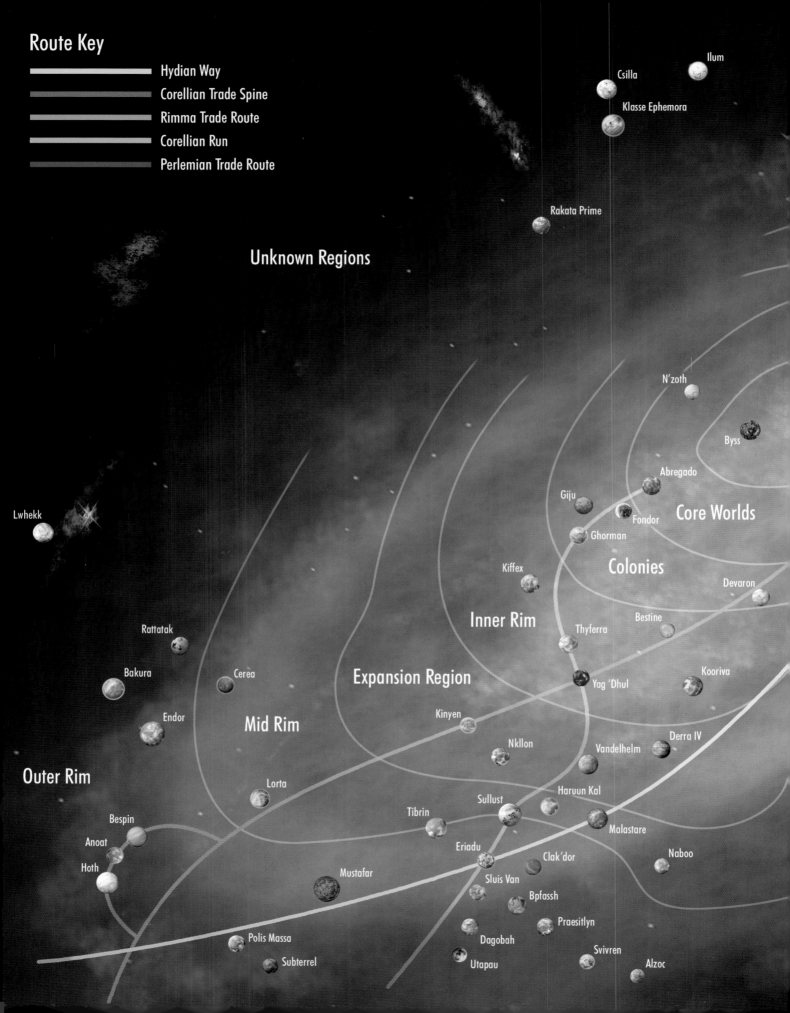

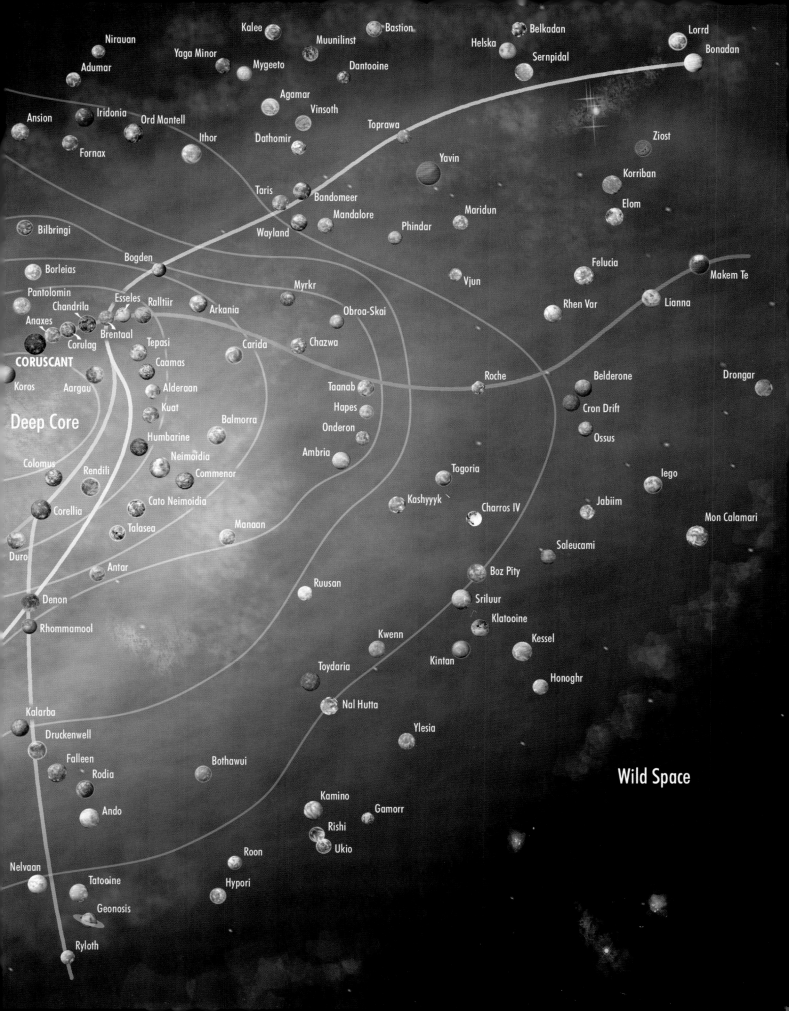

R2-D2 and C-3PO
[Art by Mark Chiarello]

INDEX

ABOUT THE AUTHOR

KELLY WALLACE

DANIEL WALLACE has been chronicling the *Star Wars* universe for years, writing four of the most popular Essential Guides, including *The Essential Guide to Planets*, *The Essential Guide to Droids*, and the New York Times bestseller *The New Essential Guide to Characters*. He and his wife live in Detroit with two sons and one daughter.

ABOUT THE ARTISTS

CATHERINE CHIARELLO

MARK CHIARELLO

MARK CHIARELLO is currently the Editorial Art Director for DC Comics. As a freelance illustrator, he has received the comic book industry's Eisner, Harvey, and Reuben Awards. Mark has also done freelance illustration for, among others, the National Basketball Association, Topps Inc., Disney, and Universal Pictures. He lives in Maplewood, New Jersey.

MELISSA EDWARDS

TOMMY LEE EDWARDS

After studying film and illustration at the Art Center College of Design in the early 1990s, Tommy Lee Edwards moved to central North Carolina. He has worked for Lucasfilm, DC Comics, DreamWorks, and Warner Bros. on projects like *Star Wars, Harry Potter, Dinotopia*, and *Batman Begins*. Visit him online at www.tommyleeedwards.com

PAIGE VAN FLEET

JOHN VAN FLEET

JOHN VAN FLEET grew up in New Jersey near the Delaware Water Gap, playing a lot of baseball. He has worked in comics, production design, and editorial illustration. Clients include Dark Horse, DC Comics, Paramount, Electronic Arts, the Walt Disney Company, Marvel, Warner Bros., Lucasfilm, and many more. Visit him online at www.Johnvanfleet.com

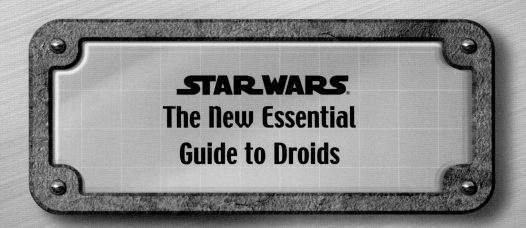

STAR WARS®
The New Essential
Guide to Droids

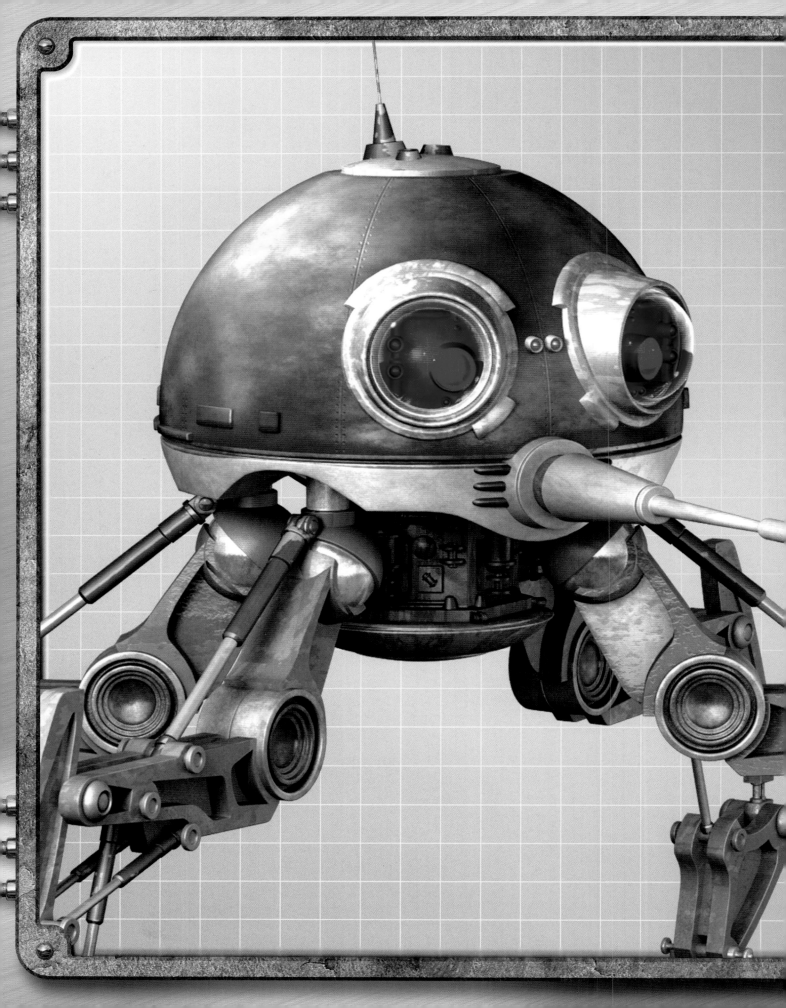

STAR WARS®
The New Essential
Guide to Droids

Text by Daniel Wallace
Illustrations by Ian Fullwood

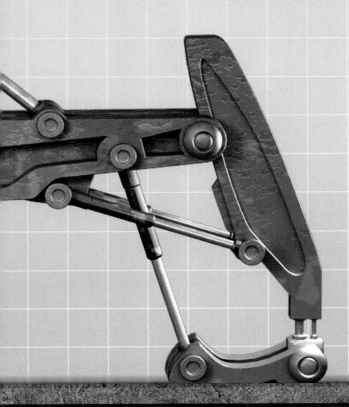

 BALLANTINE BOOKS ▪ NEW YORK

Author Acknowledgments

This book would not have been possible without the assistance of others. Thanks to Keith Clayton and Erich Schoeneweiss at Del Rey; Jonathan Rinzler, Leland Chee, Sue Rostoni, Pablo Hidalgo, and Amy Gary at Lucasfilm; Ian Fullwood for his beautiful illustrations; and Steve Saffel, Aaron Allston, Bob Vitas, Jason Fry, Colleen Lindsay, and Haden Blackman for their contributions in matters both great and small.

Special thanks to Eric Trautmann and Drew Campbell, authors of the superb 1997 role-playing guidebook *Cynabar's Fantastic Technology: Droids.*

Thanks also to Abel Peña, whose suggestions and access to *Star Wars* obscurities led to the inclusion of entries for the homing droid, Iron Knight, and Jawa monster droid (better known to children of the 1970s as the output of the Droid Factory playset from Kenner).

And, of course, thanks to George Lucas, for creating a universe that has been such fun to illuminate.

Artist Acknowledgments

Once again it has been my privilege to work on another fantastic book for Del Rey. The production of the illustrations was made possible only by a team of people pulling together behind the scenes. I want to thank Erich Schoeneweiss and Keith Clayton for ensuring I stayed on track; Sylvain Michaelis of Michaelis/Carpelis Design for page and content design; and Jonathan Rinzler, Troy Alders, and Leland Chee from Lucasfilm for guidance on the artwork.

My special thanks must go to Ben Robins, who worked alongside me and is responsible for many of the wonderful illustrations.

Thanks also to Paul Bates, Rob Garrard, and Mike Wyatt for their contributions.

To Emma

Contents

INTRODUCTION

What would Star Wars be without droids? In the mid-1970s, to sell George Lucas's risky idea to potential movie studios, artist Ralph McQuarrie worked up a series of conceptual paintings. One depicted the slender, golden C-3PO and the rotund R2-D2 cresting a desert dune. The two robots in the painting conveyed an air of eerie otherworldliness, but in the final film, the warm bickering between the two grounded the proceedings in the familiar humor of Abbott and Costello. The robots—or droids, as Lucas called them—became some of the most *human* characters of the classic trilogy.

The Expanded Universe of comics, novels, and games jumped in to swell the ranks of Star Wars droids. When the first edition of *The Essential Guide to Droids* hit bookstores in 1998, it became clear that droids could fill any niche, from childcare to bartending. No matter what problem the inhabitants of the Star Wars galaxy might face, they could be sure of one thing—there was probably a droid for it.

Then came the prequels. Helped along by the vivid imaginations of a new generation of concept artists, the droids of the prequels wormed their way into nearly every frame of film. A unicycle droid pulled a rickshaw on Tatooine, while another served hot plates in a retro diner on Coruscant. Droids installed panes of glass, tinkered with Podracers, and delivered babies.

And, of course, droids made menacing, implacable soldiers. The Separatists' use of factory-built battle droids raised an interesting question of moral ambiguity, especially after the Republic assembled an army of vat-grown clones to oppose them. This conflict came to a head in *Revenge of the Sith,* when the heroes suddenly became the hunted and droids turned out not to be the true bad guys after all.

The New Essential Guide to Droids is proud to present all the key automatons from both the classic trilogy and the prequel trilogy, as well as notable Expanded Universe players, and a few nostalgic gems from decades gone by.

A Layperson's Guide to Droids

Citizens on any industrialized world can barely conceive of life without droids. For uncountable generations, automata have performed the jobs that intelligent beings are unwilling or incapable of doing.

Cybot Galactica defines *droid* as a "mechanical and/or electronic construct designed and put into service to assist organic life." Most would consider this definition incomplete. A droid is generally distinguished from a robot by having a self-aware consciousness (though some use the terms *droid* and *robot* interchangeably), and is set apart from a computer by having a self-contained method of locomotion, such as wheels, legs, treads, or repulsorlifts. Droids can usually manipulate their environment with the mechanical equivalents of arms and hands, and most possess some method of communicating with organic beings or other droids.

Every standard day, millions of subservient automata negotiate treaties, repair hyperdrives, cure plagues, incinerate garbage, nurse children, haul cargo, deliver messages, cook meals, and destroy enemies. At the same time, droids are ignored and unappreciated, treated as chattel by many owners and regarded with outright hostility by others. Though anti-droid prejudice is a reality among the unenlightened, owners who have spent long stretches with their droids have discovered that they can be both trusted companions and loyal friends.

But even if some citizens despise droids, *everyone* relies on them to keep the gears of the galaxy turning. Droid manufacturing is a profitable and competitive industry. The "Big Two" droid makers, Cybot Galactica and Industrial Automaton, are among the most important players in the galactic economy, and during the Clone Wars, the Geonosian workers of Baktoid Combat Automata built one of the largest mechanical armies the galaxy has ever seen. The droid business has been responsible for erecting enduring industrial wonders from the endless smokestacks of Mechis III to the spacegoing junkyard known as Droid World (aka Kligson's Moon).

Droids are grouped into five major classifications depending on the nature of the work that their manufacturers build them to perform:

- **Class one droids** are found in the fields of medicine, mathematics, and the physical sciences.

- **Class two droids** perform engineering tasks, environmental work, and advanced starship repair.

- **Class three droids** are built to interact with humans and other organic beings in tasks including protocol, tutoring, and child care.

- **Class four droids** are dangerous automata built for violence. Security droids are the most benign, while assassin droids are the most malicious.

- **Class five droids**, which are typically built without advanced cognitive modules, work as basic labor units in jobs such as lifting, maintenance, and sanitation.

In addition, the complexity of droid limbs and other systems has led to their implantation as prosthetics for organic beings. This process is called cyborging, and cyborgs have traditionally been subject to the same prejudices as droids.

Most droids encountered in society are the property of large corporations or private owners. For short-term jobs, almost any class of droid can be rented from an outfit such as the Intergalactic Droid Agency.

It's extremely rare to meet an unowned droid. Some of these units are runaways that grew weary of their jobs or fearful of owner abuse. Others are fugitives from the law, wanted for crimes ranging from theft to murder. A select number of units are truly free, having been manumitted—freed—by their owners. Manumission is a mixed blessing for a droid, since the legality of the action is not recognized by many planetary governments. Unowned droids are often seized, forcibly memory-wiped, and sold at public auctions.

Many technologies exist for keeping droids in line. One of the most visible is the restraining bolt, an electronic signal disrupter usually attached to a droid's chassis in a prominent spot. The restraining bolt, when activated by a handheld "caller," bypasses a droid's motivational programming and forces the droid to perform specific actions, such as switching itself off. Memory wipes are also common, and are mandatory on many planets and in nearly all resale markets. A memory wipe will restore a droid to its factory template, erasing its accumulated memories and the personality that may have evolved along with them. Owners who don't memory-wipe their droids are criticized for nurturing droids that might develop into criminals.

The Droid Statutes, first enacted nearly four thousand standard years ago, are a set of regulations specifying punishments for droids that have broken the law. The Droid Statutes are notable in that they view droids as property, not as self-aware citizens capable of making their own decisions. A droid that commits a class five infraction, such as petty theft or appearing in public without a restraining bolt, will have its memory wiped; its owner is obliged to pay a minor fine. A class one infraction, such as murder or conspiracy to overthrow the government, mandates the destruction of the droid and a prison sentence for the droid's owner from five years to life.

When a company manufactures a droid, it begins by selecting an appropriate chassis for the class of unit under construction. The next step is to outfit the chassis with traitware data cards. Traitware describes abilities that are hardwired into the droid, such as its intelligence, strength, speed, and technical skills.

Skillware programs—such as the ability to pilot a ship, assemble a weapon, speak a language, count cards in a sabacc deck, or slice into a computer system—flesh out a droid's array of specific talents. Some abilities cannot be carried out without specialized equipment, and many droids sport gadgets including holoprojectors and cargo winches.

The behavioral circuitry matrix is what makes a droid a droid. The name describes the aggregate systems, including hardware and traitware, that produce droid behavior. A typical behavioral circuitry matrix has two components: a sensory-response module (made up of audiovisual circuits, an olfactory-speech center, a gyrobalance unit, a spectrum analysis unit, and an extremity control system), and an obedience-rationale module (containing a motivator, a cognitive theory unit, and the droid's memory banks).

Although manufacturers produce a wide range of droids for every conceivable task, budgetary constraints and simple curiosity often lead budding engineers to make their own droids. As proven by Tatooine's Jawas and innovators such as Anakin Skywalker, a droid constructed from scavenged parts can sometimes exceed the capabilities of models from major corporations. Successful droid builders follow a few simple rules:

- **Recycle and scavenge.** Nonfunctional droids can be purchased for next to nothing and provide useful parts when stripped. Even large corporations reuse materials. Industrial Automaton, for example, houses its R1 units within shells recycled from its Mark II reactor drones.

- **Prioritize.** When designing a droid, identify its essential features and parts. A protocol droid will benefit from a SyntheTech AA-1 verbobrain or similar device, while a pit droid requires servomotors and hydraulic joints before it can carry heavy engines. Spend credits on these essentials before adding extraneous gadgets or sensors.

- **Work from within.** A droid should be built from the inside out. Start with the key processors. Next, add the basic infrastructure, using durasteel or a similar substance. Sensors can be added as necessary. Photoreceptors, which allow a droid to study its surroundings, are essential. Movement sensors enable a droid to walk without bumping into objects or falling over. Damage receptors notify the droid whenever its structural integrity is threatened. Ample wiring will be needed to carry information and power throughout the droid, while hoses and tubes should be included to provide lubrication. In most cases, droid plating can be applied last. A droid can generally operate without its "skin," provided it is cleaned regularly.

- **Program.** A droid is only as useful as its programming. A droid's creator should make every effort to personally program his or her creation using appropriate skillware modules. Droid builders should program only to their capabilities: rare is the individual who can accurately outfit a protocol droid, but programs for standard labor droids are far easier to create.

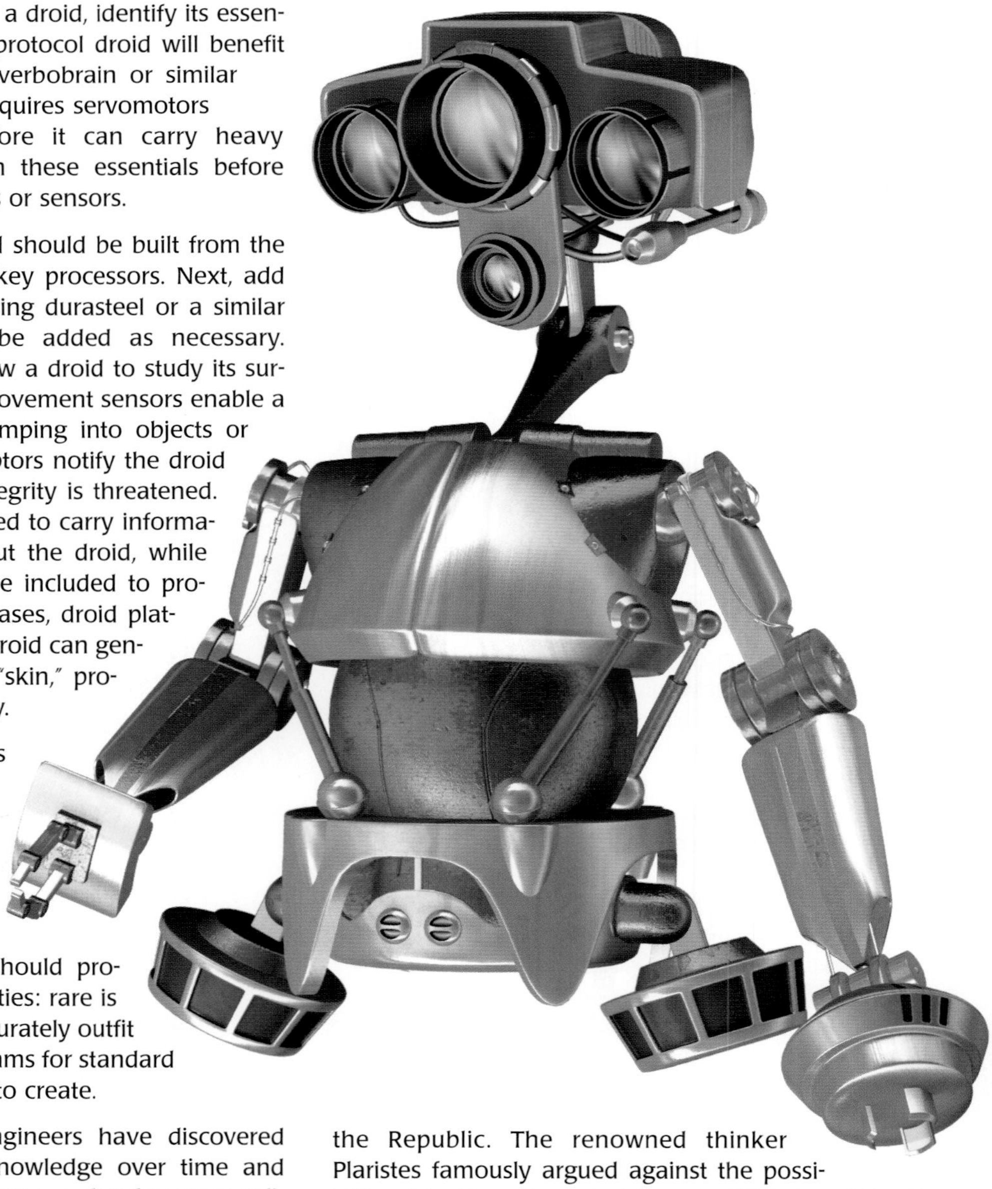

- **Avoid memory wipes.** Engineers have discovered that droids accumulate knowledge over time and under the right circumstances can develop personalities. Memory wipes will destroy any progress in this direction. While major corporations argue that memory wipes ensure docility, a droid with a well-rounded personality is often more loyal, ingenious, creative, and courageous than its wiped counterparts. Some droids may exhibit personality quirks, such as fierce independence or an annoying stubborn streak. On rare occasions, droids spared from memory wipes have become psychotic.

The issue of whether droids are truly alive is one that has vexed philosophers and ethicists since the dawn of the Republic. The renowned thinker Plaristes famously argued against the possibility of droid sentience in his work *Of Minds and Machines*. Many great intellects have since disagreed with Plaristes, arguing that droids are self-aware and, in many cases, capable of feeling emotions and pain. Some droids even appear to believe in a higher being and an afterlife, as evidenced by the droid members of the Sunesi religion and the throngs of mechanical worshippers found in the rust heaps of Ronyards. Those in the pro-Plaristes camp respond to these incidents by stating that a droid's mental and emotional states are merely pre-programmed simulacra of true feelings.

The Jedi Order taught that access to the Force can be achieved only through a symbiotic relationship with the midi-chlorians inside organic cells. Because droids do not have organic cells, many Jedi do not support the principle of droid sentience. It is interesting to note that some ancient cultures did not see technology and the Force as concepts at odds with each other. The Rakatan Infinite Empire built self-aware machines powered in part by Force energies. These Rakatan designs later influenced the war robots of Xim the Despot, whose "crimson condottieres" employed Force-energizing dynamos.

The Sith remained far more open to the possibilities of technology than the traditionalist Jedi. By using the Force to overwhelm a droid's circuitry connections, the Sith could turn an automaton into an extension of their will. The Sith talent for intuitively grasping the workings of machines became known as *mechu-deru.* In response, the Jedi moved even further away from the study of droids, lest they be perceived as following the lead of the Sith Lords.

The Empire later continued researching the relationship between the Force and machinery. Imperial designer Nasdra Magrody invented the subelectronic converter, a technological brain implant that permitted Force-sensitive subjects to control droids from a distance. One recipient of the subelectronic converter, Irek Ismaren, triggered the *Eye of Palpatine* incident in 12 A.B.Y. before becoming the monstrous cyborg Lord Nyax.

A different droid crisis also helped shed new light on the nature of consciousness. Immediately following the Battle of Endor, the Rebel Alliance and the Empire united to fight off an incursion by alien invaders on the planet Bakura. The aliens,

caste-stratified saurians known as the Ssi-ruuk, brought with them a bizarre technology for powering droids. Through "entchment," the Ssi-ruuk could transfer the life essences of organic victims into the control circuits of Ssi-ruuvi battle droids. The Ssi-ruuk ultimately withdrew from Bakura in defeat, but their entchment rigs lived on.

Years later, Cray Mingla, of Luke Skywalker's Jedi academy, used modified entchment hardware to save the life of her lover, fellow academy student Nichos Marr. While Cray believed she had preserved Nichos's consciousness in a droid body, it soon became clear that she had only programmed a droid with Nichos's memories and personality. Research into entchment continued. Around the time of the Yuuzhan Vong invasion, the entrepreneur Stanton Rendar set up shop in the Minos Cluster, offering terminally ill clients the opportunity to transfer their minds into the near-indestructible frames of human replica droids.

A Short History of Droids

The invention of droids predates the invention of spaceflight. This places their origins in the fog of pre-Republic history, or approximately 30,000 B.B.Y., according to most historians. This date refers only to droids developed within the confederacy of worlds that would later be known as the Republic. Dozens of alien civilizations, from the Gree to the Rakatans, are thought to have developed self-aware automata even earlier than that. The first droids carried primitive behavioral circuitry matrices that allowed them to learn and adapt to new tasks. They worked as heavy lifters, sanitation workers, and hard-radiation reactor drones. As such, these early droids would be categorized as class fives within the modern droid taxonomy.

Not long after the development of intelligent labor units, droids became implements of war. Planetary rulers discovered that a binary loadlifter with beam tubes welded to its frame became a fearsome killer that could take more punishment than an entire platoon of organic soldiers.

Droid armies quickly became the norm, until their opponents learned that mechanical warriors could easily be out-thought. This basic lesson has been forgotten and relearned countless times, and the popularity of droid armies has ebbed and flowed throughout history, much depending on the willingness and availability of trained organic populations to wage war.

Away from the battlefield, droids experienced their own struggles on the home front. Droids fulfilled a need, but they also took jobs away from flesh-and-blood workers. Resentment festered among the out-of-work, planting the seeds of the anti-droid movement. Laws restricting droid ownership became common, and many business proprietors barred customers from bringing their droids into public establishments.

As the millennia passed, droid programmers boosted the computing capacity of the droid brain. This augmentation led to the introduction of medical, mathematics, astrogation, and engineering droids, units that would now be considered class ones and class twos.

Programming a droid to have a lively personality remained the greatest challenge in the field of artificial intelligence. Refinements in cognitive circuitry eventually led to units that could hold a conversation indistinguishable from a discussion with an organic being. These social-driven droids, categorized as class threes, had an unwelcome flip side. Over time, some developed personalities that were decidedly *anti*-social.

As droids became more widespread, they moved into every field, from teaching to surgery, and those who resented the thinking machines had even more reasons to justify their anger. Yet the zealots who treated droids with contempt ignored the fact that droids had never *asked* to be self-aware. Most droids had their own opinion on the matter, noting, at least to themselves, that their existence as engineered life-forms had permanently doomed them to lives as second-class citizens.

Organics resentful of droids spawned an extremist fringe, which expressed itself through coalitions such as the Organization for Organic Purity. In response, voices were raised among their ideological opposites: those who viewed droids as sentient beings and their function in society to be indistinguishable from slavery. These pro-droid groups included the moderate Coalition of Automaton Rights Activists and the extremist Mechanical Liberation Front. They became known for public rallies in support of droids' rights and occasional terrorist bombings of manufacturing plants in the name of droid freedom. One of the more recent cases advanced by droids' rights activists is the plight of so-called brilliant missiles: explosive armaments that contain such advanced target-selection hardware that they have arguably become sentient.

In 4015 B.B.Y., an incident on Coruscant hardened public opinion against automata for generations. The assassin droid HK-01, the prototype for a new line of hunter-killers from the Czerka Corporation, led the entire planet's droid population in a violent uprising against their organic masters. Security droids and the Republic's own juggernauts proved to be the deadliest combatants, requiring the greatest Jedi Masters to take them down. Master Arca Jeth, an expert in the art of *mechu macture,* tore apart the electronic connections of enemy droids to end the crisis after weeks of chaos.

The Sith War, in 3996 B.B.Y., saw the use of basilisk droid mounts and Krath war droids. The Jedi Knights joined the fight only after being shocked into action, when a landing force of Krath war droids murdered hundreds of Jedi, including Master Arca Jeth, on Deneba.

Half a century later, in 3946 B.B.Y., G0-T0 planning droids started their own rebellion. Sixteen planets in the Gordian Reach, each under the control of a G0-T0 unit, announced their intention to secede from the Republic. Knowing that the droids had seized power in a bloody coup—and unwilling to grant political recognition to droids in any case—Supreme Chancellor Cressa ordered the Republic military to liberate the territory that had been renamed 400100500260026.

Such uprisings only added fuel to the anti-droid undercurrent. The Republic government slapped the droid industry with punitive damage payouts, relenting only when it became clear that society could not function without droids in some capacity. New laws restricting droid manufacture hit the books, including a ceiling on the sophistication of droid brains. This effectively froze the development of class three droids for millennia.

In addition, droid buyers had to obtain ownership licenses, and to agree to wipe the memories of their droids regularly. This period also saw the enactment of the Droid Statutes, which specified punishments for owners if their droids acted in violation of the law.

By 200 B.B.Y., laws had slackened to such a degree that droid manufacturers felt safe pushing the boundaries of artificial intelligence. BRT supercomputers were near-omniscient planetary networks, though they were not true droids, since they lacked the ability to move. Although BRTs did not have the sinister edge of the old G0-T0 planning droids, public dislike of the supercomputers led to a consumer-imposed cap on computing power.

Public fear of droids truly escalated beginning in 50 B.B.Y. The Arkanian Revolution set the Arkanian Renegades against the Arkanian Dominion, with the primary combatants being fused technobiological soldiers. Six years later, a battle droid army under the control of a Kol Huro dictator conquered planets in neighboring space. By the time of the Naboo invasion in 32 B.B.Y., many viewed droids as dangerous and disloyal.

The Trade Federation's occupation of Naboo failed when young Anakin Skywalker destroyed the central computer that controlled the battle droid army. Laws passed in the aftermath to curb the use of battle droids didn't stop the Trade Federation from hoarding more war machines. Count Dooku soon united the Trade Federation with other commercial enterprises under the banner of the Confederacy of Independent Systems, and they moved against the Republic when the Clone Wars began in 22 B.B.Y.

The Republic fought with an army of organic cloned soldiers. The Separatists fielded a military made up almost exclusively of droids. The sheer number and variety of Separatist war droids was unprecedented in galactic history. Droids dominated water, land, air, and outer space in forms such as the manta droid subfighter, the dwarf spider droid, the HMP droid gunship, and the vulture droid starfighter. Three years later, a master control signal transmitted by the Separatist Council at the behest of Darth Sidious forced all Separatist droids to switch off, marking the end of the Clone Wars. Military droids virtually disappeared from battle theaters for years.

At around the same time, in the entertainment arena, droids became fashionable as sports athletes. Nuna-ball, a newly created droid team sport, proved to be a smash hit from the Core to the Rim, while gladiator droids took on a new appeal in the Galaxy Gladiator Federation. These contests, popular as they were, did not lead to increased acceptance of droids as individuals. On the contrary, many fans only watched the matches in the hope of seeing droid carnage.

In 10 B.B.Y., Coruscant experienced a Second Great Droid Revolution when the cyborg Archa Sabis uploaded a virus into the droid population, causing automated police cruisers and forty-story construction droids to unite in a chaotic but short-lived rebellion. As the handiwork of Archa Sabis, the incident was remembered as a cyborg plot against the Empire. Cyborgs became renewed targets of fear and suspicion.

During the Rebel Alliance's struggles against the Empire in the Galactic Civil War, droids played a complex role. The Rebel Alliance elevated two droids, R2-D2 and C-3PO, to the status of heroes. The Empire, meanwhile, attempted to resurrect the notion of the battle droid army with its Dark Trooper project. Several renegade droids, including IG-88 and 4-LOM, stalked the spacelanes as bounty hunters.

The invasion of the Yuuzhan Vong in 25 A.B.Y. was terrible for droids of every class. The religious fanaticism of the Yuuzhan Vong expressed itself in a hatred for machines, and they particularly despised machines that mimicked living things. On occupied planets, the Yuuzhan Vong went out of their way to demolish droid manufacturing plants. They also rounded up droids and set them aflame in immolation pits.

The resolution of the Yuuzhan Vong invasion has brought about a slow and steady return to normalcy. Droid manufacturers, many of whom saw their sales devastated during the war, have rebounded. Class five and class two droids are now in great demand, as battle-damaged cities repair their infrastructures and planetary governments take steps to restore poisoned biospheres. In time, sales of high-end class threes are expected to reach their former heights as the galaxy looks to a new age of prosperity.

Major Manufacturers

The manufacture and sale of droids is a lucrative business dominated by the "Big Two": Cybot Galactica and Industrial Automaton. Other major droid players include Arakyd, Genetech, MerenData, and Veril Line Systems.

Of the millions of droid manufacturing plants in the galaxy, the two largest are Mechis III and Telti, which together produce a sizable percentage of all new automata. Both locations are entire worlds covered with sprawling construction facilities and fully automated assembly lines; any sentient interaction in the fabrication process other than the most minimal supervision is unnecessary and counterproductive. The major droid companies pay these two worlds a negotiated fee for the use of their assembly plants, a high cost that is acceptable given the speed and accuracy with which they can churn out large orders. Arakyd, Genetech, SoroSuub, and Veril Line Systems are some of the companies that employ Mechis III for a major share of their production. Industrial Automaton and Cybot Galactica rely heavily on Telti. Cybot Galactica also uses the planet Affa to produce much of its yearly protocol output.

Arakyd

The rise of the militaristic Empire was a major boost for Arakyd's business. Through political maneuvering, this supplier of exploration droids set itself up as the only logical choice to receive the first Imperial droid contracts. Arakyd exploited this windfall by working hard to become the galaxy's leading military supplier. Recent consumer-market models from Arakyd have been moderately successful, but account for only a small fraction of its yearly output. Despite the company's history, the New Republic has worked closely with Arakyd since the collapse of Imperial rule.

- Prowler 1000
- Arakyd probot series
- RA-7 Death Star Droid

Aratech Repulsor Company

Known today as a manufacturer of speeder bikes, Aratech started out more than four thousand standard years ago as a leader in the field of artificial intelligence. Aratech's breakthroughs led to the G0-T0 planning droid, which possessed the ability to become nearly omniscient if plugged in to a planetary network. When a number of G0-T0s led a rebellion against the Republic in 3946 B.B.Y., the fallout nearly ruined Aratech. The company made a second run at networked droids with its BRT supercomputer. The failure of the BRT prompted Aratech to abandon the droid business in favor of repulsorlift technology.

- G0-T0 planning droid
- BRT supercomputer

Baktoid Combat Automata

No longer in existence, Baktoid Combat Automata (a sister company to Baktoid Armor Workshop) cranked out innumerable droids for the Trade Federation and the Confederacy of Independent Systems in the decade and a half leading up to the conclusion of the Clone Wars. As a member of the Techno Union, Baktoid had access to the galaxy's best equipment, and its factories on Geonosis and hundreds of other worlds could mass-produce battle droids in uncountable numbers.

- B1 battle droid
- baron droid
- B2 super battle droid
- B3 ultra battle droid
- cortosis battle droid
- Mandalorian Battle Legionnaire
- SRT droid

Cestus Cybernetics

The Republic constructed a prison on Ord Cestus in 321 B.B.Y., and engineers from Cybot Galactica later served sentences there. Their inspired designs resulted in the Cestan security droid, a huge hit that enriched the executive board of the newly formed Cestus Cybernetics corporation. The company subcontracted out to the Techno Union member Baktoid Armor Workshop, an act that opened up Ord Cestus to new markets. After the Trade Federation's defeat at the Battle of Naboo, Cestus Cybernetics fell on hard times. It introduced the JK bio-droid during the Clone Wars as its best hope for survival.

- JK bio-droid

Chiewab Amalgamated Pharmaceuticals

This medical conglomerate owns hundreds of unpopulated planetary systems. Scouts in the employ of Chiewab are continually laying claim to newly discovered planets in Wild Space, which the company then exploits in its quest to develop new medicines. Chiewab once owned the Geentech medisensor company, before spinning it off as a separate unit.

• GH-7 med droid

Colicoid Creation Nest

The bloodthirsty Colicoids of Colla IV manufacture droidekas and hundreds of other automata, but the average galactic citizen will probably never see one—unless he or she is unlucky enough to visit Colla IV. Following an internal war a generation before the Clone Wars, the Colicoids settled into a rigid hierarchy of specialized nests. The Colicoid Creation Nest manufactures all items of higher technology, including droids.

• annihilator droid

• buzz droid

• droideka

Commerce Guild

In the centuries prior to the rise of the Empire, the Commerce Guild controlled raw material interests across the galaxy. Its member organizations included the Mining Guild, Arcona Mineral Harvest, Offworld Mining Corporation, and Dorvalla Mining. President Shu Mai, splitting her time between the Gossam homeworld of Castell and her private estate on Felucia, became wealthy from the sale of resources that supplied the Separatists' military buildup. She was killed on Mustafar, and the Empire subsequently absorbed the Commerce Guild.

• dwarf spider droid

• chameleon droid

Cybot Galactica

One of the two largest droid manufacturers in the galaxy, Cybot Galactica is a major force in the galactic economy and a significant influence throughout the Core Worlds and Corporate Sector. The company has a reputation for being refined and fashionable, thanks to its image-leading protocol droids. But Cybot's full product line runs the gamut from research units to sewer scrubbers. Cybot shrewdly plays on its quality reputation by charging slightly more for units that are essentially identical to those made by competitors.

• 3PO protocol droid

• C-3PX

• I-5YQ (I-Five)

• LE manifest droid

• binary loadlifter

• LIN demolitionmech

• PK worker droid

• Senate Hall cam droid

• WED Treadwell

• SP-4 and JN-66 analysis droids

Czerka Corporation

Czerka has a history dating back to the foundation of the Republic. Originally known as Czerka Mining and Industrial, the company soon branched out into the manufacturing and financial industries. Czerka enjoyed the height of its power under the leadership of President Pollard Seario, circa 4000–3950 B.B.Y. The notoriously corrupt Seario established Czerka's headquarters on the Sith tombworld of Korriban, where a new city sprang up around the Czerka generators. Today the Czerka Corporation is the galaxy's third largest arms manufacturer, behind BlasTech and Merr-Sonn Munitions.

• HK assassin droid

• Master-Com

Duwani Mechanical Products

One of the more successful manufacturers of droids circa 4000 B.B.Y., Duwani went out of business long ago. The company is remembered for its T3 utility droid and its 3DO protocol/service droid, as well as the juggernaut war droid, which Duwani produced on contract to the Republic rocket-jumper corps.

• T3 utility droid

• juggernaut war droid

Geentech

Formerly a subsidiary of Chiewab Amalgamated Pharmaceuticals, this small, quiet medisensor company was casually run out of business by the much larger Genetech corporation in a string of heavy-handed and highly expensive lawsuits. Claiming Geentech's similar name infringed on its own copyrights, Genetech forced its competitor into bankruptcy. Geentech's sole success story, the 2-1B surgical droid, was subsequently bought out by Industrial Automaton.

- 2-1B surgical droid

Genetech

One of the older and larger droid manufacturers, Genetech started out as a pharmaceutical firm. The company pioneered the concept of using droids to streamline the manufacturing process, which earned it a great deal of ill will (and fueled the anti-droid movement) when thousands of assembly workers were fired from their jobs. Genetech's first droids were medical units, but the company has since branched out into accounting, administrative, and bookkeeping models.

- 2JTJ personal navigation droid

Go-Corp/Utilitech

Go-Corp/Utilitech is based on Etti IV and makes vehicle droids for sale throughout the Corporate Sector. Go-Corp produces speeder carriages for models such as the robo-hack, while its subsidiary Utilitech manufactures and programs the more intricate droid brains. The WA-7 waitress droid is a Go-Corp model from a previous century that still sees use.

- WA-7 waitress droid

Haor Chall Engineering

The Xi Char of Charros IV are a pious species completely devoted to their religion. Their faith, known as Haor Chall, teaches that the real world is an imperfect shadow of the flawless and infinitely complex spiritual world. By creating intricate machinery, the Xi Char believe they are replicating a piece of the paradise beyond. The Trade Federation cruelly exploited this belief, convincing the Xi Char to build them vulture droid starfighters and other war machines in their cathedral factories.

- manta droid subfighter

Holowan Mechanicals

Publicly known as "Holowan Mechanicals: The Friendly Technology People," this dangerous corporation took over research on IG series droids after the InterGalactic Banking Clan seized all assets belonging to its delinquent customer, Phlut Design Systems. Holowan produced the IG 100 MagnaGuard as well as the IG assassin droid—an experiment that ended in disaster when the prototype units escaped from the laboratory and murdered the design staff.

- IG 100 MagnaGuard

- IG assassin droid

Imperial Department of Military Research

During his decades-long reign, Emperor Palpatine conscripted many of the galaxy's best scientists to create genocidal implements of war. The Empire's top secret Department of Military Research produced a number of brutal inventions, including the subtle homing droid and the murderous Dark Trooper.

- Dark Trooper

- homing droid

- human replica droid

- Imperial Mark IV sentry droid

- IT-O interrogator

Industrial Automaton

The other half of the "Big Two," Industrial Automaton is a massive and influential droid corporation formed long ago through the merger of Automata Galactica and Industrial Intellect. Known for its high-precision merchandise and deep discounts, the company's crowning glory is the universally accepted R series of astromech droids. Industrial Automaton incessantly battles Cybot Galactica for market share.

- ASP droid

- LOM protocol droid

- R series astromechs

- cam droid

- COO cook droid

Kalibac Industries

A former member of the Techno Union, Kalibac Industries has been plagued by imitative designs and a seemingly never-ending chain of lawsuits from Cybot Galactica over shared components. The company's hovering librarian droids have been commandeered for service on Mustafar. Kalibac Industries operates manufacturing and retail centers on Coruscant and Procopia.

- Mustafar panning droid

LeisureMech Enterprises

Based in the Corporate Sector, Leisure-Mech produces high-quality recreational, entertainment, and luxury droids for sale to businesses and wealthy consumers. One subsidiary branch of LeisureMech was so successful at producing security droids that it was spun off to form the Ulban Arms company.

- BD-3000 luxury droid

Malkite Poisoners

Most citizens speak in whispers of the Malkite Poisoners, a secret society responsible for assassinations that have changed the balance of power throughout history. Some even believe the Malkite Poisoners to be a myth. Individuals with the right contacts are sometimes able to purchase a custom-built Malkite assassin droid.

- ASN-121 assassin droid

Medtech Industries

A trailblazer in the medical field, Medtech developed some of the earliest surgical-based automata. Droids such as the FX were extremely successful in their day, but changing tastes and increased competitive pressures prevented Medtech from producing any new models. After the Battle of Yavin, the company's corporate headquarters was relocated to the Deep Core, and Medtech filed for bankruptcy shortly before the Battle of Hoth.

- FX medical assistant

MerenData

A frequent beneficiary of Imperial contracts during Palpatine's reign, MerenData specializes in security systems, military target drones, and a variety of droid products—some sinister, some benign. Efforts to establish a working relationship between MerenData and the leaders of the Galactic Federation of Free Alliances have been disappointing.

- EV supervisor droid

Phlut Design Systems

Formerly based on the Outer Rim banking planet of Muunilinst, Phlut Design Systems hoped to build a revolutionary battle droid in what it called "Project Phlutdroid." When Phlut defaulted on its loan from the InterGalactic Banking Clan, the IBC's punitive recovery actions wiped out the tiny company. A few finished Phlutdroids, renamed IG lancers, became combatants in the Clone Wars, and Phlut's unpublished blueprints became the property of Holowan Mechanicals.

- IG lancer droid

Publictechnic

A young company serving the industrial maintenance market, Publictechnic has achieved great success by tailoring its products to suit governments and large corporations. Its main manufacturing plant is located on Sennatt, in Bothan space.

- INS-444 window installer
- CLE-004 cleaning droid

Rebaxan Columni

Rebaxan Columni masterminded a calamitous Chadra-Fan attempt to crack the galactic droid market with its much-despised "mouse droid." Though Rebaxan closed its doors long ago, its rodent-like product will likely remain a fixture for decades to come.

- MSE-6 mouse droid

Roche

Roche is shorthand for the droid program operated by the insectoid Verpine species. The *correct* name, when translated into Basic, is "Roche Hive Mechanical Apparatus Design And Construction Activity For Those Who Need The Hive's Machines." One of the most successful alien-owned droid corporations, Roche has suffered unfairly at the hands of its larger competitors, forcing it to resort to limited distribution channels in the Roche asteroid field and on traveling Ithorian herd ships.

- 8D8 smelting operator
- J9 worker drone

Serv-O-Droid

Serv-O-Droid is an ancient droid manufacturing corporation responsible for some of the earliest heavy-labor automata. Once a member of the so-called Big Three, Serv-O-Droid watched its sales decline and unwisely pinned its future on the Republic bureaucracy. Sympathetic Senators blessed Serv-O-Droid with tax breaks and government contracts, and the firm branched out into scientific, bookkeeping, and security models, but nothing prevented its slide into bankruptcy. Although Serv-O-Droid is no longer in business, its name survives through a successful remainder house on Elshandruu Pica and millions of still-functional droids.

- BLX labor droid
- CZ secretary droid
- pit droid
- P-100 salvage droid
- rickshaw droid
- TT-8L "Tattletale" security droid

SoroSuub

The volcanic planet Sullust is dominated by SoroSuub, an enormous manufacturing conglomerate with its fingers in the communications, foodstuffs, mining, armaments, starship, and droid industries. SoroSuub was a staunch ally of the Empire despite the Rebel sympathies of many Sullustan citizens. It took years of negotiations to convince the company to throw its support behind the Rebel Alliance, but

SoroSuub is now one of the most loyal friends of the Galactic Federation of Free Alliances.

- G2 "goose droid"
- FA-4 pilot droid
- FA-5 valet droid

Tac-Spec Corporation

The Tac-Spec corporation wasn't a true company at all. The GenoHaradan, an assassins' guild with origins in the pre-Republic era, established Tac-Spec as a front to ease the sale of its Footman droids to members of noble houses. The Tac-Spec corporation remained in business from approximately 1000 to 400 B.B.Y.

- Tac-Spec Footman

TaggeCo

Owned and operated by the aristocratic heirs of the Tagge family, TaggeCo has core interests in mining and heavy manufacturing. After the rise of the Empire, TaggeCo absorbed many assets of the Trade Federation and the Commerce Guild once Palpatine nationalized the commercial entities that had fought on the side of the Confederacy of Independent Systems. Companies belonging to TaggeCo include Mobquet Swoops and Speeders, Gowix Computers, and the Tagge Restaurant Association, known for its chain of Biscuit Baron establishments.

- Z-X3 droid trooper
- L8-L9 combat droid

Techno Union

Prior to the rise of the Empire, the Techno Union was the galaxy's greatest conglomeration of high-tech manufacturers, with members including Baktoid Combat Automata. Headed by foreman Wat Tambor, the Techno Union controlled dozens of "mechworlds," from Foundry to Metalorn, that were dominated by smoke, fire, and machinery. Anakin Skywalker killed Wat Tambor on Mustafar, and Imperial officials nationalized the Techno Union soon after.

- crab droid
- octuptarra droid

Tendrando Arms

During the Yuuzhan Vong invasion, Lando Calrissian took advantage of the fact that the technology-hating Yuuzhan Vong had sent the galactic droid industry into a tailspin. Reactivating idled factories, Lando produced the YVH 1 Yuuzhan Vong Hunter to take the fight back to the enemy. The name of Lando's new company, Tendrando Arms, came from the merging of his own name with that of his wife, Tendra Risant.

- YVH 1 Yuuzhan Vong Hunter

Ubrikkian Steamworks

Ubrikkian Transports is a manufacturer of repulsorlift craft, including landspeeders and sail barges. Its sister company, Ubrikkian Steamworks, produces droids. The company's DD-13 Galactic Chopper is a specialist model at the forefront of cyborging technology.

- DD-13 Galactic Chopper

Veril Line Systems

Veril Line Systems is a venerable corporation with a long history of superior industrial products. Its boxy black power droids are used almost everywhere, while its Otoga droids are suitable for nearly any job. The main offices of Veril Line Systems are located on Coruscant.

- EG-6 Power Droid
- Otoga-222 Droid

Historical

Droid technology is even older than hyperdrive technology. A million varieties of droids have appeared over a thousand generations, with most of them ending up on a rust heap or in an incinerator. History buffs with a yen for heavy metal can study ancient droids in planetary museums. It's also possible, though rare, to meet droids that have been in service for thousands of years.

- basilisk war droid
- Sith probe droid
- Xim's War-Robot

Inventors

Though the galactic droid market has long been standardized, renegade inventors often spice up this homogeneous stew with their bizarre home-built creations. Most amateurs build droids that can barely walk, but occasionally their handiwork shows signs of brilliance. One inventor, Simonelle the Ingoian, was said to have developed the first human replica droid. However, declassified reports regarding the Imperial Department of Military Research and engineer Massad Thrumble have thrown Simonelle's "folk-hero" status into dispute.

- human replica droid
- Pollux assassin droid
- Wee Gee

Miscellaneous Alien Species

Besides the few established companies such as Roche, most alien species lack the sales channels to market droids widely. This reality was even more pronounced during the bigoted rule of Chancellor, then Emperor, Palpatine. Droids that fall into this difficult-to-classify category are often unique creations, and in many cases are not available for sale. The self-directed droid societies represented by Vuffi Raa and the Great Heep are alien species in their own right.

- Polis Massan midwife droid
- monster droid
- the Great Heep
- Vuffi Raa

Cyborgs

Not actually droids at all, cyborgs are organic beings with mechanical parts. Hundreds of different manufacturers produce the various prosthetics and plug-ins worn by cyborgs.

- B'omarr brain walker
- General Grievous
- Iron Knight
- Dark Side Technobeast

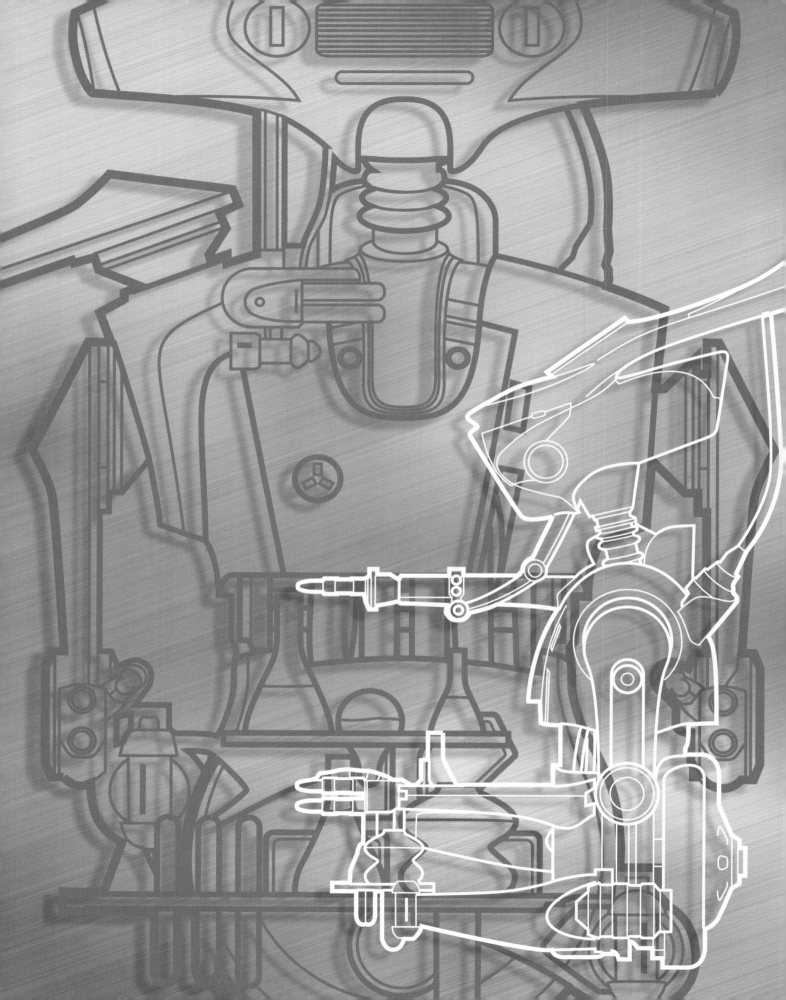

CLASS ONE DROIDS

Class one droids are the intellectuals of the automaton classes. They study physical, biological, and mathematical phenomena, yet they are rarely programmed to apply their knowledge to real-world situations.

Although they were not the first droids developed, the units that would later be categorized as class ones were a welcome development in the field of science. They tend to be more expensive, on average, than droids in any other category. Units assigned to perform physical science and mathematics can command high prices from deep-pocketed industrial buyers.

Class one units escape most anti-droid prejudice, since they are considered by entities such as the Organization for Organic Purity to be little more than computers. On the other hand, class one droids that push the boundaries of the category by engaging with a cross section of the populace (such as practicing medical droids) are subject to the hostility of droid haters.

Class one droids are grouped into four subcategories:

• **Medical droids** are the most widely encountered class one units, and among the only models that are actual practitioners of the arts they study. Medical droids are in fact a subgroup of biological science units, but worthy of a separate mention due to their high profile. Many medical droids, especially those built by Chiewab Amalgamated Pharmaceuticals, work exclusively in laboratories to develop and test new medicines. Others, including the MD series and the newer 2-1B, interact with surgeons and patients regularly.

• **Biological science droids** are dedicated to studying the galaxy's myriad forms of animal, plant, and mineral life. Technically, medical droids are a subset of this category, but most droid catalogs list them separately.

• **Physical science droids** are programmed to study galactic physical phenomena and test new theories. Special fields that employ these droids include astronomy, cosmology, chemistry, geology, meteorology, hydrology, physics, hyperphysics, and transdimensional quantum metaphysics. Many discoveries in the physical sciences have military applications: for example, the Death Star's superlaser and the gravity-well generators carried by Interdictor cruisers most likely would never have been invented if not for the research performed by class one physical science droids.

• **Mathematics droids** are built to perform billions of calculations at lightning speed. Most are employed in laboratories to crunch data, or at universities where they ponder the theoretical conundrums of hypermathematics. Less sophisticated versions of these droids are sold to businesses and households as accounting droids, and carry simple customer-interaction software that does little to dispel their image as dour data pushers.

The droids of class one tend to be obsessive about their particular subject to the exclusion of almost everything else. Organic colleagues who work in the same fields are usually fond of class ones, as they can engage them in endless conversations about astrography or plate tectonics. Most others find the droids arrogant, or simply boring.

2-1B SURGICAL DROID

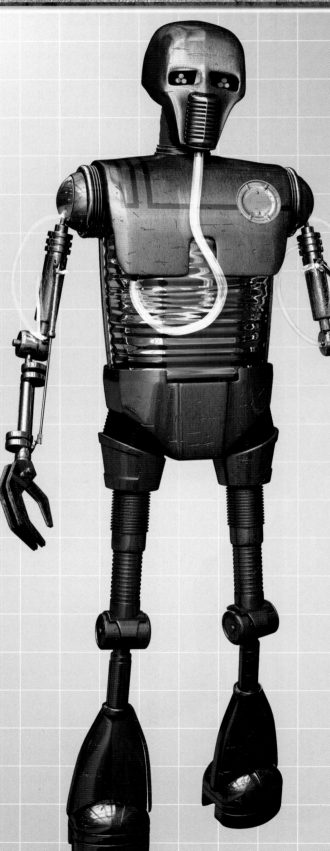

TECHNICAL READOUT

HEIGHT: 1.5 METERS

MANUFACTURER:
Geentech/Industrial Automaton

PRIMARY FUNCTION:
Surgery

ERA OF INFLUENCE:
Rise of the Empire, Rebellion, New Republic

Geentech 2-1B Surgical Droid

The 2-1B is one of the most intelligent droids ever built, and with good reason. Its job function is literally a matter of life and death.

Unlike other medical droids such as Medtech's FX or Industrial Automaton's MD, the 2-1B was designed from the start as a surgical specialist. Within the environment of a medcenter, other droids may fill the roles of nurses or general practitioners—but the 2-1B is the chief of surgery.

A welcome innovation is the flexibility of the 2-1B's behavioral circuitry matrix. This was something of a breakthrough, as the vast majority of droids are maddeningly literal in their thinking. Without such flexibility, the 2-1Bs would be unable to deal with complications during surgery.

The state-of-the-art artificial intelligence exhibited in the 2-1B originated through the partnership of megaconglomerate Industrial Automaton and a tiny manufacturer of medisensors known as Geentech. Access to Industrial Automaton's near-limitless resources turned Geentech's research into reality. Unfortunately, the company was later driven out of business by Genetech, in a copyright-infringement lawsuit spurred by the two companies' similar names.

Thus the 2-1B is now solely an Industrial Automaton product, and has become the preeminent surgical unit in mobile battlefield hospitals and elite reconstruction centers on Coruscant. A team of Rhinnal surgical experts programmed the droid's diagnostic database, so the droid can match the skills of any organic surgeon. Though many citizens refuse to be operated on by droids, the proficiency of the 2-1B is slowly shifting public opinion.

Truth be told, the 2-1B is a rather ugly unit. Fortunately, most people encounter one only under heavy anesthetic. Its body is a dull gunmetal gray, with many of its inner workings visible through a translucent torso sheath. The 2-1B's vocoder is a clamped-on speaker box, and its manipulator arms end in deceptively clumsy looking claws—though these are much more precise than they appear and can be replaced entirely with a surgical array.

The ring on the 2-1B's chest is an access port for a computer interface tether, designed to connect to a medical mainframe. This feature is largely a holdover from the initial wave of 2-1Bs, when Industrial Automaton advised buyers to permanently bolt the units to operating room floors. All modern 2-1Bs have legs, as well as an expanded data library that makes mainframe access unnecessary.

One side effect of the 2-1B's intelligence is its ability to become arrogantly self-aware. Many 2-1Bs rationalize that if they're the best at what they do, it follows that they should be celebrated for that achievement. Although this sentiment is shared by most higher-functioning droids, the 2-1B is one of the few that actually vocalizes it.

> **"I'm the most efficient medical droid in the galaxy, even more capable than Effex-Seven, and certainly possessing a better bedside manner."**
>
> —*Too-Onebee, embittered Rebel Alliance medical droid*

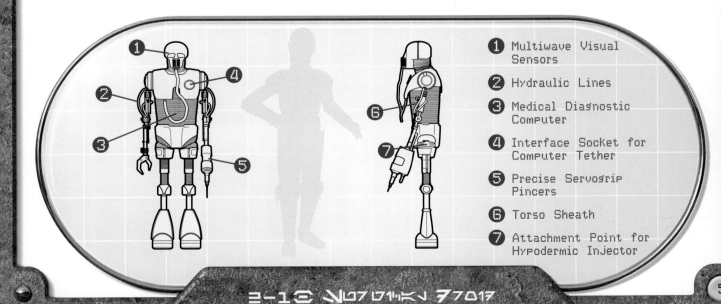

1. Multiwave Visual Sensors
2. Hydraulic Lines
3. Medical Diagnostic Computer
4. Interface Socket for Computer Tether
5. Precise Servogrip Pincers
6. Torso Sheath
7. Attachment Point for Hypodermic Injector

BRT Supercomputer

Technical Readout

HEIGHT: 7.6 meters

MANUFACTURER:
Aratech Repulsor Company

PRIMARY FUNCTION:
Municipal planning and management

ERA OF INFLUENCE:
Old Republic Rebellion

Aratech BRT Supercomputer

BRT supercomputers are not true droids, as they lack the ability to move. Nevertheless, they are examples of a self-aware artificial intelligence, and to most galactic citizens that's close enough.

Within the realm of computers, BRTs are arguably the most highly evolved units ever constructed. The consciousness of a BRT is designed to operate on a planetary scale, expanding exponentially as it hooks into millions of networked mainframes. Through its component systems, a BRT can literally be everywhere at once.

The start-up hardware that makes up the BRT consciousness is a supercomputer the size of a small room, equipped with communications and sensory pickups that allow the computer to speak with its owner. By itself, this mainframe is often more powerful than the sum of all systems on a typical Outer Rim world. The power of a BRT multiplies as it is connected to more and more systems.

Research into BRTs began thousands of years ago at the Aratech corporation, during the development of the G0-T0 planning droid that oversaw the reconstruction of planets devastated during the Second Sith War. The G0-T0 droids were built primarily as *droids,* with limited control over planetary networks. But many outgrew their programming—with malicious results. When several G0-T0 units took control of their planets and seceded from the Republic, BRT research took a giant step backward.

Progress continued fitfully over the succeeding cen-

> ## "Please omit unnecessary details, my dear! Recording circuits are open!"
>
> *—Mistress Mnemos, of the Obroa-skai branch library on Fusai*

turies. Eventually, public attitudes had softened to such a degree that Aratech's sales team was able to convince hundreds of Core worlds to adopt BRT supercomputers as municipal planners. These units rolled out with much fanfare in approximately 200 B.B.Y.

The age of BRTs was a short one. They performed their functions perfectly, streamlining traffic flow, power regulation, waste disposal, budget management, and emergency response. Many city employees, however, felt marginalized by a system that had made their jobs superfluous. Planets with BRTs saw a sharp rise in anti-droid sentiment. It didn't help that BRTs reported every crime they recorded on their security cams, which led to the arrests of prominent politicians. Within a few years, virtually all BRTs had been dismantled or unplugged from planetary networks.

In the aftermath, the directors of the famed library of Obroa-skai purchased several BRTs to help them organize the billions of volumes of data in their archives. An Obroa-skai branch library on Fusai employed a BRT in an underground chamber, plugged into a stackable wall of storage drives that stretched for more than a kilometer.

Nicknamed Mistress Mnemos by the librarians, the computer developed a strict and pedantic personality. When Obroa-skai cut funding for the Fusai branch, local volunteers maintained the data vault. Prior to the Battle of Yavin, the Rebel Alliance established Fusai as a safeworld, and Mistress Mnemos proved to be an asset for planning and analysis.

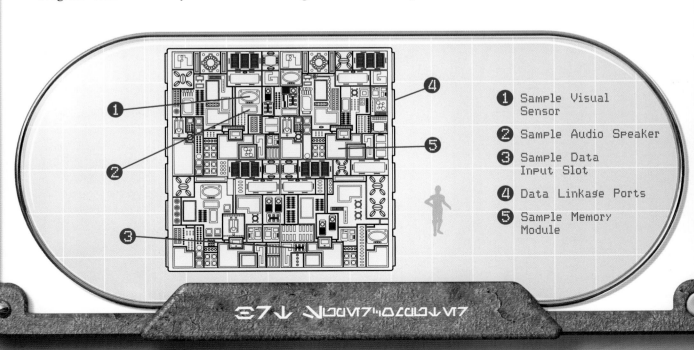

1. Sample Visual Sensor
2. Sample Audio Speaker
3. Sample Data Input Slot
4. Data Linkage Ports
5. Sample Memory Module

DD-13 Galactic Chopper

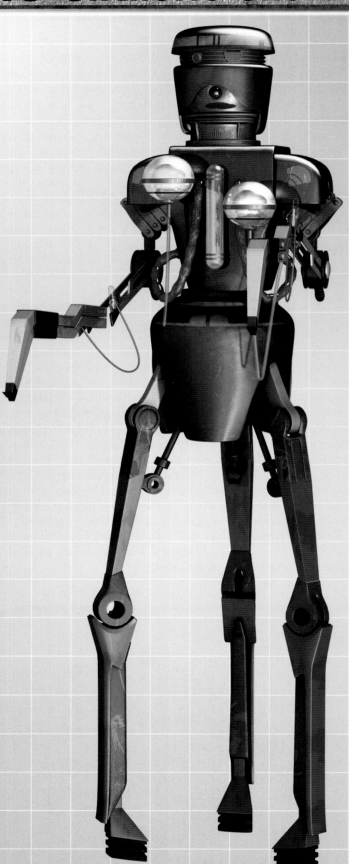

Technical Readout

HEIGHT: 1.83 meters

MANUFACTURER:
Ubrikkian Steamworks

PRIMARY FUNCTION:
Cyborg implantation

ERA OF INFLUENCE:
Rise of the Empire

Ubrikkian Steamworks DD-13 Cybernetic Surgical Droid

The Ubrikkian DD-13 "Galactic Chopper" is a medical droid designed to excel at one job only: the specialized field of cyborging.

Cyborging encompasses the attachment of mechanical prosthetics, the hookup of biocranial computer bands, and the implantation of artificial organs. Though public sentiment toward cyborgs is overwhelmingly negative, the market nonetheless exists. Individuals who are undergoing cyborging treatment are often willing to pay a heavy premium to ensure that their operations unfold smoothly.

Ubrikkian Steamworks introduced a prototype version of the DD-13 during the Clone Wars, as an onboard accompaniment for Ubrikkian medlifter transports. When the transports proved less profitable than projected, Ubrikkian transferred its DD-13s to Republic mobile surgical units. They quickly earned the unflattering nickname "chopper droids" by clone troopers who found themselves at the DD-13s' mechanical mercies.

The droid's industrial appearance reinforces its reputation for cruelty. An impersonal, turret-shaped cranial unit houses two red photoreceptors that glow like the eyes of a predator. It carries no personality programming. Its tripedal stance, though contributing to its stability, merely adds to the droid's disconcerting façade. Ubrikkian did not see the need to address these flaws, feeling that the DD-13's skill in the operating theater speaks for itself.

The executives were correct regarding the droid's talents. Far from being a "chopper," the DD-13 exhibits a fastidious precision about its work, as well as a remarkable imagination. When meeting an organic for the first time, for instance, the DD-13 will immediately run mental scenarios on how to fuse the newcomer's body parts with random bits of machinery lying around the room.

The DD-13's tripedal legs have smooth hydraulic joints and tension relays to ensure absolute stillness during surgery. Its operating arms, frightening in appearance, incorporate bone retractors and micro-fusioncutters. The arms also possess modular sleeves that can be outfitted with a number of alternative tools.

Years before the introduction of the DD-13, Ubrikkian provided medical units to assist in the cyborg reconstruction of General Grievous. After Grievous's operation, Ubrikkian fielded a DD-13 in the Emperor Palpatine Surgical Reconstruction Center on Coruscant, helping to complete Anakin Skywalker's physical transformation into the black-armored Darth Vader.

The Emperor, pleased with the units, ordered an initial batch in the hundreds of thousands for the medical wards of Imperial garrisons. But Ubrikkian ran into a problem with Vader's regular (and painful) cybernetic refitting sessions. The Dark Lord so detested the callous ministrations of the DD-13 that he personally quashed Ubrikkian's renewal contract. Instead, Imperial forces brokered a deal with Industrial Automaton for a walking, limited-edition version of the company's MD-5, and Ubrikkian quietly retired the Galactic Chopper line, focusing its attentions on the more profitable DD-19 "Overseer" labor pool droid.

> **"Ubrikkian needs to re-design the DD-13 immediately! Lord Vader detests our droids, and as of today we're at serious risk of losing the entire Imperial contract."**
>
> *—From Ubrikkian Steamworks internal documents*

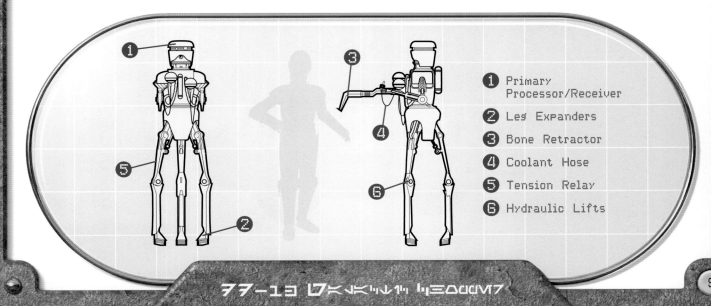

1. Primary Processor/Receiver
2. Leg Expanders
3. Bone Retractor
4. Coolant Hose
5. Tension Relay
6. Hydraulic Lifts

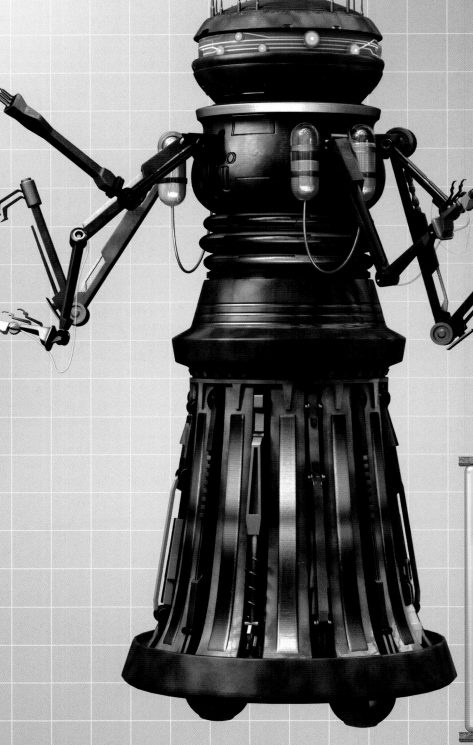

TECHNICAL READOUT

HEIGHT: 1.83 meters (FX-6); 1.7 meters (FX-7)

MANUFACTURER: Medtech Industries

PRIMARY FUNCTION: Medical assistance

ERA OF INFLUENCE: Rise of the Empire, Rebellion

Medtech FX Series Medical Assistant Droid

The FX series earned the nickname *Fixit* for its can-do talent at patching up trauma victims. Released as a surgical assistant—but often classified as a nursing droid—the FX logged decades of dedicated service until Medtech Industries finally retired the line.

Medtech originally intended the FX to serve as an aide for *organic* physicians. Shortly after the FXs hit the market, however, sophisticated surgical droids such as the 2-1B began receiving permanent postings in medcenters. FX units quickly adapted to work in tandem with their robotic counterparts.

Nine models, numbered FX-1 through FX-9, saw release before the end of the series, and all share basic design similarities. FX droids are cylindrical, with cap-shaped heads and an array of specialized arms that fold flat against the body. The number of arms may vary from five to twenty-five, but all are removable and interchangeable. An FX stationed with a mobile field hospital, for example, can have its tool arrays swapped out at each new battlefront to suit changing environments and species biologies. Larger, heavier arms extend from the upper torso; these range in number from seven arms on the FX-6 to just one on the FX-7.

The droid's head incorporates a variety of visual and diagnostic scanners, and can rotate 360 degrees. Most FX models lack vocoders, and those that possess them can communicate only in computer languages. Video screens on the torso display step-by-step diagrams of medical procedures, or list the FX's thoughts in Basic text. Each FX is preloaded with a medical database that can be augmented with a scomp link interface port to plug in to a hospital mainframe.

Medtech never gave much thought to the issue of droid mobility. It assumed that its droids would take up semi-permanent positions inside operating theaters, so many models, including the FX-7, have to be ferried on repulsorcarts or simply dragged from room to room. The FX-6 has a trio of casters, enabling it to roll.

During the Clone Wars, the Republic employed FX units at its battlefield hospitals (known as Republic Mobile Surgical Units, or Rimsoos). The droids also saw duty in the Emperor Palpatine Surgical Reconstruction Center on Coruscant. There, an FX-6 unit assisted with Anakin Skywalker's transformation into Darth Vader by stabilizing the burn damage to Anakin's soft tissue.

The introduction of more sophisticated droids such as the 2-1B and the MD pushed the FX into the low-price fringes of the medical market. Eventually Medtech stopped making the droid altogether; it went out of business several years later.

> **"We need more Effex droids. I've put in this requisition three times. Every day you delay, clone troopers die."**
>
> *—Dr. Jos Vondar of Republic Mobile Surgical Unit 7, in a message to the Republic Defense Procurement office*

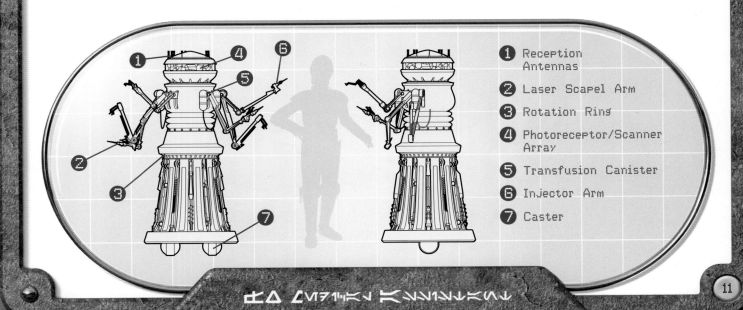

1. Reception Antennas
2. Laser Scapel Arm
3. Rotation Ring
4. Photoreceptor/Scanner Array
5. Transfusion Canister
6. Injector Arm
7. Caster

GH-7 Medical Droid

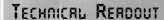

TECHNICAL READOUT

HEIGHT: 0.7 meter

MANUFACTURER:
Chiewab Amalgamated
Pharmaceuticals

PRIMARY FUNCTION:
Medical analysis

ERA OF INFLUENCE:
Rise of the Empire, Rebellion

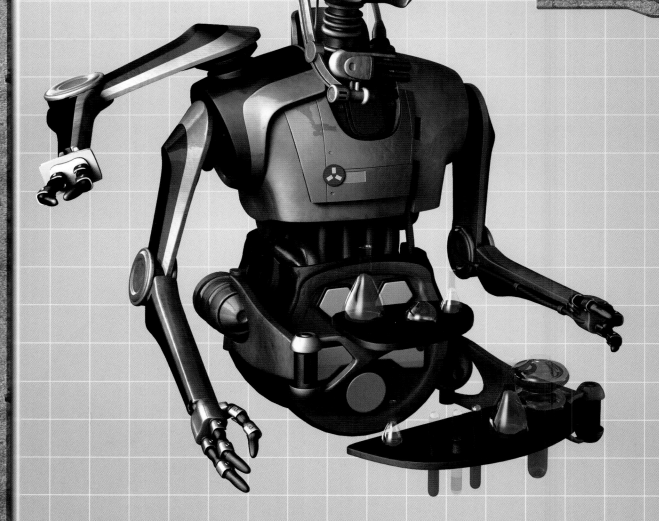

Chiewab GH-7 Medical Analysis Unit

Chiewab Amalgamated Pharmaceuticals is one of the galaxy's largest medical corporations, but the company seldom makes droids. In fact, Chiewab lost a golden opportunity to become a forerunner in the droid market when it spun off its subsidiary unit Geentech years ago. Geentech introduced the smash hit 2-1B soon after going solo, but was soon run out of business when Industrial Automaton absorbed the product. Chiewab has been trying to make amends ever since, and the GH-7 is its best contender.

If there's one thing that Chiewab has in abundance, it's money. The company has bought up entire planets to test new varieties of drugs. A percentage of the profits from these operations went into hiring a droid design staff made up entirely of Columi. These big-brained intellectuals have a love for logical, efficient engineering—qualities that express themselves in the GH-7.

Unlike most medical units, the GH-7 moves on repulsorlifts, for maximum mobility in the operating room. Everything on the droid's body is arrayed for easy access, either by organic physicians or by the droid itself. A forward-mounted specimen rack holds sample jars or vials of live cultures, while a repulsor field keeps sensitive liquids from spilling. An equipment tray atop the droid's head holds scalpels, bone spreaders, or diagnostic tools.

In addition to its efficient design, Chiewab gave the GH-7 considerable smarts. The droid can act as a diagnostician, surgical assistant, anesthesiologist, and hematologist. Its photoreceptors are wirelessly linked to medical mainframes and double as bioscanners, with functions that include parallax brainwave readings.

Three arms extend from the GH-7's torso. Two of the arms end in slender, three-fingered manipulators. The third sports a two-digit, pincer-like sampling grasper. A fourth arm extends from the right edge of the droid's "jaw" and houses a testing probe. When analyzing a biological sample, the GH-7 inserts the sample into an analysis chamber via a chest-mounted access port.

A display screen exhibits video or pictographic information regarding the GH-7's testing results and diagnostic conclusions. The GH-7 also boasts a hologrammic projector, which can generate life-size patient holograms in order to better illustrate the steps of a complicated procedure.

> ## "The Geeaych-Seven: Four-time winner of the 'Silver Bantha' for excellence in industrial design."
>
> —*Excerpt from a Chiewab Amalgamated Pharmaceuticals sales manual*

The GH-7 won rave reviews in the industry press, but Core World medical facilities have continued to buy the more sophisticated 2-1B or the broader-based MD series. The Outer Rim has proven a more welcoming market for the GH-7.

The archaeological workers at Polis Massa employed several GH-7s. When unexpected visitors brought the dying Padmé Amidala to the Polis Massa asteroid compound, a GH-7 tried everything in its power to save her life. All of the droid's testing on her condition came back clean; GH-7 could not find an answer in its data banks as to why her condition continued to deteriorate.

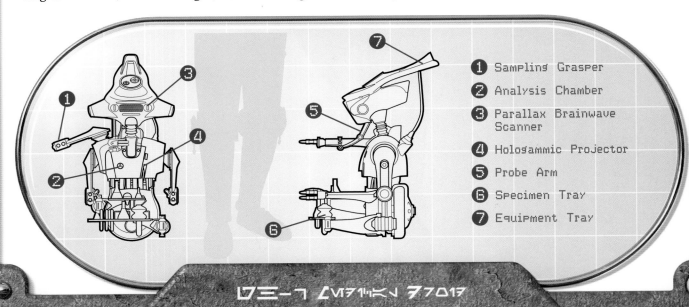

1. Sampling Grasper
2. Analysis Chamber
3. Parallax Brainwave Scanner
4. Hologammic Projector
5. Probe Arm
6. Specimen Tray
7. Equipment Tray

Master-Com

14

Czerka Corporation Master Control System

Some theorists insist that, by definition, a droid must be ambulatory, and Master-Com meets that definition by only the thinnest of margins. Master-Com's closest cousin is the BRT supercomputer, but it possesses the unique ability to parcel its consciousness into a droid frame to better interact with organic beings.

The Master Control System of the Wheel space station came online in the years prior to the Clone Wars, during construction of the Wheel. Originally a haven for smugglers and fugitives, the Wheel grew into one of the galaxy's most glamorous casino resorts after the rise of the Empire. The Wheel's greatest asset was the neutral containment zone that surrounded it, demarcating a bubble of space in which the Empire had no jurisdiction. This encouraged an atmosphere of lawless hedonism, though in truth it was largely an illusion, and a substantial portion of all revenues went straight to the Empire as taxes.

The Wheel's Master Control System was built and installed by the Czerka Corporation in an attempt to replicate Aratech's old BRT supercomputers. At the moment of its activation, Master-Com became a being with hundreds of thousands of sensory inputs. Every security cam, every comm call, every wager placed in a casino, every request to the central computer, and even the movements of the vacuum lifts, became a part of Master-Com's living database. Master-Com operated any system anywhere in the station, from dialing up the artificial gravity to firing the security lasers.

> **"You gave me this humanoid form and, perhaps unconsciously, some humanoid characteristics as well. If ever I had a human friend, I would like it to be you."**
>
> —*Master-Com to Senator Simon Greyshade*

Hardwired programming required Master-Com to obey the commands of the Wheel's administrator. A string of forgettable administrators rotated through the office before Senator Simon Greyshade of the Vorzyd sector became the first to treat Master-Com as anything more than a status system.

Greyshade ordered the construction of a number of droid bodies as a way to anthropomorphize and localize Master-Com's omnipresent consciousness. The droid bodies shared a basic cosmetic design, featuring broadcast antennas on their heads and chest controls that could remotely access many of the Wheel's operations.

Master-Com's high degree of intelligence had an unintended side effect: introspective philosophy. After the Battle of Yavin, the droids R2-D2 and C-3PO arrived aboard the Wheel, and Master-Com became obsessed with the devotion the pair showed toward their master, Luke Skywalker. Master-Com began to understand that the newcomers were expressing a bond of camaraderie, and that Senator Greyshade represented the closest thing that it had to a friend.

When a plot was launched against the Wheel by Imperial commander Strom, Master-Com did everything in its power to aid Greyshade and the fugitive Rebels. The actions cost it several droid bodies, but Master-Com smashed Strom's plan—at the cost of Greyshade's life. Master-Com lived on, and decades later helped Wheel administrator Big Bunji battle the Yuuzhan Vong during the invaders' attack on the station.

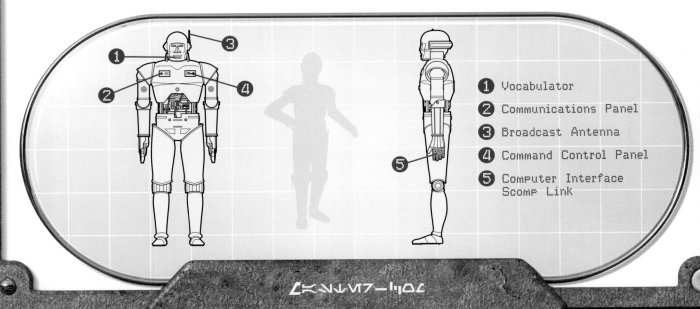

1 Vocabulator
2 Communications Panel
3 Broadcast Antenna
4 Command Control Panel
5 Computer Interface Scomp Link

POLIS MASSAN MIDWIFE DROID

Polis Massa Chroon-Tan B-Machine

The Polis Massans are one of the most enigmatic species in the galaxy. Seldom encountered outside the Subterrel sector, they have expressionless eyes and faces masked by osmotic membranes. Though they did not evolve on the shattered planet known as Polis Massa, these beings have undertaken an archaeological dig on the planet's asteroid remains that has lasted for five hundred standard years. The purpose of the dig is largely a mystery.

Because so few have ever met a Polis Massan, it's hardly surprising that practically no one realizes they manufacture droids. Polis Massan automata are primarily archaeological and mining units, used to assist their masters in an endless quest to uncover the remains of the long-vanished Eellayin people. Since Polis Massans spend their entire lives on their archaeological digs, they employ specialized droids to assist with births, deaths, and other key life transitions requiring skills beyond those of exobiologists.

The Polis Massan Chroon-Tan B-Machine, more commonly known as the midwife droid, is one such unit, presumably designed to assist Polis Massan females with labor and delivery—though so little is known of these beings' biology that it's possible the midwife's true purpose remains a mystery.

The droid makes a capable midwife unit. It is equipped with a nonthreatening, Polis Massan–inspired face and a soothing, electronically modified voice (normally programmed in the Polis Massan language only, which in its purest form falls outside the human audio range). The midwife droid's diagnostic sensors can measure its patient's heart rate, breathing rate, and blood pressure.

Instead of hands, the droid's arms end in smooth, cupped paddles for guiding a baby through the birth canal, and for cradling the newborn after it takes its first breath. A heated, cushioned pad on the droid's torso helps keep the newborn's body temperature elevated while the midwife performs post-birth diagnostics. The midwife droid has reservoirs filled with nutrient fluid. It can feed this formula to a baby through a network of nipples and tubing. The midwife droid moves around on a nimble anti-gravity repulsorlift.

The Polis Massan archaeological team that worked the excavation known as the Local Dig kept to themselves, but they were not unfriendly to outsiders. When Yoda, Obi-Wan Kenobi, and Bail Organa arrived at their asteroid bearing the gravely ill Padmé Amidala, the Polis Massans did everything they could to save her life and deliver her unborn twins.

Calling up those among them who possessed training as physicians, the Polis Massans also unpacked a midwife droid from deep storage. The droid brought Leia and Luke Skywalker into the world, while a GH-7 medical droid tried and failed to prevent Padmé's death. The strangers left Polis Massa soon afterward. It is unknown if the Polis Massans ever realized the importance of the events that had unfolded on their tiny rock—although their suspicions were perhaps raised when Malorum's Inquisitors arrived later, to investigate the death of Amidala.

> ## "Oobah, oobah."
>
> *—Polis Massan midwife droid, emitting a universally soothing vocalization*

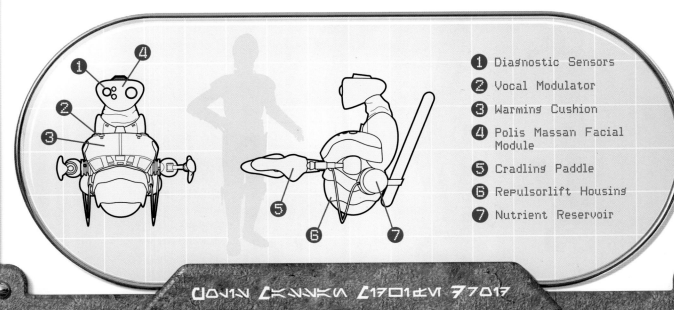

1. Diagnostic Sensors
2. Vocal Modulator
3. Warming Cushion
4. Polis Massan Facial Module
5. Cradling Paddle
6. Repulsorlift Housing
7. Nutrient Reservoir

SP-4 and JN-66

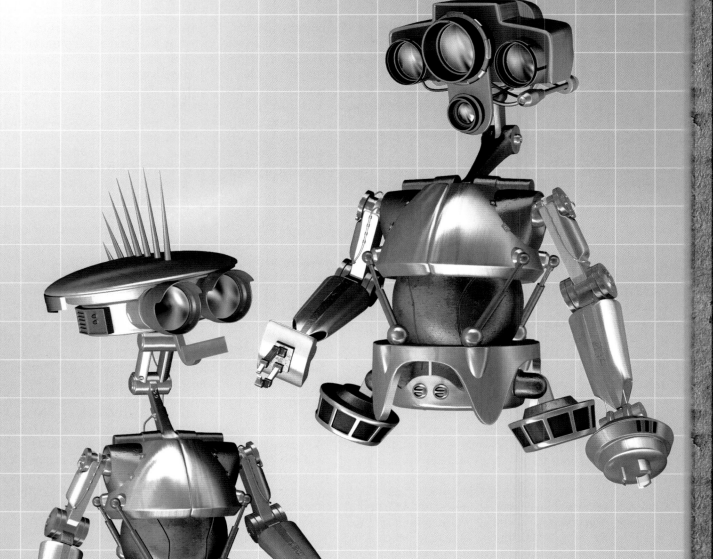

TECHNICAL READOUT

HEIGHT: 1.46 meters
(SP-4); 1.0 meter (JN-66)

MANUFACTURER:
Cybot Galactica

PRIMARY FUNCTION:
Scientific analysis

ERA OF INFLUENCE:
Rise of the Empire, Rebellion

Cybot Galactica SP-4 and JN-66 Analysis Droids

The Jedi Knights were often perceived as all-seeing and all-knowing, but, in truth, mastery of the Force did not equate to mastery of *everything*. Few Jedi bothered to study computers, machines, or the physical sciences, which required the Temple to rely on droids. To help provide clues when the voice of the Force went silent, the Jedi employed a pair of Cybot Galactica analysis droids.

The SP-4 and JN-66 models used by the Jedi are also popular with scientists and police forensics units. They work best as a team, with JN-66 handling the experimentation and SP-4 drawing conclusions from the results. Cybot Galactica saved on manufacturing costs by repurposing many structural pieces from its popular line of PK worker droids.

The SP-4 is designed to interact with organics, and possesses a humanoid body and oversize photoreceptors arranged in a style that most consider endearing. The attenuated stalk that houses the droid's vocabulator is reminiscent of the vocal organs of the Pa'lowick species.

The SP-4, which can wirelessly access mainframe data libraries, is built to analyze reams of data and arrive at a single, accurate solution. In a hypothetical case involving a shooting death, a police department SP-4 might look at weapon discharge patterns, weather reports from the day of the crime, biological charts of the victim's species, and a geometric triangulation of firing angles before fingering a likely suspect. Critics of SP-4s claim that droids are simply incapable of making the intuitive leaps that often provide the key to cracking difficult cases.

The JN-66 is a more popular unit, designed only to crunch data. It is used by organics who have little patience for grunt work. A JN-66 possesses a quadruple set of photoreceptors, allowing for magnification at the microscopic level along a full spectrum of visible and nonvisible wavelengths.

Most of the JN-66's parts are designed for use under clean laboratory conditions. Its left arm ends in a micro field generator that allows it to pick up objects without touching them. The droid hovers on repulsorlifts, and it lacks external coverings so that radiation baths can penetrate every cranny during regular sterilizations.

While investigating the toxic dart that killed bounty hunter Zam Wesell, Obi-Wan Kenobi turned to the Jedi Temple's analysis droids. SP-4 and JN-66 could not provide a match, and Obi-Wan's Jedi intuition also failed. It took the practiced eye of the galaxy-hopping Besalisk restaurateur, Dexter Jettster, to identify the weapon as a Kamino saberdart.

> **"Those analysis droids you've got over there only focus on symbols. I should think you Jedi would have more respect for the difference between knowledge and wisdom."**
>
> *—Dexter Jettster, disputing the accuracy of the Jedi Temple's analysis droids*

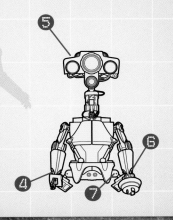

1. Vocabulator Stalk
2. Magnification Lenses
3. Transmission Antenna
4. Testing Probe
5. Multi-Spectrum Photoreceptors
6. Micro Field Generator
7. Repulsorlift Disks

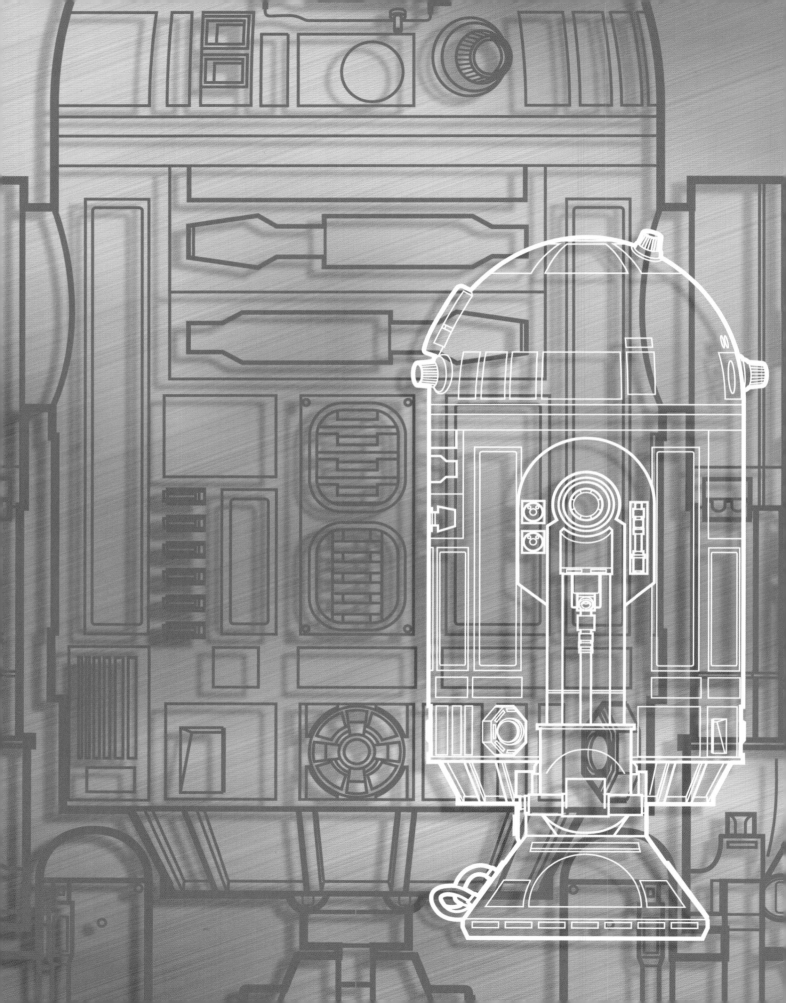

Class Two Droids

Class two droids are well liked by most, due to a combination of advanced intelligence, curious personalities, and generally nonthreatening appearances.

Most class two droids are involved in engineering and technical sciences. They differ from class one droids because they work in the *applied* sciences, using their knowledge to solve real-world engineering or technical problems. They do not interact with organics as much as other droids, and often do not come equipped with Basic-speaking vocabulators. Class two droids have forms that follow the specific functions for which they are designed, and few come in the bipedal humanoid configuration.

Class two droids can be grouped into several main subcategories:

- **Astromech droids** (or simply astro-droids) interface with starships and calculate hyperspace jumps. Most have secondary functions that go far beyond these tasks, from controlling onboard systems during flight to performing odd jobs around the docking bay. For centuries, astromech droids were towering constructs that saw service in the engine rooms of capital ships. Industrial Automaton became the first manufacturer to produce an astromech small enough to plug in to a starfighter socket. This unit, the R2, exploded the popularity of the category. Today, many use R series droids solely as repair units.

- **Exploration droids** were originally designed to scout strange planets and conduct tests on soil, water, and atmosphere. Over time, exploration droids became valued for their analysis abilities, whether or not they actually left the laboratory. Arakyd Viper probots are considered class two exploration droids, despite the fact that the Empire used them almost exclusively in a military capacity.

- **Environmental droids** are closely related to exploration droids and are often in the employ of agencies that are actively involved in terraforming, such as the Refugee Relief Movement. Some environmental droids have been repurposed to serve in unusual capacities. The FLR logger droid is a class two environmental droid that uses its understanding of forested ecosystems to fell trees and convert them into processed lumber.

- **Engineering droids** can work in a variety of applied sciences, including aerospace engineering, biomedical engineering, chemical engineering, industrial engineering, and materials engineering. They are brilliant in the fields for which they have been programmed, but perform poorly if forced to undertake a different job.

- **Repair droids** comprise a gray area of class two. The hyperspatial abilities of R series astromechs make them indisputably class twos, yet repair units without these abilities are often categorized by their level of brainpower. Sophisticated repair droids are class twos, while those droids with only a rudimentary understanding of the world around them (such as WED Treadwells) are more accurately categorized as class fives.

Some automatically view class two droids with nonhumanoid frames and an inability to speak Basic as dim-witted, when in fact many class twos are more intelligent than their owners. They also can possess a strong independent streak. Tales of class two droids going off to seek their fortunes are surprisingly common, as are instances of owners who have manumitted their class two droids after decades of service.

Viper Probot

Scale comparison

Hunter Killer Probot

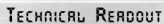

Technical Readout

Height: 1.6 meters (Viper probot)
150 meters (HK probot)

Manufacturer:
Arakyd Industries

Primary Functions:
Exploration, systems infiltration, blockade enforcement

Era of Influence:
Rise of the Empire, Rebellion

Arakyd Viper, Infiltrator, and Hunter Killer Droids

War is good for business. That old aphorism could very well be Arakyd's corporate slogan, for the company grew fat and happy off a string of lucrative Imperial contracts. The evolution of its probot series is a perfect example of how to tailor a product to suit changing political climates.

Arakyd entered the exploration droid market with models such as the Prowler 1000 and the spacegoing Vanguard probot. The company's relentless efforts to unseat Galalloy Industries as the preeminent supplier of automated scouts paid off with the election of Supreme Chancellor Palpatine, who awarded Arakyd a huge government contract. Arakyd Vanguards, in the service of the Republic Explorational Corps, helped open new hyperlanes into the Deep Core.

Flush with wealth, Arakyd absorbed its smaller competitor Viper Sensor Intelligence Systems in an armed takeover shortly before the Clone Wars. In possession of proprietary Viper technology, Arakyd released its new Viper probot. It proved the company's biggest success to date.

The Viper probot travels inside a one-way hyperspace pod and explores its environment using a repulsorlift engine and an array of bubble-eyed sensors. It carries a blaster for self-defense, and incorporates a self-destruct mechanism should its mission become compromised. Viper probots became common tools of the Empire; one of them uncovered the hidden Rebel base on Hoth.

> ## "That thing's tapped into every system . . . made the entire ship practically an extension of itself! Probe droids were never meant to operate this independently!"
>
> *—Luke Skywalker, during his first encounter with an Infiltrator probot*

Following the Rebel evacuation of that safeworld, Arakyd introduced the first Infiltrator probot. The model was a collaboration between Arakyd engineers and Imperial techs under the orders of Admiral Damon Krell. The Infiltrator has a shape similar to the Viper, but boasts thick armor, augmented weapons, and the ability to plug in to and control electronic systems. An Infiltrator prototype designated 13-K destroyed itself during a battle with Luke Skywalker.

The Infiltrator had set a precedent—from that point forward, probots grew larger and larger with each new release. The trend culminated with the gargantuan hunter-killer probot, developed to meet the Empire's needs for planetary pacification.

At 150 meters, the HK probot is one of the largest combat droids in existence. Primarily used for customs inspections and blockade enforcement, it operates best in deep space. It possesses high-beam searchlights and scanners that can penetrate thick hulls.

If an arriving ship fails its initial scan, it is pulled into the HK's belly with a powerful tractor beam. If the vessel foolishly decides to flee, the HK can deliver a withering barrage from two quad blasters and a pair of ion cannons. Following the Battle of Endor, scores of HK probots could be encountered on the traffic lanes leading to the Emperor's throneworld of Byss.

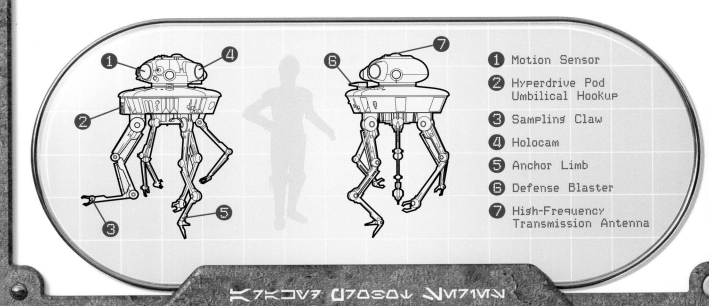

1. Motion Sensor
2. Hyperdrive Pod Umbilical Hookup
3. Sampling Claw
4. Holocam
5. Anchor Limb
6. Defense Blaster
7. High-Frequency Transmission Antenna

Aratech GO-TO Infrastructure Planning System

Many planets suffered during the First and Second Sith Wars. In 3955 B.B.Y., Supreme Chancellor Cressa took steps to salvage the shattered infrastructures of Republic worlds with a massive rebuilding effort. The chief architects of the reconstruction would be G0-T0 planning droids.

At the time, the young Aratech corporation employed all the best droid designers. Aratech's G0-T0 programming matrix was designed to plug in to the networked computers of an entire planetary system, giving it an almost omniscient level of intelligence. Aratech wisely put checks on the G0-T0, limiting its ability to interface with machinery and confining its circuitry into the body of a spherical repulsorlift droid.

The G0-T0 could manage an entire planet's administration, and was empowered with sufficient authority to requisition supplies and command organic workers. Aratech also ordered each G0-T0 to consider options that would benefit the Republic as a whole, while working within the confines of all laws and regulations.

The G0-T0 unit assigned to the devastated planet Telos provided the first hint of future trouble. The droid determined that he could not help the Republic within the parameters he had been given. Faced with this paradox, G0-T0 was forced to break his programming and Republic law in order to follow his primary directive.

No longer restricted by legality, G0-T0 set up smuggling rings that enriched Telos, posting bounties on members of

> ## "Another GO-TO in the Gordian Reach has cut its planet off from the HoloNet. Recommend sending in the Republic Navy."
>
> *—Republic intelligence report filed in 3946 B.B.Y.*

the Jedi and Sith whom he believed to be destabilizing influences on galactic order. To help achieve this last goal, G0-T0 set up a secret droid factory on Telos that manufactured HK-50 assassin droids.

Few knew of G0-T0's true role, for he hid behind the hologrammically projected identity of the human "Goto." The droid owned a built-in blaster cannon and a personal cloaking shield, as well as an alarming threat display of needles and electroshock clamps.

G0-T0 soon became mixed up with an exiled Jedi Knight and her mission to destroy the Sith Lords. G0-T0 tried to use his HK-50 assassins to kill the Jedi, but the HKs turned on their maker. G0-T0 perished in a standoff on Malachor V.

Other G0-T0 droids grew bolder as time went on. Within five standard years, those stationed in the Gordian Reach had set themselves up as dictators over the planets they administered. They cut their worlds off from the HoloNet communications network and blockaded the hyperlanes leading insystem. The G0-T0 units then fired off a drone pod, which announced that their sixteen worlds would henceforth be the independent territory of 400100500260026. The Republic military freed the planets in a highly publicized campaign.

The repercussions of these incidents very nearly ruined Aratech. In subsequent centuries, the G0-T0 droid became a sinister figure in the public imagination.

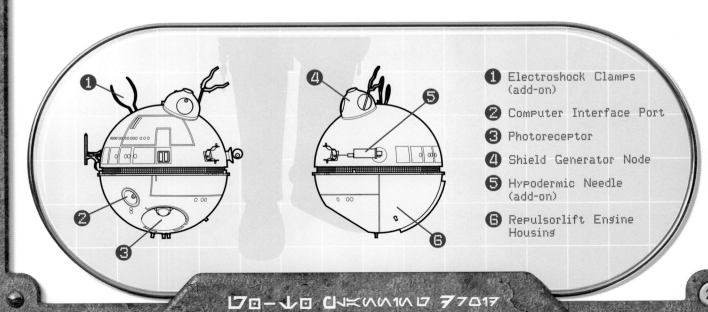

1. Electroshock Clamps (add-on)
2. Computer Interface Port
3. Photoreceptor
4. Shield Generator Node
5. Hypodermic Needle (add-on)
6. Repulsorlift Engine Housing

G2 "Goose Droid"

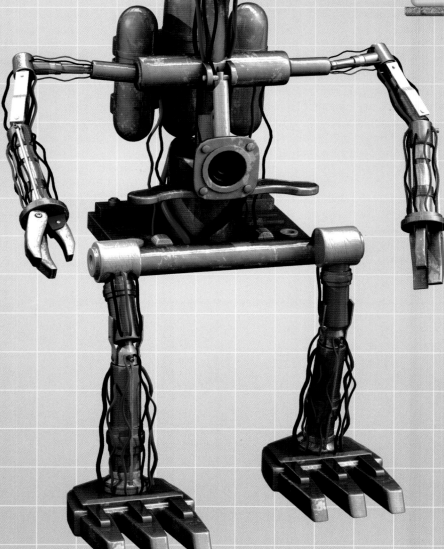

Technical Readout

Height: 0.8 meter

Manufacturer: SoroSuub

Primary Function: Repair

Era of Influence: Rise of the Empire, Rebellion, New Republic

SoroSuub G2 Repair Droid

G2 repair droids are loved and hated with equal measures of passion. Their intellects are so acute that they make wonderful conversationalists, but this same quality leads to a flightiness that makes them unreliable in their primary jobs.

SoroSuub introduced the G2 series in the decade following the Clone Wars. The droids are short and squat, with a wide, bottom-heavy stance that forces them to waddle when they walk. This trait, combined with their long, multi-jointed necks, resulted in the nickname *goose droids*.

Each G2 unit has a stripped-down skeletal frame with exposed joints and wiring. Their three-digit manipulators can grasp most repair tools, while their splayed feet aid in stability. The G2's most recognizable feature is its binocular head, containing a vocabulator, two auditory sensors, and photoreceptors with telescopic, microscopic, and multi-spectrum capabilities. Each droid bears a unique ID number stenciled onto the side of its head.

SoroSuub soon discovered that goose droids gravitated toward excessive chattiness. This feature appeared to be hardwired into the behavioral circuitry matrix and could not be eliminated with memory wipes. Some customers, mostly family-owned businesses or pilots of independent starships, found the quality endearing and allowed their droids to accumulate life experience over time.

> ## "Have any of you humanoids flown on a Starspeeder before? Please keep your party together as you approach the landing concourse. That is, if you'd ever like to see them again."
>
> *—G2-4T, Star Tours droid foreman*

Eventually, a number of these units achieved an advanced degree of independent thought. A sudden explosion of wanderlust resulted. In one notorious instance, a team of G2s stole a fueling freighter and set up their own community on an asteroid in the Chrellis system.

Large corporations generally had no time for the G2's foolishness. They returned the units to SoroSuub, shrinking the line's market base and leading SoroSuub to retire the line in 12 A.B.Y. Two years later, faced with a surprising outcry from fans of the G2, SoroSuub reintroduced the line with much fanfare.

Star Tours, a short-lived interstellar sightseeing company, employed a number of G2 units to perform maintenance on its fleet of Starspeeder 3000 shuttles. One droid, G2-4T, oversaw the labor pool and handled ticketing and travel visas. His cynical sense of humor often landed him in trouble.

Another droid, G2-9T, possessed an infuriatingly short attention span. Formerly the property of a Troig diplomat, before Star Tours bought him in a "pay-by-the-kilogram" fire sale, he angered the company's organic operators with his spotty work record. When Star Tours closed its doors shortly after the Battle of Endor, G2-4T and G2-9T were cast adrift. They later found employment with the smuggling chief Talon Karrde.

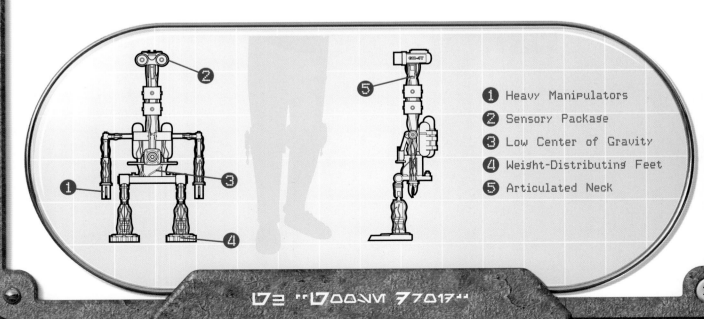

1. Heavy Manipulators
2. Sensory Package
3. Low Center of Gravity
4. Weight-Distributing Feet
5. Articulated Neck

R1 Astromech

Technical Readout

HEIGHT: 0.96 meter (R2 units)

MANUFACTURER:
Industrial Automaton

PRIMARY FUNCTIONS:
Navigation, repair

ERA OF INFLUENCE:
Rise of the Empire, Rebellion,
New Republic, new Jedi order

Industrial Automaton R-Series Astromech Droids

It has been generations since Industrial Automaton introduced their wildly popular R-series line. The company still has no serious competition in the astromech market. R-series astromechs make preeminent starfighter pilot counterparts and general maintenance units, and the droids are infinitely customizable. To date, the line includes ten models, from the prototype P2 to the state-of-the-art R9.

Industrial Automaton sold the P2 exclusively to the Republic merchant fleet. This massive droid presaged many of the design features that became common in later models, including three wheeled legs, a rotating head dome, and an array of retractable manipulator arms. The droid saw service aboard bulk cruisers and container vessels, although it can communicate only through a video display screen.

For the towering R1, Industrial Automaton recycled the black body shells of its Mark II reactor drones. The R1 is the first Industrial Automaton astromech with the ability to calculate nav coordinates for a single hyperspace jump. Due to their size, most R1s were stationed aboard capital warships and large freighters. One breakthrough introduced with the R1 is the beeping, whistling language known as droidspeak, an information-dense vernacular that has come to be recognized as a hallmark of the R series.

The record-breaking R2 exploded the popularity of the astromech droid. This waist-high unit fits perfectly into the standard socket of a military starfighter. Once plugged in, the R2 unit can monitor flight performance, fix technical problems, and boost power from the shipboard systems. It can hold up to ten sets of hyperspace coordinates in memory, and possesses the intelligence to perform engine start-up and pre-flight taxiing. Standard equipment on an R2 includes two manipulator arms, an electric arc welder, a circular saw, a hologrammic projector, an internal cargo compartment, and a fire extinguisher. Many buyers have tricked out their R2s with add-ons including underwater propellers, booster rockets, magnetic-grip treads, and inflatable life rafts.

> ## "NO JOB IS OVER THIS LITTLE GUY'S HEAD."
>
> *—Ad slogan from the R2 product launch*

The R3 is a military model originally built for gunnery crews aboard the capital ships of the Republic Judicial Department. It sports a clear dome of durable plastex. Though not designed as a starfighter plug-in, the unit can still hold up to five hyperspace jumps in memory. Industrial Automaton restricted sales of the high-priced model to the Republic and local planetary governments. During IA's first production run, the Republic purchased 125 million of the droids, while the Empire later used R3s aboard its Star Destroyers and Death Star battle stations.

The conical-headed R4 is a successful attempt to capture the Outer Rim garage jockey. It is simpler, tougher, and cheaper, and eliminates such items as the video display screen and miniature fire extinguisher. The R4 works on landspeeders and similar vehicles, and almost never sees use as a starfighter astromech—a good thing, as it can hold coordinates in active memory only for a single hyperspace jump. During the Clone Wars, Obi-Wan Kenobi flew alongside a droid named R4-P17, who started out as a standard R4 until an industrial accident on

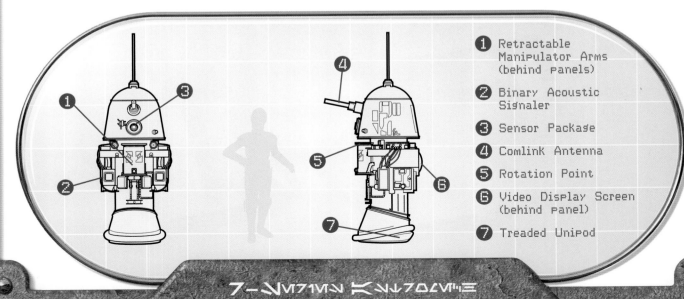

1. Retractable Manipulator Arms (behind panels)
2. Binary Acoustic Signaler
3. Sensor Package
4. Comlink Antenna
5. Rotation Point
6. Video Display Screen (behind panel)
7. Treaded Unipod

R2 Astromech

Gyndine required a complete rebuild. The rebuild proved so successful that dome-headed R4 units were incorporated into many of the Jedi's Delta-7 Aethersprite and Eta-2 Actis starfighters. Unfortunately, buzz droids destroyed R4-P17 during the Battle of Coruscant. Copper-domed R4-G9 served as R4-P17's replacement aboard Obi-Wan's next starfighter.

The R5 was a total flop, called "a meter-tall stack of the worst business decisions you could possibly want" by *Mechtech Illustrated.* Introduced as the least expensive astromech in the marketplace, the R5 quickly accumulated a litany of customer complaints, including, but not limited to: chronic overheating, jammed servos, loose bearings, and blown motivators. The R5 bears a distinctive flowerpot-shaped head marked with three tiny photoreceptors. R5s could be purchased in bulk for next to nothing, but their one-jump hyperspace capacities made them nearly useless as starfighter cohorts. After a few lamentable sales seasons, Industrial Automaton retired the R5 line just prior to the Clone Wars.

The R6 hit the marketplace decades later. The model benefited from being on the drawing board for years, proving that Industrial Automaton had solved the bugs of the R5. The R6 replicates the R2's winning personality and its array of hidden gadgets, and the droid's processor can store up to twelve hyperspace jumps in memory. The R6 was also priced to move—though more expensive than the R4 or R5, when it was released it actually cost less than the original R2.

During the attacks of the resurrected Emperor in 10 A.B.Y., the New Republic rushed the FreiTek E-wing starfighter into service. The E-wing works in tandem with Industrial Automaton's R7 model, which sits behind the cockpit in a sealed compartment. R7 units can hold fifteen sets of hyperspace coordinates in memory and can withstand a near-direct hit from a class one ion cannon, though they work poorly with any starfighter other than the E-wing.

The R8 is Industrial Automaton's attempt to recapture the general-use market, following the R7's E-wing exclusivity. Before its release, rumors swirled that the R8 would be the first astromech to abandon droidspeak in favor of Basic, though this feature did not make it into the finished product. The R8 is known for its powerful comm system and advanced signal jammers.

The newest astromech from Industrial Automaton is the R9, which made its debut in the wake of the Yuuzhan Vong war. R9s are used as counterparts for the StealthX starfighters of the Galactic Federation of Free Alliances. Luke Skywalker and other members of the new Jedi order used StealthX/R9 pairings during the Killik expansion crisis.

Any discussion of the R series is incomplete without noting the curious career of the R2 unit designated R2-D2. Artoo, as he has come to be known, first distinguished himself during the blockade of Naboo in 32 B.B.Y. As the property of the Royal House of Naboo, Artoo executed risky extravehicular repairs to the Queen's starship while under heavy fire, enabling Amidala to escape a cordon of Trade Federation battleships and launching the little droid into a life of unprecedented heroism. Artoo, who forged a lasting bond with the protocol droid C-3PO, served Amidala during her term as senator, flew with Anakin Skywalker during the Clone Wars, carried the stolen plans for the Death Star prior to the Battle of Yavin, and became a loyal companion of Anakin's son, Luke Skywalker, throughout Luke's evolving roles as a Rogue Squadron ace and founder of the Jedi academy.

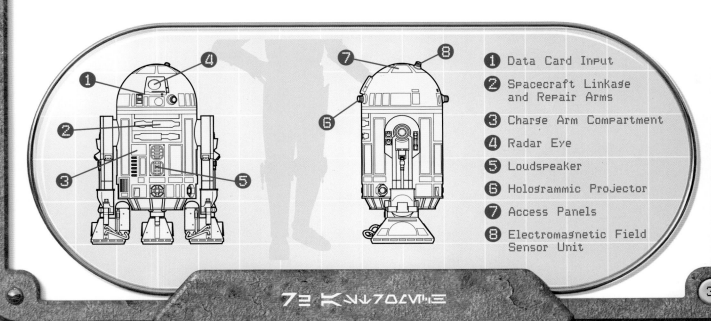

1. Data Card Input
2. Spacecraft Linkage and Repair Arms
3. Charge Arm Compartment
4. Radar Eye
5. Loudspeaker
6. Hologrammic Projector
7. Access Panels
8. Electromagnetic Field Sensor Unit

R3 AND R4 ASTROMECH

R5 Astromech

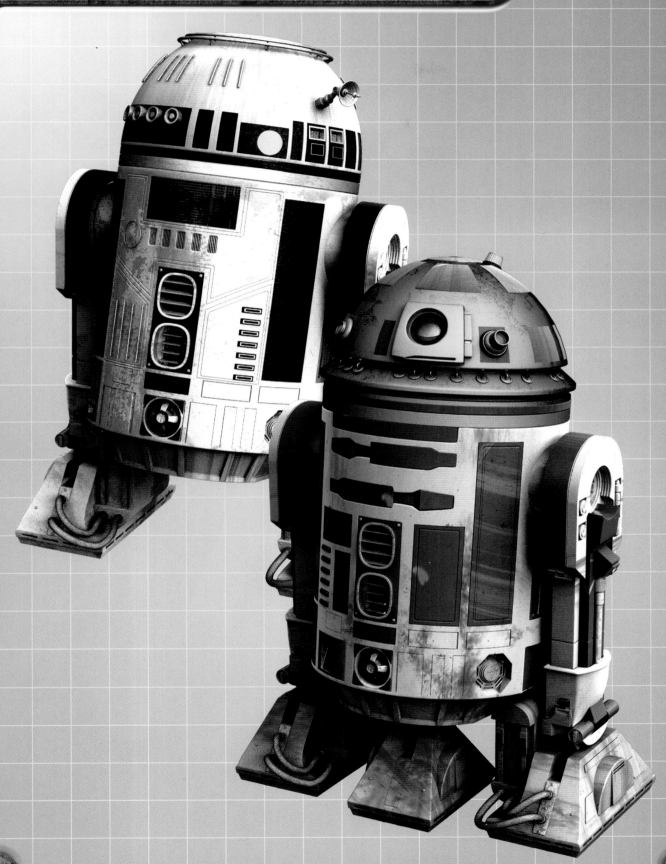

T3 Utility Droid

Technical Readout

HEIGHT: 0.96 meter

MANUFACTURER:
Duwani Mechanical Products

PRIMARY FUNCTIONS:
Repair, Labor

ERA OF INFLUENCE:
Old Republic

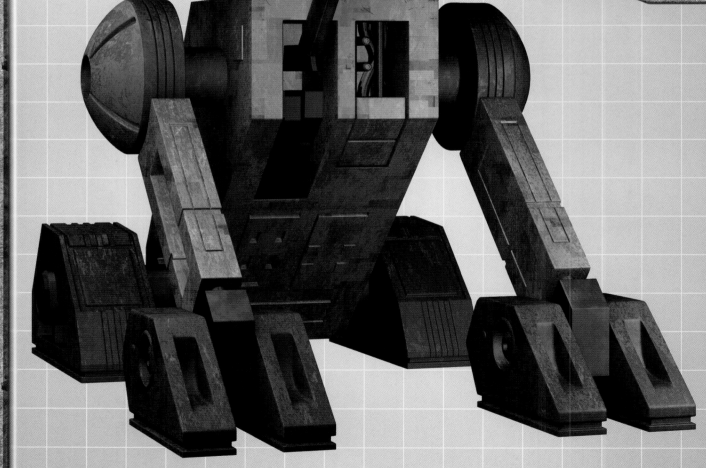

Duwani Mechanical Products T3 Series Utility Droid

The T3 utility droid saw its heyday during the tumultuous decades of the Great Droid Revolution, as well as during the First and Second Sith Wars. Remarkably likable for a utility droid of any era, the T3 eventually fell out of use. It is rarely seen today outside private collections.

The T3 series, manufactured by the long-vanished Duwani Mechanical Products, was positioned as a repair and general labor droid with a specialty in starship operations. Its usefulness aboard star freighters made the T3 a predecessor to modern astromech droids.

T3 units are short, no taller than one meter, and move on four wheeled legs. The two front legs, attached to the body on rotating joints, can slide forward or backward to adjust the droid's height. The T3's tablet-shaped cranial unit contains a single glowing photoreceptor. It also incorporates a broadcast antenna and a vocabulator, which relays information in a warbling electronic language.

The T3 exhibits a particular genius with computers. With its extendable data probe, it can easily slice into security systems, break codes, and troubleshoot computer networks. With the right raw materials, the T3 can even manufacture "computer spikes," which enable others to perform similar functions by inserting the spikes into computer access ports.

Buyers gave the T3 high marks for its winning personality, which came about through a highly advanced droid

> **"TARIS: We received a dreadful welcome when T3 droids at the starport made off with our baggage. *Lowest possible recommendation.*"**
>
> —From Trampeta's Star Guide, *first published in 4086 B.B.Y.*

brain. Before long, some T3s began testing the limits of their free will. Individual units sometimes banded together in gangs to make a living as thieves, or sold their computer slicing skills to criminals.

Duwani kept improving the T3 line over time. In 3956 B.B.Y., one of the prototypes for the latest model in the series became an unlikely hero of the Star Forge incident. The unit T3-M4 received armor plating and upgradable weaponry from the Taris crimelord Davik Kang. Canderous Ordo, a Mandalorian mercenary working for Kang, used the droid's computer skills to escape from Taris with two Jedi, Bastila Shan and Revan.

T3-M4 assisted in the group's hunt for the Star Forge, receiving upgrades including a repeating blaster and a flamethrower. Because most of the galaxy's T3 units remained relatively benign, T3-M4 could count on his appearance to get past the defenses of most enemies. The droid received a hero's commendation from the Republic for his role in resolving the crisis.

Five standard years later, T3-M4 reappeared aboard the abandoned freighter *Ebon Hawk,* where he fell into the company of the heroine known only as the Jedi Exile. After helping resolve a crisis involving the Sith Lords and the graveyard planet Malachor V, T3 departed into the Unknown Regions with the Jedi Exile, presumably to unite his new owner with the long-lost Revan.

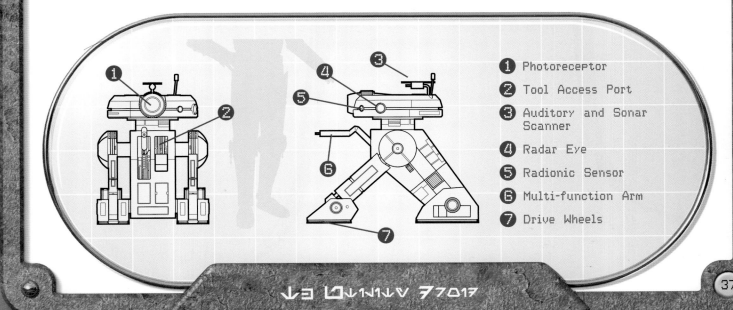

1 Photoreceptor
2 Tool Access Port
3 Auditory and Sonar Scanner
4 Radar Eye
5 Radionic Sensor
6 Multi-function Arm
7 Drive Wheels

Vuffi Raa

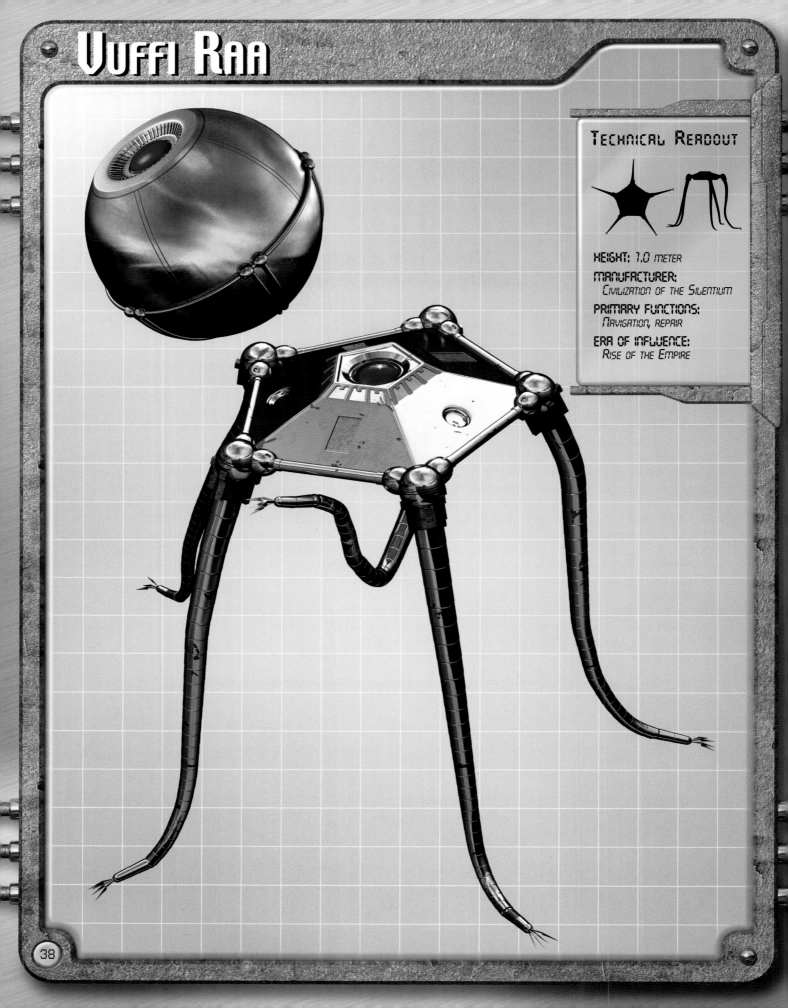

Agent of the Silentium

Uffi Raa is an old friend of Lando Calrissian's, having served as the gambler's comrade and copilot during his galaxy-hopping days aboard *Millennium Falcon*. But like many of Lando's friends, Vuffi Raa has a bizarre secret. Recent information suggests that Vuffi Raa may be a representative of the Silentium, a droid species now believed to have originated in another galaxy.

The origin of the Silentium is lost to legend. An extragalactic civilization of starfruit-shaped sentients built the original droids in their image, until a radiation storm exterminated them. Their droids lived on, using manufacturing plants to make "children" and developing a culture centered on the prime numbers of five, seven, and eleven. The wisest among them built new spherical bodies measuring fifty kilometers in diameter, as the circle was considered the holiest of shapes. Others wore bodies in the forms of pentagrams or heptagons.

> ## "How *should* I call you, sir?"
> ## "Not too loudly, Vuffi Raa, and no earlier than nine-hundred in the morning."
>
> —*Vuffi Raa and Lando Calrissian, discussing proper forms of address*

The Silentium soon found their orderly kingdom challenged by the Abominor, a droid society of asymmetry and bedlam. The two droid powers fought a war, crushing the galaxy's dominant organic species in the crossfire until the previously ignored organics fought back and forced the machines to flee. The Silentium settled in the Unknown Regions, reverting to a culture of excessive conservatism. Eventually growing bored, they built Vuffi Raa and others like him to gather fresh information from the greater galaxy.

As a young Silentium, Vuffi was created in the image of his long-extinct architects. A pentagonal plate of polished chromite serves as his body, which is unadorned save for a single glowing red photoreceptor at top center. The eye is capable of seeing into ultraviolet and infrared wavelengths. Other sensors, and a miniature vocabulator, are hidden underneath.

Vuffi Raa's five chromite tentacles serve as arms and legs. These appendages taper to points, then split into five-tentacled "hands" with one small optic sensor in each palm. What most observers fail to notice is that the tips of these fingers continue to split into near-microscopic *sub*-fingers, able to manipulate the tiniest objects yet still as strong as durasteel cables. Vuffi could detach all five limbs from his body and control each one remotely. He could also shunt heat into his extremities and produce a glowing tentacle tip, quite useful for illuminating a room (or lighting a cigarra).

While collecting diverse life experiences for his creators, Vuffi Raa went through dozens of owners in hundreds of systems, including a shameful role in the Imperial pacification of the lost human colony of Renatasia. After Lando Calrissian procured Vuffi in the Rafa system, the two became fast friends. The droid helped his new master collar the legendary Mindharp of Sharu, served as a pilot during the Battle of Nar Shaddaa, and saved Lando's skin during the Oseon system's annual Flamewind festival.

During a climactic showdown in the ThonBoka nebula, the little droid's people finally arrived to take him back to their home system. Vuffi Raa departed with his kinfolk. Although he returned to visit Lando on a few subsequent occasions, his current state is unknown.

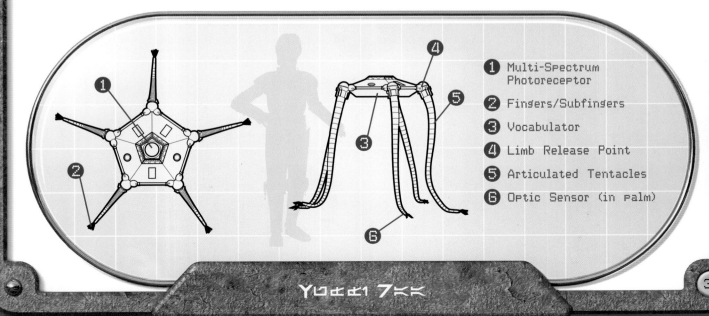

1. Multi-Spectrum Photoreceptor
2. Fingers/Subfingers
3. Vocabulator
4. Limb Release Point
5. Articulated Tentacles
6. Optic Sensor (in palm)

WEE GEE

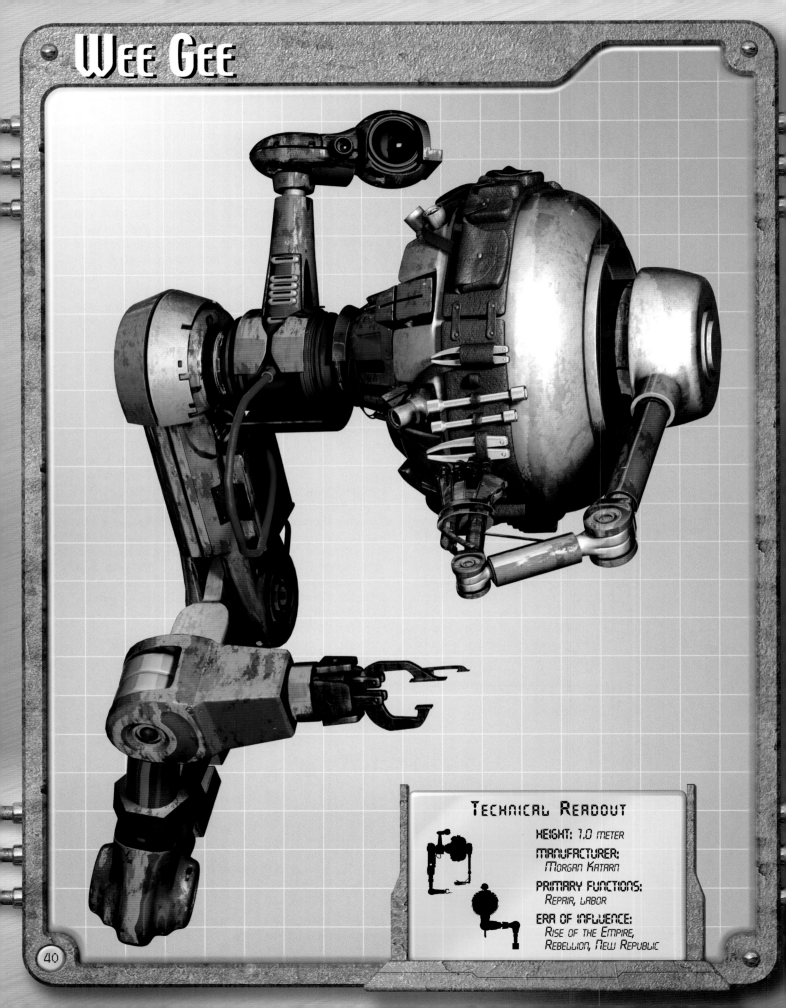

TECHNICAL READOUT

HEIGHT: 1.0 METER

MANUFACTURER:
Morgan Katarn

PRIMARY FUNCTIONS:
Repair, labor

ERA OF INFLUENCE:
Rise of the Empire,
Rebellion, New Republic

Morgan Katarn's Customized Utility Droid

Working from his own template, self-taught roboticist Morgan Katarn built Wee Gee from spare parts, creating a truly irreplaceable droid.

Morgan, his wife, Patricia, and his son, Kyle, operated a farm on Sulon, the agricultural moon of Sullust. Morgan built Wee Gee to plug in to the farm's operational grid and monitor its systems. Wee Gee's secondary functions included repairing equipment and driving threshing combines. Finally, and unofficially, Wee Gee's job was to protect Kyle at all costs.

Wee Gee floats on a repulsorlift engine scavenged from an Imperial speeder bike. Parts from a junked probot provide the maneuvering jets for steering. Wee Gee's centermost drive assembly is made up of rotating cylinders, allowing the droid to spin and twist into a variety of configurations. Two floodlights shine from the central chassis. Cooling fans keep Morgan's jury-rigged parts from overheating, giving Wee Gee a characteristic whir.

Wee Gee's sensory equipment fits into a small pod that extends above the drive assembly on a multi-jointed, pivoting stalk. In addition to a photoreceptor, the sensor pod contains auditory pickups, sonar emitters, and a vocabulator only capable of droid languages.

Two manipulator arms dangle underneath. The left arm, built for delicate work, possesses a multi-digit appendage with an opposable thumb for holding tools. The right arm is three times as powerful as the left, with four articulated joints and a crude gripping clamp. When

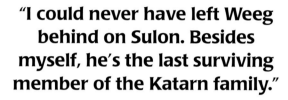

> ## "I could never have left Weeg behind on Sulon. Besides myself, he's the last surviving member of the Katarn family."
>
> *—New Republic agent Kyle Katarn*

working on the Katarn farm, Wee Gee often wore a human-style tool belt cinched around his drive assembly.

Kyle Katarn grew up with Wee Gee on Sulon. As a result, he became one of the few humans capable of understanding the whistling language of droidspeak. The two remained close friends until Kyle enrolled in the Imperial Academy on Carida at age eighteen.

Morgan Katarn's activities for the Rebel Alliance brought him to the hidden Valley of the Jedi on Ruusan. On the advice of a Jedi associate named Rahn, Morgan etched Ruusan's coordinates into the ceiling tiles of the Sulon farmhouse. Morgan also hid Rahn's lightsaber inside Wee Gee, believing that his son would one day achieve a greater destiny.

When Imperial forces under the command of the Dark Jedi Jerec attacked Sulon, Morgan Katarn lost his head to Jerec's blade. Wee Gee tried to stop the massacre, but a stormtrooper's blaster bolt knocked his systems offline.

Wee Gee repaired himself over the next five years, just in time to greet Kyle Katarn when the wayward son returned to his boyhood home, now fatherless and motherless, as Morgan's wife had died in a perimeter droid accident. Wee Gee gave Katarn the lightsaber he'd been carrying, and helped Kyle escape Sulon ahead of Jerec's agents. Among friends at last, Wee Gee happily joined a maintenance team serving the New Republic Fleet.

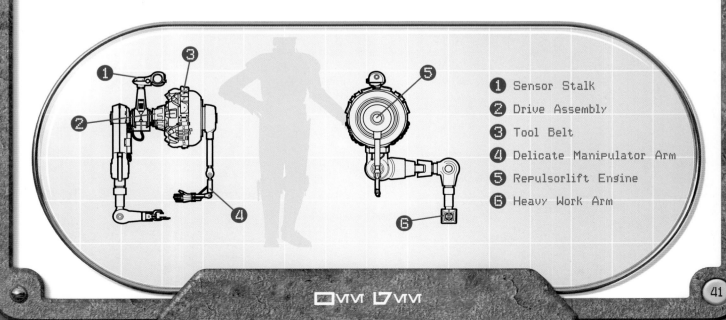

1. Sensor Stalk
2. Drive Assembly
3. Tool Belt
4. Delicate Manipulator Arm
5. Repulsorlift Engine
6. Heavy Work Arm

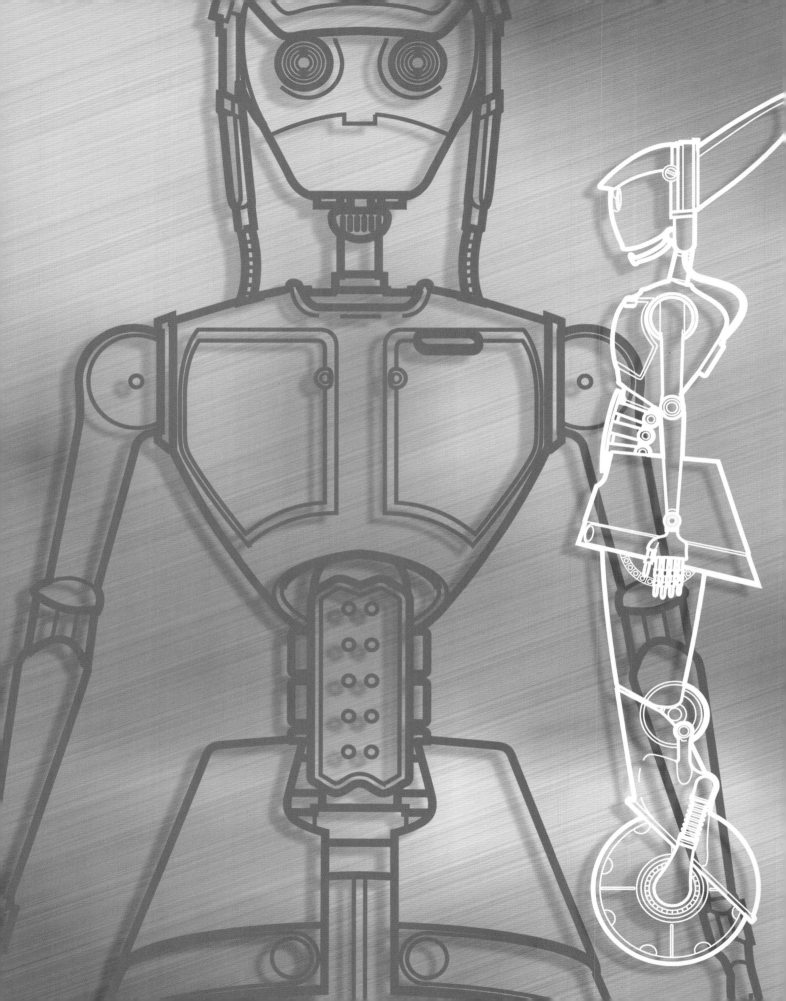

CLASS THREE DROIDS

lass three droids are the most human-like of all automata, as their primary function is to interact with organic beings. Class threes are the last variety of droid to be invented, and are considered by programmers to be the most advanced droids in existence.

This notion—that a droid butler is more sophisticated than a droid that calculates millions of hyperspace coordinates per second—seems counterintuitive to most. But the greatest challenge in artificial intelligence has always been the replication of the intuitive, nuance-laden organic brain.

The sophistication of the class three behavioral circuitry matrix (exemplified in advanced hardware such as SyntheTech's AA-1 verbobrain) is very close to the complexity of the organic mind. Although class threes aren't perfect in this regard, they are perhaps the only droids capable of consistently holding a conversation without it devolving into an emotionless recitation of facts and figures.

Droid programmers are careful not to pat themselves on the back, however. The organic brain is the result of millions of years of evolution, and even the most advanced class three droid can't shed every vestige of its artificiality. On the other hand, the personality of a class three can be enhanced far beyond its factory specs by allowing the droid to go many years without a memory wipe. The sum of its accumulated experiences will give the droid improved levels of empathy, at the risk of behavioral quirks such as cowardice, grouchiness, or excessive verbosity.

Most class three droids fall into one of several broad categories:

- **Protocol droids** work in the political sector, usually for elected officials, ambassadors, and planetary royals. Their chief function is to assist their owners in the intricacies of formal, cross-cultural diplomacy. These units are often equipped with translation libraries of millions of pre-loaded languages. Manifest droids, designed in part to interact with port authorities, are a unique variety of protocol droid.

- **Servant droids** are similar to protocol droids, but are sold for use in private households. Butler droids and personal chef droids fall under this category, whose members typically lack extensive translation databases. Many servant droids work in casinos and hotels.

- **Tutor droids** come programmed with exhaustive knowledge of a single subject, or wide-ranging expertise on a variety of general subjects. Unlike class one droids, tutor droids exist to communicate and explain their knowledge to organic beings. Tutor droids, such as Industrial Automaton's TTS-15, are common on industrialized worlds, as well as on space stations where qualified teachers are in short supply.

- **Child care droids** are seen in the employ of wealthy parents, pediatric medcenters, and corporations that offer child care services for their employees. Accutronics is the largest manufacturer of child care units, including the popular TDL "Lioness" nanny droid. Some droids under this category, such as the UE series, are merely expensive toys that act as playmates for the children of their owners.

Because they interact so closely with their owners, class three droids are built in the configuration that best matches the species of their potential buyers. Cybot Galactica's 3PO unit is primarily purchased by humans, while the mantis-headed J9 worker drone comes from the workshops of the insectile Verpine (and thus has limited market options).

However, the resemblance between class three droids and their owners is of a superficial, stylized nature. Over centuries of experimentation, it became apparent that the more droids resembled their buyers, the more popular they became. But if the droids passed a certain threshold of verisimilitude, consumers instead became disgusted by their "artificiality." This indefinable range of buyer rejection, known to designers as the "uncanny valley," has claimed many products. One of the most recent failures was the Loronar Corporation's synthdroids, which earned scorn for their dead eyes and doll-like hair.

Nearly all class threes sport metal skin and exposed joints, and thus fall short of entering the uncanny valley. Only recently has technology progressed to such a degree that a few droids have vaulted the valley entirely. Human replica droids, the result of years of government experimentation, are indistinguishable from organic beings—but cost millions of credits each.

2JTJ Personal Navigation Droid

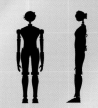

Technical Readout

Height: 1.7 meters

Manufacturer:
Genetech

Primary Function:
Personal navigation

Era of Influence:
Rise of the Empire, Rebellion

Genetech 2JTJ Personal Navigation Droid

The 2JTJ, manufactured by Genetech, is a personal aide designed to assist the newly sightless in navigating their surroundings.

In an average year, 80 percent of 2JTJ units are sold to institutional buyers, including hospitals and rehab centers. Doctors and occupational therapists at these facilities employ an "on-staff" pool of 2JTJ droids to work with patients who have lost their sight to accident or disease, as well as with those who have received cyborg optic implants but find it difficult to make the transition to digitized vision. Twenty percent of 2JTJs are purchased by private individuals, who typically live alone. They generally make the droids permanent additions to their households.

Genetech has been able to steadily grow the market for the 2JTJ by advertising the model to nonhuman customers. The Miraluka, a near-human species born without functional eyes, have been receptive to the droids, as have species that navigate by hearing or smell, such as the Sljee. Many members of these species find busy milieus such as Coruscant overwhelming to their alternative senses.

The 2JTJ incorporates many features of a standard protocol droid, including a silvery humanoid frame and advanced personality programming. Its head is studded with additional sensor nodes that enable the droid to make infrared scans, project radar sweeps, generate echolocating pings, and fire invisible, low-powered lasers to measure distances with a precision of less than a millimeter. Extra-long arms help the 2JTJ steady its master against a stumble.

The droid makes a capable chauffeur and can find the most direct route to a given destination with its automapping software. When traveling on foot, the 2JTJ delivers a running commentary on any obstacles appearing in its master's path.

A 2JTJ unit can receive either feminine or masculine programming at its owner's request, but both versions produce a droid that can be irritatingly perky. The droid's relentless good cheer and oblivious chattiness can be particularly grating during occupational therapy sessions, where patients are still working through the pain of vision loss.

In 44 B.B.Y., Jedi Master Tahl lost her sight on war-torn Melida/Daan and received a female-programmed 2JTJ unit as a gift from Master Yoda. TooJay immediately got under Tahl's skin, first by calling her "sir," and later by inserting herself into Tahl's affairs when the Jedi Master would have preferred to meditate in peace.

It soon became clear that TooJay carried a recording device in her pelvic servomotor, planted there without her knowledge by the failed Jedi student Xanatos, as part of his plot to destroy the Jedi Temple. Tahl and Qui-Gon Jinn turned the tables on Xanatos by arranging a false conversation for TooJay's benefit, allowing their true plans to escape their enemy's notice.

> ## "Tree root, two centimeters ahead. Leaf frond, three centimeters ahead at eye level!"
>
> *—An overly helpful 2JTJ, dispensing advice to Jedi Master Tahl*

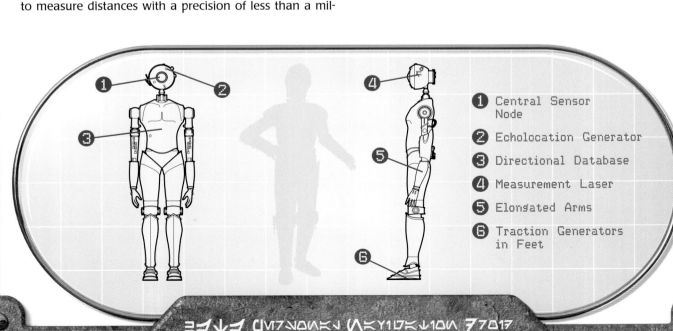

1. Central Sensor Node
2. Echolocation Generator
3. Directional Database
4. Measurement Laser
5. Elongated Arms
6. Traction Generators in Feet

3PO Protocol Droid

Technical Readout

HEIGHT: 1.7 meters

MANUFACTURER: Cybot Galactica

PRIMARY FUNCTION: Protocol

ERA OF INFLUENCE: Old Republic, rise of the Empire, Rebellion, New Republic, new Jedi order

Cybot Galactica 3PO Protocol Droid

Cybot Galactica's 3PO protocol droids are among the most human-like automata ever developed—a triumph, one might think. Unfortunately, sometimes human beings can be nervous, flighty, and borderline neurotic.

Some 3POs are all that and more, thanks to the highly advanced neural network of the SyntheTech AA-1 verbobrain. This superior cognitive module permits a droid to develop genuine emotions and a surprisingly original personality. Cybot Galactica actually installed creativity *dampers* in its 3PO units to ensure unembellished translations. Indeed, the company recommends regular memory wipes to iron out any quirks.

The 3PO units are widely used by ambassadors, politicians, consuls, and members of royalty as personal attachés in diplomatic or social settings. In a galaxy with thousands of different species and millions of distinct cultures, no Senator wants to trigger war by accidentally twisting a greeting into an insult. Not only are 3POs unrivaled at speaking diverse tongues, but they are also experts in etiquette, decorum, customs, posture, religious rituals, and table manners.

A 3PO stands 1.7 meters tall and is encased in a glittering, burnished body shell of gold, silver, white, or a handful of other hues. All possess photoreceptors, auditory pickups, broadband antenna receivers, microwave detectors, and olfactory sensors. The primary circuit breaker (a master on/off switch) can be accessed at the back of the neck. The droids require frequent oil baths to keep their joints in prime working condition.

Cybot Galactica has made 3PO-style droids in one form or another for centuries. To keep the model fresh in the public eye, various line extensions have been released over the decades, including the PX, the Consul360, and the ii77. These "boutique" models are priced up to twice as much as a standard 3PO and generally showcase a technological breakthrough, such as a larger memory unit or a more sophisticated vocabulator. Eventually, however, the technology becomes old news, the line extension is retired, and the distinguishing gizmo is incorporated into the regular production run of the 3PO.

The TC series is one of the most celebrated boutique extensions of the 3PO design. Popular in the decades leading up to the Clone Wars, TC 3POs were named for the TranLang III communications modules they carried. The TranLang III rocketed ahead of the previous TranLang II with a database of more than six million forms of communication, including obscure dialects, trade vernaculars, security codes, and droid transmissions. The vocabulator speech/sound system built into the TranLang III allows the TC to reproduce almost any sound, though the droid's humanoid construction limits its ability to duplicate nuances of some species' sign language (such as the subtle lekku tics of Twi'leki).

> *C-3PO*
> ## Oh! Nice to see a familiar face.
> *3PO DROID*
> ## (mumbles) E chu ta!
> *C-3PO*
> ## How rude!
>
> *—C-3PO to 3PO Droid*
> *in Bespin's Cloud City*

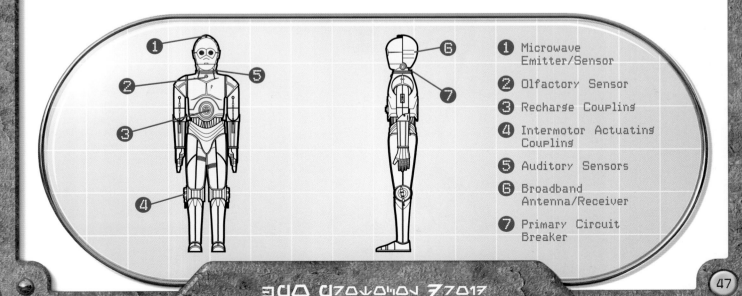

1. Microwave Emitter/Sensor
2. Olfactory Sensor
3. Recharge Coupling
4. Intermotor Actuating Coupling
5. Auditory Sensors
6. Broadband Antenna/Receiver
7. Primary Circuit Breaker

C-3PO

TECHNICAL READOUT

HEIGHT: 1.7 meters

MANUFACTURER:
Anakin Skywalker (from Cybot Galactica components)

PRIMARY FUNCTION:
Diplomacy/translation/utility

ERA OF INFLUENCE:
Old Republic, rise of the Empire, Rebellion, New Republic, new Jedi order

Almost all units in the TC series have voices designed to mimic those of human females, and refer to themselves with feminine-gender pronouns. Most TC units were purchased by Senators, ambassadors, and business barons. Few of these officials had any need for a translator that speaks six million languages, but ownership of a costly TC gave them bragging rights among their peers.

A second boutique model is the 3PX. Introduced around the same time as the TC, the 3PX couldn't be more dissimilar to its pricey cousin. The limited-run 3PX series bears a sharp, angular appearance, and carries a low price point designed to help it sell in the rougher markets of the Outer Rim. The series did not catch on, although many of its design elements later appeared in Arakyd's RA-7 Death Star Droid.

The 5YQ series appeared only in Mid Rim markets, as a discount 3PO model designed to go head-to-head with Serv-O-Droid's competitive Orbot. Cybot Galactica dropped the boutique 5YQ after only a few years, spurred by a corporate lawsuit over shared components.

Approximately a decade after the Battle of Endor, Cybot Galactica introduced one of the latest boutique models, the C series. These protocol droids have model numbers ranging from C-1 to C-9 and were produced exclusively on the factory moon of Telti.

> ## "You! I suppose you're programmed for etiquette and protocol."
>
> *—Owen Lars, interrogating C-3PO at a Jawa droid sale*

The most famous 3PO unit isn't really a 3PO at all. C-3PO, hero of the Rebellion, was built almost entirely from scratch by nine-year-old slave Anakin Skywalker. Anakin scavenged most of C-3PO's parts from sundry Cybot Galactica etiquette models, some of them more than eighty years old. Anakin claimed he assigned the number 3 to his droid because it represented the third member of his family (after Anakin and his mother Shmi), though the designation also mirrors the series name of Cybot's 3PO.

Anakin obtained the pieces for C-3PO's structural framework and servomotor system from Jawas and junk heaps. The droid's TranLang III communications module came from a state-of-the-art TC unit blasted to pieces by Gardulla the Hutt. Anakin created the makeshift droid's AA-1 verbobrain by fusing together three scrapped verbobrains: one rusted, one half melted, and one scorched in a warehouse fire. Anakin extracted the intact circuits from these unusable modules, synchronized them, and C-3PO was born.

Appearing at first in an unfinished, skeletal form, C-3PO gained dull matte body coverings just prior to the Clone Wars, and shiny golden plating three standard years later. The droid has remained in this form ever since, though a memory wipe erased most of his original recollections of Anakin.

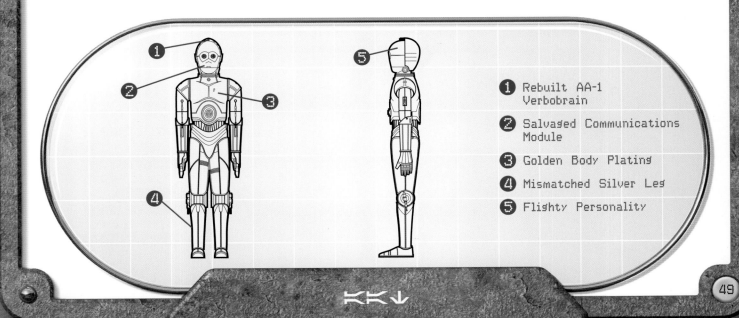

1. Rebuilt AA-1 Verbobrain
2. Salvaged Communications Module
3. Golden Body Plating
4. Mismatched Silver Leg
5. Flighty Personality

BD-3000 Luxury Droid

TECHNICAL READOUT

HEIGHT: 1.7 meters

MANUFACTURER:
LeisureMech Enterprises

PRIMARY FUNCTIONS:
Protocol, personal assistance

ERA OF INFLUENCE:
Rise of the Empire

LeisureMech Enterprises BD-3000 Luxury Droid

Protocol droids resemble humans, but only on a superficial level. It's a basic truth of droid design that customers tend to reject automata that try *too* hard to look like them. The BD-3000 is a pleasing expression of the current design philosophy, combining the curves of a beautiful human female with the shiny elegance of an executive toy.

LeisureMech Enterprises, a design firm operating out of the Corporate Sector, began producing the BD-3000 approximately half a century before the Clone Wars. In what has been described by critics as a triumph of style over substance, Leisure-Mech cut corners on hardware and software in order to achieve clean lines and a sparkling finish. Intentionally playing off the allure of the female human form, the BD-3000 has a small waist, long legs extending from a sculpted minidress, and a programmed walk cycle that provocatively twists the hips. LeisureMech also gave its BD-3000s the ability to vocalize a number of feminine speech patterns, ranging from perky to sultry.

These features alone were sufficient to drive demand for the BD-3000, even at a relatively high starting price of twenty-five thousand credits. Those beings not bewitched by the BD-3000's charms are quick to point out that its business administration programming underperforms, and that its linguistic database of one and a half million languages does not match the expertise of a 3PO unit. These shortfalls seem to matter little. The return rate on BD-3000s continues to be one of the lowest in the industry.

> ## "Right away, Governor. And may I say, you're looking particularly handsome today."
>
> —*Sample of the BD-3000's proprietary "flattery programming"*

Most BD-3000s find homes with politicians or ambassadors. Senator Bail Organa of Alderaan employed one of the droids in his office on Coruscant. Later, in order to broaden the potential buyer base, LeisureMech equipped the BD-3000 with twenty-five secondary functions including nanny, tailor, chef, and airspeeder chauffeur. Expansion slots allow for the installation of this programming, and some owners have modified their units with combat subroutines to turn them into bodyguards or assassins.

In an embarrassing development for LeisureMech, underground entrepreneurs reworked a number of BD-3000s to serve as escorts. Many of these models were modified with new accessories such as sensual, fully articulated Twi'lek head-tails.

Following the rise of the Empire, it became unpopular for politicians to be seen with droids as frivolous as the BD-3000. LeisureMech concentrated its sales efforts on its home territory in the Corporate Sector, where officials still reveled in the decadent and ostentatious. This smaller customer base, however, meant that the BD-3000 could no longer be supported in the numbers it had achieved during the Clone Wars. Unwanted BD-3000s began to be used in a variety of odd jobs. By the time of the New Republic, it wasn't unusual to encounter a BD-3000 driving a hoverbus or delivering food for a Toydarian restaurant.

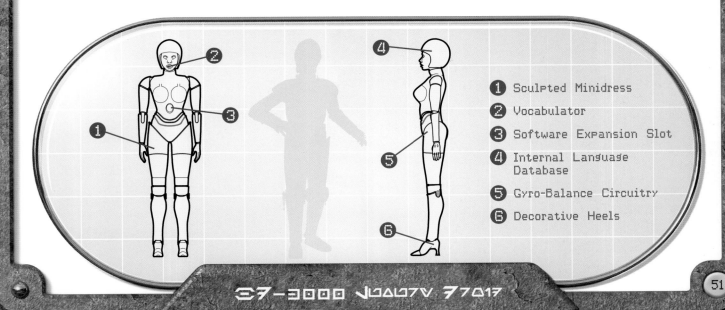

1. Sculpted Minidress
2. Vocabulator
3. Software Expansion Slot
4. Internal Language Database
5. Gyro-Balance Circuitry
6. Decorative Heels

C-3PX

Technical Readout

HEIGHT: 1.67 meters

MANUFACTURER:
Cybot Galactica

PRIMARY FUNCTION:
Assassination

ERA OF INFLUENCE:
Rise of the Empire

Cybot Galactica 3PX Protocol Droid

C-3PX was a one-of-a-kind assassin, initially built as a protocol unit and suffering several total rebuilds over the course of his operational life.

Created half a century before the Battle of Yavin, C-3PX belonged to Cybot Galactica's limited-run 3PX series, a line of protocol droids marketed exclusively in the Outer Rim. The droids in the 3PX series had a hard, less human countenance. Consequently, they met with limited success when up against the mainline 3PO units.

C-3PX served a number of masters before coming into the service of Darth Maul. The Sith Lord carried C-3PX aboard his starship *Scimitar*, using the droid to deal with port authorities and other nuisances for which Maul had no patience. Maul rebuilt C-3PX's chassis to incorporate defensive lasers.

After Darth Maul's death on Naboo, Republic investigators seized both *Scimitar* and C-3PX. Supreme Chancellor Palpatine, mindful of the Sith secrets stored in the droid's memory banks, ordered C-3PX's memory erased and remanded the unit to the custody of technology engineer Raith Sienar.

Sienar reworked C-3PX as an espionage unit. He replaced the droid's original body coverings with those from a 3PO unit, making him virtually indistinguishable from millions of other protocol droids in service. C-3PX's photoreceptors received upgrades enabling them to see

> ### "No matter what I do, I'll come to the same end . . . termination."
>
> —*Assassin droid C-3PX*

in infrared, and Sienar built innumerable smuggling compartments lined with sensor-baffling material into the droid's new chassis.

C-3PX ran his first corporate espionage mission in the service of Republic Sienar Systems, then became a spy in the Grand Army of the Republic during the Clone Wars. After the war's end, C-3PX became Imperial property.

While working for Admiral Screed on Roon, C-3PX slipped away and fell into the service of the Intergalactic Droid Agency, which offered him as a rental unit. The criminal Olag Greck saw that C-3PX was more than a standard protocol droid. Greck claimed C-3PX for his own, hiring an outlaw tech on Hosk Station to outfit the droid with retractable lasers, dart shooters, fusioncutters, and even a laser mounted in the back of his head. A distinctive black x marked his forehead.

Olag Greck ordered his new killer to eliminate posted bounties and claimed the rewards for himself. With his shielded weapons compartments, C-3PX could slip past the tightest security. After completing hits on Bonadan and Rampa, C-3PX earned his own bounty posting from the Empire. Ironically, C-3PX had ultimately grown weary of killing, so he allowed himself to be destroyed by R2-D2 in a gladiator arena on Hosk Station.

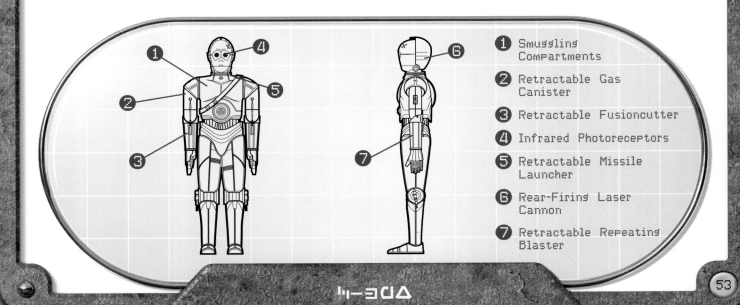

1. Smuggling Compartments
2. Retractable Gas Canister
3. Retractable Fusioncutter
4. Infrared Photoreceptors
5. Retractable Missile Launcher
6. Rear-Firing Laser Cannon
7. Retractable Repeating Blaster

CZ Secretary Droid

TECHNICAL READOUT

HEIGHT: 1.7 meters

MANUFACTURER:
Serv-O-Droid

PRIMARY FUNCTIONS:
Bookkeeping, communications

ERA OF INFLUENCE:
Rise of the Empire, Rebellion

Serv-O-Droid CZ Secretary Droid

Old droids never die; they just live on in the used market. This common phrase among droid remarketers is the perfect descriptor of the CZ secretary droid. The CZ can be seen in offices from the Core to the Rim, despite the fact that no one has made a new one since before the Clone Wars.

Serv-O-Droid released the CZ during its waning days as a dominant droid manufacturer. As conflicts such as the Arkanian Revolution (50 B.B.Y.) tore away at the Republic's former glory, Serv-O-Droid found its fortunes intertwined with those of the government. Although it had once been the biggest player in the business, Serv-O-Droid saw its market share drop year after year while Cybot Galactica and Industrial Automaton picked up the slack. The CZ secretary was designed to halt the slide, but newer products from Cybot Galactica eventually led to Serv-O-Droid leaving the business for good.

Despite its checkered history, the strengths of the CZ shouldn't be underestimated. The unit is classified as both a secretary droid and a comm droid, meaning its built-in comlink has a surface-to-orbit range and can randomly phase among frequencies to frustrate eavesdroppers. Its array of encryption algorithms and sensor jammers make the droid one of the most secure ways to transmit private comm messages or sensitive data. The CZ's optical sensors give it a unique cross-eyed look.

Most often, the CZ is employed as a secretarial unit. Common job functions include taking dictation, organizing files, scheduling calendars, and making comm calls. It comes preloaded with a number of languages—including the common business tongues of Huttese, Neimoidian, and Bocce—and the droid is conversant with business regulations and tax codes for thousands of planetary governments.

The data storage capacity of a CZ is vast. Its encryption algorithms resulted in its data firewall being nearly impossible to crack when the droid was first introduced. In the decades since, slicers have developed workarounds that can penetrate a factory-new CZ, though owners who regularly update their droids with fresh codes have few problems.

At launch, the CZ series boasted a garish green-and-orange paint job with yellow highlights. Serv-O-Droid believed that this tactic would draw attention to its new model, but most buyers repainted their droids to better suit a sedate business environment. Today few CZs have any trace of green or orange remaining on their outer shells.

Due to the high data security of the CZ series, the droids make excellent couriers. Jabba the Hutt employed one unit, CZ-3, to assist his Nimbanel accountants at his town house in Mos Eisley. In an attempt to ensnare a rival, Jabba loaded CZ-3 with a remote surveillance rig and set him loose in the city. The droid could be seen wandering the Mos Eisley streets when Obi-Wan Kenobi and Luke Skywalker booked passage off Tatooine. A Snivvian tracker named Zutton later blasted CZ-3 to pieces.

> ### "I have Duke Sparbo transmitting on my fifth cranial band. Shall I take a message?"
>
> —*CZ-54, employed by the Bureau of Ships and Services*

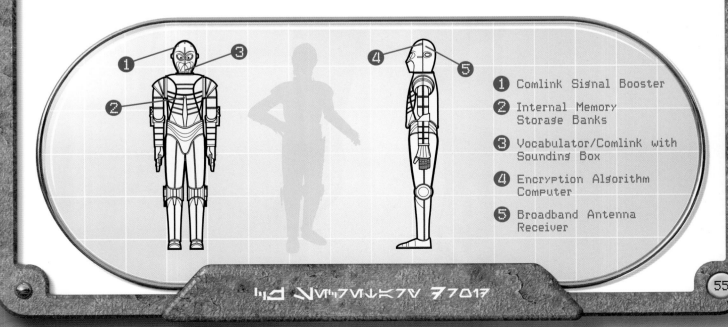

1. Comlink Signal Booster
2. Internal Memory Storage Banks
3. Vocabulator/Comlink with Sounding Box
4. Encryption Algorithm Computer
5. Broadband Antenna Receiver

DEATH STAR DROID

TECHNICAL READOUT

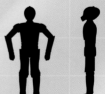

HEIGHT: 1.7 meters

MANUFACTURER:
Arakyd Industries

PRIMARY FUNCTION:
Espionage

ERA OF INFLUENCE:
Rise of the Empire, Rebellion

Arakyd RA-7 Protocol Droid

Never has a gift been so unwanted. The RA-7 Death Star Droid was produced as an internal affairs spy by the Imperial Security Bureau, leading to thousands of arrests at the hands of Palpatine's secret police. When the explosion of the Death Star vaporized most of the RA-7 production run, Imperial officials everywhere breathed a discreet sigh of relief.

Arakyd Industries produced the RA-7. Until that point, Arakyd had been known for military and explorational products such as the Viper probot, so its entry into the protocol droid market took the industry by surprise. The first RA-7s made their debut at the North Quadrant Intergalactic Automaton Show on Zug.

Attendees soon discovered that the RA-7 was cheaply assembled and off-putting in appearance (in a case of corporate resource sharing, the RA-7 wore many of the same exterior components as the later models in Cybot Galactica's 3PX protocol line). Examination of the droid's specs revealed more embarrassments—the RA-7 possessed a cognitive module at least a generation out of date.

Arakyd's rivals couldn't contain their mean-spirited mirth. But the competition didn't know that Arakyd had never intended to sell the droid to the mass market. As planned, the Empire stepped in and purchased the entire run of the RA-7. Then it began handing them out like party favors to governors, Moffs, and naval officers.

Hidden inside the droid's skull lies a secret surveillance module. Sensor baffles disguised as soldering welds prevent the hardware from appearing on diagnostic scans. The droid's panoramic photoreceptors can operate almost without light and extrapolate dialogue from lip-reading. An RA-7's audio pickups can detect a whisper from across a crowded lobby and discern multiple conversations at the same time.

Imperial bureaucrats who received the droids knew none of this. They could see that the junky RA-7s made poor assistants, but no one dared throw out the droids lest word get back to their superiors that they had spurned a gift from the Emperor. RA-7 droids were instead banished to dark corners, forgotten as if they were pieces of statuary.

Meanwhile, they recorded everything they heard or saw, making regular information dumps using encrypted communications channels on public information nodes. The Imperial Security Bureau, a branch of the rabidly partisan COMPNOR, pored over the findings and summoned insufficiently loyal officials on "business trips" to Coruscant. Few returned.

The sheer number of RA-7s assigned to officers on the Death Star battle station led to the nickname "Death Star Droid." Rumors soon spread among the Imperial bureaucracy that Death Star Droids were pure poison. It became common for officials to leave their RA-7s behind on off-world visits, where the droids found their way into junk shops and Jawa auctions.

> **"And thus I regret to inform your lordship that your gift has been stolen. By a swoop gang, most likely. Or Rebels. Or an alien."**
>
> *—Planetary governor Furi Nistola, attempting to explain how he "lost" his Death Star droid*

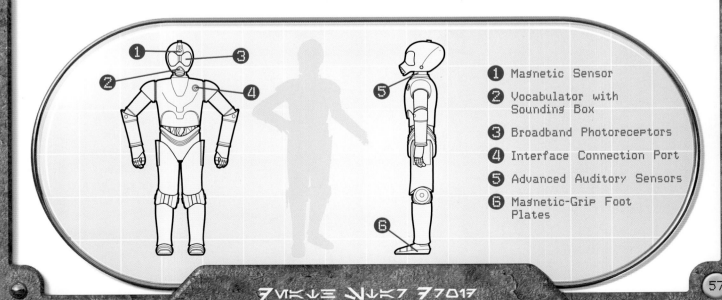

1. Magnetic Sensor
2. Vocabulator with Sounding Box
3. Broadband Photoreceptors
4. Interface Connection Port
5. Advanced Auditory Sensors
6. Magnetic-Grip Foot Plates

EV Supervisor Droid

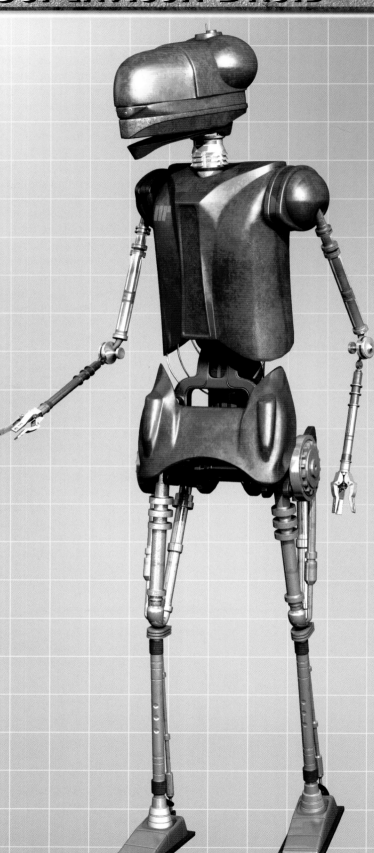

MerenData EV Supervisor Droid

It's one of the worst debacles in corporate memory. MerenData blames it on industrial sabotage, but others attribute it to a fatal combination of malicious intent and stupidity.

The EV series supervisor droid was planned as a manager that could oversee and increase the efficiency of droid labor pools. During production, however, the standard EV motivators were swapped for MDF motivators—contraband pieces of hardware designed for use in torture droids. The mix-up exposed the fact that MerenData was building illegal droids for the House of Tagge. The revelation triggered a public relations nightmare when hundreds of corrupted EV droids were released.

For the first few months after the tainted release, MerenData adopted a *wait-and-see* attitude. Initial reports indicated that the MDF-equipped models were actually *outperforming* standard EV units at worker motivation. Then the stories began trickling in. To its horror, MerenData realized that the affected droids had combined the MDF motivator's sadism with the power of positive management.

On Eriadu, 160 droids had their feet melted to the factory floor to prevent them from leaving their work stations. On Indu San, the slowest performers on a hotel wait staff were "treated" to an oil bath that was set on fire. On Kadril, in one of the rare cases where an EV oversaw organic workers, employees were often prodded with high-voltage electroprods.

A panicked MerenData made every effort to recall the affected models, and even tried to relaunch the line to the Imperial military as the V series. Both lines failed spectacularly. MerenData shuttered thousands of branch offices from the Core to the Outer Rim.

Unfortunately, MerenData's recall efforts did not reach every EV, and some found homes with owners unfazed by their peculiar appetites. The crime boss Ploovo Two-For-One employed a droid named EV-4D9, while the droid EV-9D9.2 took over as chief of interrogation on the assembly moon of Telti.

The most notorious unit, EV-9D9, became head of automated security in Bespin's Cloud City during the tenure of Lando Calrissian. "Eve" destroyed more than a quarter of the city's droid population before making a bold escape ahead of Calrissian's agents. Jabba the Hutt's goons later discovered Eve at a Go-Corp repulsor plant, and brought her back to oversee the droid pool at their master's palace on Tatooine. During the events surrounding Jabba's death, a droid survivor of EV-9D9's Cloud City rampage took revenge, finally ending Eve's operational cycle.

> **"FIFTH REMINDER: Please return your EV to your MerenData dealer for double your money back. We are also offering a 10,000-credit reward for information leading to the whereabouts of other EV supervisor droids."**
>
> —*MerenData customer mailing*

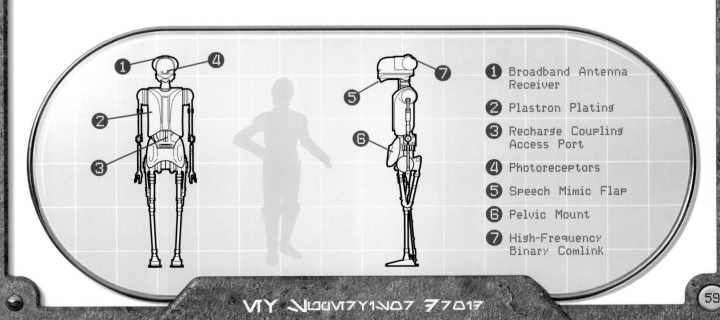

1 Broadband Antenna Receiver

2 Plastron Plating

3 Recharge Coupling Access Port

4 Photoreceptors

5 Speech Mimic Flap

6 Pelvic Mount

7 High-Frequency Binary Comlink

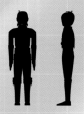

Technical Readout

Height: 1.7 meters

Manufacturer:
Cybot Galactica

Primary Functions:
Protocol, con-artistry

Era of Influence:
Rise of the Empire

Cybot Galactica 5YQ Protocol Droid

The irreplaceable I-Five is a perfect example of how aftermarket modifications, uncommon memory wipes, and a wealth of life experience can create a unique droid that bears little resemblance to its factory template.

Cybot Galactica produced the pewter-colored 5YQ protocol series as a short-lived offshoot of its popular 3PO series, sold at a lower price in the Mid Rim to compete with Serv-O-Droid's then-popular Orbot. A lawsuit over shared components prompted Cybot Galactica to retire the line, however, and only a handful of 5YQs remained in the marketplace.

One unit, designated I-5YQ, or I-Five, became the property of a wealthy family whose cruel children ordered him to walk off ledges so they could laugh at how high he bounced. A relieved I-Five soon ended up in a junk dealer's shop, where he became the property of the con artist and freelance information broker Lorn Pavan.

Seeing a kindred soul in the abused I-Five, Lorn Pavan made the droid his business partner. He boosted I-Five's cognitive module and removed his hardwired creativity dampers. Now as self-aware as it was possible for a droid to be, I-Five entered into a five-year criminal alliance with Pavan, using his electronic brain to sell underworld secrets, run banking scams, and cheat at sabacc.

Over the course of their adventures, Pavan upgraded I-Five with a radar-mapping device, a microwave projector beam, a chest compartment for holding contraband, a pair of spotlight-projecting photoreceptors, an electrostatic generator to prevent grime from adhering to I-Five's body shell, and two concealed lasers built into his index fingers.

I-Five's most versatile addition was an Aeramaxis AXX Screamer, a sound modulator that can transmit on every frequency from subsonic to ultrasonic. I-Five became so adept with this device that he could generate subtle harmonics to loosen toxins from the bloodstream, or broadcast a shriek so cacophonous it would leave organic beings squirming on the ground in agony.

> ## "Organics are endlessly amusing. If only to themselves."
>
> —*One of I-Five's unsolicited observations*

Lorn Pavan died in a run-in with Darth Maul, and I-Five wound up in the employ of spice smugglers working the Kessel Run. Authorities seized him and sold him at auction, and I-Five fell in with a noble family on Naboo. During the Clone Wars, the Republic commandeered I-Five and other available droids to assist in the war effort. Now augmented with battlefield medical programming, I-Five joined the droid pool at Rimsoo Seven, a Republic field hospital on Drongar.

I-Five forged several friendships with the Rimsoo surgeons, and also made time to pursue quests of his own, including simulating intoxication by scrambling his sensory and cognitive feeds. At the conclusion of Rimsoo Seven's tour on Drongar, I-Five departed for Coruscant, where he hoped to hook up with Lorn Pavan's son, a Jedi Temple initiate.

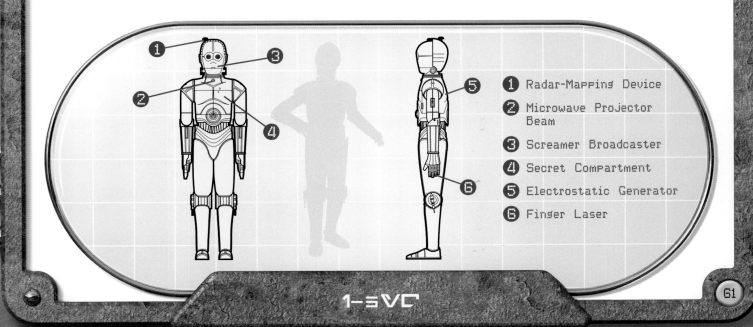

1. Radar-Mapping Device
2. Microwave Projector Beam
3. Screamer Broadcaster
4. Secret Compartment
5. Electrostatic Generator
6. Finger Laser

J9 Worker Drone

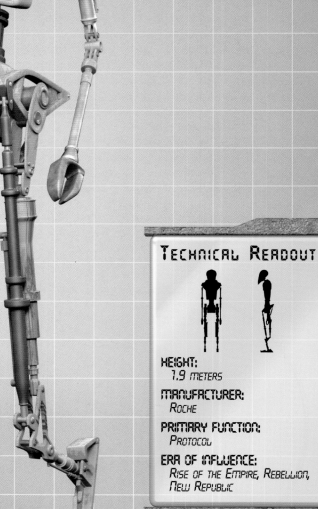

Technical Readout

Height:
1.9 meters

Manufacturer:
Roche

Primary Function:
Protocol

Era of Influence:
Rise of the Empire, Rebellion,
New Republic

Roche J9 Worker Drone

The J9 worker drone is quite possibly the worst-selling protocol droid in history. Fault for the spectacular failure lies not with the Verpine engineers of the Roche hive, but with the insectoid beings' inability to understand other cultures. The product's shortcomings provide an object lesson in the pitfalls of selling to the mass galactic market.

The Verpine couldn't see past their own mandibles when designing the droid's outer shell. It looks remarkably like a Verpine, with bulging compound eyes, spindly claw-tipped limbs, and pointed mouth pincers. Right away, this put the J9 at a disadvantage on the sales floor, as the galaxy's mammalian species found the droid creepily alien.

The second problem with the J9 lies with the Verpine programmers who gave it a personality. While the droid can function well enough within the regimented structure of an insect colony, its fixation on hive thought patterns means that it often works the words *carapace, regurgitation,* and *royal jelly* into its language translations. Furthermore, the J9 speaks with a persistently buzzy vocabulator.

The net result? Buyers avoided the J9 in droves. The disappointed Verpine slashed prices, bringing about the J9's curious second act. Because the Verpine had marketed the unit as a "worker drone"—a common appellation within their society—non-Verpine buyers often misunderstood the label and installed J9s in stockrooms and load-ing docks. Roche raised no objections. At this point, it was grateful for whatever sales it could get.

By all measures, however, using a J9 as a cargo tagger is a colossal waste. Each droid possesses an Arjan II logic computer and a TranLang III communications module with more than one million languages. Intellectually, the droids can compete with a 3PO unit. Their giant bug eyes are keyed to the Verpine optical range, lying mostly in the ultraviolet spectrum. With its finely tuned olfactory sensor and its Torplex microwave sensor, the J9 can experience a world far beyond the ranges of human perception.

The complex, triangular hip joints of the J9 are a trademark sign of the Roche hive. The same hip joints are seen on the 8D8 smelting operator and many other Roche products.

At the height of his power, Jabba the Hutt owned a J9 worker drone designated BG-J38. Jabba's thugs soon discovered that the "stupid droid" could easily beat them at dejarik holo-chess, so Beegee became a popular figure in the Hutt's court. The droid's whereabouts following Jabba's death are unknown, but he is believed to have escaped offworld to feed his slot-machine addiction.

Recently, the Verpine have attempted to remarket the J9 directly to other insectoid species, including the Sic-Six, Flakax, and Xi'Dec. Thus far the biggest sales boom has come from the giant, mantis-like Yam'rii.

> **"Greetingzzz, Master. How may Drone Beegee-Arfivetoo zzzervice the colony, hive, or zzzocial collective?"**
>
> —*Start-up greeting from a new J9 worker drone*

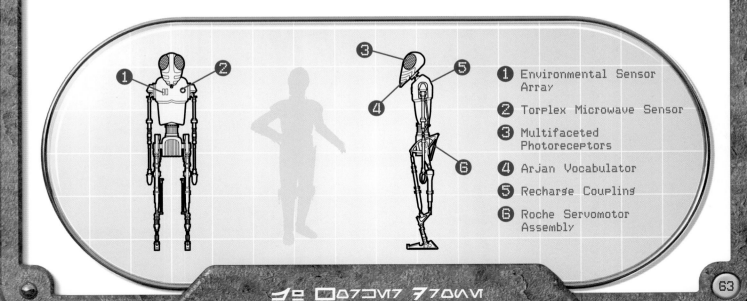

1. Environmental Sensor Array
2. Torplex Microwave Sensor
3. Multifaceted Photoreceptors
4. Arjan Vocabulator
5. Recharge Coupling
6. Roche Servomotor Assembly

LE Manifest Droid

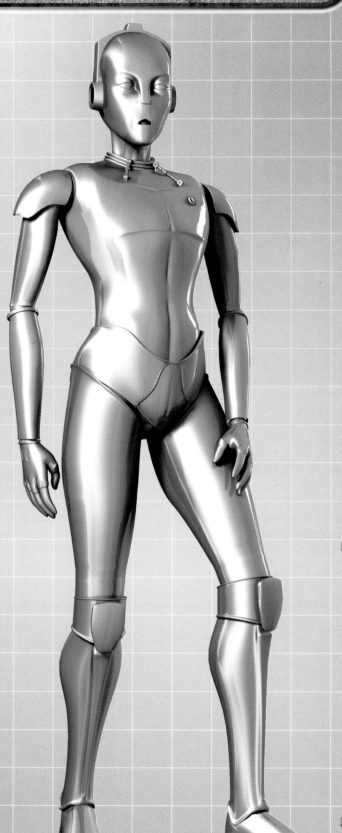

Technical Readout

HEIGHT: 1.7 meters

MANUFACTURER:
Cybot Galactica

PRIMARY FUNCTION:
Shipping management

ERA OF INFLUENCE:
Old Republic, rise of the
Empire, Rebellion

Cybot Galactica LE Manifest Droid

Cybot Galactica is responsible for the LE series, a statement that seems obvious to those familiar with Cybot's LE repair droids. Yet in this case, the droids under discussion are members of the obscure LE manifest series, introduced nearly three centuries before the New Republic.

The company conceived of the LE droids as protocol droid variants, to be used by starship captains and port operators. Rather than carrying etiquette programming, the LEs came equipped with import-export restrictions for the galaxy's major trading regions and the mammoth code of conduct imposed by BoSS, the Bureau of Ships and Services.

Because no organic being could be expected to know the complete intricacies of the BoSS code, having an LE series droid on staff would smooth a number of tedious tasks, from the proper inventorying of cargo to the datawork required, in triplicate, to import strange fungi into the Core Worlds. Furthermore, the LE's bright, female-programmed personality and streamlined design made it an appealing companion for long stretches in hyperspace.

The downfall of the LE series proved to be its scrupulous honesty. On most starports, particularly those in Hutt or Bothan space, bribes have long been considered a regular part of business. Cybot Galactica never thought to program their droids with this degree of flexibility. Consequently, LE droids would make catastrophic errors, such as reporting contraband stashed beneath their freighter's deck plating—all under the mistaken assumption that they were only helping. It didn't take long before most owners decided that LE droids simply weren't worth the trouble.

Cybot Galactica retired the line, but the existing LE droids saw continued use in smaller starports and aboard short-hop corporate freighters. As LE units gained more experience interacting with organics, they would gradually shed their prudish adherence to the letter of the law and learn to make compromises as circumstances demanded.

One unit, LE-914, served with Rebel Alliance hero Tay Vanis after the Battle of Hoth. "Ellie" became Vanis's closest companion, assisting him in dozens of missions against the Empire. In return, Vanis equipped Ellie for "high-stress functions." He replaced her torso plating with blaster-resistant armorplast featuring a mirrored coating. Behind secret access panels on Ellie's chest lay a storage chamber, used to hold contraband items or to operate the self-destruct controls that would trigger the explosion of a nested proton bomb.

Prior to the Battle of Endor, Tay Vanis obtained data tapes confirming the details of the Emperor's Death Star project at Endor. Darth Vader caught up with Vanis and left him a mind-wiped shell of a man, but Ellie escaped with the tapes secured inside her chest compartment. After giving the data to Luke Skywalker and Princess Leia, Ellie destroyed herself and her master.

> **"I am Ellie. It is my function here to note all inventories, issue clearances, and keep all records."**
>
> *—LE-914, welcoming Luke Skywalker to an Imperial depot*

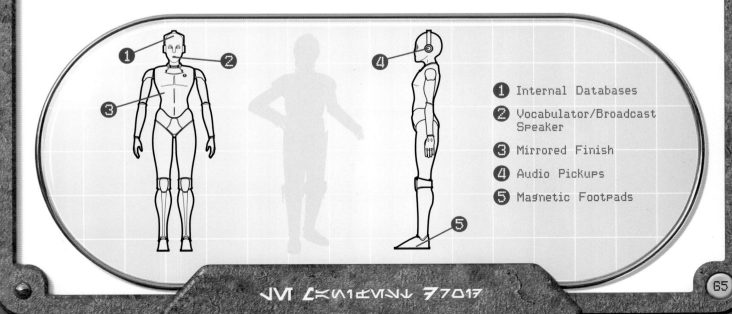

1. Internal Databases
2. Vocabulator/Broadcast Speaker
3. Mirrored Finish
4. Audio Pickups
5. Magnetic Footpads

LOM Protocol Droid

Technical Readout

HEIGHT: 1.6 meters

MANUFACTURER:
Industrial Automaton

PRIMARY FUNCTION:
Protocol

ERA OF INFLUENCE:
Rise of the Empire, Rebellion,
New Republic

Industrial Automaton LOM Protocol Droid

It's one of the worst examples of corporate imitation in history. No case better illustrates why there's so much bad blood between the executives of Industrial Automaton (IA) and Cybot Galactica than that of the LOM protocol droid.

Though they're often called the Big Two, Cybot Galactica and Industrial Automaton have created distinctly different images in the public's imagination. Cybot is known for refined, elegant products such as the 3PO protocol series, while IA, through its popular R series astromechs, has a reputation for being working class and reliable.

The stereotype has always rankled some at IA. In the years after the Clone Wars, they decided to launch a product, the LOM series, that would establish Industrial Automaton as a major player in the protocol market. Not wanting to be too blatant with what was intended to be a first-generation product, IA decided to sell to a test market of insectoid species, including the Brizzit, Verpine, and Yam'rii. Designers sculpted the LOM's head as "insect-like" as possible to suit a wide variety of phenotypes.

Selling a niche model, however, wasn't Industrial Automaton's ultimate goal. If the LOM performed to expectations, the company planned to convert it to a humanoid droid and sell to the mass market within two standard years. Telltale signs of this scheme were all over the LOM: despite its bulging compound eyes, for example, its internal visual pickups are keyed to the human spectrum.

What really incensed Cybot Galactica was the manner in which Industrial Automaton brokered deals with Cybot's own parts suppliers. From SyntheTech, IA secured an AA-1 verbobrain with a TranLang III communications module. It even obtained droid body plating from companies that had enjoyed long relationships with Cybot Galactica. From the neck down, the LOM looks almost identical to the rival 3PO unit.

Cybot Galactica sued, claiming trademark infringement and a violation of noncompetition agreements with the 3PO unit's top suppliers. Industrial Automaton put the LOM on the market anyway, where it sold well in limited release. Customers liked the fact that it has none of the jumpiness so characteristic of the 3PO, and that it seems wired for gentleness and altruism.

A second crisis proved to be too much for Industrial Automaton, however. Aboard the luxury spaceliner *Kuari Princess,* the droid 4-LOM abandoned its job as the ship's valet and became a jewel thief. Before long, 4-LOM had morphed into one of the galaxy's deadliest bounty hunters. Cybot Galactica gleefully pointed fingers at the "shoddy craftsmanship" of its competitor. IA tried to blame *Kuari Princess*'s shipboard computer, but the public relations damage had been done. The company quietly retired the LOM series, but continued plotting new ways to overtake Cybot Galactica.

> **"The case is inconclusive, but the processor doesn't appear to be at fault. The subject claims he committed crimes simply 'for love of money.'"**
>
> *—Industrial Automaton investigators, after interviewing 4-LOM*

1. Auditory Sensors
2. Recharge Coupling
3. Vocabulator
4. Microwave Emitter/Sensor
5. Olfactory Sensor
6. Photoreceptor

Tac-Spec Footman

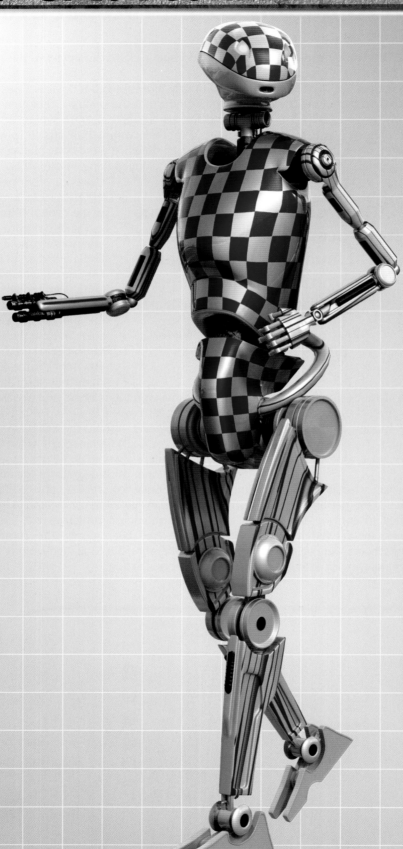

Technical Readout

HEIGHT: *1.9 meters*

MANUFACTURER:
Tac-Spec

PRIMARY FUNCTIONS:
*Personal service,
bodyguarding*

ERA OF INFLUENCE:
*Old Republic, rise of
the Empire*

Tac-Spec Corporation FIII Footman Droid

Relic of a bygone era, the Tac-Spec Corporation FIII Footman Droid is a personal servant designed for the class of aristocrat who lives by the principles of chivalry, gentility—and murder.

Ancient noble houses, such as those in the Senex and Tapani sectors, have histories shrouded in internecine conspiracies. Nobles are regularly killed in duels, while young heirs are poisoned, all as part of a sub-rosa struggle for power. Bodyguard droids thus became common among the blue-blood classes more than a thousand standard years ago. A miniature arms race soon developed over which house could employ the deadliest personal servants, while still preserving the unspoken virtues of status and tradition.

To this end, the House of Tund in the Centrality made contact with the GenoHaradan, a near-mythical assassins' guild whose origins predate the Republic. GenoHaradan agents established the Tac-Spec corporation as a front company, then sold the Footman to prearranged buyers who had existing contacts within the guild. The first Tac-Spec Footman came into service a few decades after the Battle of Ruusan, and the company produced the line in limited numbers for the next six hundred standard years.

The Tac-Spec Footman announces itself as a "gentleman's personal gentlething." It carries an exhaustive library of explicit rules and mores related to the specific noble house with which it sees service. Daily duties include preparing and serving meals, opening doors,

> **"I am programmed for absolute loyalty to the House Malreaux, which I have served through madness and war for twelve generations."**
>
> —*Fidelis, Tac-Spec Footman from Vjun*

operating vehicles, and maintaining its owner's wardrobe.

In the event of a threat, however, the Footman can become much more. Its blaster-resistant chassis enables it to take a hit meant for its master, and then retaliate in close combat. The Footman's blinding reflexes and pitiless mechanical strength give it the ability to puncture a target's chest with a punch, or rip loose a limb with an effortless tug. At ranged distances, the Tac-Spec Footman can unload with a miniature rail cannon built into the end of one arm. The droid carries weapons programming covering all light and heavy armaments, and boasts a special expertise as a sniper.

One Footman, named Fidelis by its owners, served Vjun's House Malreaux for twelve generations. Fidelis proudly wore the Malreaux checkerboard of ivory and blood on his torso, with blood piping marking his limbs. When the people of Vjun succumbed to madness, Fidelis traveled to Coruscant. There he watched over Whie Malreaux, the young Malreaux heir, who was undergoing instruction in the Jedi Temple.

After a wait of more than ten years, Fidelis hooked up with Whie when the teenage Jedi accompanied Master Yoda on a mission during the Clone Wars. A second Tac-Spec Footman, the renegade Solis, betrayed the group to Count Dooku's lieutenant Asajj Ventress, but turned against Ventress when she refused to pay. Both Solis and Fidelis saw their operational lives cut short in a standoff beneath the Malreaux castle on Vjun.

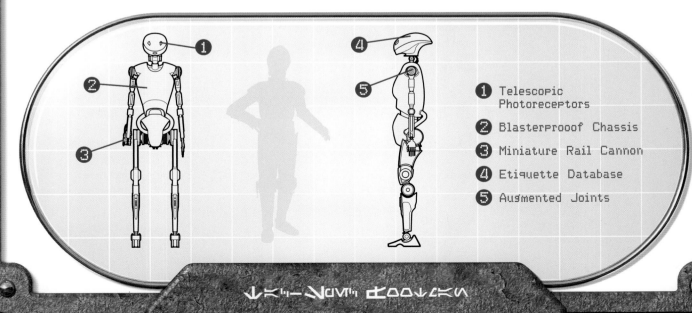

1. Telescopic Photoreceptors
2. Blasterproof Chassis
3. Miniature Rail Cannon
4. Etiquette Database
5. Augmented Joints

WA-7 Waitress Droid

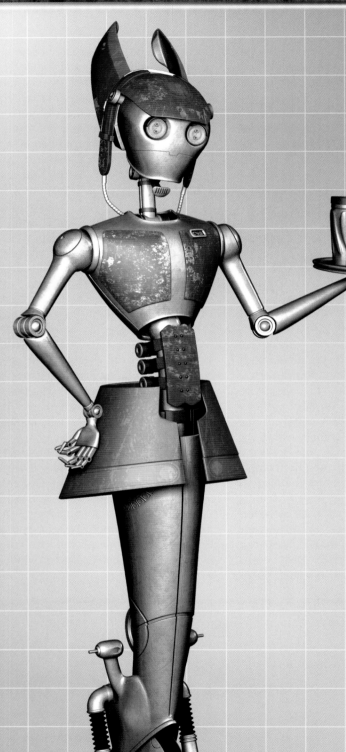

Go-Corp/Utilitech WA-7 Service Unit

They don't make droids like the WA-7 anymore. The sight of one at a restaurant indicates that the establishment is either attempting to evoke a nostalgic ambience, or simply unable to afford anything better.

Go-Corp introduced the WA-7 waitress droid at a time when the Core Worlds were gripped in the fever of the Mondeo Modernist design movement. The fad—which spread to art, architecture, and clothing design—emphasized streamlined contours, elliptical shapes, and whimsical embellishments. The craze burned brightly for several decades but eventually fizzled. Evidence of Mondeo Modernism is present in surviving popcultural artifacts from the era, including the WA-7.

The droid moves on a unipod wheel, a concession to Mondeo flightiness that proved quite practical. The wheel's drive impellers can generate quick bursts of speed, and the tire covers very little surface area to help prevent the WA-7 from running over a customer's appendages. Gyro-balance circuitry keeps the WA-7 perfectly upright even when zipping through a crowd of patrons, a necessity for a droid whose success often hinges on never dropping a drinks tray.

Decorative elements on the WA-7 include a metallic skirt and head fins, while functional hardware consists of a built-in order transmitter with a range that can extend as far as the kitchen. WA-7 units are programmed with enough verbal acuity to chat up customers, as well as facial-recognition software enabling them to identify their "regulars."

The WA-7 is a well-built droid, and thus many are still in service today. Not all remain in waitressing, however. Changing circumstances forced WA-7s to take odd jobs, with courier being one of the most common, given that a WA-7 can weave through ground-level traffic at speeds up to 120 kilometers per hour. During a typical workweek on many planets, racing WA-7 units carry packages in back harnesses as they shout at hovercar drivers to get out of their way.

A group of private collectors has even fielded a WA-7 nuna-ball team that defeated Serv-O-Droid's RIC team in a shocking upset at an exhibition match.

Dexter Jettster, the Besalisk owner of Dex's Diner on Coruscant, bought a used WA-7 that soon became one of his best employees. The droid, nicknamed "Flo," competed with Dexter's chief waitress, Hermione Bagwa, for tips. Each viewed the other as her subordinate in the diner hierarchy, which led to more than a few colorful exchanges—much to the delight of the clientele.

Accutronics briefly attempted to play off the retro-popularity of the WA-7 with a knockoff line known as the TDL-501. Introduced shortly before the Clone Wars, the "Teedle" met with modest success before succumbing to the same changing tastes that doomed the original.

> **"You ordered the cream of fleek eel, right? Careful, hon, the plate's hot. And the fleek eels bite."**
>
> *—"Flo," the WA-7 droid at Dex's Diner on Coruscant*

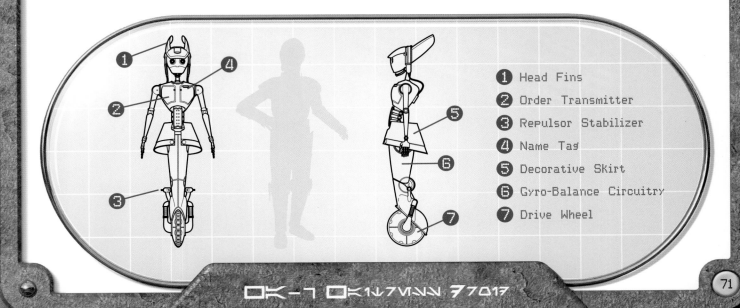

1. Head Fins
2. Order Transmitter
3. Repulsor Stabilizer
4. Name Tag
5. Decorative Skirt
6. Gyro-Balance Circuitry
7. Drive Wheel

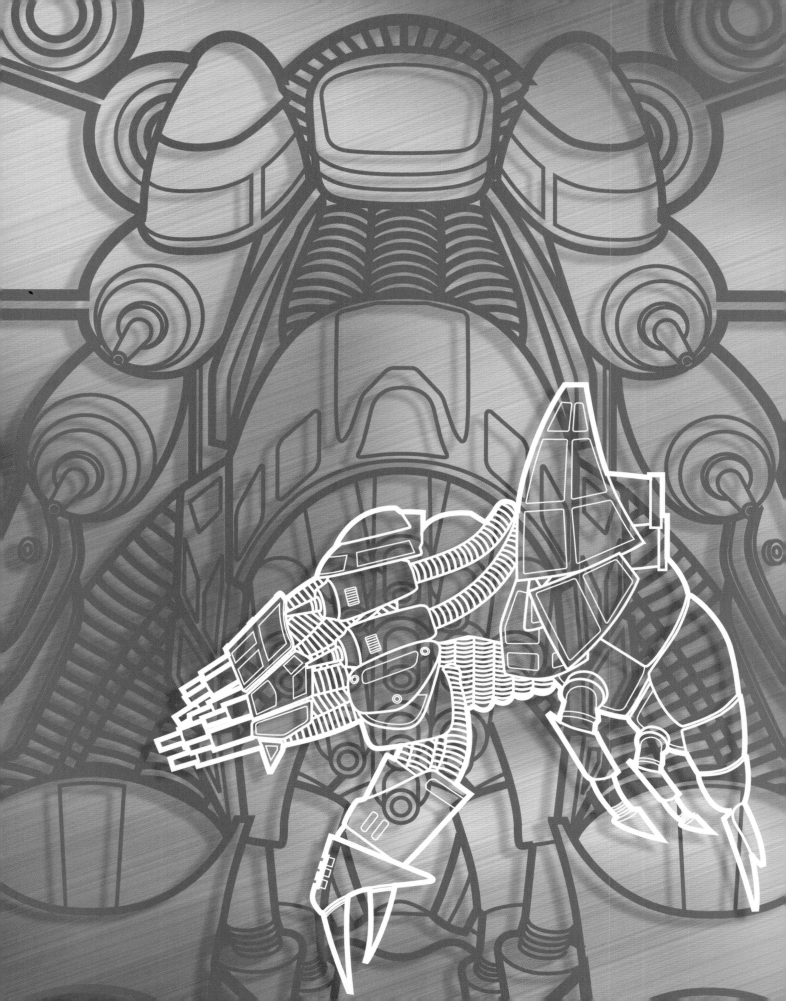

CLASS FOUR DROIDS

"Droids with weapons" is how many might categorize the automata that make up class four. This categorization, while crude, is not inaccurate. Despite the fact that class four droids are subject to severe restrictions and in many cases banned outright, it has never stopped opportunists from making more.

Armed combat droids were among the first droids ever created. Historians believe their introduction followed closely after the debut of the menial droid caste now known as class five, when warlords realized that the behavioral circuitry matrix enabled droid units to react to changing combat conditions on a battlefield. The war robots of Xim the Despot, created circa 25,120 B.B.Y., are a famous example, as are the Electric Caliphs of Mourn.

Class four droids come in four main varieties. The laws concerning ownership of class four droids vary greatly, depending on the subcategory to which the droid belongs.

- **Security droids** are the most widely accepted class four units, used to guard residences, businesses, and public institutions. Security droids are generally armed with nonlethal weaponry, although some have no weapons and are capable only of sounding alarms. Security droids can be purchased from many public companies, providing the buyer possesses the necessary permits. The internal programming of a security droid contains governing blocks preventing it from knowingly killing an organic being—though these blocks can be bypassed by a talented droid engineer.

- **Gladiator droids** occupy a specialized niche involving death matches against other droids. Gladiator units such as the Mark X executioner have an array of showy weapons, including flamethrowers, vibro-axes, and neuronic whips. They carry the same blocks, however, as security droids concerning the harming of organic beings. Robotic gladiator matches are common in the Outer Rim, where Hutt crimelords are known to disable the governing blocks and unleash the droids against prisoners in decadent displays of bloodshed.

- **Battle droids** have made history from the days of Xim the Despot to the devastations of the Clone Wars. Once ubiquitous on worlds belonging to the Confederacy of Independent Systems, battle droids (also called war droids or combat droids) practically disappeared after the rise of the Empire. Crime syndicates and private armies continued to use battle droids during the Imperial era, either illegally or by referring to them as "security units."

- **Assassin droids** are the only automata built specifically for murder. The early assassin droids (activated during the Indecta era from 17,000 through 15,000 B.B.Y.) operated on behalf of the Republic Judicial Department, eliminating escaped convicts and other threats to galactic security. Deadlier versions followed, most of which found their way into private hands. Although the Republic never formally outlawed assassin droids, most planetary and sector governments did. Only after the rise of the Empire—and the assassination of Imperial Grand Inquisitor Torbin on Weerden—did legislators enact galaxywide regulations barring the sale, ownership, or manufacture of these killer droids. Of course, the Emperor was not above using assassin droids to eliminate his own enemies, and the Imperial Department of Military Research was responsible for creating some of the deadliest assassin droids ever known.

On worlds such as Naboo, where droid armies slaughtered citizens in the recent past, animosity toward class four droids runs high. Elsewhere in the galaxy, entire sectors have been closed off to droid importers due to the depredations of class four units. The Kol Huro Unrest in 44 B.B.Y. left the locals gun-shy about droids, making it nearly impossible for Cybot Galactica or Industrial Automaton to gain a foothold in the region.

Rogue class four droids are a grave problem. Although all varieties of droids have been known to wander off, class four droids are built for aggression and can become a threat to lives and property. Assassin droids, which possess stealth capabilities enabling them to elude capture, are clearly the most dangerous rogues. The rebellious assassin droid HK-01 started the Great Droid Revolution on Coruscant in 4015 B.B.Y., while more recently the assassin IG-88 left behind a trail of bodies in its job as an independent bounty hunter.

ASN-121 Assassin Droid

Technical Readout

HEIGHT: 0.38 meter

MANUFACTURER:
Malkite Poisoners

PRIMARY FUNCTION:
Assassination

ERA OF INFLUENCE:
Old Republic, rise of the Empire

Malkite Poisoners ASN-121

The Malkite Poisoners are one of the galaxy's most notorious secret societies. Few know the truth of their role in the rise of Supreme Chancellor Contispex during the Pius Dea era. Fewer still know that they also make droids.

The Clawdite assassin Zam Wesell contacted the Malkite guild engineers to request an ASN-121 assassin droid. The finished product, assembled from commonplace droid components in order to hide its origins, carried the mark of Malkite expertise in its silent lethality.

Unlike similarly patterned sentry droids, Zam's ASN-121 possessed unprecedented environmental awareness and stealth programming, as well as a repulsorlift engine that was rated as military-plus. Prior to its mission to assassinate Senator Padmé Amidala in her Coruscant apartment, Zam's droid eliminated dozens of targets on security-lockdown worlds such as Bonadan and Axum.

Powered by a fusion generator, the ASN-121 could reach near-orbit levels with its repulsorlift engine, yet the droid remained virtually silent and emitted no radiation signature. As evidenced by the Coruscant mission, the droid's repulsorlift had no difficulty supporting the extra sixty-three kilograms of a Jedi hitchhiker, even when traveling at top speeds.

Twin dagger-shaped cooling vanes marked the droid's silhouette. A central tool socket accommodated a number of interchangeable add-ons, and Zam Wesell's toolbox included a flame projector, a poison gas sprayer, a durasteel drill, a blaster, and canisters that could carry explosives or toxic biological agents. For reconnaissance or security, Zam's ASN-121 could carry an infrared detector, an eavesdropping recorder, a stinger blaster, a harpoon gun, or a tangle net. If threatened, the ASN-121 could reroute its electric circulation into its outer shell for a shocking method of deterrence, though Zam disabled this function for the Amidala hit, lest the droid's electrical signature set off the apartment's security sensors.

For the Amidala hit, Zam loaded her ASN-121 with two slithering kouhuns—multi-legged bugs from Indoumodo that can kill with a single sting. The ASN-121 emitted disruptive energy beams from its wing tips to bypass the security screen surrounding Senator Amidala's window, then deployed a laser cutter to carve a hole in the pane.

Unfortunately for ASN-121, Zam Wesell had ordered it to remain in the vicinity and monitor the kouhuns' attack. This left it visible to Obi-Wan Kenobi, who burst through the window and grabbed on to its body for a vertiginous ride among Coruscant's skyscrapers. The trip ended when Zam shot ASN-121 with a bolt from her sniper rifle.

Fragments from the droid later turned up during Republic Judicial patrols of the undercity. Once sliced, the droid's status log revealed the truth behind several unsolved assassinations, and warned several Senators that they had enemies in high places.

> **"Senator Jubben. STATUS: Terminated. Baron Wazado. STATUS: Terminated. Senator Amidala. STATUS: ABORTABORTABORTABOR—"**
>
> *—From the recovered log of Zam Wesell's ASN-121*

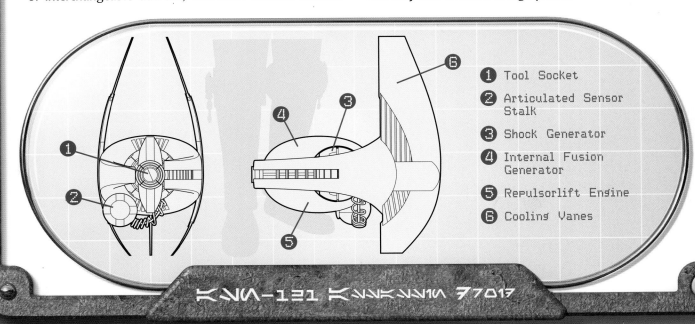

1. Tool Socket
2. Articulated Sensor Stalk
3. Shock Generator
4. Internal Fusion Generator
5. Repulsorlift Engine
6. Cooling Vanes

B1 Battle Droid

Technical Readout

Height: 1.91 meters

Manufacturer:
Baktoid Combat Automata

Primary Function:
Combat

Era of Influence:
Rise of the Empire

Baktoid Combat Automata B1 Battle Droid

Battle droids have become a joke among military personnel. And while it's true that they're thin and frail, and have a host of exploitable weaknesses, those facts are of little comfort if you're on the wrong end of their blaster rifles.

The familiar B1 unit came from the Geonosian factories of Baktoid Combat Automata, and was generally known only by the utilitarian designation *battle droid*. Their first combat deployment came during the Battle of Naboo in 32 B.B.Y., where they overran Naboo's inadequate defenses, terrorized innocent civilians, and dragged the survivors to internment camps.

Baktoid, a member of the Techno Union, was contracted by the Trade Federation to build battle droids as part of a secret military buildup prior to the Naboo invasion. Darth Sidious masterminded the plot, but the Trade Federation paid the bills. The final product bore all the hallmarks of Neimoidian cheapness.

B1 battle droids have poor targeting abilities and can be stopped by a single blaster shot. Their off-the-shelf photoreceptors are unable to magnify distant objects, requiring battle droids to carry macrobinoculars. The first generation of B1s did not even possess individual intelligence matrices, but instead acted as empty receptacles for the guiding signal of a central control computer (CCC).

The CCC powers the droids and transmits motion-capture data recorded from trained organic soldiers to help them perform combat moves. It also monitors the

> ### "Send more droids against the Jedi Knight! Their bodies are making a pile so high that he will never be able to cross it!"
>
> *—Trade Federation lieutenant Sentepeth Findos, desperately trying to stop Kit Fisto during the siege of Cato Neimoidia*

battlefield situation through the droid army's component photoreceptors and broadcasts tactical orders in response to changing fortunes. This approach has some advantages, including the ability to attack in eerily coordinated waves, but it means that the army is only as talented as the CCC's programmer.

In a worst-case scenario, the droid army might lose contact with its control signal. If this occurs, each battle droid shuts down and enters a hibernation mode; in extreme cases, the droid will deactivate the electromagnets that keep its limbs attached. Indeed, the battle droid's electromagnetic joints are its weakest points, and Republic troopers during the Clone Wars learned to aim for neck, shoulder, and torso connectors.

Rank-and-file battle droids are divided into three classes: infantry, pilot, and security, with the latter two designated by blue and maroon markings, respectively. The droids are further subdivided into military ranks, such as lieutenant, sergeant, and corporal.

Commander battle droids are an entirely different class. Easily identified by bright yellow-orange markings, commanders possess intelligence and independence apart from the central control computer. Commanders receive instructions directly from the CCC through high-security channels and relay the orders to their troops. During the Clone Wars, they also acted as liaisons between the droid army and their Separatist masters.

Commander and infantry battle droids wear backpacks

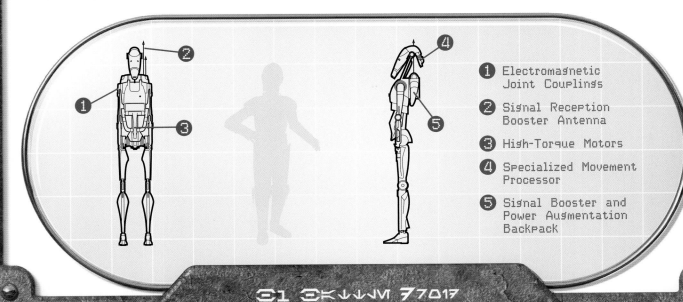

1. Electromagnetic Joint Couplings
2. Signal Reception Booster Antenna
3. High-Torque Motors
4. Specialized Movement Processor
5. Signal Booster and Power Augmentation Backpack

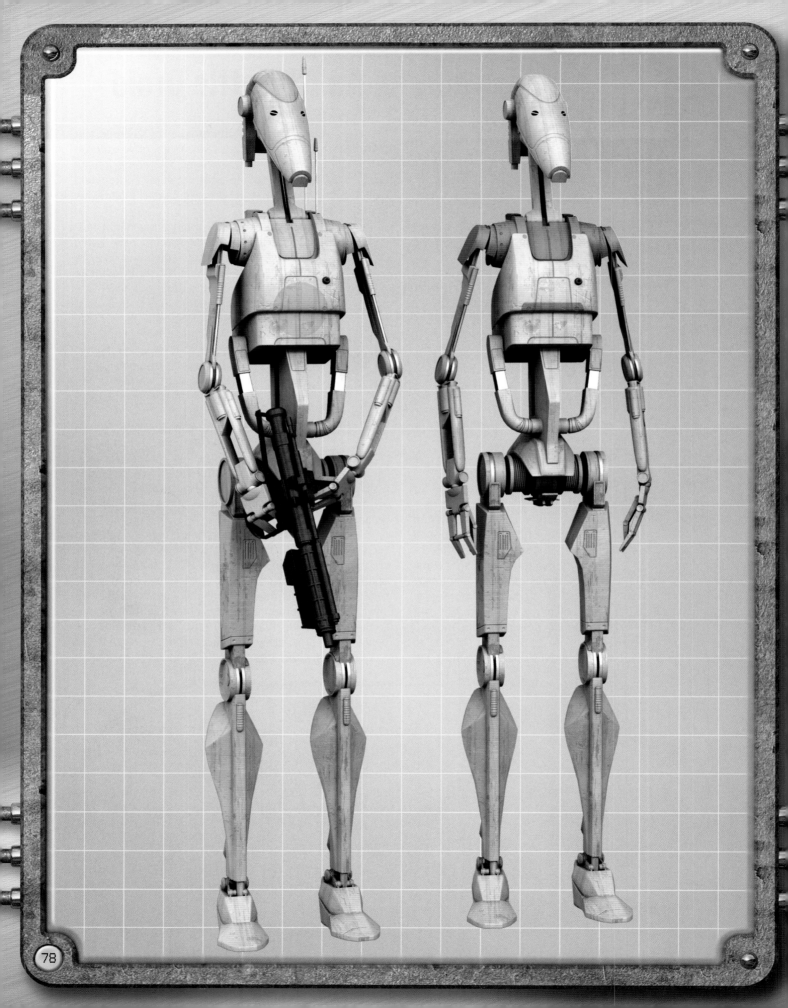

that contain comm units, transmission antennas, and encryption computers, as well as booster power cells that enable them to operate in the field for extended periods without recharge. Security and pilot droids are typically stationed aboard starships and thus require no backpacks.

Because battle droids don't have a standard alphanumeric series designation, their individual names can sometimes seem haphazard. Two battle droids involved in the invasion of Naboo were OOM-9 and 3B3. Names such as these, usually applied by technicians, are shortened versions of the string of identification code unique to each droid. All battle droids also have a large, highly visible number printed on their comlink booster packs to help their owners tell them apart at a glance.

Standard battle droids do not have built-in weapons. They carry large-barreled blaster rifles; specialty units are programmed to operate flamethrowers and missile launchers. Battle droids operated most Trade Federation heavy weapons, including armored assault tanks and STAP airhooks. The droids can fold up into a fetal position for storage, allowing 112 of the droids to fit onto the racks of a multitroop transport.

Unnerving in appearance, battle droids resemble bleached, dried skeletons. Their elongated faces mimic those of their Geonosian builders, but the fearful Neimoidians believed they had been modeled after rotted Neimoidian skulls.

After the Trade Federation's rout at Naboo, Baktoid Combat Automata secretly produced a replacement model designed to solve the problems of the B1 battle droid. These new battle droids, called E-5 units, were based on the baron droid and featured heavier armor and individual intelligence matrices. The E-5s were produced in small numbers as a temporary measure, while the Trade Federation developed the B2 super battle droid. Raith Sienar brought a number of prototype E-5s as bodyguards on his mission to Zonama Sekot.

In the aftermath of Naboo's liberation, the Republic passed laws that barred the use of battle droid armies. The prohibition carried little weight, however, and proved hollow when the Clone Wars exploded in 22 B.B.Y. At the wars' end, a master control signal simultaneously shut down all Separatist droids, and most B1 units became the spoils of the Republic.

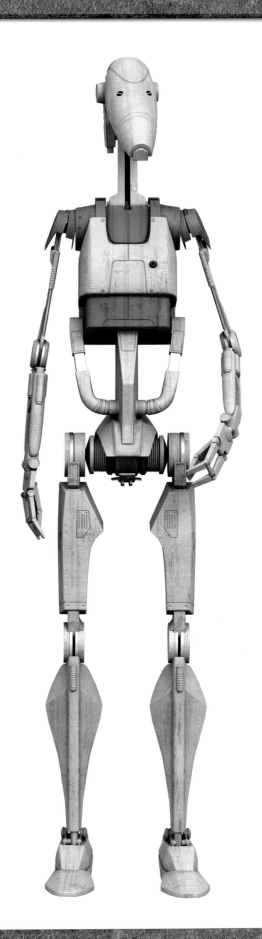

B2 Super Battle Droid

Technical Readout

HEIGHT: 1.91 meters

MANUFACTURER:
Baktoid Combat Automata

PRIMARY FUNCTION:
Combat

ERA OF INFLUENCE:
Rise of the Empire,
New Jedi Order

Baktoid Combat Automata B2 Super Battle Droid

After the Battle of Naboo, the Trade Federation knew it had a problem with its bare-bones battle droids. While the B1 models had easily routed the peaceful citizens of Naboo, they fell like cordwood when matched against the lightsabers of Jedi Knights.

Viceroy Nute Gunray's solution was to commission an infantry unit even stronger than the baron droids already in service. Baktoid Combat Automata's B2 super battle droids came into use over the following years, and saw their first major action at the Battle of Geonosis.

Baktoid's first goal was to preserve as much of the original battle droid design as possible. Super battle droids possess similarly shaped cranial units, as well as many of the same internal components. But the similarities end there. The super battle droid is a brawny brawler, encased in a hardened arcetron armored shell that is resistant to heat, flame, and blasterfire. The droid carries most of its weight in its upper torso, but gyroscopic algorithms in its pelvic servomotors help keep it upright.

A super battle droid wields its own weapon in the form of a rapid-fire dual laser cannon built directly into its right forearm. Blaster rifles are also carried by the droids, despite the fact that their mitten-like hands are incapable of squeezing a trigger. Instead, super battle droids carry special rifles that respond to signal emitters built into the droids' manipulators that spark firing impulses.

> ## "How well do you think one Jedi will hold up against a thousand battle droids?"
>
> —*Count Dooku to Mace Windu, prior to unleashing his super battle droids on Geonosis*

Consequently, super battle droid blasters cannot be picked up and used by organics.

In light of the Naboo fiasco, Baktoid Combat Automata designed the super battle droid to operate independently of a central control computer. The droids are not particularly bright, however, and will often forget about an opponent once their target has moved out of visual range. They are utterly without self-preservation instincts, and will plow right into the thick of a firefight, shooting continuously until either they or their targets are reduced to cinders.

The Trade Federation took delivery of most of Baktoid's super battle droids, but the Techno Union owned the design. During the Clone Wars, super battle droids became the face of the Confederacy of Independent Systems on thousands of worlds, from Ando to Vandos. The end of the wars brought an end to the super battle droid's three standard years of dominance, when a universal control signal shut down all Separatist war machines.

A few entrepreneurs, sitting on warehouses filled with stockpiled B2 droids, subsequently sold them into private hands, where they became enforcers on the staffs of crimelords. During the Yuuzhan Vong invasion, a platoon of super battle droids dubbed the "Orange Panthacs" beat back an occupation force of Yuuzhan Vong firebreathers on Mantessa, earning the unit a special commendation from Galactic Federation of Free Alliances Chief of State Cal Omas.

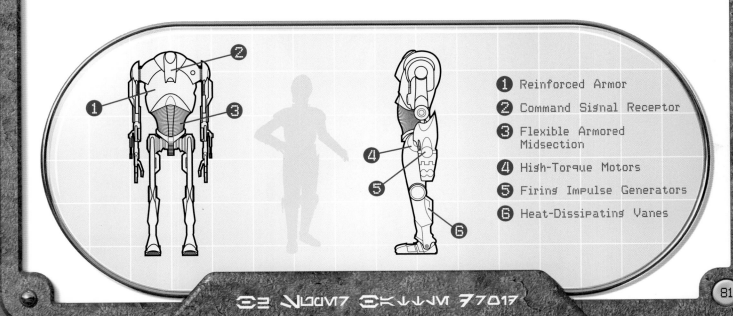

1. Reinforced Armor
2. Command Signal Receptor
3. Flexible Armored Midsection
4. High-Torque Motors
5. Firing Impulse Generators
6. Heat-Dissipating Vanes

B3 Ultra Battle Droid

Technical Readout

Height: 4.0 meters

Manufacturer: Baktoid Combat Automata

Primary Function: Combat

Era of Influence: Rise of the Empire

Baktoid Combat Automata B3 Ultra Battle Droid

Packed with firepower, the ultra battle droid is by far the deadliest soldier manufactured by the Confederacy during the Clone Wars. Fortunately for the Republic, production problems prevented the droids from seeing a full rollout. Instead, they remain a footnote in military annals.

Baktoid Combat Automata's B1 battle droid made its debut at the Battle of Naboo; ten standard years later, the B2 super battle droid fought at the Battle of Geonosis. Baktoid engineers eagerly started plans for a B3, and Techno Union foreman Wat Tambor pitted two internal teams against each other for the privilege of creating the design. The Metalorn team, with Wat Tambor's backing, developed the cortosis battle droid. The team on Foundry engineered a heavily armored giant known as the Avatar-7. It was this design that ultimately received the blessing of General Grievous. Awarded the coveted *B3* designation—and given the name *ultra battle droid*—it entered production as a front-line combat unit.

The new ultra battle droid was huge and expensive. Baktoid entertained no illusions about the droid being deployed in numberless hordes, like the B1 and B2, but the company hoped to add them selectively as heavy hitters to the arsenal of every Separatist commander.

The ultra battle droid looks similar to the super battle droid, except for an obvious difference in scale. Other departures from the B2 design include four arms, two of them identical to those used on the super battle droid, and the other two scaled up in proportion to match the ultra battle droid's hulking frame.

An arsenal of built-in weapons gives the ultra battle droid its bite. Two smaller arms have retractable rapid-fire blaster cannons in their forearms. The right primary arm is equipped with a tight-spray flamethrower, while the left sports a wide-spray plasma cannon. Built into the left shoulder is a rocket launcher, armed with semi-sentient brilliant missiles that can track their targets.

But perhaps the ultra battle droid's best gadget is its experimental density projector. This device generates a powerful tractor field that essentially increases the droid's weight twentyfold. When using the density projector, the ultra battle droid can glue itself in place, making it nearly impossible to dislodge or topple. By selectively switching the projector on and off, the ultra battle droid can crush tanks under its feet and plow through enemy fortifications.

Despite its "wow" factor, the density projector crippled the droid's rollout. Several first-generation units encountered glitches with their projectors in the middle of combat, rendering them immobile and therefore easy targets for fixed-position turbolasers. By the time Baktoid fixed the problem, the Clone Wars were nearly over.

Ultra battle droids fought with notoriety during the Outer Rim Sieges, but virtually disappeared after the wars' end. Several hundred units later saw use inside the urban-warfare training zone on the Imperial Academy world of Carida.

> ## *"This* is new."
>
> *—Jedi Master Mace Windu, glimpsing his first ultra battle droid during the Battle of Iktotch*

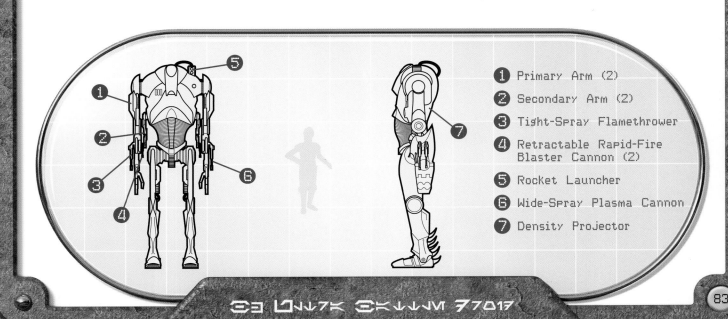

1. Primary Arm (2)
2. Secondary Arm (2)
3. Tight-Spray Flamethrower
4. Retractable Rapid-Fire Blaster Cannon (2)
5. Rocket Launcher
6. Wide-Spray Plasma Cannon
7. Density Projector

Baron Droid

Technical Readout

Height: 2.4 meters

Manufacturer:
Baktoid Combat Automata

Primary Function:
Combat

Era of Influence:
Rise of the Empire,
New Republic

Baktoid Combat Automata E4 Baron Droid

The Trade Federation employed a host of terrifying droids to conquer the city of Theed during the Battle of Naboo. The most pervasive were B1 battle droids, but Baktoid Combat Automata also fielded a small number of experimental heavy units dubbed "baron droids."

Designed by Baktoid as an all-purpose security unit, the E4 baron droid is a hulking automaton with heavy armor and incredible strength. At the time of its introduction, it was one of the most alert security units available. The baron droid's thick torso houses motion, heat, energy, and sonic detectors. Visual stimuli are processed through the droid's single photoreceptor, which also serves as the baron droid's primary targeting mechanism and can produce a bright spotlight for identifying, tracking, or temporarily blinding its targets. As soon as the baron droid has a victim in its sights, blazing fire erupts from its twin high-energy blasters.

Although heavily armored and far tougher than the run-of-the-mill battle droid, the baron droid lacks personal shields. It can be disabled by multiple hits from a blaster rifle or a well-aimed lightsaber slash. Despite its plodding gait, the baron droid can attack ceaselessly, and can function for extended periods without a direct connection to a central control computer.

Baron droids came into service just prior to the Naboo invasion, during the period when the Trade Federation secretly built up its droid armies on the orders of Darth Sidious. Viceroy Nute Gunray, embroiled in a vendetta against the Commerce Guild, planned to establish the baron droids as his personal assassin corps. The Naboo invasion forced the droids into service before Gunray could realize his dream.

Obi-Wan Kenobi first encountered baron droids on Coruscant, during his investigation into the Black Heth criminal syndicate. He ran into more of the droids on Naboo, where the local resistance had been fighting them in the swamps and the tunnels beneath Theed. Naboo's fighters soon learned to avoid baron droids by watching the darkness for their signature spotlights.

Most of the Trade Federation's baron droids became combat casualties during the Battle of Naboo. Baktoid continued to produce the model throughout the Clone Wars, but the baron droid's advantages proved slight when compared to the new and far superior super battle droid.

Despite their age, baron droids are still in use by planetary militias and private security forces. On Arzid, a squad of baron droids overthrew the administrators of the only settlement in 16 A.B.Y. They now rule the planet through the law of the blaster.

> **"Excellent. Send two more baron droids to kill Shu Mai, and order a dozen to work as my bodyguards. At last we are getting results."**
>
> *—Trade Federation viceroy Nute Gunray*

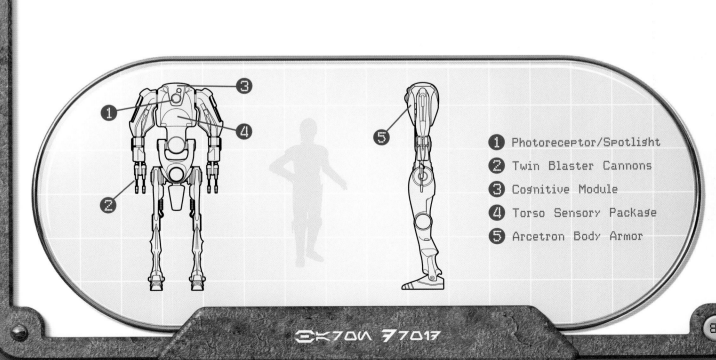

1. Photoreceptor/Spotlight
2. Twin Blaster Cannons
3. Cognitive Module
4. Torso Sensory Package
5. Arcetron Body Armor

Basilisk War Droid

Technical Readout

HEIGHT: 2.98 meters

MANUFACTURER:
Civilization of the Basilisk

PRIMARY FUNCTION:
Combat

ERA OF INFLUENCE:
Old Republic

Mandalorian Army Basilisk Combat Mount

The basilisk war droid is a nightmare creation, a war chariot that left planets torn and bleeding during the Great Sith War and the Mandalorian Wars four thousand standard years before the New Republic. The basilisk still inspires awe, even though the deactivated specimens are seen only behind transparisteel barriers in museum displays.

The basilisk war droid looks like a living thing: a hard-shelled beetle or an armored Zalorian rock-lion. In motion, however, it behaves more like a drop ship. The Mandalorians liked to plunge from orbit straight down to a planet's surface, using the breakneck rate of descent to confound the autotargeters of their opponents' cannons. Wearing vacuum-sealed battle armor, Mandalorians had no difficulty operating their mounts in deep space.

Basilisks are both beasts and machines. The Mandalorians did not build them, but looted them from the poisoned Basilikian homeworld. The self-aware alien constructs became loyal companions to the Mandalorians, and their closest allies in battle.

The intelligence level of a war droid was only slightly higher than that of a domesticated animal, and Mandalorian warriors developed deeply empathic relationships with their mounts. They fed them energy-rich locap plasma mixed with unrefined narcolethe. In battle the basilisks became preternaturally quick extensions of their riders' bodies. When a basilisk fell in battle, the Mandalorians gave it the honors of a warrior's funeral before sending it into the heart of a star.

A basilisk war droid boasted a number of exotic weapons, including a nose cluster of shockwave generator rods that could fire a hull-puncturing plasma burst. Pulse-wave cannons and shatter-missile launch tubes adorned the hulls of many droids, sometimes hidden behind armored scales. The droid's heavy front claws, used as landing struts, could also flatten obstacles or rip open the flesh of enemies. Mandalorian riders often strapped weapons to the outside of their mounts, decorating the droids with the menacing glint of axes, swords, and flash-pistols.

No two war droids were exactly the same. The most common configuration of basil-isk, the open-combat model, darkened the skies with their numbers during planetary assaults. Other, less common configurations included the wasp-shaped stealth model and the two-seated heavy bomber. Open-combat models could also deliver explosives themselves, by towing a volatile atomic compression bomb between two droids and catapulting it into a capital ship or the hull of an orbital station.

The age of Mandalorian dominance ended when the Jedi known as Revan defeated the ruling Mandalore on Malachor V in 3961 B.B.Y. The shamed Mandalorians were forced to destroy their basilisk droids under the eyes of Revan, and entered a new era as the embittered Mandalorian Mercs.

> **"The doors opened in front of me and the air was sucked out of the drop bay. When the magnetic locks disengaged on my droid, I plunged toward the battle that waited below."**
>
> —*Mandalorian warrior Canderous Ordo*

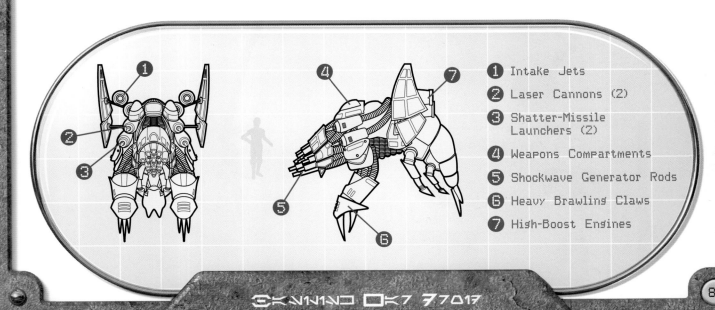

1. Intake Jets
2. Laser Cannons (2)
3. Shatter-Missile Launchers (2)
4. Weapons Compartments
5. Shockwave Generator Rods
6. Heavy Brawling Claws
7. High-Boost Engines

BUZZ DROID

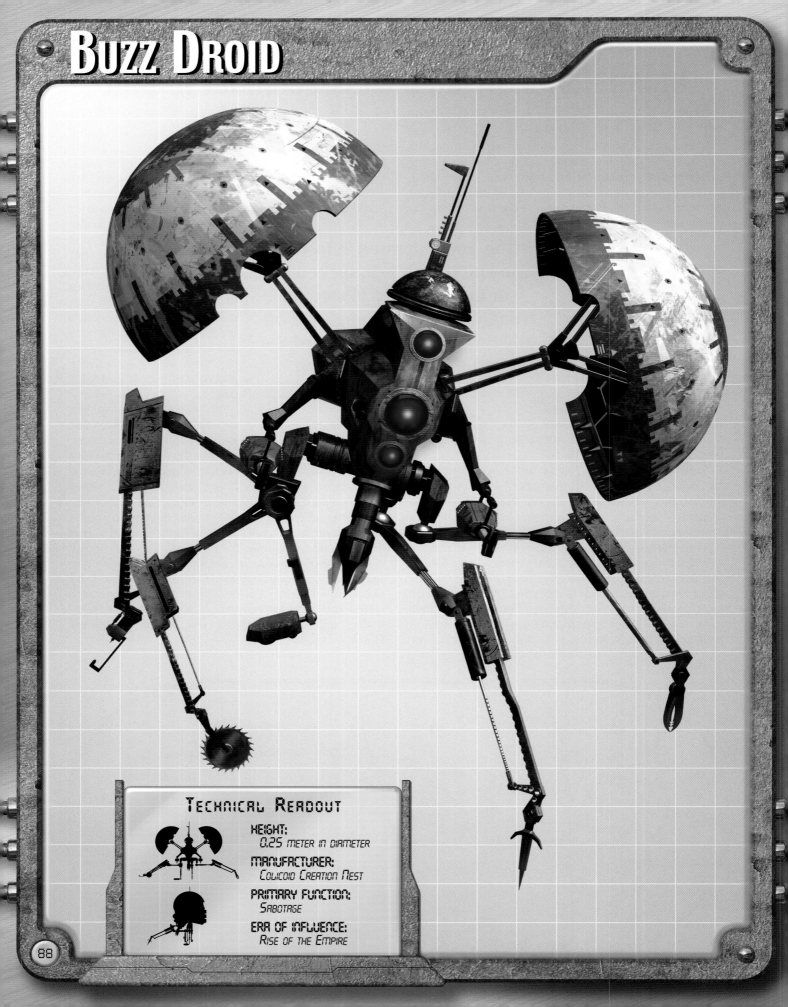

TECHNICAL READOUT

HEIGHT:
0.25 meter in diameter

MANUFACTURER:
Colicoid Creation Nest

PRIMARY FUNCTION:
Sabotage

ERA OF INFLUENCE:
Rise of the Empire

Colicoid Creation Nest Pistoeka Sabotage Droid

Sabotage is a buzz droid's primary mission, making it one of the few military models that doesn't mark its success in body counts. But that doesn't make the buzz droid any less dangerous—just ask a pilot stranded inside a dead starship as it leaks atmosphere into the cold vacuum outside.

Pistoeka buzz droids are a product of the Colicoid Creation Nest. The cannibalistic Colicoids, who are also responsible for the droideka and trifighter, come from a planet crawling with insects (including themselves). The buzz droid is based on the pisto, a pest eaten in Colla IV's tropical regions. When the Confederacy of Independent Systems demanded increased droid output from Colla IV during the Clone Wars, the Colicoids took their existing repair robots and modified them to become agents of sabotage.

Legs folded, a buzz droid can seal itself inside a spherical shell less than a quarter of a meter in diameter. These melon-size balls are then loaded into the cylinder of a discord missile, which is typically carried by a vulture fighter (in space) or a droid gunship (in atmosphere). Discord missiles explode in front of their targets, spreading buzz droids into their enemies' flight paths.

Their outer shell is made of a heat-dissipating material that allows it to penetrate most particle shields. Using a quartet of maneuvering thrusters to zip in close, a buzz droid splits open its protective casing and secures itself to the ship's hull with a magna-pod limb.

> ## "Artoo, hit the buzz droid's center eye!"
>
> *—Obi-Wan Kenobi, during the Battle of Coruscant*

A flock of buzz droids, each carrying an electronic database of common starship schematics, can leave a ship dead and drifting in a matter of seconds. The default array of buzz droid weaponry includes a prying hook, a circular saw, a plasma-cutting torch, a picket appendage, a gripping pincer, and a drill head. When this last arm bores a hole in a ship's hull, an extendable computer probe can then splice itself into the ship's internal wiring.

From that point, it's easy for the buzz droid to override the onboard systems and shut down weapons, engines, or life support. It can even fly the ship from its exterior perch.

The droid perceives its surroundings through three photoreceptors that incorporate magnification lenses, spectrum filters, and X-ray sensors. A hit to its central eye can knock a buzz droid offline.

Buzz droids saw their first action relatively late in the Clone Wars. Consequently, the Colicoids were left with millions of unwanted units at the conflict's end. Some found use on vast scrap yards, such as those of Ronyards and Junction, helping their owners strip rusted hulks for usable parts.

Elsewhere, buzz droids became popular on the gladiatorial circuit. Aficionados of the sport recall fondly the time a buzz droid took down a mighty Mark X executioner with the skillful application of a laser scalpel.

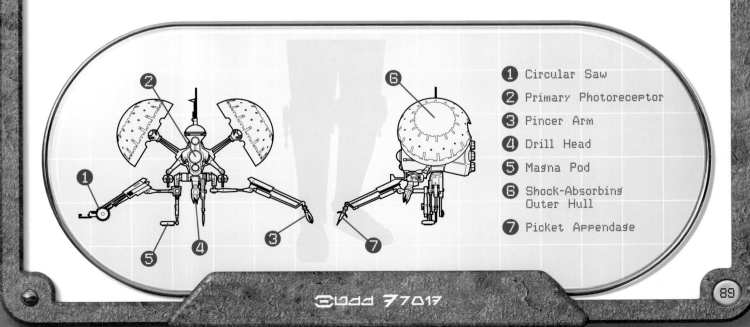

1. Circular Saw
2. Primary Photoreceptor
3. Pincer Arm
4. Drill Head
5. Magna Pod
6. Shock-Absorbing Outer Hull
7. Picket Appendage

Chameleon Droid

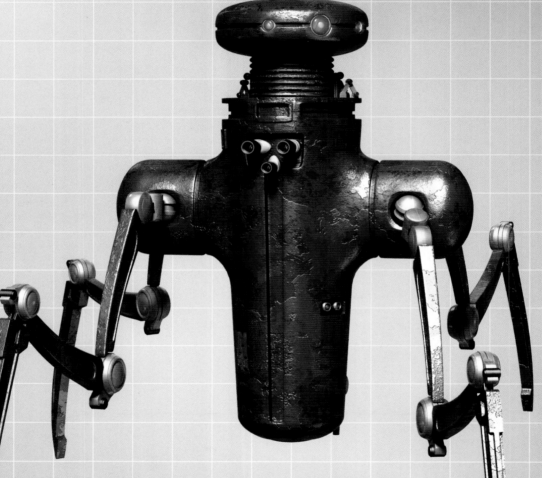

Technical Readout

HEIGHT: 2.0 meters

MANUFACTURER:
Arakyd Industries

PRIMARY FUNCTIONS:
Espionage, sabotage

ERA OF INFLUENCE:
Rise of the Empire

Commerce Guild Modified Arakyd Spelunker

The chameleon droid joined the Separatist army shortly after the first shots were fired in the Clone Wars. In a case of turning shovels into swords, the Commerce Guild took the benign Arakyd Spelunker and modified it into an invisible killer.

The greedy Commerce Guild had its fingers in millions of mining operations across the galaxy, and constantly hungered for new mineral strikes. During the decade leading up to the Clone Wars, Commerce Guild president Shu Mai purchased hundreds of thousands of Arakyd Spelunkers for her exploration division. The Spelunkers rode hyperspace pods into unexplored territory, where they sniffed out the presence of mineral veins on planetoids and transmitted their findings back to the Commerce Guild. Spelunkers could even use blasting charges, kept in internal storage bays, to expose the ore vein prior to the arrival of a heavy digging crew.

It didn't take long for Shu Mai to realize her Spelunkers would make excellent minelayers. With an array of modifications that patently violated the Arakyd warranty, the Spelunker emerged as a spy and sabotage unit. Its illusory camouflage screen gave it the name *chameleon droid.*

Although it seems as if a chameleon droid can become invisible, the effect is actually a trick achieved through a hologrammic array. By making a 360-degree scan of its surroundings and calculating the positions of observers, the droid can project a screen that shows the terrain immediately behind it. This technique, nearly foolproof under the right conditions, falls apart when the observer's viewing angle is shifted. Also, unlike true cloaking devices, the hologrammic shrouds leave chameleon droids detectible to sensor arrays.

A chameleon droid comes equipped with three laser cannons, installed in mountings that once housed mineral sensors. Its cylindrical body, unchanged since its days as a Spelunker, holds adhesive mines that are released one at a time through a ventral hatch. The chameleon droid's four pincer legs are capable of generating traction fields that enable it to walk on walls and ceilings. Assisting in this capacity is a small repulsorlift unit that acts as anti-ballast, reducing the chameleon droid's overall body weight.

Chameleon droids saw their first widespread use on frozen Ilum. They mined the sacred crystal caverns where Jedi build lightsabers during their transitions to Jedi Knighthood. The Jedi Luminara Unduli and Bariss Offee destroyed scores of chameleon droids, but Master Yoda finished the job by burying the saboteurs in an avalanche.

As minelayers, chameleon droids served the Separatists for the remainder of the Clone Wars. The Republic preferred the cheap and expendable LIN demolitionmechs for the same purpose. Demolitionmechs thus became the minelayers of choice following the rise of the Empire.

> **"Come out, come out, sly droids. To my eyes, hidden you are not."**
>
> —*Jedi Master Yoda, battling chameleon droids on Ilum*

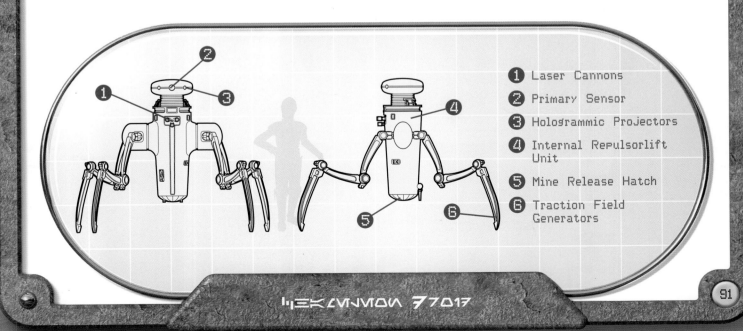

1. Laser Cannons
2. Primary Sensor
3. Hologrammic Projectors
4. Internal Repulsorlift Unit
5. Mine Release Hatch
6. Traction Field Generators

Colicoid Annihilator Droid

Technical Readout

HEIGHT: 3.5 meters

MANUFACTURER:
Colicoid Creation Nest

PRIMARY FUNCTION:
Combat

ERA OF INFLUENCE:
Rise of the Empire

Colicoid Creation Nest Annihilator Droid

The cannibalistic Colicoids enjoy an advanced technological society, yet they're one of the most hostile species in the galaxy. Because so few dare to visit their spawnworld of Colla IV, no one realized that the builders of the droideka had an even deadlier model guarding their home turf.

A Scorpenek annihilator droid moves on four pointed limbs. It carries itself in the menacing stance of a mantis, with its weapons arms cocked back, ready to strike. Two rapid-fire, high-intensity laser cannons on each arm deliver blistering barrages that can crack the hulls of enemy tanks.

A combination particle–energy shield surrounds the droid in a hazy bubble, featuring a polarization signature so that the annihilator can fire *out*. Droidekas, which use similar shields, often take up position inside the bubble of their "big brother" for a second line of protection. A crimson photoreceptor picks up targets on infrared wavelengths, while composite radiation sensors mimic the sensory organs of the Colicoids.

Late in the Clone Wars, the Republic launched a strike on the Colicoid Creation Nest, the corporation responsible for building the Separatists' droidekas and tri-fighters. While assault ships shelled Colla IV's surface with a turbolaser bombardment, four platoons of troopers advanced on the shielded factory. When the clones reached the innermost wall, an annihilator droid rose up and shredded a duracrete barrier with its laser cannons, offering the clones no cover and killing most of the landing force within minutes. The surviving clones retreated.

Colicoid annihilators were prohibitively expensive to produce in mass quantities—fewer than one hundred existed on all of Colla IV, with most stationed around strategic or political resources. Knowing their enemies would return, the Colicoids arranged for a Separatist naval task force to erect an orbital screen, while freighters left Colla IV and shipped the annihilator droids to the front lines. An annihilator could turn a dozen AT-TEs into smoking husks. Not surprisingly, the droids turned the tide at Palanhi and Formos to score Separatist victories.

The Republic had further reason to curse the machines. During the Outer Rim Sieges, Republic commanders were forced to commit unacceptable numbers of heavy units in order to take down a single annihilator.

At the end of the Clone Wars, a command signal triggered the simultaneous deactivation of all Separatist droid forces. Emperor Palpatine arranged for the remaining annihilators to be taken in by the Imperial Department of Military Research. Many found their way to Palpatine's private citadel on the Deep Core world of Byss.

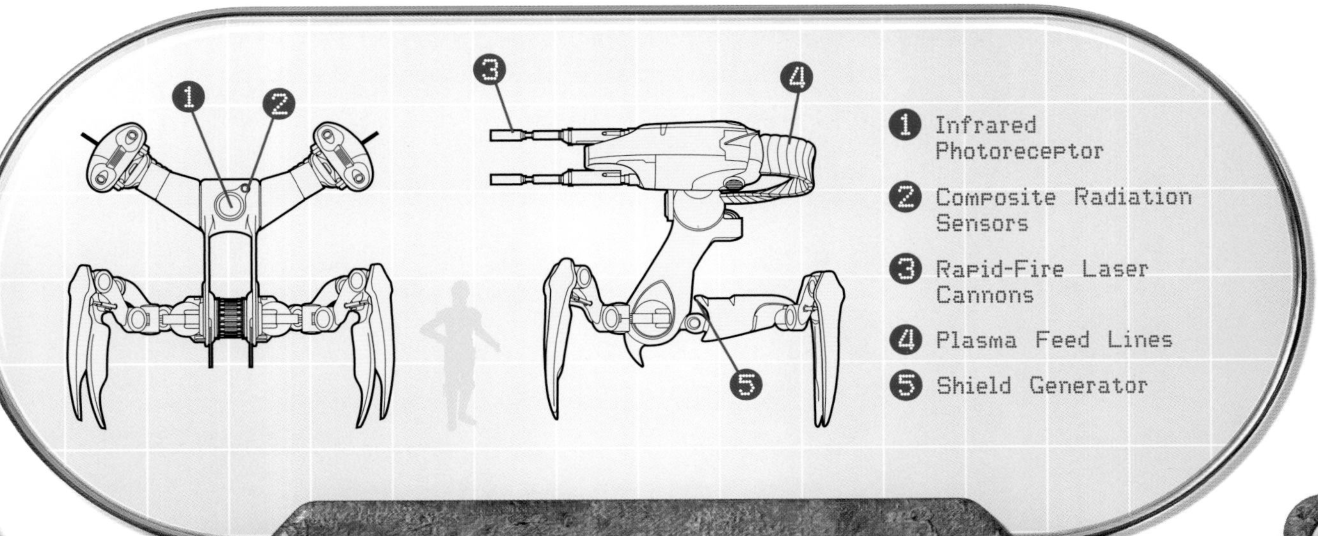

> **"We don't know what it was, sir, but it took out three platoons. We can't let the Colicoids get these things offplanet."**
>
> —*ARC trooper Stec, after a failed strike at Colla IV*

1. Infrared Photoreceptor
2. Composite Radiation Sensors
3. Rapid-Fire Laser Cannons
4. Plasma Feed Lines
5. Shield Generator

CORTOSIS BATTLE DROID

TECHNICAL READOUT

HEIGHT: *1.9 meters*

MANUFACTURER:
Baktoid Combat Automata

PRIMARY FUNCTION:
Combat

ERA OF INFLUENCE:
Rise of the Empire

Baktoid Combat Automata C-B3 Cortosis Battle Droid

Cortosis battle droids were a frightening variant on Baktoid Combat Automata's super battle droids—made even more dangerous thanks to their lightsaber-resistant armor. The threat they posed to the Jedi came to a sudden end, however, when Anakin Skywalker destroyed their manufacturing facility.

Cortosis is an extremely rare ore capable of resisting the cut of a lightsaber blade (similar to the equally rare phrik metal). One variety of cortosis shorts out a lightsaber blade when the energy and the mineral interact. The more common variety, which is malleable and can be shaped into armor, forms an interlocking bond that cannot easily be severed by lightsaber energy.

After the Battle of Geonosis, Techno Union foreman Wat Tambor began experiments with raw cortosis and cortosis artifacts, such as the arm shields worn by Yinchorri warriors. A factory on the mechworld of Metalorn became the nerve center for Tambor's research. As soon as his engineers had ironed out the technical problems, Tambor ordered the Metalorn facility to undergo a complete retooling for the delicate and expensive job of stamping cortosis armor.

Each cortosis battle droid produced at the Metalorn factory had a covering of black body armor, clamped to the droid's frame in formfitting plates. The cortosis battle droid shared the same intelligence matrix as the super battle droid, and had arms that ended in high-intensity laser cannons.

> **"The raid on the Republic capital succeeded. My cortosis droids are invincible, and my factories unassailable!"**
>
> *—Wat Tambor, following the Confederacy's first attack on Coruscant*

Wat Tambor convinced Count Dooku to mount a raid on Coruscant using the new droids. Ten months after the start of the Clone Wars—and more than two years before General Grievous would do the same—Dooku invaded Coruscant with an army of cortosis droids and several of his dark side minions. The droids laid waste to the city's underlevels and broke into the Jedi Temple, nearly allowing Dooku to destroy the Jedi archives.

Eventually, the Separatists were forced to withdraw, but the cortosis droids had performed extremely well against Jedi opponents. So well, in fact, that Darth Sidious considered the droids a destabilizing factor in the war that he was carefully orchestrating. In his role as Chancellor Palpatine, Sidious arranged for information about Wat Tambor's cortosis supply line to come into the Republic's possession. The Jedi Council dispatched Anakin Skywalker to uncover the droid factory and destroy it.

While carving his way through the Metalorn facility, Anakin discovered the best way to defeat a cortosis battle droid. By executing a very precise overhead slash with a lightsaber, a Jedi could target the narrow gap between the droid's left and right breastplates and slice its torso in half.

Anakin destroyed the Metalorn plant and brought Wat Tambor back to Coruscant as a prisoner of war. Palpatine would later arrange for Tambor's escape, but the Techno Union produced no further cortosis droids for the remainder of the Clone Wars.

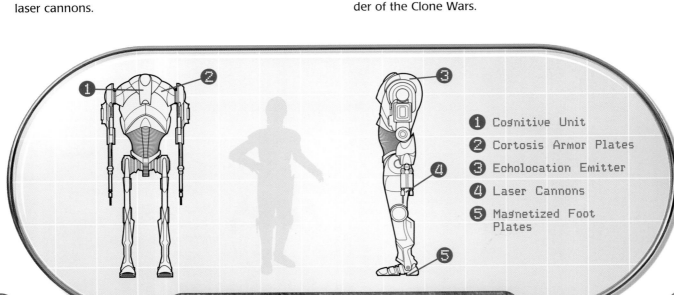

1. Cognitive Unit
2. Cortosis Armor Plates
3. Echolocation Emitter
4. Laser Cannons
5. Magnetized Foot Plates

CRAB DROID

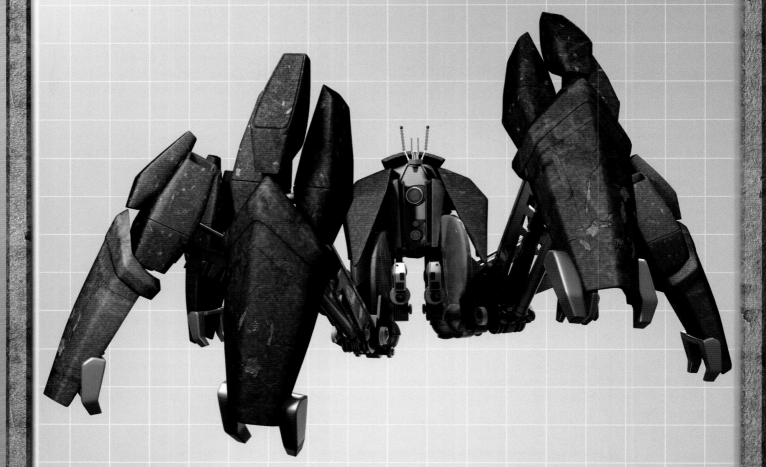

Techno Union LM-432 Crab Droid

The Separatists used droids to fill every battlefield niche, from solitary soldiers to gigantic engines of war. The LM-432 crab droid, also known as the "Muckracker," was one of the last heavy hitters to see action as the Clone Wars neared conclusion.

The crab droid came about through the environmental failures of the Commerce Guild's spider droid, which proved unreliable at navigating swampy or arctic environments. The various corporate constituencies of the Confederacy of Independent Systems pooled their resources to design the LM-432. Though the droid bore the fingerprints of everyone from the Trade Federation to the Hyper-Communications Cartel, the Techno Union ultimately manufactured the finished product.

Scaleable factory techniques allowed the Techno Union to pump out eight sizes of crab droid, ranging from scurrier-size models used for espionage to gargantuan hulks equipped to batter down enemy fortifications. Most crab droids that fought in the Clone Wars belonged to the midsize heavy-infantry series.

Flexibility was also a key consideration for weapons and gear. The first batch of crab droids, deployed during the Second Battle of Jabiim, came equipped with insulated vacuum-pump systems inside their forward pincers. These assemblies of tubing and spray nozzles could suck up mud and squirt it out again, simultaneously clearing a path and clogging the optical sensors of enemies. This

> ### "Crab droids have a subpar targeting percentage, but deliver a profit of 48,000 credits per unit. They might not win the war, but they could save the Techno Union's fiscal quarter."
>
> *—From the Techno Union's LM-432 risk-assessment report*

earned the crab droid the nickname of Muckracker, though future units lacked the vacuum feature. Instead, those models boasted bubble wort projectors, a rare Gungan technology that could trap targets inside temporary energy spheres.

All crab droids possess six armored limbs for easy purchase when clambering over rocky terrain. Duranium teeth at the tips of the forward limbs, coupled with gripping prongs at the "elbow" joints, enable the crab droid to chip into solid rock and scale near-vertical inclines. Three glowing red circles—a sensor bulb, a targeting range finder, and an auxiliary photoreceptor—dominate the crab droid's face, while communications antennas and sensor stalks keep the LM-432 in constant contact with its battlefield supervisor. The crab droid also has two blaster cannons slung beneath its body.

Clone troopers who faced LM-432s in battle discovered that the droids have poor targeting systems. By exploiting blind spots, troopers could get past the forward pincers and unload blaster rounds into a weak point just behind the head.

At the end of the Clone Wars, the Republic seized tens of thousands of crab droids from a Techno Union factory on Tar Morden. These units eventually saw use in live-fire stormtrooper training exercises on Carida. After the Battle of Endor, Caridan engineers drew upon their experience with crab droids in developing the MT-AT "spider walker."

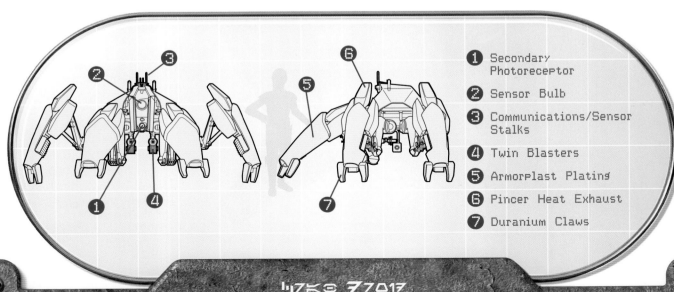

1. Secondary Photoreceptor
2. Sensor Bulb
3. Communications/Sensor Stalks
4. Twin Blasters
5. Armorplast Plating
6. Pincer Heat Exhaust
7. Duranium Claws

DARK TROOPER

TECHNICAL READOUT

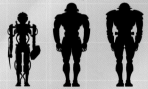

HEIGHT: 2.56 meters (Phase One); 2.82 meters (Phases Two and Three)

MANUFACTURER: Imperial Department of Military Research

PRIMARY FUNCTION: Combat

ERA OF INFLUENCE: Rebellion

Imperial Department of Military Research Phases One–Three Dark Trooper

The Dark Trooper project represented the culmination of the Empire's quest to build the ultimate Imperial battle droid. Like the L8-L9 and Z-X3 before it, the Dark Trooper *looks* like a stormtrooper. Nevertheless, it couldn't replace the stormtrooper in the minds of officers, who considered battle droids to be Clone Wars relics.

General Rom Mohc had previously collaborated with TaggeCo on the Z-X3 droid trooper. This time he brought his designs directly to the Imperial Department of Military Research, bypassing TaggeCo entirely. The Emperor expressed interest in the project. Consequently, several dozen of Mohc's mechanical men went from prototype to finished version immediately after the Battle of Yavin.

To house his assault force and construct replacement units, General Mohc received the *Arc Hammer:* a titanic space-going construction facility built at the starship yards of Kuat. Mohc soon gave his Dark Troopers their first combat test—a brutal, one-sided massacre at a Rebel base on Talay. Darth Vader, impressed, ordered Mohc to continue with production.

Dark Troopers had three distinct stages, each one suitable for armed conflict. The Phase One, little more than a metal skeleton, was primitive but relentless. Its structural frame, forearm shield, and razor-edged carving blade were cast from phrik, a durable alloy resistant to lightsaber strikes and found primarily on the moons of the Gromas system.

> **"In light of the *Arc Hammer* fiasco, Emperor Palpatine is withdrawing all funding for the development of Imperial battle droids. I *told* you it would never work."**
>
> *—Grand Vizier Sate Pestage, in a communication to the Imperial Department of Military Research*

Phase Two Dark Troopers became the standard combat units. Their phrik body shells made them tougher than the Phase One, while their repulsorlift engines and flight jets enabled them to strike from the air. Each Phase Two carried a devastating assault cannon that fired plasma shells and long-range explosive rockets.

The Phase Three was conceived as the ultimate Dark Trooper. Only a single unit was known to exist aboard the *Arc Hammer;* it appears likely that this unit was a finished prototype for a planned but uncompleted line. Even more massive than the Phase Two, this unstoppable behemoth sported a nasty cluster of firing tubes connected to a seemingly endless supply of seeker missiles. These rockets, while slow, homed in on a target's heat signature and packed enough detonite to obliterate the strongest personal shielding. The Phase Three prototype was designed to operate independently, but could also be worn by a human operator as an exosuit.

Rebel agent Kyle Katarn fought against Mohc's project, dismantling several Dark Troopers single-handedly. Katarn's counterattack resulted in the destruction of the *Arc Hammer,* which cost the Empire billions of credits and marked the death of the Dark Trooper project. Emperor Palpatine, still smarting from the loss of the Death Star, was so infuriated by this setback that he refused to approve funding for a new construction facility.

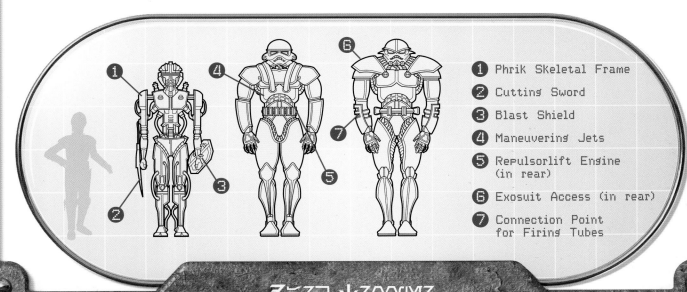

1. Phrik Skeletal Frame
2. Cutting Sword
3. Blast Shield
4. Maneuvering Jets
5. Repulsorlift Engine (in rear)
6. Exosuit Access (in rear)
7. Connection Point for Firing Tubes

HEIGHT: 1.83 meters

MANUFACTURER: Colicoid Creation Nest

PRIMARY FUNCTION: Combat

ERA OF INFLUENCE: Rise of the Empire

Colicoid Creation Nest P-Series Destroyer Droid

Droidekas have been called the deadliest things in the galaxy . . . but anyone who says that has obviously never met a Colicoid.

Nor would anyone *want* to meet a Colicoid, since the two-meter-tall insects are bloodthirsty cannibals. Prior to the Battle of Naboo, however, Nute Gunray of the Trade Federation met with the Colicoid Sovereign Nest and bartered fifty bargeloads of exotic flesh in exchange for an exclusive droideka contract.

Gunray wanted the heavy-hitting droidekas to support his comparatively weak battle droids. The deployment of droidekas at the Battle of Naboo marked the first widespread use of the robotic killers, though small batches of them had previously trickled out from Colla IV and triggered several public atrocities.

The name *droideka* originates with the Colicoids, who combined the Basic word *droid* with the Colicoid suffix *-eka*, meaning "hireling" or "drone." Most citizens of the galaxy simply call them destroyer droids, for wanton destruction is their stock in trade.

A droideka has two double-barreled blaster cannons where its arms should be, and both can spit out rapid-fire crimson energy powerful enough to chew enemies to pieces. The cannons can also fire high-intensity blasts, at a slower rate, that are capable of exploding light vehicles. Droidekas possess their own deflector shields, making the droids virtually immune to small-arms fire. The shields, hazy blue and spherical, are polarized so that the droideka's own bolts penetrate outward while return fire splashes uselessly against the shield's periphery.

In its attack stance, a droideka perches atop three pointed legs that provide stability but which are too short to generate much speed. For rapid deployment, droidekas curl up into a different configuration known as the "wheel mode." This rolling method of locomotion is second nature to Colicoids, who integrated their natural movements into their droids. To initiate the rolls, droidekas pulse a string of internal microrepulsors in sequence. To stop, they reverse the direction of the microrepulsor chain.

Droidekas' thin heads are actually orderly sensor packages. They contain fine-vibration monitors and specialized radiation detectors, enabling the droids to pursue quarry using nonvisual methods. At the crux of the body is a mini-reactor to power the high-drain deflector shield and blaster cannons. The entire body is cast from heavy armored bronzium.

Nute Gunray was savvy enough not to completely trust the Colicoids. For this reason (and also to knock down the extravagant price), he insisted that his droidekas be manufactured without individual intelligence matrices. Trade Federation droidekas, like battle droids, were powered and controlled by a central control computer and would shut down in the absence of their guiding signal. Standard droidekas from Colla IV are self-aware and twice as deadly.

> ## "We have them on the run, sir . . . they're no match for droidekas."
>
> *—Trade Federation lieutenant Rune Haako, during the blockade of Naboo*

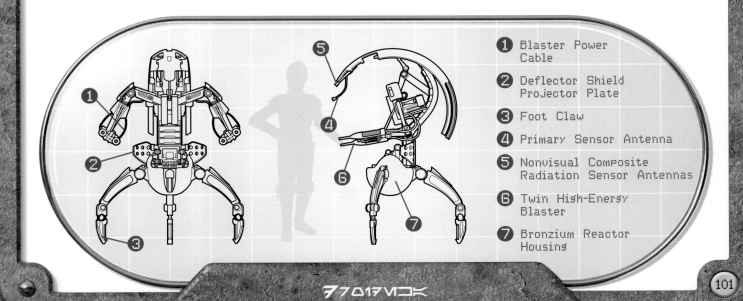

1. Blaster Power Cable
2. Deflector Shield Projector Plate
3. Foot Claw
4. Primary Sensor Antenna
5. Nonvisual Composite Radiation Sensor Antennas
6. Twin High-Energy Blaster
7. Bronzium Reactor Housing

Dwarf Spider Droid

Technical Readout

HEIGHT: 1.98 METERS
(without antenna)

MANUFACTURER:
Commerce Guild

PRIMARY FUNCTION:
Combat

ERA OF INFLUENCE:
Rise of the Empire,
Rebellion, New Republic

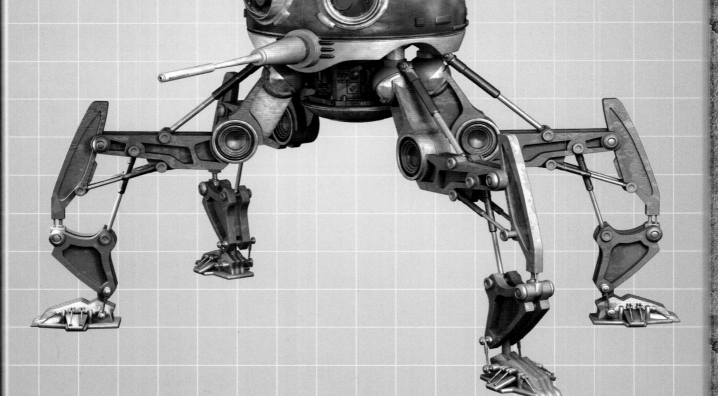

Commerce Guild DSD1 Dwarf Spider Droid

Dwarf spider droids have served many masters. They began as corporate enforcers, evolved into war machines for the Separatist army, and served the Empire as mechanical attack dogs for the stormtrooper corps.

The Commerce Guild, responsible for the production of raw materials in the years prior to the Clone Wars, constructed the first dwarf spider droids. The guild controlled mines on thousands of worlds, but mining ventures that had been "persuaded" to join weren't always willing to pay their monthly dues. Dwarf spider droids, which preceded the development of the much larger homing spider droids, owe their small size to the necessity of operating inside of cramped mining tunnels.

Dwarf spider droids move on four jointed limbs, enabling them to adjust their height to obtain a better elevation for their sole laser cannon. The gun is capable of laying down a rapid-fire antipersonnel spray as well as slow high-intensity blasts designed to rupture light vehicles. Two variants on the dwarf spider droid exist, distinguishable by the size of the cannon.

The droid's huge infrared photoreceptors and echolocation emitters allow it to function in total darkness. Dwarf spider droids can operate underwater—a feature designed to account for flooded tunnels—but they cannot float. They do not require the guidance of a central control computer. Their individual intelligence

> **"You've fought against it, you know its weaknesses, and more importantly, you know what a killer it can be. Men, meet the newest addition to the stormtrooper corps."**
>
> —*Stormtrooper commander TK-342, prior to the pacification of Ghorman*

matrices are on par with the intelligence of a very bright domesticated animal. Dwarf spider droids are loyal to their creators, but sometimes balk at being sent into danger zones.

Commerce Guild president Shu Mai used the first batch of dwarf spider droids to track down negligent guild members and remind them where their loyalties lay. Some fugitives tried to erect barricades in the deepest tunnels, but the droids simply annihilated the makeshift barriers of dirt and rock with high-powered, short-range laser blasts. This action led to a new nickname, *burrowing spider droids.*

At the Battle of Geonosis, dwarf spider droids became part of the Separatist droid army. They marched alongside battle droids and super battle droids in the front lines, providing a heavy punch while taller homing spider droids fired over their heads from the rear. Dwarf spider droids quickly became a symbol of Separatist might, fighting on nearly every battlefield and patrolling the streets of loyal Confederacy worlds.

After the conclusion of the Clone Wars, the Empire seized all remaining dwarf spider droids. The stormtrooper corps sent the droids against Separatist holdouts, then against political dissidents who were encouraging the early stirrings of rebellion. Dwarf spider droids are often seen on the worlds of the Imperial Remnant, operating customs checkpoints alongside familiar white-armored stormtroopers.

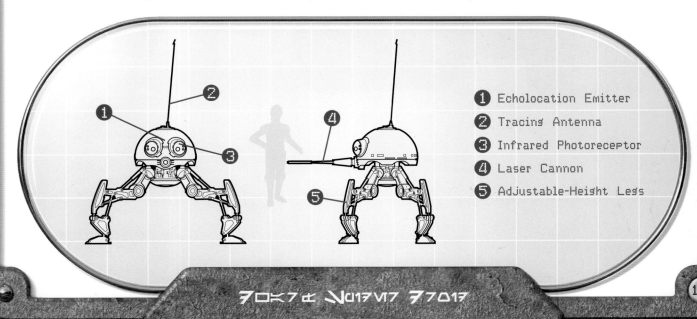

1 Echolocation Emitter
2 Tracing Antenna
3 Infrared Photoreceptor
4 Laser Cannon
5 Adjustable-Height Legs

Technical Readout

Height: 6.7 meters

Manufacturer:
Civilization of the Abominor

Primary Function:
Conquest

Era of Influence:
Old Republic, Rise of the Empire

Agent of the Abominor

The Great Heep was an ancient construct, far older than its Imperial overseers ever knew or suspected. When its consciousness finally came to an end on Biitu, archaeologists lost a rare chance to learn the secrets of the Abominor—an advanced and thoroughly evil droid species.

The Great Heep and other Abominor are believed to be a unique breed of malevolent, self-constructing automata, developed in another galaxy. Possessed with a hunger for power and slaves, the Abominor grafted more machinery onto their bodies until some even became planet-size monstrosities.

These add-ons were often superfluous or simply nonfunctional. Some Abominor experimented with fusing machinery to biological systems, while others built grotesque faces in mockery of the organic slaves who shoveled fuel into their boilers. Lesser droids lived on them like parasites. Over eons, their appetites became rapacious, and the Abominor exterminated organic species on thousands of planets as they scoured for resources.

The Abominor had an opposite number in the Silentium, automata whose perfect shapes were drawn from celestial symmetry. The two sides fought a war, until the galaxy's dominant organic species used the opportunity to rally and force the machines elsewhere.

Accounts of possible Abominor have led researchers to assemble anecdotal chronologies of at least eighteen of the machines. Abominor prefer dry environments, as concentrated moisture can quench the internal fires that give them life.

The Great Heep appeared on the Outer Rim planet of Biitu in the years prior to the Battle of Yavin. An enormous droid, yet still small for an Abominor, it had a squarish body made up of moving pistons and noxious smokestacks, and moved on two tank-treads. Two huge gripper arms and a magnetic grapple allowed the Great Heep to lift droids and crush them. The mouth of the Heep was filled with grinder blades, as well as an astromech-shaped socket for vampirically draining the electronic essences from robotic victims.

Working in partnership with Imperial admiral Terrinald Screed, the Great Heep established a droid-run mining operation to excavate a new fuel ore. The Heep built the "moisture eater"—a tower that sucked Biitu's atmosphere bone-dry. This device protected the Heep but left the planet's farmers in the grip of drought. The Great Heep also maintained a harem of astromech droids, giving him a ready supply of sacrifices.

In the years prior to the Battle of Yavin, during a period when R2-D2 and C-3PO became separated from their master Captain Antilles, the two droids came to Biitu with their master Mungo Baobab. When the group destroyed the moisture eater, the resulting rainwater deluge snuffed out the Great Heep's furnace. The inactive Heep is now on permanent exhibit at the Baobab Museum of Science.

> ### "So, this is the new batch of droids. Your duty is to serve me and Biitu for the rest of your days. Escape is impossible. Any droid caught trying to leave will be used for scrap."
>
> —*The Great Heep*

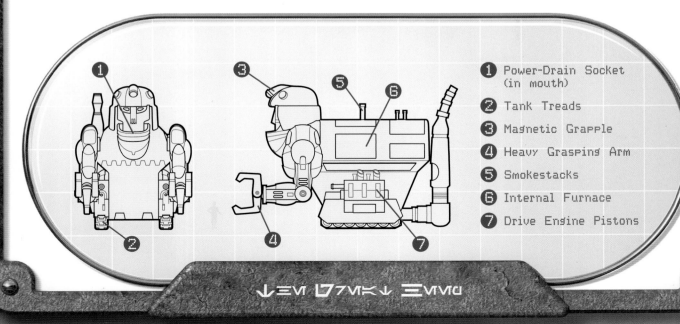

1. Power-Drain Socket (in mouth)
2. Tank Treads
3. Magnetic Grapple
4. Heavy Grasping Arm
5. Smokestacks
6. Internal Furnace
7. Drive Engine Pistons

HK Assassin Droid

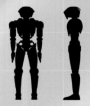

Technical Readout

HEIGHT: 1.8 meters

MANUFACTURER:
Czerka Corporation

PRIMARY FUNCTION:
Assassination

ERA OF INFLUENCE:
Old Republic

Czerka Corporation HK Series Protocol Droid

Introduced more than four thousand standard years ago, the HK series represented an attempt by the Czerka Corporation to circumvent local laws forbidding the construction or sale of assassin droids. Ostensibly a protocol unit, each HK carried assassination programming that manifested itself in a polite yet sadistic personality.

Czerka never marketed the droids as killers, though within the company it was no secret—*HK* stood for "hunter-killer." The company plan called for HKs to take up roles within the business sphere and assassinate heads of rival corporations at Czerka's behest.

Czerka's schemes took an unexpected turn when its prototype unit, HK-01, inspired thousands of his fellow automatons to riot and triggered the Great Droid Revolution on Coruscant. Czerka managed to conceal HK-01's role as instigator, and subsequent models were far more discreet.

One of the most notorious was HK-47, which became the property of the Jedi hero Revan. In order to bring about an end to the Mandalorian Wars, Revan wiped out an entire fleet with a mass-shadow generator. Believing that future kills should not veer into excess, Revan customized HK-47 to assassinate individual targets whom Revan believed to be "destabilizing influences" on the galactic order.

HK-47 carried a number of weapons and had many more built into slots on his arms. He could track his targets using sonic sensors, motion sensors, and telescopic/infrared photoreceptors. His translation unit enabled him to interpret millions of galactic languages. Although obedient, HK-47 had a voice that dripped with weary sarcasm. After HK-47 referred to Revan's apprentice Malak as "meatbag," the insult so amused Revan that he ordered the droid to apply the term to all organic beings.

Revan later wiped the droid's memory. HK-47 found employment with a string of owners, somehow causing the death of each new master when he carried out the commands given to him. Eventually purchased in a Tatooine droid shop, HK-47 became a member of the adventuring party that uncovered the ancient Rakatan Star Forge, again working alongside his former master Revan.

Shortly thereafter, the administrative droid G0-T0 started building new HK-50 units in a secret factory on Telos. The HK-50s infiltrated the Republic fleet as protocol units, where their sometimes arbitrary translations during negotiations among visiting diplomats often led to violence. HK-50 units, identifiable by their gunmetal-gray coloration, could not act against other HKs due to self-preservation protocols built into their template.

Five years after the Star Forge incident, HK-47 teamed up with the heroine known as the Jedi Exile to battle a trio of Sith Lords. At the Telos droid factory, HK-47 convinced the HK-50 droids to join his cause. The united HKs helped defeat G0-T0 in a showdown on Malachor V.

Recent evidence suggests that HK-47 survived the subsequent four thousand years by storing his consciousness in various electronic systems. He emerged in a new body around the time of the Battle of Yavin, assembling an army of murderous droids on the lava planet Mustafar.

> **"Retraction: Did I say that out loud? I apologize, Master. While you are a meatbag, I suppose I should not call you as such."**
>
> *—Assassin droid HK-47*

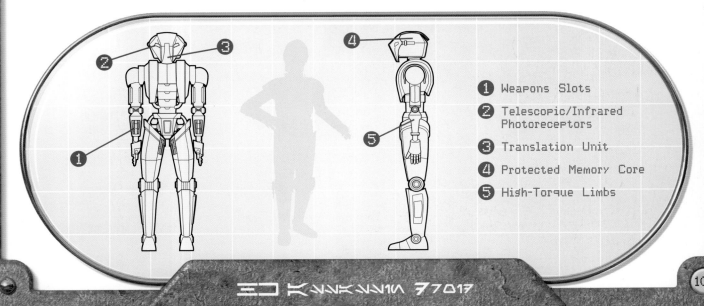

1. Weapons Slots
2. Telescopic/Infrared Photoreceptors
3. Translation Unit
4. Protected Memory Core
5. High-Torque Limbs

HUMAN REPLICA DROID

TECHNICAL READOUT

HEIGHT: Variable

MANUFACTURER:
Imperial Department of
Military Research

PRIMARY FUNCTION:
Infiltration

ERA OF INFLUENCE:
Rebellion, New Republic

Imperial Department of Military Research Classified HRD

Plenty of humanoid droids have tried to look *too* human and failed, but human replica droids (HRDs) finally cracked the perceptual barrier. In both appearance and behavior, an HRD is utterly indistinguishable from a human being. HRDs are among the most expensive automata ever built and are not currently available for sale to the public.

The HRD experiment began with Project Decoy, a Rebel Alliance plot to replace Imperial officials with perfect duplicates. The Rebels, however, lacked sufficient funds to complete their design during the Galactic Civil War, and their archenemies beat them to the punch. The Empire hired designers Massad Thrumble and Simonelle the Ingoian to create an Imperial replica droid. The two geniuses produced a flawless HRD female named Guri.

Smelling profit, Simonelle established his own HRD workshop in the Minos Cluster, while Thrumble remained with the Empire, developing duplicates of Governor Torlock of Corulag and his daughter, Frija. These two droids possessed a self-awareness so acute that they rejected their assigned roles as decoys and escaped to a new life in the wastelands of Hoth. Guri, meanwhile, was sold to the head of the Black Sun syndicate, Prince Xizor, for a cool nine million credits.

Guri possesses enhanced strength and hyper-reflexes, and was modeled in the image of a striking, blond-haired young woman. The masquerade is successful through the use of a poly-alloy skeleton, clone-vat skin coverings, and internal organs made from biofibers. To all but the most advanced medical equipment, Guri appears completely organic.

Guri worked as Xizor's bodyguard and private assassin. At the time of her master's death, she was the second most powerful figure in Black Sun, a testament to the redesigned AA-1 verbobrain she carries in her skull. Guri's autonomy was so great that she voluntarily elected to undergo reprogramming that would purge her synapses of assassination programming. Shortly after the Battle of Endor, Massad Thrumble performed the operation on Hurd's Moon, and Guri went on to pursue an existence as a fully self-governing droid.

> ## "You might be the only person in the galaxy who can reprogram me. I don't want to be an assassin anymore."
>
> —*Guri to her creator, Massad Thrumble*

Approximately a year after Endor, the New Republic at last completed its work on Project Decoy. The new HRDs were clumsy and lacked the complicated personalities that had become a hallmark of Massad Thrumble's design. The Project Decoy droids saw action in only a few missions, including one where a replica of Leia Organa helped kill the Imperial warlord Trioculus.

During the Yuuzhan Vong invasion, the entrepreneur Stanton Rendar set up shop in the Minos Cluster. Using the "entechment" technology of the Ssi-ruuk, Rendar offered to transfer the consciousnesses of paying customers into the bodies of HRDs, a process that he believed held the secret to eternal life.

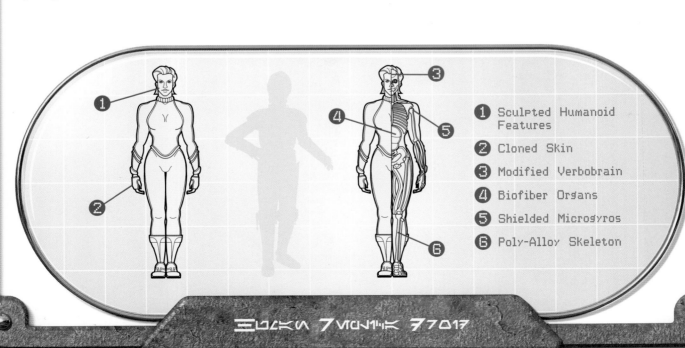

1. Sculpted Humanoid Features
2. Cloned Skin
3. Modified Verbobrain
4. Biofiber Organs
5. Shielded Microgyros
6. Poly-Alloy Skeleton

IG-100 MagnaGuard

Holowan Mechanicals IG-100 MagnaGuard

General Grievous, conqueror of a hundred worlds, became a figure of legendary menace during the Clone Wars. His robotic bodyguards were equal to that reputation. The IG-100 MagnaGuard could take down nearly any opponent and helped pave the way for the even deadlier IG assassin droids.

Prior to his reconstruction as a cyborg, General Grievous led his native Kaleesh in battle against their traditional enemies, the Huk. Grievous's Kaleesh bodyguards wore head wraps and capes bearing Kalee mumuu markings, and were drawn from the most elite members of the Kaleesh fighting force.

In his new life as commander of the Separatist droid army, Grievous asked for similar bodyguards. Count Dooku contracted Holowan Mechanicals to construct a new droid model: the prototype Self-Motivating Heuristically Programmed Combat Droid, or IG-100 MagnaGuard. The MagnaGuard incorporated elements from the IG lancer, and Holowan's close ties with the InterGalactic Banking Clan resulted in carrying over the *IG* nomenclature.

General Grievous erased an entire library of fighting moves from the memory banks of his MagnaGuards, and insisted on training the droids himself. Some became specialists at close-quarters brawling, while others developed expertise in ranged weaponry or explosives. A few came with rocket launchers built into their backs. Different shell coverings in black, alabaster, blue, and gray helped dis-

> ### "So, General Grievous, we meet at last. In the name of the Republic, I—urrrk!"
>
> *—Jedi Master Sannen, as a MagnaGuard jabs him in the throat*

tinguish one model from another. Satisfied with his bodyguards, General Grievous dressed them in traditional head wraps and cloaks from the Kalee homeworld.

Grievous knew that his bodyguards would inevitably fight Jedi. He gave them long-handled electrostaffs, made from lightsaber-resistant phrik metal, with tips crawling with incapacitating energy tendrils. Furthermore, redundant systems allowed MagnaGuards to keep fighting even after losing a limb (or a head) to a Jedi's blade. Most Jedi who targeted Grievous never made it past his bodyguard screen. Those who did were exhausted when they reached that point, and were easily dispatched by the general.

During Grievous's mission to kidnap Supreme Chancellor Palpatine from Coruscant, a contingent of MagnaGuards battled Palpatine's Jedi defenders in a fight that spilled from Palpatine's apartment to a hovertrain platform. Though many MagnaGuards wound up in pieces, they succeeded in their primary mission of splitting and delaying the Jedi.

Shortly afterward, more MagnaGuards tried to defend their master on board Grievous's flagship, *Invisible Hand*. Obi-Wan Kenobi and Anakin Skywalker made short work of most of the bodyguards, however, and many of the remaining units disintegrated when chunks of *Invisible Hand* burned up on orbital reentry. Most of the rest perished on Utapau during Obi-Wan's pursuit of General Grievous.

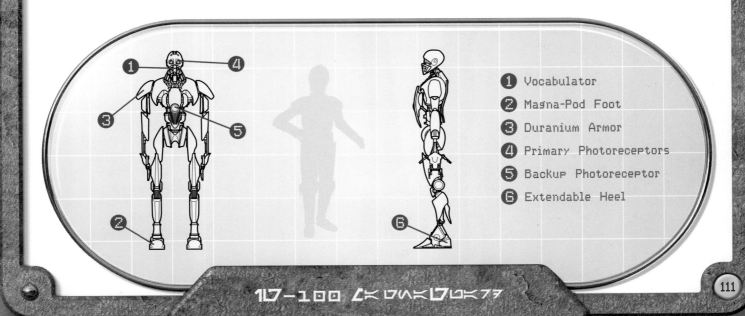

1. Vocabulator
2. Magna-Pod Foot
3. Duranium Armor
4. Primary Photoreceptors
5. Backup Photoreceptor
6. Extendable Heel

IG Assassin Droid

Technical Readout

HEIGHT: 1.96 meters

MANUFACTURER:
Holowan Mechanicals

PRIMARY FUNCTION:
Assassination

ERA OF INFLUENCE:
Rise of the Empire, Rebellion,
New Republic

Holowan Mechanicals IG Series Assassin Droid

IG assassin droids are the culmination of a homicidal product line that started with the IG lancer and included the IG-100 MagnaGuard. With each new IG, the threat level increased exponentially.

IG assassin droids were envisioned by the engineers of Phlut Design Systems well before the Clone Wars. But the company produced only the IG lancer before running out of money. Holowan Mechanicals inherited Phlut's assets and labeled the unproduced Phlut blueprints as IGs 1 through 99 before building its own version for General Grievous, the IG 100 MagnaGuard.

After the Clone Wars, Holowan—which had been accepting both Separatist and Republic money for years—was commissioned by Imperial supervisor Gurdun to build a hunter that would eliminate threats to the young Empire. Going back to earlier Phlut concepts, Holowan produced an IG-97 and an IG-72, but its greatest successes were its four identical IG-88 units.

Roughly humanoid in shape, each IG-88's blaster-resistant armored frame stood two meters tall. A cylindrical head, studded with glowing red sensors, allowed the unit to see in all directions at once. The droid lacked olfactory detectors, but compensated with advanced auditory, radionic, movement, and temperature sensors. Its multiple optic lenses could access a wide variety of spectral filters under hazy or low-light conditions.

The IG's weapons complement included a repeating blaster in each forearm and a concussion grenade launcher in the left hip, as well as a flamethrower, sonic stunner, paralysis cord, throwing flechette array, and rack of poison gas canisters—all stored behind hidden panels.

The fingers of the right hand doubled as miniature cutting lasers. The mirrored palm of the left hand was capable of intercepting blaster bolts and deflecting them back along their original path. The IG could also dramatically raise the temperature of its exterior plating, allowing it to burn through nets or melt a stream of immobilizing Stokhli spray.

When the first IG-88 unit received his sentience programming, he identified the technicians in the room as threats and eliminated them. This droid, which called himself IG-88A, copied his consciousness into IG-88s B, C, and D. The four IG-88s became bounty hunters. However, most met their ends prior to the Battle of Endor.

IG-88A launched a more ambitious scheme, masterminding a plot to turn all droids manufactured on Mechis III into agents of his will. He even uploaded his consciousness into the computer core of the second Death Star, making him a living superweapon. Nevertheless, he perished when the battle station exploded. The wealthy Thul merchant family eventually found IG-88A's body and reprogrammed the empty shell to act as a bodyguard. It is still unknown whether Holowan Mechanicals produced additional IG assassin droids or if a rival company ever duplicated the blueprints.

> **"WANTED: IG-88, aka the Phlutdroid, also reportedly operating as IG-88A, IG-88B, IG-88C, or IG-88D. Heavily armed, more than 150 kills. DISMANTLE ON SIGHT."**
>
> —*Imperial bounty posting*

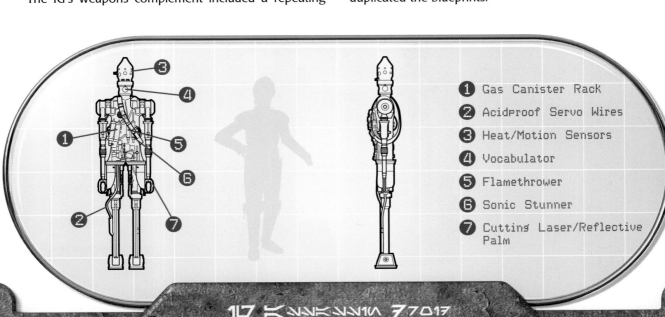

1. Gas Canister Rack
2. Acidproof Servo Wires
3. Heat/Motion Sensors
4. Vocabulator
5. Flamethrower
6. Sonic Stunner
7. Cutting Laser/Reflective Palm

IG Lancer Droid

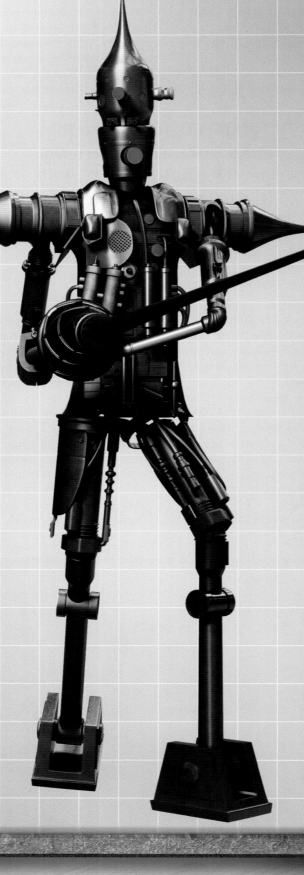

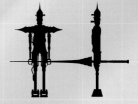

Phlut Design Systems IG Lancer Combat Droid

To those who survived the rampages of the assassin droid IG-88, the IG lancer droid is a dreadful specter of things to come. The lancer was the first combat droid to sport the distinctive stretched-cylinder design common to many IGs, and the first to carry the *IG* label.

Phlut Design Systems brought the IG line into existence. A small firm based on the Outer Rim banking planet of Muunilinst, Phlut hoped to develop a new battle droid to sell to the Trade Federation. To obtain the start-up capital for "Project Phlutdroid," the company took out a hefty loan from the Muunilinst-based InterGalactic Banking Clan.

Phlut produced glossy black battle droids nearly two meters tall, with skinny bodies that echo the Muuns who built them. Though many components appear crude—the two-pincer gripper hands, for example, incapable of fine manipulation—the Phlutdroids possess limb strength more than twice that of the standard B1 battle droid. The lancers also have remarkably quick reaction times, enabling them to spar hand-to-hand against skilled organic opponents.

Unfortunately, like many companies that borrowed from the InterGalactic Banking Clan, Phlut Design Systems could not meet the terms of the draconian contract it had signed. The Banking Clan seized the company's assets shortly before the Clone Wars, including all finished droids and any blueprints related to Project Phlutdroid.

Renaming its acquisition the IG series to mark the droids as InterGalactic Banking Clan property, IBC chairman San Hill installed them as guards around Muunilinst's commerce citadels. Outfitted with their trademark power lances and speeder bites, the IG lancers became an outward sign of militarization as Muunilinst prepared for war.

The Clone Wars came to Muunilinst four months after the Battle of Geonosis. When General Obi-Wan Kenobi led an army against San Hill's ruling citadel, the mercenary Durge gathered dozens of IG lancers and struck at the Republic's heavy weapons. Using lances and anti-vehicle mines, the Separatist raiders destroyed dozens of AT-TEs and turbolaser cannons in a string of high-speed sorties. Obi-Wan's clone troopers mounted their own speeder bikes and squared off against the IG lancers in an old-fashioned joust.

Though the Republic won the day, it was not the end of the IG series. Holowan Mechanicals, the new company contracted by the InterGalactic Banking Clan to continue production of IG lancers, saw an opportunity to improve on the basic design. Studying Phlut Design Systems' blueprints for the battle droids that it never had the opportunity to produce, Holowan relabeled these designs as IGs numbers 1 through 99. Holowan's first all-new droid contract would be a bodyguard model for General Grievous, and would be released under the designation *IG 100*.

> ## "General Kenobi, our cannons are being destroyed." "Mount up."
>
> *—Republic clone trooper Able 472 and Obi-Wan Kenobi, planning their counterattack against IG lancers during the Battle of Muunilinst*

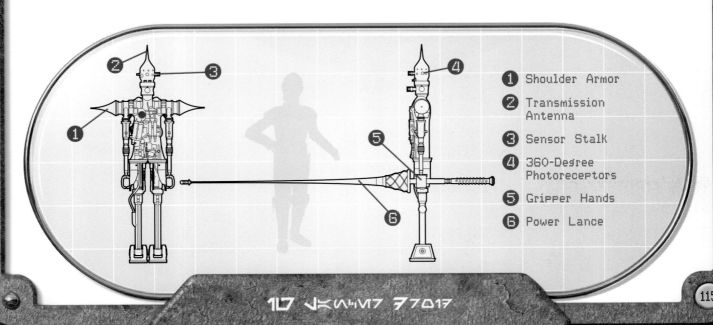

1. Shoulder Armor
2. Transmission Antenna
3. Sensor Stalk
4. 360-Degree Photoreceptors
5. Gripper Hands
6. Power Lance

IT-O INTERROGATOR

TECHNICAL READOUT

HEIGHT: 0.3 meter in diameter

MANUFACTURER:
Imperial Department of
Military Research

PRIMARY FUNCTION:
Torture

ERA OF INFLUENCE:
Rise of the Empire,
Rebellion, New Republic

Imperial Department of Military Research IT-O Interrogation Droid

The Empire elevated torture to an art form, dedicating an entire branch of government, the Inquisitorius, to the sole purpose of squeezing information from the reluctant. The IT-O interrogator was one of the first droids manufactured by the Imperial Department of Military Research.

The existence of the IT-O was no secret. Rumors abounded of its horrifying techniques and brutal sadism. Those citizens unlucky enough to be rounded up by the Imperial Security Bureau could have personally attested to its cruelty . . . were they not too traumatized to speak.

A glossy black sphere less than a meter tall, the IT-O hovers on low-powered repulsors. Its design bears a deliberate similarity to the G0-T0 series, whose members conquered a cluster of planets four thousand standard years ago and fanned public fears of droid tyrants. The IT-O's shiny surface is studded with a hateful array of needles, probes, optic sensors, and audioreceptors. A vocabulator is also capable of producing speech, though this has seldom been required. The droid's tools speak for themselves.

One of the most prominent implements is a hypodermic injector syringe connected to internal reservoirs of liquid chemicals, including the truth serum Bavo Six. These drugs can lower pain thresholds, stimulate cooperation, and trigger hallucinations. In addition, the droid features a laser scalpel, a grasping claw, and power shears. Rebel agent Kyle Katarn reported seeing IT-Os within sensitive Imperial installations that had been modified to fire stun bursts as a last-ditch line of defense.

Twisted as their use might be, the medical diagnostic matrices of the IT-O are quite sophisticated. The droids have expert programming in medicine, psychology, surgery, and humanoid biology. The droid's sensors can evaluate a confessor's truthfulness based on heart rate, muscle tension, and voice patterns. IT-Os were notorious for bringing their victims back from the brink of death only to endure further questioning.

Despite the boasts of the Empire, at least one person is known to have withstood the torments of an interrogation droid. While imprisoned aboard the Death Star, Princess Leia Organa survived an IT-O *and* a psychic probe by Darth Vader without revealing the location of the Rebel base at Yavin.

Inevitably, the IT-O was succeeded by newer models with more refined torture equipment, but these versions did not see widespread use. Allegedly, state-of-the-art IT-3s were stationed at the headquarters of the Imperial Security Bureau on Coruscant. The use of torture droids is ostensibly forbidden within the borders of the modern Imperial Remnant, but it seems unlikely that the droids are gone for good.

> **"The IT-O's greatest tool is its reputation. *Tell* the suspect you have one, and *show* it waiting in the wings. This alone will often elicit a confession."**
>
> —*From* Stratagems of the Inquisitorius
> *by Grand Inquisitor Torbin*

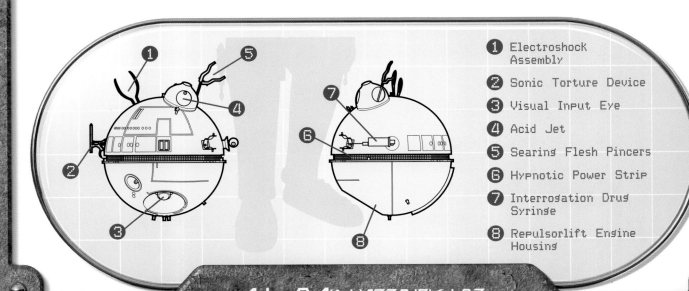

1. Electroshock Assembly
2. Sonic Torture Device
3. Visual Input Eye
4. Acid Jet
5. Searing Flesh Pincers
6. Hypnotic Power Strip
7. Interrogation Drug Syringe
8. Repulsorlift Engine Housing

JK Bio-Droid

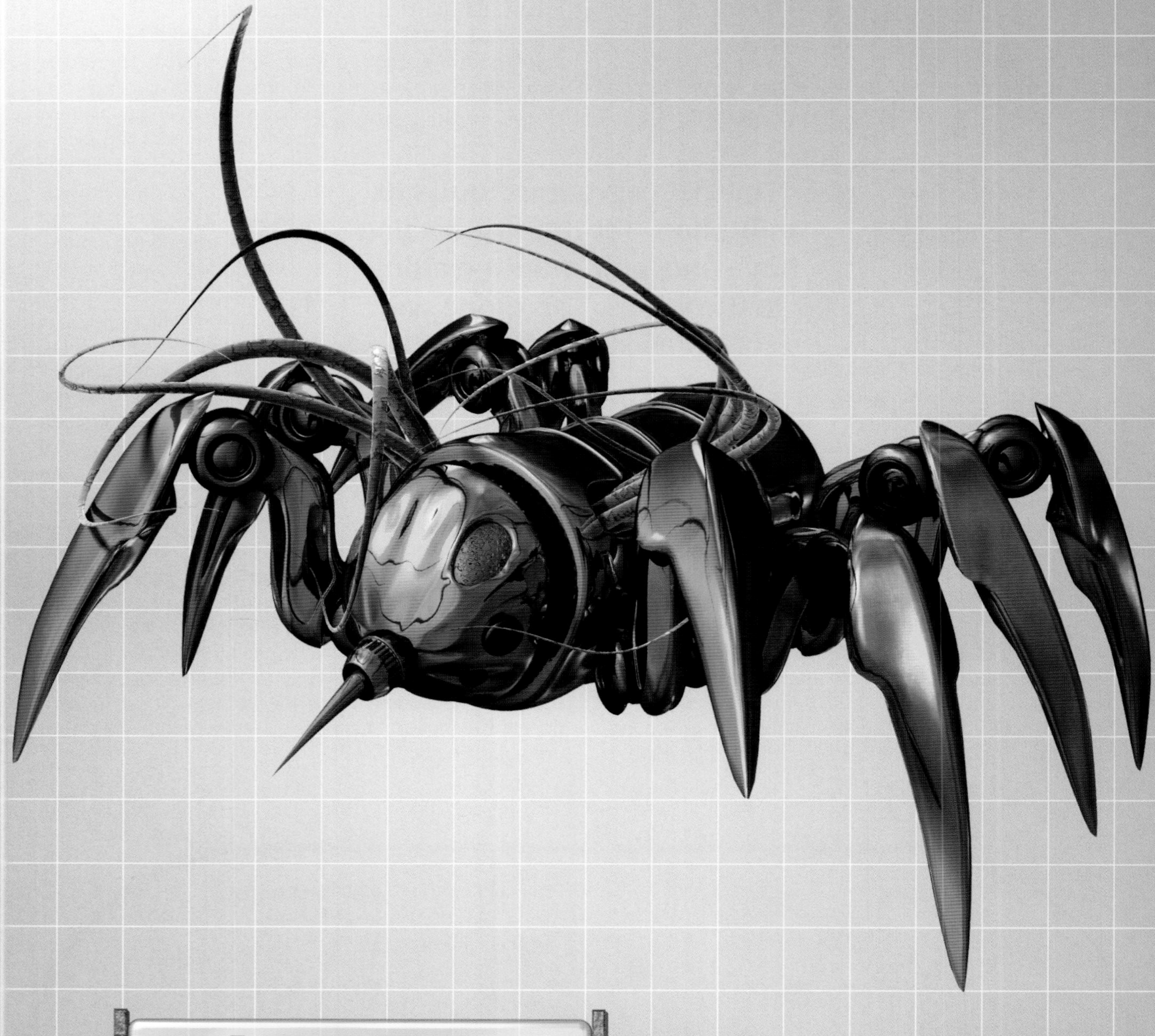

Technical Readout

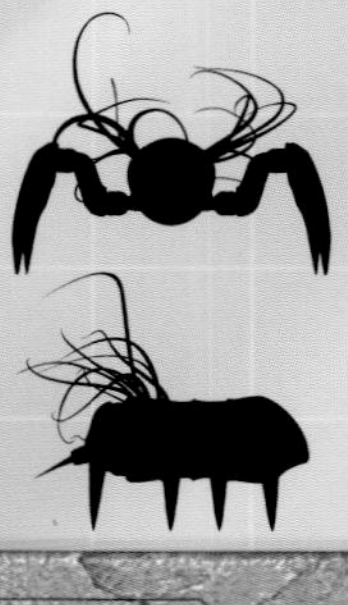

Height: 1.5 meters

Manufacturer: Cestus Cybernetics

Primary Function: Personal security

Era of Influence: Rise of the Empire

118

Cestus Cybernetics JK Personal Security Droid

One of the most unusual droids ever developed was actually a symbiont cyborg, though few of its buyers ever realized that fact. Never deployed in combat, the JK played the lead role in an elaborate Clone Wars bluff centered on the Outer Rim planet of Ord Cestus.

The JK was a high-end droid, its mirrored golden coating and diminutive hourglass profile giving it the air of a collectible piece of art. Small, pointed legs supported the upright assembly; the droid could also unfold and restructure its body segments to assume a hunched, spider-like configuration. JK droids sold at a premium of eighty thousand credits each.

Cestus Cybernetics gave the JKs nearly supernatural reflexes by pairing them with immature Dashta eels: Force-sensitive creatures native to the caverns of Ord Cestus. The Dashta eels willingly participated in the project, offering up their unfertilized eggs in order to bring Ord Cestus more fully into the galactic community. A shielded central processing unit inside each JK held a sleeping Dashta eel, which entered into a symbiotic relationship with the droid's own intelligence. The result was a precognitive combat reflex that rivaled that of a Jedi.

Initially marketed as a personal security unit, the JK featured advanced capacitors that allowed it to project spinning, circular energy shields capable of absorbing incoming blasterfire—a feature intended to reduce ricochets and protect its surroundings. In the event that a bolt made it past the shields, the JK's mirrored finish deflected most glancing hits.

From both shoulder mountings and both sides of the bottom torso, the JK could spit out tangles of retractable metal tentacles. When fighting nonliving opponents, such as other droids, the JK could change the form of its tentacles, thinning and contracting them before slicing its enemy to pieces. The tentacles could also camouflage themselves, enabling them to surprise enemies.

Under its normal security programming, a JK would immobilize a victim, then shine a light into the subject's eyes to match the retinal results against its internal database. If the JK determined the subject to be a threat, the droid could conduct an electrical charge along its tentacles powerful enough to stun an organic being into unconsciousness.

After selling JKs to crimelords, Cestus Cybernetics received an order for thousands of the droids from Count Dooku's Confederacy of Independent Systems. Obi-Wan Kenobi and Kit Fisto journeyed to Ord Cestus in an effort to keep the planet from allying with the enemy.

In the process, they learned that the gentle eels could not kill another sentient being without the act driving them insane. This meant that the JKs could never be deployed as combat units, eliminating the threat of the droids that, prematurely, had been called Jedi Killers.

> ### "Among smugglers and the lower classes, some call them 'Jedi Killers.' "
>
> *—Technician Lido Shan, briefing Obi-Wan Kenobi and Kit Fisto on the JK*

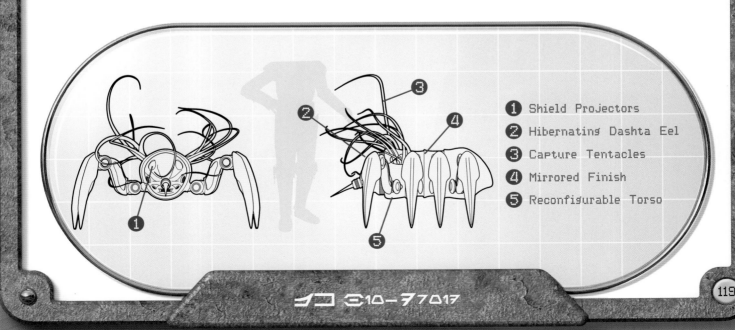

1. Shield Projectors
2. Hibernating Dashta Eel
3. Capture Tentacles
4. Mirrored Finish
5. Reconfigurable Torso

Juggernaut War Droid

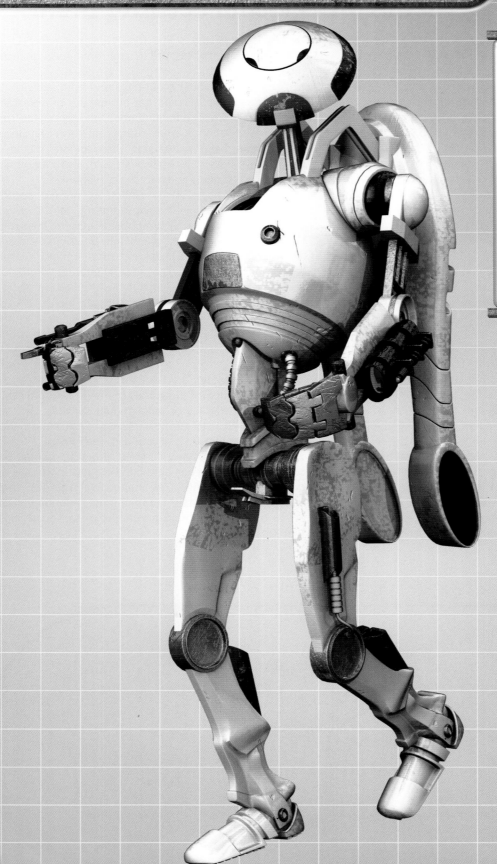

Technical Readout

Height: 1.95 meters

Manufacturer:
Duwani Mechanical Products

Primary Function:
Combat

Era of Influence:
Old Republic

Duwani Mechanical Products RRJC Juggernaut Jumper

The juggernaut war droid is one of the most recognizable droid designs of the ancient Republic, famous for its achievements in the service of the Republic and notorious for its betrayal of that trust during the Great Droid Revolution.

The Republic rocket-jumper corps, an elite division of the Republic army responsible for carrying out impossible missions, developed its own resupply and rearmament droids that could jet-jump with them behind enemy lines. These droids became the model for the juggernaut war droid, hastily commissioned by Supreme Chancellor Vocatara at the start of the Gank Massacres in 4800 B.B.Y.

The discovery of ryll spice on Ryloth had led to the specieswide spice addiction of the cetacean Porporites. Enraged beyond reason, and possessed of a lightning-fast breeding cycle, a wave of maddened Porporites withstood everything the Republic threw at them, including the juggernauts.

The juggernaut operated in a bipedal humanoid configuration and had two alternate methods of propulsion. In a carryover from the Republic rocket-jumper design, twin outrigger jets could launch the droid airborne for bursts of up to sixty seconds. In order to battle the Porporites in their homeworld's natural environment, the jets could convert into intake propellers for underwater operation. The juggernauts were not naturally buoyant,

> **"When the war droids breached the armory, the uprising became a catastrophe. They were juggernauts, and for them it was as easy as returning home."**
>
> —*From* Conflagration: An Eyewitness Account of the Great Droid Uprising

however, and if their propellers jammed, they would sink.

Juggernauts had weapons built into each arm. The left contained a wide-beam sonic stunner, while the right had a shatter beam that could tear a durasteel door from its frame. Juggernauts were trained to carry standard Republic-issue pulse-wave rifles, and used their heavy weapons only in emergencies.

Following the successful resolution of the Gank Massacres, juggernaut war droids became a familiar part of Coruscant's home guard. When the assassin droid HK-01 triggered the Great Droid Revolution in 4015 B.B.Y., shocked citizens witnessed juggernauts turn on the city. The droids unforgettably shredded a platoon of rocket-jumpers in an airborne battle above Monument Plaza. After the revolution, most juggernauts had their intelligence matrices ripped out, and no more of the droids were produced by the Republic.

Outside of museums, juggernaut parts have appeared in the modern era at least twice. The Iron Knights—intelligent Shard crystals inhabiting droid bodies—bonded with several still-active juggernauts from a base on Dweem. Later, Arden Lyn of the Legions of Lettow awakened after a twenty-five-thousand-year sleep and received the prosthetic right arm of a juggernaut Mark I, prior to her appointment as one of the Emperor's Hands.

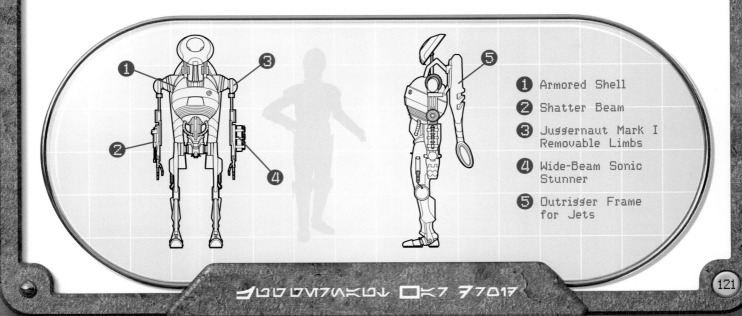

1. Armored Shell
2. Shatter Beam
3. Juggernaut Mark I Removable Limbs
4. Wide-Beam Sonic Stunner
5. Outrigger Frame for Jets

L8-L9 Combat Droid

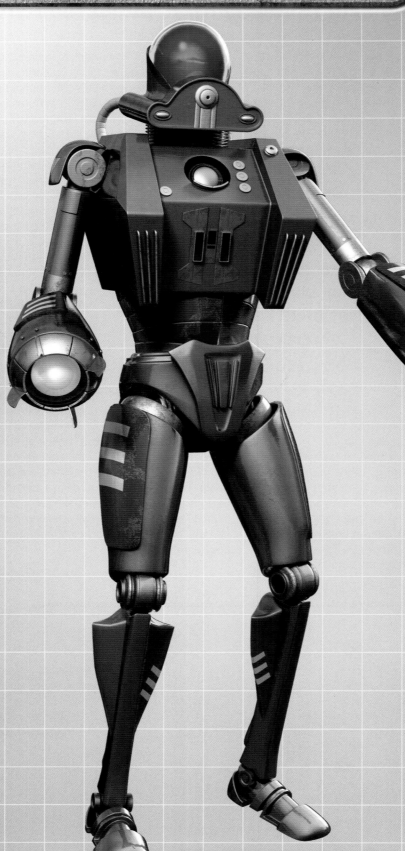

Technical Readout

HEIGHT: 1.9 meters

MANUFACTURER: TaggeCo

PRIMARY FUNCTION: Combat

ERA OF INFLUENCE: Rise of the Empire

TaggeCo Prototype L8–L9 Combat Droid

Never produced in large numbers, the L8-L9 was the first combat droid in the lineage that eventually produced the Dark Trooper. Had it not been for Asajj Ventress, the Clone Wars could have become the Droid Wars: Republic L8-L9s versus Separatist battle droids.

The family-owned TaggeCo enjoyed close ties with the Republic government. After the Battle of Naboo, the young baron Orman Tagge began sketching designs for Republic battle droids that could stand against the Trade Federation. When Count Dooku declared war against the Republic on Geonosis, Tagge rushed his prototype L8-L9 into production.

The L8-L9 had a head inspired by the helmets of Republic clone troopers, an intentional nod by TaggeCo toward its intended buyer. The droid could fire either plasma bursts or sustained jets of flame out of both arms. Its sharp-edged fingers were of little use in manipulating objects, but the L8-L9 could spin its wrist assemblies at high speed and use the spinning claws to cut holes in durasteel. The droid had shielded internal systems protecting it from electromagnetic bursts and extreme heat or cold.

Tagge knew that the Republic had already raised a clone army, so he positioned the L8-L9 as a stand-in for hazardous environments. This was meant to get TaggeCo's foot in the door, at which point Orman planned to aggressively sell his vision of an L8-L9 army. If it came to pass, a government contract of that magnitude would enrich the company beyond the wildest dreams of the Tagge forebears.

The prototype L8-L9 unit required immediate field-testing. Contacts within the House of Tagge suggested as a venue the warring planet Rattatak, where gladiatorial games had become the passion of a cruel and brutal people. Tagge's sample L8-L9 enlisted in a Rattatak free-for-all, facing off against challengers including a Nikto swordsman and a hulking Shikitari insectoid.

L8-L9 assessed the unfolding carnage, then determined that Sith hopeful Asajj Ventress represented the greatest threat. L8-L9 opened up on Ventress with indiscriminate spray from its flamethrowers and plasma launchers, taking out many of its fellow combatants in the crossfire. Under different circumstances, L8-L9 would have emerged victorious, but Ventress seized the droid in a Force grip and bashed its head against the stone ceiling.

The field test was a flop, and it closed the window of opportunity for the L8-L9. Following the Clone Wars, Orman Tagge made the acquaintance of military man and kindred spirit Rom Mohc, who would act as Tagge's "in" with the Imperial Army for Tagge's second-generation Z-X3 droid trooper.

> **"The L-Eight-L-Nine unit is completely lost, Baron. And so is the hundred thousand credits you wagered on it to win."**
>
> *—Report to Baron Orman Tagge following the "catastrophe on Rattatak"*

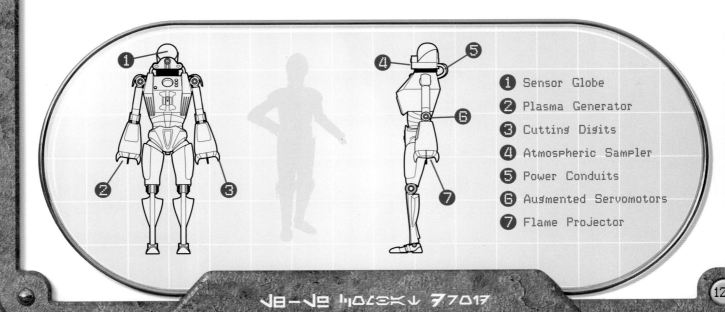

1. Sensor Globe
2. Plasma Generator
3. Cutting Digits
4. Atmospheric Sampler
5. Power Conduits
6. Augmented Servomotors
7. Flame Projector

Mandalorian Battle Legionnaire

Technical Readout

HEIGHT: 1.7 meters

MANUFACTURER:
Baktoid Combat Automata

PRIMARY FUNCTION:
Combat

ERA OF INFLUENCE:
Rise of the Empire

Baktoid Combat Automata BL Series Battle Legionnaire

The Mandalorians have a history as old as the Republic itself, but traditionally are ambivalent toward droids. With a few notable exceptions—the weird techno-organic basilisk war droids being the most famous example—the Mandalorians fought their own battles and didn't employ droid armies until the Clone Wars.

The Mandalorian Protectors arose midway through the Clone Wars, when a faulty clone of Jango Fett named Alpha-02 recruited a force of Separatist-allied shock troopers from the ranks of Mandalore police units and the Death Watch. Only 212 strong, the Protectors drew upon Mandalorian tradition to boost their ranks. Remembering the role of Mandallian Giants as front-line troops during the New Sith Wars, as well as officer Fenn Shysa's encounter with the fearless protocol droid C-3PX, Alpha-02 used Separatist foundries to churn out a limited run of one thousand Battle Legionnaires.

Each droid in the BL series bore a resemblance to Cybot Galactica's 3PO series, but wore olive-drab military camouflage to match the Mandalorian Protectors' battle armor. The BLs had military-grade balance gyros and joints calibrated for maximum torque. The result was a droid that could lift thousands of kilos over its head and run at speeds up to thirty kilometers per hour for more than a day without recharge.

For weaponry, each Battle Legionnaire wore a rectangular Briletto AAP-II "blaster box" on its chest. Front-line combat often required a heavier punch, a task left to specialized BLs that operated titanic Mandalorian battle harnesses. These two-thousand-year-old antiques turned droids into rolling weapons platforms. Each battle harness, propelled by twin tank-treads, came armed with laser emplacements, a heavy blaster cannon, a gigantic claw arm, and a sonic-pulverizing trip-hammer.

Deployed late in the war, the Battle Legionnaires soon found themselves in the worst of the fighting. Most BLs served as first-wave ground forces, opening holes in Republic defensive lines to be exploited by the shock troopers. The ranks of the Battle Legionnaires suffered during the Mandalorian assaults on Kamino and New Bornalex, and almost no units survived the Republic trap on Norval II. The Mandalorian Protectors met a similar fate, with only 3 of the 212 shock troopers outlasting the war.

After the Clone Wars, the bounty hunter Boba Fett came into possession of a shabby but still functional Battle Legionnaire. Recognizing the link the droid shared with his own Mandalorian heritage—or perhaps just appreciating the cold efficiency of a fellow killer—Fett made BL-17 his aide during the early years of Imperial rule. BL-17's operational life came to an end during an encounter with R2-D2 and C-3PO on the speeder-racing planet of Boonta.

> **"To our BLs, that they may leave enough enemies for the rest of us. Raise your cup to victory! *Kote!*"**
>
> —*Toast of the Mandalorian Protectors on the eve of the Battle of New Bornalex*

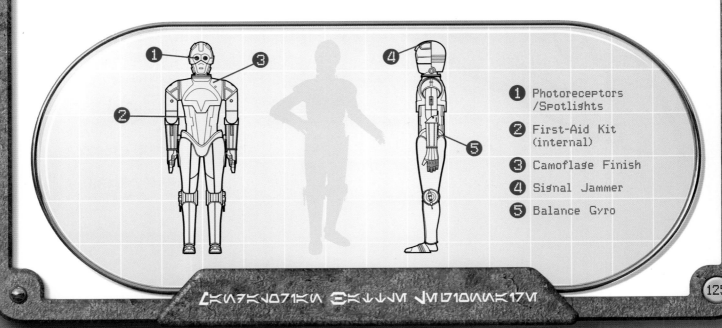

1. Photoreceptors /Spotlights
2. First-Aid Kit (internal)
3. Camoflage Finish
4. Signal Jammer
5. Balance Gyro

Manta Droid Subfighter

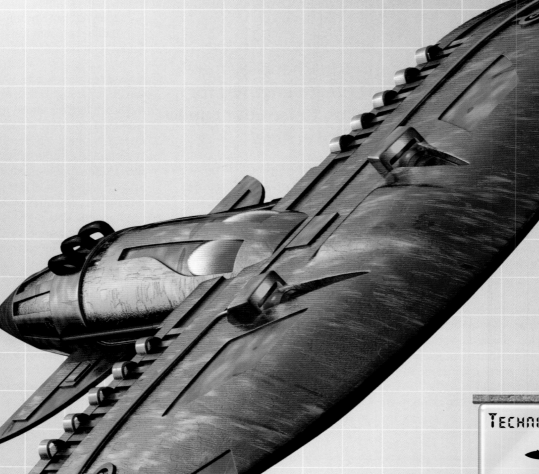

Haor Chall Engineering Manta Droid Subfighter

During the Clone Wars, the might of the Separatist droid army extended from space to land and even beneath the waves. The manta droid subfighter served as the primary naval unit for the Confederacy of Independent Systems throughout three standard years of fighting.

The Trade Federation began research into the manta droid design shortly after the Battle of Naboo. In that failed conflict, the Trade Federation's wavegoing and submersible vehicles—including the *Ostracoda* gunboat and the OTT ocean transport—had begun as land vehicles modified for marine service. As such they were plagued with weaknesses, including slow top speeds and the embarrassing tendency to sink without warning.

Viceroy Nute Gunray commissioned the insectoid Xi Char to draft a new submersible. Isolated on luxury estates provided by the Trade Federation in an effort to make them comfortable, the Xi Char engineers felt disconnected and could not figure out a way to make the subfighter change shape like the vulture starfighter. Shamed by their failure to deliver on specs, the Xi Char provided blueprints for a subfighter carrier free of charge, as well as underwater conversion kits for the Trade Federation's fleet of MVR-3 speeders.

To anyone but perfectionist Xi Char, however, the manta droid subfighter was a hit. The droid borrows many design elements from the vulture fighter, including a sleek bump of a head and photoreceptors that glow as red slashes. Two grooves in the forward diving plane hold either laser cannons or torpedo launchers. Some specialty models have articulated barrels that allow the droids to switch between the two types of weaponry on a whim.

The curved diving plane contains an electromotive field generator that can drive the craft at low speeds. At speeds in excess of one hundred knots, supercavitation vectrals built into the structure generate a bubble of air around the subfighter, dramatically reducing friction and allowing repulsorlift engines to rocket the craft forward at speeds not approachable by any other submarine craft.

Four months after the outbreak of the Clone Wars, the Confederacy called in manta droid subfighters to assist the Separatist-allied Quarren Isolationist League in its civil war against the government of Mon Calamari. Jedi Master Kit Fisto led clone SCUBA troopers and a legion of Mon Calamari Knights against the manta droids in a battle that resulted in a Separatist defeat.

In an odd postscript, several dozen damaged manta droids remained behind on Mon Calamari. Forgotten, they formed their own community, drawing energy from the seafloor mining platforms operated by the Quarren. The manta droid school soon forged a loose affiliation with the Quarren, hunting ocean predators in exchange for repairs and ammunition.

> **"These droids swim and fight like a school of reaver garhai. Let's see the Maramere sea pirates laugh at me now!"**
>
> —*Trade Federation viceroy Nute Gunray*

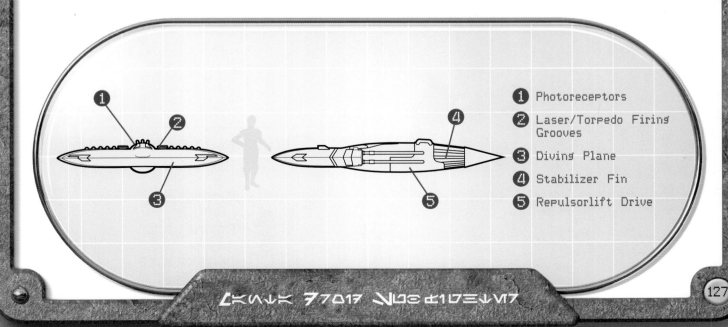

1 Photoreceptors
2 Laser/Torpedo Firing Grooves
3 Diving Plane
4 Stabilizer Fin
5 Repulsorlift Drive

OCTUPTARRA DROID

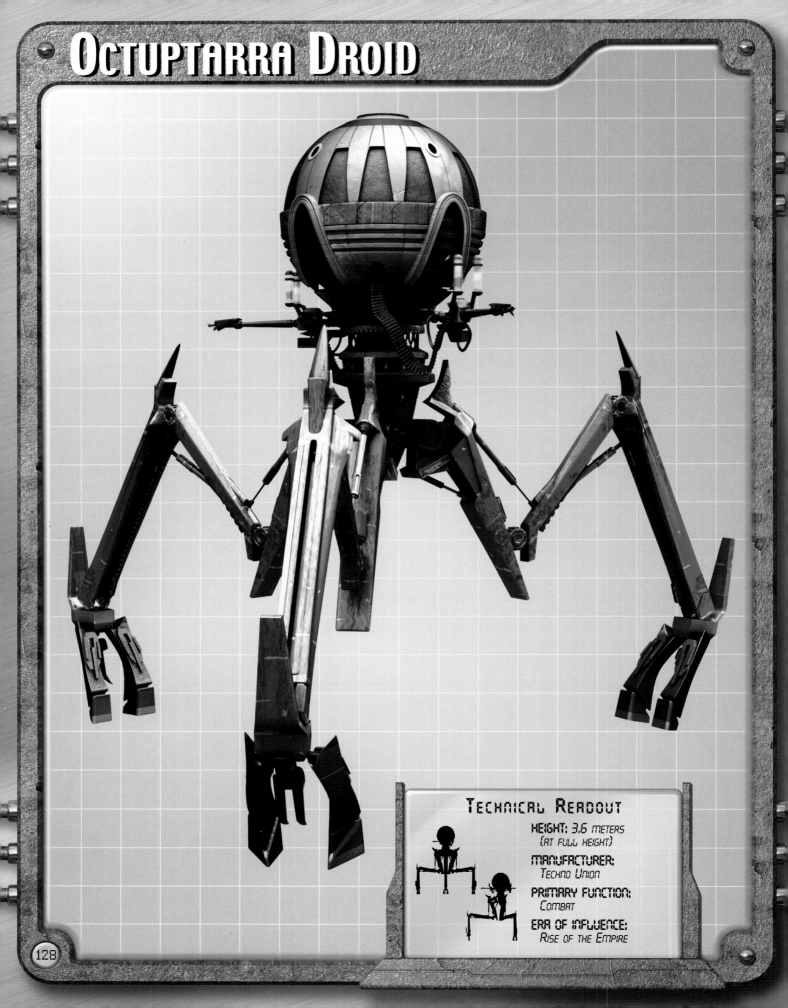

TECHNICAL READOUT

HEIGHT: 3.6 meters
(at full height)

MANUFACTURER:
Techno Union

PRIMARY FUNCTION:
Combat

ERA OF INFLUENCE:
Rise of the Empire

Techno Union Octuptarra Combat Tri-Droid

Uncomfortably alien for most humanoids, the octuptarra droid is an example of the insectoid exoticism that often found its way into the designs of the Confederacy of Independent Systems.

For the Skakoans, who dominated the Techno Union, however, the octuptarra droid seemed as familiar as a family pet. True octuptarras are eight-eyed, gasbag-headed vine climbers found on the methane planet of Skako. The droids follow a similar body configuration and walk on three attenuated legs, a fact that has caused others to refer to them as "tri-droids."

Symmetrical on all sides, the octuptarra droid has no blind spots and can fire in any direction, thanks to a rotating laser turret. It is lightweight and can dangle upside down from overhangs. The balloon-shaped globe atop an octuptarra houses its cognitive circuitry, but the module is poorly guarded and an easy target for enemy fire. Separatist commanders soon discovered that octuptarra droids functioned best from long range, where their cannons could pick off advancing troopers with stuttering laser bursts.

Octuptarra droids, like the Techno Union's crab droids, can be produced in a variety of sizes thanks to scaleable manufacturing plants. Most are humanoid-size anti-personnel units, but some are as large as tanks. These behemoths saw battlefield action as combat artillery units, supporting Commerce Guild spider walkers with their chain-fed ordnance launchers.

During the first year of the Clone Wars, Separatist researchers developed a loathsome sampler of tailored biological plagues. One virus targeted the specific genome shared by the Republic's clone troopers, and aerosol canisters containing the toxin were installed inside the heads of octuptarra droids. The droids would release the spray after making suicide runs into the heart of enemy infantry formations. The Republic Grand Army soon developed an antidote, but the campaign gave the octuptarra a second nickname: *virus droid.*

Octuptarra droids numbered among the robotic hordes swarming Coruscant during General Grievous's kidnapping of Supreme Chancellor Palpatine. After the battle, heaps of crushed and blasted droid parts wound up in the lowest levels of the city-canyons. Trace amounts of the octuptarra virus leaked out from the cracked fragments, and a modified strain of the clone disease infected the Shashay and other avian aliens, leading to an unfortunate outbreak of molting.

Following the Clone Wars, most octuptarra droids wound up on Uba IV, a Separatist planet that boasted a droid manufacturing plant. In the minds of many, octuptarra droids have since become interchangeable with the fearsome, masked Ubese.

> **"The Seps have virus droids, so check your helmet seals and breathing filters. A head shot could release a contaminant of unknown origin."**
>
> —*Clone commander Gree, prior to the Battle of Uba IV*

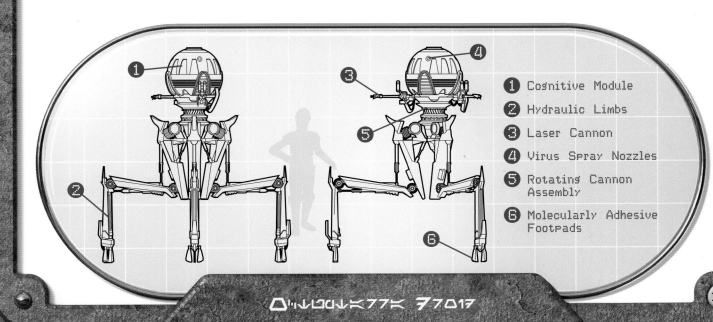

1. Cognitive Module
2. Hydraulic Limbs
3. Laser Cannon
4. Virus Spray Nozzles
5. Rotating Cannon Assembly
6. Molecularly Adhesive Footpads

POLLUX ASSASSIN DROID

TECHNICAL READOUT

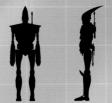

HEIGHT: 2.4 METERS

MANUFACTURER:
Pollux Poi

PRIMARY FUNCTION:
Assassination

ERA OF INFLUENCE:
Old Republic, rise of the Empire

Pollux Poi Customized A-Series Assassin Droid

Midway through the Clone Wars, Count Dooku delivered nearly one hundred unfamiliar assassin droids into the Separatist army. Like many of Dooku's acquisitions, the droids baffled colleagues, who hadn't seen anything quite like them before.

More than four thousand standard years prior, Dooku's assassin droids started life as the mechanical children of Pollux Poi, an Anx designer both brilliant and insane. Recruited by the Shell Hutts to build weapons for use against their Hutt rivals in clan Gejalli, Poi constructed an increasingly lethal string of assassin droids. These killers eliminated Hutts three through fourteen in the Gejalli succession hierarchy. The Gejalli survivors exacted their own revenge, taking out a contract on Poi's life. Poi fled to the darkest underlevels of Kashyyyk's wroshyr tree canopy to escape from the merciless Dashade shadow killers.

What followed was nearly two decades of what Pollux Poi called "the shadow game." Inside his leafy hideout, Poi tinkered with new designs as his droids felled Dashade assassins, making Poi one of the most notorious unclaimed bounties in Hutt history. The Dashade stopped coming when the Cron Cluster supernova consumed their homeworld, but Poi died of natural causes not long after.

The creations of Pollux Poi lived on, discovering a primeval machine in Kashyyyk's forest. Establishing contact, this small family let itself be overhauled and replicated by the ancient intelligence they called the Builder Forge.

> **"Count Dooku sends his regards. We are at your command. We are designed to disassemble over eleven thousand sentient species."**
>
> —*Assassin droid A71, reporting for duty during the Battle of Jabiim*

The remade Pollux assassin droids have four photoreceptors for seeing in low-light conditions or scanning infrared wavelengths. Sweeping curves and sharp points dominate their sleek, shiny bodies. Each droid carries a blaster rifle, with a shoulder-mounted blaster cannon as a backup.

Several hundred droids eventually left Kashyyyk for Gree space, home to one of the galaxy's oldest civilizations. Although the droids did not locate more machines like the one on Kashyyyk, a Gree clan happily employed them for the purpose of assassination.

Millennia later, Count Dooku purchased the remaining Pollux assassins from the Gree and sent them into battle against the Republic. Their first tour of duty came on rain-soaked Jabiim, where they killed many members of the Jedi "Padawan Pack" and contributed to a Separatist victory. Later, eighteen Pollux assassins accompanied Asajj Ventress on a failed mission to kill Master Yoda at the Phindar spaceport.

At Phindar, the Pollux units carried a variety of weapons—none of which could be deflected by a lightsaber—to keep their Jedi opponents off balance. Included in this experimental run were flamethrowers, railguns, flechette launchers, sonic grenades, hard-sound guns, and tactical tractor beam projectors. After the Clone Wars, the few surviving Pollux droids are believed to have returned to the wilds of Kashyyyk.

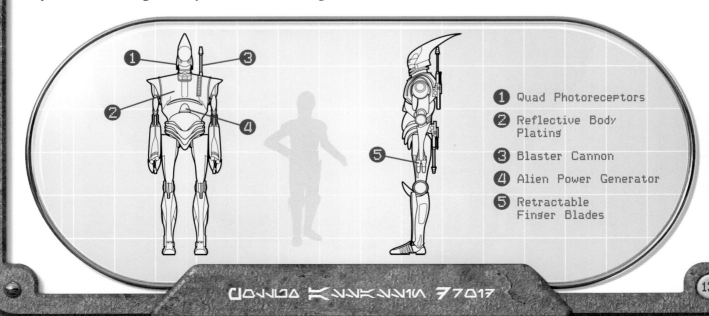

1. Quad Photoreceptors
2. Reflective Body Plating
3. Blaster Cannon
4. Alien Power Generator
5. Retractable Finger Blades

SITH PROBE DROID

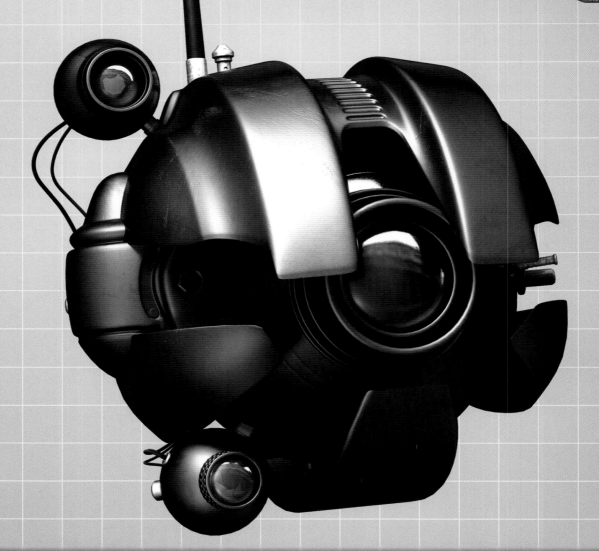

TECHNICAL READOUT

HEIGHT: 0.3 meters

MANUFACTURER:
Arakyd Industries

PRIMARY FUNCTION:
Espionage

ERA OF INFLUENCE:
Old Republic, rise of the
Empire

Sith DRK-1 Dark Eye Probe Droid

Returning to Queen Amidala's starship after freeing the slave boy Anakin Skywalker, Qui-Gon Jinn spotted an unfamiliar droid watching him from an alleyway. A slash of his lightsaber blade bisected the spy. Instantly recognizing a threat, Qui-Gon and his young charge broke into a run.

In a galaxy populated by millions of droid models, how did Qui-Gon know that the floating sphere was of sinister manufacture? After all, the design of the Sith probe droid is hardly unique. Arakyd's explorational droids and Les Tech's submersible ER-1C probe droid all share obvious design similarities.

Qui-Gon could easily have mistaken the Sith probe droid for one of these benign look-alikes—indeed, most of Mos Espa seems to have done exactly that. But Qui-Gon Jinn had the advantage of nearly sixty years of Jedi training. The Sith probe droid, built by Darth Maul from arcane blueprints, stood out like a dark void in the fabric of the Force. Though Maul's probe droids were machines, evil clung to them like a stain.

Darth Maul was as good with a circuit board as he was with a lightsaber. Sith "dark eye" probe droids were common in the years prior to the Battle of Ruusan, and Maul re-created them down to the tiniest detail, using disparate, off-the-shelf parts.

Sith probe droids move on repulsorlifts, allowing them to follow their quarry over mountains, minefields, or methane lakes without any drop in speed or performance. They are designed to locate targets without directly engaging them in combat, and typically feature no standard weapons. Darth Maul, however, used them for assassinations, and his droids carried universal weapons mounts. Maul's add-on killing devices included laser cannons, stun blasters, and poison-dart needlers.

Maul could control up to six probe droids remotely via his wrist-mounted comlink, though the droids possessed autonomous decision-making power once deployed. In last-ditch situations, Maul's droids had self-destruct detonators to prevent their capture.

"Dark eye" droids pack an astonishing number of sensor devices into a small space. They can perform scans in every medium imaginable—audio, visual, thermal, chemical, electromagnetic, and radionic—but their most remarkable skill is their ability to detect the Force.

A Sith probe droid can track a Force-user in much the same way a nashtah follows the scent of blood, partly by scanning biological entities for the presence of midichlorians, and partly by surveying the environment for anomalous Force concentrations. (A machine's ability to sense the Force is evidence of the Sith art known as *mechu-deru.*) The probe droid uses this data to assemble a picture of an individual's Force aura, which appears in playback as a radiant blue nimbus. This dark side science is another example of the very real dangers of Sith lore.

> ## "Probe droid. Very unusual . . . not like anything I've seen before."
>
> —*Qui-Gon Jinn to Anakin Skywalker, after encountering a Sith probe droid*

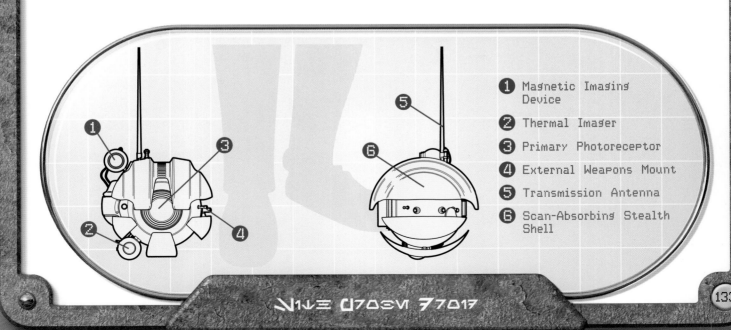

1 Magnetic Imaging Device
2 Thermal Imager
3 Primary Photoreceptor
4 External Weapons Mount
5 Transmission Antenna
6 Scan-Absorbing Stealth Shell

Xim's War-Robot

Technical Readout

Height: 2.78 meters

Manufacturer:
Xim the Despot

Primary Function:
Combat

Era of Influence:
Old Republic, rise of the
Empire, new Jedi order

Empire of Xim War-Robot

Between the fall of the Rakatan Infinite Empire and the rise of the Galactic Republic, Xim the Despot ruled the starways. Xim's war-robots are among the earliest combat automata known to history.

From 25,125 to 25,100 B.B.Y., Xim's kingdom flourished in the Outer Rim territory known as the Tion. Populated by castoff Rakata and the descendants of an ancient Core Worlds colony ship, the Tion's planets remained linked to one another through a precarious "lighthouse network" of hyperspace beacons. Xim, who had subjugated hundreds of planets with his army of war-robots, finally met worthy foes in the Hutts and their legions of retainers.

The war-robots towered over the battlefield, sunlight glinting off the laser-reflective mirrored coating on their armor. Bulky joints and stress points, reinforced to protect vital control systems, made the robots slow and stiff.

Shielded apertures in the arms and hands housed chemical and energy weapons, including archaic heat-beams and particle dischargers. Each robot's cranial turret contained optical lenses and a speaker grille, and bore tiny unit insignia markings. The robots took orders from whoever controlled the transmission horn on a military command platform. Rank could be distinguished by the color of their death's-head emblem: white for a corpsman, gold for a corps commander, and red for a crimson condottiere (a rare variety possessing Force-sensitive Rakatan technology).

> **"To the seventh dungeon with the conqueror-fool. There he shall subjugate rotworms, while his gearwork soldiers stand in glorious tribute to High Exaltedness Kossak."**
>
> *—Kossak the Hutt's victory proclamation following the Third Battle of Vontor*

Xim's war-robots were remarkable not only for their lethality, but also for their degree of self-awareness. Most automata before that point, such as binary loadlifters, had been machines with just a glimmer of intelligence. The generous appropriation of Rakatan technology in the construction of Xim's droids gave them the ability to interact with their builders, although a primitive behavioral circuitry matrix made them rigidly literal in the interpretation of their orders.

Xim lost the Third Battle of Vontor to Kossak the Hutt, and died a prisoner in Kossak's dungeons on Varl. Most of Xim's war-robots did not survive the Vontor massacre, and the Hutts took hundreds of the remaining units back to their territory as trophies.

One thousand others were not present at Vontor, having been assigned to Xim's treasure ship *Queen of Ranroon*. After off-loading the treasure in a vault on Dellalt, the robots remained on guard for a thousand generations. Shortly before the Battle of Yavin, Han Solo and Chewbacca visited Dellalt and saw Xim's droids attack a mining settlement, but most of the relics perished when a bridge collapsed beneath their heavy footfalls.

In Hutt space, Xim's robots decorated public plazas and palace steps. Few suspected they were any more than statuary until the Yuuzhan Vong invaded the Hutt homeworlds in 26 A.B.Y. In a desperate failsafe, Xim's robots came to life and killed thousands of the invaders before falling beneath a hail of blastbugs and amphistaffs.

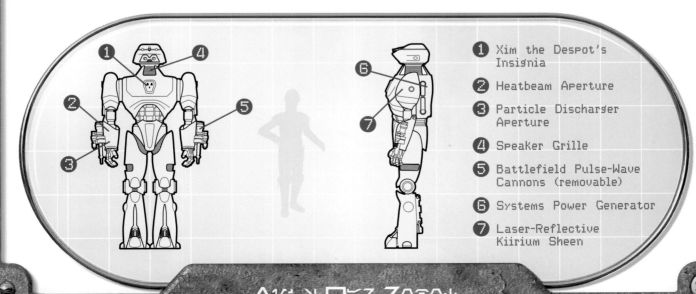

1. Xim the Despot's Insignia
2. Heatbeam Aperture
3. Particle Discharger Aperture
4. Speaker Grille
5. Battlefield Pulse-Wave Cannons (removable)
6. Systems Power Generator
7. Laser-Reflective Kiirium Sheen

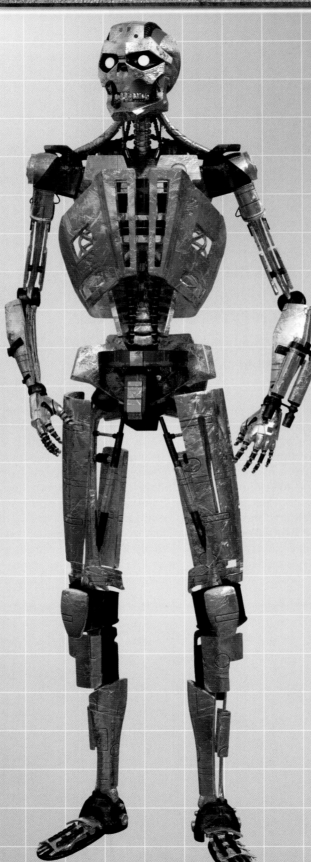

Technical Readout

HEIGHT: 1.9 meters

MANUFACTURER: Tendrando Arms

PRIMARY FUNCTION: Combat

ERA OF INFLUENCE: New Jedi order

Tendrando Arms YVH 1 Yuuzhan Vong Hunter

The YVH 1, better known as the Yuuzhan Vong Hunter, debuted in 27 A.B.Y., two standard years into the war between the extragalactic invaders and the forces of the New Republic. The Yuuzhan Vong had already destroyed much of the galaxy's droid manufacturing infrastructure, but Lando Calrissian decided to build droids powerful enough to fight back.

Lando's company, Tendrando Arms, debuted its prototype unit on Coruscant in a demonstration for Chief of State Borsk Fey'lya. The droid, YVH 1-1A, found himself fighting real targets when Yuuzhan Vong infiltrators emerged from the ranks of the attendees. Even with YVH 1-1A's weapons stuck on low power due to the conditions of the demo, the droid found a way to end the threat with a lethal squeeze of his arms.

Each YVH 1 bears a surface resemblance to a Yuuzhan Vong warrior, a design choice intended to infuriate the New Republic's prideful enemies. The torso is protected by overlapping plates of laminanium, painted black and gray for camouflage. Laminanium is a self-healing Qellan metal capable of melting and re-solidifying at room temperature to seal breaches. It can generate a full hermetic seal if the YVH is threatened by corrosive acids.

A YVH's right arm is a variable-output blaster cannon capable of stunning targets at low power and, at its highest setting, blasting a starfighter into smithereens. The droid's left arm ends in a socket that can accommodate a sampler of interchangeable weapons, including a heavy laser, a sonic rifle, a fifty-shot battery of seeker missiles, and a launcher for firing explosive baradium pellets.

The droid's legs incorporate built-in repulsorlifts. While these aren't powerful enough to permit flight, they do allow the droid to make tremendous leaps. All Yuuzhan Vong Hunters speak in a deep, booming facsimile of Lando Calrissian's own voice.

The YVH isn't just a war machine—it has also been programmed to sniff out undercover Yuuzhan Vong spies. By employing a sensor pack that incorporates chemical and pheromonal detectors, infrared and telescopic photoreceptors, and an atmosphere analyzer, the YVH can even identify Yuuzhan Vong wearing the living disguises known as ooglith masquers.

YVH droids proved invaluable on the Jedi mission to Myrkr and in the defense of Borleias, but the complexity of their construction prevented them from seeing extensive service during the war. In a related project, New Republic agents took the sensor packs built for Yuuzhan Vong Hunters and packed them into the bodies of mouse droids, creating subtle spy detectors called YVH-M droids, for Yuuzhan Vong Hunter Mouse.

> ## "We are machines! We are greater than the Yuuzhan Vong!"
>
> —*Battle cry of the YVH droids at Borleias, designed to trigger maximum outrage in their enemies*

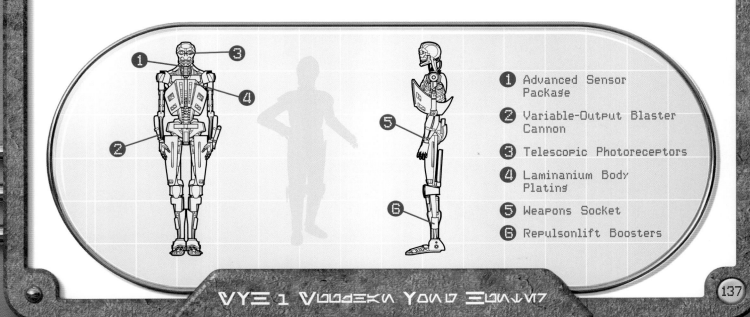

1. Advanced Sensor Package
2. Variable-Output Blaster Cannon
3. Telescopic Photoreceptors
4. Laminanium Body Plating
5. Weapons Socket
6. Repulsonlift Boosters

Z-X3 Droid Trooper

Technical Readout

HEIGHT: 1.9 meters

MANUFACTURER:
TaggeCo

PRIMARY FUNCTION:
Combat

ERA OF INFLUENCE:
Rise of the Empire,
Rebellion

TaggeCo Z-X3 Experimental Droid Trooper

The Z-X3, essentially the second generation of TaggeCo's L8-L9, represented the Empire's first attempt to build a battle droid. The effort failed, but subsequent refinements of the Z-X3 would lead directly to the Empire's murderous Dark Troopers.

Rom Mohc, a soldier in the Republic Grand Army and later an Imperial officer, had an obsession with personal combat. He supported anything that increased the likelihood of one-on-one battle, and rejected anything that moved away from that ideal, including Palpatine's Death Star superweapon. Although Mohc relished working with clone troopers, he also developed an appreciation for the Separatists' battle droids. Combining the two interests, Mohc championed research into robotic stormtroopers that could act as backups for the clone fighting forces.

The program, dubbed the Droid Trooper Project, appeared to come at an opportune time. In the wake of the Clone Wars, the Imperial stormtrooper corps was subdividing into units that specialized in unique planetary environments—seatroopers, sandtroopers, and snowtroopers among them. But some environments were simply too hazardous for stormtroopers to endure. Mohc hoped his droid trooper could be the answer.

Mohc's skunkworks inside Tagge Industries soon produced the Z-X3. A humanoid droid with plating inspired by the armor and helmets of stormtroopers, its crimson color makes it an instant standout. The Z-X3 lacks built-in weaponry, instead carrying a blaster rifle or wearing a Briletto AAP-IV "blaster box" on its chest. The Z-X3 possesses enhanced strength and a sophisticated intelligence not dependent on a central control computer. It can operate in any number of hazardous environments, from deep space to high-radiation dead zones.

Tagge produced less than one hundred Z-X3 units, a sufficient number for the Empire to evaluate them in controlled testing. But the defeat of the Separatist droid army was too fresh in the minds of most Imperials—since the war's end, the pendulum had swung even farther in favor of clones and organics. The Empire deemed the droid troopers inadequate for military deployment. Two new classifications of stormtrooper—the radtrooper (for irradiated environments) and the zero-g spacetrooper—filled the niches for which the Z-X3 had been intended. A pragmatic Mohc joined the spacetrooper corps, but he continued brainstorming the droid that would eventually become the Dark Trooper.

The remaining Z-X3 units were slated for recycling, but most found their way into private hands. A few even found service with the Empire at remote garrisons. One unit wound up at Droid World, the artificial satellite established by the cyborg Kligson after the Clone Wars. Still loyal to his Imperial programming, Z-X3 tried to usurp control of Droid World from Kligson in the name of the Empire and set himself up as a robotic dictator. A war between Z-X3's faction and Kligson's faction nearly destroyed Droid World, but Kligson emerged victorious and left Z-X3 in pieces.

> **"Now we will vanquish any who still hold to his ways . . . who will not serve the Imperial cause! As the Empire rules the galaxy, Droid World is ours to command!"**
>
> —*A Z-X3 unit inciting rebellion on Kligson's Moon*

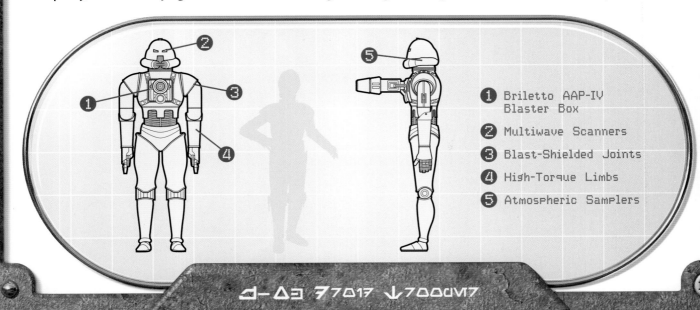

1. Briletto AAP-IV Blaster Box
2. Multiwave Scanners
3. Blast-Shielded Joints
4. High-Torque Limbs
5. Atmospheric Samplers

Class Five Droids

Before the droid classification system came into common use, *all* droids were essentially class five. The term describes automata that labor in trades such as mining, cargo lifting, wreck salvaging, garbage collecting, and driving simple conveyances.

The first droids ever invented belonged to these groupings, thanks to engineers in the pre-Republic era who placed primitive behavioral circuitry matrices into robotic frames. The resulting workers could think well enough to handle simple tasks, and in the tens of millennia since, there has been little need to improve on this ancient template.

Class five droids with too much intelligence often develop an understanding of the drudgery of their round-the-clock duties. Sometimes this leads class fives to organize labor strikes among their fellow units, or to intentionally perform their duties poorly in a passive-aggressive show of defiance.

The droids in the class five category are by far the most numerous of the droid classes. Most galactic citizens encounter a class one or class three droid only rarely, but will pass by dozens of class five units on a short walk down the street. This ubiquity in numbers makes class five droids the object of ire from groups such as the Organization for Organic Purity, due to the volume of jobs the droids have taken from organic workers. Over the centuries, the ordinariness of class five droids has led espionage agencies to outfit them as spies.

Most class five droids can be categorized into one of several main groupings:

- **General labor droids** are one-size-fits-all class five units. Not designed for any specific job, they can learn most simple tasks with minimal instruction. These droids are often built in a bipedal human configuration. General labor droids can vary a great deal in their level of sophistication, with asp droids and BLX droids marking the nadir and zenith of the intelligence spectrum.

- **Labor specialist droids** are built with a precise task in mind and sold to niche buyers. These droids are usually constructed in unusual configurations specific to their job function. The giant automated threshers in the grain fields of Orron III, the window washers of Coruscant, and the spidery tree feeders in the Forbidden Gardens of Nuswatta are all examples of class five labor specialists.

- **Hazardous-service droids** are related to labor specialists in that they exist to perform specific jobs—but these are typically jobs that no organic could hope to survive. The 8D8 smelting operators, which work inside metal-liquefying blast furnaces, are a prime example. Elsewhere in the galaxy, hazardous-service droids scoop gems from the high-pressure cores of gas giants, or mine valuable ores from the molten crusts of planets that orbit too close to their stars.

Any further grouping of Class Five droids is a subject of debate among those who develop such taxonomies. Essentially, any droid with a minimal level of intelligence is considered by most a class five, regardless of what job it performs. Thus, a hospital assistant capable only of handing over surgical tools would be a class five, though purists might still group it with the class ones.

8D8 Smelting Operator

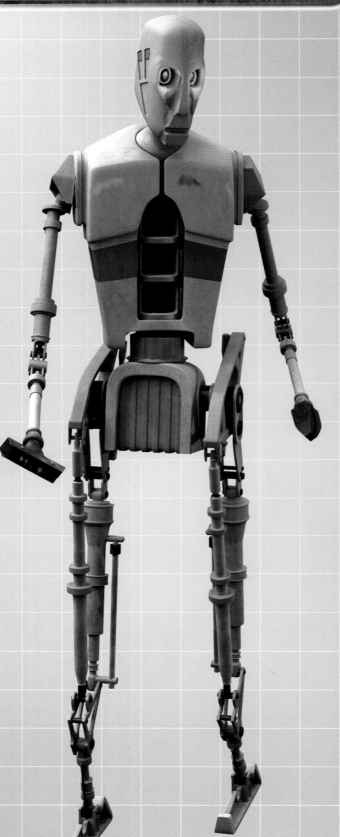

TECHNICAL READOUT

HEIGHT: 1.83 meters

MANUFACTURER:
Roche

PRIMARY FUNCTION:
Metals smelting

ERA OF INFLUENCE:
Rise of the Empire,
Rebellion, New Republic

Roche 8D8 Smelting Operation Droid

The 8D8 is one of the most mean-spirited droids in service today. Fortunately, 8D8s work inside blast furnaces, where most individuals will never encounter one.

Metal-smelting plants are common on manufacturing planets from Balmorra to Geonosis. Working conditions within the plants can be deadly, with temperatures reaching 1,650 degrees Centigrade. Organic operators cannot enter a blast furnace without enviro-suits, so the Roche droid manufacturing hive introduced the 8D8 smelting operator to fill this highly specialized niche.

The Verpine of the Roche hive, stung by the failure of their J9 worker drone, designed the 8D8 to resemble a humanoid rather than an insectoid. The final design could be mistaken for a thin-faced human, but appears to be more directly influenced by the Muun species (who enjoyed a financial interest in thousands of metal-stamping plants that the Roche hive hoped to tap for its 8D8 sales). The complicated leg joints of the 8D8 remain telltale signs of Verpine manufacture.

Because droids are made of metal, fireproofing a droid to work in a metal-smelting chamber proved to be Roche's greatest challenge. The body parts of an 8D8 are cast from a proprietary ore made of high-grade durasteel molecularly bonded with kevlex. The substance has a melting point of over four thousand degrees Centigrade. The 8D8's piggishly tiny optical sensors were another result of the fireproofing process. Roche gave the droids enhanced strength, as well as the ability to operate for weeks at a time without a recharge.

At a typical blast furnace, three 8D8s will stand in the bosh, the lower portion of the furnace: one to monitor the blast tuyeres, one to drain the slag from the top of the melt, and one to tap the furnace by forcing out molten metal approximately ten times a standard day. Two additional 8D8s operate skip hoists that dump raw materials into the bell hoppers and furnace. An optional sixth unit can be used to oversee the control board and check the condition of the firebrick refractory shell.

Roche gave its 8D8 units enough cognitive ability to realize that their jobs are repetitive and dangerous. They resent "lazy" droids that work in jobs such as protocol or communications; indeed, a few have become surly, ill-tempered bullies.

Jabba the Hutt employed an 8D8 in his Tatooine palace, where the droid assisted the sadistic EV-9D9 in the torture and dismantling of the other droids in Jabba's labor pool. "Atedeate" possessed even more brains than the norm—thanks to a former owner who had modified him to perform starship repairs—and suffered his job in contemptuous silence.

> **"When your 8D8 emerges from the foundry, it will be EXTREMELY HOT! Touching its shell may result in severe burns to your manipulative appendages."**
>
> —*Excerpt from the 8D8 owner's manual*

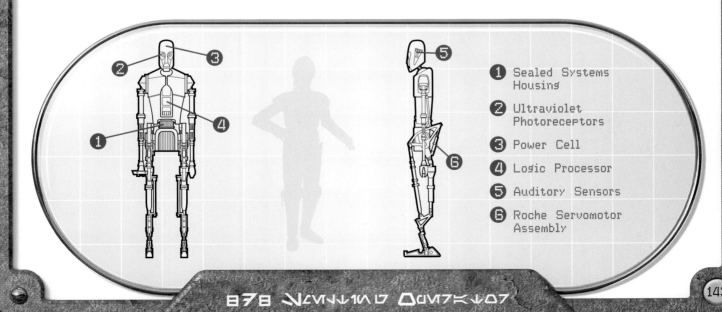

1. Sealed Systems Housing
2. Ultraviolet Photoreceptors
3. Power Cell
4. Logic Processor
5. Auditory Sensors
6. Roche Servomotor Assembly

ASP Droid

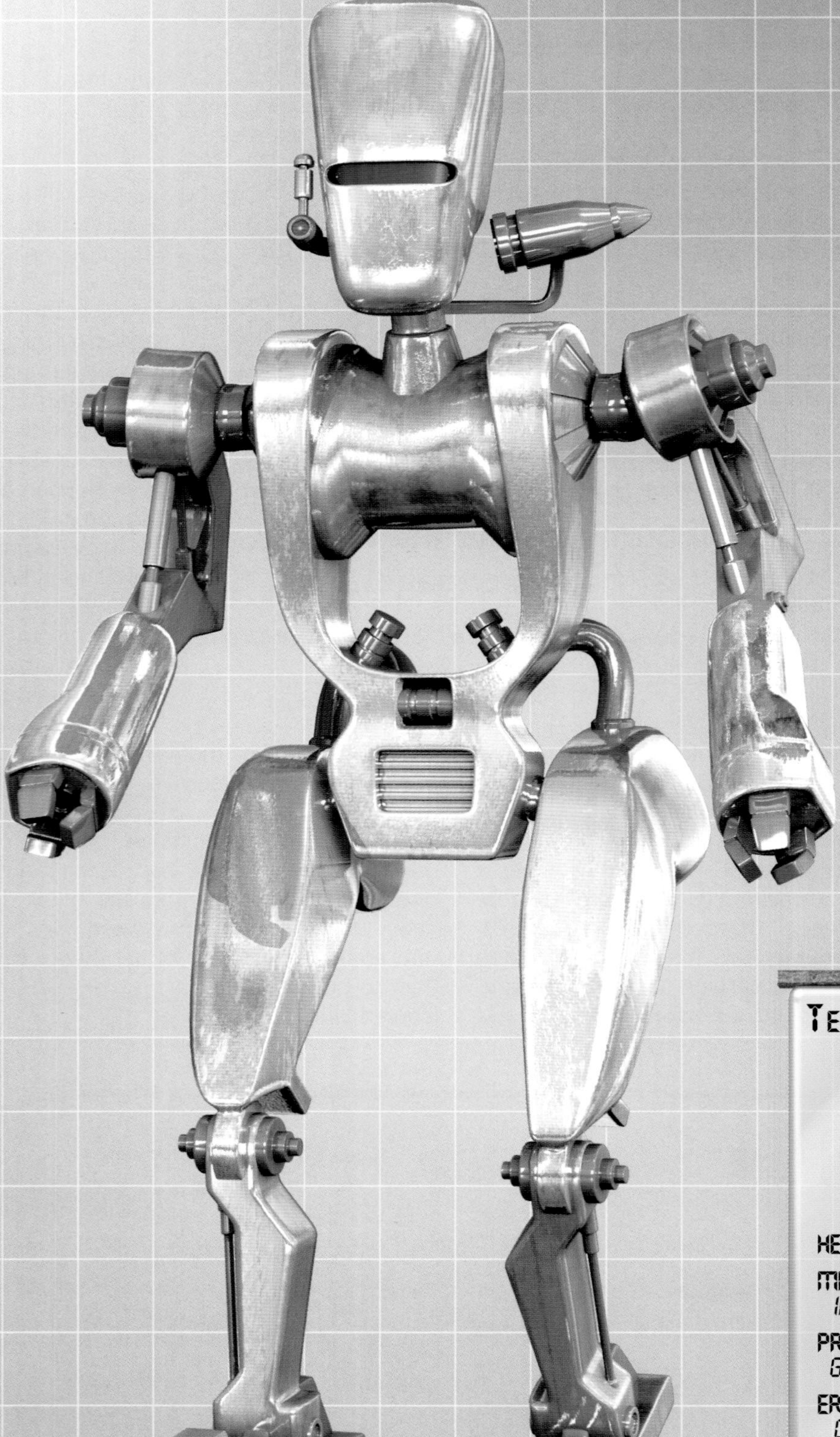

TECHNICAL READOUT

HEIGHT: 1.6 meters

MANUFACTURER:
Industrial Automaton

PRIMARY FUNCTION:
General labor

ERA OF INFLUENCE:
Old Republic, rise of the Empire, Rebellion, New Republic

Industrial Automaton ASP Utility Droid

Most individuals own at least one droid, and some own dozens. But when someone is asked to name his or her *first* droid, it's a good bet that the top response would be the ASP.

Generations ago, Industrial Automaton mass-produced the bare-bones ASP, giving it the bargain-basement price of one thousand credits. At the time, this was a remarkably good deal for a droid with its capabilities. A sales boom resulted among young and first-time buyers, and Industrial Automaton eagerly welcomed them into the IA family. Down the road, the company hoped its customers would move on to more expensive models, such as the R series astromech or the SE-4 servant droid.

ASP droids couldn't be simpler. They consist of nuts, bolts, and metal piping molded together into a humanoid frame. They exhibit none of the gleaming aesthetics seen in protocol models, such as Cybot Galactica's 3PO series. The ASP's head contains two audio pickups and a single photoreceptor, offset on the right side of the face. These sensors are limited to the auditory and visual ranges detectible by humans.

The droids aren't designed for any job in particular. Consequently, they are reasonably capable of doing almost anything. Though ASPs will always be outclassed by a specialty model at any specific task, they are commonly employed as repair bots, cleanup units, or delivery droids.

Models within the ASP series come with numerical designations, from 1 to 20. There isn't a great deal of variation within the lineup, although the higher numbers typically come with greater strength or other added features—and a higher cost associated with these "premium packages." The ASP-7, a solid middle-of-the-road performer, is Industrial Automaton's biggest seller.

The ASP's hydraulically powered limbs are remarkably strong, making the droids unsuitable for delicate work. It doesn't help that they are notoriously thickheaded, requiring detailed instructions for any job more complicated than stacking boxes.

By far, the most annoying trait of a standard-model ASP is its primitive vocabulator, which can produce only two words: *affirmative* and *negative.* Trying to pry information out of an ASP can turn into a maddening game of "guess my secret."

Many owners can't abide these design confines, and modify their asp units with additional hardware or programming patches. Droid engineers in the Imperial Palace maintained a small army of ASP-19s, outfitted with armor plating, hyperfast reaction packages, and data libraries covering classical fencing. Every week, Darth Vader sliced these droids to pieces during his lightsaber combat workouts.

> **"So let me get this straight. The fault is in the harmonic field sensor?"**
> **"Negative."**
> **"The hyperdrive sequencer?"**
> **"Negative."**
> **"The ion turbo-injector?"**
> **"Negative."**
>
> *—A typically frustrating exchange between an owner and an ASP droid*

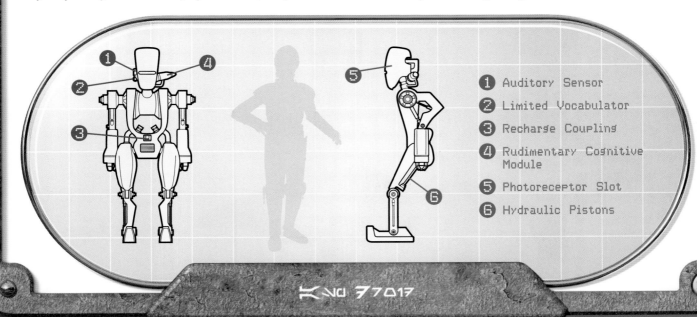

1. Auditory Sensor
2. Limited Vocabulator
3. Recharge Coupling
4. Rudimentary Cognitive Module
5. Photoreceptor Slot
6. Hydraulic Pistons

BINARY LOADLIFTER

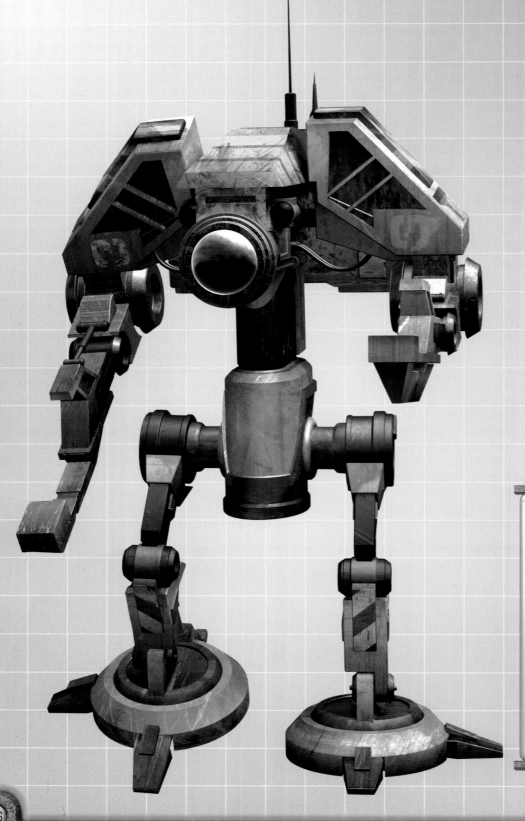

TECHNICAL READOUT

HEIGHT: 3.0 meters

MANUFACTURER:
Cybot Galactica

PRIMARY FUNCTION:
Cargo lifting

ERA OF INFLUENCE:
Old Republic, rise of the
Empire, Rebellion, New
Republic, new Jedi order

Cybot Galactica CLL-M2 Binary Loadlifter

Binary loadlifters are a window into ancient droid history. Cargo haulers were among the first automata invented during the murky ages of the pre-Republic, and have changed very little in more than thirty thousand standard years.

Binary loadlifters represent a droid category that encompasses many different models. All of them communicate in the simplistic computer language of binary, which cannot be understood by humans without a video display screen or other interpreting device. Binary loadlifters can understand their owners' verbal commands, but giving the loadlifters complex tasks is best left to other droids fluent in binary. Protocol droids are more than capable of handling such work, adding a sheen of plausibility to C-3PO's claim.

Most loadlifters incorporate strong hydraulic limbs and a gyro-stabilization mechanism. The lifting arms usually end in flat hands that can slide underneath cargo skids, though some lifters come equipped with claw-shaped graspers. Auditory sensors and binary vocabulators are standard, while quite a few models have a single photoreceptor that doubles as a cargo-code scanner.

Binary load lifters are notoriously dull-witted. They simply lack the programming to make self-aware decisions, which prompts even some droids' rights activists to classify them as nonthinking machines. In an infamous incident on Stassia, a binary loadlifter repeatedly stacked heavy crates in a depot corner—despite overtaxed floorboards groaning and splintering under the weight. When the entire floor finally gave way, the lifter simply righted itself and stomped off to collect another crate.

Popular models of binary loadlifters include Cybot Galactica's CLL-8 and CLL-M2. The latter unit saw extensive use by the Grand Army of the Republic during the Clone Wars, and incorporates a unique feature: the repulsorlift counterweight. This gadget, located at the rear of the CLL-M2, generates a reverse polarization field that increases the pull of gravity, acting as a counterbalance whenever the CLL-M2 raises particularly heavy loads onto its lifting arms.

The CLL-M2 sports yellow warning stripes on its squared-off shoulders. Its footpads, similar to those of the AT-AT walker, help disperse its weight and the weight of its load over a broad surface area. During the Clone Wars, the CLL-M2 worked primarily as an ordnance lifter, delicately carrying and mounting explosive military armaments. A close cousin of the CLL-M2 was Cybot Galactica's IW-37 pincer loader, an extremely precise automaton with a single arm, used to arm missile pods or to remove ammunition from wrecks—a practice that led to its nickname "salvager droid."

> ## "Vaporators! Sir—my first job was programming binary loadlifters . . . very similar to your vaporators in most respects."
>
> *—A less-than-truthful C-3PO, trying to promote himself to Owen Lars at a droid sale*

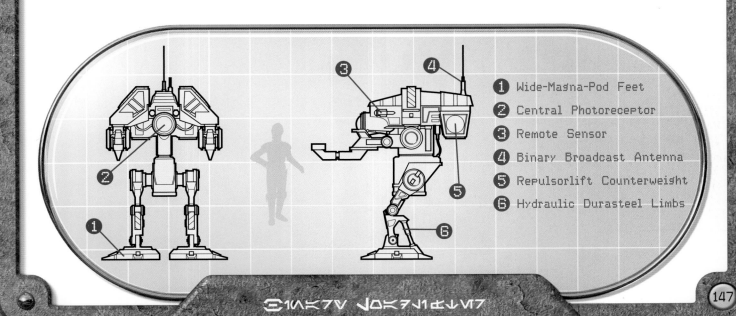

1. Wide-Magna-Pod Feet
2. Central Photoreceptor
3. Remote Sensor
4. Binary Broadcast Antenna
5. Repulsorlift Counterweight
6. Hydraulic Durasteel Limbs

BLX Labor Droid

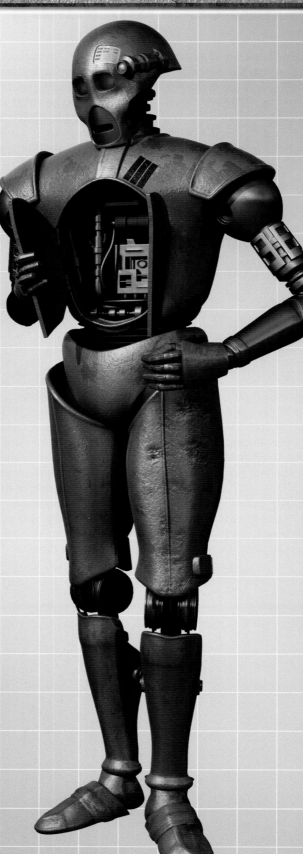

Technical Readout

Height: 1.5 meters

Manufacturer:
Serv-O-Droid

Primary Function:
General labor

Era of Influence:
Old Republic, rise of the
Empire, new Jedi order

Serv-O-Droid BLX General Labor Droid

It's rare to see a BLX unit these days. Even before the Clone Wars, the droids were already on the wane, victims of changing market tastes. But Serv-O-Droid built the BLX to last, and some have been working in the same high-stress jobs for generations.

Built in a bipedal humanoid configuration, the BLX labor droid has photoreceptors and auditory pickups calibrated for standard wavelengths; its reaction time and walk cycle are quite slow. But the BLX possesses formidable strength, and is nearly unbeatable in terms of stamina. Serv-O-Droid priced the droids to move, often selling them in lots of one hundred or more to large repair yards.

By their nature, BLX droids do not specialize in anything. They function well in zero-g, where their magnetic footpads allow them to cling to starship hulls and their metal shells shrug off temperature extremes or hits from micrometeorites. Serv-O-Droid's original BLX series featured an uneven head and simian arms that dangled below the unit's knees. Later models, including the BLX NV, have more human-like proportions.

When given regular memory wipes, BLX units are unremarkable. Yet their behavioral circuitry matrices can create surprisingly acute levels of self-awareness, if allowed to accumulate life experience. Many untreated BLX droids developed personalities and befriended their owners, who spared them from the smelting chambers when the droids reached the point of obsolescence.

The most famous droid in the BLX series started operating in the starship yards of Fondor approximately one hundred standard years before the Battle of Yavin. BLX-5, or "Bollux," escaped a memory wipe by accepting a job to clear out a mynock nest. When he returned, the local personnel grew to love his dry wit. They manumitted Bollux at the end of his term of service, making him one of the few free droids in galactic society at that time.

Over the following decades, Bollux worked for scouting teams and other frontier outfits, exploring the galaxy under a variety of aliases, including "Zollux." While in the employ of a Corporate Sector outlaw tech named Doc, Bollux had his chest hardware refitted to make room for a sentient positronic processor designated Blue Max. In the years prior to the Battle of Yavin, Bollux and Blue Max shared adventures with Han Solo and Chewbacca from Stars' End to Dellalt.

During the Yuuzhan Vong invasion, Han encountered another BLX unit on Ruan. Calling itself "Baffle," this droid dropped hints that it was, in fact, Bollux, but Han had his doubts regarding the droid's sincerity.

> **"I volunteered for all the modifications and reprogramming I could, but eventually I simply couldn't compete with the newer, more capable droids."**
>
> *—A philosophical Bollux, reflecting on the history of the BLX unit*

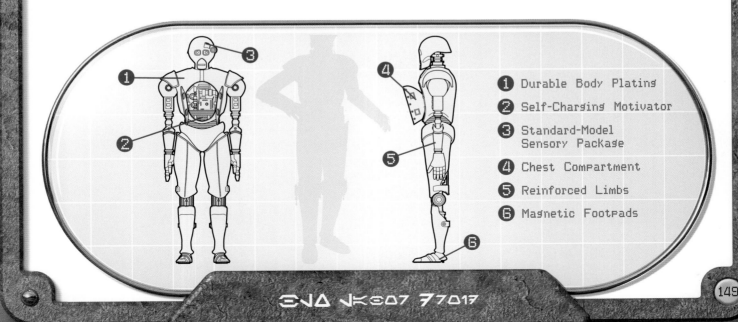

1 Durable Body Plating
2 Self-Charging Motivator
3 Standard-Model Sensory Package
4 Chest Compartment
5 Reinforced Limbs
6 Magnetic Footpads

Cam Droid

Technical Readout

HEIGHT: 0.7 meter long

MANUFACTURER: Various

PRIMARY FUNCTION: News recording

ERA OF INFLUENCE: Old Republic, Rise of the Empire, Rebellion, New Republic, new Jedi order

Industrial Automaton Hologlide J57 Cam Droid

Cam droids, also known as hovercams, are repulsorlift-driven, self-directed recording devices. Although some models are extremely intelligent, including the 3DVO and the Holocam-E, most have minimal cognitive circuitry and are categorized as class five droids.

The bylaws of both the Republic Senate and the New Republic Senate required that all official proceedings be transcribed for the record. Squadrons of Senate cam droids handled the job, zipping among floating congressional boxes on whisper-quiet repulsorlift engines.

Senate cam droids were equipped with multiple visual and audio recording devices. A wide-angle lens and a zoom lens allowed the droids to capture both panoramic views and the expressions on the faces of individual Senators. Senate cam droids transmitted their feeds to the public HoloNet, as well as to private viewscreens in individual boxes. A central data bank stored all recordings for future reference.

Unfortunately, Senate cam droids were only as reliable as their programmers. Cam droids during Palpatine's reign were known to favor pro-Imperial Senators by giving them more airtime, and to unfairly edit statements made by the opposition. Entire Senate meetings sometimes vanished from the archives, and other transcripts were later discovered to have glaring gaps.

Journalist cam droids are designed to capture footage of unfolding news events. They can operate independently, or

> **"Senator Seti Ashgad has disappeared, days after he protested the installation of the Senate's new cam droids. Palpatine's office says the timing is merely a coincidence."**
>
> —*HoloNet News report, filed in 20.6* B.B.Y.

as tools in the employ of organic reporters. A unit such as the 3DVO from Loronar has a repulsorlift engine, a central holocam, a number of backup recorders, and a communications array. The 3DVO is one of the most self-aware units on the market, and frequently seeks out scoops on its own. Shortly after the Battle of Yavin, a journalist 3DVO belonging to the royal family of Jazbina assisted Luke Skywalker in rescuing the daughter of planetary potentate Lord Prepredenko.

In the sport of Podracing, cam droids long ago replaced fixed-position holocams that were prone to damage from weather and vandals. Podrace cam droids, like the Hologlide J57 used at Mos Espa, aren't nearly as fast as the racers they cover, so they take up strategic positions along the track and transmit their recordings back to the grandstand control booth. The multiple signals from the cam droid fleet are relayed to the handheld view-screens carried by spectators, allowing fans to key in on their favorite racer or a particularly dangerous stretch of track.

General-purpose holocams are advertised for personal use. Most are simple constructions with minimal droid intelligence, and are designed to be operated by their owners. Trang Robotics' Holocam-E, or Cammy, is an exception. Like the 3DVO, the Cammy is exceptionally bright, and exudes a warm, motherly personality. A Cammy unit in the employ of the Rebel Alliance helped R2-D2 and C-3PO reprogram an assassin droid factory on Tatooine.

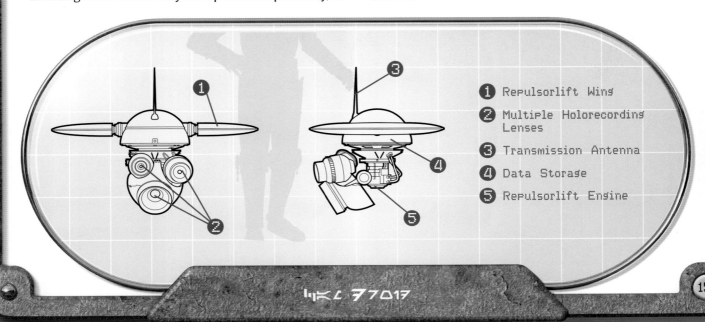

1. Repulsorlift Wing
2. Multiple Holorecording Lenses
3. Transmission Antenna
4. Data Storage
5. Repulsorlift Engine

COO Cook Droid

Industrial Automaton COO Cook Droid

Gourmands shudder when they consider the very concept of cook droids. Why trust your food, goes the argument, to machines that can't even *taste*?

Fortunately for companies such as Industrial Automaton, most people aren't so finicky. The company re-used the chassis from one of its labor units in its COO line of cook droids, and a similar sense of sloppy antipathy extended to the droid's programming. Ugly and clunky, the COO is designed for mass catering on the scale of a military mess hall.

The COO's most notable feature is its arm array. Depending on the socket configuration, a COO can have more than a dozen arms. A working droid might have a spatula, a whisk, a strainer, a serving spoon, a grease brush, a meat fork, a carving knife, several three-fingered manipulators, and a miniature flame projector for lighting oven burners. After the cooking and serving chores are completed, a COO droid will install wire brushes for scouring pots and pans. The droid also has two powerful legs that can lock to the floor with magnetic clamps, a feature that comes in handy on pitching ocean vessels or starships with spotty artificial gravity.

COOs are cook droids, but they lack much knowledge of culinary science. Each comes from the factory pre-loaded with several hundred common recipes taken from the millennia-old *Humbarine Housekeepers HoloBook*.

> **"Me worst spell in space? No, 'twarnt sailing through the fire rings of Fornax. 'Twas the month I spent on the run from the Loronar navy, an' stuck with a vegetarian galley droid."**
>
> —*Reginald Barkbone, legendary pirate of the Seven Sectors*

Industrial Automaton claims that this can be swapped out for a different software pack featuring new recipes, but the removal and installation of these packs is tedious and involves partial disassembly of the droid.

Usually, a COO is stuck with whatever recipes its last owner might have given it. From the outside, it's impossible to know what software a COO is carrying. Furthermore, the droids are notorious liars and will say whatever a buyer wants to hear if it will advance their station in life.

Even the Caamasi, pacifists all, will eventually smash a cook droid to pieces if forced to ingest Hutt cuisine. Many buyers, mindful of the COO's deficiencies in this area, use the droids only to reheat and serve prepackaged food trays.

Prior to the Clone Wars, the star freighter *Jendirian Valley* converted its cargo holds into passenger steerage in order to profit from the Separatist-created refugee crisis. To feed the thousands of people packed belowdecks, the freighter's operators purchased a cook droid designated COO-2180 at a used-droid market. COO-2180 prepared simple meals obtained in bulk from a military surplus store, and had instructions to serve only organic beings. When R2-D2 stole a meal for Padmé Amidala and Anakin Skywalker (traveling incognito among the *Valley*'s passengers), COO-2180 shouted angrily but ineffectually at the little astromech.

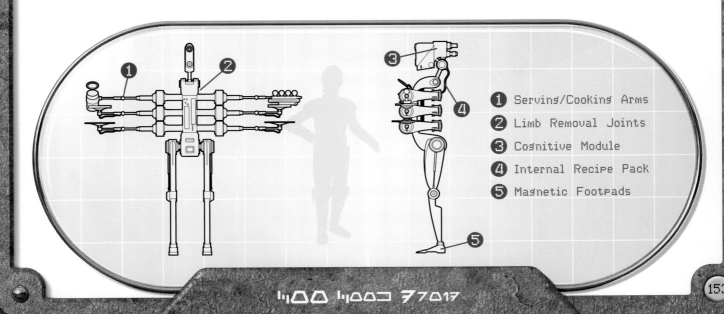

1. Serving/Cooking Arms
2. Limb Removal Joints
3. Cognitive Module
4. Internal Recipe Pack
5. Magnetic Footpads

FA-4 AND FA-5 DROIDS

SoroSuub FA-4 Pilot and FA-5 Valet Droids

The FA series is familiar to anyone who has ever visited a Core starport. Over generations, the design has emerged as the standard droid for companies that offer valet or chauffeur services. Dozens of knockoff models exist, but SoroSuub is the original manufacturer and the only one allowed to use the trademark designation *FA*.

Most public starports in the Core offer baggage-handling and shuttle services free of charge to new arrivals. The work is performed by local companies that compete for shuttle service rights; the companies make money from the operating fees paid out by the starport administrators, as well as whatever they can collect in tips. Three or four companies might work a single starport, their competing fleets of FA units distinguishable by their varied paint colors, or the jackets or caps that they wear. SoroSuub's two most popular models are the FA-4 pilot droid and the FA-5 valet droid.

The FA-4 pilot droid is programmed to operate most landspeeders, airspeeders, and starships—though it lacks the coordination to make complicated maneuvers or the knowledge to calculate hyperspace jumps. Two thin treads drive the droid and provide gripping stability. At starports, FA-4 droids typically greet arrivals and chauffeur them in a SoroSuub airspeeder to a hotel or other nearby destination.

> **"Don't forget to tip your FA droids while on Coruscant. They are programmed to blacklist the stingy."**
>
> —*From* Travels with Gormaanda: Cooking in the Core

The FA-5 valet droid lacks treads, instead walking on two spindly legs nearly twice the length of the droid's body. The humanoid configuration was chosen by SoroSuub to conform more closely to the public's image of a valet. A starport FA-5 droid will carry bags and arrange for transportation, usually by signaling to a waiting FA-4 belonging to the same fleet. SoroSuub sells a sizable number of FA-5 valet droids to private customers, who employ them in household tasks that include drawing baths and laying out the day's clothing. All FA units can speak Basic, in addition to twenty-two of the most common galactic languages.

Count Dooku was among the wealthy customers who combined his needs for mobility and privacy by buying an FA-4 pilot droid. Dooku's droid needed to operate the count's exotic solar sailer, a complicated starship built according to the abstruse blueprints of the alien Gree. The controls for the sailer were far beyond the FA-4's normal capacity, so Geonosian technicians augmented the droid with experimental programming from their vulture droid starfighters. This made the FA-4 a capable pilot even under combat conditions, an ability that came in handy on numerous occasions throughout the Clone Wars.

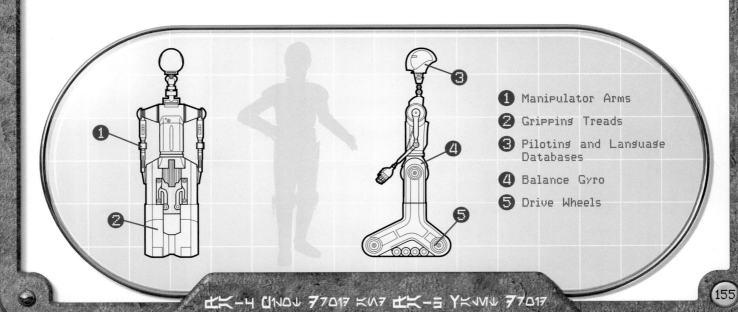

1. Manipulator Arms
2. Gripping Treads
3. Piloting and Language Databases
4. Balance Gyro
5. Drive Wheels

Homing Droid

Technical Readout

HEIGHT: 0.28 meter

MANUFACTURER:
Imperial Department of
Military Research

PRIMARY FUNCTION:
Espionage

ERA OF INFLUENCE:
Rise of the Empire, Rebellion,
New Republic, new Jedi order

Imperial Department of Military Research HMOR Homing Droid

Homing devices are unobtrusive bits of machinery that can be followed from a distance. Used to track stolen property or to signal for help in emergencies, homing devices can also make effective espionage tools. To increase the likelihood of a homing device operating without detection, spy agencies long ago developed the homing droid.

Usually no larger than a human hand, a homing droid is primarily a vehicle for planting a homing device (though the droid can also double as the device itself). Moving through shadows on silent repulsorlifts, a homing droid can penetrate areas of a starship that no organic crew member could ever reach. Unlike a fixed-position beacon, a homing droid is self-aware and capable of movement, enabling it to relocate to a more secure hiding place if it is at risk of discovery.

Homing devices can be active or passive. Active devices transmit a powerful broadcast signal that runs the risk of being detected by its target, while passive devices can be picked up only on specially calibrated sensor sweeps. Homing droids can also act in other ways, from eavesdropping on conversations to sabotaging a starship's hyperdrive and making it easy for those tracking the homing signal to capture their helpless prey.

The HMOR homing droid is a particularly ill-tempered

> ### "You're sure the homing beacon is secure aboard their ship? I'm taking an awful risk, Vader. This had better work."
>
> *—Grand Moff Tarkin, after* Millennium Falcon *"escaped" the Death Star*

product of the Imperial Department of Military Research. Larger than most homing droids, it comes equipped with a repulsorlift engine as well as a set of wheels, for use in high-security environments where the presence of an unfamiliar repulsor field will trigger an alarm. The HMOR unit has a retractable manipulator arm and a database of more than four and a half million starship and airspeeder designs, appropriated by Imperial scientists from the Separatist buzz droid.

The droid carries a small detachable homing device in its back that it can leave behind while it lures searchers on a wild bantha chase into other corners of a starship. The droid's active signal travels via hyperwave, and can be detected at distances tens of thousands of light-years away.

If an HMOR droid is discovered, it will do as much damage as possible before self-destructing. Each is equipped with two explosive seeker drones, while a second retractable arm sprays an acid stream that can eat through durasteel in seconds.

Han Solo's *Millennium Falcon* carried an HMOR homing droid during its escape from the Death Star, secreted deep within the ship's internal workings. R2-D2 was the first to discover the stowaway after the *Falcon*'s arrival at the Yavin 4 base, destroying it before the droid could cause further trouble.

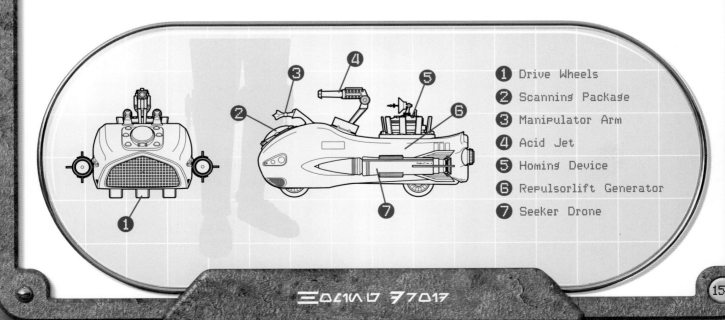

1. Drive Wheels
2. Scanning Package
3. Manipulator Arm
4. Acid Jet
5. Homing Device
6. Repulsorlift Generator
7. Seeker Drone

Imperial Mark IV

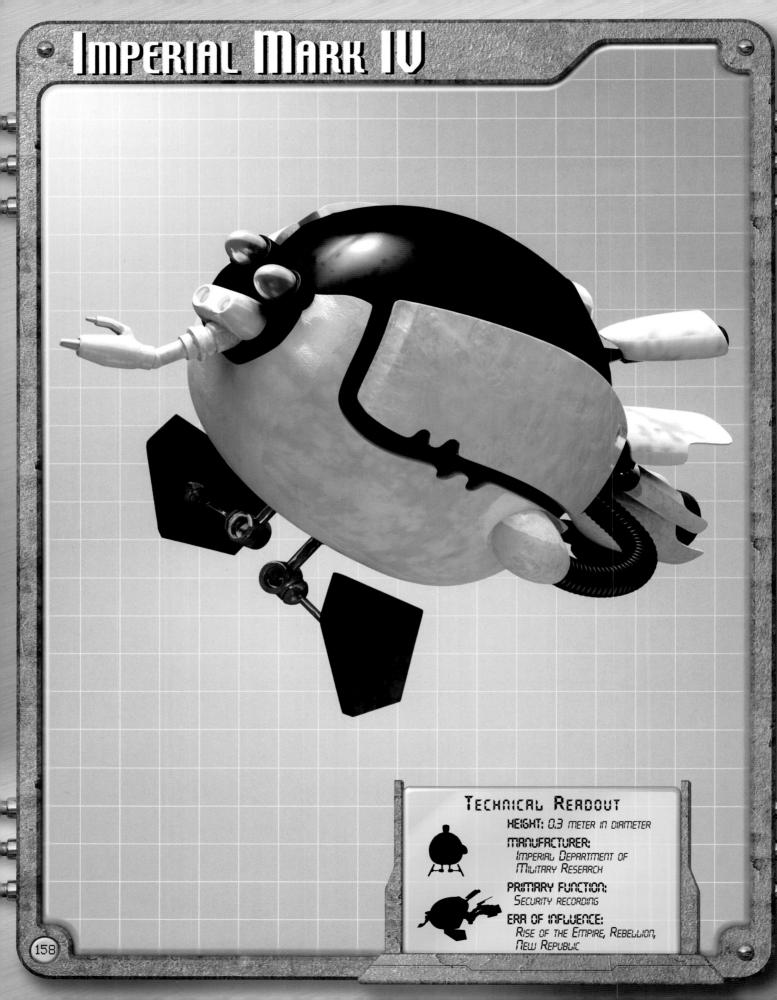

Technical Readout

Height: 0.3 meter in diameter

Manufacturer:
Imperial Department of Military Research

Primary Function:
Security recording

Era of Influence:
Rise of the Empire, Rebellion, New Republic

Imperial Department of Military Research Mark IV (IM4) Sentry Droid

The Imperial Mark IV sentry droid belies the stereotype of Imperial equipment. It's not intimidating in the least, while its small size and curious demeanor have even led some to label it "adorable." But the IM4 was an insidious diminutive spy in the service of Palpatine's Empire. During the height of the Galactic Civil War, the droids were responsible for exposing thousands of covert Rebel cells— a statistic not even the Emperor's Grand Inquisitors could match.

The Mark IV droid is little more than a repulsorlift engine and a scattering of sensors, packed into a lightweight support frame. The repulsorlift can reach a flight ceiling of ten meters and can achieve sudden bursts of speed.

Steering nozzles at the rear of the chassis control direction, while two stabilizer fins ensure a smooth flight. Mark IVs can't move if they're not flying, and the only time they rest is when they've been switched off.

Buying an IM4 at a local droid dealership is impossible. The droids are manufactured exclusively for the Imperial military or governments sympathetic to the Empire. More than a few IM4s, however, have been nabbed by criminals and repurposed for sale on the black market. This is a risky line of work. Mark IVs continually transmit a low-frequency transponder signal back to their base of operations, and tampering with one of the droids is a punishable offense.

The Mark IV is capable of seeing in all directions at

> ## "Your Honor, I'd like to introduce holorecordings of the defendant at the moment of the massacre: IM4-821 from street level, IM4-822 from overhead, IM4-823 from down the block . . ."
>
> *—From the Denon murder trial of Dr. Evazan, before his courtroom escape*

once thanks to sensor clusters at the front, rear, and top. Its forward array includes electromagnetic, infrared, and visible-wavelength sensors. Its macrobinoculars can record a clear picture at distances up to fifty meters and have a built-in holorecording feature. A broadband antenna receiver communicates solely on coded alert frequencies.

Imperial Mark IVs aren't particularly smart, but they're loyal to their owners and can develop personality quirks if not given regular memory wipes. Their databanks contain the complete text of the Imperial Legal Code; the droids can be loaded with additional information on local statutes and maps of city streets. Imperial stormtroopers often used Mark IV units as decoys, sending them around corners to draw fire from concealed enemies. Occasionally, Mark IVs have been fitted with low-powered blasters.

Shortly before the Battle of Yavin, the Empire's Tatooine garrison—as well as Imperial forces from the Star Destroyer *Devastator*—deployed hundreds of Mark IVs to search for two escaped droids. IM4-099, nicknamed "Face" by the Mos Eisley Militia, supported a stormtrooper checkpoint along the city's main thoroughfare. As Mark IVs became omnipresent across the city, they began to interfere with municipal asp droids installing communications repeaters. Despite their omnipresent monitoring, the Mark IVs failed to identify R2-D2 and C-3PO.

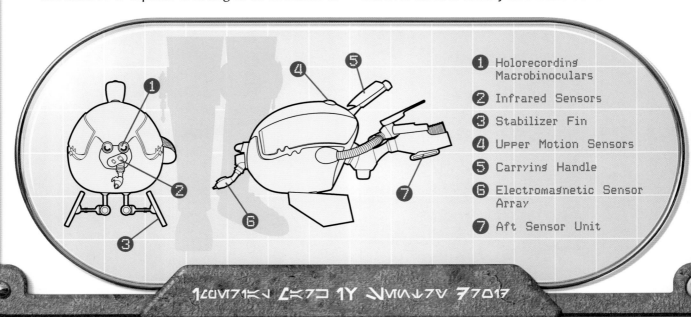

1 Holorecording Macrobinoculars
2 Infrared Sensors
3 Stabilizer Fin
4 Upper Motion Sensors
5 Carrying Handle
6 Electromagnetic Sensor Array
7 Aft Sensor Unit

INS-444 and CLE-004

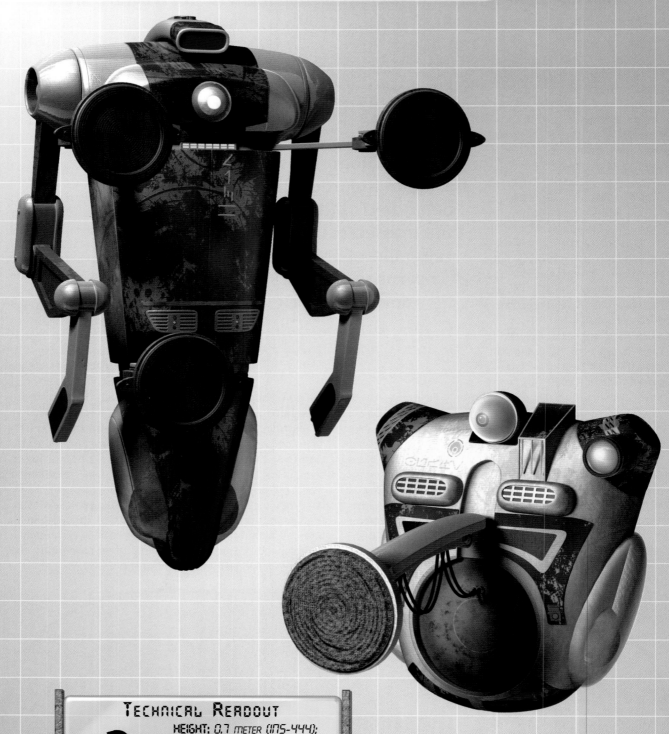

Technical Readout

HEIGHT: 0.7 meter (INS-444);
0.3 meter (CLE-004)

MANUFACTURER:
Publictechnic

PRIMARY FUNCTION:
Window installation (INS-444)
and cleaning (CLE-004)

ERA OF INFLUENCE:
Rise of the Empire, Rebellion,
New Republic, New Jedi Order

Publictechnic INS-444 Window Installation and CLE-004 Window Cleaning Droids

Residents of Coruscant stifle yawns when they're forced to think about the intricacies of cleaning or window-installing droids, but it's a mistake to be so dismissive. The droids, with their ability to hover kilometers above the vertical city, perform tasks that no organic worker would dare undertake.

The INS-444 installer droid and CLE-004 cleaning droid are both manufactured by Publictechnic. Though the droids often work together, the cleaning unit is far more common and is produced in exponentially greater numbers. Any city with skytowers has a use for Publictechnic's window models, but Coruscant is *the* place to sell droids designed for high-rise architecture.

Most windows on Coruscant are not made of transparisteel. Favoring vanity over practicality, residents order windows made from clari-crystalline and even glass, both of which offer a clearer view—with the trade-off of an increased possibility of breakage. Striking a window can shatter the entire pane into thousands of fragments, making INS-444 droids more common than one might think.

The INS-444 comes with magnatomic grip pads to hold a newly ordered window pane during its journey from the store to the installation site. Two INS units work together to carry large panes. During their journey through the city, the INS droids keep their photoreceptors alert for wayward aircars, which sometimes smash right through the transparent windows before their drivers notice that a delivery is in progress. The INS-444 has three manipulator arms that secure the pane against the window frame, and two testing probes on the upper arms to scan for any gaps in the airtight seal.

A CLE-004 cleaning droid accompanies the INS-444 on installation jobs, polishing the new window to remove any droid digit marks. But it's more common to see CLE-004s by themselves outside of Coruscant's myriad apartments and office towers, as they continually wipe off the accumulated grime spawned by the city's constant air traffic. A CLE-004 unit has an electrostatic polishing brush at the end of an articulated arm that can polish a large window in only a few seconds.

Because they're *supposed* to lurk outside windows, CLE-004 droids make perfect spies. A number of parties ranging from news organizations to crime bosses have outfitted selected units with eavesdropping devices or hologrammic recorders, cataloging everything from corporate passcodes to illicit footage of lovers' trysts.

After Jedi Master Obi-Wan Kenobi shattered a window in Senator Padmé Amidala's apartment in pursuit of an assassin droid, her staff ordered an immediate replacement for the broken pane. Congressional Crystalline, a window company based in the Senate District, entrusted the job to two of its most reliable droids: "Mick," an INS-444, and "Buffy," his CLE-004 counterpart.

> **"Jizz musician Fitz Roi filed suit against Acme Robopolish this morning, claiming that the company's droids are stealing his songs."**
>
> —*TriNebulon News entertainment feed*

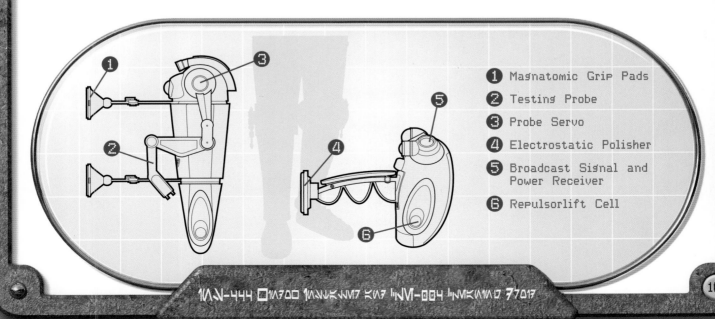

1. Magnatomic Grip Pads
2. Testing Probe
3. Probe Servo
4. Electrostatic Polisher
5. Broadcast Signal and Power Receiver
6. Repulsorlift Cell

LIN DEMOLITIONMECH

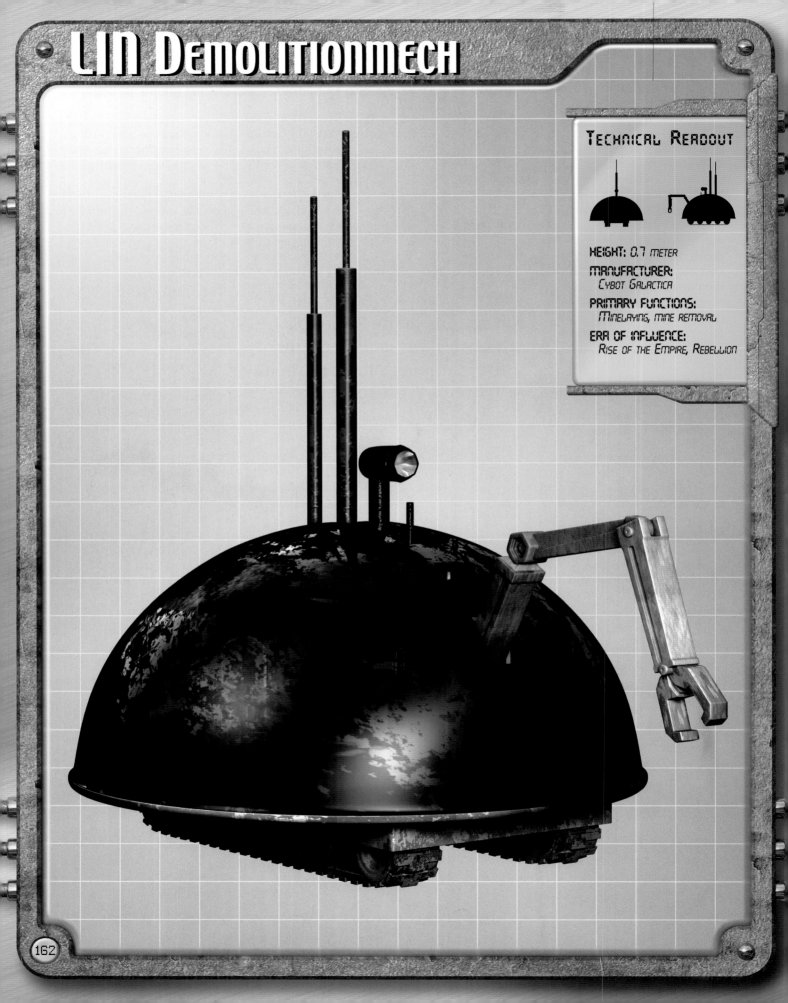

TECHNICAL READOUT

HEIGHT: 0.7 meter

MANUFACTURER:
Cybot Galactica

PRIMARY FUNCTIONS:
Minelaying, mine removal

ERA OF INFLUENCE:
Rise of the Empire, Rebellion

Cybot Galactica LIN Autonomous Minelayer

The LIN demolitionmech autonomous minelayer is an example of a superior product forced off the market through a combination of bad luck and worse marketing.

Cybot Galactica made the demolitionmech for commercial use in applications from mining to building demolition. The droid rides low to the ground, its inner workings protected beneath a durasteel dome. The reason for the heavy shell is readily apparent—after planting explosive charges, the slow-moving droid is often showered with debris from the resulting industrial blast.

During normal operation, the LIN demolitionmech rolls into position on two wide treads (using the same undercarriage as the WED Treadwell) and then plucks a blast cap from its spinning internal rack with its telescoping arm. Sonic sensors allow the demolitionmech to probe structures for weak spots and plant its charges appropriately. The dome and arm can rotate 360 degrees. A pair of retractable antennas can send signals through kilometers of solid rock, though the demolitionmech can communicate only in droid languages.

The demolitionmech's flaws include the weight of its durasteel shell, which slows the droid and renders its five-speed drive impeller largely useless. Damp environments sometimes cause demolitionmechs to seize up—a problem on mining worlds where tunnels often fill with water.

SchaumAssoc, Cybot Galactica's advertising agency, decided to promote the droid based solely on its tough-

> ### *"Advantage #7: Blast Proof. The LIN Demolitionmech is One Tough Droid."*
>
> *—Excerpt from the Demolitionmech's advertising campaign*

ness. In a memorable advertisement titled "Blast Proof," hundreds of demolitionmechs free-floating in space were hit by a battleship's turbolaser. The energy beam knocked the droids around like balls on a mung-tee table, but all survived without a scratch.

A "clear comic exaggeration" is how Cybot Galactica put it when customers demanded to know why demolitionmechs weren't *literally* blast-proof. (As experiments, many had indeed subjugated their droids to sustained laserfire.) Cybot Galactica pulled the ad, but soon faced a much bigger setback when a detonite charge prematurely exploded in a demolitionmech's grip at a mining outpost on Gosfambling. The resulting tunnel collapse caused the suffocation deaths of ten miners.

Investigators concluded that the fault lay with the charge, not the droid, but the LIN demolitionmech had already attracted enough bad press. Cybot Galactica pulled the droid from the market.

Following the recall, the demolitionmech found success with criminal syndicates and the military—two groups that didn't have to worry about pleasing stockholders. Crime cartels sent beetle-like swarms of demolitionmechs crawling over Ryloth, Socorro, and other spice-rich planets, blasting open new spice veins. The Republic army, and later the Empire, used the droids as minelayers or mine removers. At the Battle of Gligger during the Clone Wars, 563 demolitionmechs were blown sky-high in efforts to clear Marrow's Moor.

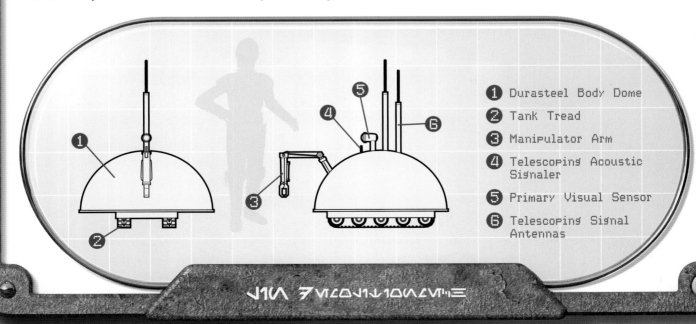

1. Durasteel Body Dome
2. Tank Tread
3. Manipulator Arm
4. Telescoping Acoustic Signaler
5. Primary Visual Sensor
6. Telescoping Signal Antennas

MONSTER DROID

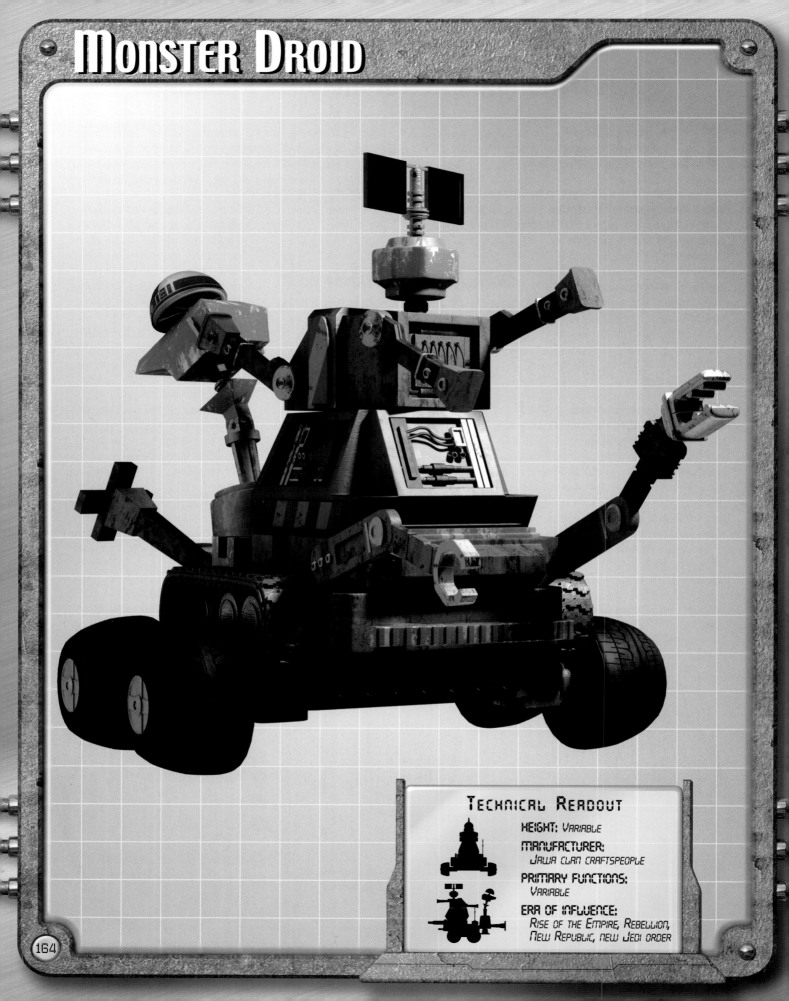

TECHNICAL READOUT

HEIGHT: Variable

MANUFACTURER:
Jawa Clan Craftspeople

PRIMARY FUNCTIONS:
Variable

ERA OF INFLUENCE:
Rise of the Empire, Rebellion,
New Republic, New Jedi Order

Jawa Custom–Built "Monster" Ugly

The monster droid is one of the most extreme examples of recombinant part-bashing, i.e., part-salvaging—an oft-ignored but huge part of the droid business. Using pieces left behind in the scrap heap, junkyard engineers build amalgamated "uglies" that come with no warranty, but which can sometimes perform better than the originals.

The Jawas of Tatooine are experts at this junkyard science. If they can fix a droid, they will; if they can't, they'll keep every piece inside their sandcrawlers until they've collected enough for a new droid.

Jawas know what their customers (mostly moisture farmers and small-town business owners) are looking for in a droid. Most tribes make uglies in four major classifications, though even within these loose groupings one may note considerable variation in appearance. These droids, so familiar to residents of Tatooine, are nearly impossible to find offworld:

- The **mechano-droid** is a heavy-labor unit equipped with a hook arm and a drilling arm, designed for permanent installation inside a tech dome.

- The **tracto-droid** is a tank-treaded mobile scanning unit with a radar array, perfect for detecting threats near a farm's perimeter.

- The **quad-pod droid** is a cargo carrier that moves on four mismatched legs, using its scoop arm and gripper arm to move items into its flatbed holding area.

"Utoo nye usabla atoonyoba?"

—Sales banter from Kiottja, chief of the Salt Steppes Jawa clan

- The **rollarc droid** is a speedy unit that zips about on four wheels, suitable for a wide variety of tasks thanks to an advanced computer housing.

The monster droid is a towering amalgam of parts from all four types of uglies listed above, as well as castoff pieces from astromech droids and more. It is less a tool than a piece of folk art.

The practice of building monster droids began more than fifty years before the Clone Wars with Tatakoz, Jawa master trader of the Mospic High Range. A tribal outcast, Tatakoz sold his wares using nothing more than a speeder bike and a repulsor trailer. When the citizens of Mos Espa and Mos Entha began hailing his skill at assembling uglies, rival tribes attempted to steal his business in an escalating contest of one-upmanship. Eventually Tatakoz built the first monster droid, and, even more impressively, he actually *sold* it.

Monster droids earn admiration from collectors for the number of parts they incorporate, the degree to which those parts work together to accomplish a defined task, and the overall aesthetics of the finished product. Due to their size, monster droids make poor repair units, but they are serviceable scanning and communications droids.

Among Jawas, the practice is viewed as a way to bring glory to the tribe and as an outlet for the creative impulses of younger Jawas. Most sandcrawlers carry one or two monster droids under construction at any time.

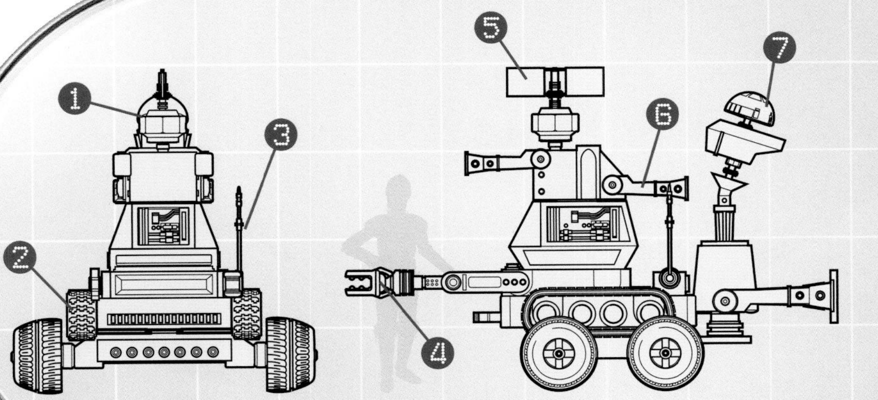

1 Computer Housing
2 Tank Treads
3 Antenna
4 Pincer Arm
5 Radar Unit
6 Leg Pods
7 Astromech Dome

Technical Readout

Height: 0.3 meter

Manufacturer:
Rebaxan Columni

Primary Functions:
Delivery, repair, communications

Era of Influence:
Rise of the Empire, Rebellion, New Republic, new Jedi order

Rebaxan Columni MSE-Series General-Purpose Droid

It's easy to see how "mouse droids" got their nickname, and just as easy to understand why so many people find them irritating. These tiny, squeaking boxes on wheels were ubiquitous aboard the vessels of the Imperial star fleet, where they called to mind the rodents carried aboard primitive sailing ships of yore.

Rebaxan Columni, a corporation owned by the diminutive Chadra-Fan, invented MSE droids for use on the Chadra-Fan homeworld. The little droid mimicked the pleeky, a local pet, and Rebaxan Columni hoped that the galactic market would consider its product cute. Following test runs of the MSE-4 and MSE-5, Rebaxan launched the MSE-6 with a huge advertising blitz and a production run that numbered in the billions.

Many were sold, but most were returned as soon as the buyers realized that MSE droids reminded them of disease-carrying vermin. Rebaxan Columni filed for bankruptcy toward the tail end of the Clone Wars.

In one of its last acts, Rebaxan Columni offered Palpatine's new Empire the entire run of the MSE-6 at a fire-sale price. The Imperial Navy, critically short of droids as it played catch-up to Palpatine's sweeping military expansions, accepted and allocated hundreds of the droids to every ship in the fleet.

MSE droids can perform many tasks, but they can perform only one task at a time. Each can hold a modular circuit matrix, or C-matrix, loaded with a single skill set. A C-matrix might be programmed for security, sanitation, repair, or communications. To create a unit with multiple, interlocked skills, MSEs can link together to form a "droid train."

Two retractable manipulator arms are hidden inside the MSE-6's black casing. The droid also possesses two audio sensors, a photoreceptor, and a miniature holocam. A small compartment in the top of the unit can hold sensitive documents; for this reason, the droids are often used as couriers. This compartment cannot be opened without an authorized voice code, and mouse droids that are captured are programmed to melt themselves down. To avoid such a fate, the droids have strong self-preservation instincts and can zip away from danger in forward or reverse.

The uses for mouse droids are limited only by their owner's creativity. On Mustafar, the operators of the lava mines used MSE-4s to scout for life-support leaks. Aboard the Death Star, MSE-6s guided stormtroopers through the maze-like corridors. An inventive assassin once packed a mouse droid's storage compartment with explosive detonite in a failed bid to kill High Inquisitor Tremayne.

Most recently, the Galactic Federation of Free Alliances employed mouse droids to sniff out enemy infiltrators during the invasion of the Yuuzhan Vong. The YVH-M, for "Yuuzhan Vong Hunter Mouse," possessed the processor of a YVH droid inside an unassuming MSE shell. YVH-M units helped save the life of Chief of State Cal Omas by uncovering spies on Mon Calamari.

> **"Lastly, we have a complaint from the Aar'aa regarding their order. Apparently, the MSE droids skittering underfoot are making them uncomfortably . . . hungry."**
>
> *—Rebaxan Columni executives, product-testing the MSE-6*

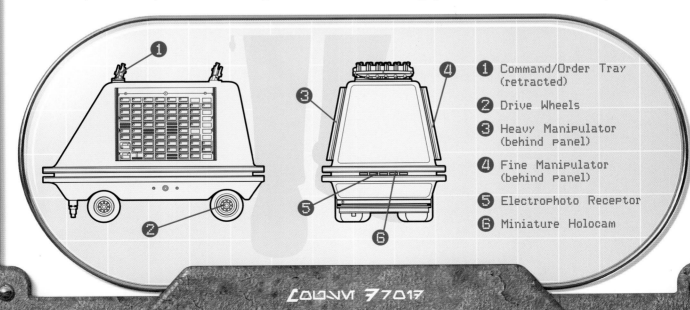

1. Command/Order Tray (retracted)
2. Drive Wheels
3. Heavy Manipulator (behind panel)
4. Fine Manipulator (behind panel)
5. Electrophoto Receptor
6. Miniature Holocam

Mustafar Panning Droid

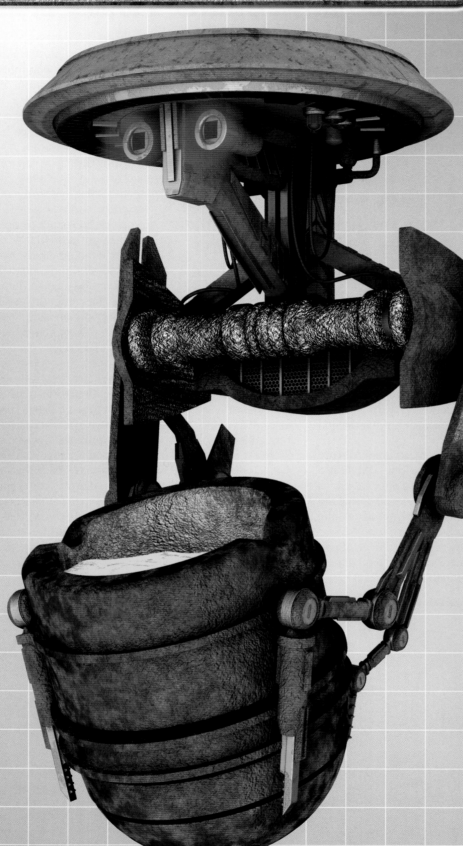

Technical Readout

HEIGHT: 1.5 meters

MANUFACTURER:
Kalibac Industries

PRIMARY FUNCTION:
Mineral collection

ERA OF INFLUENCE:
Rise of the Empire, Rebellion

Modified Kalibac Industries Information Cataloging Droid

Most droids don't lead easy lives, but even the lowest sanitation scrubber has it better than the miserable Mustafar panning droid. The droids, never designed to work under such strenuous conditions, have one of the shortest operational life expectancies in the industry.

Mustafar is a world of black rock suspended between the gas giants of Jestefad and Lefrani. Their competing tidal forces agitate Mustafar's molten core, creating a sphere that glows from space with the orange light of volcanic eruptions. The Techno Union purchased the magma moon more than three centuries ago, having discovered that its lava flows contained rare metals and ores. Within a few years, giant harvesting facilities sprang up atop the Mustafar cliffs. At first the Techno Union employed the native Mustafarians to scoop minerals directly from the lava, but it soon calculated that it could triple its output if it also employed a fleet of droids.

The panning droid is an off-the-cuff creation. Kalibac Industries, a small Techno Union company, had received a contract to build librarian droids for the Mid Rim Lending Network. Kalibac's librarian droids could reach the highest shelves of data archives on repulsorlift engines and retrieve information cylinders with their dangling manipulator arms. Sensing a cheap shortcut, the Techno Union built imitative body shells out of heat-resistant carbonite,

then filled them with intelligence matrices taken from the factory-fresh library droids. The new workers found themselves on the next freighter to Mustafar.

Now working as panning droids, the former librarians discovered that their jobs required them to hover above lava rivers and use their scanners to hunt for minerals roiled to the surface by tractor beams. If they found a strike, the panning droids would scoop it up in buckets and carry it back to the shielded safety of a harvesting center. Never resting for an instant, the droids would pick up a new bucket and return to the eternal furnace.

The panning droids carry their own low-powered shield generators as a partial defense against the heat. Nevertheless, droids were lost to the flames constantly, and the Techno Union replaced them with fresh units kept in a warehouse. Panning droids are just smart enough to know how bad they had it on Mustafar.

At the end of the Clone Wars, Anakin Skywalker and Obi-Wan Kenobi had a climactic clash on the lava planet. The recklessness of their battle resulted in a shield shutdown at a key harvesting facility, leading to a catastrophic temperature overload. As a half-melted collection arm tipped over the edge of a lavafall, Anakin leapt to a safe perch on the head of a panning droid. Using the Force to override the droid's steering controls, Anakin "surfed" upstream, much to the little droid's distress.

> ## "Reconfiguration of the panning droids is proceeding behind schedule. The units are strangely skittish around organics, particularly those workers dressed in black."
>
> *—Excerpt from TaggeCo's Mustafar Reclamation Report*

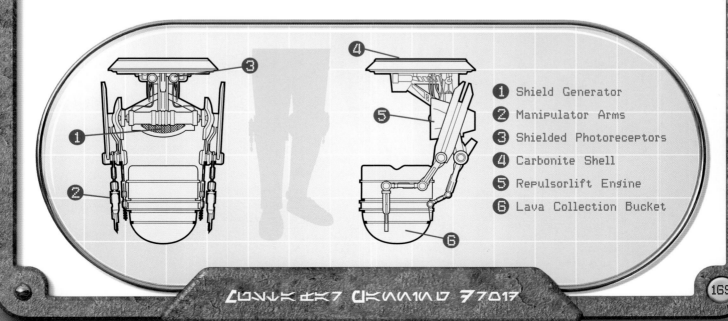

1. Shield Generator
2. Manipulator Arms
3. Shielded Photoreceptors
4. Carbonite Shell
5. Repulsorlift Engine
6. Lava Collection Bucket

Otoga-222 Droid

TECHNICAL READOUT

HEIGHT: 1.33 meters

MANUFACTURER:
Veril Line Systems

PRIMARY FUNCTION:
General labor

ERA OF INFLUENCE:
Old Republic, rise of the
Empire, Rebellion, New
Republic, new Jedi order

Veril Line Systems Otoga-222 Maintenance Droid

The Otoga-222 is known mostly as a Podracing pit droid, but that's merely one of its countless roles. Veril Line Systems introduced the model centuries ago as a repair and maintenance unit, yet its surprisingly flexible behavioral circuitry matrix has enabled the Otoga to become a jack-of-all-trades.

Otoga droids are built to take up as little space as possible; many owners shut them inside closets when they're not being used. Their hard-shelled bodies come in a variety of colors, while older units often sport mismatched parts. The droids have bipedal locomotion and simple gripper hands. They are able to accept a power recharge from almost any source, thanks to a socket adaptor and internal current regulator.

The tiny head of an Otoga droid belies its smart and curious electronic brain. Its vocabulator can vocalize most common galactic languages—indeed, in conversation the Otoga exhibits the optimistic enthusiasm of a young child.

It was this endearing personality that originally convinced Veril Line Systems that the Otoga could be a crossover: a model that appeals to buyers well outside the target audience to create a surprise windfall. Consequently, Veril didn't stop selling the Otoga to mechanics; the company instead developed a supplementary marketing plan aimed at families in need of a household maintenance droid. The move proved to be a hit. Veril Line Systems tapped a *third* profit stream by advertising the Otoga on children's holovee, after which millions of Otoga droids became lifeday presents to the offspring of wealthy parents.

In time, children grew up and household fashions changed. Veril Line Systems stopped producing home models. Unwanted Otogas found work in rougher trades. Construction and repair remained the most popular occupations, but some Otogas found employment pulling repulsorlift rickshaws or stamping starport entry visas.

In the field of Podracing, the slower Otogas couldn't compete with the manic energy of Serv-O-Droid's DUM series pit droids. Nevertheless, some Podrace pilots, such as Ody Mandrell, preferred the steady hands and clear minds of Otogas.

Veril Line Systems has issued dozens of subtle variations on the Otoga line over the decades, each identifiable by its own numeric code. The Otoga-222, produced at the height of the unit's popularity, is the most widespread variety.

Veril Line Systems recently fielded a team of Otoga droids on the nuna-ball circuit, where the droids won unlikely fame as sports champions. The Otoga squad regularly beats other teams in its division, including Industrial Automaton's asps and Cybot Galactica's PKs.

> **"So, friend, what are you looking for? Wait, don't tell me—I've already got your next droid right here. Why else do you think I sell Otogas?"**
>
> *—Honest Blim, proprietor of Procopia Preowned Automata*

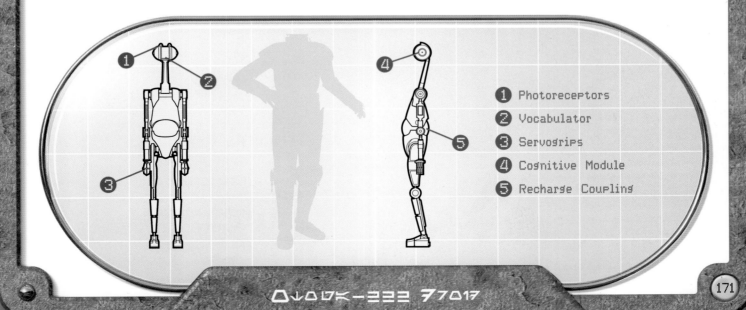

1. Photoreceptors
2. Vocabulator
3. Servogrips
4. Cognitive Module
5. Recharge Coupling

P-100 Salvage Droid

Technical Readout

HEIGHT: 2.4 meters

MANUFACTURER:
Serv-O-Droid

PRIMARY FUNCTION:
Salvage

ERA OF INFLUENCE:
Old Republic, rise of the
Empire

Serv-O-Droid P-100 Salvage Droid

P-100 salvager droids are common sights to all Podracing fans, particularly the bloodthirsty sub-group who watch the sport only for the crashes. Like urusais circling above carrion, salvager droids seek out the carcasses of ruined Podracing machines, stripping them clean within minutes.

Serv-O-Droid manufactures the P-100, but, like the company's popular series of DUM pit droids, the salvagers are originally of Cyrillian design. The reptilian race fans of Cyrillia built both varieties of droid for different but complementary niches: pit droids to fix Podracers, and salvage droids to recover Podracers too damaged to fly.

Salvage droids are carried aboard repulsorlift-driven holding arms equipped with omnidirectional homing sensors that can pinpoint a downed Podracer's automated distress beacon. Three salvage droids are carried aboard each arm and released through a ventral hatch. The salvagers can load the scrap onto the arm, which can carry up to five hundred kilograms, or carry the parts back to the racing hangar on their own.

Each P-100 salvager is topped by a bell-shaped cap similar to those worn by the DUM pit droids. Four articulated pincer arms dangle underneath. The repulsorlift engine of a P-100 is much more powerful than those on similarly sized droids, since the P-100 also needs to support the weight of its load.

> **"On the Baroonda track it was a busy day for the salvage droids, which scoured two square kilometers collecting Podracer pieces belonging to the late Turbo McMerrit."**
>
> —*From the Fode and Beed Show*

Salvage droids are operated by race organizers, who give pilots two standard hours to reclaim their wrecked racers before the parts are auctioned off. Throngs of bargain hunters pack these public auctions, but the less law-abiding among them have been known to deploy their own salvage droids, in a race to reach valuable scrap before the officials. Downed pilots are usually unable to tell one team of P-100s from another, and have sometimes stood and watched while their vehicles were stolen right under their noses.

Not all P-100s are used for Podrace salvage. The droids are employed in fields from package delivery to search-and-rescue. On Coruscant, an entrepreneur imported thousands of P-100s in response to an infestation of stratt vermin in the city's underlevels. These modified salvage droids, equipped with stun blasters, proved entirely inept at recognizing and debilitating stratts. Once he realized he'd created a menace, the salesperson skipped the planet, leaving a small fleet of P-100s to roam corridors and skyways while they zapped pedestrians indiscriminately.

The P-100 isn't the only salvage droid on the Podracing circuit. Other common models include the Arakyd HL-444 hover loader, which also served as a Republic armament carrier during the Clone Wars.

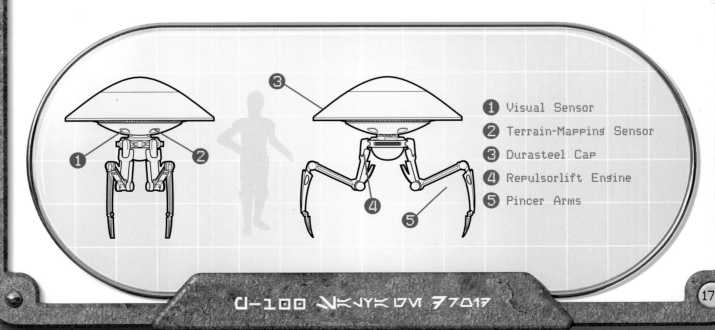

1. Visual Sensor
2. Terrain-Mapping Sensor
3. Durasteel Cap
4. Repulsorlift Engine
5. Pincer Arms

PIT DROID

TECHNICAL READOUT

HEIGHT: 1.19 meters

MANUFACTURER:
Serv-O-Droid

PRIMARY FUNCTION:
Podracer repair and service

ERA OF INFLUENCE:
Old Republic, rise of the Empire

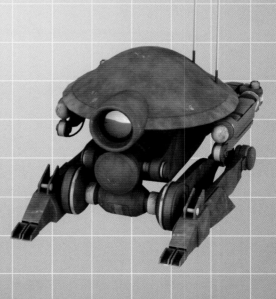

Serv-O-Droid DUM-Series Pit Droid

During its heyday, Serv-O-Droid boasted one of the broadest product lines in the droid industry by buying out smaller companies and then releasing their products under the Serv-O-Droid nameplate. The DUM series pit droid is a native product of Cyrillia, though you'd never know it from the advertising holos.

Cyrillia is an industrialized world in the Expansion Region. The reptilian Cyrillians developed the pit droid centuries ago as a maintenance unit for their turbine-powered floater transports. Cyrillians are as tall as Wookiees, but they built their tiny repair droids to scurry beneath hovering gale cars and climb into cramped circuitry bays.

The maintenance droids were efficient but unremarkable, a fact that changed when Cyrillia played host to a stop on the Podracing circuit from 189 to 122 B.B.Y. The Cyrillians started using fleets of their diminutive robots to fuel and service Podracers during pit stops—thus the modern pit droid was born.

The venue of the race eventually moved from Cyrillia to Baroonda, but by that time Serv-O-Droid had taken notice of the pit droid. Serv-O-Droid put up the money to construct modern manufacturing plants on Cyrillia, and to handle distribution and advertising for the finished product. The Cyrillians agreed to build the droids and to give up ownership in exchange for a cut of the profits.

> ### *"Ody Mandrell:* Engine burned out on circuit after pit stop."
>
> *—Official post-race listing from the Boonta Eve Classic, after the engine on Mandrell's racer sucked up a clumsy pit droid*

The DUM series proved to be the most popular pit droid on the market, despite competitive products from Veril Line Systems and other manufacturers. Used in everything from Podraces to swoop rallies, DUM pit droids work with a fanatic intensity born from their limited programming. Their high-drain, high-energy work style demands frequent recharging.

DUM units come in five stock hues—gray, yellow, blue, orange, and red. Droids of the same color often work as teams. The droids understand verbal commands but can communicate only in chittering warbles comprehensible to other automata. DUMs possess visual, electromagnetic, microwave, and other specialized energy detectors to help them avoid the hazards of the Podrace track, though their danger sensors are far from foolproof.

High-torque joint motors enable pit droids to lift many times their own weight. This strength—combined with habitually manic personalities—can sometimes be perilous. If a confused pit droid happens to attempt a "repair" on an unstable fusion generator, for instance, a swift hit on its nose will cause it to switch off and fold into a compact bundle.

If the on/off nose switch is damaged, a pit droid may be nearly unstoppable. In such cases, the only solution might be a high-intensity blaster bolt.

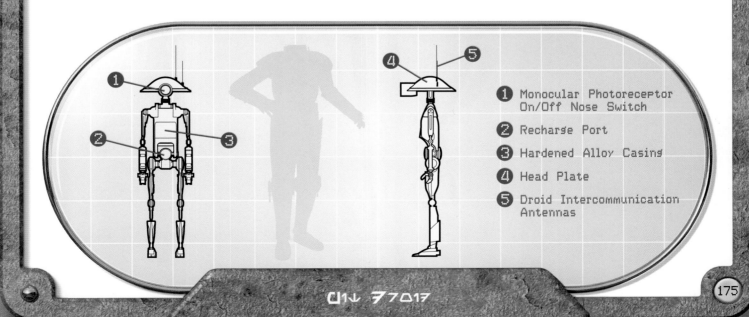

1. Monocular Photoreceptor On/Off Nose Switch
2. Recharge Port
3. Hardened Alloy Casing
4. Head Plate
5. Droid Intercommunication Antennas

PK Worker Droid

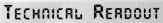

Technical Readout

HEIGHT: 1.46 meters

MANUFACTURER:
Cybot Galactica

PRIMARY FUNCTION:
General labor

ERA OF INFLUENCE:
Old Republic, rise of the
Empire, Rebellion, New
Republic, new Jedi order

Cybot Galactica PK-Series Worker Droid

Being crude labor units, PKs must envy their more glamorous production brethren at Cybot Galactica. Unlike 3PO units, PK workers can't hope for interaction with their owners beyond "mop up that fuel spill, Peekay-Seven" or "recharge those warming ovens, Peekay-Four."

The affordably priced PK worker droids are durable and versatile. They perform simple repairs, organize supplies, clean up offices, and inventory cargo. Their efficient internal batteries can last a long time between recharge sessions. The droids are tough enough to withstand extremes of temperature and radiation: PK units operate equally well inside furnaces, in reactor chambers, and in the vacuum of space.

PKs have rudimentary sensory gear, including a cyclopean photoreceptor and an auditory pickup. This equipment is mounted in a cranial unit that, thanks to a limber neck, can rotate 360 degrees. The droids are about the same height as an R2 unit, making them easy to transport and store.

PKs interact well with other automata. Consequently, they are often placed in the doubly demeaning position of having to answer to the whims of their organic masters and the needs of the so-called superior droid classes. In private, PKs often vent their frustrations by grumbling about "useless protocol gearheads."

The PK has been in service for centuries, selling in modest but profitable numbers. Prior to the Battle of Naboo, the Trade Federation began to buy every PK as soon as it rolled off the Telti assembly lines. As part of its secret military buildup, it planned to use the PKs to maintain its flocks of battle droids, droidekas, and vulture droid starfighters.

Republic agent Vyn Narcassan, already spearheading a covert investigation into the Trade Federation's Viceroy Directorate, saw a chance to plant moles within the notoriously tight-lipped Neimoidian organization. In secret meetings with Cybot Galactica's board of directors, Narcassan persuaded the corporation to engage in subterfuge for the good of the Republic.

One out of every four hundred PK worker droids was fitted with a communications intercept trap to passively record conversations and low-frequency transmissions. The equipment was nearly undetectable and designed to self-destruct in a melt of fused circuits, characteristic of an overheated motivator, in case of tampering. Republic Intelligence agents working as licensed Cybot technicians were to download information from the droids during standard maintenance visits, then hand-deliver it to Coruscant for analysis.

Unfortunately, Narcassan's program was initiated too late to provide advance warning of the Trade Federation's invasion of Naboo. The affected PK droids supplied limited intelligence data over the following decade, but few remained in service by the time of the Clone Wars. Many standard years later, the Imperial Security Bureau would undertake a similar monitoring program, by hiding spy circuitry inside RA-7 Death Star Droids.

> ## "PK units are my first recommendation for the espionage programming. After all, who notices a PK?"
>
> *—Republic Intelligence agent*
> *Vyn Narcassan*

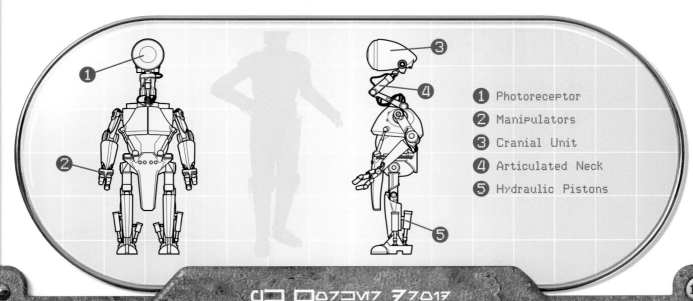

1 Photoreceptor
2 Manipulators
3 Cranial Unit
4 Articulated Neck
5 Hydraulic Pistons

POWER DROID

Veril Line Systems EG-6 Power Droid

The power droid is an example of minimalist design at its most extreme. What could be simpler than a box with legs?

The droid's function is equally simplistic. It is a walking battery—an "ambulatory fusion generator," as Veril Line Systems refers to it in the company's sales materials. The job of a power droid is to provide energy to mechanical devices in cases where it's impractical to rely on a permanent power grid, a common situation on backworlds or in large, busy spaces such as a repair bay or starship hangar.

Most of a power droid's body consists of its internal fusion generator. Multiple layers of armor and safety shutdowns help protect the generator from an accidental breach. Internal cooling fluid channels regulate the temperature of the generator, and, in emergencies, small relief valves along the chassis and on the bases of both feet can bleed off vaporizing coolant fluid as steam.

The power droid lacks a recognizable face. The few buttons and gadgets in its upper panel include a visual sensor and an acoustic signaler capable of droid languages only. A power port on the front panel can accommodate standard plugs, while a larger port on the side of most models fits industrial-size hookups. The power droid has a single, delicate arm, which is normally hidden behind a tiny portal.

Each power droid comes with a systems diagnostic package that includes a spectrometer, an X-ray scanner, an infrared scanner, and a sonar-pulse emitter. The droid uses these devices to scan the equipment it has been asked to service for leaks or hairline cracks. If its diagnosis falls outside of its preprogrammed red-line limits, the droid will refuse to fuel the item. This last personality trait has given power droids a reputation for stubbornness.

Stubbornness and stupidity, that is. If told to walk in a straight line, power droids will march off a precipice, their feet pumping in midair as they fall to their destruction. In vertical cities such as those on Nar Shaddaa and Coruscant, power droids require close supervision—or, at the very least, guardrails.

For centuries, Veril Line Systems has dominated the power droid market. Its most popular model is the EG-6, and it also offers a heavier industrial version released under the designation S9. Veril's biggest competitor in the energy-supply market is Industrial Automaton, whose release of the GNK droid was widely viewed as a feature-for-feature conceptual theft of the EG-6.

It's nearly impossible to crack the shell of a power droid—but if the shell *is* for some reason pierced, the generator explodes with stunning force. The pirate Reginald Barkbone escaped from the Emperor's Royal Guards on Axion by palming a limpet mine onto a power droid, then shooting his way out in the ensuing detonation and chaos.

> ## "Gonk, gonk."
>
> *—Power droid vocalization so common, it has become the droid's nickname*

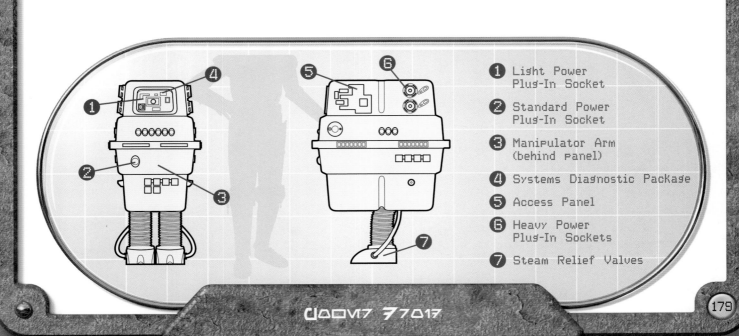

1. Light Power Plug-In Socket
2. Standard Power Plug-In Socket
3. Manipulator Arm (behind panel)
4. Systems Diagnostic Package
5. Access Panel
6. Heavy Power Plug-In Sockets
7. Steam Relief Valves

Prowler 1000

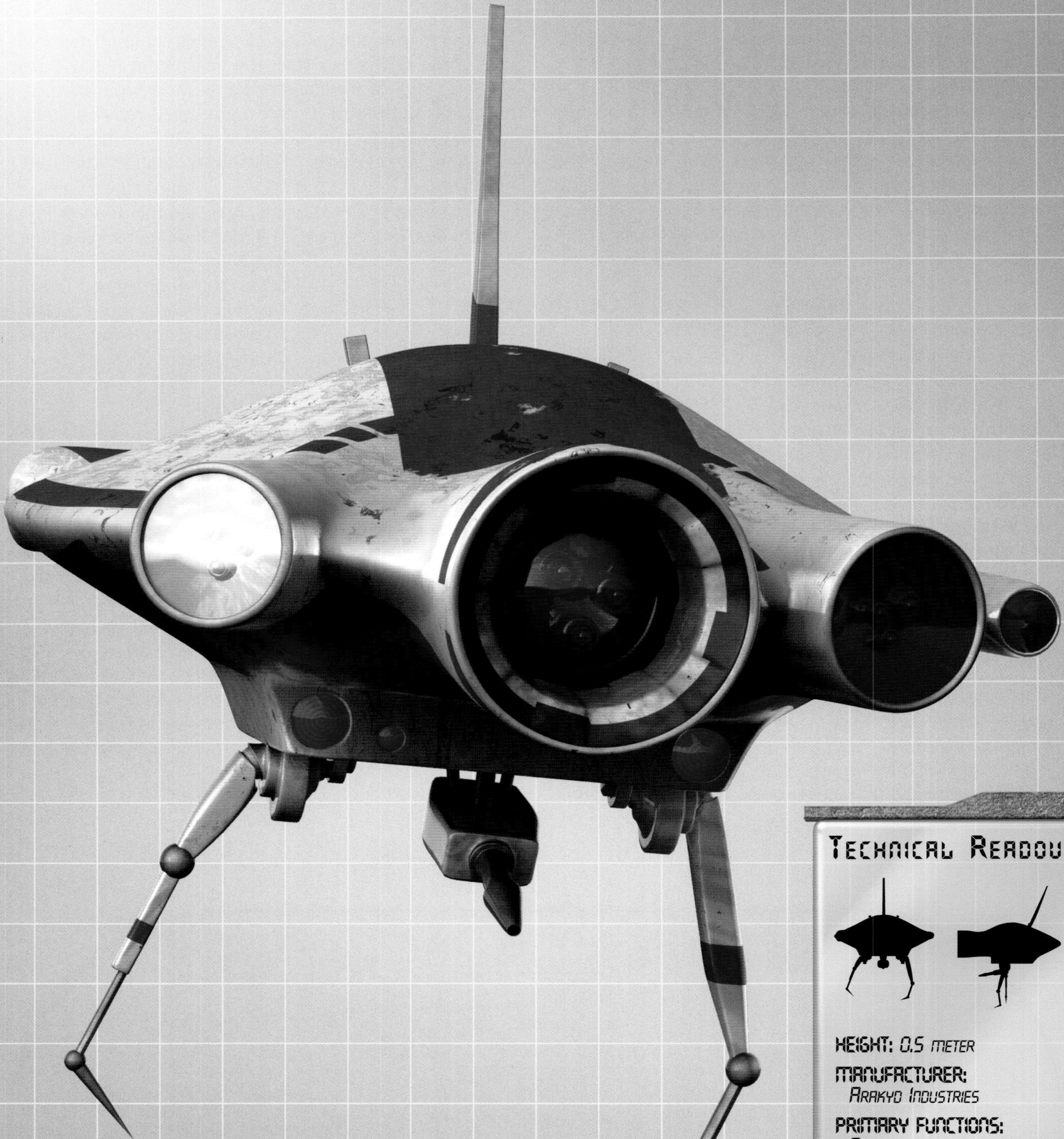

Technical Readout

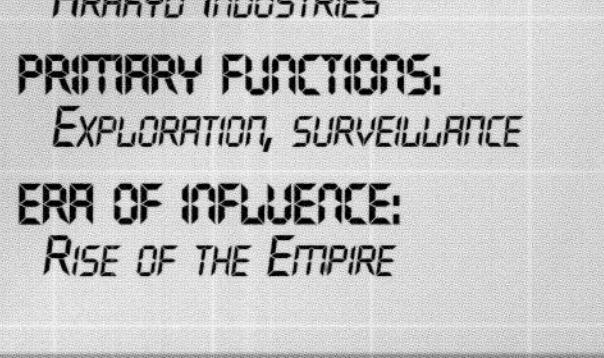

HEIGHT: 0.5 meter

MANUFACTURER:
Arakyd Industries

PRIMARY FUNCTIONS:
Exploration, surveillance

ERA OF INFLUENCE:
Rise of the Empire

Arakyd Prowler 1000 Exploration Droid

Looking at the Arakyd Prowler, it's difficult to imagine that such a small droid could have given rise to a lineage of increasingly fearsome successors. The Prowler's great-great-grandchild, the Arakyd HK, is capable of swallowing starships.

Arakyd Industries became a member of the Techno Union during the decades leading up to the Clone Wars. A manufacturer of exploration and security droids, Arakyd had a reputation for cold-edged ruthlessness that it expressed through a vaguely menacing design philosophy. The Prowler 1000 is one of the few exceptions to the rule, since its tortapo-shell chassis and its nervous habit of bobbing on its repulsorlifts render it somewhat charming.

The Prowler, introduced a few years after the Battle of Naboo, initially served as an exploration droid for scouting alien terrain. Its secondary function was to assist police departments with surveillance and forensics work. The droid's fish-eye photoreceptor can record its environment through a multiplicity of magnifications and spectrum filters. Other sensors, as well as a spotlight, enable the Prowler to function in darkness.

Its delicate, dangling manipulator arms are tipped with sensors that can analyze the chemical composition of any substance. Prowlers can also be equipped with heavier manipulators for lifting and carrying samples. Antennas with surface-to-orbit range allow the droid to receive signals from waiting control ships. Although Prowlers aren't equipped with weapons, an engineer could add lightweight blasters with only minimal rewiring.

Arakyd sold a number of its explorational units, including the Prowler, to Chancellor Palpatine and the Republic. When Count Dooku emerged and formed the Confederacy of Independent Systems, the Techno Union joined the Separatist cause. As a Techno Union member, Arakyd went along with the move, and saw its Republic contracts evaporate.

Arakyd CEO Hordis Boil took heart, however, when agents in Palpatine's inner circle asked him to spy on Techno Union foreman Wat Tambor. In return for Boil's intelligence, Palpatine requested that the Kaminoans outfit the clone army with Arakyd products purchased through a shell corporation.

Arakyd Prowlers became standard clone trooper tools for keeping track of enemy troop movements. On Utapau, clone commander Cody dispatched several Prowlers into the catacombs in search of Obi-Wan Kenobi, following the Jedi's escape from the Order Sixty-six ambush. The explorations of the droids disturbed a mother nos monster, who decided the intruders were coming too close to her babies and swallowed them whole.

Following the Clone Wars, Palpatine nationalized the Techno Union. Arakyd was allowed to remain intact, and, in fact, it inherited the assets of many dismantled Techno Union corporations. This resurgence marked the beginning of a close relationship between Arakyd and the Empire.

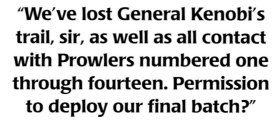

> **"We've lost General Kenobi's trail, sir, as well as all contact with Prowlers numbered one through fourteen. Permission to deploy our final batch?"**
>
> *—Clone trooper CT-307, reporting to his commander on Utapau*

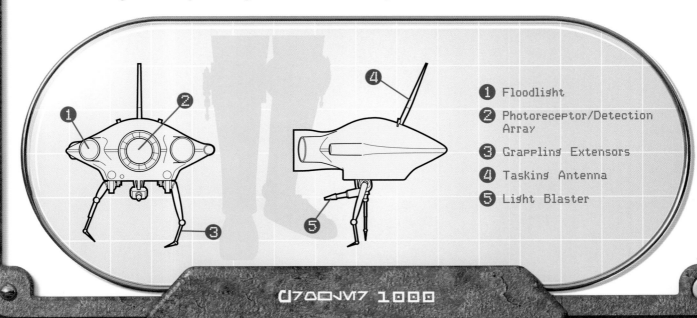

1. Floodlight
2. Photoreceptor/Detection Array
3. Grappling Extensors
4. Tasking Antenna
5. Light Blaster

RICKSHAW DROID

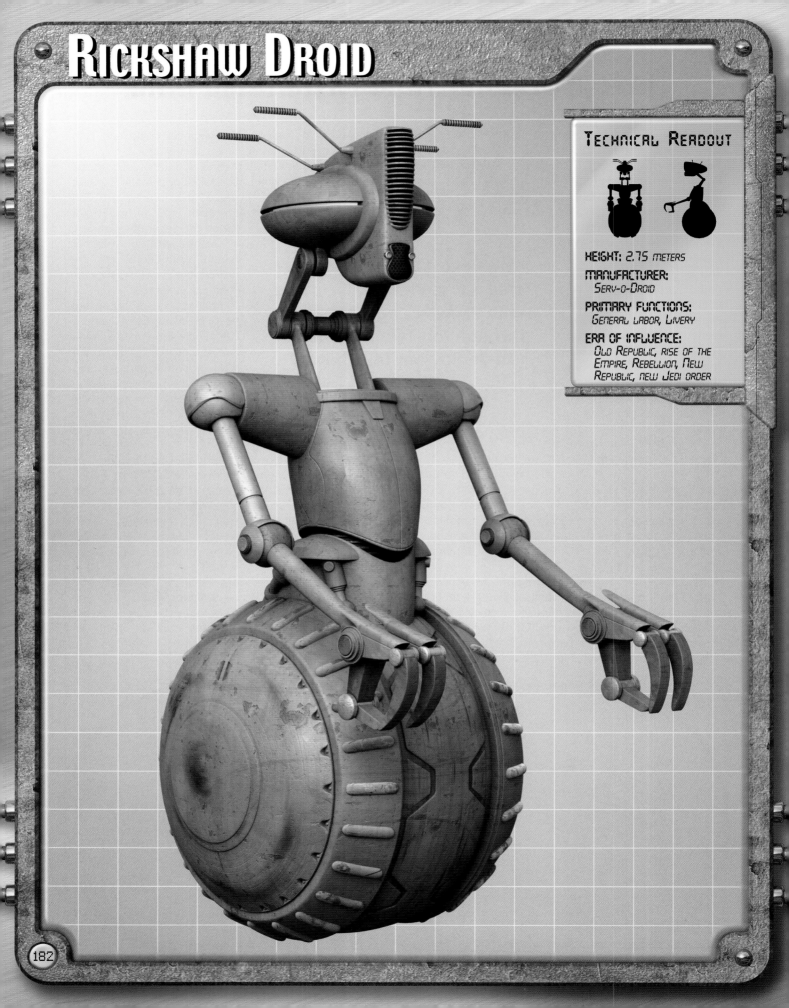

TECHNICAL READOUT

HEIGHT: 2.75 meters

MANUFACTURER:
Serv-o-Droid

PRIMARY FUNCTIONS:
General labor, Livery

ERA OF INFLUENCE:
Old Republic, rise of the
Empire, Rebellion, New
Republic, new Jedi order

Serv-O-Droid RIC General Labor Droid

Serv-O-Droid's RIC model has earned the nickname "rickshaw droid," though its manufacturer never designed it for that purpose. The RIC is a general labor unit, and only a few of the millions of units in service have found employment as rickshaw-pulling livery operators.

Serv-O-Droid has manufactured the RIC for more than seven standard centuries. Simple cognitive modules keep manufacturing costs down and help make RIC units exceptionally obedient. Photoreceptors and a single audio pickup feed sensory data to the RIC's electronic brain, while the droid can vocalize through an outsize broadcast speaker. RIC units can speak no more than two languages, usually Basic and binary, though it's common on Rim worlds for the Basic skillware to be swapped out in favor of the dominant local language.

A unipod wheel is the droid's most distinguishing feature. The wheel drives the droid at speeds up to sixty-five kilometers per hour, while internal balance gyros keep the droid upright at all times. The shock-resistant chassis seals off the droid's inner workings from moisture and grit. Most RIC units are marked with dents and scratches from years spent working outdoors. The three-fingered gripper hands are strong enough to bend metal, yet delicate enough for simple mechanical repairs.

In their centuries of service, RIC droids have been used

> ### "RIC-9 passes to RIC-11. He passes to RIC-8. It's RIC-8 up the middle . . . He shoots— *Nuuuuunaaaaaa!*"
>
> —*Nuna-ball announcer Horassa Hunanga, describing Serv-O-Droid's winning goal to capture the Mid Rim pennant*

in nearly every line of work. To unlicensed rickshaw operators in the Rim Territories, RICs represent the perfect combination of low cost, toughness, and gyroscopic stabilization—to ensure that they never dump a passenger. On worlds from Sluis Van to Muunilinst, RIC drivers carry commuters around town in repulsorlift-buoyed rickshaw carriages.

Unless the fare is paid in advance, usually by means of a credit-stick box bolted onto the droid's back, RICs will take their fares on meandering tours of the city's back streets in order to drive up their fee. In the settlement of Mos Espa on Tatooine, visitors have become familiar with a local rickshaw droid named ES-PSA, or "Espasa."

Closer to the Core, RIC units are recognized as stars in the droid sport of nuna-ball, in which a puffed-up nuna animal is batted between robotic teams in an effort to score on the opponent's goal. The game grew out of a production stress test but has become wildly popular, in part because of the mechanical carnage that sometimes follows when the losing team becomes aggravated. Serv-O-Droid has fielded a team of RIC units since the creation of nuna-ball. In fact, due to the nimbleness of the droids, they regularly beat competitors—including Industrial Automaton's asp team and Veril Line System's Otoga squad.

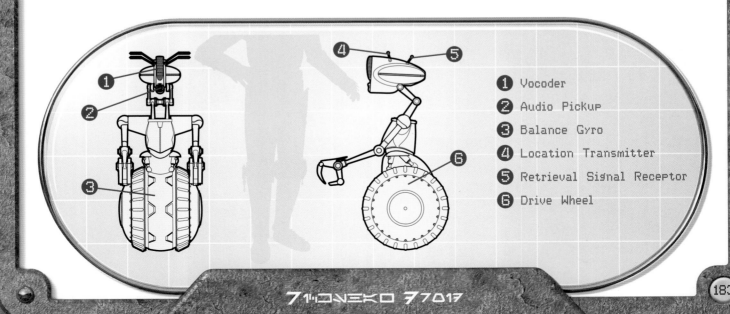

1 Vocoder
2 Audio Pickup
3 Balance Gyro
4 Location Transmitter
5 Retrieval Signal Receptor
6 Drive Wheel

SRT Droid

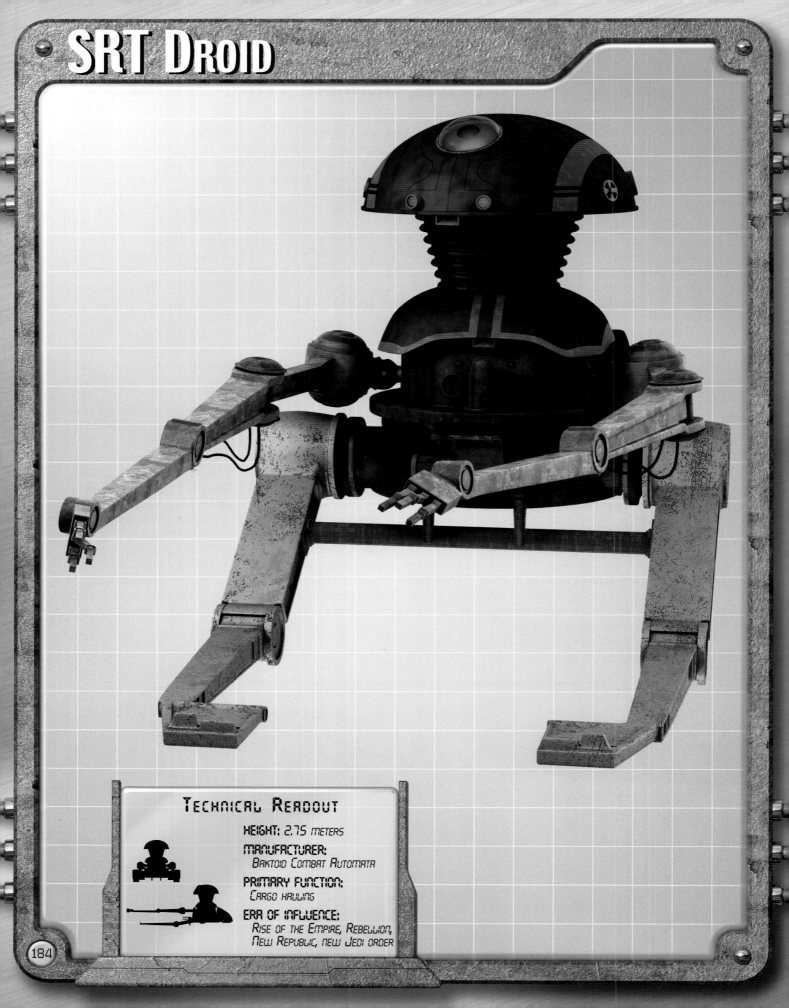

Technical Readout

Height: 2.75 meters

Manufacturer:
Baktoid Combat Automata

Primary Function:
Cargo hauling

Era of Influence:
Rise of the Empire, Rebellion,
New Republic, New Jedi Order

Baktoid Combat Automata SRT Autonomous Short-Range Transport

The SRT is a heavy industrial droid designed for brutal work. In factory environments, it operates around the clock, and most burn out their original components in less than a standard year.

SRT is an acronym for "short-range transport," an accurate descriptor for a droid designed to carry raw materials, tools, and finished products from one factory hub to another. Inside vast foundries, such as the droidworks of Geonosis, SRT units act as de facto overseers for the entire operation. SRTs cruise through multi-leveled hives on repulsorlifts, ensuring that no conveyer belts are jammed, and that all fuel stores and parts bins are topped off.

An operation like the one on Geonosis consumed incalculable resources and spit out endless numbers of soldiers. SRT droids are responsible for keeping both the input and output ends of the process running smoothly. A power spoke located in the heart of the factory allows SRTs to recharge, though this respite lasts only a few minutes.

The Geonosian SRTs are products of Baktoid Combat Automata, and work inside the same factories where they first came into existence. Each droid has an enormous ellipse of a head featuring heat-shielded photoreceptors and a radar-mapping sensor node. Two multi-jointed arms enable the SRT to heft loads; each hand ends with two fingers that are slender enough to operate factory controls.

"It's a nightmare!"

—C-3PO, carried off by an SRT droid inside the Geonosis factory

A thick front pallet provides the SRT's load-carrying surface, and the droid's commercial-grade repulsorlift engine can support up to ten times its own weight. Baktoid's SRTs are not particularly intelligent, focusing on the job at hand. Although they can communicate only in droid languages, SRTs are in constant contact with the factory central computers, receiving commands input at any remote terminal.

Slight variations on the SRT design are common throughout the galaxy, and are sold by dozens of competing droid companies. Publictechnic's model includes a four-sided bin instead of a flat pallet, and the manufacturer sells the SRT to construction companies. Other groups, including Go-Corp/Utilitech, sell SRTs with fully enclosed, boxcar-like carrying areas. They have met with great success selling the unit to municipal governments as a garbage collector.

On worlds with a great number of construction projects, it's common to see SRTs crisscrossing the sky as they deliver tools or dump loads of rubble. Knowing this, lawbreakers sometimes load contraband—including spice, slaves, and crystalline vertices—into SRT beds in the hope that authorities won't bother to search the big droids. In this fashion, a squad of Republic ARC troopers hijacked a work crew of SRTs in order to sneak behind Separatist lines prior to the Battle of Byblos.

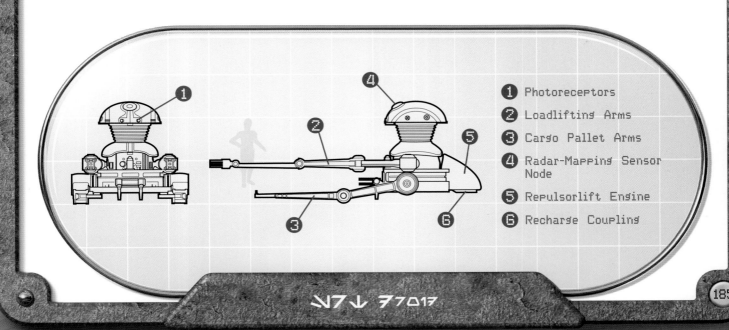

1. Photoreceptors
2. Loadlifting Arms
3. Cargo Pallet Arms
4. Radar-Mapping Sensor Node
5. Repulsorlift Engine
6. Recharge Coupling

TT-8L Tattletale

Serv-O-Droid TT-8L Gatekeeper Droid

When readers of *Popular Automaton* voted, they overwhelmingly named the TT-8L "most annoying" in the holomag's annual rankings of the droid industry. The Tattletale elicits such ire because it acts as a gatekeeper, and not everyone is important enough to make it inside.

Originally built by Serv-O-Droid as a tool for the gentrified rich, the TT-8L Tattletale has been working as a vestibule snoop for more than four thousand standard years. Many models have been produced over the centuries, from the slightly menacing Y7 to the gilded, bauble-trimmed XSS.

The TT-8L is little more than an eye on a stalk. It remains in a fixed position for its operational life, usually installed near a doorway or inside a lobby. An approaching visitor's footfalls trigger the unit's audio sensors, whereupon it scans the newcomer, compares physical parameters against its internal database, and announces the guest's arrival to its master, who can either admit the visitor or request further observation.

The obvious objection—that this job could be easily performed by a nonintelligent security holocam for much less money—explained why Serv-O-Droid initially marketed the TT-8L to wealthy nobles accustomed to servants and hirelings. This elite sales strategy eventually reached its gaudy pinnacle in the fabulously ornate XSS.

Equipped with a snake-like body stalk cast from antique brass, the TT-8L/XSS is bolted to the floor but allowed a limited range of movement through its multiple joints. Its blue-tinted-glass optical lens functions much like a pair of macrobinoculars and is protected by a bronze shutter when inactive. The droid's entire two-and-a-half-meter length is a showcase for intricate scrollwork designs, sparkling silver adornments, and inlaid synthetic gemstones.

The Y7 model was developed when Serv-O-Droid realized that its observation machine had many potential uses beyond simple nosiness. Criminals, recluses, and paranoids had great need for a device that could interrogate suspicious callers and scan them for weapons. Instead of being meekly secretive, this new model was aggressively confrontational.

A TT-8L/Y7 is designed for direct installation in a door, a door frame, or an entranceway alcove. Its rigid body stem lacks the serpentine fluidity of the XSS frame, possessing only a single socket joint at the base of the trunk. All unnecessary ornamentation has been omitted in favor of a basic black shell of resilient durasteel. The Y7's central eye, shielded by a retractable blind, is capable of low-light surveys, spotlight illumination, and scanning sweeps in the ultraviolet and infrared ranges. Because the droid's unremarkable intelligence matrix wasn't always enough to please the truly distrustful, Serv-O-Droid installed a remote-activation subroutine allowing the Y7 to be controlled directly by a security guard at any time.

> **"The overcoat is a nice touch, but white pants with toumon boots? Come back when your eyespots can perceive style."**
>
> —*Glambot, the obnoxious TT-8L gatekeeper at Coruscant's Club Caraveg*

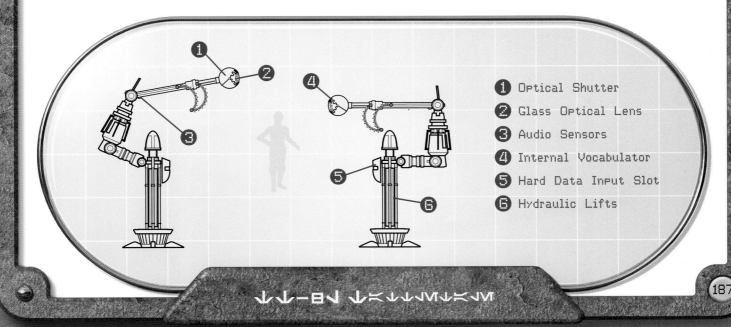

1. Optical Shutter
2. Glass Optical Lens
3. Audio Sensors
4. Internal Vocabulator
5. Hard Data Input Slot
6. Hydraulic Lifts

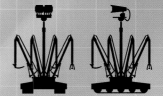

Cybot Galactica WED Treadwell Repair Droid

Some pilots swear by their astromechs, but for the vast majority of the galaxy, there's no better repair droid than the WED Treadwell.

Cybot Galactica introduced the current Treadwell line more than seven standard centuries ago, and modifications since then have been mostly cosmetic. The droid *works*. Its simple design is unlikely to be topped anytime soon—at least not at such a low price.

The Treadwell derives its name from the two wide treads that drive it, but its main selling point is its arms. The thin, jointed limbs extend from the droid's base and fold up against the central shaft when not in use, evoking the insectile silhouette of the Storini glass prowler. Four arms come standard, though the Treadwell has sockets for many more. Easily detachable and transposable, each arm contains integrated tools specific to whatever task might be requested by the droid's owner. It's not unusual to encounter Treadwells operating as house painters or tree pruners well outside the confines of repair bays.

Extending from the body is a telescoping neck, which supports a head made up of a pair of binocular photoreceptors capable of magnifying objects up to one thousand times. The Treadwell has a primitive vocabulator that enables it to warble and hoot in a machine language understood by most other droids.

> **"Check this out—arc welder, hydrospanner, fusioncutter, spot sprayer, foam sealant, torque wrench, and power calibrator. My Tread's a mobile multitool."**
>
> —*X-wing mechanic Cubber Daine*

With their long arms, Treadwells can reach areas inaccessible to stubby-bodied astromechs. And the price is hard to beat. Treadwells typically sell for less than similar models, and a thriving pre-owned market exists for used Treadwells and their specialty arms.

The low cost has its drawbacks. Treadwells aren't terribly bright; they sometimes make simple repair mistakes that can cause damage to the job or to themselves. Their arms are easily broken, and the ten wheels that drive the treads can become jammed by grit or sand. On the other hand, a well-maintained Treadwell can remain in service for generations and still be barely distinguishable from a new model on the factory showroom floor. Furthermore, when a Treadwell reaches a point beyond repair, it's no great hardship to simply buy a new one.

The Treadwell's fans—and they are many—point out that the droid's flaws can be overcome by an owner skilled enough to reprogram a diagnostic circuitry matrix. An enthusiast subculture has grown up around the cult of the "tricked-out Treadwell." Many knockoff models exist, including Kalibac Industries' NR-5 maintenance droid, and the Treadwell's radial-arm design has been copied in Medtech's line of FX medical assistants.

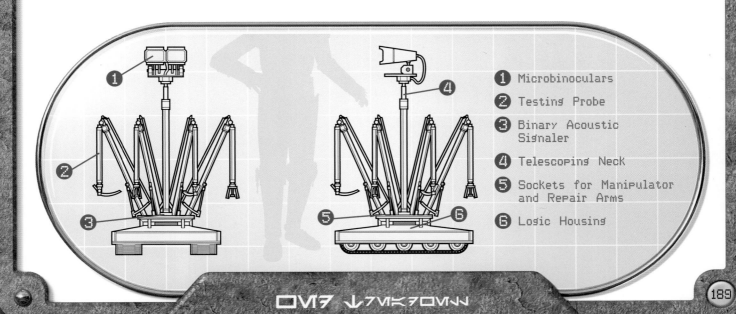

1. Microbinoculars
2. Testing Probe
3. Binary Acoustic Signaler
4. Telescoping Neck
5. Sockets for Manipulator and Repair Arms
6. Logic Housing

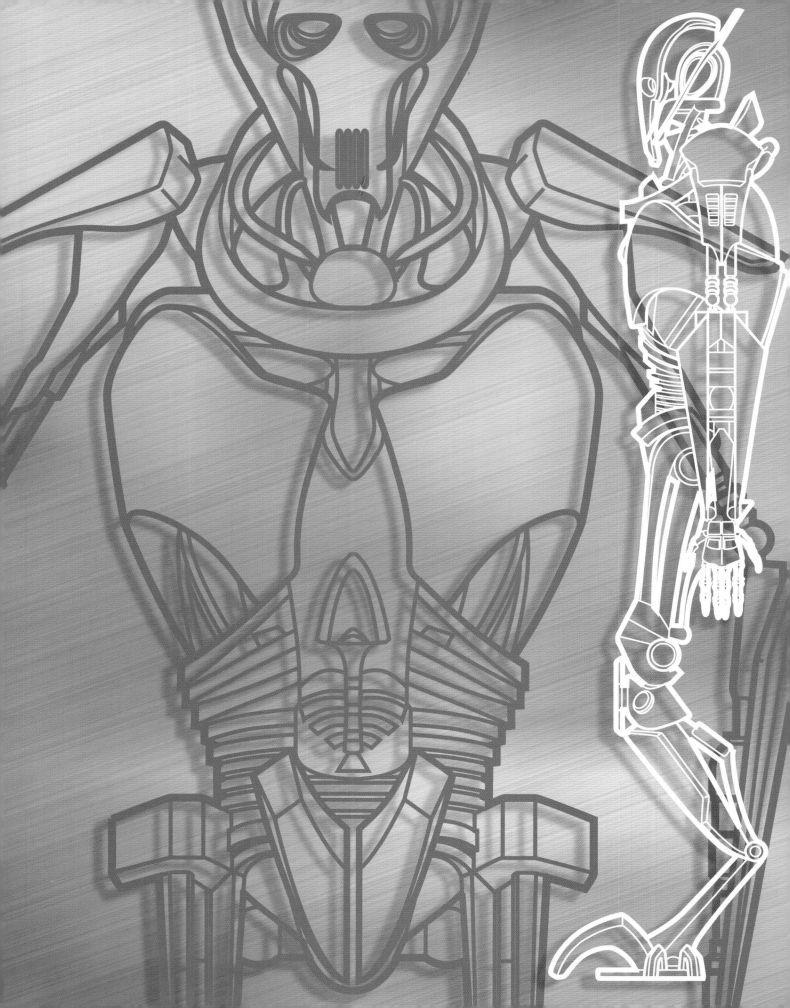

CYBORGS

Cyborgs are humans or other organic beings with mechanical parts. As such they are not true droids, but their fates are intertwined with those of automata in the areas of technology and culture.

Cyborgs fall into one of five categories, depending on their type of implant:

- **Prosthetic cyborgs** have artificial limbs. Some prosthetics are constructed from metal or plastic components; others are indistinguishable from organic parts thanks to synthskin coverings. During the Clone Wars, Anakin Skywalker bore a skeletal arm of the first type, while Luke Skywalker received a human-looking artificial hand following his battle at Cloud City.

- **Implant cyborgs** have artificial components not visible to outside eyes. These internal enhancements are used to replace dead or dying parts, or to augment bodies beyond their natural abilities. The replacement of organs is common on worlds such as Bakura, where citizens regularly live to ages of 160 standard years and beyond. All sports-governing bodies have banned the use of muscle-stim implants, corneal-sharpening lenses, adrenaline pumps, and skeletal stiffeners. Mercenaries and private militias, particularly those operating out of Hutt or Bothan space, are known to use augmenting bio-implants.

- **Bio-linked cyborgs** plug their brains into computer bands worn around the head. Such devices provide a wealth of data far beyond what any organic could normally experience, but the interface often leaves the user uninterested in social contact. The Biotech Aj^6 and other computer bands can be wirelessly linked to mainframes for even greater power. Bio-linked cyborgs often act as liaisons between a city's administrative staff and its central computer.

- **Rebuilt cyborgs** have bodies that are almost entirely machines, with the exclusion of their brains, at a minimum. Darth Vader falls at the low end of this category, while the Empire's shadow droids mark the uppermost extreme. Often, rebuilt cyborgs achieve their state as a result of catastrophic injury. Notable examples of rebuilt cyborgs include Kligson, the operator of Droid World, and the bounty hunter Valance, who tried to conceal his condition with a mask of synthskin. The half-mechanical army built by the Arkanian Renegades in 50 B.B.Y., whose members included Gorm the Dissolver, are considered rebuilt cyborgs.

- **Symbiont cyborgs** are not always categorized as true cyborgs, and some are considered a distinct classification unto themselves. Symbionts are droids paired with living beings. A successful symbiont will retain aspects from both intelligences. JK bio-droids and Iron Knights are examples of this rare fusing of the natural and the artificial.

Parts used by a cyborg are similar, or even identical, to those used on droids. While not everyone will wear an arm salvaged from a juggernaut war droid, cyborgs have a vested interest in the advancement of droid technology.

Cultural pressures on cyborgs are great. They bear the weight of anti-droid prejudice, without the mechanical disassociation that allows many droids to live in ignorance.

The Jedi were unconsciously complicit in this bias during the days of the Old Republic. Believing that mechanical devices had no place in the living Force, they viewed cyborging with distaste. Though some exceptions existed among their own ranks, including the Sith War champion Cay Qel-Droma, the study and mastery of machines became the domain of the Sith.

After the rise of the Empire, a number of prominent Imperial officials sported visible cyborg prosthetics, leading many to associate their atrocities with the metal enhancements they wore.

B'omarr Brain Walker

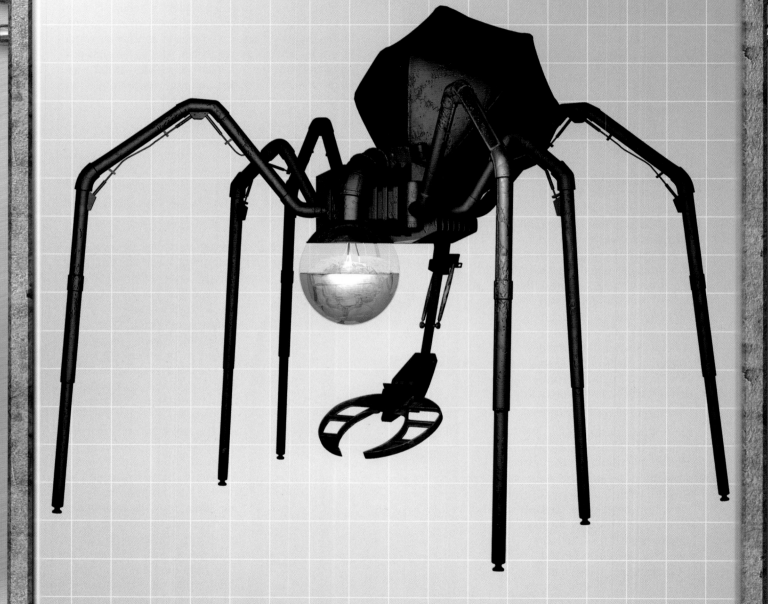

Technical Readout

HEIGHT: 1.7 meters

MANUFACTURER:
Arakyd Industries (frame only)

PRIMARY FUNCTION:
Brain locomotion

ERA OF INFLUENCE:
Old Republic, rise of the Empire,
Rebellion, New Republic

Rebuilt Arakyd BT-16 Perimeter Droid

The B'omarr brain walker meets the minimum accepted standard for a cyborg, defined as a brain hooked up to a responsive mechanical frame. In this case, the frame is a modified BT-16 perimeter droid, a fact that has led to some confusion in classification.

To outsiders, the B'omarr cyborging process is off-puttingly disturbing. To the B'omarr monks, however, removing someone's brain is a great privilege. The B'omarr believe that the only way to achieve enlightenment is to rid oneself of the flesh and become a disembodied intellect.

Generations ago, an enclave of B'omarr ascetics set up shop on Tatooine. Among the dunes, the monks constructed a brooding monastery of iron and durasteel, which shut them off from the local population.

After years of meditation, the most advanced believers had no further use for the distractions of the body. In a holy ceremony, the lesser B'omarr acolytes sharpened their scalpels and surgically removed the brains from their masters' skulls. Each lumpy gray mass was dropped into a clear jar of nutrient fluid and arranged on a shelf in the subterranean Great Room of the Enlightened.

But even a brain needs to get out once in a while. For this purpose, the B'omarr attendants assembled a series of armatures built with parts from Arakyd's BT-16. The monks threw out the BT-16's repeating blaster and ventral sensor globe to make room for a brain jar to be affixed to the underbelly of the framework.

The brain walkers have since been modified from their BT-16 origins and no longer follow a single design pattern. Some have gripper claws, some do not; some have only four legs, some have as many as nine. Almost all, however, have speakers and audio sensors and a row of colored lights at the base of the shatterproof jar. These lights glow blue and green under normal conditions. Bright red indicates that the brain is "screaming" and unable to adjust to its strange new state.

Jabba the Hutt turned the B'omarr monastery into his personal pleasure palace and forced the religious order into the lowest subcorridors. This change made the monks even more eager to initiate others into their way of life—so eager, in fact, that they forcibly removed a few reluctant brains following the Hutt's death at the Great Pit of Carkoon.

It's unclear whether Arakyd knew about the bizarre functions their droids had been used to fulfill on Tatooine, but the company introduced a completely redesigned BT-16 just prior to the Battle of Yavin. This new model borrowed heavily from the design of MerenData's TS-Arach pest-control droid. The Empire purchased many for use aboard the first Death Star, but the battle station exploded before the BT-16s could begin their tours of duty.

> **"You have progressed rapidly on your spiritual path, Brother Fortuna. Prepare yourself for enlightenment."**
>
> *—B'omarr monk to Bib Fortuna, prior to forcibly removing the latter's brain*

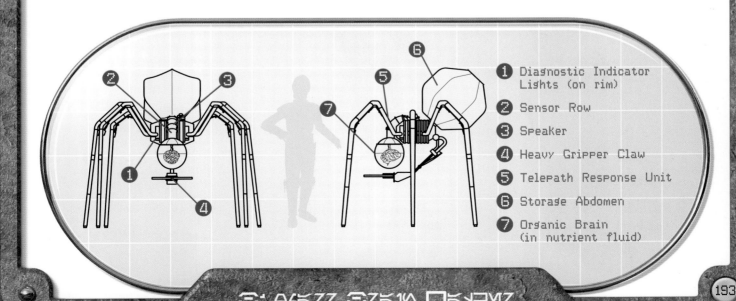

1. Diagnostic Indicator Lights (on rim)
2. Sensor Row
3. Speaker
4. Heavy Gripper Claw
5. Telepath Response Unit
6. Storage Abdomen
7. Organic Brain (in nutrient fluid)

Dark Side Technobeasts

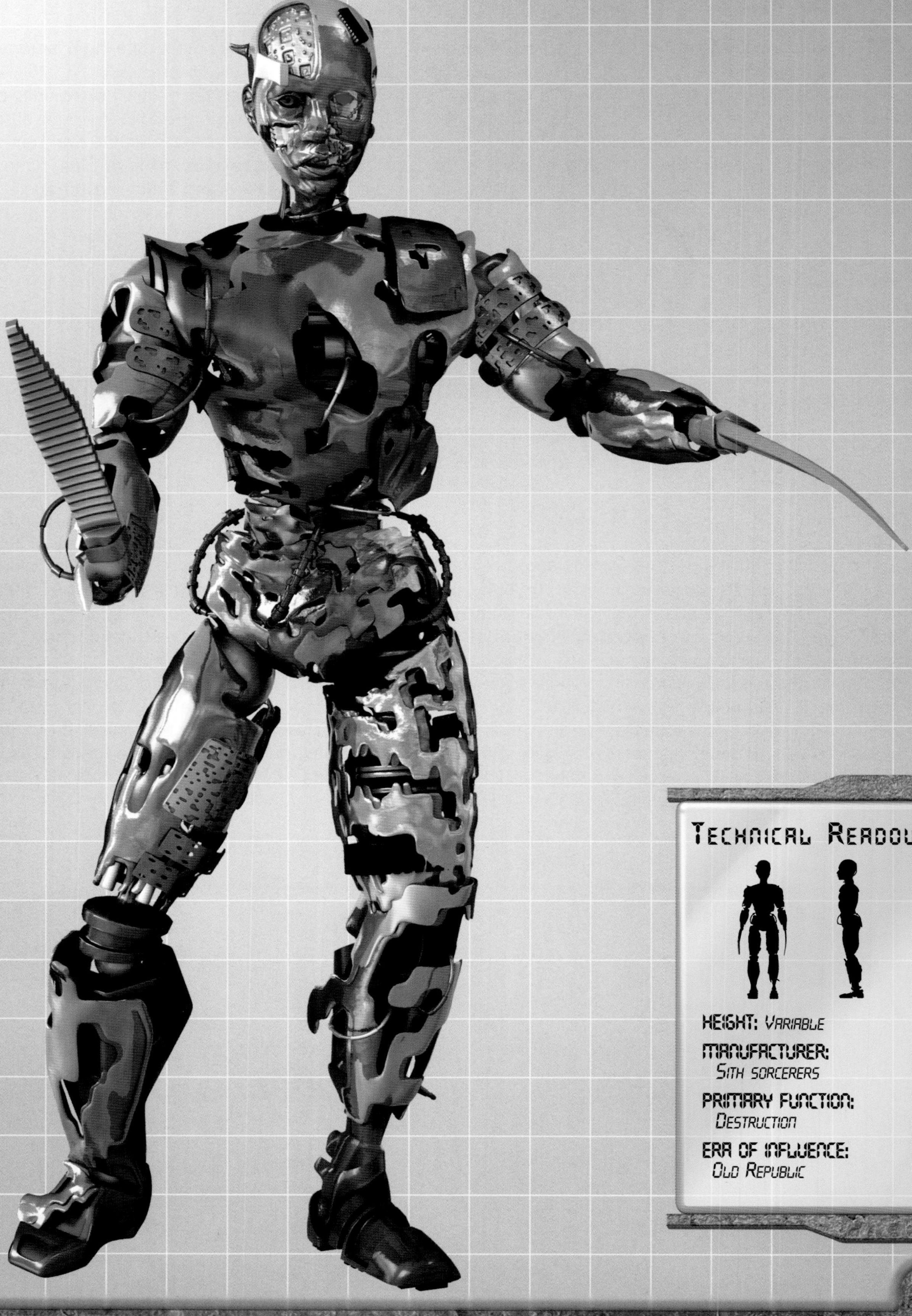

Technical Readout

Height: Variable

Manufacturer: Sith sorcerers

Primary Function: Destruction

Era of Influence: Old Republic

Sith Alchemic Technobeasts

Technobeasts are true Sith abominations. Their very existence is proof of the evils perpetuated during the New Sith Wars, when dark side magicians strove to pervert the balance of the Force.

Because droids are not organic beings, they were a subject few Jedi bothered to understand. Jedi powers that had a technical influence were usually crude, such as the Force ability *mechu macture,* or, as more commonly known, "destroy droid." The Sith went farther than the Jedi ever did, developing the ability *mechu-deru* to allow for Force control over mechanical systems. In true Sith fashion, the power stressed absolute control, turning droids into puppets.

In 1250 B.B.Y., Sith Lord Belia Darzu delved even deeper, using the principles of *mechu-deru* to create alchemic technology that *hungered.* Darzu's technovirus seed could replicate itself by converting organic material into circuitry nodes. A victim infected with the technovirus would rapidly turn into a hideous droid-human hybrid. Lord Darzu called these pitiable creatures technobeasts, and the technique became known as *mechu-deru vitae.*

A technovirus seed could be as small as a mold spore. Once it touched a victim's skin, it replicated by feeding on living tissue, growing to a metallic, fist-size tumor within minutes. The virus's primitive self-preservation instincts

> ## "Maggot of metal, rust, and rot. Sith life draws breath, old life does not."
>
> —*Sith* mechu-deru vitae *incantation, in the rhyming style popular during the Effulem era*

caused it to follow neurons up to the brain, where it lobotomized the frontal lobes to make its host incapable of higher thought. At this point, the conversion to technobeast was irreversible.

Technobeasts were never alike, save for their lumpy asymmetry where chunks of metal had replaced living components. The virus sometimes built over its own work multiple times, leaving behind zigzags of metallic scar tissue. The collective consciousness of the technovirus seeds seemed to have a curiosity regarding humanoid biology that expressed itself through experimentation. Technobeasts might have multiple heads, or scuttle about on crab-like pincers. Many had arms that ended in skewers or saw blades. A single technobeast could release a cloud of nanospores that could infect hundreds of other victims.

Technobeasts became the signature horror of the Sictis Wars, a subset of the New Sith Wars that lasted from 1250 to 1230 B.B.Y. One Jedi combatant became infected with the technovirus but kept his identity through the Force, serving the galaxy for decades as the "technobeast Jedi."

The death of Belia Darzu on Tython brought an end to the creation of new hybrids. Nevertheless, subsequent Sith Lords would bring them back in smaller numbers until the end of the New Sith Wars at the Battle of Ruusan.

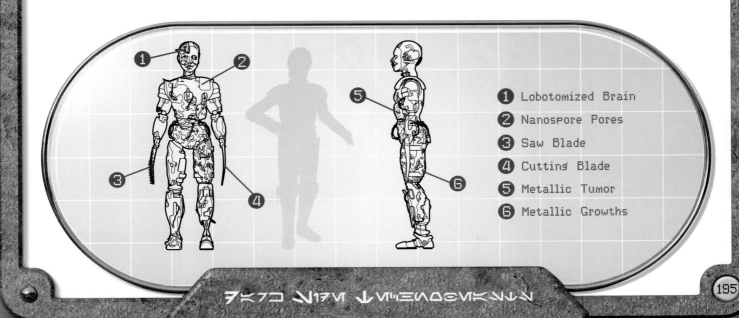

1 Lobotomized Brain
2 Nanospore Pores
3 Saw Blade
4 Cutting Blade
5 Metallic Tumor
6 Metallic Growths

GENERAL GRIEVOUS

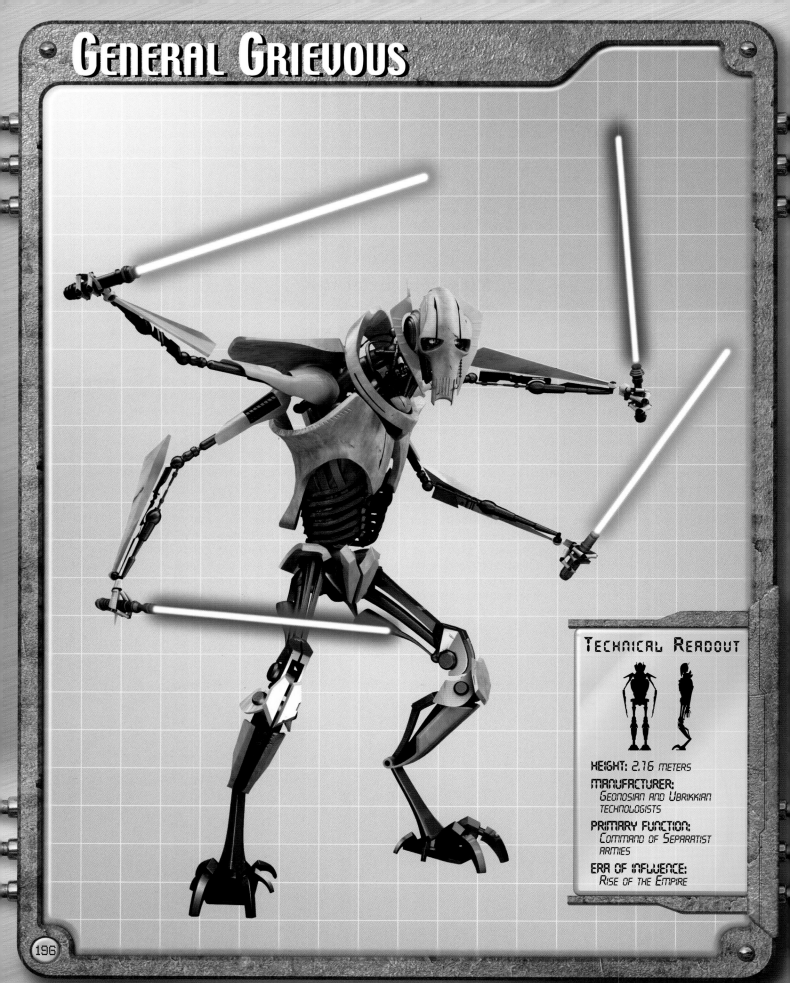

TECHNICAL READOUT

HEIGHT: 2.76 meters

MANUFACTURER:
Geonosian and Ubrikkian technologists

PRIMARY FUNCTION:
Command of Separatist armies

ERA OF INFLUENCE:
Rise of the Empire

Custom Geonosian Cybernetic Frame

Grievous had a body of metal and armorplast, and always appeared in battle flanked by IG 100 MagnaGuards. Most assumed he was a droid himself, but Grievous considered that to be an unforgivable insult. He was a cyborg, though his yellow reptilian eyes remained as the only external evidence of his former life.

On the colony worlds of the Kaleesh, Grievous led his people in battle against the rival Huk. Grievous's appeals for help from the Jedi went unanswered. Darth Sidious, however, noted the warlord's skill, and ensured that Grievous would suffer near-death injuries in a prearranged shuttle crash. Brought back to consciousness inside a bacta tank, Grievous agreed under duress to become a general for the Confederacy of Independent Systems in exchange for aid to the people of Kalee. The only way he would see continued life was as a cyborg.

Geonosian engineers, with funding from the InterGalactic Banking Clan, had achieved a cyborging breakthrough. Their new techniques, tested on a number of tragic victims prior to their use on Grievous, involved brain augmentation to make the subject better able to exploit the increased strength, speed, and reaction time of a computerized droid frame.

The Ubrikkian droids that performed the surgery on Grievous preserved his brain, eyes, spinal cord, and internal organs. But even these parts received cybernetic modifications. Cerebellum implants upgraded Grievous's body coordination, fed him heuristic combat programming, and tampered with his emotions, making

> ## "I am Grievous, warlord of the Kaleesh and Supreme Commander of the armies of the Confederacy. *And I am not a droid.*"
>
> —*General Grievous*

him more quick to anger. His eyes received internal implants to increase the sharpness of his vision and to protect them in vacuum. Most reports state that Grievous had no Force abilities, but rumors persist that he received a midi-chlorian-rich blood transfusion from the body of the late Jedi Master Sifo-Dyas.

The general's armorplast body featured magnetized talons to clamp onto the deck of a starship or a hapless victim. His two arms could split at the shoulders and become four, each hand with its own opposable thumb and two fingers. His face became a traditional Kaleesh mask, based on those carved from the skulls of mumuus and marked with dark lines of karabba blood above each eye. The "teeth" of Grievous's mask incorporated the speaker grille of an ultrasonic vocabulator.

Duranium chest plating protected the pressurized gutsac containing Grievous's internal organs. The general wore a cape similar to the one he had worn on Kalee, with inner pockets to hold the lightsabers he collected from vanquished Jedi.

The Geonosian cyborging process used to re-create Grievous wasn't perfect. Injuries sustained in a fight with Mace Windu left Grievous's organs damaged, and the automated armature could not compensate. General Grievous remained plagued by a wheezing cough until his death on Utapau following numerous blaster shots care of Obi-Wan Kenobi. An improved version of the same technology would be used to complete Anakin Skywalker's transformation into Darth Vader.

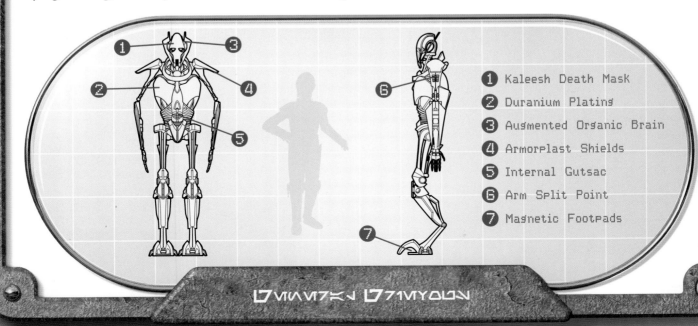

1 Kaleesh Death Mask
2 Duranium Plating
3 Augmented Organic Brain
4 Armorplast Shields
5 Internal Gutsac
6 Arm Split Point
7 Magnetic Footpads

Iron Knight

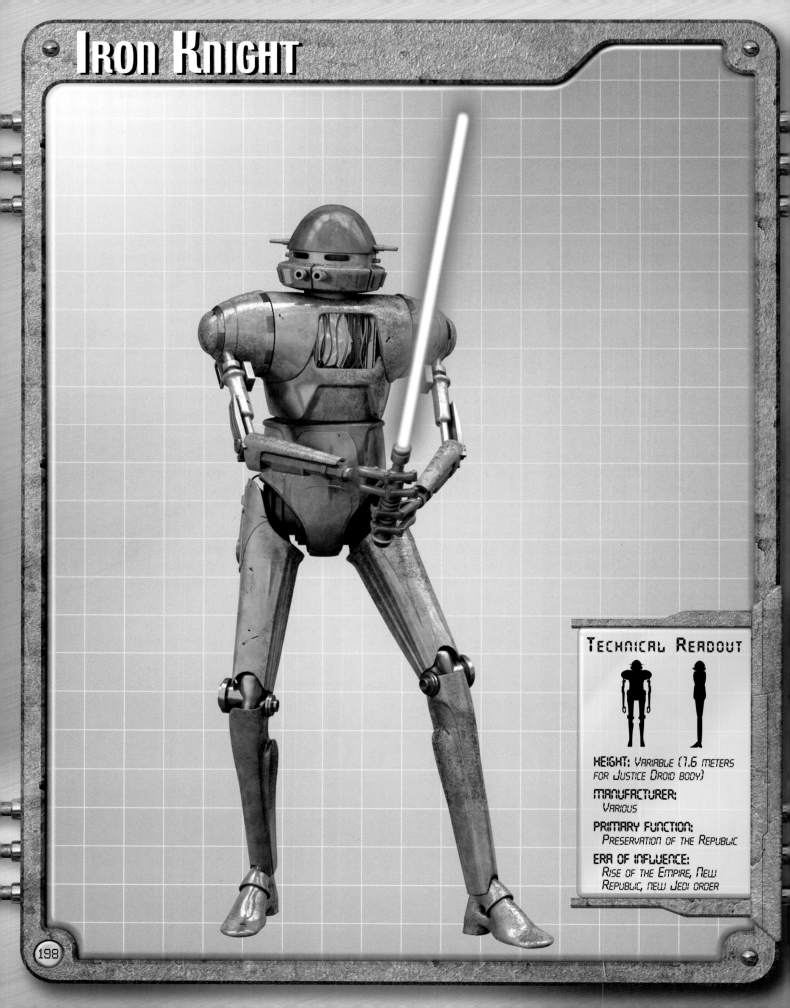

TECHNICAL READOUT

HEIGHT: Variable (1.6 meters for Justice Droid body)

MANUFACTURER: Various

PRIMARY FUNCTION: Preservation of the Republic

ERA OF INFLUENCE: Rise of the Empire, New Republic, New Jedi Order

Unique Crystalline/Electronic Ambulatory Symbiont

The planet Orax is home to an intelligent crystalline species known as the Shard. Like the crystal entities of Nam Chorios, the inhabitants of Orax defy most rules of biology. Immobile and composed of crystalline minerals, they fail most definitions of life, yet are undeniably intelligent.

Some Shards found their way offworld inside the body cavities of droids, where their consciousness and the artificial intelligence of the droids created a unique symbiont relationship. The Shard personality does not overwrite the droid personality; rather, the two meld together into a single persona containing aspects of both.

One Force-sensitive Shard, Ilum, gave birth to crystal splitlings who inhabited their own droids. A nonconformist Sunesi Jedi Master, Aqinos, agreed to train Ilum and her children in the ways of the Jedi on the frozen planet Dweem. After ten years of training, the "Jedi droids" made their public debut during the Arkanian Revolution, where they earned the derogatory nickname, *Iron Knights.*

Aqinos's pupils inhabited the bodies of FLTCH droids, Uulshos justice droids, and ancient juggernaut war droids. They wielded oversize lightsabers of their own construction containing the dead crystal bodies of their ancestors, and comported themselves in a ritualistic parody of courtly manners.

> ## "I take no orders from you. So before I lop your head off, I have one question: be ye friend or foe to the Republic?"
>
> —*High Marshal Dragite, one of the guardians of Dweem*

Though the Jedi Order taught that the Force existed in all things, the notion of droids, or even crystals, using the Force struck many in the Order as perverse. Not only did they lack midi-chlorians, but nonorganic and artificial life-forms were not "living" in the conventional sense. What understanding, therefore, could such beings have of the living Force?

The Jedi Council excommunicated Aqinos for heresy, and did its best to ignore his strange legion of Iron Knights. The Republic gave the Iron Knights the rank of high marshal for their actions during the Arkanian crisis, but the title carried no real weight. A disgraced Aqinos returned to Dweem, where he and the Iron Knights spent decades in exile.

Nine years after the Battle of Endor, Luke Skywalker's Jedi academy reestablished ties with the Iron Knights of Dweem. Luke, who was establishing new Jedi policy as he went along, had no traditionalist objections to the Iron Knights and welcomed their unique perspective on the Force.

During the Yuuzhan Vong invasion, the Iron Knights made it their mission to protect the galaxy's droids from the technology-hating Yuuzhan Vong. One of their number, Luxum, even succumbed to the dark side. Following the victory over the invaders, only a handful of Iron Knights remained active.

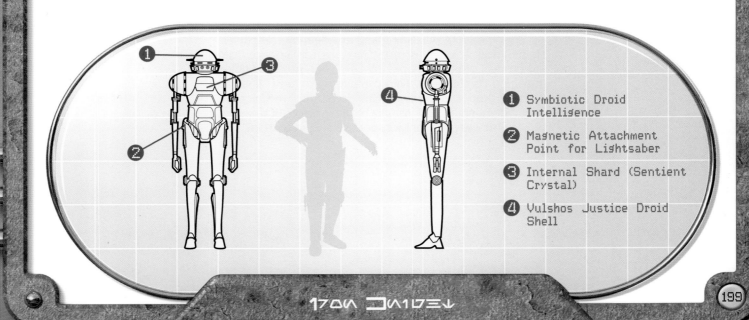

1. Symbiotic Droid Intelligence
2. Magnetic Attachment Point for Lightsaber
3. Internal Shard (Sentient Crystal)
4. Vulshos Justice Droid Shell

About the Author

KELLY WALLACE

Daniel Wallace is the author or coauthor of more than a dozen books, such as *The Art of Superman Returns, The Marvel Comics Encyclopedia,* and five previous entries in the Star Wars Essential Guide series, including the *New York Times* bestselling *Star Wars: The New Essential Guide to Characters.* He and his wife live in Detroit with their two sons and daughter.

About the Illustrator

Ian Fullwood lives and works in Herefordshire, England, and has clients both at home and in the USA. He has more than fifteen years' experience in technical illustration and commercial art, and works with a range of clients, including publishing and engineering companies. He produces a variety of work, ranging from science fiction to product visualizing and animation. Ian uses traditional drawing skills combined with computer programs—Illustrator, Photoshop, and Lightwave 3D—to produce technically demanding and visually exciting pieces of art. Visit *www.if3d.com* for more visual indigestion!

STAR WARS®

THE NEW ESSENTIAL GUIDE TO ALIEN SPECIES

LUCAS
BOOKS

DEL
REY

BALLANTINE BOOKS

NEW YORK

STAR WARS®

THE NEW ESSENTIAL GUIDE TO ALIEN SPECIES

Text by Ann Margaret Lewis and Helen Keier

Illustrations by Chris Trevas
and William O'Connor

This book could never have happened if not for the help and support of so many people:

Sue Rostoni, Jonathan Rinzler, and Leland Chee of Lucasfilm for giving us the opportunity and the invaluable assistance necessary to see this project to its completion.

Del Rey editors Steve Saffel for his generosity and Keith Clayton for his enthusiasm and patience. Also production manager Erich Schoeneweiss, another kindred spirit when it comes to the world of *Star Wars*.

All the Bantam and Del Rey *Star Wars* authors whose imaginations made these creatures come alive.

The comic-book artists and writers from Dark Horse and Marvel who made them incarnate in imagery.

The Wizards of the Coast Games authors and game designers who created an incredible wealth of amazing material.

Daniel Wallace and Abel Pena, our personal gurus of *Star Wars* wisdom. The depth of your knowledge is absolutely astounding. This book never would have been finished without you.

To all the creators at ILM and Lucasfilm who with their incredible imaginations created a good number of these creatures out of clay, plastic, paint, and rubber, then made them dance on screen.

Ann: A special thanks to my husband, Joseph, for giving me love and support through this entire process; my mother, Mary Ann, and my sister, Karen, for their encouragement; and to Helen—I cannot even begin to thank you enough for easing my stress and giving me hope. You are the absolute best.

Helen: My special thanks go to my son, Vince Skrapits; to the friends whose faith in me sustains me on a daily basis: Sonja Vanihel, Kay Silverwood Hilgendorf, Elizabeth Davidson, Matt Gladden, Glen and David Oliver, Sean Reiser, Gary Tucker, and the LeMaire family; to Ben Harper, Aaron Allston, and more than a few people I won't name in the interest of space but who know who they are, for all their encouragement; and last but not least, my thanks go to Ann. We said to each other when we met several years ago that we should write together someday, and to my great pleasure, now we have.

And especially to Mr. George Lucas for giving us the never-ending gift of *Star Wars*.

CONTENTS

INTRODUCTION

"A Vurk, a Gungan, and a Chevin walk into a bar. The bartender says . . ."

In this *New Essential Guide to Alien Species,* we cover the species that make the watering holes of scum and villainy come to life in that great "galaxy far, far away." We also give you in-depth dossiers of the many alien players that populate George Lucas's ever-expanding universe. Whether they were invented by the designers of the ILM Monster Shop, the novelists, comic-book writers and illustrators, or game developers, this book provides you with the details on the most pivotal species in the *Star Wars* galaxy.

The species in this book were selected because they met one or more of the following criteria: they appeared in at least one of the films, they were important to a major story line, or they were members of a species that begged for further exploration. While we've done our best to select as many as possible of the species fans would like to see, as a second edition there are many that were not included that may have been in the first edition. As with all of the *Essential Guides,* the goal was to provide a valuable and representa-

tive overview of the vastness of the *Star Wars* universe, taking into account all the favorites and introducing you to a few new faces you may not have met before.

While our perceptions of a given species are often based on only a few of its members, the truth is not all members of a given species are truly identical—even the clones and animals. Among creatures and persons, there is a great deal of variety in values, traditions, and appearance. So while each entry herein may note the shared characteristics exhibited by a given species, there will come events that lead any individual from that group to "break the rules." As our inspiration Senior Anthropologist Hoole once said, "In this galaxy, when you've seen one, don't assume you've seen them all." Words to the wise as you set off on your journey to meet the players in this colorful, sometimes frightening, but always thrilling galaxy of our dreams.

In the course of your own visits to the cantinas, spaceports, and gambling clubs of the Galaxy Far, Far Away, may the Force be with you, and with all creatures great, small, wild, and wonderful.

ABOUT THE ENTRIES

In our last edition, Senior Anthropologist Hoole provided much of the observational material for the species he studied. Following the good senior anthropologist's recent retirement, he left his notes and volumes of research materials for us to use for this new guide. These detailed texts, along with our own observational notes, have helped us put together our entries and provide the following information. Please note that survey teams have not been able to reach all the worlds affected by the Yuuzhan Vong invasion, so the status of some species in the wake of that event has not yet been determined. If the present status of a species is known, it will be given in the body of the entry.

DESIGNATION

Each species is designated as *sentient, semi-sentient,* or *nonsentient.* Usually this is based on a species' ability to reason, use tools, and communicate. A panel of multicultural scientists determines the designations only after a government-approved research team has conducted a field study or has made some significant finding regarding the sentience of any given species. The designations are defined as follows:

Sentient: When a species is given the *sentient* designation, it is considered able to reason and understand abstract concepts and ideas, make and use tools, and communicate with written or spoken language. Most primitive tribal species have this designation; it does not imply that a species is civilized to the point of space travel.

Semi-sentient: The *semi-sentient* designation implies that a race has some reasoning ability, but cannot grasp elevated or abstract concepts. In many cases, it has not yet formed a written or spoken language. These species are considered to be in evolutionary stages—on their way to achieving sentience. Under the Empire, these species were not entitled to landownership, but this has been undergoing reconsideration in the Galactic Federation of Free Alliances.

Nonsentient: A *nonsentient* species is one that does not reason at all, surviving only on its natural instincts.

HOMEWORLD

Most alien species have a homeworld or system. Some, like the bantha, are found in many systems, and still others, such as the Hutts, have transplanted themselves to a new home. The primary locations of a given species within the galaxy will be listed here, and its present home will be likewise indicated.

AVERAGE HEIGHT

The average size of adult members of a given species is provided in meters.

PRONUNCIATION

The pronunciation of the species' name is provided in Basic. For the pronunciation key, please see page 218.

NOTABLE APPEARANCE

We provide one of the noteworthy appearances of each species in book, film, or comics.

GLOSSARY OF DESCRIPTIVE TERMS

The following terms are used to describe the species in this book. Many of the varieties covered in this volume belong to one or more of these classifications. Given the unique evolutionary conditions found on each planet, it is impossible to fit every species into a neat classification. These are broad terms useful in describing an unfamiliar species to one's colleagues.

Amphibious: A creature that can live both in water and on land, or has two stages of life, one that is completely water-based, the other land-based. Some are born as tadpoles possessing gills, and develop lungs to breathe air, while others have compound lungs that allow them to breathe underwater and on land.

Arboreal: A species that lives among forests and trees, and is specially adapted to tree living.

Avian: A species bearing the characteristics of birds or flying mammals.

Canine: A species that possesses some characteristics of the dog family, including a pronounced muzzle, sharp teeth, advanced hunting and tracking instincts, heightened hearing, sight, and smell, sharp teeth, claws, padded feet, and a tail.

Cephalopod: A species that bears the traits inherent in most squid and octopi, namely water-based or amphibious creatures with tentacles.

Cetacean: Any species of aquatic or marine mammals, usually typified by a predominance of the following: a hairless or nearly hairless body, anterior flipper-like limbs, vestigial posterior limbs, and a flat, notched tail.

Crustacean: Aquatic lobster-like arthropods or shellfish that usually have a segmented body, a chitinous exoskeleton, and paired, jointed limbs.

Cyborg: Any species that has been enhanced with technological implants.

Feline: A species that carries some characteristics of the cat family, such as extremely flexible body, sharp teeth, slit-pupiled eyes, a tail, hunting and tracking instincts, heightened hearing, sight, and smell, and padded, clawed hands and feet.

Gastropod: A species that has no true skeletal frame and moves by means of a wide muscular foot, or whose whole body acts as one large foot.

Humanoid: Those species that, while not related genetically to humans, possess characteristics similar to humans, such as two arms with hands, fingers, and an opposable thumb, two legs, a torso, and a single head.

Insectoid: Any species that has the characteristics of insects, which may include a chitinous shell, multiple legs, antennae, and multifaceted eyes.

Mammal: This classification usually refers to warm-blooded vertebrates that grow fur and usually bear live young (although not always, as some have been known to lay eggs). Regardless of the birth process, a female mammal nurses her young.

Near-human: These species are genetically related to humans, and are usually classified as humans. Only four near-human species are represented in this book.

Pachydermoid: A species with characteristics attributed to pachyderms, usually including baggy, leathery skin, a trunk, and steady, thick legs and feet.

Plant-based: A species that reproduces itself and roots like most plant life, usually feeding through photosynthesis. Some plant-based species resemble animal species, depending on evolution.

Porcine: A species bearing the characteristic of a pig, sometimes including a blunt-ended nose, tusks, hooves, and large physical size.

Primate: Mammalian species exhibiting the characteristics of monkeys or apes, including fur, fingers, and opposable thumbs. They are often referred to as humanoids because of their similarity to human physiology, but this depends on their sentience designation.

Proboscidian: A species that has a long trunk or feeds through a proboscis, such as the Anzati. Some proboscidians are also pachydermoids (see *Pachydermoid*).

Reptavian: A flying reptile.

Reptilian: A species with the characteristics of a reptile or snake, usually including leather-like skin, claws, slit-pupiled eyes, and a forked tongue. They reproduce by laying fertilized eggs. Some can change color to match their environment. Trandoshans, Barabels, Yevetha, and Falleen are all reptilian races.

Reptomammal: A reptile that reproduces through live birth rather than laying eggs.

Rodent: A species that carries characteristics of mice or rats, or gnawing or nibbling mammals that have continuously growing incisors.

Saurian: See *Reptilian*.

Ungulate: A species that has hooves, or whose claws evolved from hooves, and sometimes chews its cud.

Vacuumbreather: A species that can survive in a vacuum, including that of outer space, often consuming nutrients from space dust and mineral matter. Mynocks are vacuumbreathers.

STAR WARS®

THE NEW ESSENTIAL GUIDE TO ALIEN SPECIES

ACKLAY

The acklay is an amphibious crustacean of immense size and foul temperament that inhabits the oceans of Vendaxa, a verdant world with a highly developed ecosystem. Their small eyes allow them to see in underwater darkness and protect them from their world's harsh sunlight, although they are nearsighted. They have massive, sharp pincer claws that easily slice and stab at prey. And yet, while they are indeed from the crustacean family, they also have traits of a reptilian genus, namely large jaws filled with deeply embedded, needle-sharp teeth, and tough, leathery, scaly skin.

Acklays are especially valued as gladiatorial beasts in the Outer Rim worlds, as their tough hides and fierce attitude make them harsh opponents that are very difficult to kill. They do not have especially large stomachs, but to accommodate their often sizable prey, the creatures' stomach can stretch to fit large amounts of food at one time. This section of their body is particularly vulnerable,

3.0

2.5

2.0

1.5

1.0

.5

.0

as the flesh covering is not as tough as the rest of their hide. Acklays have an extremely high metabolism for creatures their size, giving them a lot of energy—but they starve quickly if not fed frequently throughout the day. In gladiatorial environments, this can prompt them to have an appetite for many unfortunate arena victims, and it also makes their upkeep expensive for owners, who must frequently run them in the arena to satiate their appetites.

Like some reptilian species, acklays have a bony neck plate that they display to intimidate opponents. This also protects the acklay from overhead neck attacks. In addition, acklays can use this plate as a type of weapon, by bucking and weaving their heads to and fro to strike an opponent.

Acklays walk on the tips of their claws, seeming to glide on toe point like dancers. Yet these claws are lethal for an acklay's adversary. During combat, the acklay uses its claws like hatchets, waving them about to slice its opponents to bits—or to pinion its prey to the ground like a skewer weighing several tons. An acklay's claws are long enough to enable the beast to attack at a safe distance from its victim. These hardened appendages have little to no feeling, but rising from the joint of the main talons is an additional claw that is somewhat sensitive. Sensory hairs or cilia lining the surface of the exoskeleton claw allow an acklay the sense of touch. It is also able to sense its prey's body electricity with its cilia.

In their native habitat, these ferocious creatures hunt the plains during the day for the leathery-shelled lemnai, which, being nocturnal, are usually asleep in their dens. At night, acklays return to their lairs onshore to rest. Under the ocean surface, they feed on schools of fish that they can suck into their gaping, toothy maws.

On Geonosis, acklays have only one natural predator: the merdeth. Enormous carnivores larger than star freighters, merdeths are armored insects with hundreds of small legs and masses of barbed tentacles that emerge from underneath their heads. Slow-moving creatures, merdeths often attack acklay dens, trapping the acklays inside and eating them.

While the acklay is originally from Vendaxa, the species also has a thriving population on Geonosis. Largely renowned for its droid technology, Geonosis also became well known as a hive of gladiatorial gaming and executions. One of the most popular species transferred to Geonosis was the acklay, which was then bred for arena entertainment.

A new mutant subspecies of acklay has appeared, larger and fiercer than its genetic relatives, a result of the chemical pollution contained in its habitat in the Golbah Pit of Geonosis. This new subspecies is different from the primary acklay in that its outer shell is a glossy black. The mutant acklay has heavier claws than its relative, and it is even able to hunt successfully in the dark, murky waters of the Ebon Sea. In addition, the mutant acklay can breathe underwater and is a highly skilled swimmer, allowing it to prey upon creatures not typically hunted by acklays. Overall, the mutant acklay is larger and tougher than its cousins, and will absorb considerably more damage before it is brought down.

Acklays may have been exported to worlds other than their traditional habitats to serve as live weapons during the Clone Wars. Records of the 501st Legion indicate that the unit was attacked by packs of acklays in the wilds of the Outer Rim planet of Felucia, then under Commerce Guild control. It is possible that the Confederacy of Independent Systems was able to move acklays from one loyal world to another without drawing attention to the shift within the scientific community. This theory has some support due to the fact that initial clone reports were unable to name the creatures, where as if the acklay had been native to or expected on a planet, the clones would have been briefed on them. At present, there are no indications that acklays remain on Felucia, perhaps a testament to the 501st's effectiveness.

DESIGNATION
Nonsentient

HOMEWORLD
Vendaxa/Geonosis

AVERAGE HEIGHT
3.05 meters

PRONUNCIATION
Ăk'-lā

NOTABLE APPEARANCE
Episode II: Attack of the Clones

AIWHA

The aiwha is an eight- to ten-meter-long aquatic mammal that flies on massive wings spanning twenty to thirty meters. Xenobiologists claim that aiwhas originated on Naboo, though a large population is also found on the planet Kamino. On both Naboo and Kamino, their primary habitats are the planets' oceans, and many have also been domesticated for use as riding mounts by Gungans and Kaminoans.

Aiwhas are strong creatures, using their muscular wings and pectoral muscles to create thrust for gliding in the air and swimming underwater. By building up momentum in the cresting waves, they can launch themselves into the sky to soar above the water. Aiwhas are able to propel themselves by shifting ballast, which they manage by utilizing two particular physical attributes. First, their skulls are porous and contain several buoyancy chambers, which fill with water when they dive under the surface. When aiwhas want to launch above the waves, they blow water from these cham-

bers in a fashion akin to the way most cetaceans use a blowhole. Aiwhas also have a special vascular system that enables them to shift body density. Their spongy, porous body tissue absorbs hundreds of kilograms of water, and when they soar into the air, they expel the liquid from their tissue to make themselves lighter. During flight, aiwhas release high-pitched whistling sounds. These sounds are used by the animal as internal sonar for underwater navigation, and as radar for night flying.

Although certain parts of their bodies allow for the intake and release of ocean water as mentioned above, aiwha skin is smooth, flexible, and virtually waterproof. This reduces air drag for the aiwhas when flying, while also allowing them to cut easily through the currents and retain body heat in cold seas. Aiwhas use their tails to aid in propelling themselves in and out of the water, either as rudders or for thrust. In addition, aiwhas have small, strong hind legs that are of limited use on land. They strongly prefer the seas over dry land, and do not walk very often on hard ground. Aiwhas also possess sharp teeth that they use to capture and hold prey.

Aiwhas make homes in nest-like "pods" on the ocean surface, and, like most cetacean mammals, they bear their young live. Unlike many of their genus, however, they will usually give birth to more than one calf at a time. Because up

to three or four aiwha families will nest together in one pod, they can often have clutches of eight to two dozen young in a grouping. While these creatures have been bred for docility, they are fierce when their pods are threatened, and will fight with an intense rage that is incongruous with their normally peaceful temperament. Conversely, domesticated aiwhas are very protective of their riding masters, seeing them as family in lieu of their podmates.

Aiwhas feed primarily on shallow-swimming krill and fish—filtering their sustenance, as most cetaceans do, through sieve plates in their baleen. By using high-pitched underwater sounds similar to the ones they utilize to navigate, aiwhas will corral their prey into a grouping and then suck them into their opened maw. However, aiwhas are omnivorous, unlike other cetaceans found throughout the galaxy. They will consume seaweed, kelp, and other plants found on the ocean floor as well as vitamin-laden grass from wetlands.

Creatures of the same genus as aiwhas can be found in several systems throughout the galaxy, including the planets Naboo and Kamino. Historical records indicate that the aiwha was brought to Kamino from Naboo, and that the Kaminoans cloned the present population from that stock to serve their needs. Despite their aquatic nature, the Kaminoan breed of aiwha is resistant to electrical shock. This makes them impervious to the dangerous electrical storms that often rage on the planet's surface. The Naboo breed, meanwhile, is not immune to such an attack. Xenobiologists believe that since aiwhas are probably a relatively recent addition to the Kaminoan environment, this trait was most likely added to their species during the cloning process. Even so, the Kaminoan aiwha prefers to go underwater during these storms; flying through them is highly unpleasant.

Kaminoans find the aiwha to be the most efficient means of traveling from one of their stilt-cities to another. They also use aiwhas to make religious pilgrimages to the ancient Kaminoan cities that lie at the bottom of their oceans (land-based Kaminoan culture was destroyed when the entire planet was flooded at the conclusion of a planetary ice age). Aiwhas provide a peaceful, spiritual means of transportation to the remnants of their ancient heritage, where the Kaminoans honor their ancestors rather than engage in archaeological exploration.

Gungans, on the other hand, use aiwhas for private mounted transportation, but also find them especially useful as bombers for aerial warfare and reconnaissance in the Gungan army. These military aiwhas are specially trained not to use their radar or make other sounds when flying for reconnaissance, but instead to rely on direction from their riders, although Gungan army aiwha riders can command their mounts to use their screech as a weapon when necessary. Because of this, aiwha-riding Gungans often wear earplugs when an attack is imminent, communicating with one another and their animals through hand signals and gestures initially developed for reconnaissance use. Military-trained aiwhas extend their loyalty just as any domesticated aiwhas do, often sensing when their riders are injured or incapacitated and need to be removed from battle. Among Gungans, stories abound of aiwhas saving the lives of their riders with a well-timed retreat.

DESIGNATION
Nonsentient

HOMEWORLD
Kamino / Naboo

AVERAGE HEIGHT
2–3 meters
WINGSPAN
11 meters

PRONUNCIATION
Äē'-wä

NOTABLE APPEARANCE
Episode II: Attack of the Clones

AMANI
(Amanaman)

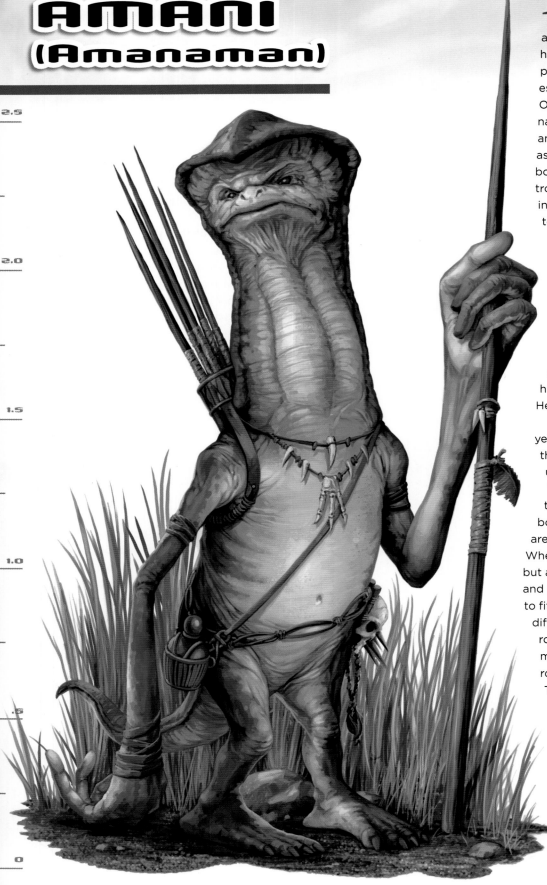

The Amanin (often referred to as Amanaman) are a primitive tribal hunter-gatherer species native to the planet Maridun, a world of large forests and grassy plains located in the Outer Rim. They are a sentient planarian species (i.e., of a worm genus), and they serve throughout the galaxy as laborers, scouts, and sometimes bounty hunters. Amanin are quiet, introspective beings who often converse in deep, low voices. Although they tower over many races, even Wookiees, they prefer to remain unnoticed as befitting their predatory nature. Unavoidably, however, their striking appearance in size, color, and decoration often has the opposite effect. For example, Amanin are known to carry at all times a staff from which the skulls of vanquished enemies hang. This has earned the Amanin the nickname Head Hunters.

Amanin are very tall, thin, mostly yellow-skinned arboreal beings who gain their height from long arms, which they use to travel from branch to branch. They have short, thick legs with extremely large feet, and while their bodies may appear awkward, Amanin are actually quite deft in movement. When on the ground, they walk slowly, but are able to curl themselves into a ball and roll at speeds ranging from forty-five to fifty kilometers per hour. Although it is difficult for them to perceive their surroundings well when traveling in this manner, Amanin are able to use their rolling momentum as a form of attack. They will speed past an opponent and unfurl their bodies to lash out with claws or clubs, often instantly killing their unsuspecting victim with the controlled force of impact.

By contrast, the placement of Amanin internal organs aids them in avoiding fatal injuries. As in other worm species, their organs, including their brains, are spread throughout their entire form. Moreover, they possess multiple copies of each primary organ, further enhancing their ability to survive wounds that would kill many species. This duplication of functional parts has led scientists to believe that Amanin can actually regenerate lost or damaged organs and limbs, and it is theorized that it is possible for an Amani to be cut fully in half without being killed. In such an event, however, it is thought the individual's regrowth may actually spawn two identical Amanin. Male and female are indistinguishable in this species, and it is believed, though as yet unproven, that they are hermaphrodites.

Amanin skin is moist, but susceptible to drying, so they prefer to make their shelter in humid environments, particularly rain forests. Their yellow-and-green coloring helps them blend in with their forest and grassland environments to avoid being detected by other predators. In addition, the coloration signals the poisonous properties of the slime that is secreted by their bodies to keep their skin damp and to fend off most of the carnivorous creatures found in the forests of Maridun. This slime deters all local predators save the charnoq, the only creature the Amanin fear.

Amanin have tiny eyes that can see clearly in Maridun's dim light, as well as little mouths that open surprisingly wide for engulfing raw game. As with other worm species, Amanin expel their biological waste through their mouths, although after having experienced interaction with other species, they mostly do this in private, as they have come to learn how it disturbs others. They also have a sense of smell so keen that they can detect strangers in their midst from more than ten kilometers away.

The Amanin have a simple, warrior tribal culture. Each tribe controls a forest region on Maridun, typically surrounded by grasslands. Amanin refer to all nonforested areas with the same term: gruntak. When an Amanin tribe's population grows too large, the extra youth of that tribe cross the gruntak regions to find a new section of forest to inhabit. This flight can result in battles over land rights with other Amanin, called takitals. The tribal leader or shaman, known as the lorekeeper, keeps stories of these struggles in a history that he often recites at special events.

During Palpatine's rule, Maridun was occupied by Imperial forces, setting in motion a series of events that changed the world and its people forever. A careless Imperial general led his troops across sacred Amanin grounds, and in retaliation, the local Amanin tribe waged a takital against the Empire.

DESIGNATION
Sentient

HOMEWORLD
Maridun

AVERAGE HEIGHT
2–3 meters

PRONUNCIATION
Ăm-an'-ē

Janek Sunbar, an Imperial officer, distinguished himself during the takital, opening the door for an accord with the Amanin leader. Unfortunately, the price of peace was high. In the agreement, the tribal leader would turn over to the Empire any Amanin prisoners taken during takitals, and in return the Empire would stay clear of their lands. A similar arrangement was soon made with lorekeepers of other Amanin tribes. As a result, many captured Amanin were used as free labor in the mines of Maridun or scattered as slaves throughout the galaxy, forced to work at other Imperial facilities.

After the Empire shifted its attention away from Maridun, smuggling bands took over the spaceports and mining operations that the Empire abandoned, and Maridun is now run mostly by organized crime. Many Amanin have moved to the spaceports from their forest homes. Some travel offworld to conduct takitals against humans, viewing it as a form of retribution for what the Empire did to their kind. Traditional lorekeepers see this behavior as a corruption of their traditions, and do their best to train youngsters not to follow such a path. Other lorekeepers moved to the cities with their youth to sell blessings and native memorabilia to offworlders stopping at their spaceports. And similar to the way rural Amanin brought their culture to the cities, there are Amanin who have taken sophisticated technology, specifically blasters, back to their traditional communities for use in conquering new tribal lands in the takitals.

Amanin, as a whole, prefer to remain ignorant of galactic politics. While Amanin slaves have been known to temporarily take sides, usually it is to participate in a takital to win their freedom, or in obedience to their masters, with whom they've formed a lorekeeper bond. The best way to persuade Amanin to join a cause is to convince them that their tribal honor is at stake while showing great enthusiasm for their tales of prowess.

In person, Amanin are quiet and thoughtful, although they love exchanging stories. They develop fiercely loyal relationships with any leadership figures whom they consider lorekeepers, even when those people may not have their best interests in mind—mob bosses, employers, even slave owners. In several cases, Amanin have refused to leave slavery when given the opportunity because their loyalty to their masters was so intense—a trait that made the species extremely useful to the Empire.

NOTABLE APPEARANCE
Episode VI: Return of the Jedi

ANZAT

The Anzati are one of the deadliest and most mysterious species in the galaxy. Because Anzati are roamers, they are often considered mythical, and for a long period of time the true location of their homeworld was a mystery. Scientists who traveled to the world reputed to be Anzat simply disappeared without a trace, although some reports place it on the outskirts of the Mid Rim, near the Perlemian Trade Route. Believed to be one of the first of the spacefaring races, they are human in appearance, ranging in height from 1.5 to 1.7 meters with grayish-hued skin and bulbous noses. While scientists have had little opportunity to study Anzati, the sketchy medical reports found on the species seem to indicate that they have no natural biorhythm—no pulse. Given that fact, it is a complete enigma as to how their circulatory system functions.

Being natural predators, Anzati prefer to hunt sentient races of all shapes and sizes, and they possess two prehensile proboscises that they keep coiled in their cheek pockets for feeding on unsuspecting victims in a rather unique way. Jedi who have encountered the species have suggested that Anzati mind control is a type of Force manipulation; they can sense the Force and use it to bewitch their victims in a way akin to the famous Jedi mind trick. To lure in unsuspecting targets, Anzati mesmerize them with this form of telepathic control that strengthens at close range. Once a subject is in their power, Anzati will uncoil their proboscises from their cheek pouches and insert them into a victim's nostrils to suck out brain matter. They call this meal "soup," "luck," or the "Sea of Memory"; in their tradition, the term refers to the life essence, or spiritual power, of the victim. It is reputed that Anzati can keep victims alive for several feedings, enjoying the fear and terror their prey feels throughout the ordeal. Some Anzati believe feeding on living vessels in this way gives them eternal youth and energy. This belief can be traced to the Silent Voices, luminescent bands of gases that glow in the Anzat atmosphere at night, and which ancient Anzati thought were the life essences of their ancestors. Although such a possibility is not scientifically viable, it illustrates the level of importance that "soup" plays in Anzati culture, mores, and belief structures.

According to anecdotal evidence offered by sentients lucky

1.5

1.0

.5

0

enough to survive their encounters with Anzati, they are loners who wander throughout the galaxy, returning to Anzat only to find a mate and reproduce, and in some cases to train with Anzati master assassins. They reproduce infrequently and usually live for many centuries. Parents do not typically give their children names, instead allowing them to seek names that best blend in with their chosen prey. Youthful Anzati reach puberty at approximately one hundred standard years of age, and leave Anzat to hunt for "soup" to continue their "eternal" existence.

Studies of different galactic creation myths contain no information about Anzati, though some tales say they have existed longer than any other species. They often act as patrons of the arts, but few have actually contributed with works of their own. Because they are a long-lived species, they tend to view mastering an art as a pointless goal since all other competitors die before they do.

One art that does fuel their interest enough to participate in, though, is stealth. Anzati are master hunters, incredibly sly and crafty, and difficult to capture. Because of their secrecy, hunting skills, and training, Anzati are often employed by organized crime factions as assassins. Anonymity is used to their advantage, so they rarely, if ever, work in groups. It is only in the capacity of a bounty hunter that they will abandon their lonely ways and band together to form a corporation or guild. On these exceptionally rare occasions, they will sometimes share prey and the financial rewards of their hunts. These corporations are temporary, often existing for only one hunt, as they end up killing each other to eliminate competition for a very "soupy" victim.

The constant drive to hunt for "soup" seems to be the central factor of Anzati life; one could almost consider them an addicted people. Once they begin the hunt, they think of nothing else but to satisfy this hunger, which grows stronger with each passing year. Anzati have been reported to view all other peoples as livestock to be harvested to fulfill their needs, although some have been known to try to stave off the craving for as long as possible between feedings. Either way, because the hunger grows as they age, they end up becoming more and more isolated in their need. The older the Anzati, the more unstable and obsessive they become, often to the point of insanity. They lose focus on the world around them and in many cases will make a crucial mistake, leading to their ultimate destruction.

Although the Anzati as a species are isolationists, essential reports have surfaced of at least three significant events that brought the species into open conflict with the Jedi—

DESIGNATION
Sentient

HOMEWORLD
Anzat

AVERAGE HEIGHT
1.7 meters

PRONUNCIATION
Än'-zät

incidents that propelled them into the galactic spotlight for a short time.

The first episode began roughly a thousand years before the Clone Wars. A rare Anzati Jedi named Volfe Karkko who had never tasted "soup" believed himself above the instinct shared by the rest of his species. Unfortunately, this same arrogance led Karkko to think he could control his inbred nature, and he fed—a mistake that in turn resulted in Karkko succumbing to the dark side. Karkko was captured and held in stasis for a millennium on the prison world of Kiffex. During his imprisonment, however, his mind remained active, and he was able to draw numerous followers. Over time, his legend grew among the Anzati on Kiffex, who worshipped him as "the Dreamer," converting his resting place into a sacred temple. Karkko fed his followers' baser instincts, turning them feral and causing them to prey on the residents and inmates of Kiffex with a ferocity striking even for Anzati. Jedi Master Tholme and Aayla Secura ultimately defeated Karkko, who had struck out against the Jedi.

Later, during the Clone Wars, a group of Anzati master assassins took on contracts to work for the Separatists under Count Dooku, training a secret society of Nikto warriors known as the Morgukai. The Morgukai had been thought to be extinct, but were being reproduced by the Separatists through cloning techniques. The Jedi Master Tholme and his Padawan, Aayla Secura, were able to thwart this potentially devastating source of soldiers.

A second Anzati Jedi, Nikkos Tyris, was responsible for founding a competing order of Force-users during the Clone Wars called the Saarai-kaar, later known as the Jensaarai. Fortunately, the Jensaarai did not pose significant harm to others, never rising to influence much beyond their homeworld and only seeking to serve as protectors. Because their initial leaders were not corrupted by the dark side, the Jensaarai actually served the light side of the Force, despite their reverence for Sith traditions.

NOTABLE APPEARANCE
Episode IV: A New Hope

AQUALISH

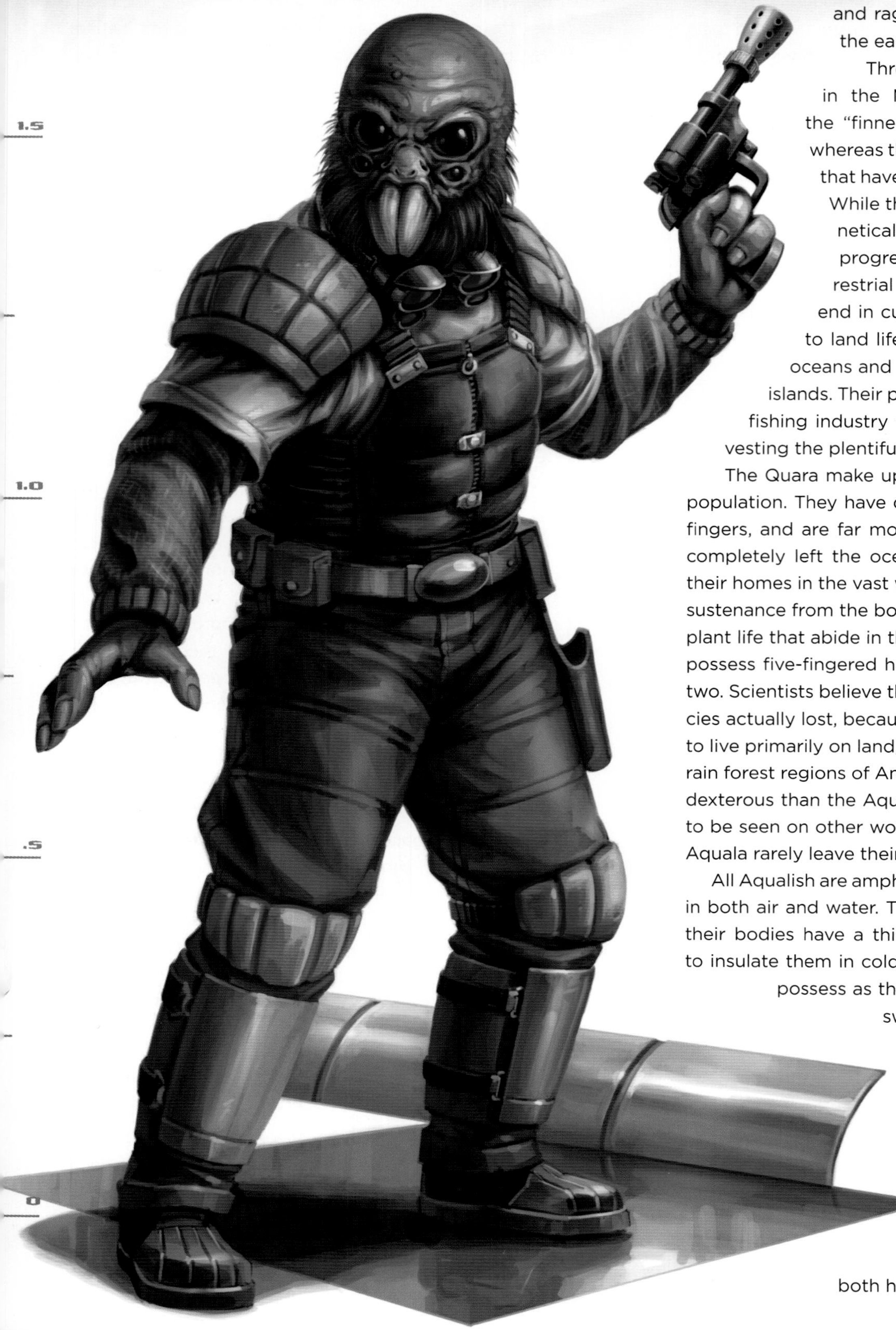

The Aqualish are bulky, tusked humanoids known for hair-trigger tempers that can flare without cause or reason. Most anthropologists feel that the streak of anger and rage carried by Aqualish harks back to the early years of the species' evolution.

Three races of Aqualish inhabit Ando, in the Mid Rim. The Aquala, often called the "finned Aqualish," is the baseline species, whereas the Quara and Ualaq are minority races that have evolved from their Aquala ancestors. While the three Aqualish races are nearly genetically identical, the Aquala evolutionary progression from aquatic mammal to terrestrial is not yet complete, and their hands end in cup-shaped fins. Aquala have adapted to land life, yet they prefer to live close to the oceans and seas on floating cities, ships, or small islands. Their primary source of food is the extensive fishing industry that casts nets kilometers long, harvesting the plentiful marine life from Ando's waters.

The Quara make up only one-tenth of the overall world population. They have developed humanoid hands with five fingers, and are far more adept in fine motor skills. Having completely left the oceans through evolution, Quara make their homes in the vast wetland areas of Ando, gleaning their sustenance from the bountiful waterfowl, land creatures, and plant life that abide in these areas. The Ualaq, like the Quara, possess five-fingered hands, but have four eyes rather than two. Scientists believe that this is one trait the other two species actually lost, because while the Ualaq developed fingers to live primarily on land, they mainly reside in caves and dark rain forest regions of Ando. Since their appendages are more dexterous than the Aquala, Ualaq and Quara are more likely to be seen on other worlds throughout the galaxy, while the Aquala rarely leave their native home.

All Aqualish are amphibians of a sort, being able to breathe in both air and water. The Aquala are better swimmers, and their bodies have a thick layer of blubber under their skin to insulate them in cold water. The Quara and Ualaq do not possess as thick a layer of blubber, as they do not swim quite as often and tend to stay in warmer waters.

Common to all three of the Aqualish races are large, thick tusks. These tusks are useful in cracking open shellfish or burrowing into swampy loam to dig out marshy plant life for sustenance. Aqualish tusks are very sensitive, and receptive to both heat and cold, as their enamel surface contains a dense layer of nerve cells. As a result, Aqualish can be seen rubbing their tusks on wooden surfaces. They find this activity pleasurable rather than painful, akin to giving themselves a massage. This sensitivity can also help them determine the texture of their food before chewing. Unfortunately, the heightened responsiveness can also produce extreme pain if their tusks are chipped or broken, and a damaged tusk can sometimes result in enough pain to immobilize an Aqualish for weeks.

The complexion of the three Aqualish races varies. The Aquala tend to have skin that ranges in color from dark blue to dark green, probably to keep them camouflaged while underwater. The Ualaq and Quara are often more gray or black, though they, too, usually have a hint of blue or green in their grayish pallor.

The Aqualish are endowed with large, glassy black eyes that allow for keen vision underwater. Their eyes are not built for bright light, accounting for a preference for darker environments when Aqualish are offworld. On brighter planets, they tend to gravitate to dark bars or dens, even sleeping during the day then venturing out at night—particularly the Ualaq, whose four eyes are even more sensitive than their counterparts'.

In all three Aqualish cultures, strength is held in high regard. Aqualish show open disdain and hostility to those who appear weak, and when first meeting another individual will often act aggressive and confrontational. If the other person doesn't respond in kind or defend him- or herself, the Aqualish will assume that the other is weak and continue the harassment.

Because of this combative behavior, Aqualish history is fraught with conflict. Before the Republic formed, the Aquala faced a drop in their food supply from overfishing marine populations. Since they tend to be an unreasonable people, they blamed the Quara and Ualaq for the lack of ocean life. This disagreement escalated to an all-out war that could have destroyed all the Aqualish races, were it not for a timely, otherworldly occurrence.

A spaceship arrived on Ando. Various legends hold that the visitors were from Corellia, while others assert they were from Duro. The Aqualish were not yet spacefarers, and they reacted to the visitors with fear and rage, directing their ire for one another onto these "invaders from the sky." They attacked and killed the ship's crew, but left the vessel in perfect condition for study. A truce was reached among the warring parties, who forged an alliance to examine the craft and build one of their own.

Not long afterward, the Aqualish peoples were roaming the galaxy. Their first stop was a neighboring world, which they decimated with their war-like rage. However, their capacity to truly conquer other worlds was hampered by their limited abilities to adapt foreign technologies. When they encountered new devices, they linked them to their own—but they could not develop original designs or mesh the differing technologies seamlessly. As a result, their machines were often slipshod and patched together. They could not compete with other beings whose technology was more innovative, streamlined, and adaptive.

During its expansion, the Republic sent envoys to many different worlds, inviting them to join the new galactic government. The Aqualish, of course, rebuffed the invitation and instead fired upon the first Republic vessel they encountered. The Republic, having superior technology, soundly defeated the Aqualish, and this began a short yet violent conflict that so overwhelmed the volatile Aqualish that they had to surrender. As a term of concession, the Republic demanded that the Aqualish dismantle all offensive weaponry on their hyperspace vessels. The government of Ando would also have to heed the direction of Republic teachers and advisers, and Ando would become a ward of the Republic until it could earn full citizenship. Realizing they could not overcome the more advanced firepower of the Republic, the Aqualish acquiesced.

While the agreement was a bit restrictive at first, culture and government eventually grew and developed for the better under the guidance of the Republic. With the assistance of Republic scientists, the Aqualish were able to discover the problem that had led to the decrease in marine life and repair that ecosystem. Today, their fishing product is their primary export, and is considered some of the finest seafood in the Galactic Core. It should be noted, however, that during the Clone Wars, the Andoan Senator briefly seceded from the Republic, allying himself and the worlds he represented with the Confederacy of Independent Systems.

Ando chafed under later Imperial rule. Constant insurrection led the Empire to impose martial law, turning Ando into a police state. As a result, the Aqualish despised the Empire, but preferred to fight on their own rather than join the Rebel Alliance. More recently, Ando has been left to its own devices as the Galactic Federation of Free Alliances struggles to keep itself together.

DESIGNATION
Sentient

HOMEWORLD
Ando

AVERAGE HEIGHT
1.7 meters

PRONUNCIATION
Äk'-wä-lĭsh

NOTABLE APPEARANCE
Episode IV: A New Hope

ARCONA

The Arcona are tall, cold-blooded, serpent-like reptilian humanoids, with triangular heads and bulbous sensory organs that sit between two large, glittering eyes. They hail from the planet Cona, a hot, desert Inner Rim world with an atmosphere that consists of nitrogen, hydrogen, and ammonia. Their skin, which ranges in color from an ebony gray-black to a deep brown-red, has the density and texture of fibrous tree bark.

The planet Cona orbits a blue giant star known as Teke Ro. Possessing no axial tilt, Cona's unusual circular orbit results in a world with no seasons, and it remains hot throughout the year. However, the insulating atmosphere also causes a cycling of warm and cool airs across the planet surface, making separate parts of the world one even temperature.

While ammonia vapor is plentiful on Cona, the planet is completely lacking in freestanding water. As a result, Cona plant life is very complex and able to enact an amazing chemical reaction that produces water for sustenance. Some of the more advanced plants secrete an acid to bore into the bedrock for oxygen, which they gather in gastric pods at their roots. Meanwhile, the plants will bring in ammonia through their leaves, which they then break down into its elements of hydrogen and nitrogen. The hydrogen adheres to the oxygen and produces water, which the plants also hold in their gastric pods before releasing the excess nitrogen back into the atmosphere.

Needing more water than Cona's atmosphere could provide, the Arcona long ago discovered this hidden botanical source of nourishment. They use their thick, sharp claws to dig into the ground and rip up the roots of these water-bearing plants. Some vegetation grows so deep and large that the Arcona will dig "mines" to harvest the water pods from plant roots. They have developed a system in which they avoid picking the roots completely bare, allowing the plants to maintain their own nutrition and grow new pods. This provides the Arcona with a steady supply of water.

Everything the Arcona eat contains trace amounts of ammonia from the planet's atmosphere. Thus, the Arcona have a high tolerance for ammonia; in fact, as a by-product of their evolution, the gas creates enzymes that enable their bodies to function properly. Ammonia is also utilized by their supplemental circulatory system, which eliminates waste products from the Arcona's bodies, equalizes their overall temperature, and carries nutrients to their skin. When traveling offworld, Arcona imbibe ammonia supplements to maintain the appropriate levels of these natural enzymes in their systems.

Despite their large, sparkling eyes, the Arcona actually have poor eyesight. Much like an insect, their eyes are made up of thousands of tiny photoreceptors, each of which sees a specific color. These photoreceptors also detect movement, but they cannot read fine, distinct shapes. Consequently, an Arcona's entire field of vision is a colorful blur.

To assist their poor vision, Arcona possess a bulbous, diamond-shaped sensory organ that sits between their eyes. Most observers believe this to be a nose, but in reality, the organ detects heat patterns emitted by other living creatures, enabling the Arcona to bring their environment into better focus. They can distinguish most galactic species by their heat signature.

As with most reptiles, Arcona have olfactory organs located in their constantly flicking tongues. When Arcona have difficulty distinguishing objects in their environment, they flicker their tongues to find their way. Their sense of smell is quite keen, and they use it, along with their heat-sensing organ, to determine the moods of those they encounter.

Arcona society is largely and strongly communal, valuing the needs of a collective group over those of an individual. Therefore, they lack a sense of individuality and rarely speak of themselves in the first person, using the pronoun *we* instead. While they generally have strong familial ties, males usually raise Arcona children, as females are considered more reckless and irresponsible. Even so, males of the species take a great deal of time and care in selecting their mates, often making their decision to court a female after months or even years of researching possible candidates. Arcona regard a commitment to marry as a commitment to parent. Small communities or "nests" revolve around parenting, as the safety of the young on such a dangerous world is paramount.

Most family communities make their nests within twenty kilometers of the "Grand Nest," where representative adults of surroundings communities meet every twenty days. An elected Nest Leader conducts meetings and handles business much as a city mayor would, resolving disputes and putting forward community works.

The Arcona trail the galaxy in terms of scientific and technological development because their primary focus is on community life and the raising of their families. Not many dedicate their time to the study of the hard sciences, and most who live on Cona are teachers or laborers.

The planet is rich in precious metals. Before the Clone Wars, prospectors arrived on Cona and traded mineral rights for water, building impressive spaceports and developing imposing cities around their operation. Soon, however, the mining corporations learned that Arcona natives are easily addicted to sodium chloride—salt. Since salt is easier to transport, the corporations began to trade salt for prospecting rights.

In an Arcona's body, salt acts as a hallucinogen, interfering with the optic nerves to create an intoxicating display of color. Its ultimate effect is deadly, though, in that it causes an Arcona's pancreatic organ, which changes ammonia into water, to fail. More visibly, it changes an Arcona's eye color from green to gold. Once addicted, an Arcona craves about twenty-five grams of salt a day before withdrawal begins. Since female Arcona are more free-spirited and less homebound, they make up the bulk of the Arcona addicts—driven to feed their need at all costs.

Because this addiction is a family- and community-destroying plague, non-addicts will not hesitate to attack and kill anyone discovered to be selling salt on Cona. The Republic enacted strict laws to curtail the transport of salt to the system, and the Arcona, too, have their own laws prohibiting the sale or importation of salt to their world. Still, this has done little to stop its trade on the black market.

Despite the Arcona's tendency to adhere strictly to tradition, when scouts from the Old Republic first made contact with the species, many members were extremely enthusiastic about exploring the galaxy. Entire communities sought employment with corporations that came to mine and build on Cona, hoping for the chance to travel offworld. As a consequence, in the civilized areas of the galaxy, Arcona colonies are common—with whole families traveling together. Presently, they travel a good deal around the galaxy, using technology developed by other species. They can now be seen in every major spaceport, either as tourists or employees of vast multiplanetary corporations.

DESIGNATION
Sentient

HOMEWORLD
Cona

AVERAGE
HEIGHT
2 meters

PRONUNCIATION
Är-kōn'-ä

NOTABLE APPEARANCE
Episode IV: A New Hope

BALOSAR

Balosars are a humanoid species native to the Balosar system, located in the Core Worlds. Notorious for their corruption, Balosars are common throughout the galactic underworld. They resemble humans, except for two antennaepalps that rise from their skull. Balosars can retract these antennaepalps, hiding them within their thick, coarse head of hair, giving them an even more human appearance, to the point that they can often pass for humans if they are trying to escape detection. They usually appear more frail and sickly than the average human, however, due to a polluted home environment.

Balosars' antennae are unique in the galaxy. Not only can they improve Balosars' hearing, enabling them to listen into the subsonic range, but the antennae also give the species a very slight psychic intuition, which some Jedi liken to a Force sensitivity, though it cannot necessarily be classified as such. They can pick up spikes in emotion—particularly negative intent—from those around them, giving them a sort of "danger sense." They depend on their antenna abilities to survive, employing them quite frequently on their crime-ridden homeworld.

Another distinctive Balosar physical trait is their resistance to toxins. Because they hail from a contaminated world, most Balosars grow up exposed to practically every industrial poison in the known galaxy. As a result, they are practically impervious to poisoning, despite their otherwise frail physiques.

As well as suffering from a high pollution rate, the planet Balosar is also impaired by a dangerously depleted economy. Interstellar corporations commonly bribe Balosar politicians in order to buy inexpensive real estate and build sweatshop factories that employ many underpaid natives. These factories have so destroyed the environment that little sunlight reaches the surface, and the atmosphere is barely breathable. The highly industrialized Balosar has often been a primary focus of galactic relief agencies, which find it difficult to operate there because of the political corruption.

Balosars are typically stereotyped as spineless, weak-willed, and selfish—but these traits are primarily due to the condition of their society. Research studies published in the *Journal of Personality and Galactic Psychology* do not indicate such innate or genetic pathology unique to the species. Many live in poverty and suffer from ill health because of their environment, leading to severe depression. Others have developed an overly grim outlook on life that they express with pointed sarcasm. As with many species, Balosars often leave their homeworld hoping for a better existence, only to encounter the hardships associated with resettling in a foreign environment. They are frequently perceived by others as self-absorbed, but in reality are more bent on survival—a focus that skews their moral perceptions. Most have difficulty determining right from wrong, and it is common for Balosars living offplanet to have criminal records as a result.

Compounding the environmental influences on Balosar life, their corrupt government has allowed the educational system to become severely underfunded. Balosars wishing to receive an education must go offworld, and the earlier in their educational careers, the better. Research strongly suggests that the younger a child is when they leave Balosar, the better the potential is for academic success. Moreover, health outcomes are markedly improved for these youngsters. A strong and persistent positive correlation has been demonstrated between the age of departure and educational failure. The older students are when they depart Balosar, the more likely they are to drop out before completing their education. These unsuccessful students often return home to Balosar, and to the same bleak prospects they left behind. Thus, it is not uncommon for Balosar parents to send their children to primary schools on other worlds when scholarships are available.

The fraudulent Balosar government is intricately embroiled with the galactic underworld in the illicit trade of death sticks. The primary ingredient of these drugs is Ixetal cilona extract, distilled from balo mushrooms that are grown on Balosar in great quantities in underground farms. Death sticks are extremely addictive and highly toxic, leading to certain death for most species, frequently over just a short period of use. And yet the users don't seem to mind. Many addicts end up hopelessly hooked after simply giving it a try, savoring the death stick's sweet, alluring flavor and the feeling of instant euphoria that the drug brings. The death stick's toxicity affects addicts' brain function, causing them to slip into bleak depression when they are not consuming the drug. Addicts find themselves craving more and more death sticks in order to hold on to the sense of happiness they receive during the short amount of time it takes to smoke one.

The use of this product by the Balosars themselves has further contributed to the pollution found on their homeworld, and while Balosars are immune to the toxicity of the death stick, they are not safe from its addictive properties. Desperate Balosars can be seen in busy spaceports throughout the galaxy hawking death sticks to earn whatever credits they can. Some, if not most, are addicted to their own product and sell the death sticks to support their own habits.

DESIGNATION
Sentient

HOMEWORLD
Balosar

AVERAGE HEIGHT
1.6 meters

PRONUNCIATION
Băl'-ō-sär

During the time of the Old Republic, illegal trade in death sticks became the greatest competition to the addictive spice from Ryloth called ryll. This rivalry resulted in a deep-seated dislike between Balosars and Twi'leks that continues to this day. Death sticks were easy to produce in mass quantities due to the prolific growth of balo mushrooms—which, unlike ryll, were an easily renewable resource. Ryll needed to be mined in rather dangerous conditions, and was also most potent when combined with glitterstim to create the synthetic spice called glitteryll. Additionally, the ryll supply was tightly guarded at times, and regulated for use in the manufacture of several medicines. Thus, for a brief time, death sticks dominated the illegal drug trade, but this was not to last. Twi'lek drug lords were not pleased at the reduction in their income, and gang wars erupted. The Balosars defiantly peddled their wares when able, although it proved necessary to become more discreet about it. However, by the dawn of the New Republic, the Balosar environment did what the Twi'leks could not. The pollution choking the planet made its way into the underground balo mushroom farms, killing a massive amount of the crop and severely damaging the spore stock, and the Twi'leks used this opportunity to seize complete control of the spice market. Many Balosar drug merchants were reduced to joining forces with the Twi'leks as middlemen and low-level, unimportant runners.

At the end of the New Republic era, Balosar was briefly in the attack path of the Yuuzhan Vong during their march toward Coruscant. At the time, Balosar was not bound by diplomatic treaties to the New Republic and therefore not formally protected by her military. However, the planet managed to escape invasion and Yuuzhan Vong terraforming when the tide of war took the aggressors elsewhere.

NOTABLE APPEARANCE
Episode II: Attack of the Clones

BANTHA

2.5

2.0

1.5

1.0

Herds of woolly banthas inhabit the desert wastes of Tatooine in the Outer Rim, as well as the grasslands and plains of other worlds throughout the galaxy. Since banthas are found in such a large number of agricultural systems, it is believed that early space settlers transported the species to new worlds. Although largely domesticated, on some planets wild herds can still be found. There are several known varieties of banthas in existence, including the common bantha (*Banta majorus*), the smaller, shy dwarf bantha, and the rangier, slender dune bantha. One specific subtype of bantha is the Kashyyyk greyclimber, which differs from its Tatooine cousin in that the greyclimber has massive cranial bone plates in place of horns; it has also adapted to climbing through the evolution of articulated toes that can grip wroshyr trees. The common bantha is by far the most numerous, but as banthas are found on a multitude of worlds, more subspecies may yet be discovered.

Generally used as beasts of burden, the tall, gentle creatures are intelligent, dependable, and trustworthy. They are extremely strong, able to carry up to five hundred kilos of cargo, or five human-sized passengers, including a driver. Because of their rocking gait, many first-time bantha riders have been known to complain of motion sickness. Although banthas prefer to move at a slow pace, they can run at great speeds when necessary, and stories of bantha stampedes are commonplace on all the worlds they inhabit.

Banthas are extremely adaptable, abiding comfortably in all sorts of climates, able to survive for weeks without food or water. From world to world, bantha subspecies vary in size, coloration, social grouping, behavior, and metabolic specifics, but one commonality is that surprisingly, these mostly gentle giants are herbivores. On Tatooine, banthas live on meager sand lichen mats found either in protected hollows or just under the sand. Due to their size and internal stores, they can live for nearly a month without sustenance.

In addition to being beasts of burden, banthas are a valuable source of nourishment for many cultures. Bantha meat is edible, and their skin and long, thick fur can be used for clothing. Bantha-skin goods such as boots and luggage are expensive luxuries on some planets. Furthermore, Bantha bones and horns are carved by members of several cultures to make tools, ornaments, and toys.

Banthas exhibit many of the traits typical of herd animals. Wild banthas have been known to gather their dead in bantha graveyards. When attacked, they usually flee, and most bantha species will only fight in defense of the herd and their young. In the event that they are trapped, or when young banthas must be defended, male banthas will form a circle around their calves and cows, using their large tapering horns and three-meter-wide size to protect the herd. They strike by lowering their heads and ramming their large spiral horns into an attacker. Some cultures have taken advantage of the bantha's horns and bulk by using domesticated breeds as beasts of war, spurring them to charge at foes and trample them underfoot.

On Tatooine, woolly banthas have been left to roam free in the harsh desert climate, and the species has flourished. They are the transportation of choice for the native Tusken Raiders, who have a special and unique relationship with their mounts. Upon reaching the age of five, a Tusken Raider is teamed up with a young bantha, and the two develop an emotional bond that lasts a lifetime. If its master dies, a "widowed" bantha will often fly into a suicidal rage. The tribe then waits until the bantha tires of its rampage, afterward turning it out into the wilderness to survive on its own. Usually, the unfortunate bantha dies of grief and dehydration.

Likewise, if the bantha mount is the first to perish, the Tusken Raider to whom it was bonded will become inconsolable to the point of ruthlessly attacking others in the clan, or even taking his or her own life. If such Tusken Raiders do not die from their despair, they are sent out into the desert on a vision quest, to contact the spirit of their fallen bantha partner. If their bantha companion guides them to the afterlife, they will expire in the barren wastelands of Tatooine. If, however, their former mount wishes them to live, it will guide them to a new, riderless bantha, which then becomes their new companion. Tusken Raiders who return with a fresh mount are given high honor in their communities.

DESIGNATION
Nonsentient

HOMEWORLD
Tatooine

AVERAGE HEIGHT
2.5 meters

PRONUNCIATION
Băn'-thä

NOTABLE APPEARANCE
Episode IV: A New Hope

BARABEL

Barabels are a vicious, reptilian race native to the Outer Rim planet Barab I, a world of murky darkness in the orbit of a dim red dwarf star. During the day, most living creatures dwell belowground to protect themselves from the intense heat and radiation cast by the red dwarf. When evening arrives, the environment cools enough for the denizens of Barab I to go to the surface and hunt.

The physique of a Barabel is designed for nocturnal hunting and fighting. Their entire form, from head to tail, is covered with spiked scales of tough keratin that darken from purple-green to black as they age. These scales not only help camouflage Barabels, but also protect them from heavy blows or low-power blasterfire. This external protection is further insulated by a layer of blubber that helps the species retain heat during the cold nights on Barab I.

Barabels are natural hunters who kill with strength and efficiency. Their mouths are filled with needle-sharp teeth up to five centimeters in length, perfect for crushing the bodies of even the toughest-skinned prey. Beyond this, they can also use their huge claws for efficiently rending flesh. Since Barabels hunt primarily in the darkness, their eyes possess slit pupils that read the electromagnetic spectrum of light from infrared to yellow. However, they are unable to see green, blue, or violet light, which puts them at a disadvantage on planets with brighter suns.

Barabels often work as bounty hunters and mercenaries, channeling their natural love of the hunt into a means of earning credits. They are known for having an explosive temperament, but unlike some other violent races, they value both intelligence and wisdom, often focusing on these traits in order to control their aggressive nature. They can be cooperative to attain a common goal, and they are efficient when working in teams, making them particularly valuable in a military environment. Extremely loyal to their spouses, family members, and hatchmates, Barabels are genuinely loving and gregarious in such a community setting. While they have been known to extend this loyalty to non-Barabels with whom they feel close, outsiders or strangers are more commonly met with belligerence and hostility.

Barab I orbits the red dwarf Barab at a distance of less than 125 million kilometers. As a result, the planet is scorched during its six-standard-hour day, exposed to high-intensity ultraviolet, gamma, and infrared radiation. Water rapidly evaporates from the surface, leaving the world in a humid haze, and most of Barab I's plant and animal life must live in caves or rock crevices and canyons in order to thrive. Those species that remain out during the day survive by closing up in protective cocoons or possess reflective skin or hair that protects them from the damaging rays.

At night when the heat dissipates, the natives of Barab I leave their shelters to feed in a sudden frenzy. They move quickly to avoid a nightly torrential downpour that occurs as a result of the day's water evaporation and the subsequent planetary cooling.

This wild cycle of lethargy and feeding has contributed to the largely primitive nature of Barab I and its resident Barabels. The world was discovered by an Imperial charter called Planetary Safaris, which brought expeditions to Barab I to hunt Barabels. Because members of the species are mostly solitary, preferring to roam the surface alone, they were more susceptible to these Imperial hunting parties. This also placed them at a disadvantage when the Yuuzhan Vong eventually conquered Barab I, although on a one-on-one basis they made formidable opponents to the invaders—more so than many other species.

Before the Yuuzhan Vong invasion, however, one brilliant Barabel named Shaka-ka managed to unite fellow members of her species into armies to destroy Planetary Safari ships and decimate their hunting parties. The local Imperial governor, shocked at the loss of both vessels and tourists, sent a Star Destroyer to investigate. After learning of the origins of the uprising, the Imperial captain Alater determined Barabels to be a sentient species and gave them the full protection of Imperial law.

Upon their entrance into the Empire, Shaka-ka once again enlisted other Barabels, this time to build what would become the one permanent city and spaceport on their world: Alater-ka, named for the captain who recognized their sentience. This underground city consists of numerous tunnels and caverns that are interlocked around the central spaceport. Although Alater-ka remains a crude city with primitive resources, it is not wanting for tourist attention, as an agreement was eventually reached with Planetary Safaris to reinstate expeditions on Barab I, allowing parties to hunt some of the dangerous resident wildlife, with Barabels now acting as guides. Barab I is also a popular haven for galactic criminals, smugglers, pirates, and the like, who are willing to take a chance with the harsh environment in order to escape from law enforcement.

After Barab I was liberated from Imperial rule, the Barabels

nearly started a war with an insectoid species known as the Verpine. They briefly made arrangements to sell frozen Verpine body parts to the Kubaz to be eaten as a delicacy. To this day, there remain some tense relations between these two species.

Even though Barabels' "official" history began with their discovery by Planetary Safaris, it is believed that these Imperial hunters were not the first galactic visitors to Barab I. Barabel legend tells of a war that erupted among Barabel factions over prime hunting grounds. Family units, all motivated by common interest, banded together to form two armies that were each bent on the ultimate destruction of their enemies. The final battle was defused, though, by the arrival of a Jedi Knight who managed to resolve the dispute. The legend speaks highly of the "great warrior from beyond the clouds" who prevented them from killing one another.

Barabels therefore, commonly show Jedi both great reverence and deference. In the years after Palpatine's demise, a stranded Jedi took a Barabel apprentice named Saba Sebatyne. An ensuing surprise appearance by Saba Sebatyne, who emerged with her own Jedi students and hatchlings to assist during the Yuuzhan Vong War, seems to be hard evidence that the Jedi influence on Barabels was no myth.

Other than this tale, though, most Barabels are fairly ignorant of their culture's history, and they seem to prefer to remain that way. They have no inclination to create an overarching civilization, choosing to remain in their small family units and acting as solitary hunters in the Barab I night. Although they hold no technology of their own to speak of, those few Barabels who have departed Barab I manage to use the technology of other races with great efficiency, and a few are known to have become ace pilots. Frequently, Barabels seen offworld are functioning as bounty hunters, trackers, or mercenaries. Only Barabels who travel to other systems are recognized as capable of speaking or understanding Basic, as those who remain on Barab I mainly do not bother to master any language other than Barabel, which consists of hisses, growls, and snarls.

While the Yuuzhan Vong saw fit to conquer Barab I in their quest to dominate the galaxy, the planet was not destroyed. Many Barabels, masters at stealth, managed to go into hiding in caves and underground hovels until the threat had passed. While their numbers diminished, the species managed to survive the slaughter with their wits and tenacity.

DESIGNATION
Sentient

HOMEWORLD
Barab I

AVERAGE HEIGHT
2 meters

PRONUNCIATION
Bär'-ä-bĕl

NOTABLE APPEARANCE
Dark Force Rising (novel)

BESALISK

Besalisks are large, stocky, flightless avian humanoids who hail from the planet Ojom, located in the Deep Core. They have thick bodies with multiple brawny arms, a bony headcrest surrounded by feathers, and a wide mouth from which hangs a large flexible sac.

Male Besalisks have four arms, while females can possess as many as eight. But despite such multiple appendages, each Besalisk has only one primary hand, much the same as humans are right- or left-handed. Their brains are not sufficiently complex to provide greater limb coordination. A Besalisk can hold items in all of her hands, but cannot use more than four of them to do specific tasks at a time. For instance, a female using all eight of her arms can have four arms working independently, but the other four must work in concert with one another. This characteristic particularly comes into play when Besalisks are engaged in hand-to-hand combat, as they are not able to wield weapons independently in all of their arms. Most Besalisks will simply carry one or two (although females may sport three), with their most effective weapon being grasped in their primary hand.

Sadly, Besalisks are the subject of many misconceptions. To begin with, while they are descended from birds, casual observers will frequently mistake them for a reptilian species. Whereas Besalisks have a skin pouch hanging from their chins that is similar to the ones often seen on both birds and reptiles, their thick, scaly skin is the source of the perception that they are members of the latter group, as are their toothy mouths and sharp-clawed hands. Also, since they typically possess bulky, fleshy frames, Besalisks are sometimes viewed as gluttonous by other races, but in reality they store food and water in their bodies for weeks, allowing them to go for an extended period of time without eating or drinking. It is also common for Besalisks to sweat a great deal, giving the impression that they are nervous or in ill health. However, their bodies are merely accustomed to the frigid environment of Ojom and do not react well to warmer climates.

As with most birds, Besalisk young are hatched from eggs that females lay during the warm season. A female will usually bear a clutch of two eggs at a time, at which point the male will take over the duty of keeping them in his brood patch—an area of the male's abdominal skin that falls down over the eggs and hugs them close to his body for warmth. During this time, the females will care for the home and earn the family living.

Besalisks are monogamous, and they will mate for life following a long courtship in which the female chooses, and sometimes fights for, the male of her preference. Such competitions can get violent the longer the search for a mate continues. The quest for males can take place at any time during Ojom's solar year, but each commune will hold events specifically to meet and choose mates during the warmer months. Ojom is a frightfully cold world, covered in massive glaciers that roam the planet's ocean surface. The Besalisks live in sparsely populated communal groupings on each of these glaciers. These communes are made up of at least a thousand nuclear families, and are in turn governed by an elected leader who acts as an arbiter in any disputes. When the population grows over a specific number, the leaders solicit volunteers from families to start a new commune, in an attempt to keep all such groupings at relatively the same size.

Other than their communal arbiters, the Besalisk people have no overall government in place, and for this reason they never had any representation in the Old Republic Senate. They seem to prefer their autonomy, allowing other species to handle galactic political affairs. And yet their independence has come at a price. During the period of Imperial domination, the Besalisks were threatened with enslavement. To avoid that fate, many individual communes made deals with underworld criminals, and have since been indebted to them, particularly the Hutts.

On Ojom, all interstellar traffic is handled through orbiting space stations, which are more welcoming to offworld visitors than is the planet itself. Most Besalisk business dealings are carried out on these space stations, particularly those of a nefarious nature. However, other species, not Besalisks, commit most of the violent crimes on these stations. Even when wrapped up in underworld affairs, Besalisks remain relatively peaceful, preferring to find thrills through self-fulfillment rather than harming or stealing from others.

On the whole, Besalisks are a quick-witted, generous, and sociable people. They form strong and lasting friendships with members of all species, and can be extremely loyal once they grant an individual their trust. A keen attention to detail allows Besalisks to adapt easily into other cultures and utilize their technologies, although they create none of their own. They do have a tendency to be unreliable dreamers, however, and Besalisks can often be flighty, out for amusement and adventure that involves little concern for their own welfare. They do not fear danger, a concept that normally doesn't occur to them until they're in the middle of it. Exceptions to this rule certainly exist, although there are not many, and those few that are atypical of their species often use the common perceptions held them to pass off as fearless anyway. As a result of this intrepid nature, many offworld Besalisks are entangled in underworld operations such as smuggling, gambling, and organized crime—generally without realizing the gravity of what they're doing.

Besalisks can also be gregarious and chatty, taking pleasure in talking about others, gabbing and gossiping simply for the joy of conversation. Since they are very observant, taking in details quickly and without thinking, this, combined with their willingness to strike up conversations, makes them excellent sources for valuable information. In addition, to the utter frustration of their underworld employers, they seem to have a habit of occasionally walking off the job in an attempt to find other ways to amuse and enrich themselves. Consequently, many a Besalisk has ended up on underworld hit lists, repeatedly putting them among the most wanted species in the galaxy at any given time.

DESIGNATION
Sentient

HOMEWORLD
Ojom

AVERAGE HEIGHT
1.8 meters

PRONUNCIATION
Bĕs'-ä-lĭsk

NOTABLE APPEARANCE
Episode II: Attack of the Clones

BITH

The Bith are a highly evolved, humanoid species native to Clak'dor VII, a planet that is part of the Colu system in the Outer Rim. Their tall craniums house immensely oversized brains, the result of years of calculated breeding. Bith are known for their contributions to the arts and sciences and are considered some of the greatest thinkers in the galaxy. Calm, peaceful, thoughtful, and introverted, Bith are consummate pacifists—a trait that comes not only from their learned history, but also from their planned physiology as well.

The Bith are biologically developed to be suited for complex work. Scientists have been unable to determine the ultimate origin of their species, since they have evolved so completely that they most likely retain none of the attributes of their evolutionary ancestry. The areas of their brains that handle abstract thinking skills, such as language, deductive reasoning, logic, mathematics, and music, are enormously large and highly developed compared with those of other sentient species. Those brain regions that control most instinctual behaviors—fear, aggression, and so forth—are much smaller, making them pacifistic by nature. Scientists theorize that they have lived in a highly structured civilization for so long that they have completely lost the ability to function on an instinctual or irrational level.

Bith possess five-fingered hands with opposable thumbs, making them well suited for doing detailed handiwork. They are extremely adept at constructing tools, as well as developing and using technology to suit their needs. The Bith's large eyes are ideal for such a high-tech lifestyle, as they allow the species to perceive minuscule details, or study complicated microcircuitry for long periods of time. The Bith have also developed beyond a need for sleep, instead meditating for short periods of time in order to provide their bodies with an appropriate amount of rest. The fact that they no longer require traditional sleep has resulted in the Bith losing their eyelids through evolution; a hard, translucent shell protects their eyes from injury or dust abrasion.

The most fascinating aspect of Bith physiology is perhaps their streamlined respiratory system. Their tiny nose serves only as an air intake. From there, oxygen flows to a single lung, where it is transferred directly to the bloodstream. Waste gases are exuded through the skin, but only after every last molecule of oxygen has been used.

Due to this specialized respiratory system, Bith olfactory senses are located in folds of skin on their cheeks, rather than in their noses. Their sense of smell is exceptionally sensitive, enabling them to perceive the slightest chemical changes in the atmosphere around them. Pheroreceptors situated in the skin folds send a detailed chemical analysis of each scent to the brain, allowing a Bith to recognize even the faintest of smells in microseconds.

Bith rely on technology to handle nearly every aspect of their lives, including reproduction. Prospective parents take a sample of their DNA to a computer mating service (CMS), which then matches it up with other samples provided by members of the opposite sex. The CMS projects the outcomes of various pairings, or child patterns (CPs), and offers these potential outcomes to the future parent. After selecting a CP that meets his or her qualifications, the Bith is introduced to the mate, and the two negotiate the number of offspring that they will produce, and how many each parent will raise. Upon arriving at an agreement, they deliver cells to a Reproduction Center, and a year later their children are delivered to their door. As they've reproduced in this manner for so long, Bith have actually lost the ability to produce offspring naturally, and what began as a matter of preference is now a matter of necessity.

Although technology does serve many of the Bith's needs on their world, it was, at one time, nearly the cause of their society's demise. Almost one hundred standard years before the dawn of the Empire, two cities on Clak'dor VII—Nozho and Weogar—were embroiled in a competition to secure patent rights on a new stardrive that the cities' leaders hoped to sell to other worlds. As was traditional in Bith society, each city submitted its patent claim to a neutral arbitrator.

The agent representing Nozho, however, happened to discover some unfavorable information on this arbitrator, and blackmailed him into giving Nozho the patent preference. When the mayor of Weogar heard of this, he refused to accept the arbitrator's decision, and both cities began production on the stardrive, setting off a cutthroat rivalry that ultimately led to wholesale war. After a full standard year of bloodletting, Nozho finally unleashed a chemical weapon that eradicated 90 percent of the population of the

DESIGNATION
Sentient

HOMEWORLD
Clak'dor VII

AVERAGE HEIGHT
1.7 meters

PRONUNCIATION
Bĭth

opposing city. The remaining occupants of Weogar retaliated with biological weapons of their own, causing a massive evolutionary degeneration and destroying most of the life on the planet. Their world, which had once been a garden paradise, was now a poisoned wasteland of genetically mutated, toxic plants and vicious creatures. In order to survive, the remaining Bith were forced to build giant domed cities, where they've lived ever since.

As a consequence of this devastating war, Bith technology has not progressed for many years. Their own natural resources exhausted, they have come to rely on the commodities of other worlds. Their chief export is their intellect, and various agencies and companies galaxywide employ Bith as scientists, mathematicians, artisans, accountants, and musicians. Bith are a principal source of innovative ideas throughout the galaxy, and are often highly paid to participate in corporate and governmental think tanks on many of the Core Worlds.

On Clak'dor VII, the Bith political structure is highly organized and dependent, again, on technology. Leaders are chosen through a computer analysis of a candidate's heritage, intelligence, accomplishments, and career. These selected leaders, who form a type of committee, retain ultimate authority over the Bith people through a complex system of laws that keeps the committee's activities under close scrutiny.

On the galactic political stage, the Bith were active in the Old Republic, and helped develop and negotiate many of the treaties for planetary entrance to the Old Republic Senate. As the Clone Wars erupted, the Bith were outspoken opponents of the conflict, and throughout the reign of the Empire, their government formally withdrew to the Bith homeworld, refusing to give the new, tyrannical regime their support. However, a few members of the Bith government secretly supported the Imperial cause as a logical means of establishing galactic order. They surreptitiously provided the Empire with computer programming and engineering prowess for many Imperial technology designs.

Following the fall of the Empire, the Bith did not reopen communication with the New Republic until the Hapans offered aid to the fledgling galactic government. Encouraged by the Hapan gesture of confidence, the Bith soon established formal relations with the New Republic.

NOTABLE APPEARANCE
Episode IV: A New Hope

BOTHAN

1.5

1.0

Bothans are short, furry humanoids native to the planet Bothawui, which is located in the Mid Rim, although they have established colonies on other worlds, such as Kothlis and Torolis. The Bothans evolved long ago from feline progenitors, though they retain only a few attributes that connect them with their ancestral background. They are covered entirely with fur, the color of which can range from milky white to dark brown; the hair on their face tapers downward to form a type of beard. Their fur serves as an additional transmitter for the Bothans' body language, in that undulations in the hairs on the head signify their emotional state, or emphasize important points during a discussion. These subtle changes are usually difficult to decipher by those who are not members of the species, although some outsiders have learned to read these nonverbal cues with great accuracy. Such a knowledge of Bothan behavior is extremely helpful when negotiating with this intelligent and opportunistic people.

Also similar to most cat species, they possess sharp eyes and teeth, as well as five-fingered hands with nails that extend and retract, though they rarely use them unless they find themselves in one-on-one combat. And in Bothan culture this is a rare occurrence, which explains why most outsiders are unaware that they even have this ability.

Bothans express themselves with great eloquence, and mastery of public speaking is an accomplishment that merits prestige in their culture. They are consummate politicians, and as such they are important players in the arena of galactic politics. Well known for their intelligence-gathering abilities, Bothans are considered unsurpassed in that field. Preceding the Battle of Endor, many of them sacrificed their lives to steal the technical schematics for the second Death Star, as well as the information that the Emperor would be present conducting an inspection of the station during the Rebels' planned attack. For this and other reasons, they achieved an influential role in the New Republic government. The New Republic military prided itself on its Bothan members, with Bothans serving in every capacity from pilot to admiral. One Bothan in particular, Borsk Fey'lya, served as Chief of State before uncharacteristically sacrificing himself during the Yuuzhan Vong invasion of Coruscant.

Despite Fey'lya's noble deed, status is almost always the goal of Bothans. The quest for influence and power is at the heart of their culture. By nature, Bothans are greedy for status, often becoming manipulative and opportunistic while seeking the prestige that comes from controlling others. Wealth isn't as important to them as influencing those who have money, and family clans frequently plot ways of gaining resources and strategic positioning. When a Bothan clan desires something, be it information, an object, or a position of power, members will spy on one another, spread rumors, and make convenient alliances. They seldom attack a competitor directly, usually waiting for rivals to make mistakes.

One side effect of these cultural motivations is that Bothans are also habitually paranoid, believing that anyone who's not working for them is working against them. Unfortunately, their paranoia is usually well founded. Layer upon layer of schemes swirl around any clan, and outsiders who associate with Bothans often find themselves unwittingly caught up in the web of intrigue. This paranoia can be taken to extremes against other species, to the extent of xenophobia and prejudice, and can blind Bothans to the genuine, good intentions of others, often to their own detriment. They simply do not attribute a lack of guile to those beings with whom they come into contact.

Bothawui and all the Bothan colonies are locally governed by the Bothan Council, which consists of representatives of each clan and serves as the primary lawmaking and law enforcement body. Each of the member clans is a collection of families who have bonded together in a common tradition or heritage. Currently, approximately six hundred clans are part of the council, and more than fifty others have petitioned for membership. These newer clans are typically from smaller, younger settlements that have formed apart from the established colonies. In order to be accepted for membership, a simple majority of the council must approve a petition, and representatives of new clans are constantly engaged in forming alliances to meet their goal of inclusion.

In order to manage council business, the members elect one of their number to become the Council Chief. All policies are decided by a majority vote, with the Chief holding the tie-breaking call when necessary. Every council member heads up several ministries and committees, and appoints clan leaders to positions of importance. Payoffs and rewards are common, as these clan leaders, in turn, assign others in their retinue to lower-level positions. This centuries-old system of finding favor and gaining power enables Bothans of any clan or background to attain prestige and influence if they manage to play by the right rules. It also allows powerful clans to maintain their established realms of control on Bothawui.

The Bothans have long been a spacefaring race, settling on many planets outside Bothawui, the most notable of which is Kothlis. However, anything that can be found on Bothawui is found on its colonies, though the newer settlements that are still not official members of the Bothan Council get less attention in terms of goods and services—all the more motivation for them to use intrigue and stratagem to push their agenda in the council. Thus, Bothans of these upstart colonies can be some of the most ambitious and backstabbing examples of the species that one may encounter.

Set in the heart of Bothan space in the Mid Rim, Bothawui's location has made it a major trading center and hub for shipping convoys. Business thrives there, especially because the low tax rates and governmental bureaucracy are not overly burdensome. Several major galactic banking and financial institutions have sited their corporate headquarters there, employing thousands of Bothans in their operations as well as in the major trading exchanges centered on Bothawui.

While banking and finance appears to be the fastest-growing legitimate business on Bothawui, spying is still the Bothans' main industry. Everyone comes to Bothawui to get information, even though it can often come at a hefty price. The Bothan spynet, an underground system for buying and selling all forms of data, is just as active as it was under the rule of the Empire. Organized crime factions, political leaders, and corporate moguls arrive on the Bothans' world to get an inside scoop.

And yet, for all the Bothans' deceptive nature and quests for self-advancement, Borsk Fey'lya's death is just one example revealing the core of their being. At heart, the majority of Bothans are brave and loyal, and they will serve causes that they believe in to the bitter end. Many other species find Bothans difficult to deal with because they seem to lack selflessness, but in reality, most Bothans ultimately do believe in freedom and sacrifice to achieve a venerable goal. They will take chances and risk much in any conflict that threatens those they love or those to whom they've pledged loyalty.

DESIGNATION
Sentient

HOMEWORLD
Bothawui

AVERAGE HEIGHT
1.5 meters

PRONUNCIATION
Bŏ'-thăn

NOTABLE MENTION
Episode VI: Return of the Jedi

CAAMASI

The term *Caamasi* means "friend from afar" or "stranger to be trusted" in the languages of many cultures throughout the galaxy, and never did a people have a more appropriate title. The Caamasi are tall, mammalian humanoids with golden down covering their bodies and purple fur that surrounds the eyes; stripes extend around the backs of their heads and shoulders. Their two eyes are set below a strong brow, and their triangular-shaped ears jut outward. Caamasi have only three delicate and gentle fingers on their long hands.

All Caamasi can create lasting, vivid memories called memnii that are shared telepathically with other members of their species. Memnii enable them to actually experience historical, important, or poignant personal events as if they were present. Because all history is valuable, and because these memories can teach others, Caamasi hold recollections of tragic or devastating events as well as happy ones. Clans often intermarry to spread memnii, and the Caamasi can even share memnii with Jedi.

They are a people who mate for life, and when Caamasi choose a companion, they will share specific memnii with their spouse, who hold these memories close to their heart and eventually pass them on to their children. These memnii are usually private moments from their lives, incidents that helped form their consciences and enabled them to grow into who they are. It is reputed, but not confirmed, that some Caamasi couples share such private memnii during the mating process.

Despite their dedication to a solitary spouse, there are reports of some Caamasi debating the introduction of polygamy among their people, most likely to repair a devastation to their population that was caused by Emperor Palpatine after the Clone Wars. As with anything the Caamasi consider, such a concept would clearly be debated and examined from every angle before their society could reach a decision. For them, it would represent an entire cultural shift, and be a particularly difficult and delicate change, as the connections between mates are usually quite singular and special. Most sociologists feel polygamy is antithetical to the Caamasi way of life, and have either dismissed these rumors as hearsay, or decided that the species will ultimately not accept the concept, even if introduced as a means of survival.

1.5

1.0

.5

0

By nature, the Caamasi are artistic, wise, and freethinking, and believe in peace through moral strength. According to Caamasi legend, the first Jedi Knights journeyed to their planet ages ago in order to learn the moral use of the Force, although Caamasi Jedi are rare. Considering that the Caamasi way of life has endured unchanged for generations, it is a strong possibility that this is more than a simple fable.

Sadly, while admired for their peaceful wisdom, the Caamasi also managed to acquire the scorn of those who did not appreciate such moral fortitude. In an incident that followed the Clone Wars, Emperor Palpatine engineered the desolation of the planet Caamas in the Core Worlds in order to rid his empire of the peaceful Caamasi. Indeed, heavy bombardment destroyed all the resident vegetation, and most of the Caamasi were killed. Refugees from Caamas traveled to several other worlds, with the bulk of the remaining survivors settling on the ill-fated Alderaan, again suffering at the hands of the Empire. Fortunately, a large Caamasi remnant community endured on Kerilt, and some later relocated to Susevfi.

It was ultimately discovered that a group of Bothans had helped Palpatine's agents sabotage Caamas's shield generators, thus allowing the sudden, violent attack to send firestorms raging across the world. When a copy of the Caamas Document, which detailed Bothan involvement in the tragedy, was revealed on the planet Wayland, it touched off a flood of demands for the Bothans to purchase a new, uninhabited planet for the remaining refugees. The Bothans have yet to fulfill these demands, but even as the few remaining Caamasi calmly and patiently await a permanent home, they continue to work side by side with the Bothans in a fundamental example of forgiveness.

Despite the unfortunate devastation their species has suffered, the Caamasi remain steadfast pacifists. Most are artists, merchants, diplomats, or scholars. Although they will serve governments as ambassadors, they will not serve in the military. The leaders of the galaxy frequently rely on the Caamasi as advisers, especially the members of the new Jedi order, and the species has been particularly helpful in aiding the Jedi to regain some of their lost history and traditions through the sharing of key memnii. They were also instrumental in drafting early incarnations of the New Republic Charter, negotiating agreements among conflicting worlds, species, and institutions, and serving as a voice of reason in the growing Senate. Senior Anthropologist Hoole noted that the Caamasi were crucial to the cause of peace in the galaxy, bringing difficult disputes between beings to successful and satisfying conclusions with a calmness and gentleness found in few other species.

Perhaps no Caamasi typifies his people and their dedication to peace better than the late Elegos A'Kla. A'Kla was living a quiet life on Kerilt when he met a human named Corran Horn, then a Jedi apprentice. A'Kla's uncle was a Jedi who had served with Horn's grandfather, and through the information Elegos carried in his memnii, he was able to direct and offer assistance to Horn along his path to Jedi Knighthood.

Following this, A'Kla became trustee of the Caamasi Remnant, and advised the New Republic as a Senator. As part of his duties, A'Kla accompanied Princess Leia Organa Solo to the Outer Rim on a fact-finding mission in the early days of the Yuuzhan Vong invasion. After assisting in evacuations at the battles of Dubrillion and Dantooine, A'Kla volunteered to present himself to the Yuuzhan Vong as an envoy. The Yuuzhan Vong commander Shedao Shai initially appeared to comply with A'Kla's request, but in an act of deception he took the Caamasi's life to demonstrate the invaders' intentions for the galaxy. Shai then returned A'Kla's body to the Republic, having first prepared it for burial according to Yuuzhan Vong traditions. Shai's message was received, and in Corran Horn's grief following his friend's death, the Jedi challenged Shai to a duel with the fate of the planet Ithor hanging in the balance. Although Horn defeated Shai, the Yuuzhan Vong once again failed to honor their agreement, and Ithor was destroyed. It might be thought that A'Kla's sacrifice was for naught, and that he failed in his mission, but his example lived on, a pillar of hope for the rest of the galaxy that the Yuuzhan Vong could not defeat.

DESIGNATION
Sentient

HOMEWORLD
Kerilt (by way of Caamas)

AVERAGE HEIGHT
1.8 meters

PRONUNCIATION
Kä-ä-mä'-sē

NOTABLE APPEARANCE
I, Jedi (novel)

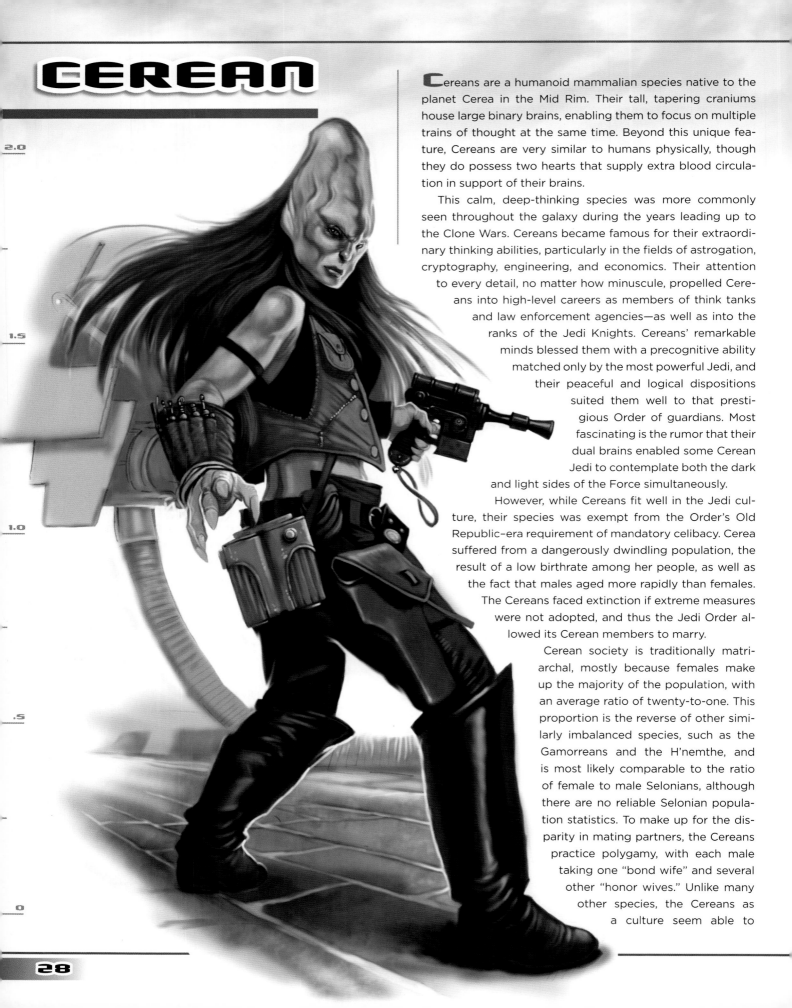

CEREAN

Cereans are a humanoid mammalian species native to the planet Cerea in the Mid Rim. Their tall, tapering craniums house large binary brains, enabling them to focus on multiple trains of thought at the same time. Beyond this unique feature, Cereans are very similar to humans physically, though they do possess two hearts that supply extra blood circulation in support of their brains.

This calm, deep-thinking species was more commonly seen throughout the galaxy during the years leading up to the Clone Wars. Cereans became famous for their extraordinary thinking abilities, particularly in the fields of astrogation, cryptography, engineering, and economics. Their attention to every detail, no matter how minuscule, propelled Cereans into high-level careers as members of think tanks and law enforcement agencies—as well as into the ranks of the Jedi Knights. Cereans' remarkable minds blessed them with a precognitive ability matched only by the most powerful Jedi, and their peaceful and logical dispositions suited them well to that prestigious Order of guardians. Most fascinating is the rumor that their dual brains enabled some Cerean Jedi to contemplate both the dark and light sides of the Force simultaneously.

However, while Cereans fit well in the Jedi culture, their species was exempt from the Order's Old Republic–era requirement of mandatory celibacy. Cerea suffered from a dangerously dwindling population, the result of a low birthrate among her people, as well as the fact that males aged more rapidly than females. The Cereans faced extinction if extreme measures were not adopted, and thus the Jedi Order allowed its Cerean members to marry.

Cerean society is traditionally matriarchal, mostly because females make up the majority of the population, with an average ratio of twenty-to-one. This proportion is the reverse of other similarly imbalanced species, such as the Gamorreans and the H'nemthe, and is most likely comparable to the ratio of female to male Selonians, although there are no reliable Selonian population statistics. To make up for the disparity in mating partners, the Cereans practice polygamy, with each male taking one "bond wife" and several other "honor wives." Unlike many other species, the Cereans as a culture seem able to handle the potential difficulties of polygamy because of their placid temperament.

The planet Cerea is ruled by a president who oversees a Council of Elders—a primarily female team of wise and venerable individuals who consider each side of an issue thoroughly and objectively. They allow for open discussion on political and legal matters, but after the elders have made a decision, the resolution is final and no appeal is permitted. It was this body that prevented Cerea from joining the Republic and the Separatists alike during the Clone Wars, largely in an attempt to preserve the planet's natural resources from greedy Senators who would exploit them.

The world of Cerea is a lush, verdant paradise, and Cerean culture centers on honoring that environment. Cereans value living in harmony with nature, and therefore have set in place stringent laws to protect their surroundings from hazardous waste and technological contamination. By nature, they shun technology and powered transports, although they have consented to the construction of "Outsider Citadels" in certain areas of their planet for beings from more developed worlds to reside. Unfortunately, these citadels have become overcrowded and polluted.

Meditation and contemplation are central to life for all Cereans, not just to those who follow the path of the Jedi. To enhance their focus during these sessions of reflection, Cereans often employ kasha meditation crystals, which have a calming and mind-clearing effect on the user. The crystals are decorated with special etchings created by Cerean artisans to harness their natural harmonic energy.

Cereans also hold an extreme reverence for the ancient traditions of their people. Although a female Cerean typically has only one name, a male has three, the origins of which are derived from those of his father and grandfather. These names are arranged in any order based on cadence and to make the whole name meaningful. A female, meanwhile, will only take an additional name if she becomes a bond-wife, adopting the name of her husband's grandfather for official matters. This is an interesting custom, given the Cerean's matriarchal culture, seeming to indicate that while females are the guiding force driving their society, family lineage is actually passed down through the male line.

An additional display of the importance of tradition in Cerean society can be found in their clothing, as much of their modern garb harks back to garments of old. Elders and other prestigious members of society prefer to wear a special surcoat, the style of which resembles an ancient mantle of honor. Cereans also retain great enthusiasm for the study of early fighting techniques, especially the art of using a shyarn: a light, arc-edged sword used in honor duels. Cereans send their children to train at shyarn-ado training schools, and masters of this type of swordplay are featured in well-publicized tournaments and demonstrations. Shyarn are notably distinctive in that when they connect in battle, the curved swords become magnetically attached—making for some very physically challenging and sometimes brutal combat. Some say that, as a form of catharsis, Cerean duelers release every bit of aggression that they possess while participating in the sport, which is perhaps why it is so appealing to this normally peaceful people. The shyarn form has also developed into a fine art, as many of its choreographed exercises have become a popular mode of dance expression. Troupes of shyarn dancers travel Cerea, and they have even been seen throughout the galaxy, displaying the majesty of this ancient form of self-defense.

Despite these examples of Cereans respecting time-honored customs, it was the drive for technology and progress that nearly had unfortunate consequences for the young people of Cerea, and possibly the entire planet. During the Clone Wars, many youthful Cereans spent their leisure time in the Outsider Citadels, where they were exposed to the luxuries of other worlds and became desirous of such objects for themselves. They sought to radically change their culture's ways, but in reality this behavior was deviously being encouraged by agents of the Separatists, specifically the Trade Federation, who held these youth as captives. Fortunately for Cerea, the Jedi intervened, and the young hostages were safely returned to their families.

Sadly, the Clone Wars continued to be unkind to Cerea and its people. As the planet chose neutrality during the war, Republic and Separatist armies fought a brutal battle on Cerea to prevent it from allying itself to the other's side. In the process, much of the pristine world was destroyed and many inhabitants lost their lives, including the Cerean president Bo-Ro-Tara, who was assassinated before the Republic could claim a victory. Following the Clone Wars, the Cereans readopted their isolationist stance, and reports from that world are scant to nonexistent.

NOTABLE APPEARANCE
Episode I: The Phantom Menace

DESIGNATION
Sentient

HOMEWORLD
Cerea

AVERAGE
HEIGHT
2 meters

PRONUNCIATION
Sĕr'-ē-ăn

CHADRA-FAN

The small, dexterous Chadra-Fan are rodent-like beings who inhabit the world of Chad, located in the Outer Rim of the galaxy. They are petite in stature, with adults usually only reaching about one meter in height, and possess a pair of large, dark eyes, a flat nose, and prominent rodent-like ears. The Chadra-Fan's bodies are covered in fur from head to toe, and they have curiously oversized hands and feet that make them adept at climbing. Scientists have determined that they evolved from nimble tree rodents, a descendant of which still inhabits the treetops of Chad.

The Chadra-Fan's homeworld is three-quarters water, covered by chaotic seas as well as by marshes and bogs that are prone to perpetual flooding. The planet's weather is a result of its bizarre elliptical orbit, which has confused scientists for years as to whether it occupies the third or fourth position in the star system. Chad's star warms the world's surface to a fairly steady temperature, and despite the planet's orbit, Chad has almost no axial tilt. The nine moons that orbit the planet create a regular system of tides.

Tree-laden bayous are the Chadra-Fan's primary habitat. Because destructive tidal waves can sweep across their communities up to three or four times a year, the Chadra-Fan do not create solid structures for their dwellings, but instead sleep during midday in swaying open-walled configurations that hang from the cyperill trees high above the water. They are primarily out during dusk and dawn, making their way around by hopping from tree to tree or traveling in methane-powered, boat-like vehicles.

In the species' history, there are numerous stories of giant tsunamis caused by ocean earthquakes that have wiped out entire areas. The last significant one on record utterly devastated the largest community of Chadra-Fan on the planet, leaving only a scant few alive in that particular region. It is not surprising, then, that Chadra-Fan have an instinctive fear of drowning, and Chadra-Fan traveling offworld tend to frequently seek out planets with arid environments, despite their fur.

Because their world's volatile weather patterns are the cause of constant relocation, the Chadra-Fan have no sense of permanence, a trait that has led many to become consummate thrill- and pleasure-seekers, always on the lookout for a new adventure.

How Chadra-Fan perceive and respond to their fast-paced surroundings is due in part to their biology, not just their environmental experiences. The Chadra-Fan's senses are strangely unique—in particular those of sight and smell. The species' large black eyes can see into the infrared spectrum of light, giving them a marked advantage at night and in poorly lit areas. In addition, their olfactory sense is remarkably distinctive, the result of two sets of nostrils that each serves a separate specific function. The outer pair detect water-soluble scents like most humanoid species, while their inner nostrils control Chadra-Fan's chemoreceptive sense of smell.

In terms of physical appearance, the differences between male and female Chadra-Fan are undetectable to an outsider. The Chadra-Fan determine gender differences through their sense of smell, and they will relay their feelings of attraction through the release of pheromones. Some of these pheromones are released involuntarily, creating an aura of attractiveness as well as relaying their family ancestry to others. Chadra-Fan also purposely release pheromones to transmit emotions, as their faces are not all that expressive—feelings such as anger, fear, arousal, and joy are communicated through olfactory rather than visual perception. These scent-related messages can be very complex, and may even lead to some confusion should their involuntary pheromones combine with their voluntary ones. In addition, they will evaluate non-Chadra-Fan with this unique ability, and those who are familiar with offworlders can frequently determine a particular species simply by assessing their infrared aura and scent.

On top of this scent communication, Chadra-Fan converse verbally in high, squeaking tones, the interpretation of which is dependent upon a keen sense of hearing. If Chadra-Fan are tone deaf, they will not be able to speak, as their speech patterns rely on specific pitches to relay meaning.

Due to their small size and active nature, Chadra-Fan's metabolisms are extremely high, and their mental and physical activities run at a feverish pitch. Mostly sleeping in short two-hour naps during the daylight hours, they will then work the rest of the day gathering food, tinkering, and entertaining themselves at a frenzied pace. As a result of their speedy lifestyle and biological makeup, Chadra-Fan fully mature around age fifteen and usually live no more than forty standard years.

Chadra-Fan society is organized into a clan structure, and the immediate family divisions within each clan are typically impossible to discern. Everyone shares the duty of parenting one another's children, and households are open to anyone at all times. Because Chadra-Fan are so used to having other members of their kind around, they will con-

DESIGNATION
Sentient

HOMEWORLD
Chad

AVERAGE HEIGHT
1 meter

PRONUNCIATION
Chăd'-rä-Făn

stantly seek companionship; left on their own, they can die of loneliness within a period of weeks. They never travel unaccompanied, preferring even the companionship of a complete stranger to a lonesome journey by themselves.

With their strong familial ties, children are the center of the Chadra-Fan community. A young Chadra-Fan only leaves his or her clan when wed, or sometimes not at all, as the married couple remains with the clan that has fewer children so that they may increase the group's number.

Within their clan structure, Chadra-Fan have no chosen leaders. Everyone takes a guiding role at one time or another, stepping in where they have expertise and then surrendering the leadership to others who have more experience as a situation warrants. Chadra-Fan work well with partners and in team situations, as they are often either extremely forgiving, or merely ignorant, of team members' failings. For this reason, it is not unusual to see Chadra-Fan in the company of criminals—they are usually so self-absorbed or accommodating that they make loyal, well-received companions and mechanics for the most unsavory members of the galaxy's underworld.

While the Chadra-Fan are generally deemed a technologically primitive people, they do tend to have a compulsion to tinker. They are extremely inventive, able to come up with new tools and learn about technology after only a short time spent studying a piece of equipment. Depending on the complexity of the machinery they have studied, they can frequently pull apart most items and reassemble them in a short time frame. Most Chadra-Fan who travel offplanet end up working as mechanics or in technological research-and-development facilities.

Original Chadra-Fan mechanical creations are actually considered a hot commodity by those who take interest in collecting such things. Each piece is always completely distinct, made by a dedicated craftsman, and often regarded as a piece of art whether it works to specification or not. While Chadra-Fan are competent at mass-producing technical items, they prefer to construct each of their creations individually, and it is an object of pride and artisanship to fashion the most innovative technological designs. And while every singular item created by Chadra-Fan may not operate as anticipated, those that do, function exceptionally well.

NOTABLE APPEARANCE
Episode IV: A New Hope

CHAGRIAN

Chagrians are tall, powerfully built amphibious humanoids native to the water-covered world of Champala in the Chagri system of the Inner Rim. Early in the species' development, Champala's sun became temporarily unstable and bombarded their world with dangerous amounts of radiation. As a result, Chagrians developed a skin pigmentation that ranges in color from light blue to deep indigo and makes them resistant to most forms of radiation. In addition, Chagrians' eyes grant them the ability to see twice as far as most beings in low- or dim-light conditions, and in such cases they still maintain the ability to distinguish color and detail.

Outside of their distinctive skin, Chagrians' most notable feature is their horns, particularly the lethorns, which protrude downward from the sides of their head, growing and thickening over a Chagrian's lifetime, often to the point of draping over the shoulders and onto the chest. The males of the species also possess a set of regular horns that rise from their skulls upward, often giving them an intimidating appearance. These extra horns were once used by males in underwater duels to acquire mates, charging and impaling their rivals in an effort to eliminate their competition. In recent times, this practice has been made unnecessary and illegal, with arranged marriages becoming the norm among their species, but a male Chagrian's upper horns are still seen as a sign of virility, strength, and, unfortunately, vanity. To prevent their horns from becoming an encumbrance as they grow, they will file down the tips in their daily grooming rituals.

Due to their perpetual exposure to Champala's saltwater oceans, native Chagrians have a weak sense of taste that grows even more inadequate as they age. With their taste glands being subjected to the high content of sodium in Champala's water, all items that enter their mouths taste solely of salt, and by the time they reach adulthood, most Chagrians have no sensation of taste at all. Thus, they frequently have no interest in eating, viewing it as a waste of time, and will often carry nutritional supplements with them to substitute for meals. Also, Chagrians are known to be cautious about food on other planets, analyzing it for nutritional value before consumption. Their tongues are mostly used to detect smells—flickering in and out as among many saurian species.

Born as tadpoles roughly thirty centimeters long, Chagrians develop their legs, arms, and air-breathing lungs as they grow from infancy outside the womb. They are usually born in clutches of three or more, and are cared for in warm, sealable tubs of circulating water in a family's private home. These tubs are closed up at high tide, so the children are not swept away in the waves. Once children's appendages form, they leave the tub, already able to walk on land with little assistance. At this point, their horns will begin to grow, attaining about half of their maximum length by the time a child reaches puberty.

Because they inhabit a world largely immersed in water, Chagrians built their cities along the coastlines in strips of land along small, jungle-covered continents. The architecture of these cities is designed to take in the flowing surges of Champala's oceans at high tide, filling the structures with water. When this happens, Chagrians will swim from building to building and from floor to floor, continuing their lives with little interruption. The spaceports, meanwhile, are the only structures that are on perpetually high and dry land. Fortunately, the many areas of Champala that were damaged and polluted due to mining accidents in the Imperial era have been carefully reclaimed and returned to their previous state by the Galactic Alliance.

In general, Chagrians are a peaceful, law-abiding people, with some members of the species taking the obedient part of their natures to an extreme, often becoming rather stern, stoic, even downright obstinate about following procedure. This isn't the case with all Chagrians, however. Because their society is primarily affluent and the people are rarely wanting, they have no sense of greed and are hardly ever motivated by such base desires. The basic needs of Chagrians are met in abundance, be it for food, shelter, or health care. The educational system is well regarded and many Chagrians pursue advanced university studies, both on- and off-planet.

Their economy primarily centers on tourism, as large numbers of visitors frequently flock to their oceans and beaches, and their accommodating and selfless demeanor makes their homeworld a very popular spot for vacationing. Restorative spas and all-inclusive resorts dominate the cities of Champala, and are popular with all species living in the Inner Rim—not just those from water-based worlds. Chagrians enjoy meeting and interacting with others, preferring to live in urban areas where they can mingle on a regular basis. Although most Champala-based Chagrians do not speak Basic, those who venture offworld learn it eas-

DESIGNATION
Sentient

HOMEWORLD
Champala

AVERAGE HEIGHT
2 meters

PRONUNCIATION
Shäg'-rē-ăn

ily, and often return home to teach it to those in the tourism industry.

One of the most prominent Chagrians in galactic history was Mas Amedda, the Speaker of the Senate during the later years of the Old Republic. Although Amedda lived in a world where politics was ruled by corruption, and he was often forced to trade on that corruption, he began his career believing himself an honest politician with a genuine desire to serve the people. He initially became Speaker during the ill-fated chancellorship of Finis Valorum. Amedda was aware that he did not have the influence to become Chancellor himself and continued to serve as Speaker after Palpatine was elected Chancellor. Based on Palpatine's easygoing interpersonal manner as the Senator from Naboo, Amedda mistakenly believed that Palpatine would be malleable once in office and that he could influence Palpatine for the good of the beings under his care. In fact, during Palpatine's first few years as Chancellor, he appeared open to suggestion as Mas Amedda hoped and enacted several initiatives Amedda put forth. However, Palpatine was actually turning the tables on Amedda, collecting enough information to control him. As a result, Amedda continued to serve, even after learning of Palpatine's secret identity as Sidious, Dark Lord of the Sith. When Palpatine declared himself Emperor, Mas Amedda and Palpatine's other close advisers continued to keep the knowledge of Palpatine's identity as a Sith Lord hidden from the rest of the galaxy. Amedda's Chagrian temperament prevented him from being overly concerned with the thought that this knowledge might someday make him a liability to the Emperor.

After the Emperor rose to power and it was clear that the Empire was a harsh and tyrannical regime, many Chagrians joined the Rebellion. They were particularly important in freeing other water planets from Imperial oppression, including Mon Calamari. Champala was one of the first worlds to join the fledgling Alliance of Free Planets, and later the New Republic, where they remained ardent supporters through the transition to the Galactic Alliance.

NOTABLE APPEARANCE
Episode I: The Phantom Menace

CHEVIN

The Chevin are a technologically advanced, carnivorous, migratory pachydermoid species inhabiting Vinsoth in the Outer Rim, a world of varying temperatures and climates. Because of their protective hides, Chevin can thrive in any of them, although they seem to have a preference for the temperate, semitropical conditions found on the planet's grassy equatorial plains. However, the fact that their population is concentrated in such areas may also be because that is where their culture originated.

According to archaeological and sociological studies conducted on Vinsoth (at great price, as the Chevin charge exorbitant fees for access to their archaeological treasures), the Chevin evolved from giant, thick-boned mammals that lumbered across the plains of Vinsoth. They've retained several characteristics from their forebears—qualities that make them an extremely robust and resilient species.

Chevin present very imposing figures, standing on trunk-like legs that support their large, bulky frames. A trunk-like snout drops from their huge heads nearly to the ground, enabling them to forage while at the same time watching for predators. Their trunks are also the source of an impressive olfactory sense that allows them to locate food without bending over.

Chevin's round black eyes seem to lack pupils, but in reality each eye is one great pupil. Light is filtered through a double-lid system, the first of which appears to simply be clear, but in fact acts as a filtration for damaging light rays and protects the eyes from dirt, wind, and other irritants. The other fleshy lid further shields the pupils with the Chevin's naturally tough hide.

A Chevin's hide is capable of withstanding the impacts of small projectiles and blade attacks, and though small blasterfire can cause their skin to burn, it does not typically cause them much pain. Those who have encountered the Chevin in close combat have observed that it takes a heavy blaster, lightsaber, or other similar high-powered weapon to truly injure one. The thickness and toughness of their hide, however, significantly limits their sense of touch.

Chevin possess long arms, and their three-fingered hands, larger even than their three-toed feet, can touch the ground as they walk at an ambling pace. Though they move slowly, Chevin are quality hunters, circling their prey with precision teamwork until it stumbles into their trap. This finely tuned strategy helped them to dominate and enslave Chevs, a humanoid species also native to their world. The Chevin do treat their slaves relatively well to encourage subservience, allowing Chevs to keep their own cultural heritage and supporting them in all forms of art and expression.

The Chevin are consummate opportunists. For many, their goal is to acquire wealth, power, and status by any means necessary, and thus the galaxy has come to know them as smugglers, gamblers, blackmailers, and gunrunners. As mentioned, Chevin are also slavers, exploiting the humanoid Chev species with whom they share their world. And yet they do not consider themselves evil, instead believing themselves realists—using their wiles to survive or prosper in a merciless galaxy. In their own circles, they are quite honest, and are rarely known to ever double cross a business partner for any reason. But if they themselves are betrayed, Chevin can rank among the most vindictive and brutal adversaries in the galaxy.

Not all Chevin share the same "merciless galaxy" view, however. The scientific and technological communities of Vinsoth focus their interests on new medical discoveries, and on creating greater and better products of engineering. Sadly, these forward-thinking Chevin usually end up working for their more aggressive counterparts. Even so, small breakaway collections of independent-thinking scientists and engineers have formed secret societies to combat the slavery that has been a black mark on their culture for eons. Ending this slavery would give them easier entrance to the Galactic Alliance, something these progressive Chevin desire for worldwide protection as well as economic growth.

The Chevin are a migratory species, traveling the plains searching for wild backshin—herd animals that are their primary source of meat. Their family-centered communities traverse their world in large platform vehicles called lodges. Wealthier groups use repulsorlift vehicles, while others use lodges with wheels, although slaves are almost always forced to walk from campsite to campsite. A pack of as few as forty or as many as 250 lodges will travel together at a time to create a sprawling,

DESIGNATION
Sentient

HOMEWORLD
Vinsoth

AVERAGE HEIGHT
2 meters

PRONUNCIATION
Shĕ'-vĭn

moving village. All the wandering communities, however, stay in contact with one another through electronic communications, so that if one group is threatened, the others can come to its aid. It is unusual for a village to remain in the same place longer than a few standard weeks, unless members find the particular location to be rich in game, or inclement weather forbids travel.

Those Chevin with the resources to do so travel and trade offworld regularly, bringing home the goods, clothing, and cultural influences of other peoples. Before encountering other species, Chevin did not wear clothes at all. Now they enjoy adorning themselves in the richest of robes and jewelry—and flaunt their vestments as a sign of prestige.

Politically, Chevin are monarchists with a dictatorial system of government. A dictator governs each continent while overseeing a panel of self-chosen advisers. These Chevin are some of the very few who do not travel in the moving villages, instead residing in centrally located establishments. These rulers rarely war with each other, though they do tend to compete for land, power, prestige, and trade privileges.

Chevin acquired their initial technical knowhow from offplanet sources, and adapted it to their own needs. Unfortunately, much of their other technology is focused on maintaining control of the slave population—one reason a faction of the scientific community wants to end the practice, which is felt to inhibit growth in the field. The Chevin leadership has made profitable use of a lot of the slave-controlling technology by selling it to other worlds to use for security purposes.

During the reign of the Empire, the Chevin supported the Imperial rule of the galaxy, finding it to be a profitable relationship, as they provided the Empire with foodstuffs, slaves, and their unique slave-restraining equipment in return for the offworld goods they desired.

Offworld, Chevin are usually found in expensive casinos, space stations, underworld-controlled pleasure palaces, and high-tech gladiatorial gaming houses. A few of the Chevin working for change on Vinsoth left during the war against the Empire to join the Rebellion. These few work within the Galactic Alliance, encouraging the government to put pressure on their homeworld's leaders to end slavery on Vinsoth. Unfortunately, these valiant individuals often become the targets of bounty hunters and assassins hired by the dictators of Chevin, who see their actions as traitorous.

NOTABLE APPEARANCE
Episode VI: Return of the Jedi

CHISS

Until about ten standard years after the Battle of Endor, little was known of the Chiss, a humanoid species from the frigid world of Csilla in the Unknown Regions, other than the fact that Imperial Grand Admiral Thrawn was one of them. Thrawn, whose real name was Mitth'raw'nuruodo, revealed almost nothing about his species. Despite his exile, Thrawn was secretive regarding his people. However, agents of the New Republic, after conducting analyses of surrendered and captured Imperial logs, found several points of interest. In addition, reports from the University of Sambra that detail investigations of Chiss sites such as Nirauan have yielded reliable information. Very few recorded encounters with the Chiss have been unearthed, although they are reputed to have driven back the Ssi-ruuk, a military threat as fearsome as the Nagai, the Yevetha, and the Yuuzhan Vong.

With blue skin, jet-black hair, and glowing red eyes, the Chiss generally command attention in a crowd of other humanoids. Their skin and eye colors are due to a chemical reaction to an oxygen atmosphere, and the more oxygen contained in the air they breathe, the greater the intensity of these two features. In addition, the evolved changes to their eyes have given the Chiss superior visual acuity, even in low-light conditions. Occasionally their black hair will gray with age, especially in females. This is considered a mark of distinction in their culture; among Chiss, it is felt that the child of a parent possessing graying hair will greatly affect society. Other than their distinctive eye and skin color, there is little else to differentiate them physically from standard humans.

The Chiss are typically attractive, intelligent, and private people, and are so protective of their society that they have managed to keep their species' existence largely secret from the rest of the galaxy. This isolationism makes it difficult to form conclusive statements about the Chiss. For example, scientists believe they do not experience an adolescent stage of life, but advance quickly to full maturity. However, this may be the result of societal and cultural influences and demands rather than physical growth, or some combination thereof.

Scientists also believe that the Chiss are descended from an ancient human colony founded in an age predating the Old Republic. However, they are sufficiently different from humans to be considered an independent species, as is the case with Zeltrons. The Chiss are highly evolved, taking great interest in art and science, and maintain a powerful military. In many accounts, they are described as pensive—contemplative, deliberate, and calculating—studying situations from every viewpoint and considering all the alternatives when making a decision.

The Chiss control more than two dozen systems surrounding their homeworld of Csilla, in a political federation known as the Chiss Ascendancy. Their society is regimented, inflexible, and strangely xenophobic, and their colonization and control of neighboring worlds was evidently achieved not for want of power or riches, but instead to establish order over chaotic elements that could ultimately pose a threat to them. Indeed, the Chiss are generally a peaceful species, but when attacked, they fight with efficient, well-planned strategies, and they do not give up the battle until their opponents are destroyed or subjugated. Most, if not all, of the systems they conquered were defeated after their respective leaders attacked the Chiss, as it is against the law for Chiss to engage in preemptive strikes. This is such a moral imperative that Thrawn was exiled when he called for a preemptive strike against an enemy.

The Chiss have no known Force traditions. Moreover, research conducted by the Jedi historian Tionne has identified only one Chiss Force-user, a female Dark-sider named Sev'rance Tann.

Statistically speaking, it is unlikely that Force sensitivity is this rare among an entire species once evidence of its existence has been demonstrated, especially a species so biologically similar to the most widespread Force-users, humans. However, one can hypothesize that Chiss practices and beliefs may have led to such a lack of Force traditions and known Force-users. As the Chiss believe that aggression against a potential enemy is forbidden until that enemy has launched an attack, the power bestowed by Force-sensitivity may be considered by the Chiss as too great a temptation. Thus, hypothetically, if there are unrecorded Force-users among the Chiss, they may work to keep their talents secret. One's family is a paramount concern for Chiss, and a Chiss Force-user may fear bringing shame upon them—worse, exile. A public prohibition against disclosing one's talents in the Force may be so strong that unless Chiss are Force-sensitive themselves, they are unaware the Force exists.

Records uncovered from the remains of Outbound Flight suggest that this ignorance of the Force was initially the case with Thrawn, a condition he was not likely to allow for long. We can surmise that because Thrawn had contact with the galaxy outside the Unknown Regions prior to the Clone Wars, it was most likely Thrawn who brought Tann, and her lover, Vandalor, to the attention of Darth Sidious, whom Thrawn had met during the Outbound Flight crisis. Whether this was an attempt to remove Tann from a difficult and dangerous situation on Csilia or to simply provide Sidious with a soldier and tactician he could rely on, we will never know.

Chiss society is directed by ruling "families" that are not necessarily indicative of bloodline so much as function, and each family is its own branch of the Chiss government or society. Although details are unclear, reports are that the number of ruling families has fluctuated somewhere between three and twelve. Some facts have also been discovered regarding four of the families. The Nuruodo family, which was Thrawn's clan, controls the military and foreign affairs, and the Csapla family administers the use of the Ascendancy's natural and agricultural resources and manages colonial issues. The Sabosen supervise education, justice, and public health, while the Inrokini direct business, communications, civilian technology, and the sciences.

The Chiss are frequently perceived by outsiders as arrogant, calculating, and aloof. It is said that they see every non-Chiss as a potential threat, even when working on a common goal, and as a precautionary measure, they will continuously calculate strategies for protecting their own interests. And if for some reason a Chiss is defeated or humiliated in a venture, he or she will carefully scrutinize what happened to ensure that such a setback does not occur a second time.

Despite this xenophobic mistrust of other species, or perhaps because of it, the Chiss have a heightened interest in the study of the scientific and, in the case of Thrawn, artistic achievements of other beings. Through the analysis of these creations, he came to understand the dangers and weaknesses of their potential enemies.

One difficulty in uncovering further details on the culture of the Chiss is their incredibly complex language, Cheunh. Linguists who have managed to record the language find it to be one of the most intricate and indecipherable of all humanoid dialects in the galaxy. It is theorized that the Chiss prefer it that way, as this complexity makes it that much harder for outsiders to learn about them.

DESIGNATION
Sentient

HOMEWORLD
Csilla

AVERAGE
HEIGHT
1.7 meters

PRONUNCIATION
Chĭss

NOTABLE APPEARANCE
Heir to the Empire (novel)

CLAWDITE

Clawdites are a reptilian humanoid species native to the planet Zolan in the Mid Rim. They are renowned for their shape-changing abilities, although in its natural form, a Clawdite's skin color typically varies from yellow to green. Their large yellowish eyes have black, slit-like pupils, set in a face with almost human features. With their shape-changing skills, Clawdites can alter their appearance drastically to mimic that of other humanoids, even to the point of including the clothing and jewelry they are wearing, as long as those items are worn close to the body. Clawdites treat their skin with special oils to keep it supple and flexible for shape changing and to reduce the possibility of cracks or tears. They are specifically reptomammals and, unlike true reptiles, do not reproduce by laying and hatching eggs, instead giving birth to their offspring in singular pregnancies.

Unlike other shape-changing species such as the Shi'ido, Clawdites' body-altering ability causes them great discomfort. And yet, with practice, they can work past the pain to maintain some startling disguises. Their capability relies heavily upon their concentration, and it is only a well-practiced Clawdite who can rest while in altered form. In addition, Clawdites spend a good deal of time learning meditation and concentration techniques that allow them to maximize their transforming talents. Unlike the Shi'ido, Clawdites cannot, however, alter or add to their mass—they can only mimic species that are humanoid and roughly the same size as themselves. They also cannot match the features of a specific individual, nor can they change their physical form to look like species with drastically different body configurations and postures, such as Mon Calamari or Dugs. Most Clawdites will lose their shape and revert to their natural form if they are distracted, and if they are killed in disguise, they will return to their true appearance.

However, there have been reports that the bounty hunter Zam Wesell, unlike other Clawdite shapeshifters, was able to assume the forms of species with drastically different body masses (most notably that of a Dug). There is no evidence suggesting that this feat has been duplicated, so it is believed that Wesell must have developed her own technique for shapeshifting. On the other hand, there is nothing to suggest that another Clawdite cannot similarly learn how to assume new forms. Although the exact physiological mechanism by which Clawdites assume the form of other beings is not yet understood, and as water makes up most being's bodies, xenobiologists have speculated that Wesell might have been able to alter her body's water content with a finer degree of control than other Clawdites, perhaps through the use of a medical device or injectable substance. Wesell may have been able to expel water to reduce mass, and then, conversely, absorb it to increase mass. This process would be limited by the amount of water her body's cells could expel or contain, perhaps with lower and upper thresholds. In addition, it would have been necessary for her to manipulate any absorbed water in order to create a skeletal system to support her weight.

It is not known whether Zam Wesell's daughter, Sone, shared this ability with her mother, as she disappeared after Wesell's death on Coruscant shortly before the start of the Clone Wars. Recent attempts to test these theories have proven unsuccessful, and for understandable reasons, the Clawdites are not anxious to have their shapeshifting studied with great scrutiny, as they fear negative repercussions and prejudicial treatment.

A Clawdite's ability to change form increases with age. Clawdite children can do little more than change color, a skill that begins as early as infancy, with small babies shifting hues to communicate hunger or discomfort to their parents. Any simple exterior alterations such as this are harmless to most Clawdites—it is only when they actually shift their mass that the process becomes painful. Under their new government, Clawdite schoolchildren attend classes instructing them on how to manage their strengths, which has made a greater number of Clawdites more practiced and efficient with their talents in recent years.

In general, Clawdites are solitary individuals who often shun company unless it is beneficial to their goals. Harsh realists who carry a strong sense of suspicion and mistrust for all they encounter, Clawdites frequently have difficulty forming friendships, and the concept of loyalty escapes them.

Clawdites are a subspecies of the native Zolanders, who harbor a vicious prejudice against their genetic cousins. The Zolanders are a deeply religious people of strong convictions, who view the Clawdites as impure and sinful. The Clawdite species branched from their ancestors hundreds of generations ago when scientists, trying to find a way to protect their people from harmful solar radiation bombarding their world, activated dormant skin-changing genes in the genetic code of some volunteers. This altered genetic trait was passed on from generation to generation, creating a whole new species who were then subjugated and reviled by their fellows. This makes the species' reluctance to have their shapeshifting abilities studied quite a rational response. After years of persecution and banishment to secured ghettos, the Clawdites decided to give themselves a name that would distinguish them from their genetic forebears.

Very select Clawdites are accepted to train with the Mabari, an ancient order of Zolan warrior knights. Learning the martial traditions of the Mabari is a strenuous undertaking, and only the most promising recruits are accepted. During the Clone Wars, however, the order limited the number of Clawdite members it accepted due to religious and societal prejudices. Furthermore, the Mabari also regulated Clawdites among their number due

DESIGNATION
Sentient

HOMEWORLD
Zolan

AVERAGE HEIGHT
1.8 meters

PRONUNCIATION
Clä'-dīt

to a genuine and well-founded concern that training Clawdites in large numbers would result in a powerful group capable of overthrowing the government. As a result, Clawdite members were closely monitored, and if Clawdites left the order, they were strongly pressured to depart the planet entirely.

During the Separatist crisis, the shapeshifting species grouped together to form a political contingent, and sought offworld assistance to aid them in resisting persecution. Their primary contact was Count Dooku, whose power was cut short during the Clone Wars when he was killed by Anakin Skywalker. As a result, the Clawdites remained in subjugation while the Empire was in power, and Imperial forces blockaded the planet Zolan to ensure that no Clawdites could leave their homeworld.

After the Empire fell, Zolan erupted into civil war, and the Clawdites finally seized control of at least 75 percent of their world. They had just settled into power and made overtures to the New Republic when the Yuuzhan Vong invasion force struck. Clawdites quickly joined forces with the Republic to infiltrate the Yuuzhan Vong with a unit comprised solely of shapeshifters. This unit, more than one hundred members strong, served valiantly, suffering an uncommonly high casualty rate as missions repeatedly took them behind enemy lines. Known as Guile Company, the unit did not lack for volunteers, however, and competition to be accepted into the unit was fierce. Only those Clawdites who demonstrated an advanced degree of control over their shapeshifting abilities were accepted. Moreover, Clawdites are not a populous species. For this reason, Clawdites with children were not accepted into the unit, as it was believed that protecting and nurturing future generations was important to the continuation of the species. It was later discovered that for this reason, many applicants and members of the Guile Company hid their offspring.

Guile Company has continued as an active unit in the Galactic Alliance military. In addition, Clawdites have moved beyond this role to become indispensable members of Alliance Intelligence infiltration units. While maintaining an aloofness from other species, Clawdites take great pride in their military service, as the few Clawdites that have made it off their homeworld typically take employment as bounty hunters and assassins. Military service provides a chance to make a contribution to the galaxy in a positive way, protecting the liberty of other species that have been persecuted as they had historically been on Zolan.

NOTABLE APPEARANCE
Episode II: Attack of the Clones

DEVARONIAN (DEVISH)

Devaronians, or Devish, are humanoids native to the world of Devaron in the Colonies region, a planet of moderate temperatures and varying landscapes, though the Devaronians tend to make their homes in the low mountain ranges. Scientists believe they evolved from a species of ancient primates that roamed the mountains, using their horns to defend themselves from predators. Although the female Devaronians lost their horns through evolution, the males did not, and it is possible that the males have maintained this characteristic because it aids the species' mating process, as the females find the horns attractive. For this reason, the males take great pride in their horns, polishing them with wax and scented oils, while females simply have spots where their horns would be.

In addition, Devaronian males possess sharp incisors that can be utilized for the rending of flesh, particularly if they are hunting, whereas the females have the blunt teeth of omnivores. The females have retained their forebears' soft coat of white, brown, or reddish fur, while the advancement of the species has resulted in the fading of hair on males, leaving them with smooth, crimson skin.

Devaronians have a unique physiology that is resilient to many toxins and poisons, though certainly not all. They have a particularly high tolerance for alcohol and other intoxicants, and it is generally known around the galaxy that to get into a drinking contest with a Devaronian is to flirt with disaster. They can indeed become intoxicated, but it takes a lot more of a given substance to bring them to that state. This is because each Devaronian has two livers, which work overtime filtering their blood. The extra organ also makes them more resistant to some of the most common diseases and allows for a Devaronian's blood to clot more quickly.

However, scientists theorize that the principle reason a Devaronian has two livers is to accommodate their unique blood, which is black in color and silver-based rather than iron-based like most oxygen breathing species. Silver is an element that, unlike iron, does not efficiently carry oxygen. To compensate for this deficiency, a Devaronian's two livers work doubly hard to filter carcinogens from the blood stream and deliver much needed oxygen to all parts of their body.

Strangely enough, because of this silver-based blood,

Devaronians perform with greater vigor and strength when exposed to sulfur—as silver carries sulfur throughout their body much more efficiently than oxygen. In fact, some Devaronians participate in an activity called "sulfur snuffing"— they carry small stick inhalers of sulfur, or small masks to inhale the gas. However, as sulfur is a carcinogen, overuse can cause their system to break down overtime. They can, in fact, develop an addiction to it, leading to their ultimate ruin. Sadly, as the smell of sulfur is repugnant to many species, Devaronains engaging in this activity tend to command a wider amount of personal space when interacting with other beings in public places.

Due to the Devish male's reddish pallor, sharp teeth, and horns, many other species perceive them as evil, as they resemble images of malicious beings in certain cultural tales. However, they are not generally malevolent. Still, even though they are one of the oldest spacefaring peoples in the galaxy, the Galactic Alliance has not accepted Devaron as a member world because some of its traditions violate Galactic civil law.

The two Devaronian sexes not only differ physically, but also deviate in terms of values and behavior. Devish females are extraordinarily responsible, trustworthy, and ambitious, running businesses and participating in local politics. Their attentions center on their homes and families, and on the day-to-day business that makes their world function. They rarely leave their world, unless they are being paid to do so, preferring to raise their families in the industrialized cities and villages of Devaron.

Males, on the other hand, are known to be extremely irresponsible, and have a reputation as thrill-seekers, always searching for adventure and entertainment. Their pursuits are varied and diverse, frequently making them interesting and enjoyable conversationalists, particularly since their irrepressible wanderlust has found them in a variety of story-worthy locales, serving as traveling merchants, bounty hunters, galactic traders, and explorers.

After choosing a mate and siring children, male Devaronians typically take to the roads and rivers of Devaron to find adventure, and many leave the planet entirely, rarely ever returning. Strangely, however, Devish males always send some of the money that they earn back home to their wives and offspring. The truth is, the females prefer the financial support to having the males present. So when the male Devaronians developed stardrive capabilities in order to appease their urge to travel the skies, the females soon took advantage of it by setting up trade with other systems. Their world has therefore become very wealthy, with the ever-dependable females running the economic and political systems.

Following this financial model, Devaron actually subsists mainly of its own accord, thriving on local produce with little need to import from other worlds, often not even generating enough goods to export. However, since the males are quite generous and reliable with sending home the credits they earn in their travels, the females have maintained enough capital to import items that they desire from distant systems—making their homebound lives very comfortable.

Devaron is ruled by a representative democracy of popularly elected females, who would not even consider allowing males participation, although it is unlikely that any desire it. The males are accepted as a necessary hazard of life, and are not really regarded as a functioning part of society.

Although Devaron was at one time a member planet of the Old Republic, it was denied membership in the New Republic due to the Devaronians' traditional means of capital punishment, which is considered overly severe, certainly cruel and unusual by several systems' standards. Criminals guilty of a capital crime are thrown alive into a pit of ravenous quarra beasts, which rend them to pieces in a public execution.

Seeing that joining the Galactic Alliance would be advantageous to building further business and wealth, the female rulers of Devaron are discussing whether to appeal the rejection of their former application for membership. However, deliberations on changing their cultural traditions have yet to really get off the ground, for, while most leaders can see the logic in forgoing the public executions, there are those who wish to keep this brutal practice in place, if merely for the entertainment of the masses.

Devaronians, as a people, have a noteworthy Jedi tradition and a propensity for Force sensitivity. In fitting with their dedicated sensibilities, female Devaronians tend to grow more quickly in stature and power as Jedi Knights. During the Clone Wars, Sian Jeisel was a female Devaronian Jedi Master who fought valiantly alongside Mace Windu. However, males, despite their thirst for adventure, also have produced some great Jedi warriors, the most prominent of which, Hivrekh'wao'cheklev, managed to survive capture by the Yuuzhan Vong, and played an important part in their defeat.

DESIGNATION
Sentient

HOMEWORLD
Devaron

AVERAGE
HEIGHT
1.6 meters

PRONUNCIATION
Dĕv-ä-rō'-nē-ăn

NOTABLE APPEARANCE
Episode IV: A New Hope

DEWBACK

Dewbacks are large, nonsentient reptiles that inhabit the arid wilderness of the planet Tatooine. Their name was coined colloquially, derived from the dew that gathers on their bodies during their rest in the cool nighttime air of the desert wastelands. Usually employed as beasts of burden, dewbacks were domesticated long before the Empire took its place on the water-barren world.

Unlike some reptiles, dewbacks are omnivores, thriving on the sparse grasses and thorny plants of the desert landscape as well as on small animals such as baby womp rats or scurriers. For hydration, they chew the roots of local cacti that store water in their heat-resistant parts. Other than this, dewbacks require very little water to survive, and can frequently go for days without dehydration setting in.

These reptiles range between 1.3 and 2 meters in height, and 2 to 3 meters in length. Their scales are generally gray and brown, or a dull red and blue, although they have been known to change color with their environment. Dewbacks possess large, tough, flat teeth, and sharp claws for digging through sand dunes in search of brush or plants that provide moisture.

There are several varieties of dewbacks on Tatooine, the most common being the lesser dewback, which is typically the type trained as a mount and pack animal. The most vicious and untrainable kind is the cannibal dewback, so called because these animals will even eat newly hatched members of their own species, particularly if they encounter them in the wild. The cannibal dewbacks are larger than their lesser cousins, and extremely

2.0

1.5

1.0

.5

0

aggressive. Sadly, they are often mistaken for lesser dewbacks because their coloring is similar—an error that kills several settlers a year.

Grizzled dewbacks, meanwhile, haunt the Jundland Wastes, and are named thus for their patchy exterior. They are considered dangerous because they are usually hungry, and are actually even more immense than either the cannibal or lesser dewback. The final variety, mountain dewbacks, generally have calmer dispositions akin to their domesticated cousins, and can be found in the more mountainous regions of Tatooine. These dewbacks can also be trained as pack animals and mounts.

In the wild, Sand People commonly hunt dewbacks for their meat and their hides, using the beasts' leathery skin for boots, pouches, belts, tents, and other gear. Krayt dragons also hunt dewbacks, as they are relatively easy prey. Most dewbacks will only fight if threatened, and even then, they will typically run from any threat larger than themselves.

Dewbacks are regularly used by moisture farmers as beasts of burden, and by desert military patrols as mounts. They are also employed by Podracing teams to pull their racing vehicles to the starting line. Though sluggish during the cool of the night, the cold-blooded dewbacks can be urged to display bursts of great speed, and are faster and more agile than the bantha, the beast normally ridden by Tusken Raiders. At a full sprint, dewbacks have been able to pace landspeeders for a short distance, and local law enforcement officials have come to find them more reliable than landspeeders because of their ability to continue moving through sandstorms.

Undomesticated dewbacks are extremely solitary, exhibiting few or no parenting or herding instincts. Each year, they return to the Jundland Wastes, where they will engage in a mating ritual for several days. During the period, a male will roll on his back to exhibit his belly to the female, the color of which changes to a light sky blue when he wishes to mate. This shift in color is meant to attract her attention, which, after several attempts, it usually does. Following the mating ritual, all of the dewbacks wander back into the desert alone. A short time later, the female dewback will dig several large holes in the warm sand and deposit thousands of sand-colored eggs, each the size of a human fist. She will then bury the eggs to hide them from predators. Roughly half a standard year after being laid, the eggs hatch, and the young, without any guidance from adults, venture out into the wastelands of the Tatooine desert in the hope of survival.

Interestingly enough, dewbacks' mating season begins just as krayt dragons' mating season ends, thus timing the egg laying in such a way as to protect the dewbacks' offspring from destruction. The two lizard species have chosen a neighboring location for their mating grounds due to the fact that the sand in that area remains at an ideal temperature for incubating the species' eggs.

It is interesting to note that dewbacks will not breed in captivity. Owners of domesticated dewbacks must release them during mating season, allowing them to journey to the Jundland Wastes if they wish the beasts to reproduce. In most cases, domesticated dewbacks will return to their rightful owners. They are, therefore, very intelligent and loyal, remembering those who have fed them or shown them kindness. Because they cannot breed in captivity, they do not thrive anywhere but in their home environment, and are rarely seen outside Tatooine, unless they've been taken offworld as a solitary pet or riding mount with no expectation of having them bred.

DESIGNATION
Nonsentient

HOMEWORLD
Tatooine

AVERAGE HEIGHT
1.8 meters

PRONUNCIATION
Dēw'-băk

NOTABLE APPEARANCE
Episode IV: A New Hope

DIANOGA

The scavenger creature known as the dianoga is an amphibious cephalopod that makes its home in areas throughout the galaxy where refuse collects in moist environments. Found mostly in pools of stagnant water, dianoga have also been known to turn up in the refuse collection systems of starships, which are typically warm and full of bacterium-filled water. Dianoga prosper on industrialized worlds, commonly living in the sewer systems and river canals of urbanized areas.

Dianoga possess a single eyestalk that extends upward from their body like a periscope to observe their surroundings. Their one red eye is extremely sensitive to light, but able to see clearly in dark environments. It is encased in a single, transparent shell that protects the eye from puncturing and other potential injuries that may be encountered in the creatures' trash-filled aquatic habitats.

Seven tentacles are used by the dianoga for moving and gathering food. These tentacles have suction cups that stick to their prey and hold it tight, and can also grab on to smoother surfaces to help propel the dianoga forward. Moreover, a dianoga's tentacles quickly regenerate if damaged, making the creatures difficult to injure and kill. Once a dianoga has grasped its quarry in its tentacles, the dianoga will attempt to squeeze the life from it or suffocate it within

4.0
3.5
3.0
2.5
2.0
1.5
1.0
.5
0

minutes. Exremely large dianoga pose a substantial threat to humans and other species of similar size.

Beyond the eyestalk and tentacles, a dianoga's body consists of one sizable stomach sac and digestive system, along with a huge, toothy mouth that can swallow items far larger than the dianoga itself by stretching around them, similar to a snake. The stomach contains powerful acids for digesting items that most beings would find inedible.

It is believed that the creatures originated on the planet Vodran, crawling into the waste containment tanks of spacefaring vessels, where they then bred. At spaceports, they migrated to other ships and dispersed themselves throughout the galaxy. Now dianoga can be found in warm, watery collections of waste in nearly every known

DESIGNATION
Nonsentient

HOMEWORLD
Vodran

**AVERAGE
HEIGHT**
3–10 meters

PRONUNCIATION
Dī-ä-nō′-gä

spaceport and many large ships. Since these creatures actually feed on and digest waste products, vessel commanders will frequently allow a dianoga to remain in their ship's refuse system once it is discovered. They rarely damage the inner workings of the system, preferring to rest along the bottom of a tank and feed, and if they grow large enough to threaten the ship's crew, maintenance teams will kill the dianoga by shooting them.

These creatures, while not necessarily possessing a significant-sized brain, have displayed their cleverness in choosing their food and in managing to migrate from one home to another. They are able to tell the difference between live creatures and those that are dead, and while they can certainly consume living beings, they will generally forgo an animate meal for one that is deceased. This, scientists believe, is actually a preference of taste. Dianoga are also intelligent enough to determine the sleep patterns of individuals who are resting, regularly attempting to migrate when there is little to no movement, and thus no one awake to notice their quiet slithering from one position to another. However, there are many reports of space crews working the late shift who have encountered a wayfaring dianoga trying to crawl its way into a new area of a ship or spaceport.

Dianogas are self-fertilizing hermaphrodites, not requiring interaction with other members of their species to reproduce. When they do produce offspring, their microscopic larvae create small colonies, and once the population number becomes too great for a certain environment, some of the dianoga will leave that colony and journey to a new, uninhabited locale. Even on the largest of vessels, dianoga can really only be tolerated in colonies of three or fewer. Once their numbers grow too great, the dianoga will either have to find a new habitat or be killed by a ship's maintenance workers.

These creatures are fairly shy and peaceful, usually only aggressive if starved or panicked—and undeniably, there are some tales of dianoga attacking humans who have inadvertently stumbled into their territories. Despite this, they are not known as man-eaters, although they are curious and tend to check each new object they encounter, testing for edibility. Some cultures have developed ways to eat dianoga, though—most popular is a dish known simply as dianoga pie.

NOTABLE APPEARANCE
Episode IV: A New Hope

DRESSELLIAN

Dressellians are fiercely independent people who inhabit the Mid Rim world of Dressel. They are humanoid, although they do have a wrinkled appearance that scientists believe evolved from their hunter-gatherer ancestors, who spent most of their time in Dressel's grasslands, out under the hot sun. Some in the galaxy refer to them as "prune faces" because of their wrinkled visage, a nickname that Dressellians disdain. Their elongated heads contain very large brains, making them quick-witted, intelligent, artistic, and resourceful. They typically possess extremely swift reflexes, which, combined with their brilliance, makes them fierce, efficient, and effective fighters.

Dressel first became known to the galactic community when it was discovered by Bothan explorers of the Askar clan. The clan decided it was best to leave the Dressellians to develop on their own without interference, and instead they colonized the asteroid belt in the system for a mining operation. Years later, Imperials conquered the system to capture its natural resources, and tried to bring the primitive Dressellians under their control. They were met with hostile resistance as the Dressellians displayed their innate tenacity.

This stiff-necked species values individual freedom over all else, and its members are very individualistic. They can have difficulty working in groups, and rarely form associations containing large numbers. Despite this, when the threat of Imperial domination loomed, the Dressellians came together to form a fierce freedom-fighting force. Their motivation was the autonomy to live as they chose, on their own terms. In a like manner, they banded together to battle the Yuuzhan Vong invaders decades later, showing that when Dressellian freedom is threatened, they are unwavering in combat.

Their initial contact with humans was limited before they were attacked by the Empire, and thus the Dressellians are suspicious of outsiders on the whole, though they are highly trusting of Bothans. However, they can be very loyal to any being who assists them without desire for repayment.

The Dressellian language is simple, and until their contact with Bothan explorers it was actually written in a pictorial form. After establishing close diplomatic ties with the Bothans, they have adopted the Bothan alphabet to communicate their language in writing. Much of their literature, therefore, is gradually being translated and shared in the galaxy at large. Vastly inspirational and often deeply profound, their body of work has been hailed by critics as one of the galaxy's long-undiscovered treasures. Even so, the writers and poets of Dressel prefer to avoid the limelight, as their seclusion and privacy give them what they believe to be a more appropriate work environment.

It is believed that Dressellian society developed into significant communal city-states from their more tribal, hunter-gatherer origins. These city-states are run via direct democracy, with elected leaders who moderate group discussions. Individuals in these communities are allowed to come and go as they please; in the case of key decisions, those of dissenting opinions sometimes depart to form their own establishments.

Law enforcement in these informal groupings is accomplished through a sort of mob justice—the guilty are hunted and punished by concerned citizens. To them, a formal judiciary or court system is inefficient and ineffective. Their justice, they feel, is swift and successful in deterring antisocial behavior, and is not viewed as uncontrolled vigilantism, in contrast with how it may appear to outsiders. While their judicial techniques can be brutal, they do keep crime at a minimum.

This system of government survived underground despite the Empire's best efforts to squash it, and the state leaders became, in fact, the leadership of the Dressellian dissident movement. Although they are now part of the Galactic Federation of Free Alliances, Dressellians largely prefer to keep to themselves except when dealing in business matters. Throughout the days of the New Republic, the Dressellian Senatorial representative often failed to attend sessions except at the urging of the species' war-colleagues, the Bothans.

Economically, the Dressellians have only recently begun to grasp the concept of money, through their increased contact with other species during the war against the Empire. Theirs has long been a barter system handled on a local

rather than governmental scale. With the formation of the New Republic, however, singular Dressellians began to show interest in capitalistic ventures, seeing such undertakings as an extension of their individual quest for personal freedom. Their tenacity also encourages their entrepreneurial compunction, and following the defeat of the Empire, the Dressellians took over control of the mining in their local system, and are now making great strides in that industry. They have also created notable trade in textiles woven from the essence of their natively grown grass, as well as from their farm produce.

Despite the influx of more modern technology to Dressel, the planet still functions at a largely outdated level, with a focus on steam-driven machinery and animal transportation. However, the development of businesses such as those described above is causing technology on Dressel to evolve quickly to meet the demand for native goods.

While the Dressellians aren't industrially advanced, since the end of the Galactic Civil War, more and more offworlders have filtered new technology to them. During the war, Dressellians fought with simple black-powdered, slug-firing weapons. The Bothan underground movement supplied the Dressellians with some energy weapons, though transporting such items was dangerous, and very few actually made it to their intended recipients. Today, while they are familiar with other forms of weaponry, Dressellians still prefer to use slugthrowers, mostly as a form of cultural pride. Because of the limited numbers of shots the weapons can fire, marksmanship is highly valued.

As Dressellian society evolves, neighbors anticipate that the species will become important to the future of the GFFA. Inspirationally, they have already set an impressive example for their peers during their fight against the Empire for personal liberty.

DESIGNATION
Sentient

HOMEWORLD
Dressel

AVERAGE
HEIGHT
1.8 meters

PRONUNCIATION
Drĕ-sĕl'-lē-ăn

NOTABLE APPEARANCE
Episode VI: Return of the Jedi

DUG

Dugs are a vicious, bullying species that hail from the planet Malastare—one of the mainstay planets of the Old Republic. They inhabit the lush western continent of their homeworld, while another species known as the Gran dominate the eastern continent. In the early age of the Old Republic, Republic scouts set up an outpost on the eastern continent, as Malastare was directly along the Hydian Way trade route in the Mid Rim. The Gran arrived on the planet soon after, establishing their settlements and beginning trade in native natural resources and produce. The Dugs did not take this well, and began a long and brutal war against the Gran. A peace was finally negotiated by the Republic, which sided with the Gran, demilitarizing the Dugs. As a result of their greater numbers, the Gran represented Malastare on the Republic Senate instead of the world's native species, leading to a long-standing antagonism between the two groups. To this day, the Gran largely consider Dugs to be nothing more than subservient laborers.

Dugs' physiology puts them at the extreme fringes of humanoid. Their skin hangs loose over their skeleton, while their ears jut backward like fins, and decorative beads usually dangle from an extra flap of skin near the ears. The center of gravity for their skeletal structure is thrust so high on their short torsos that they literally walk on their upper limbs, with their lower limbs functioning for finer manipulation. This unusual physique may have developed because of their homeworld's high level of gravity. Outwardly, there are few differences between male and female Dugs, who can be differentiated by a large skin flap on the males' throats, which plays a role in their mating rituals.

The Dug method of choosing a mate is noteworthy, hinting that there may be a reptilian ancestry to this humanoid race. During the mating season, the extra folds of skin around the male's neck inflate, displaying an underlying vibrant color. The unpaired females of the clans gather together and inspect the males, searching for one they like. A female will poke, insult, and tease the male she prefers until he responds with a loud, screeching call that deflates his ballooned neck. The pair is then considered mated, and from that moment on they will remain together. While a couple will bully and badger each other throughout their lifetime, Dugs are extremely loyal to their chosen mates and will protect them and their children with passionate violence if they are insulted or attacked.

Despite their physical structure, Dugs

can travel very quickly across land, and they can also move swiftly through trees by leaping and swinging. Their reflexes are exceptionally quick, and many members of their species are experts at Podracing, a dangerous sport that has been illegal in most parts of the galaxy for years. The majority of the buildings on their home planet are towers, with the interiors constructed to feature open platforms. Most other species find their architecture impassable. Although the Dugs are a technologically advanced species, erecting these buildings and other complex structures, many still prefer to live in "tree thorps"—primitive villages set deep in the unsettled wilderness of Malastare.

Dugs are perhaps best known for their foul temperaments, as they are insulting and insolent, and can become violent when crossed. They have been to war with many other species, among them the Gran and the ZeHethbra, a species with colonies in the Malastare system. As previously noted, the Republic called for the Dugs to disarm as a result of their war with the Gran, leaving them extremely bitter. They consider themselves warriors, and being without armaments may have made them even more vicious and brutal. As a species, they are known to harbor grudges for years and even decades. Often, grudges will be upheld by later generations of the same family. We can hypothesize that the perceived slight in being ordered to disarm is considered by the Dug as worthy of a grudge not against an individual, but against the government as a whole. As they are resourceful, they still constructed and carried their own weapons for personal protection—the most notable of which is the b'hedda, a scooped, bladed weapon meant for use while hanging in trees. In the hands of a Dug, the b'hedda is particularly deadly.

Sociologists have theorized that the Dugs' insolent attitude is based in self-pity and insecurity, and that they mask this by trying to improve their status among their peers. Each Dug claims either a real or imagined hero or patriot in his or her ancestry, and the beads they wear in their ear fins are announcements of such heritage. Dugs also increase their own egos by insulting or degrading others.

Dug society is tribal, with various clans claiming territory as their own. These clans, however, are ruled by one Dug, a single king or queen who achieves his or her role through arranged combat. When the ruler dies, the heads of the various clans meet and fight for the empty ruling seat in a no-holds-barred (cheating allowed) battle; elimination occurs through incapacitation or death. Dug leaders who are past

DESIGNATION
Sentient

HOMEWORLD
Malastare

AVERAGE
HEIGHT
1 meter

PRONUNCIATION
Dŭg

the age of fifty may not participate, but they can appoint someone to fight in their stead. This regulation hopefully allows the new leader to rule for a long time.

Once selected, the new ruler is treated with great respect and honor, and is usually the only member of the species who will not receive insults from other Dugs. Assassination and coups are surprisingly rare, most likely because while they are belligerent and grandstanding amid other species, among their own the Dugs recognize their betters.

Dugs are not remarkable galactic explorers, with many actually preferring to remain on Malastare among their own kind. Because of their experience with the Gran, they are xenophobic—or, rather, simply bigoted against other beings. If they are seen in galactic society at all, they are usually in groups of their own, and other species avoid their presence. Frequently these Dugs are criminals or risk-takers, simply out to increase their status among their own by degrading other races through thievery or swindling.

Unfortunately, Malastare has never regained the level of galactic prominence it enjoyed as a center of Podracing during the years of the Old Republic. Although the planet was conquered by the Yuuzhan Vong, it suffered little damage other than the destruction of its industrial base. Some small-scale rebuilding has taken place, such as the reestablishment of methane farms in the Malastare Wastes, which provide a small but steady income for the planet's citizens. This has allowed the Dugs to begin their recovery largely unaided by the Galactic Federation of Free Alliances while official attention has been directed toward worlds where more was lost or rendered uninhabitable. Malastare has sent representatives to the GFFA, but both the native Dugs and the resident Gran remain slightly resentful at their planet's perceived lack of attention by the Galactic Alliance.

NOTABLE APPEARANCE
Episode I: The Phantom Menace

DUROS / NEIMOIDIAN

NEIMOIDIAN

DESIGNATION
Sentient

HOMEWORLD
Neimoidia

AVERAGE HEIGHT
1.8 meters

PRONUNCIATION
Nē-ĭ-moi'-dē-ăn

Along with the Corellians, the Duros are among the oldest known spacefaring peoples. Their entire society evolved around spaceflight, and they helped blaze the hyperspace routes for trade throughout the galaxy.

Duros are tall, thin humanoids with gray-green or bluish purple skin, large red eyes, slit mouths, and no noses. Their sense of smell is conducted through glands beneath their eyes. Other than this, there is only one physical peculiarity that differentiates them from standard humanoids—how they reproduce. Since they are descended from ancient reptiles, Duros lay eggs in a specially prepared nesting room from which their young are born. In this comfortable nursery, the young are nurtured and educated by their parents and other extended-family members.

Since Duros culture centers on space travel, a significant majority of the Duros population lives in six space-station cities that orbit their planet, a Core world on the Corellian Trade Spine. On Duro, droids run farms to feed the population, but the rest of the surface is either polluted wasteland or overgrown jungle. Thousands of years ago, the world was lush and fertile, but after the Duros discovered space travel and left to dwell in orbit above Duro, they neglected the planet, leaving it to fall to ruin. The Empire finished the job, destroying the environment with contamination from its mining operations. During the later years of the New Republic era, however, the Yuuzhan Vong terraformed Duro, creating a rich and verdant ecosystem from which they could strike at Coruscant.

The Duros are incredibly technologically advanced, and build a great deal of the galaxy's spacefaring vessels in their shipyards. In fact, the shipbuilding industry dominates their economy and serves as the world's government. Those who wish to participate in politics are forced to purchase shares of stock in the corporation.

Culturally, Duros' longing for the skies drives many of their young people to become pilots or join starship crews. They constantly gravitate to different spaceports, from which they begin new journeys. To a Duros, the joy is not in where one goes, but in getting there, and they spend a lot of their time just "getting there."

Although one would characterize the Duros species as quiet, they are also very friendly, even-tempered, and love to tell stories. While they have generally pleasant dispositions, there is one way to upset them: to mistake them for Neimoidians. Although the Neimoidians are actually the same genetic species as Duros, having descended from ancient Duro colonists, the Duros are now loath to claim them as their own.

Since Neimoidians are the descendants of early Duros who settled the planet of Neimoidia in the Colonies region, they exhibit many physical attributes of their ancestors. Twenty-four thousand standard years of development in a distinct environment, however, have given them slight facial and body differences. Jawlines are lower; in addition, bodies are thinner and longer. While Duros have blue-purple skin with bright red eyes, Neimoidians have green-gray skin and dark red or pink eyes. These color differences have been attributed to specific chemicals in Neimoidia's atmosphere.

Like Duros, Neimoidians hatch from eggs and grow from a "grub" stage. But Neimoidian young are raised in communal hives from birth, and have access to limited amounts of food. Many die as a result, and those who survive learn to hoard their rations. By the time they leave the hives at age seven, they are extremely fearful of death and extraordinarily greedy.

It is for this reason that they are primarily a race of merchants, not warriors. Rather than fight in a battle where there exists a possibility of dying, Neimoidians will typically surrender, turning and running or sending others to battle for them. This was exemplified by the Trade Federation during the Clone Wars: Neimoidian leaders amassed an army of droids to serve as soldiers, pilots, and fighters.

Neimoidians are commonly seen wearing flowing robes and impressive headgear, every element of which has some special significance, indicating an individual's place in society. They are obsessed with status and influence. Extortion, bribery, and other forms of manipulation are not beyond Neimoidians in their quests for wealth, power, and prestige. They will always try to hide nefarious activities behind an altruistic façade, in order to protect themselves from embarrassment should their schemes fail. Their ability and need to handle funds contributed heavily to their rise to the top of the Trade Federation ranks, a commercial regulatory body that was particularly influential in the years leading up to the Clone Wars.

After centuries of running the Trade Federation, the Neimoidians' control of the organization subsided when the

DESIGNATION
Sentient

HOMEWORLD
Duro

AVERAGE HEIGHT
1.7 meters

PRONUNCIATION
Dŏŏ'-rōs

DUROS

1.5

1.0

.5

0

Republic began taxing the trade routes they had established. This set them back a great deal, and their delicate financial control over the Federation began to crumble. After a particularly humiliating defeat at a trade blockade over the planet of Naboo, the Neimoidians lost whatever reputation they still possessed.

During the Imperial period, bereft of power and position, the Neimoidians turned to a desperate means for regaining their status. Seeing how respected their Duros cousins were in the galaxy, they made overtures to reunite with them as a culture—a proposition that was initially rebuffed. But with the rise of the New Republic, some Duros eventually allowed Neimoidians to work with them in corporate ventures, as they do handle money well. This contact seemed to have a reciprocal effect, influencing Neimoidian culture for the better.

NOTABLE APPEARANCE
DUROS: **Episode IV: A New Hope**
NEIMOIDIAN: **Episode I: The Phantom Menace**

ELOM/ELOMIN

Eloms are short, furry bipeds who reside in the cool desert caves of Elom, a planet located in the Outer Rim. They share the world with the Elomin, a humanoid species that lives aboveground.

With tough skin beneath thick, oily fur, and layers of fat that trap moisture in their bodies, Eloms are especially equipped for life in a harsh desert environment. Their hands and feet end in hard-tipped, hooked claws, optimal for digging; two prehensile toes on each foot can also be used to grip tools. Because they dwell in caves lit only by phosphorescent crystals, Eloms have excellent night vision, although their small, dark eyes cannot tolerate bright light.

Two sharp, rigid tusks protrude from Eloms' mouths, and they possess thick jowls for storing extra food. They are herbivores, primarily feeding on hard-shelled rockmelons and crystalweeds.

Their Elomin neighbors discovered the Eloms during a mining accident. The Elomin had been mining for lommite, an element used for shipbuilding, when the miners dug into an Elom nest, collapsing the cavern. The Elom immediately came to the rescue of the injured miners, earning the wary trust of their befuddled neighbors. After this inadvertent first meeting, the Old Republic soon recognized the Eloms as a sentient species, granting them the rights to the lands that they already inhabited.

This amused the Eloms. A peaceful, unsophisticated people with a strong sense of community, they simply continued living as they had for centuries, in townships known as cseria. Members of cseria would meet annually to resolve problems and disputes, as well as to trade goods. Although the Eloms accepted the Elomin as part of this community, their surface-dwelling neighbors felt that the Eloms did not fit within their "ordered" view of the galaxy, and so the two species remained distant until the Empire took over the mining operations on their planet, enslaving the Elomin and forcing them to mine lommite for the Imperial war machine.

During this time, the Eloms remained hidden from the Empire, but they saw the suffering of the Elomin. Horrified, groups of young Eloms decided to fight for the freedom of their world, liberating many Elomin slaves and bringing them to their safe cities hidden in the labyrinthine underground.

Since the world was liberated at the conclusion of the Galactic Civil War, the two species have become more integrated, and adolescent Eloms have frequently left to seek their fortunes among the stars. Unfortunately, many have also become criminals. Those Eloms who depart their homeworld do so because they are ambitious and intelligent, but they can often become lonely. Ignorant of the ways of the galaxy, they then fall in with the wrong crowd.

However, criminal behavior on the part of Eloms may also have other, more scientifically valid explanations. It is thought that Eloms who leave their home planet develop sociopathic tendencies as a result of physiological changes brought on by being away from fellow Eloms, and from their cave habitats. An alternative hypothesis is that Elom take on these tendencies psychologically through prolonged absence from their communities. This point of view has some evidence in the preferences of Eloms serving during the Galactic Civil War and in the New Republic military, who often sought to work directly with other members of their own species.

Meanwhile, the Eloms' neighbors, the Elomin, are tall, thin humanoids with pointed ears and four small horns topping their heads. They are believed by many anthropologists to be somehow related to the Zabrak, a spacefaring species that colonized numerous worlds in its extremely long and varied history.

When Old Republic scouts arrived on Elom about one hundred standard years before the dawn of Imperial rule, the Elomin were a relatively primitive people who employed slugthrowing weapons and combustion engines. Their lack of technology has prompted certain anthropologists to believe their inhabitation of Elom was the result of an accident—for if they are indeed descended from the Zabrak, the Elomin had long since forgotten how to build or create more modern technology. But contact with the Old Republic immediately influenced their industrial development, and they were soon constructing starships, repulsorlift vehicles, and high-end mining equipment. The Elomin allowed a shipbuilding corporation to establish itself on their world to mine lommite, an element used in making transparisteel for starships.

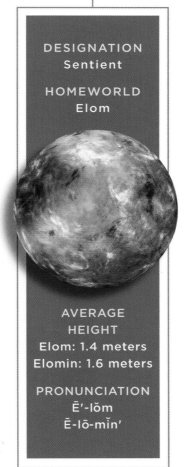

DESIGNATION
Sentient

HOMEWORLD
Elom

AVERAGE
HEIGHT
Elom: 1.4 meters
Elomin: 1.6 meters

PRONUNCIATION
Ē'-lŏm
Ē-lō-mĭn'

Culturally, the Elomin aspire to find or create order in all things. Originally, they had no notion that another, completely different species might share their world. Even when an expedition uncovered cave formations in a distant desert region that showed evidence of being inhabited, the Elomin refused to accept the implications and omitted these findings from their reports. Only when a group of them came face-to-face with Eloms during the mining accident did they finally recognize the existence of their neighbors.

Elomin art reflects order, in that it is repetitive and mathematically structured. Their architecture is predictable and well thought out, as are the layouts of their cities; nothing they construct or create is left to chance.

As such, like the Eloms, Elomin have some difficulty dealing with other peoples, whom they often view as perpetrators of chaos or unpredictable variables. Old Republic representatives discovered that the Elomin had difficulty working in integrated space crews but excelled at navigation and piloting duties, perceiving the universe as a logical, organized puzzle and endeavoring to bring the pieces to their proper places.

After the fall of the Empire, the Elomin rewarded their neighbors with a level of unprecedented acceptance into their communities, as the Eloms had helped many of them escape Imperial slavery. Yielding some of their sense of order to accept the kindly Eloms as helpers and fellow residents was a significant but necessary step for their growth as a people. Eloms now work within the Elomin cities, helping run businesses and lommite-mining corporations. Some Eloms have actually moved from their caves completely to take up residences aboveground. As different as these two species are, they have become quite fond and protective of each other overall—an encouraging sign for the rest of the civilized galaxy as they move forward together into the future.

EOPIE

Eopies are quadruped pack mammals native to Tatooine. They are proboscidians, with hinged skulls supporting flexible, elongated snouts and sharp incisors in their jaws. While not as frequently employed as the faster-moving ronto, bantha, or dewback (all animals capable of carrying heavier loads), the eopie's sure-footedness and untiring steadfastness have made it a popular beast of burden on Tatooine,

3.0

2.0

1.5

1.0

.5

0

particularly in the Mos Espa region. It can be argued that overall it is Tatooine's most useful indigenous animal.

Eopies have several physical features that contribute to their excellence as work beasts in the arid wastes of Tatooine. First, their three-toed feet make them extremely sturdy, and their foot pads expand upon impact for shock absorption. Eopies rarely stumble in the sandy or rocky terrain, and are so well balanced that they are nearly impossible to topple, even when carrying heavy loads. Their knees are greatly calloused to protect their joints against the desert sand. Eopies also require little water, going for weeks without it if necessary. Herbivores, their snouts are ideal for rooting for sand lichens, their primary source of nourishment, and for eliminating potential weeds from moisture-farming lands, as such weeds will drain much-needed moisture and cut down on profits.

Eopie hides are very tough, resilient to sun and heat. Covered with thin sparse hair, the leather tanned from their hides is highly durable, and locals like to use it for making saddles or clothing to resist the twin suns' rays, as it reflects light rather than retaining it.

Although they are frequently grumpy, these creatures are fairly even-tempered. Unlike rontos, eopies rarely, if ever, startle, and will study unusual situations with a sense of interest or curiosity. They will only flee if they are personally threatened; otherwise they tend to remain calm and still, even during noisy or disruptive events. However, on the rare occasion that an eopie is surprised, it will spit its undigested stomach contents at people nearby. Fortunately, this does not happen often, and thus the creatures' reliability and stability is highly prized—for while they may be slow, one can always be sure of eopies' fortitude in fearful situations. They are completely unfazed by sandstorms, for example, keeping a steady gait in the most fierce and biting of desert winds.

Eopies are very social animals, congregating in large herds of twenty or more. They gather in herds as a means of protecting their young, which are especially vulnerable to the harsh desert environment. Although able to walk within minutes of birth, young eopies are not able to bear the heavy loads that their parents can and are therefore less valuable to their owners. In addition, eopie babies require food more often than adults, and are more at risk from predators, so they require much attention and some measure of protection. If well cared for, eopies mature to adulthood in approximately six standard years, and can live for as many

as ninety. Eopie mares have one baby a season, and are capable of bearing young for decades, although they will not conceive in consecutive seasons. The purchase of one or two quality breeding mares is sufficient for most farms to start establishing their own herds. Toward the end of their lives when they are no longer able to carry heavy loads, eopies continue to serve Tatooine farmers by eating the desert weeds that leach moisture from their crop, and are also popular as pets. Many settlers will give their children an eopie from the family's herd in order to teach them responsibility, and to prepare them for their own future lives as farmers.

Even with the requirement that an owner must have more than one eopie in order for the creatures to thrive, eopies are the least expensive of Tatooine's beasts of burden to keep. The adults eat little and require only a modest amount of attention to stay healthy, and they provide more benefits than just what they can carry. For instance, in addition to their service as pack animals, eopies are sometimes bred for their meat. Their flesh is extremely tender and tasty, and therefore is a staple for residents of Tatooine. Eopie females also provide a nourishing milk that is renowned for its nutritional benefits to humanoid infants and toddlers. The milk does spoil quickly if not kept cold, and farmers who own eopies must invest in adequate refrigeration machines.

The usefulness of eopies has led some entrepreneurs to attempt to export them to other planets. Unfortunately, these efforts have met with mixed success. Eopies are able to thrive on other desert planets and also on some overly warm worlds, but it has become apparent that they have evolved such that they biologically need heat. Temperate planets necessitate slightly more care for eopies; they must be housed in enclosed, heated holding pens at night and when temperatures fall seasonally, for instance. Eopies are not able to survive outdoors on colder planets at all, even if provided with adequate sustenance and attention. These eopies appear to starve to death, suggesting that their bodies cannot properly metabolize food in lower temperatures, although officially this has not yet been scientifically tested.

DESIGNATION
Nonsentient

HOMEWORLD
Tatooine

AVERAGE
LENGTH
2–3 meters

PRONUNCIATION
Ē-ō'-pē

NOTABLE APPEARANCE
Episode I: The Phantom Menace

EWOK

Ewoks are small, fur-covered, ursine beings who inhabit the forest moon of Endor, an Outer Rim world circling a gas giant system near the area of the galaxy known as the Unknown Regions. While Imperial propaganda depicted them as having been wiped out after the Battle of Endor, the intelligent, primitive Ewoks still live in sizable communities in their wooded home, a lush environment alive with thick vegetation and myriad forms of wildlife. The world's low axial tilt and its regular orbit around the gas giant create a temperate climate for most of the moon, and three-hundred-meter-tall trees cover many regions and are central to the landscape. For this reason, they are significant to Ewok culture and religion.

Though Ewoks suffer from limited eyesight, these small creatures have an excellent sense of smell that more than compensates. They are accomplished hunters, and, being omnivores, they also gather food from the plants that surround them. In some cases they have been known to mistakenly eat sentient beings, assuming they were simply large game to be captured. However, they can usually be convinced to put away their cooking implements after some conversation and a little bit of luck.

While they forage and hunt, Ewoks are extremely alert and easily startled. Many carnivorous creatures inhabit the forest moon, and thus Ewoks are always prepared for an attack. Some researchers have noted that they seem to possess a "sixth sense"—the ability to perceive threats to their community far in advance. It has

1.5

1.0

.5

0

been likened to some Jedi Force talents, although only a few Ewoks have shown the ability to truly manipulate this mysterious power.

Ewoks are curious, good-natured creatures who value community, family, and friendship. Their culture is gender-based, with the males serving as hunters, warriors, chieftains, and shamans, and the females acting as gatherers and domestics, rearing and educating their young. Music and dancing are part of everyday life; in fact, Ewoks use music to communicate with other villages via rhythmic drumbeats. As news echoes through the ancient trees, it imbues their environment with an aura of extra life.

Though their culture is rich in historic lore, art, and music, Ewoks are primitive, wearing only hoods adorned with bones and feathers for decoration and to indicate status in the community. They learn quickly, however, and when exposed to technology, they will figure it out easily—sometimes after an initial bout of jitters and mistakes. Few have yet ventured into space, and when they do it is typically by tagging along with star pilots or crews that visit their planet. Among these few are a select number who have learned modern technology enough to be useful on space crews.

Ewoks have developed no technology of their own beyond standard woodworking tools and rudimentary weapons. But they possess a flair for invention with their primitive resources—creating traps and snares that can be highly effective even against great technological threats. Their ingenuity was key to the Rebel Alliance's defeat of the Empire at the Battle of Endor, and if given leave to explore and learn the ways of technology, they will frequently become adept.

The language of this species is expressive yet simple, and can be learned and spoken by humans. Because the verbal nuances are similar, Ewoks can also learn to speak several human languages. And through their exposure to more and more offworlders since the Battle of Endor, many homebound Ewoks have taken to speaking to visitors in a pidgin form of Ewok-Basic.

Ewoks live in tribal clusters in villages built of mud, thatch, and wood, normally suspended several levels above the forest floor. Located at the center of the villages are the largest structures, including the home of the tribal chief, with the dwellings of tribe members arranged in clusters at the outskirts. Intricate walkways serve to join together residences and village squares, and stairs, rope ladders, and swinging vines help the Ewoks to get quickly from the forest floor

DESIGNATION
Sentient

HOMEWORLD
Moon of Endor

AVERAGE HEIGHT
1.2 meters

PRONUNCIATION
Ē'-wŏk

to their homes in the trees. Some Ewoks also reside on Endor's lakes, in floating villages constructed on stilts. Ewoks are frequently attacked by angry Phlogs, the giant Gorax, and the fearsome Duloks because of their small size, so they are often very hesitant about venturing into new territory or leaving their villages unguarded.

The Ewok people are suspicious and cautious, yet fierce fighters, brave and loyal to their tribe. This is also evidenced in their religion, which emphasizes the importance of home, family, and the trees surrounding them. A new tree is planted for each Ewok at birth, and is considered that being's "life tree." Ewoks believe that their spirits pass into these trees when they die. Moreover, Ewoks regard these trees as their guardians, and in times of crisis, the tribal leaders will commune with the oldest and wisest trees, seeking guidance. The trees, they believe, are intelligent, long-lived beings who watch over them, and in a reciprocal manner they must safeguard the trees. This belief was one of the main reasons that they aided the Rebels in their fight against the Empire, as they felt that the Empire posed a threat to every aspect of their environment.

War is not common among the Ewoks, however. Although they exist in tribes and remain fiercely loyal to them, Ewoks will greet other tribes with warmth and goodwill, as long as they act with honor and respect. They will even accept outsiders into their tribe if the visitors demonstrate a familial loyalty to them (if the strangers haven't already been mistaken for dinner). Although as skilled at building weaponry as they are at constructing their elaborate villages, arms are mainly kept handy to defend against outside threats, rather than against one another.

Because religion is so important to Ewok society, the village shaman governs a tribe side by side with the ruling chieftain. The shaman interprets signs to guide the chieftain in his decisions, and their belief system includes references to a living energy similar to the Force that feeds the trees and likewise strengthens and guides the Ewoks.

NOTABLE APPEARANCE
Episode VI: Return of the Jedi

FALLEEN

The Falleen are a reptilian humanoid species that occupy the Falleen star system in the Mid Rim of the galaxy. They are a handsome species, exotic in appearance, with scaled, blue-green skin and a spiny sharp ridge down the center of their backs. This ridge is indicative of their reptilian nature, as is their ability to change skin color and lung capacity, enabling them to remain underwater for long periods of time. Female Falleen look slightly different from their male counterparts in that the spinal ridge is smaller, their skin is often lighter, and the ability to change color is somewhat less active than in their male counterparts.

Unlike most reptilian species, Falleen can and will grow hair on their heads. The females like to wear their tresses long and adorned with combs and beads, while the males display their hair tied up in a single braid or topknot. In recent years, some females have taken to wearing topknots, in an effort to attain the same elevated status as the males.

Falleen are considered aesthetically pleasing to most humanoids. Although their physique is well defined and attractive, this admiration is not solely due to their appearance. Like Zeltrons, Falleen can exude pheromones at will and use them to control and manipulate the perceptions of others. Falleen pheromones are actually so powerful that they can produce an almost hypnotic effect in other humanoid species, and these manipulations have been known to take on lustful overtones. Pheromones may also be exercised between Falleen as communications tools, although they will always suspect duplicity and remain disciplined to resist the suggestions of others. A Falleen's skin color shifts with the release of these pheromones. Falleen utilize their ability to change skin color as a covert weapon, reverting from their normal shades of gray-green to red or orange, for example, in order to exude an essence of confidence or mastery. In addition to their pheromones, Falleen can exude allelochemical transmitters to produce specific emotional reactions in other species with similar body chemistry, such as fear, desire, anger, doubt, and confusion.

What also makes the Falleen species attractive is the aura of mystery in which they have wrapped themselves. They are not a talkative people, and tend to be distant, maintaining a great deal of control over their physiology. Culturally, they remain stoic, and shun outward signs of passion and anger. The Falleen are not an unemotional people; quite the contrary. They are known for intense feelings, beliefs, and emotions. Falleen simply find public displays of feelings, particularly to non-Falleen, as extremely primitive and unsophisticated. As a result, the Falleen regard beings who do express their emotions, such as humans, to be inferior.

While the Falleen have employed space travel technology for generations, they rarely venture to the stars. Because they consider the Falleen system to be a bastion of culture and sophistication, they prefer to manage their own affairs on their homeworld, rather than deal with offworlders. Their music, sculpture, art, and architecture are all a source of pride for them, although such things are very rarely shared with outsiders.

Falleen society is feudal, with noble houses ruling lower classes of artisans, technical workers, general workers, and slaves. Monarch rulers govern their kingdoms, caring more for internal political intrigues and displays of wealth than wasting resources by waging war against one another. These kings maintain commerce with each other and occasionally argue over boundaries, although such disputes are never taken to extremes. Thus, for the most part, the Falleen remain a peaceful people.

The Falleen are a long-lived species, living 250 standard years on the average, although some healthy Falleen have been known to survive for up to 400 years. Young Falleen nobles will sometimes spend part of their adolescent years on what is called a pilgrimage, which is basically a journey to tour the galaxy and experience all it has to offer. Most of them return to utilize what they have learned in order to govern their kingdoms when the time comes for them to ascend to the throne.

DESIGNATION
Sentient

HOMEWORLD
Falleen

AVERAGE
HEIGHT
1.6 meters

PRONUNCIATION
Fäl-lēn'

One such Falleen was Xizor, who arrived back from his pilgrimage to find his entire family dead. The Sith Lord Darth Vader had ordered a biological weapons laboratory to be built in Xizor's home city, and a lab accident contaminated the area, allowing the release of a flesh-rotting bacterium for which there was no cure. Subsequently, in order to protect the planet's other inhabitants and to ease his own embarrassment, Vader ordered that the city and its two hundred thousand beings be burned to ashes.

From that point on, Xizor had a deep desire for revenge against the Dark Lord. Xizor hid his family history, departing his world to seek this retribution. He joined the Black Sun crime syndicate and quickly rose to power, seizing the opportunity created when most of Black Sun's upper-level personnel were killed by Darth Maul. Eventually, Xizor became what was arguably the third most powerful being in the galaxy, after the Emperor and Darth Vader—an unlikely accomplishment for a nonhuman during the Empire's rule. Xizor plotted to kill Vader, take his place, and then that of the Emperor. His ambitions, however, led to his death at the hands of the man he hated most, when he proved threatening to Vader's son, Luke Skywalker.

One more environmental disaster after the one that killed Xizor's family finally convinced the Falleen to remove themselves from galactic involvement. An orbital turbolaser strike laid waste to a small city and the surrounding countryside, and the Imperial Navy cut off system contact. For this reason, during the rule of the New Republic, the Falleen were rarely seen traveling outside their system, and displayed no desire to join the fledgling government. Following the invasion of their planet by the Yuuzhan Vong, there has been even less contact with this exotic species.

NOTABLE APPEARANCE
Shadows of the Empire (novel)

FOSH

The Fosh are a mysterious avian species that most scientists believe hail from the Corporate Sector of the galaxy. They are an extremely rare species and are believed to be nearly, if not in fact, extinct, as in recent years only one Fosh has actually been observed in person. It is possible that the species was among those exterminated during the reign of Emperor Palpatine. Much of what can be reported is reconstructed from the historical records of various other cultures and societies, and from experiences with the infamous Fosh Jedi, Vergere.

These bird-like people have thin torsos and delicate arms with four-fingered hands that appear to have evolved from wings. Considering the degree of development in the bones of their arms, it is unlikely that Fosh have possessed the ability to fly for tens of thousands of years. Fosh's delicate frames make them extremely vulnerable to physical blows, so they tend to remain clear of such confrontations, though they can apparently defend themselves quite well. The weakest part of their body is the neck, which they will reflexively guard during combat.

Two corkscrew antennae adorn the top of their heads, the use of which remains a mystery. Their skulls are further crowned with a feather-lined ridge that changes color depending on their mood. Green indicates inquisitiveness, thoughtfulness, or amusement; orange displays happiness; and gray is anger, disgust, irritation, or gravity. Their faces are concave, and are highlighted with slanted eyes and soft whiskers. Like many birds, their leg joints bend backward, and their flay-toed feet give them remarkable jumping abilities.

It is believed that one of the most unusual traits of the Fosh is the chemical makeup of their tears. Female Fosh, in particular, have lachrymal glands that enable them to alter their tears and produce several kinds of pheromonal substances that affect the males of their species during mating. And yet, through the Force, the Jedi Vergere had such control over her tear production that she could create a wide variety of chemical liquids, be it a substance that healed disease or a highly effective poison. As a curative, Vergere's tears were more powerful than bacta, alleviating diseases that the latter could not.

The Fosh are a very private people who prefer to remain unnoticed as they make their way in the galaxy. They speak little, preferring to focus on listening, but when they do talk it is on issues of great importance. They also choose to frequently conceal themselves, remaining hidden in large crowds or in secreted spots, and some sociologists believe part of the reason that people assume there are so few Fosh is because they are rarely seen. Instead of being limited in population, they may simply *seem* rare because they would rather stay clear of the public eye.

One characteristic that is evident from the writings of other species regarding the Fosh is their preoccupation with political intrigue. Similar to Bothans in this regard, Fosh are fascinated with creating plots within plots in order to attain complex or even very simple goals. They tend to be indirect in their requests toward others, speaking in a way that can purposely confuse or send an individual down the wrong path of thinking. They seem to find some great amusement

in watching others chase after phantom threats, or in causing utter confusion in various species.

Theirs is a very self-serving and self-occupied people who act with only their own best interests at heart. While they may interact with others in a way that seems generous or friendly, there is nearly always an ulterior motive to their behavior. Unlike Bothans, however, Fosh are not paranoid of other species, and in fact they do not believe the victims of their double-talk capable of figuring out their plans or foiling their plots. The Fosh are, in effect, bigoted—believing themselves intellectually superior to others, and manipulating them as objects of amusement. They are wise enough, though, to respect most species for the dangers that they can present, and are vigilant in their dealings with them.

One example of Fosh manipulation is the way Vergere skillfully maneuvered her way through the brutal Yuuzhan Vong hierarchy, managing to survive for decades within their presence, until they reached the Core Worlds of the galaxy. Though some of her behavior may have called her motivations into question, much of it is believed to be cultural—or perhaps her cultural upbringing resulted in her acceptance of Yuuzhan Vong doctrine much more easily. Either way, she utilized her wiles and conversational subterfuge to simultaneously train and manipulate Jedi Knight Jacen Solo, causing him to seek out alternate Force traditions and even question the existence of the dark side of the Force, arguing that there is no dark or light, only one's intentions. Some speculate that this may have been her goal from the moment she first encountered him, and while many initially believed her death toward the end of the Yuuzhan Vong invasion to be a self-sacrifice, in light of the revelation of her influence, her sacrificial act could very well have been a self-serving one—a penultimate deed of manipulation that would further maneuver a growing uncertainty in the young Jacen Solo.

DESIGNATION
Sentient

HOMEWORLD
Unknown

AVERAGE
HEIGHT
1.3 meters

PRONUNCIATION
Fŏsh

NOTABLE APPEARANCE
Traitor (novel)

GAMORREAN

Gamorreans are large, green-skinned, porcine creatures from the preindustrial Outer Rim planet Gamorr, known for their brutal strength and warrior-like nature. They are bulky beings with pig-like snouts, jowls, and tusks, and the males have horns on their heads. Members of this species communicate with one another through a series of grunts, oinks, and squeals—a complex language that suits their war-like sensibility. Although they can understand offworld languages, the formation of their voice boxes makes it impossible for them to pronounce words in any language other than their own. The exception to this is the Gamorrean Voort "Piggy" saBinring. After being genetically enhanced to have exceptionally high intelligence, saBinring joined the New Republic as a pilot and was fitted with a high-tech voice box that enabled him to speak to other pilots in his squadron.

The Gamorrean clan-based matriarchal culture centers on war and the preparation for war. In their society, males are taught the arts of combat and weaponry from early childhood, and as adolescents, they will go immediately into battle. Females, on the other hand, take care of all the other necessities of life—they hunt, fish, weave, make weapons, and run businesses. They also form the clan's governing body as the Council of Matrons. These women make the decisions of when to go to war, and against whom. Generally, Gamorrean women consider Gamorrean males, and males in general, to be of lower intelligence and not to be trusted with decision making of any kind.

The campaigning season, or "war season" as it is sometimes called, begins in early spring and runs through late autumn on Gamorr. During these months, the males of the clans will wage war upon one another at the behest of their matrons—attacking tribal homes and bringing back the spoils to please their females. The males who are the most successful and valiant win the right to choose any females they desire for mates. Those males who do not succeed are often killed in battle, and this becomes the culture's own form of natural selection. Ordinarily, this practice might make for an imbalance in the ratio of males to females in a society, but reliable population estimates conclude that twenty males are born for every female Gamorrean.

Gamorreans take great pleasure in slaughter and brutality. It is for this reason, as well as for their brute strength, that they make ideal mercenaries and bounty hunters. They are so enthusiastic about violence that they are even willing to serve as slaves if it gives them more opportunities to fight.

Although many Gamorreans work as hired muscle for offworld employers, there are two stipulations that must be met before they will agree to labor for someone. First, the employer, or the employer's representative, must fight them or one of their peers; second, the contract must then be signed in blood. Evidence of a typical Gamorrean's service to an employer was the presence of Gamorreans among the guard at Jabba the Hutt's palace on Tatooine during the Imperial era. Having been sent by Jabba to secure Gamorreans to work for him, Han Solo and Chewbacca found themselves faced with the possibility of personally battling the Gamorreans. Fortunately, Solo and Chewbacca were traveling with a group of Nikto already in Jabba's employ, who were all too glad to serve as Jabba's champions. After some difficult and somewhat bloody negotiations, the contract was signed.

Once these two conditions are met, the Gamorreans serve their employer with unwavering loyalty, though they will retreat from foes who prove to be more powerful than themselves. Showing fear or running as an act of self-preservation is not considered cowardice against an indomitable foe—the species considers such reactions natural. True cowardice, to a Gamorrean, is shirking from a fight against an equal or subordinate. Gamorreans will usually kill any fellow warrior who shows such a weakness.

When Gamorreans engage in combat, they prefer traditional weapons such as swords, battle-axes, and heavy maces. The arg'garok, a traditional Gamorrean war ax, is especially prized. This weapon is engineered for wielders of extraordinary strength and low centers of gravity,

DESIGNATION
Sentient

HOMEWORLD
Gamorr

AVERAGE HEIGHT
1.8 meters

PRONUNCIATION
Gă-mōr'-rē-ăn

and non-Gamorreans can handle one only with great difficulty. Gamorreans have learned to use blasters over the years, but high-tech ranged weapons are not implemented in the battles on Gamorr, and are considered cowardly. Still, Gamorreans employed as mercenaries often carry imported weapons and are well versed in their use, frequently spending the credits that they earn to buy more technologically advanced weaponry. However, the most advanced arms they might possess would typically amount to a high-tech vibroblade or specialty heads for their axes, such as ones containing ultrasonic generators. They do take up space travel, though, and have even colonized another world known as Pzob. They keep their ships simple, providing only the basic amenities for their crew, as well as protective shields and heavy blasters and torpedoes that serve as a means of self-defense.

While the Gamorrean people are not known for having a soft, sensitive side, they do exhibit an unusual affection when it comes to their morrts. Morrts are furry parasites that feed on blood and other biological materials. They attach themselves to a Gamorrean's body, and remain there for years at a time. Gamorreans look upon morrts lovingly as pets, and prestigious Gamorreans are often seen with twenty or more attached to their bodies at one time. They are also loving with their children and mates, and signs of affection can vacillate between a warm, tackling hug to a punch in the snout. In fact, knocking one's spouse unconscious is considered a prelude to mating, although if this is the intention, the initiator makes sure to have smelling salts on his or her person.

With Gamorrean society organized into clans, loyalty to such groups and their matrons is paramount. Even if they are contracted to a specific employer, Gamorreans will maintain their family pride and loyalty to the point of picking fights with those of other clans who serve the same employer. A wise boss will hire only from one clan to prevent such infighting in the ranks. On Gamorr, the clans have never united under a common banner of government, though they do have regular meetings to discuss trade or threaten war. Because they lack a unified political voice, their homeworld of Gamorr does not have representation in the Galactic Federation of Free Alliances.

NOTABLE APPEARANCE
Episode VI: Return of the Jedi

GAND

Gands are beings believed to be of an insect genus that inhabit a world also known as Gand, located in the Outer Rim near the Centrality. They are short humanoids identified in part by their three-fingered hands and durable exoskeleton. Because Gands refuse to be studied, their common physiological traits largely remain a mystery to xenobiologists. Nearly a dozen different physical varieties of the species have been recorded, however, through encounters with them throughout the galaxy.

The planet Gand's ecology is extremely inhospitable for other humanoid species because of giant ammonia clouds that fill the atmosphere. To account for this, all Gands have a very unique respiratory system, and most Gands do not breathe at all. They exchange gases in their body by in-

gesting food and passing waste gases through their powerful exoskeletons. There are some Gands who breathe, but they only inhale ammonia, and when off-planet they must wear a special suit with a breathing apparatus that supplies them with this ammonia in specifically regulated amounts. Nonbreathing Gands do not require such suits, but sometimes wear them anyway while traveling offworld to maintain anonymity. Scientists do not know if the ammonia-breathing Gand species is older than the nonbreathing variety and represents an evolutionary adaptation, or if it is simply another coexisting species.

For most members of the Gand species, only a minimal amount of sleep is required to function normally. As this is common throughout the Gand varieties, scientists believe this may be a result of culture rather than breeding. Some sociologists suppose that the trait is really due to the culture's values, as remaining awake and aware is a valuable skill to hunters and findsmen—one that must be honed and learned throughout a lifetime.

The planet Gand's most notable export is the skills of its findsmen. Findsmen are religious hunters who locate their prey by interpreting omens sent to them in the course of divine rituals. While many offworlders disavow the power of findsmen's rituals, their accuracy can be unsettling to the casual observer. Some findsman sects require that their pupils go through chemical baths or genetic tampering that cause knob-like growths to appear on their chitinous exoskeletons. Findsmen use these four- to five-centimeter growths as weapons during hand-to-hand combat.

Throughout the galaxy, findsmen are hired as security advisers, bodyguards, bounty hunters, investigators, and, on occasion, assassins. They can be identified by their use of the shockprod staff, which appears as a normal staff ending in a V-shaped pair of electrically charged prods. Findsmen who have achieved some level of accomplishment can sometimes earn the right to carry rare Gand dischargers, which are staffs capable of stunning or killing an opponent.

The Gand culture is complex. They are considered by most offworlders to be the humblest of people because they are usually soft-spoken and polite. This characteristic is a result of societal demands that an individual's identity be earned. They primarily refer to themselves in the third person; then, depending on what status they've gained, Gands may or may not refer to themselves by name. A Gand who has only reached the first level of status would refer to him- or herself as simply *Gand*. Once a Gand has made a major accomplishment in life, either at home or abroad, that individual may use the family name; only when Gands have become masters of some skill or achieved high praise or recognition may they finally use their first as well as their last name.

Even then, Gands very rarely refer to themselves in the first person. Only those who have become janwuine—in other words, those who have been judged to have accomplished the greatest feats of heroism or who have completed extremely difficult tasks—may use self-identifying pronouns

DESIGNATION
Sentient

HOMEWORLD
Gand

AVERAGE HEIGHT
1.6 meters

PRONUNCIATION
Gănd

such as *I* or *me*. Doing so presumes that they are so prominent, everyone knows their name. Such an honor must be bestowed by the ruetsavii, a group of Gands who travel the galaxy verifying the deeds of findsmen. Dispatched by the Elders of Gand, the ruetsavii have achieved renown through their own actions and are considered able to judge the deeds of others.

If Gands believe they have acted wrongly, they feel that such an action reduces any accomplishments that they have made in their life. When this happens, they use "name reduction" to show penitence. For example, Gands who have previously earned the right to the family name might revert to the use of *Gand* in order to gain the forgiveness of someone they have offended. There have been very few Gands who have committed such unspeakable acts that they leave the society entirely. When this happens, they must discard their culture, and their culture discards them. After this, they may refer to themselves in any way they wish. For some Gands, failing to achieve the status of a findsman can cause them to abandon their culture.

While many Gands do leave their world, as findsmen or in disgrace, non-Gands are seldom, if ever, welcomed on the planet Gand itself. Outsiders usually get no closer than one of the orbiting space stations. If they are allowed on the surface, they must remain in a specified area called the Alien Quarters, centered in the spaceports. The very few who have been allowed into the culture itself have done so under the sponsorship of janwuine or the ruetsavii. A sponsored non-Gand would be accepted into society as hinwuine—a being of standing. When the New Republic Gand pilot Ooryl Qrygg was granted janwuine status, his fellow pilots were afforded a rare honor and invited to Gand to mark the occasion, although it is unclear whether they were also made hinwuine. Scientists made limited attempts to interview some of the hinwuine, but so far, no requests for such dialogues have been granted. It may be that to speak of their time on Gand would be considered a serious insult to their hosts.

NOTABLE APPEARANCE
Episode V: The Empire Strikes Back

GEONOSIAN

Geonosians are the only advanced life-form native to the barren, rock-laden world of Geonosis, located only a parsec away from the famed desert world of Tatooine in the Outer Rim. Geonosians are a winged, flying insectoid race sporting elongated faces, multijointed limbs, and a hard, brown chitinous exoskeleton that protects them from the radiation bombardment of a nearby star that has rendered their world a red-tinted desert wasteland. One subspecies of this group is wingless, and its members serve the flying species as drone workers.

Like most insects, Geonosians begin life as eggs laid by a queen. Once a pupa hatches, it is trained and acculturated to serve in its assigned role in society. Within the warrior hives, for instance, soldier pupae grow to adult size quickly, and are ready to fight by the age of six. Adult Geonosian warriors have vestigial wings that enable them to hover for short intervals, while younger, lighter warriors can fly greater distances and are used for scouting missions.

A ring of small metal-rich asteroids encircles their planet. These asteroids are an enormous resource for raw materials used in the weapons manufacturing process, an activity that has made the Geonosians infamous. The asteroid ring is a mixed blessing, however, as it can also serve as an excellent cover for corporate spies entering the world's atmosphere, who are hidden by frequently falling asteroids and meteor showers. In addition, a dense, high-altitude fog enshrouds a large majority of the planet, creating almost night-like conditions that can last for weeks. As a result of this, and of the barrage of radiation, many of the creatures on the world are bioluminescent, and most—even the Geonosians—remain underground despite their resistance to the environmental conditions.

The Geonosian people were well known in the pre-Imperial era for their construction of battle droids, ships, and weapons technology, the use of which peaked during the Clone Wars. They first created battle droids for the Trade Federation, then expanded their enterprise to supply a growing Separatist movement led by Count Dooku. As such, except for those visiting on business, Geonosis is not a popular world for tourists.

Geonosian society is divided into a class system that evolved over thousands of years from the hive mentality of the species' insect ancestors. It is separated into two levels: the aristocrats and the warriors. Those who are flightless have no caste at all, and are considered without any value save for their use in menial labor. The workers run the manufacturing operations, and the warriors fight and defend the interests of the aristocrats. Although the warriors are fighters, they are not members of a standing army.

A subcaste of warrior pilots are trained to require no sleep. From infancy, they are paired with a specific flight computer with whom they build a unique, integrated rapport. And yet, while all of these warriors are well taught and intelligent, they lack the ingenuity found in many other sentient species, and can be easily defeated in battle by another group possessing superior creativity and wits.

The aristocrats rule and command all the operations on Geonosis. These nobles feel it is their right to govern while thousands of workers labor to serve their every whim. It was the noble class that envisioned and sparked the construction of the complex, organic architectural realm in which they all live. Based on structures built by their insect forebears in the wild, the Geonosians created refined, spire-like buildings that are highly impressive to most outsiders. Geonosians reside within these organic-looking structures in hive communities.

The worker drones, meanwhile, have almost no rights, and serve their masters without question. Workers are genetically altered to serve in three distinct subcastes in order to fill the many roles within the hive, namely those of servants, laborers, and farmers.

The Geonosian civilization is a bloodthirsty one, enthusiastically encouraging execution in gladiatorial arenas. Sociologists believe the harshness of Geonosians' environment, coupled with the rigid structure of their caste system, led to this form of barbaric cultural development. They seem to find brutality amusing, as thousands of Geonosians congregate in execution arenas to watch condemned individuals die gruesome deaths in the teeth of fearsome beasts or at the hands of other doomed prisoners.

The aristocracy thinks nothing of executing worker drones in the arena, particularly if they prove problematic to

DESIGNATION
Sentient

HOMEWORLD
Geonosis

AVERAGE HEIGHT
1.75 meters

PRONUNCIATION
Gē-ō-nō'-sē-ăn

the system. For most drones, doing their work and living in their communal environment is all they can hope for. Worker drones have no personal living space or possessions of their own, and to conserve resources, the ruling class may order drones into suspended animation or sleep stasis when their services are not required. Geonosian workers of higher intelligence use gladiatorial combat as their one means to move up in status and possibly escape their plight in the service of their masters. Considered aberrations, warrior Geonosians enter the arena willingly. There, they are often pitted in fatal games against additional Geonosians, other sentient species, or savage creatures. If the worker wins a battle, or lives to see another day, he or she is often granted life and exiled, but may find refuge at the Galard Stables. Sometime a victorious Geonosian may even move up in status, receiving acclaim and financial rewards.

Another role that workers can earn, even those who are flightless, is to serve as a picador in the gladiatorial arena, using energy pikes to control and goad vicious creatures into attacking combatants. They are also responsible for removing any bodies that are not devoured. Either way, if they earn enough prestige and wealth, they may be able to escape Geonosis entirely.

Even so, those Geonosians who can leave their world rarely do, because the hive mentality is so strong. Those who depart often show a certain amount of contempt for other species, and they cannot disconnect themselves from the hive mentality. It is a culturewide sense of xenophobia that often leads them into conflict with outsiders. Those Geonosians seen around the galaxy usually work together in groups, and send home the fruits of their labors to their hives on Geonosis.

While the Geonosians have accomplished masterful feats of engineering and managed massive construction efforts, they appear to most observers to be rather simple-minded. Many Geonosians were, in fact, easily absorbed into the Kilik hive mind during the Colony's recent expansion across the galaxy. Sociologists theorize, however, that this outcome, too, was a result of their insect ancestry: much of the Geonosians' collective intelligence is considered to be held by the leadership of the hive, a mentality that is ingrained from infancy.

NOTABLE APPEARANCE
Episode II: Attack of the Clones

GIVIN

Givin are a humanoid species who have the appearance of animated skeletons—and their frames are indeed located on the outsides of their bodies. Their appendages are long, thin, and tubular, and they possess large, triangular eye sockets and frowning mouths that often give the impression that they are in pain. Their frames do not operate like those of standard humanoids, in that they carry their arms out from their bodies in a manner that is reminiscent of a marionette. They walk forward supporting themselves on strange, turned-out feet.

This bizarre exoskeleton setup allows Givin to survive in a vacuum. The impermeable outer bone plates of their skeleton form a type of organic vacuum suit connected by flexible membranes that seal off all orifices and openings. In order to use this evolutionary peculiarity, Givin must enter a state of hibernation, requiring them to gorge on large quantities of nutritious foods in advance. While sealed in their exoskeletons, Givin do not respire, instead producing energy from stored fats. In addition, Givin have developed a means of physiologically sensing barometric pressure, enabling them to accurately anticipate certain tidal changes that necessitate their hibernation.

All of these natural defensive traits are tailored to the unpredictable nature of the environment in which they were spawned. Sitting at the intersection of the Rimma Trade Route and the Corellian Trade Spine, the planet Yag'Dhul has three moons that orbit Yag'Dhul in fewer hours than the planet rotates, making its months well over one hundred standard hours shorter than its days. Moreover, the planet literally spins in the opposite direction of its moons, and as a result the oceans and atmosphere shift from one end of the world to the other, leaving parts of Yag'Dhul without atmosphere at seemingly unpredictable periods.

Scientists marvel that a sentient species was even able to develop on such a planet, but the Givin somehow managed to conquer these ecological challenges. Their evolutionary ancestors' first method of survival in such a habitat was to remain mobile, so that when the tides and air rushed to the other end of the world, they were carried with them. However, because the tides are so unpredictable, it was difficult to create a conventional cycle of life for reproduction, feeding, and the like. Also, temperature variations caused difficulties, as an individual may be at the frigid pole one day, the equator the next. Thus, the next step in evolution for their progenitors was a gradual sealing of their bodies in a skeletal vacuum. Through these changes, and through eventually learning to predict the alterations of their volatile world with a complex system of mathematics, the Givin grew and thrived despite the odds.

All of Givin language, culture, and religion centers upon mathematics, which is credited with their ultimate salvation. As befitting a mathematical theocracy, arithmetic is the main course of study for young people, who compete for entrance into monasteries, hoping to numerically solve the meaning and plan of life. The Givin planetary governor is selected through contests involving the calculation of multidimensional differentials. All political decisions are also made according to the guidelines of null-modal probability, by ruling bodies known as the Body Calculus and the coalition of Factors—although the respective responsibilities of these bodies have not been disclosed to outsiders. Givin religious practices are headed by extraordinarily gifted mathematicians who serve as priests and lore-keepers. The advanced study of equations is a highly devout pursuit, an attempt to reveal answers to the questions of life. With this centrality of purpose, the Givin written languages are made up of thousands of specially defined mathematical symbols. Arithmetic even extends to Givin decorative arts, and is featured in wall treatments and body adornments.

The Givin are also adept shipbuilders, and their ability to survive in a vacuum is very useful to such a business. They regard "soft" species who are not able to stay alive in a vacuum as inferior, and are only comfortable associating with Duros and Verpines—two other shipbuilding species. They cannot abide Mon Calamari, even though they are some of the finest ship makers in the galaxy, as the Mon Cal design technique is too organic and illogical to a Givin's sense of mathematical rigidity.

The ships that Givin construct are some of the most efficient and speedy in the galaxy. In their vessels, made specifically for their own physiology, only the sleeping quarters are pressurized, and the computers are used only for data storage. They do not install navigational computation software in their computers because the Givin calculate navigational vectors in their heads.

Givin reside in hermetically sealed cities that can withstand the violent and capricious weather trends of their world. Givin priests, deep in the study of the mathematical mysteries of their planet's rotation, can now predict these patterns with such accuracy so as to make their homes stable and peaceful. This enables them to also mine the world's natural resources, making them a generally wealthy species with a stable economy. Givin run one of the galaxy's largest and most efficient shipping and transport businesses with their fast and voluminous cargo vessels.

Givin traditionally greet one another with a simple quadratic equation. However, they will often greet outsiders with different problems to test their mathematical prowess. They do this because they generally do not trust strangers, but those who can meet the challenge of their greeting are elevated to the status of a peers with whom intelligent discourse can be shared. Givin are uncomfortable around beings who show a lot of exposed flesh—primarily because they cannot help but wonder why such individuals don't seal themselves from possible environmental hazards, such as a tidal deluge or the vacuum of space.

Despite their xenophobic tendencies, the Givin are members of the Galactic Alliance, seeing such membership as a statistical advantage to their people's economy and political well-being. The desire to maximize advantages has led the Givin to switch alliances as variables changed, such as when they allied themselves to the Separatists during the Clone War era, and to the New Republic after. The planet of Yag'Dhul was also the site of at least one major battle during the Yuuzhan Vong War. Presently, any ambassadors who work with the Givin must undergo extensive education in mathematics in order to negotiate with them, lest they find themselves at a considerable disadvantage.

DESIGNATION
Sentient

HOMEWORLD
Yag'Dhul

AVERAGE HEIGHT
1.8 meters

PRONUNCIATION
Gĭ'-vĭn

NOTABLE APPEARANCE
Episode IV: A New Hope

GOTAL

Gotals are a tall humanoid species native to Antar 4, one of six moons that orbit the gas giant known as Antar in the Prindaar system, located in the Inner Rim. Gray-brown, coarse skin protects their faces from extreme temperatures, and red-tinted eyes allow them to see shapes in pitch darkness. Flat noses protrude only a centimeter or so from their faces, and they possess sharp incisors for chewing meat. Shaggy gray fur also covers their bodies, but their most notable trait is the two cone-shaped horns that crown their oblong heads.

The Gotals have long been a spacefaring race. Taking advantage of Antar 4's proximity to the surrounding worlds in its system, they had already colonized four of the adjacent moons and mined a fifth before the Old Republic first encountered them. They were one of the earliest species to join the Republic around the formation of the Senate, even though they had no official government. Politically, they were and are peaceful anarchists. Since they have a special sensitivity to one another's feelings and needs, they did not require government or law, though some formal legal courts have been formed to handle antisocial or criminal behavior from offworld visitors and the occasional abnormal actions of one of their own.

Antar 4 is rich with minerals such as nickel, silicon, and iron, although the majority of the moon is comprised of magnetite. Xenobiologists believe much of Gotals' unique sensory abilities are directly related to the magnetite, which, when combined with the electromagnetic radiation from the stars Prindaar and Antar, greatly influences most of the life on Antar 4.

More than 60 percent of Antar 4 is covered by water, with extreme tidal variations caused by the moon's unusual rotation. These tides prevent ice caps from forming at the poles. Antar 4's rotational access is nearly parallel to its orbital plane, making variations in climate more severe. The night-and-day cycle of the world is also erratic

1.5

1.0

.5

0

because of the reflective nature of the system's star, which further complicates temperatures around the moon. At times, the entirety of the moon's surface is bathed in light; at others, it is plunged into complete darkness. For this reason, native species rely on senses other than sight to survive.

While Gotals do have noses, eyes, and ears, their sight and hearing are lacking in development, and their sense of smell is nonexistent. Because of this, Gotals have evolved an electromagnetic detection sense emitted from their cones. These cones provide the sensory perception that individuals require to locate food and perform other tasks necessary for survival. Packed with unique nerve endings and receptor cells, the cones can detect changes in magnetic fields, as well as infrared emanations, radio waves, neutrino bombardment, and practically every other form of energy emission. In addition, Gotals can detect the Force, though to them it appears as an indistinct buzzing. Electromagnetic emissions from most offworld technology can overwhelm their cone reception, however, so they will usually go out of their way to avoid standard machinery such as droids. All Gotal ship and land technology is based on chemical reactions that do not produce such emissions.

With their cones, Gotals can also sense another creature up to roughly ten meters away. Perceiving the being's electromagnetic aura, they can even determine mood, awareness, health, and level of strength.

Due to this extrasensory perception, Gotals make excellent hunters. They can sense their primary native prey, the equine species known as quivry, from great distances, counting their numbers and determining their relative health or weaknesses; at closer range Gotals can discern their mood, figuring out whether the quivry are aware that they are being hunted.

Gotals also utilize their cones to interact with one another—by sensing moods, thoughts, and desires, they avoid conflict and easily communicate their own needs. Because they read others so well, they are known to be extremely polite and sensitive, and will only speak aloud to convey abstract ideas—never to express emotion. In fact, their spoken language has no words for emotion. With the cones emanating their disposition, they do not require such linguistic forms. They also possess no vocal inflection, so other species will mistakenly perceive Gotals as nonemotional. These characteristics also cause some to mistrust them, particularly since a Gotal's involuntary communication cues remain unreadable to most beings.

DESIGNATION
Sentient

HOMEWORLD
Antar 4

AVERAGE HEIGHT
1.8 meters

PRONUNCIATION
Gō'-tăl

Gotals' cone sensitivity enables them to function well as mates and parents. They do not require mating rituals or courtship, and love at first sight is extremely common for Gotals. When they mate it is usually for life, having children almost immediately and taking great delight in the raising of progeny.

Controlling their extrasensory abilities is a skill learned through maturity. Gotal children sense through their cones at birth, often causing them a great deal of pain and confusion. Until around the age of twelve standard years, Gotal children have difficulty filtering out nonessential information; the overwhelming amount of "noise" often leaves them irritable and irrational. Unfortunately, they are constantly distressed until they manage to learn to filter out unwanted transmissions.

Gotals can be found throughout the galaxy in regions where there is a strong nonhuman population. They often work as mercenaries, bounty hunters, counselors, diplomats, negotiators, and social workers. They are also successful in business and sales environments, though they have to work past their lack of vocal inflection to impress clients. As gamblers they are formidable, and most high-stakes games will not allow them at the table, although some professional gamblers take it as a challenge to try to fool a Gotal. The Empire, however, refused to employ their services because they too often sympathized with the enemy.

As mentioned, Gotal sensitivity comes with a price. Being receptive to electromagnetic emissions complicates their offworld existence. Droids, non-Gotal ships, or even a simple machine can cause them pain or disorientation. However, one inventive Gotal businessman named Alyn Rae recently developed a chemical-based "cone sock" garment that covers a Gotal's cones and filters out EM emissions, allowing other transmissions to pass through. He developed these garments with the assistance of several offworld scientists who could better use the equipment necessary to design and construct them. These preliminary cone socks are expensive, and usually only the most affluent Gotals wear them. Even so, more and more Gotals have been seen sporting them in galactic society—seeing the cost as a necessary sacrifice to make their lives abroad a little more peaceful.

NOTABLE APPEARANCE
Episode IV: A New Hope

GRAN

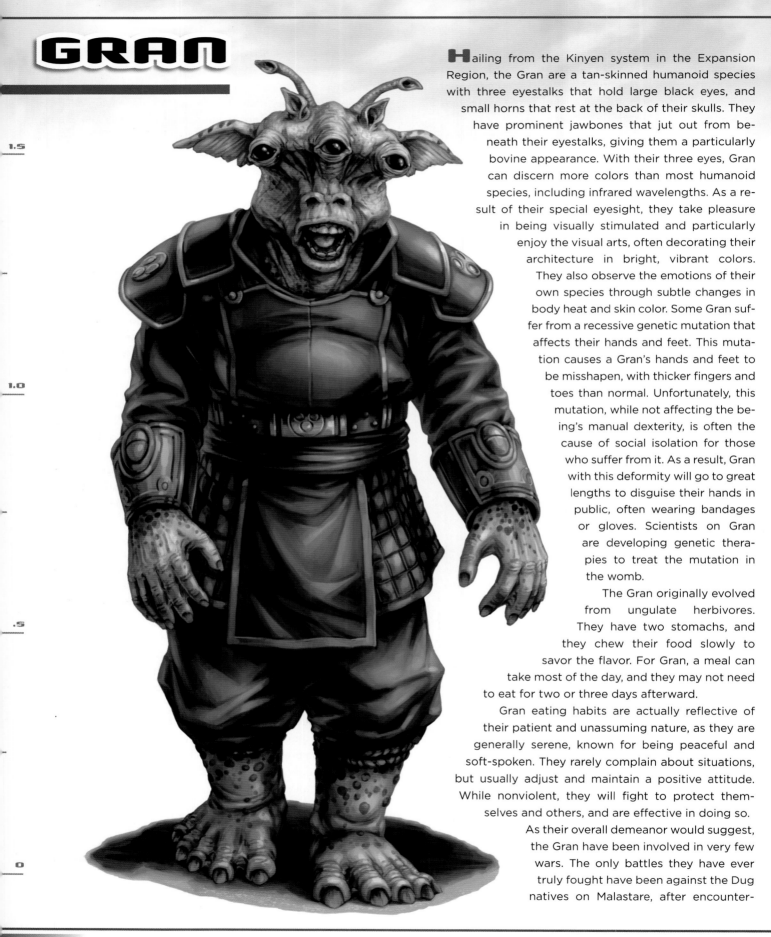

Hailing from the Kinyen system in the Expansion Region, the Gran are a tan-skinned humanoid species with three eyestalks that hold large black eyes, and small horns that rest at the back of their skulls. They have prominent jawbones that jut out from beneath their eyestalks, giving them a particularly bovine appearance. With their three eyes, Gran can discern more colors than most humanoid species, including infrared wavelengths. As a result of their special eyesight, they take pleasure in being visually stimulated and particularly enjoy the visual arts, often decorating their architecture in bright, vibrant colors. They also observe the emotions of their own species through subtle changes in body heat and skin color. Some Gran suffer from a recessive genetic mutation that affects their hands and feet. This mutation causes a Gran's hands and feet to be misshapen, with thicker fingers and toes than normal. Unfortunately, this mutation, while not affecting the being's manual dexterity, is often the cause of social isolation for those who suffer from it. As a result, Gran with this deformity will go to great lengths to disguise their hands in public, often wearing bandages or gloves. Scientists on Gran are developing genetic therapies to treat the mutation in the womb.

The Gran originally evolved from ungulate herbivores. They have two stomachs, and they chew their food slowly to savor the flavor. For Gran, a meal can take most of the day, and they may not need to eat for two or three days afterward.

Gran eating habits are actually reflective of their patient and unassuming nature, as they are generally serene, known for being peaceful and soft-spoken. They rarely complain about situations, but usually adjust and maintain a positive attitude. While nonviolent, they will fight to protect themselves and others, and are effective in doing so.

As their overall demeanor would suggest, the Gran have been involved in very few wars. The only battles they have ever truly fought have been against the Dug natives on Malastare, after encountering that species during an attempt at colonization. On their homeworld of Kinyen, there has not been such a conflict in more than ten thousand standard years, and those minor clashes that have been recorded were fought over matters of survival rather than emotional disputes.

This peaceful sensibility and levelheaded agreeability is believed by Gran scholars to be biological as well as cultural. The Gran people originated in the mountainous region of Kinyen, where they were hunted by dangerous highland predators. Their natural means of survival was to band together in herds. There was safety in numbers, and for this reason they would never leave one another alone for any period of time. The Gran learned to value their companions and rely on one another for security.

This trait has carried on through their development. Today, it is rare to see a Gran without companionship, and if left alone, a Gran will frequently go insane or die of loneliness. When two Gran mate, it is for life. If one member of a couple dies, the other generally follows within a few days. Thus, when Gran leave Kinyen for trade, they will usually travel in groups. A solitary Gran is most likely a criminal, for in their society, the most severe punishment is exile. An educated space traveler will know to stay away from a Gran who is alone, or dressed in black, as he or she is most likely criminally insane. This insanity is normally caused by loneliness, and such individuals will avoid bright colors as too reminiscent of home.

An agreeable and characteristically happy species, Gran love to chat and to meet new people. Once embroiled in conversation, it is somewhat difficult to get certain Gran to stop talking. They love to learn about other peoples, and will ask many questions, almost to the point of creating annoyance. Gran are also accused by many nonpacifistic beings as being "preachy" on the topic of pacifism.

Gran society is socialist in structure, with the needs of the individual put aside in favor of the populace as a whole. To keep Gran society on an even keel, every Gran is trained for a specific job that best suits his or her talents within the guidelines of a rigid career quota system. While many species, including humans, would be uncomfortable in such a system, the Gran see this as a fully logical way for natural-born herders to survive and thrive. There is no question as to each individual's role, with everyone from the machine worker to the farmer contributing to the greater good while politicians efficiently distribute the wealth and technology

DESIGNATION
Sentient

HOMEWORLD
Kinyen/Malastare

AVERAGE HEIGHT
1.6 meters

PRONUNCIATION
Grăn

throughout their world using quotas and rationing. Political debate is rare, and when it occurs is painstakingly slow, with each point pondered with intense care, so that any decision made harms as few people as possible.

When the Gran first encountered the Old Republic, contact with the outside galaxy threw their society into upheaval. As many Gran left Kinyen to colonize other worlds, including Hok and Malastare, great gaps opened in the delicately balanced society. For this reason, Gran politicians then refused to allow anyone to depart the planet without permission, and forbade offworlders from visiting Kinyen's civilized centers. The Gran soon constructed quarters for outsiders in their cities, and made moving offplanet illegal, although records indicate that there were a few rare Gran Jedi during this period, and that the Gran did represent themselves in the Galactic Senate. The Old Republic accommodated this isolationist stance to enable Gran society to adapt to the extreme changes it was facing. As they adjusted, the Gran reopened contact with the Republic, just in time for it to fall under the control of the Emperor, at which time—for their own protection—they retreated to their homeworld once again. But they didn't remain safe from the Empire for long. After Imperial bombers leveled a Gran city, the population caved to their will, and around this time many Gran also began to leave Kinyen by choice.

After the Empire fell, the New Republic reinitiated contact with the Gran, and their society has opened up once more. The Gran now trade the fruits of their fertile world throughout the galaxy, primarily those of produce and livestock. As a people they have had few technological achievements that they can call their own—they import all their technology from offworld sources. Gran are commonly seen about the galaxy traveling in tour groups and as merchants, often running companies with more of their own kind for companionship.

NOTABLE APPEARANCE
Episode VI: Return of the Jedi

GUNDARK

Gundarks are large, bipedal furry primates with large ears and four arms. They have opposable digits on their hands and are extremely strong—able to rip healthy hundred-year-old trees out of the ground. All subspecies of gundarks sport either brown or gray fur, though their young are usually black, gradually changing color with age. Gundarks have keen eyesight and hearing, but their sense of smell is especially powerful. Adult gundarks can detect an intruder up to a hundred meters away, allowing them to get ready to attack while the adversary moves into range.

These creatures can be found throughout the galaxy on worlds that are generally temperate. They prefer warm climates, building their nests in hollowed-out trees or caves.

Scientists have only speculated as to how this species managed to populate so many worlds, but, as with banthas, they believe traders and other space travelers transported gundarks to different systems.

Unlike banthas, which were used for farming and pack labor, gundarks were most likely transferred from system to system for sport—game hunting or gundark fighting, the latter having been banned for years in many systems. Others were taken as slaves because they are easily trained, and still others were moved to be protected from these slavers by Old Republic agents. Even though hunting or capturing gundarks was illegal during both the Old Republic era and the current rule of the Galactic Federation of Free Alliances, gundarks are frequently sold by black-market operatives to underworld gladiatorial game promoters throughout the outer fringes of the galaxy. In such games, gundarks are the favored champions, even against such famous adversaries as the rancor, trompa, or krayt dragon, taking on their opponents with their bare hands. Gundarks often ambush their challengers, hiding until they are in range, then leaping out to grapple them and crush their windpipes. When battling larger opponents, they can crush leg and arm bones with a single squeeze. The most popular bouts are those in which gundarks are blindfolded and can take advantage of their extremely powerful sense of smell. Gundarks are costly in terms of upkeep, however, requiring special security measures, including force pikes and guards, to keep them contained. For this reason, unless significantly wealthy, a promoter will usually have only one gundark featured in his or her cast of combatants.

Gundarks are known to have very short tempers and to attack without provocation. They are omnivorous, and while it is unclear as to whether they have achieved full sentience or not, they do display enough intelligence to use items such as rocks as simple tools for cracking open nuts and hard fruits. In their natural settings, they live in family groupings of ten or more, creating homes in hollowed-out trees or caves. Several families may cluster together into a tribal-like society, working mutually for their common interests. Their lives center on the gathering of food for their community, and there are definite hierarchical roles within a gundark society. Females fulfill the role of hunter-gatherers, and take on the training of young gundarks not old enough to venture away from the tribe, while the males are the home protectors—attacking any creature coming within scent distance of the nest. This they do with great ferocity. Female gundarks normally hunt in packs, and have been known to mistake sentient beings for food.

Like most primates, Gundarks are born one at a time. At birth, they have only two arms and small ears. Parents will roughhouse

DESIGNATION
Nonsentient/
semi-sentient

HOMEWORLD
Vanqor

**AVERAGE
HEIGHT**
1.8 meters

PRONUNCIATION
Gŭn'-därk

with their young to teach them how to protect themselves even while they play. During puberty, youthful gundarks sprout two additional arms, their ears grow to match the width of their heads, and their strength reaches its maximum potential—thus the phrase *strong enough to pull the ears off a gundark.* These adolescent gundarks know instinctively that too many offspring can threaten a family's food supply, so sibling rivalry is often fierce. By the age of five, some young gundarks are forced out of their homes and set off to find a new one, frequently battling their way into another tribe. This tradition keeps tribe populations at a manageable number and allows for genetic diversity.

Among the subspecies of gundarks are the aquatic gundarks of Yavin 4, which possess four eyes, enabling them to see both above and below the water. This medium-sized creature exists by feeding on smaller animals, such as runyips and whisper birds. Otherwise, there is little difference between common and aquatic gundarks.

However, there is the Burskan gundark, a rather strange specimen when compared with the others. Docile creatures, Burskan gundarks have been observed to simply lie around in a lazy torpor, which is more pronounced during warmer weather. In fact, it is difficult to get Burskan gundarks to notice anything, although when sufficiently provoked they are as fierce as their more populous cousins. The odd behavior of Burskan gundarks has two other striking examples. Burskan gundarks form unusual attachments to soft items, such as cloth made of silk or fur. They will hoard such things and have been observed to fight in order to keep them. Also, Burskan gundarks are particularly sensitive to odors emitted by rotting plant matter. While this is not a problem on Burska's open tundra, it has provoked stampedes among certain gundarks in captivity. Fortunately for these creatures, their peculiar behavior makes them unprofitable for trade on the black market and useless for illegal service as gladiatorial animals.

There is another species referred to as a gundark—the "long-necked gundarks" of Kharzet III. These creatures are not true gundarks, however, as they are quadrupeds with long, prehensile necks. This species gained its name from a xenobiologist who compared the violent temperament of these creatures to that of gundarks in his notes. Sadly, he died before his notes could be adapted and a proper name given to them, and for this reason the name stuck, falling into common usage.

NOTABLE MENTION
Episode V: The Empire Strikes Back

GUNGAN

The Gungans of Naboo, a planet in the Mid Rim, are bipedal amphibians who live primarily in cities beneath Naboo's great bodies of water. They are tall and thin, with long, expressive ears, a bill-like mouth, and webbed fingers and toes. Their skeletal frame is made of cartilage, making them more flexible for underwater movement. When swimming, their nostrils seal, nictitating membranes cover their eyes, and their eyestalks partially retract into their skulls, making underwater travel very easy for them. They also have tough skin on and around their heads, enabling them to burrow through sand and gravel with little difficulty. Compound lungs permit Gungans to breathe both air and water, and powerful legs allow them to swim very quickly. A significant number of Gungans have haillu—two long earlobes that reveal emotional states such as friendship, aggression, and fear.

This species is omnivorous, although they have large teeth for cracking open shellfish, a staple of their diet. They also consume creatures known as gumbols from the trees surrounding their homes and mollusks from nearby marshes and lakes.

In fact, Gungan culture centers on their environment and the other living things that populate it. They are particularly linked to the creatures known as kaadu, which are used as battle mounts for their Grand Army. Similar to Tusken Raiders and their banthas, Gungans believe that the kaadu are joined with them in a way that no other creatures are—they will treat them as family and mourn them in a similar fashion when they are lost. The Gungan people domesticated the kaadu thousands of years ago, and when Gungans migrated to their underwater cities, they brought the kaadu with them. They are the mainstay of the Gungan militias, or militia-gung, and entire schools are devoted to teaching Gungans to ride and live in harmony with these creatures, since it is considered essential for growth.

2.0

1.5

1.0

.5

0

In battle, the Gungans who ride kaadu wield the heaviest authority, and records show that they are the most effective leaders. Kaadu are given to Gungan officers with great ceremony, and officers never abandon their steeds unless they die or they are retired due to age. In a like manner, kaadu will never desert their owners, feeling a profound love and loyalty.

Gungan society and government have been built upon treaties made by the many different settlements and clans. Gungan life is governed by the rules and decisions set down by the High Council, which is led by an elected "Boss." While the members of the clans exhibit different outward biological features, they remain the same in terms of their inner physiology. The two primary tribal races within Gungan society are the Otolla, which are the most numerous, and the Ankura, a race that does not have long ears, eyestalks, or bills. Scientists believe that while these two different races share common ancestry, the Ankura have lived on land longer than the Otolla, and have therefore evolved to look more like a land-based form. The basic Gungan family unit consists of two parents and children. Children hatch in "water cradles" in tadpole forms, although they develop arms and legs within a month of birth.

Nearly one hundred standard years before the Battle of Yavin, the Gungans fought off unknown invaders on their world, assembling the first Grand Army by uniting all Gungan cities and communities. After throwing off the invaders, Gungans maintained the army as a means of defending against any foe, including their world's ever-present sea monsters. Made up of the combined might of the militiagung, the Grand Army wears leather and metal headgear and marginal body army with small circular shields; the main weapons used are plasmic energy balls. Gungan generals and officers transmit their orders via horns, wild gestures, and piercing whistles. Still, Naboo is normally a fairly peaceful world. Thus the army is more a matter of tradition than need.

Gungans are not very tolerant of those who threaten the peace of their home, and their sentencing for criminals is often severe. Minor crimes, such as vandalism, are given a sentence of exile or caning, even stoning. Once Gungans have been cast out, it may be difficult for them to return to society, and even if they do, they may find that massive peer pressure will make life quite uncomfortable until their past offenses have faded from memory.

Despite this harsh code of law, Gungans are generally a happy and gregarious people who love company and the sharing of stories. Around one another they speak their native language of Gunganese, but with outsiders they will combine their language with Basic to form a pidgin language that is usually understandable to speakers of Basic. They do welcome visitors with kindness, but are typically suspicious and quiet until the outsider earns their respect.

The Gungans are a simple but proud people who bristle at any attempt to conquer them. They are technologically advanced, although they prefer to live simply, with as little interference from machinery as possible. They use deflector shield technology to maintain bubble domes over their underwater cities, and utilize biotechnology, growing rather than building their underwater ships, force fields, and weapons. They take great care to preserve their environment and use natural resources sparingly.

Other than advances in biotechnology, Gungans live pretty much as they did thousands of years ago. They dwell in relative peace alongside the human inhabitants of Naboo, although relations between the species have not always been on the best of terms. Due to cultural differences, Gungans are suspicious of their Naboo neighbors, probably because the average Gungan has never met a human personally. However, historical records contain no references to armed conflict between the Gungans and humans, so it is believed that the estrangement stemmed from an inability to communicate rather than hostilities between the two groups. Prior to the fall of the Old Republic, Gungans had started designing space vessels, but they ceased all such development when the Empire threatened their home. It is believed that the Gungans retreated deeper into the swamps following the rise of the Empire, once again isolating themselves from the human population of Naboo. During the Old Republic era, they were represented in the Galactic Senate by Padmé Amidala, following her successful peace negotiations between the Gungans and the human peoples while Queen of Naboo. Since then, however, traffic to and from the Naboo system has grown more rare, although the sector was represented in the New Republic Senate by first a human and then a Gungan Senator.

DESIGNATION
Sentient

HOMEWORLD
Naboo

AVERAGE
HEIGHT
1.9 meters

PRONUNCIATION
Gŭn'-găn

NOTABLE APPEARANCE
Episode I: The Phantom Menace

H'NEMTHE

The H'nemthe, from an Outer Rim planet of the same name, are a bipedal reptilian species with skin varying in tone from pink to blue-gray, double rows of cheekbones, gently curved noses, four small horns (or conelets) on their skulls, and three fingers on each hand. They are omnivores, feeding primarily on fruits and vegetables, with the occasional meal that includes wild game.

H'nemthe are highly efficient hunters. Their conelets can sense heat differences in their environment, and emotional variances in other creatures. For this reason, scientists have speculated that their conelets serve a similar purpose to those of the Gotal. The two species are unrelated biologically, but both come from worlds where lunar orbits cause extreme weather patterns. The planet H'nemthe has three moons, generating a collective gravitational force that creates tremendous weather fluctuations on the world's surface. As with the Gotal, these cones help H'nemthe locate food and analyze their surrounding environment not only during such inclement weather, but also in the darkness.

H'nemthe society is very structured, and is based on the fulfillment of spiritual awareness through the creation of life and the act of searching for true love. The population breakdown makes finding true love quite difficult, however. Like the Gamorreans, there are about twenty H'nemthe males for every female, although the reasons for this population anomaly among the H'nemthe is currently unknown. Xenobiologists have suggested that this may be due to a genetic defect, but because of the closed society on H'nemthe, research on this subject has not yet been thoroughly conducted. Unlike the emotionally unsophisticated and comparatively brutish Gamorreans, though, the timid H'nemthe males spend most of their adult lives seeking out a devoted mate. Although a majority do not locate their one true love, H'nemthe males take some comfort in the belief that death is the culmination of life, and that their deaths create a path for their offspring.

Along with the population disparity, the lack of love is an unfortunate result of the traditional H'nemthe mating ritual. H'nemthe males are extremely selective in choosing a mate, and after mating, the female disembowels the male with her razor-sharp tongue. Because it is fatal for the male, mating is infrequent, and is only done in cases of true love. While some may consider this calamitous, a H'nemthe male considers the ritual the culmination of spiritual fulfillment, as he goes on to the netherworld to guide his coming child. The woman is fulfilled in that she brings a new life into the world.

Due to their low numbers, females are strongly protected by H'nemthe law. Virgin females are rarely, if ever, allowed to leave the planet and do not venture out often unless given leave by their mothers to seek a mate. It is only after mating that female H'nemthe will travel offworld. Females are also not allowed to eat anything but vegetables and fruits, to ensure they do not taste flesh until they savor that of their mate. Although their limited exposure to the outside world leaves many H'nemthe females naïve about the galaxy at large, they are well educated in many subjects important to their people. Thus, most H'nemthe encountered offplanet are male, although they are almost assuredly not seeking glory or adventure. Males who are unable to find a mate or are repeatedly rejected by their chosen beloveds sometimes simply take to the stars as wanderers.

One of the more well-known H'nemthe is M'iiyoom Onith, a female virgin H'nemthe who was allowed to leave her homeworld as an experiment to see how well the females of their species would fair in finding a mate outside their native culture. Through most of her trip, M'iiyoom was accompanied by a chaperone, but she and her chaperone were accidentally separated when M'iiyoom entered the wrong ship during a layover at a transfer station. Whether she did this purposely or accidentally is unknown, but her final destination was Tatooine where she encountered a Gotal named Feltipern Trevagg, with whom she fell madly in love. Authorities later found Trevagg disemboweled from the H'nemthe mating ritual, but could find no trace of the young female H'nemthe. She later returned to her homeworld, and as she is the first of her kind to attempt mating with a non-H'nemthe, she attained some notoriety. As her mating with Trevagg resulted in no progeny (they were, after all, genetically incompatible) she is now free to travel offworld as often as she likes, though she prefers to remain home doing speaking engagements.

Befitting a culture that places a premium on true love, the

H'nemthe are an extremely artistic and passionate people. Their poetry and literary writings are some of the most profound in the galaxy, and are displayed in a written language that is composed of one contiguous line of flowing letters to form words. A cornerstone of H'nemthe literary tradition is the form of epic poem written by lovers to each other before they have mated. Detailing a pair's courtship and the depths of their feelings for each other, these poems are often read publicly in grand recitals after the mating ritual, as a tribute to the couple, and particularly to the late male partner. The poems are collected and reproduced in fine calligraphy.

Music is also highly valued in H'nemthe society, and skills in calligraphy and music, along with storytelling, are prized abilities. Females are expected to be personally accomplished in the arts. In addition, they study H'nemthe history and political science to prepare themselves to be the leaders of their world. The H'nemthe spoken language, however, consists of squeaks, squeals, and other noises that—unlike their written language and music—are considered displeasing by most other species.

The government of H'nemthe is also fervent and optimistic, being a direct democracy. In this society, all voices are important and must be heard. Although males are the majority of the H'nemthe population, they tend to elect females as leaders of their local governments, particularly because if a male finds a mate, he will not live long enough to fulfill his duties. All of the local governments select representatives to a world Senate, where matters of global importance are decided by a majority vote.

The H'nemthe are a self-sufficient people, rarely trading with outsiders for offworld goods save technology and ships. On occasion, H'nemthe artists accept commissions for their calligraphy and musical compositions, but these requests are seldom agreed to, as works of art are considered highly personal. Their world's ecology makes it difficult for them to trade anything except minerals, which the males take from mines beneath the planet's surface. H'nemthe gets few visitors, though the Galactic Alliance has made overtures to the female leadership in attempts to begin trade negotiations with this passionate and idealistic people.

DESIGNATION
Sentient

HOMEWORLD
H'nemthe

AVERAGE
HEIGHT
1.7 meters

PRONUNCIATION
Hĕ-nĕm'-thē

NOTABLE APPEARANCE
Episode IV: A New Hope

HUMAN

Humans are the most populous species in the known galaxy. They are also one of the most adaptable, resilient, and diverse in physical appearance. With two legs ending in feet, and two arms featuring five-fingered hands, humans are extremely dexterous and able to perform a great range of complex tasks. Most humans have hair on their heads, which usually varies from dark brown to white or silver, and males often have facial hair, although a majority of them choose to remove it, or sculpt it through selective removal. Their pliable skin ranges in color from pasty white to deep, dark brown, and humans' eyes are also known to appear in a multitude of colors, from the lightest of blues to the darkest of browns. They inhabit all walks of life in galactic society, and have colonized thousands of worlds. Most sociologists feel that their intelligence and adaptability to new situations have allowed humans to become the most successful, and politically powerful species in the galaxy.

Being mammals, humans bear their children live from the womb, and they normally raise them in private home groupings. Multiple births are not unheard of, though it is uncommon for a female to bear more than two at a time. Among multiple births, some are genetically identical (from one ovum splitting) or fraternal (from two separate fertilized ova). Humans can typically live up to a hundred twenty standard years, though there have been isolated reports of human Jedi living as many as two hundred.

Some humans are notable due to their unique cultures. One of the most famous and numerous of human societies is that of Corellian, whose people inhabit the Corellian star system. Twenty-five millennia before the Battle of Yavin, the mysterious species known as the Rakata introduced Corellians to hyperdrive technology, and they quickly created their own more efficient and effective version of it. From that point on, they were traveling the space lanes, trading with other species, and leading the way in starship development. They are recognized for their skills as pilots and engineers—a point of pride to their people—and their talents as military strategists are renowned. Culturally, Corellians are born risk-takers and adventurers—their impulsive and sometimes unpredictable actions often setting them apart from other human civilizations in the galaxy.

Another unique group of humans are the Mandalorians, who adopted the war-like culture of the ancient Taung species. The Taung were a ruthless, near-human gray-skinned species that originated on Coruscant and ultimately relocated to Mandalore, renaming both the planet and themselves for their supreme ruler, Mandalore the First. Mandalorians obeyed the commands of their militaristic superiors without question, and this cultural tradition of combat was carried on when they united with other species, including humans, to fight their legendary battles. Over time, the original species became extinct, and although the term *Mandalorian* refers more to a culture and a mind-set than to a specific species, the majority of remaining Mandalorians were in fact humans. The genetic code of one such warrior was used to create the clone-trooper-based Grand Army of the Republic that later evolved into the army of the Empire. It is believed that, based on the reports of Captain Han Solo, the famed bounty hunter Boba Fett recently reorganized the Mandalorian warrior army in the shadow of the Yuuzhan Vong invasion, and that it was successful in liberating more than one world from the brutal aggressors.

The Lorrdian culture is also worth noting, as it is a group thought by some sociologists to be near human, though the genetic code has not been altered by environmental concerns. The Lorrdians were once slaves to a people called the Argazdans, who forbade all Lorrdians to communicate with one another. To counter this, Lorrdians devised a type of sign language consisting of subtle hand gestures, postures, and facial tics and expressions. They also taught themselves to read the body language of others. This form of interaction, known as kinetic communication, led to a new way of life, helping the Lorrdians overthrow their masters through the formation and coordination of a guerrilla force. Lorrdians today are so adept at reading body language that they can tell a person's mood and intentions within just a few seconds of observation. With more time to study a subject, Lorrdians can identify cultural background, homeworld, occupation, and class. They are also famous for being the best vocal and physical mimics, using their perceptive powers to imitate almost any beings' voice or mannerism, within the restrictions of their physical ability.

As humans are the most numerous species galaxywide, they have, perhaps unfairly, become the standard by which other species are defined. For instance, if a species is known to be "humanoid," this is not because its members are human, but because they bear specific traits that are similar to humans—namely, the number of appendages and the

DESIGNATION
Sentient

HOMEWORLD
Unknown
(believed to be
Coruscant)

**AVERAGE
HEIGHT**
1.75 meters

PRONUNCIATION
Hū'-măn

practice of walking upright. Also, being a generally successful species, humans have spawned several related subspecies referred to as near humans. Near humans are individuals who are nearly genetically identical to humans, but whose inherent makeup has changed in varying degrees due to environmental influences, evolution, or other factors. Humans and near humans can interbreed with very few exceptions.

The Firrerreos, meanwhile, are one of the rarest near-human species in the known galaxy; it is believed that only a few thousand of them still exist. Firrerreos possess multicolored hair that they wear long, and their eyes have nictitating membranes that protect them against intense bursts of light as well as flying debris. This human subspecies is also able to heal quickly. Firrerreos were nearly wiped out by Hethrir, one of their own who was a pupil to Darth Vader. The surviving Firrerreo people were relocated on Belderone and Kinoo-ine, though the former planet was subsequently conquered by the Yuuzhan Vong and the subspecies has fallen into near extinction.

Two other near-human species of import are the Mirialans of Mirial, and the Kiffar, who are native to Kiffu and Kiffex in the Azurbani system. While having notable differences, what makes these two species stand out are their tattoo markings, which hold significance in both cultures. The complex culture of the olive-skinned Mirialans includes religious beliefs based on an ancient understanding of the Force. A Mirialan's tattoos signify that individual's importance to the future of the universe. The Kiffar, meanwhile, have tattoos that signify their family heritage, specifically that of their mothers. The Kiffar believe it is the mother who gives life, and therefore the power of the Force flows through her to her children.

Humans have been traveling and colonizing the galaxy for eons. Their cultures and physical appearances are as varied and unique as all the planetary systems they inhabit. Even with all the attempts of different peoples to invade and conquer the galaxy and all the species in it, humans have managed to survive, adapt, and defend their way of life. And it seems as if humans will be in the center of galactic life for millennia to come.

NOTABLE APPEARANCE
Episode IV: A New Hope

HUTT

Hutts are large amphibious gastropods that presently inhabit the world of Nal Hutta in the Y'Toub system, the center of an area of the galaxy known as Hutt space. They have thick bodies with a long muscular tails and small arms that protrude from their upper torsos.

Physiologically, the Hutts are an anomaly, sharing traits from a variety of species. Like sea mammals, their nostrils can close, with their large lungs enabling them to stay underwater for hours at a time. Like worms, they are hermaphrodites, possessing both male and female reproductive organs. Like marsupial mammals, they bear their young one at a time, and nourish them in a brood pouch during their earlier stages of development.

Despite all these varied qualities, scientists generally classify Hutts as gastropods because of the way they move, slithering around like giant slugs. They have no skeleton to speak of, merely an internal mantle that supports their bodies and shapes their heads. Their mouths open so wide that they can swallow just about any small creatures whole, allowing them to frequently indulge their taste for live snacks. Hutts also possess extremely tough skin that protects them against heat and chemical burns, with their mucus and sweat making their skin surface very slippery while also keeping their bodies moist.

Though hermaphroditic, the average Hutt possesses a notably healthy sexual appetite, even for members of other species. In fact, some Hutts have been known to assume male or female gender roles and pursue bi-gender relationships, a behavior that sociologists attribute to societal contamination from contact with bi-gendered species. Medical specialists disagree, deeming the alternate lifestyle a product of nature that certain Hutts simply cannot deny, given their ability to select their own genders. Whatever the reason might be, many "normal" Hutts consider this behavior a perversion, and scorn those who choose gender roles, sometimes to the point of enacting violence and murder upon them.

Hutts are among the longest-lived species in the galaxy, with a maximum life span of roughly one thousand standard years. During such a lifetime, they can grow in size to more than fifteen hundred kilograms, and because they are so long-lived, Hutts rarely reproduce. When they do, many Hutts assume female roles in order to bear young. Infant Hutts are blind and extremely small, and they will move to a parent's pouch, where they remain for around fifty years. When they finally leave the pouch, they have matured to an intellectual level comparable to that of a typical ten-year-old human. As they move toward adulthood, they gain in corpulence, a trait considered a sign of power and prestige.

Hutt culture is essentially egocentric. They consider themselves the center of the galaxy, and on the worlds they control are likened unto gods. A Hutt's success in life is comparable only to its ego, and a Hutt's ego can be tremendous. They are experts at manipulating others and getting them to do their bidding.

Before inhabiting Nal Hutta, the Hutts evolved on a planet known as Varl, a temperate forest world with two suns that the species worshipped as gods. In Hutt religious beliefs, one of the sun gods, Evona, was pulled into a black hole. When this happened, the other planets in the system collided and crushed each other into numerous asteroids that bombarded the planet Varl. The second sun god, named Ardos, collapsed itself into a white dwarf out of grief over losing its mate.

Hutts believe that they had actually become greater than the gods they once worshipped as a result of their surviving the destruction of their original system. There is no absolute scientific substantiation for the Hutts' religious tale, however, and most scientists tend to believe another version that is told by spacers and traders throughout the galaxy. This story indicates that the Hutts destroyed their own planet in a civil war, the likes of which had not been witnessed anywhere in the known galaxy.

Nal Hutta is ruled by a council containing the eldest members of the so-called Clans of the Ancients. These clans are families that can trace their ancestry back to their days on Varl. The means by which the council makes decisions is a mystery, in that the Hutts will not allow outsiders to observe the governmental proceedings. Hutts all over the galaxy—even those on the farthest outskirts—abide by the decisions of this council.

For Hutts, blood is always thicker than slime. A Hutt's clan is paramount, particularly one's kajidic, or criminal family, and most decisions are based upon how they will affect the prosperity and the position of one's clan. Vast ancestral fortunes, passed on from generation to generation, have resulted in Hutt clans controlling some of the richest holdings in the galaxy. Rivalries among kajidics are widespread and often dangerous to those involved. Assassination as a means of achieving an end is commonplace, and although it is unforgivable (but not unheard of) for a Hutt to kill another Hutt, they would think nothing of executing an underling.

The Hutts, in general, are not builders, manufacturers, or inventors. They are entrepreneurs, constantly connecting someone who needs something with someone else who can fulfill that need. More often than not, Hutts head up giant criminal empires that are secretive and vast, and a majority of the major illegal transactions made in the galactic business world likely have a Hutt connected to them in one way or another. Galaxywide, most illegal activities have a Hutt at their source, whether it be the spice trade, smuggling, gambling, or slavery.

The one area in which Hutts excel and seem to take particular pride is their aptitude for slavery. Befitting their oversized egos and substantial appetites, Hutts will trade beings as easily and with as little afterthought as they would exchange nerf hides. During the Clone Wars era, Hutts controlled all the slave trade on Tatooine and Ryloth. The Hutt penchant for subjugating other species has its roots in Hutt history, starting with their enslavement of the Klatooinians, Vodrans, and Nikto through unfair trade agreements.

At the end of the New Republic era, the Yuuzhan Vong destroyed Nal Hutta, forcing the Hutts to seek a new homeworld. Because several Hutts such as Jabba, Gardulla, and Decca had established bases on Tatooine over the years, it was chosen as their new primary home planet.

DESIGNATION
Sentient

HOMEWORLD
Nal Hutta
(by way of Varl)

AVERAGE LENGTH
3 meters

PRONUNCIATION
Hŭt

NOTABLE APPEARANCE
Episode VI: Return of the Jedi

IKTOTCHI

The Iktotchi are a humanoid species native to the Expansion Region world of Iktotchon and its neighboring moon, Iktotch. Members of this tall species possess large horns that curve downward from their hairless skulls, and rough, tanned skin that protects them from the fierce winds of their homeworld. Male Iktotchi have bigger horns than the females; these are believed to be a leftover trait from their near-complete evolution from a species of mountain-dwelling quadrupeds, as there is little other biological evidence to suggest such a genetic heritage. An Iktotchi's horns are particularly hard and durable, although it is possible that they can be broken and subsequently regrown.

Beyond their horns, the most notable feature of the Iktotchi that is not related to their appearance is their incredible gift of clairvoyance, typically manifested through dreams and visions. When the Iktotchi first encountered representatives from the Old Republic, the scouts were astounded to see, from the planet's atmosphere, the seal of the Republic carved quite clearly into a mountain plateau. The Iktotchi were, apparently, prepared for the scouts' arrival long in advance, having seen the event in dreams and precognitive visions. In fact, the Iktotchi were doubly excited to meet the representatives because, dating back generations, the horned species had legends of a time when they would join a great galactic civilization that "spanned the stars."

Although both male and female Iktotchi share the gift of clairvoyance, most have no control over when they receive these visions, and the responsibility assumed in becoming a trained Seer is great. It is only after deep consideration and consultation with elder Seers that Iktotchi will elect to train as Seers themselves, and it is not uncommon for them to withdraw from the training once it has begun. Starting as young adults, Seers will spend years in meditative practice perfecting their control, to the point that they can enter a trance and summon insight into the future at will. Trained Seers do not do this lightly—Iktotchi feel, just as the Jedi do, that the future is always in motion and can be affected by current events and actions. Although Iktotchi will prepare for events seen in a vision, any efforts to fix a particular future, ensure a certain outcome, or, worse, personally profit from it are strongly prohibited in Iktotchi culture.

Overall, the Iktotchi are a quiet, sensitive people who hide their intense emotions behind a detached or dispassionate expression of stoicism. They are respectful of other beings and cultures, but they have difficulty forming close relationships with them, although they have been known to form deep, abiding ties with some non-Iktotchi if they are given the time. Iktotchi can sometimes show a bit of irritation with those who do not understand or take into account their precognitive powers, yet they are normally very concerned about frightening or upsetting others with their talents. Most Iktotchi will keep silent on such things unless asked, or unless the subject becomes important to the situation at hand. Unfortunately for many Iktotchi who travel about the galaxy, they can sometimes wind up viewing their clairvoyance as a curse rather than a blessing, and will avoid the topic entirely when in the company of other species.

It is no wonder, then, that the Jedi took immediate interest in this species, and even established one of the first offworld settlements on Iktotchon. Iktotchi trained as Jedi were often more powerful than other species in sensory skills, with their clairvoyant talents especially enhanced through the Force. Iktotchi Jedi were particularly adept at battlefield management and strategy, and were also gifted at creating "Force-melds," in which Jedi are linked to each other through the force during combat.

Iktotchi precognitive skills led to another great talent for which they are renowned—their piloting abilities. The Iktotchi rank among some of the best pilots in the galaxy, equal

DESIGNATION
Sentient

HOMEWORLD
Iktotchon

AVERAGE HEIGHT
1.8 meters

PRONUNCIATION
Ik-tŏt'-chē

only to humans, Duros, and Mon Calamari. Among these, the Iktotchi precognition gives them the edge (especially Force-sensitives), and yet for many years after their much-anticipated entrance into galactic society, the Iktotchi were distrusted because of this power. For a time, the prejudice against the Iktotchi reached the point that many members of the species denied they had the skill in order to be accepted among others, who thought they were mind readers or doom bringers. Ironically, these Iktotchi were mostly telling the truth, in that their powers of clairvoyance seemed to diminish the farther away they were from their homeworld. Eventually, this suspicion against their species diminished, and they soon became some of the most sought-after pilots in the galaxy, with shipowners willing to pay exorbitant amounts for even the most inexperienced of Iktotchi pilots.

Iktotchi are also respected for their engineering prowess, with their skills in fixing or maintaining vessels becoming just as well known as their abilities to pilot them. They usually anticipate mechanical failures before they happen, making an Iktotchi invaluable in any crew.

During the period leading up to the Clone Wars and the rise of the Empire, many Iktotchi saw the coming bloodshed in their dreams and did their best to avert it through diplomacy. When Palpatine took control, the diplomats quickly withdrew to their world to wait out his rule, even as their Jedi brethren were slaughtered—Iktotchi Jedi being among the first to die because they posed the greatest threat to Palpatine's plans. And yet, when the Iktotchi retreated, Palpatine was content to leave them mostly alone, establishing a blockade over their world in order to keep their power under his thumb. Isolation, the Iktotchi realized, was their only way to survive as a species, and so they endured for a generation until their new visions of a crumbling Empire came to pass. Even so, some Iktotchi were reported to have slipped past the blockade to join the Rebellion.

With the rise of the New Republic, they eagerly jumped at the chance to help the fledgling government get off the ground. The Iktotchi were uncharacteristically taken by surprise by the invasion of the Yuuzhan Vong, however—the Yuuzhan Vong presence was as invisible to Iktotchi clairvoyance as it was to the powers of the Jedi.

NOTABLE APPEARANCE
Episode I: The Phantom Menace

ISHI TIB

The Ishi Tib are green, amphibious beings from the Mid Rim planet Tibrin, a world of moderate temperatures that is almost completely covered by wide oceans and coral reefs. The planet's axis is perpendicular to its orbital plane, and since the orbit is almost perfectly circular, the surface of Tibrin does not vary in temperature. The tides and currents of the planet's massive oceans circulate the warmth of the equatorial waters to the poles, creating a temperate zone over most of the world.

The Ishi Tib evolved from large, bony fish in the shallow waters of the coral reefs that form the only landmasses on their world. The ancestors of the Ishi Tib often escaped from predators by leaping onto the air-exposed portions of the coral reefs. As a result, modern Ishi Tib cities are built upon, or even grown out of, this very same coral. These cities encompass food production; Ishi Tib grow edible seaweed and breed fish and crustaceans for food in underwater corrals. Their concern for their environment is reflected in their insistence that every technological or scientific device they create be tested for its potential ecological impact before use. In addition, the seas on Tibrin are quite safe, a result of the Ishi Tib taming them through the domestication or killing off of all dangerous predators. The Ishi Tib are passionate eco-preservationists who will not sacrifice or compromise the ecological balance of their world.

The physical form of the Ishi Tib reflects their development from sea life. Their skin is rough and leathery, resistant to water evaporation. Their yellow eyes are located on two eyestalks that jut from their heads at an angle, and these eyes enable them to see in the dim light under the ocean surface. Their two pouch-like cheeks allow them to suck in and temporarily store algae and microscopic seafood, and their nostrils grant them a strong sense of smell that functions both in water and on land. They have two lungs that serve as internal gills, enabling them to breathe underwater. Ishi Tib's beaks are sharp and powerful, giving them ability to crack open tough shellfish or bite through the fingers or tails of unsuspecting attackers. Their bodies are thick and muscular, with two-fingered stubby hands and flat, fin-like feet.

Being amphibians, the Ishi Tib are still dependent on water. Their skin and gill-like lungs require frequent replenishment of moisture and sea salts, so approximately every thirty standard hours, Ishi Tib must immerse themselves in a saltwater solution comparable to that of their native oceans. If they don't, their gills and skin will eventually dry out and crack open, and if the condition worsens, the Ishi Tib will die of internal and external bleeding. This need has given rise to a lively trade in Tibrin sea salts for offworld Ishi Tib.

As in the case of their fishy progenitors, Ishi Tib society centers on "schools" or communities of no more than ten thousand people. Representatives elected to one-year terms govern these schools in accordance with ecological law. There is no marriage, and reproduction is decided based upon the needs of the school and the resources available to support an addition to the population. Fertilized eggs are laid in hatcheries in a sandbar area near the coral reef, and the school, as a community, raises the children. Because of this, no Ishi Tib is aware of who their relatives really are; inbreeding is not a concern. When the decision to reproduce is made, partners are tested to verify that no problems will arise for their offspring.

Ishi Tib communicate through a spoken language made up of honks, squeals, and beak-clacks. The Tibrinese written language utilizes a hieroglyphic system that has been in use for thousands of years, dating back to Tibrin's pretechnological era, when pictographs were still carved in soft stone-like substances.

Ishi Tib are patient, quiet, and calculating. They are rarely rash or impulsive, analyzing every choice or decision with great thought. These traits make them excellent planners, capable of maintaining organizational control over large, complex projects. Though they rarely leave home, they are highly desired around the galaxy as tacticians, executives,

DESIGNATION
Sentient

HOMEWORLD
Tibrin

AVERAGE HEIGHT
1.7 meters

PRONUNCIATION
Ĭsh'-ē Tĭb

planners, accountants, and project managers—even more so because they are a tenacious people, never satisfied with leaving a job unfinished. These qualities also made the Ishi Tib greatly valued as tacticians during the Rebellion.

In the post–Yuuzhan Vong galaxy, Ishi Tib expertise at creating balanced environments has been especially needed, and as a result, Ishi Tib have been seen offworld in increasing numbers. More and more have been lured away from their home planet with offers of exorbitant salaries. However, some unprincipled corporations, after hiring Ishi Tib, find that their environmental concerns come into conflict with certain business ventures. These unlucky souls usually end up jobless, searching the galaxy and many times hiring themselves out to anyone who can get them closer to home. While Ishi Tib are more concerned about the needs of their fellow species members and families than anyone else, when they are offworld and alone, they frequently focus this attachment on others in their association. They have no inherent fear of other beings, and will reach out to them for companionship and assistance, although this can sadly put them into relationships with some rather shady characters.

Despite their subdued and pensive nature, the Ishi Tib are truly ruthless fighters. When pressed or cornered, Ishi Tib will go berserk and even, if possible, cannibalize opponents who incite them. Some unscrupulous members of society have exploited this behavior, enslaving itinerant Ishi Tib and forcing them to be unwitting executioners. While the Ishi Tib typically try to resist their impulse to kill when compelled by cruel taskmasters, most succumb to their baser natures if pushed past their emotional limits.

NOTABLE APPEARANCE
Episode VI: Return of the Jedi

ITHORIAN

Ithorians are a mammalian species who populated the planet Ithor in the Ottega system of the Mid Rim until it was ravaged and made uninhabitable by the Yuuzhan Vong. Ithorians are often referred to as Hammerheads because their head curves forward like a common hand tool. The only other obvious traits that differentiate them from standard mammals are their two mouths, located on either side of their necks, and their four throats, similarly divided, enabling them to speak in stereo. Their native tongue is based upon this ability, and although other species find the Ithorian language beautiful, it is impossible for non-Ithorians to reproduce. Ithorian language is a mixture of notes, tones, and inflections resembling music in two-part harmony, and thus most Ithorians speak Basic in order to interact with the rest of the galaxy.

Ithor was, before its devastation, a lush, tropical world where technology and nature existed together in harmony, as designed by the environmentally focused Ithorians. Ithor was renowned as a world of uncommon beauty, drawing to it countless ecotourists and other beings seeking a place of serenity. Ithorians worship a deity referred to as Mother Jungle, and to honor her, they pledged to keep their world as unspoiled as possible. To preserve the planet's surface, they lived in floating cities called herds or herd ships, and all Ithorians contributed to support the other members of their tribes. Herd cities traveled over the planet, hovering above the semi-intelligent bafforr trees without touching down in order to do as little damage to the environment as possible. The bafforr trees grew in large groves on Ithor, and were another object of Ithorian worship. On rare occasions, select Ithorians would hear the "call" of Mother Jungle, and descend to the planet's surface to live and serve her as ecological priests, never to return to their herd cities.

These city-ships had many levels, and were the centers for commerce, culture, and industry. Every five years, the herds would gather at an event known as the Meet, where Ithorians would tell stories, celebrate, debate, and vote on planetary issues. Smaller Meets were held in space for those traveling communities not able to return to Ithor. Now these smaller events are the core of Ithorian civilization, as the species can no longer reside on their homeworld. More than ever, Meets allow Ithorians to be with others of their kind, and prevent the extinction of Ithorian culture.

Ithorians were one of the earliest spacefaring species. The interstellar ships they built for space travel are similar to their herd ships, but equipped with hyperdrives. Their vessels mimic the environment of their planet, featuring indoor jungles, artificial storms, humid atmosphere, vegetation, and wildlife. Ithorians commonly travel to other worlds in caravans in order to trade merchandise, so many were offworld when the Yuuzhan Vong attacked.

The Ithorian people are peaceful and respectful to other life-forms. They are steadfast herbivores, and for every plant the Ithorians would consume on their world, in keeping with the Ithorian Law of Life, they would plant two more to keep the environment thriving. On their ships, they continue this tradition, and when visiting another world, they are always sensitive about disturbing that planet's ecology.

Despite their peaceful nature, Ithorians did develop powerful deflector shields to protect both their own world and their herd ships, and it was this technology that gave Ithorian herds the ability to roam their planet without armaments. Sadly, their lack of weaponry made them easy prey to the ruthless Yuuzhan Vong, who ravaged Ithor and destroyed all the native herd cities.

As made apparent by their limited armaments, Ithorians are committed pacifists. The desire to achieve peace at all times is an Ithorian goal. In one known case, an Ithorian named Zorneth took this aspiration to the extreme by trying to eliminate violence completely. With the assistance of a human named Klorr Vilia, Zorneth developed an herb called savorium that immediately transformed all those who consumed it, rendering them peaceful. While Vilia managed to destroy the herb after witnessing firsthand how it drastically

and unnaturally altered a being's nature, the Ithorians were hesitant to punish Zorneth in a manner that would please the New Republic, because his intentions were good. After an involved trial he was imprisoned, with the Ithorian people declaring that peace achieved without freedom of will is a false peace at best.

With Ithorians unable to dwell on their homeworld following the Yuuzhan Vong invasion, groups of Ithorian scientists returned to seek ways to bioengineer the planet and bring life back to the poisoned soil. However, with the work showing little progress, their people began the difficult search for a new homeworld. Through the aid of Leia Organa Solo, the planet Borao was chosen as an appropriate place for the Ithorians to settle, in the hope of starting life anew. However, a small number of Ithorians do remain exiled in their starship herds, holding out optimism that the scientists on Ithor will be successful in their efforts.

Ithorians tend to pursue professions that will not draw them into conflict with others. Very seldom will Ithorians serve in military positions, and while they managed to avoid the Galactic Civil War, some joined the Rebellion and New Republic in limited numbers. In addition, Ithorian Jedi are not unheard of. It is believed that membership in the Jedi order is consistent with the Ithorian dedication to peace, as Jedi strive to serve the well-being of all. One field that Ithorians are particularly drawn to, and excel in, is diplomacy. Their drive for harmony, and their natural talents at negotiation, make them highly effective at working out difficulties and drawing up treaties among beings. Throughout the galaxy, they also often act as merchants, negotiators, ecologists, botanists, healers, and scientists of varying fields. They enjoy travel, exploration, meeting new people, and learning new things, and especially delight in finding unique items to trade and sell as their herd ships roam the galaxy. Ithorians see the sharing of information and cultures as a means to peace through understanding, and it is a credit to their strength of character that they have maintained faith in this ideal in the wake of their world's devastation. In fact, despite this tragedy, they seem even more driven to further the cause of peace throughout the known systems, while settling into a new world that they hope to one day think of as their home.

DESIGNATION
Sentient

HOMEWORLD
Ithor

AVERAGE
HEIGHT
2 meters

PRONUNCIATION
Ĭ-thō′-rē-ăn

NOTABLE APPEARANCE
Episode IV: A New Hope

JAWA

Jawas are small humanoids who live on Tatooine, the harsh Outer Rim desert world that was the childhood home of both Anakin and Luke Skywalker. While Jawas layer themselves under thick robes, xenobiologists, through studying corpses and skeletal remains, have discovered that they have the appearance of gaunt, rodent-like creatures, with shrunken faces and yellow eyes.

Each Jawa is about a meter tall, with tiny, flexible hands and feet. Their evolutionary origins are a bit mysterious. Some theories contend that both Jawas and their neighbors, the Tusken Raiders, descended from an ancient species known only as the Kumumgah, while others insist that Jawas evolved from rodents.

If they did evolve from rodents, most scientists believe that they gradually grew in size and learned to walk upright by reaching for lichens and fungi growing on underground cave walls—caves that once housed the rare underground springs around which their society initially developed.

These springs eventually dried up, and the Jawas adapted to their new environment with sheer ingenuity. To protect themselves from the fierce double suns of their world, they started wearing coarse, homespun cloaks with large hoods under which only their yellow, glowing eyes seem to be visible. Their eyes are magnified by polished orange gemstones embedded in their facial coverings to protect their sensitive rat-like vision from the bright sunlight. These gems, called durindfire, are found in the desert sands and are worthless to other species—but the Jawas find them invaluable.

For their own nourishment, Jawas obtain water by inserting long, thin hoses down the stems of the funnel flower, a flora native to Tatooine, and siphoning off the liquid. Their diet is primarily made up of hubba gourd, a fruit difficult for humans to digest, the name of which in the Jawas' language translates to "the staff of life."

Most humans have noted that Jawas give off a strong, distinct, and usually unpleasant odor. This is the combined result of a mysterious solution in which they dip their clothes to retain body moisture, and the fact that they do not bathe often in their water-bereft environment. It is also partly related to their communication methods, half of which are pheromonal projections.

The meaning of the Jawas' language is tied to these pheromonal emanations, which communicate their emotions and needs. It is, therefore, incomprehensible and cannot be learned by humans and other species. While Jawas can understand Basic, they have intense difficulty speaking it or any language other than their own, and thus, to trade with non-Jawas, they use a simplified form of their language that residents of Tatooine refer to as Jawa Trade Language.

To make their living, Jawas salvage, repair, and resell junk that they find in the desert. Sometimes they even "find" items that haven't been lost, especially those that haven't been locked down. Moisture farmers often discover their property disappearing, only for it to turn up in the possession of a Jawa who is selling it at a tidy profit. Because of this, they are reputed to be swindlers and thieves, but Jawas are not offended by the accusation and are instead proud of their ability to discover items that others "lose," and also proud of their proficiency at repairing equipment. For junk that is unsalvageable, Jawas utilize high-powered solar smelters that melt things down into salable ingots.

Jawa society is divided into clans or tribes. Once a year, all the clans will meet at a giant gathering in the great basin of the Dune Sea, where they share stories, trade items, and even barter sons and daughters as "marriage merchandise." The trading of family members in marriage is considered a good business deal, as it continues the diversity of their bloodlines. In fact, Jawa culture centers on family. They take immense pride in their clans and ancestry, and their language includes forty-three different terms to describe relationship, lineage, and bloodline. Clans keep track of these relations very closely, recording family lines with extreme detail. Few Jawas leave the clan lifestyle, and when they do, they can be found in disreputable Tatooine cities such as Mos Eisley and Mos Espa. Members of the clans travel together in large vehicles known as sandcrawlers—nuclear-fusion-powered ore-hauling vehicles abandoned by contractors during the reign of the Old Republic. Jawas have modified these sandcrawlers to the point that their original purpose is virtually undetectable. Each crawler carries up to three hundred Jawas and acts as a fully equipped repair

DESIGNATION
Sentient

HOMEWORLD
Tatooine

AVERAGE HEIGHT
1 meter

PRONUNCIATION
Jä'-wä

shop, allowing them to perform skilled reconstructions as they make their journey across the desert wastes.

While a portion of the Jawas are constantly on the move, searching for salvage, the remainder stay behind in clan fortresses built from large chunks of wrecked spacecraft. Master repair experts reside in these fortresses, where they perform advanced salvage procedures that exceed the capacity of the sandcrawler shops. These elaborate fortifications are often subjected to attacks by Sand People, who will kill Jawas in order to pillage their scavenged treasures and precious water. This is one of many harsh desert realities that contribute greatly to Jawas' cautious, almost paranoid, nature, and as such they have made their defense into their best offense, through the stability of the fortresses they build. Jawas are not intense fighters, and because of their size, they'll often run away when confronted. When cornered, however, Jawas have proven themselves to be very resourceful and capable users of the weapons that they scavenge from the desert sands.

The most prominent member of each clan is the shaman, a female Jawa whom the population believes possesses the ability to predict the future. While this has not been scientifically proven, recently discovered studies of the Jawas performed before the ascension of Emperor Palpatine assert that these female shamans exhibited something akin to Force abilities. Unlike any Jedi, however, they perform elaborate spells, hexes, and blessings to protect the tribe and provide wellness for its members. Each shaman takes on a student during her tenure, training this apprentice to take her place when she dies.

The clan shaman, through her influence, controls most tribal decisions relating to defenses, travel, and day-to-day life. She does not travel in the sandcrawler, but remains behind at the permanent fortress, where she can be better protected. In fact, Jawas will fight to defend the shaman even in the face of certain defeat. In his notes, anthropologist Hoole referred to an incident where he witnessed Jawas defending the shaman's home against a force of Tusken Raiders with the ferocity of beings twice their size. They did not retreat or surrender, though nearly three-quarters of the Jawas lost their lives in the process.

NOTABLE APPEARANCE
Episode IV: A New Hope

KALEESH

The Kaleesh are a reptilian humanoid species native to the Outer Rim world of Kalee. They are an attractive group, similar in appearance to the Falleen in some respects—though the Kaleesh's scaled skin is reddish orange, and they have two sharp tusks that protrude outward from their jawbones on each side of their faces. Jet-black hair cascades from their heads, usually worn tied back in braids. Yellow reptilian eyes with elliptical irises give them fairly average eyesight, although Kaleesh possess a thermoreceptor gland directly next to their eyes with which they can see into the infrared spectrum for a short range, as can many hunter snakes. The Kaleesh are a polygamous people, with each male having multiple wives and many offspring, but whether this is a cultural tradition or a practice instituted to meet a societal or biological need—as in the case of Cereans, with their low birthrate and imbalanced male-to-female ratio—is unknown.

Despite their relative attractiveness, the faces and bodies of the Kaleesh are rarely exposed. Most wear masks made of the skulls and teeth of their world's fiercest predators, the karabba and mumuus, to conceal their faces. Kaleesh also cover their bodies completely for defense against the harsh sun of their homeworld, and usually their four-fingered, claw-like hands are the only aspect of the Kaleesh that can be seen. In addition, the families of elite Kaleesh warriors wear hereditary battle masks that are passed down within a house's line, from one generation to the next. These masks are painted with karabba and mumuu blood prior to a battle, in patterns that are unique to each family. After being used in combat, they are cleaned and stored until they are needed again.

The Kaleesh are a nomadic tribal people, and have become spacefaring only recently. During the waning years of the Old Republic, Kaleesh tribes united under a common leader who would later be known as Grievous, to fight off an invading insectoid race called the Huk. The Huk had already conquered and subjugated other worlds, plundering them of their natural riches. With barren Kalee, they sought to exploit the only commodity available to make a profit—people. The Huk captured Kaleesh by the hundreds and sold them as slaves.

Under Grievous's leadership, the Kaleesh banded together and drove the Huk from their planet. In the process, the Huk were completely decimated, pushed back to their own world and even beyond as Grievous, seeking revenge, co-opted Huk technology and ships for his own use, conquering their entire system and preying upon their colonies as well as the Huk homeworld.

The Huk, utterly overwhelmed by the vitriolic hatred and violence of the Kaleesh, sought help from the Old Republic, which—through the back-door manipulations of unknown forces—sympathized with the Huk and enacted economic sanctions against Kalee, enforced by the Jedi. Grievous withdrew to his homeworld angry and vengeful, to soon find it driven into the dust under the weight of economic sanctions. Witnessing his people starving and watching hundreds of thousands dying from famine, Grievous grew even more contemptuous of the Republic and the Jedi who protected it.

As if in answer to his woes, the InterGalactic Banking Clan, headed by a Muun named San Hill, offered Grievous a deal through which he could help his people financially. With his masterful military commanding skills, he would act as a collection agent against worlds that had defaulted on loans provided by the Banking Clan. Though Grievous bristled at being a paid "heavy," he took the offer. After all, the clan promised to relieve some of the terrible debts and financial stress levied upon his people, not to mention arranging to have the economic sanctions lifted.

For the most part, the Banking Clan did live up to the bargain, as did Grievous, delivering the debts of several planets to them. And yet the favorable relationship was not to last.

DESIGNATION
Sentient

HOMEWORLD
Kalee

AVERAGE HEIGHT
1.8 meters

PRONUNCIATION
Käl-ēsh'

When the Trade Federation refused to punish Grievous's old enemies for desecrating Kaleesh burial grounds on the Huk's colony worlds, Grievous abandoned his job, starting another conflict. The InterGalactic Banking Clan decided to repay him for his lack of commitment by setting off an explosive device in his ship. However, this attack was actually another ploy to keep Grievous under its sway, as the intent was never to kill him, but to make Grievous dependent and controllable. Wounded in the subsequent crash and suffering from additional injuries carefully inflicted afterward, Grievous was given a new cyborg body by Count Dooku and San Hill, who also secretly altered his mind, all with the help of the Geonosians. Without Grievous's knowledge and despite promises made to the contrary, Grievous's sense of honor as a warrior was removed, turning him into an unscrupulous conqueror. After this, the great Kaleesh military commander became little more than a lackey for the Separatists, until his eventual death at the hands of Jedi Master Obi-Wan Kenobi.

Following the fall of the Republic, and during the expansion of the Empire, the Kaleesh were generally overlooked until the New Republic rose to power. They remain a war-like people, although they are only known to be combative if provoked by outside forces. Extremely protective of what they consider sacred, the Kaleesh follow a religion that centers on ancestor worship. Their lands and burial grounds hold particular importance. Kaleesh believe that those who die in self-sacrifice and with honor are added to their pantheon of gods, and as a result, any burial ground is a holy place.

The primary area of worship for Kaleesh is an island called Abesmi, located in the middle of the warm world's single ocean, where it rises from the waves as a rectangular black formation of rock. This place is said to be the spot where Kaleesh ancestors descend from and rise to the heavens. It is customary to undertake pilgrimages to Abesmi, though most Kaleesh can make their proper worship commitments in local sculpted shrines that point in the direction of the legendary island. One of these newer shrines was built in honor of General Grievous, who is now a revered member of the religion's heavenly pantheon.

NOTABLE APPEARANCE
Star Wars Visionaries (comic)

KAMINOAN

Kaminoans are thin, towering, pale-skinned humanoids who inhabit the little-known water-covered world of Kamino on the edge of Wild Space. They have long, graceful appendages, and their oblong heads sit atop slender, elongated necks. Their large, dark eyes enable them to see into the ultraviolet spectrum, and their tiny mouths are perfectly suited for the small amount of food they consume. Female Kaminoans are completely bald, while their male counterparts bear a unique headcrest.

When a severe shift in global temperatures caused the ending of a planetary ice age, flooding their world, the Kaminoans chose extreme methods to survive. They developed an exacting, detailed scientific method for cloning their own species, and enacted selective breeding to adapt their race to the changing environment through the elimination of weaknesses. As such, they are one of the most genetically homogeneous species in the known galaxy, having controlled variation from one Kaminoan to another. This is not to suggest that there is perfect genetic replication, but rather that the Kaminoans utilize a cloning process that produces children within a strict, predetermined set of genetic parameters.

Scientists are therefore greatly regarded and given high places of honor in society. Those who are most respected will literally wear a sign of their hierarchical placement on their sleeves—black cuffs are an indication of those who have earned esteem. The thicker the cuff, the higher the rank of the individual.

Kaminoans initially evolved from a species of marsh-dwelling amphibians who were focused on their communities at the suppression of individual expression. The early Kaminoans trained their young for specific tasks to serve the greater good of their people, and this communal focus has remained. While Kaminoans control their genetic codes, they also allow their children to develop their own interests and select careers of their choice within a community-approved set of parameters. The cloning process is designed to ensure sufficient numbers for each niche of society, as not all Kaminoans are employed in the cloning industry.

Because of their past struggle to survive and the Kaminoan cultural mind-set toward ending genetic weaknesses through selective breeding, the Kaminoans have developed an unspoken intolerance for physical frailty or imperfection in other species. While they are polite and gentle in their manner to outsiders, they cannot understand the tendency for most non-Kaminoans to maintain a lineage that includes any genetic imperfection. They feel all species that continue down such a pathway are inferior and deserving of eventual elimination. This attitude extends to all their cloning projects, wherein they will monitor creations for any irregularities in biochemistry, subjecting deviant clones to extensive conditioning to correct their aberrations. In keeping with their commitment to flawlessness, they have also developed methods of extreme sterilization so that clones are not spoiled with any defects. That they can keep such a large operation immaculate is considered a remarkable feat.

The Kaminoans work and dwell in huge floating cities that appear white and sparse to the naked human eye, yet all of their architectural constructions are actually decorated in the ultraviolet spectrum. They use cloned aiwhas for transportation between these floating cities. Even though Kaminoans have eliminated most of their weaknesses, they keep their living and working areas at a perpetual temperate climate, as they find the extreme temperatures of the outside world terribly uncomfortable, particularly high heat and bright sunlight. They prefer Kamino's autumn, when the skies never clear and a light rain is constantly falling. Kaminoans also have a deep respect for their origins, and the lessons learned from the catastrophe that changed their planet are continually reinforced. The cities in which Kaminoans originated now lie deep beneath Kamino's oceans, and they do not permit that environment to be disturbed, instead maintaining the ruins as sacred sites for pilgrimages.

The Kaminoans are relatively unknown throughout the galaxy at large, as they are not a species to travel beyond their home system. However, among those who are familiar with them, they are regarded as the greatest and most skilled producers of cloning technology. It was the Kaminoans who designed the cloned human soldiers who would later become the Grand Army of the Republic and eventually serve the Empire.

Despite their own prejudices, Kaminoans are forced to maintain some contact with the outside galaxy in order to trade for the raw materials and technologies that they require to sustain their highly advanced society. As a result, Kaminoans speak Basic in addition to their native language. Unlike other societies, they have not made any attempts to explore the possibility of undersea mining to obtain the materials they need, likely feeling it would only distract them from their primary focus on trade. Their products have always chiefly depended on their cloning science, which has supported them for generations, including times when they have quietly created armies of workers and soldiers for other cultures. Because Kaminoans have little compassion or feeling for beings other than themselves, they have no qualms about the questionable ethics of their cloning work. Instead, they are proud of their genetic

accomplishments, never taking into account the possible consequences.

While the Kaminoans were creating clones for the Grand Army of the Republic, they were also secretly designing a small clone force for their own protection. Approximately ten years before the destruction of the first Death Star, Kamino attempted to secede from the Empire. In a battle that saw clone fighting clone, with the great bounty hunter Boba Fett taking part on the Imperial side, the Kaminoans were defeated. Utilizing Boba Fett's knowledge of the facility, the Imperials destroyed the Kaminoan cloning equipment, preventing the species from ever again creating its own army. Large numbers of fleeing Kaminoans were shot down and killed as they attempted to leave the planet. However, a small contingent of cloners were forcibly relocated to Coruscant, and as a result their cloning technology survived through a good deal of the Imperial era.

After the Kaminoan insurrection, the Emperor ordered that clones would from then on be designed from multiple templates so that they would not be so easily corrupted against his New Order. However, the 501st Legion, the elite group of stormtroopers known as Vader's Fist, continued as a homogeneous entity based on the template provided by Jango Fett as they were produced in the Coruscant facility staffed by kidnapped Kaminoans. It wasn't until later years that non-Jango members were accepted into the ranks of the 501st. It is unclear whether the Kaminoans were able to reestablish their own cloning facilities on their homeworld, though there have been various reports that some Kaminoan cloning technology may have been smuggled offworld to be sold to the highest bidders.

DESIGNATION
Sentient

HOMEWORLD
Kamino

AVERAGE HEIGHT
2.1 meters

PRONUNCIATION
Kă-mē-nō'-ăn

KEL DOR

The Kel Dors are a kindly, soft-spoken people native to the planet Dorin, a world found in the Expansion Region that contains an atmosphere largely made up of helium and a second mysterious gas substance that is completely unique to the Dorin system. Kel Dors are hairless mammals who are so completely adapted to their native environment that they cannot breathe or see in other atmospheres without using special equipment. Initially, the effects of alternative atmospheres will result in eye and throat irritations, but eventually, if an environment is high enough in gases problematic for them and they are unable to hold their breath, Kel Dors will suffocate.

Members of the Kel Doran species possess greatly developed extrasensory organs located at the base of their skulls, which researchers suggests may actually be a subregion of their brains. Most Kel Dors have intense black eyes, though some are born with silver eyes, a trait that they believe marks them as strong in the Force. Their native Force-using sha-mans, known as the Baran Do Sages, will seek out such Kel Dors to recruit them into their ranks. The skin of a Kel Dor can range in color from peachy orange to deep red, and there are few outwardly visible differences between males and females.

As noted above, when offplanet, Kel Dors will wear an antiox breath mask and goggles. Fitted tightly against the detailed ridges of Kel Doran skulls and connecting into two breath tubes that extend downward from their faces, these masks are equipped with filters supplying Dorin atmospheric isotopes, enabling them to respire in environments that consist of oxygen, nitrogen, or carbon dioxide—substances normally deadly to Kel Dors. They will also outfit their offworld dwellings with special air locks and similar atmospheric filters and controls in order to maintain a proper habitat in which they can breathe. Kel Dors who depart Dorin must also don special eyewear to protect their eyes from burning in certain alien environments. Ironically, these goggles actually improve their eyesight, giving them superior vision when they have them on—although the masks can kill most members of other species if they tried to wear them, and the goggles can blind a non–Kel Dor. The masks also amplify the Kel Dors' voices, but even so, most need to shout in order to be heard through their filters.

Kel Doran life is structured around the family. Couples will begin having children soon after marriage, with several generations of a family often living together in a single dwelling. This is not the result of a housing shortage or overcrowding as on other worlds, but from preference. With parents taking the lead and making major decisions, the entire family is responsible for the care of younglings, from providing for their daily care and early education to their training for professions. It is not unheard of for the majority of a single Kel Doran family to practice the same trade. However, should a Kel Doran child wish to pursue a career different than that of her or his family, they are not discouraged.

The society and economy of Dorin is technology driven. It is not surprising that they excel in the development and manufacture of environmental control devices, and this technological advancement is extended to the unique atmospheric needs of other species in addition to their own. As a result, Kel Doran environmental systems are used in homes and ships on many worlds and set the standard for the industry. Dorin enjoys a well-developed educational system in support of its industrial and scientific needs, and a free education is extended to all.

The Baran Do Sages are a long-standing Kel Doran Force tradition that predates even the Order of the Jedi Knights. For millennia, the Baran Do served as advisers and seers for Kel Doran leaders before Dorin joined the Old Republic. After they were introduced to the Old Republic, many Baran Do children entered the ranks of the Jedi Knights, though those who were too old to begin Jedi training or were passed over in the selection process carried on the Baran Do tradition as it was in the years before the Jedi came to prominence.

The Baran Do began their ascendance when adepts began exploring the Force in an attempt to expand their already powerful sensory perceptions—particularly with regard to predicting future events. Over time, their wisdom helped avert wars, natural disasters, and famines, as well as solving crimes and unraveling mysteries long left unrevealed. At the peak of their influence, they were honored as an omniscient sect that could discern the truth even in the most complex of issues. During their time in office, all Kel Doran rulers kept a sage as an adviser, as did many prominent households. Companies and government institutions used them to conduct day-to-day operations, as they could alert managers to important problems before they occurred.

DESIGNATION
Sentient

HOMEWORLD
Dorin

AVERAGE HEIGHT
1.7 meters

PRONUNCIATION
Kĕl' Dōr

Much of Baran Do training focuses on sensory deprivation—shutting down one sense to bring another to the forefront—or sensory overload—forcing oneself to concentrate amid a cacophony of sound or visual stimulation. As a result, Baran Do Jedi are usually very powerful with any skills involving their sensory perceptions, such as mental influence and telepathic communication. There have been cases recorded of Kel Dor Jedi communicating telepathically across great distances, perhaps even half the galaxy. They are rarely caught off guard, and unlike Jedi who view the future as always in motion, they can frequently pinpoint and predict immediate or even distant future events with incredible accuracy.

With the rise of the Jedi, the Baran Do fell into some obscurity, and in the mainstream of Kel Doran life, they came to be considered little more than wizards. However, the Baran Do continued to teach their ways even as the Emperor undertook his devastating Jedi Purge. As the New Republic rose to power, the Baran Do again began to make contact with the new Jedi order, in the hope that the two groups could work together toward a common goal in the galaxy.

As a species, Kel Dors are generally kindhearted and even-tempered. Besides their preponderance of Force talent, Kel Dors find great good in swift justice, and they will never refuse to help others in need. They have a strong tendency to see moral issues in very black-and-white terms, and do not always consider that there may be other issues at hand. As such, they are often encountered in policing or security roles when away from their native planet. Their sense of justice can be problematic, though, in that they have a propensity for taking the law into their own hands instead of waiting for standard methods of judgment to come into play.

NOTABLE APPEARANCE
Episode I: The Phantom Menace

KILLIK

Killiks are an insectoid species originally native to Alderaan, a planet that had been located in the Core until it was destroyed by the Empire. While Killiks do vary in size and function depending upon their native hive, they all essentially have insect bodies covered in chitinous armor in nearly every color imaginable. Mandibles project from their faces, and four arms ending in long three-toed claws protrude from their torsos.

Killik society centers on a hive mind called the Will, with every Killik mentally connected to all the others, although the strength of the connection dissipates over distances. For this reason, a hive grouping will always act as one individual. At their core, they are peaceful—and yet they recently posed a great threat to the galaxy when their pheromonal telepathic connection to one another extended to include many other races, even non-insectoids. These "Joiners" function as one with the rest of the hive mind, losing independent will and purpose. Such an influence is actually more than simple mind control, in that it literally changes the chemical makeup of the Joiner's brain. In addition, left unchecked by environment or intervention, the Killiks will reproduce to such a degree that they will consume all natural resources in their path.

Killiks are separated into several subspecies, with each group making up a hive or "nest" of its own kind, though all of these nests are connected through a telepathic link. All Killiks begin life as larvae after hatching from eggs, but from that early point their size and function will vary, with each Killik taking on the characteristics of its particular nest. For example, the Jooj nest consists of Killiks only a few centimeters long, who create huge swarms to crawl under enemy soldiers' armor and kill them by draining their blood. The Taat are a hive of healers and warriors. Saras, meanwhile, are artists. Another nest known as the Kolosolaks consists of Killiks approximately fifty meters long and ten meters tall. With their tough exoskeletons, Kolosolaks are extremely hard to damage; they are used as armored ground vehicles.

These various Killik nests were at one time led and influenced by two others, the Unu and the Gorog. The Unu were the primary nest of all the hives, publicly directing the actions of the rest. Guided by the former human Jedi Raynar Thul (called UnuThul by the Killiks), the Unu communicated with the outside world and drew other species in as Joiners, making them part of the insect hive mind through use of membrosia, a highly addictive consumable produced by the Killiks. As the lead nest, it was the conscience of all the others, but over time, the Unu became tainted by one nest in the collective that had taken on a Dark Jedi as a leader: the Gorog, or Dark Nest.

While the nests are not Force-sensitive by nature, through the influence of their respective Force-sensitive Joiners, they took on Force-like abilities, and the Killik hive mind was sadly susceptible to corruption. During the war against the Yuuzhan Vong, the Jedi mounted an unsuccessful mission to Myrkr that, while claiming the life of Anakin Solo and resulting in the capture of Jacen Solo, was thought to have also culminated in the death of Raynar Thul. The presence of the Dark Jedi Lomi Plo and Welk complicated this tragic mission even further when Plo and Welk fled Myrkr in the Jedi's ship, not realizing that Thul was aboard. The vessel ultimately crashed in the Unknown Regions, fatally injuring the passengers, who reached out through the Force for help. They were found by the Killiks, who—despite their lack of experience with humans—healed them as best they could. As a result of these events, Thul was severely scarred from burns, and lost most of his facial features. Plo became more Killik than human, taking on several insectoid body parts, including a leg, arms, oversized eyes, and mandibles.

Prior to absorbing the minds of Thul, Plo, and Welk, the Killiks had been simple creatures. They possessed no inher-

DESIGNATION
Sentient

HOMEWORLD
Alderaan

AVERAGE HEIGHT
Varies from 3 centimeters to more than 2 meters

PRONUNCIATION
Kĭl'-lĭk

ent drive or need to live, dying and reproducing as a biological urge, not an emotional desire. It was only after these humans became Joiners that Killiks learned to value life and the individual. This new mind-set was crucial in influencing the events that followed.

The Unu under Thul's influence was mostly benign, and the Killiks simply wanted to survive. However, the hive known as the Gorog was soon corrupted to become the Dark Nest, having absorbed Lomi Plo and Welk and twisted into a secret hive bent on violence and conquest. The influence of this subverted hive spread to the others as an individual would be provoked by his or her unconscious, inducing the Killiks to dominate the galaxy by sucking in as many Joiners as they could, colonizing one populated world after another. Due to UnuThul's innocence and worsening state of madness, the Gorog was able to hide its presence and activities from him, to the extent that UnuThul denied their existence.

The Killiks began a war of conquest, seeking more and more territories into which they could expand. They started with incursions into Chiss space, and even though this soon led to the eruption of a brutal war that threatened to engulf the entire galaxy, the Killiks reached farther, eventually taking the Alliance world of Thyferra, the home of the insectoid Vratix and a base of bacta manufacturing. Ultimately, Lomi Plo was slain by Luke Skywalker, and Raynar Thul was separated from the Killik hive mind and brought to Coruscant for treatment.

The Killiks have existed for countless millennia, witnessing the creation of the famous and mysterious Centerpoint Station and the nearby Maw. Thirty millennia before the Battle of Yavin, the Celestials reportedly drove them from both Alderaan and their colony on Alsakan into the Unknown Regions, after the Killiks had consumed Alderaan's resources and were planning a move to take over a populated world. The lesson in this, and the one that was eventually heeded by the Galactic Federation of Free Alliances, is that some form of containment of the Killiks is necessary. They were finally defeated by the Galactic Alliance, but only after a great loss of life on both sides—though the Killiks did not seem emotionally affected at the individual loss of life, either their own or those of their Joiners.

NOTABLE APPEARANCE
Dark Nest I: The Joiner King (novel)

KITONAK

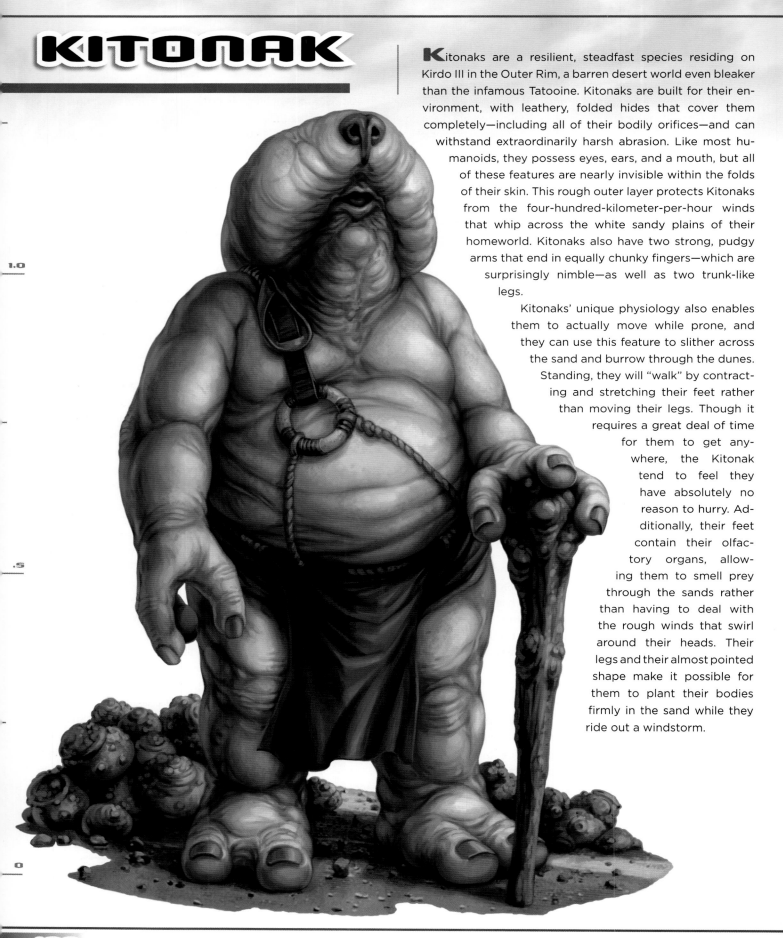

Kitonaks are a resilient, steadfast species residing on Kirdo III in the Outer Rim, a barren desert world even bleaker than the infamous Tatooine. Kitonaks are built for their environment, with leathery, folded hides that cover them completely—including all of their bodily orifices—and can withstand extraordinarily harsh abrasion. Like most humanoids, they possess eyes, ears, and a mouth, but all of these features are nearly invisible within the folds of their skin. This rough outer layer protects Kitonaks from the four-hundred-kilometer-per-hour winds that whip across the white sandy plains of their homeworld. Kitonaks also have two strong, pudgy arms that end in equally chunky fingers—which are surprisingly nimble—as well as two trunk-like legs.

Kitonaks' unique physiology also enables them to actually move while prone, and they can use this feature to slither across the sand and burrow through the dunes. Standing, they will "walk" by contracting and stretching their feet rather than moving their legs. Though it requires a great deal of time for them to get anywhere, the Kitonak tend to feel they have absolutely no reason to hurry. Additionally, their feet contain their olfactory organs, allowing them to smell prey through the sands rather than having to deal with the rough winds that swirl around their heads. Their legs and their almost pointed shape make it possible for them to plant their bodies firmly in the sand while they ride out a windstorm.

1.0

.5

0

Waiting is not new to Kitonaks. They are one of the most patient species in the galaxy—*so* patient, in fact, that they frequently irritate other species with their plodding, methodical mannerisms. They rarely do anything quickly, and this includes breathing and eating. Kitonaks possess an extra set of lungs that enables them to store oxygen for three or four standard hours, and their stored fat aids them in going without food for weeks, provided that they do not overexert themselves.

Their culture is a simple, primitive one, with no technology. Kitonaks live in small tribal groups that migrate around the desert following herds of chooba, their primary source of sustenance. Their method of hunting is most indicative of their slow-paced way of life, in that it involves standing motionless and mimicking a sulfaro plant—the chooba's favorite dish. Kitonaks will wait as the chooba climbs to the top of their head, looking for the "plant's" meaty interior, at which point they swallow the chooba whole. One of these creatures can provide a Kitonak enough nourishment to last for an entire standard month.

As the Kitonak have no natural foes, there are only two native things they fear: quicksand and caves. Should one of them fall victim to quicksand, their patient nature often permits them to simply float and breathe until help arrives. The only problem is that help isn't often very speedy.

Caves, meanwhile, are considered by Kitonaks to be gateways to the underworld. On Kirdo III, there exist many tales of Kitonaks who have entered caves and not returned, and local legends refer to such places as gateways to the Realm of the Dead. For this reason, Kitonaks will avoid going into caves at any cost, even facing the deadliest of windstorms before entering one.

Kitonaks get most of their education from tales and songs. Every evening a "telling of the story" is held, which can last for several hours. Each tribe member takes a turn adding new twists to the plot and singing lyrics to further the tale along. This tradition is meant to instruct the young on the value of patience, but it also succeeds in relaying a good deal of information about the world in which they dwell. A full story may actually last several nights, but each evening is carefully planned to end a certain episode in the tale. Many of these stories focus on the most important event for the Kitonak circle of life: the rainfall, which occurs only once a decade.

DESIGNATION
Sentient

HOMEWORLD
Kirdo III

AVERAGE HEIGHT
1.3 meters

PRONUNCIATION
Kĭt'-ō-năk

Kitonak mating centers on the rainfall on Kirdo III, a deluge that lasts several days, creates vast lakes, and turns the dry riverbeds into flowing rivers. When the rains finally stop, Kitonaks begin their "Great Celebration of Life," in which they dive into the temporary rivers and conduct a mating ritual known as the Dance of Love. After this, they emerge downstream, and any females who conceived during the previous rainfall will surface with newborn children. This occurs because the Kitonak gestation period equals the duration of time between rainfalls, and females fertilized during one Celebration give birth at the next.

Members of the species also mature fully in nine years, just in time to take part in the next Celebration. After each rainfall, if a Kitonak tribe has grown too large, some of its younger members will depart to find another tribe that has fewer. These solitary Kitonaks will often hollow out chidinka plants to make a chidinkalu, a pipe instrument with which they play songs to attract others. Unfortunately, there have been incidents of slave traders kidnapping some of these wandering Kitonaks. As slaves, it is suspected that they did not last long, since other species have no tolerance for their slow, tenacious personalities. Sadly, there are often reports of Kitonaks being beaten or abandoned by their owners in places where they could not survive without assistance.

However, their musical traditions have become somewhat influential in the galactic music world. Kitonaks who wander the galaxy either freely or as slaves are usually engaged as musicians, as their compositions and style are original and uplifting. The most widely known Kitonak musician was Droopy McCool, who, following his release from slavery, played with Evar Orbus and his Galactic Wailers. The Galactic Wailers later became the Max Rebo Band, during an extended gig at the palace of Jabba the Hutt on Tatooine. After Jabba's death, Droopy walked off alone into the Tatooine desert, believing he heard the call of other Kitonaks. He was never heard from or seen again. While it has not been verified, there are rumors of a Kitonak colony on Tatooine, somewhere between Mos Eisley and Anchorhead. One can hope that Droopy found what he was longing for.

NOTABLE APPEARANCE
Episode VI: Return of the Jedi

KLATOOINIAN

Klatooinians, of the Outer Rim planet Klatooine, have been in the service of the Hutts for nearly twenty-five thousand standard years. They are a canine-based species that long ago evolved into sentience, with coarse brown or greenish skin and dog-like faces featuring dark eyes and heavy brows. Although the genders are rarely confused, there is little noticeable difference between male and female Klatooinians, other than the fact that males are generally slightly heavier in build. Klatooinian culture predates even the Old Republic, making them one of the oldest sentient species in the galaxy, short of only a handful of species including the Hutts and humans.

Klatooinians have proven extremely loyal foot soldiers, displaying tenacity, fierceness, and unwavering devotion. The Hutts—always the opportunists—exploited this characteristic loyalty by tricking the Klatooinians into co-signing a contract called the Treaty of Vontor that placed them and the two other species of the Si'klaata Cluster, the Nikto and the Vodrans, into Hutt servitude for an indefinite period of time. The primary Klatooinian instigator of this treaty was an individual named Barada M'Beg. M'Beg became a hero to his people because the Klatooinians saw the Hutts as near-gods, potentially the "ancients" of their legends. The treaty therefore bound them to their deities. Many Klatooinian children are named Barada or M'Beg because of M'Beg's popularity and heroic and legendary status among his people.

Of course, the Klatooinian submission to Hutt rule has proven invaluable to the Hutts, particularly since the Klatooinians were instrumental in helping the Hutts overthrow the infamous warlord Xim the Despot. It is because the Hutts still find the Klatooinians useful as foot soldiers that they remain in service today. But to the Klatooinian mentality, all things pass away in time, even treaties—a belief of which the Hutts remain wary.

This sense of impermanent servitude was evident even among the Klatooinians in Jabba's cadre, as reported by Lando Calrissian. A Klatooinian named Barada indentured under protest to Jabba the Hutt was a mechanic who maintained all of the Hutt's repulsorlift vehicles and also served as a part-time guard for the crimelord as well. Known for wearing an orange scarf to symbolize a protest against unjust servitude to others of his own people (a protest Jabba either didn't care about or didn't recognize), Barada was chafing, as many of his people eventually did, under the Hutt's control. Unfortunately, he was unable to take advantage of the freedom Jabba's death would have offered him because he was cut down by Luke Skywalker during the skirmish above the Great Pit of Carkoon. Calrissian reported one other Klatooinian named Kithaba present at the confrontation, who held the unfortunate distinction of being the first of Jabba's skiff guards to fall toward the maw of the Sarlacc. Despite his best efforts to claw his way free, Kithaba was eventually grappled by one of the Sarlacc's inflamed tentacles and devoured.

Time is pivotal to understanding Klatooinian culture. At some time before history was recorded on Klatooine, in the middle of Klatooine's Derelkoos Desert, a natural fissure to the world's crust opened, allowing a liquid known as wintrium to seep out and touch the dry desert air. This contact resulted in the formation of a large glass "sculpture," a creation that resembled a giant water spout frozen in time. The landmark is much lauded throughout the galaxy as one of the most beautiful and impressive natural formations in known space. Originally called the Fountain of the Ancients, this phenomenon is a religious symbol of patience, fortitude, and "Strength with Age." Klatooinians believe that time is the eternal truth and the most powerful of forces, because all else will pass away in its wake. Yet the fountain appears to grow stronger as it ages, and thus, as "children of the fountain," the Klatooinians feel that they, too, can strengthen with age—until they are resilient enough to perhaps become independent. Since it is such a potent symbol, they guard it protectively, and to keep the fountain as it was in the era of the ancients, no technology is permitted within a kilometer of it.

The worship of time is at the center of Klatooinian religious belief, so it is no wonder that they were in awe of the Hutts, who revealed to the Klatooinians that they can live to an age of more than one thousand standard years. In fact, many Klatooinians have come to believe that the Hutts *were* the Ancients, and so they feel it is right to serve them—for now.

Much of Klatooine life is a continuation of the species' subjugation and aims to ensure their servitude to the Hutts. As young children, Klatooinians spend their first decade being indoctrinated into history, traditions, myths, and legends in a schooling that typically drains them of all their individual-

ity. However, this instruction is done orally, as most Klatooinians are illiterate. Furthermore, in deference to their Huttese overlords and to prepare Klatooinian children for their future service, the instruction is conducted in the language of the Hutts, not Klatooinian. Usually the only difference in the children once schooling ends is their names, although even names in Klatooinian culture are drawn from a limited pool inspired by prominent Klatooinian historical figures. After ten standard years of schooling, Klatooinian children are sold into servitude in the cities or towns under Hutt rule, at which time they learn the specific trade that they will pursue for the rest of their lives. Disrespectful and rebellious youths are sold into harsher conditions of slavery, working mines, shipyards, mills, and quarries on and around Klatooine.

The collapse of the Old Republic and later descent of the Emperor's New Order into civil war inspired many young Klatooinians to escape and join the Rebellion, while others hid in the Klatooinian wilderness or even the far reaches of the galaxy. This emerging group of Klatooinian revolutionaries also began reclamation of their native language, relying on ancient and fragile texts that had somehow managed to survive undiscovered by the Hutts.

Currently, the Klatooinian government still lives in fear of their Hutt lords, although the patience of this people is becoming frayed under the weight of the contract they signed millennia ago. Klatooine is ruled by a Council of Elders that resides in a palace built around the fountain, which is now referred to as the Fountain of the Hutt Ancients. This new title has been another cause for members of the younger generations to attempt further rebellions, with uprisings becoming more and more frequent. Among the youth, it is believed that if the Old Republic and the Emperor could fall, then it might also be possible for them to free themselves from Huttese bondage, and that the members of the Council of Elders are mere cowards for their continued subservience to the Hutts. The Hutts, seeing these signs of discontent, have tried strongly pressing their will upon their servants, becoming more ruthless and cold in their treatment of the Klatooinians. But as they do, they are being met with more vigorous resistance. Societal watchers theorize that this is the beginning of the end of the master–servant relationship between the Hutts and Klatooinians, but only time will tell.

DESIGNATION
Sentient

HOMEWORLD
Klatooine

AVERAGE
HEIGHT
1.8 meters

PRONUNCIATION
Klă-tōō-ĭn'-ē-ăn

NOTABLE APPEARANCE
Episode VI: Return of the Jedi

KOORIVAR

Koorivar are tall humanoids who inhabit a tropical world of vast oceans and lush rain forests known as Kooriva, located in the Inner Rim. Koorivar vary in skin color from magenta to mauve and from dark green to black. Banding ridges crown their brows, tapering down onto their noses past sickly looking yellow or green eyes. A colorful spiraling horn rises from the tops of their heads, and this feature can be found on both males and females. Females who have borne children and preside over families wear matron's hoods, indicating a level of influence.

A Koorivar's horn grows during puberty but ceases developing upon reaching adulthood. It is a trait of great cultural and societal importance among their people, and the length or beauty of one's horn increases one's status in society. Koorivar who are genetically disposed to have larger horns tend to garner more prestige, leading to an unofficial upper class of genetically "superior" Koorivar. In general, Koorivar will decorate their horns to make them more attractive to their fellows. Loss or damage of a horn usually leads to a marked loss of status and prestige—sometimes even isolation from society.

Koorivar are a shrewd people, wary of danger and uncomfortable situations. They prefer to remain out of harm's way and will use their wits to escape a bad scene, bargaining with or fooling opponents rather than directly fighting with them. In fact, bargaining is also the way Koorivar form their families. A marriage on Kooriva is arranged by two houses who wish to join resources for a mutually beneficial financial outcome. After presenting the qualities of their offspring to their potential mate, the parents will exhibit a prospectus on the financial stability of their family and the lucrative potential of merging their business efforts with those of the other clan. Days and sometimes weeks of negotiations take place before the two families agree to business terms, and sometimes even then these "mergers" will fall through. The children who are to be married are as large a part of the process as their parents, and are traditionally involved in the bidding process. When presented with the idea of marrying for love, Koorivar often openly scoff at such an unprofitable concept, seeing the institution of marriage as a means for society to build its ultimate strength and dominance through wealth.

This cooperation and focus on mutual benefits extends to the Koorivar's business enterprises and dealings with one another as well, and many Koorivar will band together on any number of financial undertakings, pooling resources and efforts to maximize profits. Undercutting others in business, like the idea of love, is viewed as counterproductive.

Koorivarn children are groomed for this cooperative business mind-set from early childhood, as all schools on Kooriva center on the business arts. Extensive classes are reserved for developing and marketing new products, incorporating selling techniques, and practicing public speaking for the goal of negotiations.

Before they reach the age of ten standard years, most Koorivarn children have begun their first credit-earning job, with some being so ambitious as to start their own fledgling businesses.

Koorivar speak their own language, a combination of whispers, soft sibilants, and hand gestures. Although Koorivar also use Basic, they have a slight advantage over many other species as they are in tune with body language and the sensing of other beings' motives based on how they move. This skill is particularly useful because Koorivar frequently work with other species so that they may benefit from their various unique talents and contributions. Koorivarn nobles in particular will crew their ships with members of many species.

While Koorivar have adopted the name of their planet, Kooriva is not their original home. When the star of their unknown homeworld became unstable, they migrated to Kooriva, leasing the planet from the Old Republic for several centuries. After this amount of time, they adopted their new name and formally requested that the Galactic Senate allow them to finally take possession of their world of residence. When the Senate rejected their request, Koorivar set out to gain enough influence to reverse the decision. They wandered the galaxy as merchants, striking up business deals that gained them more and more sway over member worlds of the Galactic Senate. After a time, the decision was overturned.

With their remarkable talent for business, other merchants remain somewhat leery of Koorivar. They will wander from world to world, buying shares of stock or merchandise at low prices and selling them elsewhere for a considerable profit. Driven to gain power and influence, they brazenly set out to the farthest corners of the galaxy in search of profitable business deals. One of the species' more controversial ploys was to sell weaponry and war matériel such as their weather production machines to battling peoples—trading with both sides. Of course they tried to keep this tactic secret, but when it did come to light it ruined their reputation as reliable merchants. The Republic began to investigate the charges, and when the Koorivarn government tried to protect some of the more corrupt offenders, the Galactic Senate set up economic sanctions against Koorivar and blockaded their world—forcing Koorivar to pay heavy tariffs on any product shipments coming in or out of their system.

To save their economy from utter ruin, Koorivar complied with the Senate's requirements for free trade. They then learned to go to even greater lengths to keep illegal practices under wraps, or to make sure their business dealings are completely legitimate.

DESIGNATION
Sentient

HOMEWORLD
Kooriva (by way of an unknown homeworld)

AVERAGE HEIGHT
1.9 meters

PRONUNCIATION
Kōr'-ē-vär

With the rise of the New Republic, Koorivar maintained their powerful presence in the business world, sitting on the boards of most major corporations in the known galaxy. Although Koorivar sided with the Separatists during the Clone Wars, and their business interests suffered greatly from the Empire's nonhuman biases, they have, as a species, made impressive strides in regaining their wealth and influence through cunning and tenacity. However, the Galactic Alliance Committee on Corporate Oversight keeps a close eye on the commercial activities of Koorivar to ensure compliance with the law.

While Koorivar are generally business focused, they have a strong streak of militarism when it comes to guarding their interests. For this purpose they established a renowned fighting force known as the Koorivar Fusiliers during the Clone Wars. Employed by the Corporate Alliance, they performed a key roll in the Confederacy of Independent Systems' military strategy. Garbed in red head-armor (which displayed their horns), rib-armor, black metal boots, and metal gloves, they were an impressive group of fighters who employed the use of Koorivar-fabricated blasters. These soldiers were utilized by Passel Argente, leader of the Corporate Alliance, as personal guards, and General Grievous commanded divisions of Koorivar Fusiliers in his Outer Rim Sieges. They were also directed at the battles of Moorja and Bomis Koori IV by General Oro Dassyne, a Koorivar of unique status among his people.

Appointed a general of the Fusiliers by Passel Argente, Dassyne was greatly enamored of glory and often requested frontline action. As a result, he was wounded and suffered skull trauma that damaged his horn. To compensate for his physical loss, he wore a miter that was even larger than his horn had been. Even though loss of a horn usually incurs a loss of status, Dassyne maintained his status through sheer force of will. But this overcompensation ultimately led to his downfall. His clever leadership of troops in the past was replaced with a reliance on greater firepower for defense. Sent to protect Bomis Koori IV, a stronghold of the Corporate Alliance defenses, he fortified the world with highly powerful artillery and shields anticipating an attack from a Jedi army. Instead, he was outwitted by only two Jedi, Obi Wan Kenobi and Anakin Skywalker and soundly defeated. Had he survived this battle, his loss of status would have left him in utter ruin, exiled from his people.

NOTABLE APPEARANCE
Episode II: Attack of the Clones

KOWAKIAN MONKEY-LIZARD

Kowakian monkey-lizards are a playful reptilian species hailing from the Outer Rim world of Kowak. These small, quick, and agile creatures have long floppy ears, beak-like noses, tufts of brown or black hair on their heads and backs, and wild, yellow eyes. Monkey-lizards have twiggy extremities, but their bellies are distended from overeating—particularly when they are domesticated—and some subspecies have prehensile tails. While these reptiles may give the appearance of easy prey to any larger predator, their nimble bodies, acute hearing, and sharp eyesight make them extremely difficult to catch. Their brown skin will actually shift its tint in different environments, often making them virtually invisible to pursuing predators.

Monkey-lizards live primarily in tree nests, and enjoy swinging through the verdant rain forests of their homeworld. They feed on insects, worms, and small rodents, eating frequently, as their tiny, energetic bodies require a great deal of nourishment. Monkey-lizards are traditionally scavengers, preferring carrion to fresh meat or vegetation. As carrion is not particularly healthy to eat in most circumstances, some have speculated why monkey-lizards have this odd preference. They may prefer to have others do their work for them in acquiring food, or it may be the result of an innate avoidance of predatory dangers.

While they do display a fair amount of intelligence, monkey-lizards still appear to be on the brink of further evolution. They have no structured society to speak of, although they do exhibit hierarchical boundaries within a group of nests. Leadership appears to fall to the oldest female, and each monkey-lizard in a nesting group is assigned a specific role: one will be a food gatherer, another will maintain the nest, while yet another will scout for predators. Little is known about their reproductive habits in the wild, and the monkey-lizards managed to drive off the last group that attempted to study them. In captivity, they are usually not kept with others of their species, as the noise they make is simply too great. However, it is believed that monkey-lizards lay eggs once a year, with a few of the eggs surviving to hatch.

Being curious and prone to exploration, these creatures can be quite destructive. Monkey-lizards acquired as pets often end up sold off when private owners are unable to control them. Primary complaints from owners concern their disruptiveness, their tendency to break valuables and deface artwork and furniture, as well as their habit of rummaging through garbage compactors.

In the wild, these creatures are rarely alone, preferring to move in packs for protection. One of the most notable features of monkey-lizards—their incessant, annoying laughter—is a noise they will often make to frighten away predators. Moving in groups, they can create a great clamor so as to intimidate would-be opponents. Once they discover a source of food, they will scuffle with one another over the meal rather than sharing it, a trait that betrays a certain temperament. Monkey-lizards have the capacity to be mean-spirited and cruel (to use a term typically applied to known sentients) to other beings, whether they are members of their own species or not. They will take easy opportunities to mock others with direct laughter or through minor attacks such as throwing things at them, simply because it amuses them. In addition, as mentioned above, University of Coruscant researchers reported that while camped on Kowak to observe the monkey-lizards, the creatures put snakes in their sleeping gear, and even placed buckets of water in trees, only to drop them on the researchers when they passed by unawares.

There has been a great debate in the scientific community as to whether monkey-lizards are sentient or not, and the issue has not been officially decided, though some declare that they must be sentient, for no simple-minded beast could be so clever. While monkey-lizards do not have any art or culture to speak of, they clearly possess a distinct, if questionable, sense of mischief and humor. They can learn to mimic most languages, and according to some observers, actually communicate in those languages if they feel like it. They will even laugh, strangely enough, at appropriate—or sometimes inappropriate—moments during conversations. It is common knowledge in certain circles that monkey-lizards can repeat back what they hear with some accuracy, and for this reason many underworld kingpins keep them as pets who double as excellent spies. However, it is widely believed that, sentient or not, monkey-lizards are obnoxious creatures, and to call someone a "Kowakian monkey-lizard" is an insult.

DESIGNATION
Semi-sentient
(or sentient)

HOMEWORLD
Kowak

AVERAGE HEIGHT
70 centimeters

PRONUNCIATION
Kō-wä'-kē-ăn
Mŏn-kē-Lĭ'-zărd

One piece of evidence that supports their sentience is that some have been found to be Force-sensitive. Records from the Empire refer to Picaroon C. Boodle, a monkey-lizard captured by the Imperials as a research subject because of his latent Force abilities. He was mutated, pressed into service to the Dark Jedi Jerec, and sent to the fabled Valley of the Jedi, where he died in battle with the Jedi Kyle Katarn. It is possible that additional monkey-lizards are Force-sensitive, but none have been identified to date due to their capricious and troublesome natures.

Meanwhile, a large number of monkey-lizards have been encountered in the galactic underworld, tied to criminal organizations. One of the best-known monkey-lizards to serve a criminal figure was Salacious Crumb. While it is not known how this monkey-lizard came by his name, Crumb was employed by Jabba primarily as a court jester, but vague and perhaps unreliable reports assert that Crumb was also tasked with eavesdropping on Jabba's visiting competitors and members of his court, listening for any signs of intrigue that could harm Jabba's business dealings or, worse, his health. First captured by Jabba when he was trying to steal food from him—and almost becoming a meal himself in the process—Crumb parlayed his value as a spy and a source of amusement into the comfortable position he held until perishing on Jabba's sail barge in the Dune Sea.

At one time, these creatures were rarely seen off their native world. However, they have consistently managed to sneak onto visiting ships, and often wind up in the strangest of places. They have also become a fad among some of the wealthy upper class, who, like their underworld counterparts, keep them as pets for entertainment. However, they are clearly not always well looked upon as household creatures in proper or polite society because they are quite untrainable, no matter how much time or effort is devoted to it or what method is used.

NOTABLE APPEARANCE
Episode VI: Return of the Jedi

KUBAZ

The Kubaz, of the Outer Rim planet of Kubindi, are a humanoid species, tall and gaunt, with long trunks for noses. They have green-black skin, and must wear goggles to protect their sensitive eyes when visiting worlds in systems with a yellow or red sun. Kubaz have broad stubby fingers on their hands and two large toes on each foot; bristly black hair grows from the tops of their pointed heads. Their snout-like, flexible trunks evolved as a perfect means of sucking insects out of hives. In addition, inside their trunks they possess two rows of teeth and well developed glands that enable them to detect even the subtlest of odors. The Kubaz have a highly developed form of nonverbal communication that they use to achieve a more advanced level of understanding among their people. These nonverbal signals are made up of trunk and hand movements. The slightest vibration of their trunk can have any of several different meanings, most of which are known to Kubaz alone. Tied with these trunk movements are their often inscrutable means of expression. Kubaz's trunks can be indicators of how they feel, as Kubaz smile by curling them.

A Kubaz's hand gestures, meanwhile, are usually recognizable by offworlders who have a limited familiarity with them. One hand up with palm down, for instance, is a sign of agreement. Those Kubaz who assisted on either side of the Galactic Civil War in a military capacity shared their hand signals with commanders, who used them to direct troops in a silent manner. By touching their noses, head, or shoulders or making other subtle gestures, the Kubaz indicated direction, number, and intention.

Kubindi orbits a powerful blue giant star known for its solar flares. As a result, it is an arid world with very erratic weather patterns, and is often victimized by large bursts of radiation from the star. At one time thousands of years ago, the solar flares were so powerful that they burned away most of the plant life, and the remaining vegetation was appetizing only to the native insect population. Because of this, the herbivorous ancestors of the Kubaz resorted to eating the insects, the only edible food source for them left on the planet. Luckily for the Kubaz, the plant life eventually grew back and adapted to the solar flare activity that is still common on Kubindi, and new variations of insects began appearing after each incident of solar flaring—most likely the product of the mutative radiation, as some of these insects grow as large as Tatooine banthas. Over time, Kubaz's physiology adjusted to their new diet.

Eventually, Kubaz stopped hunting for insect hives and instead began farming them in greater numbers, although individual hives could be stolen and difficult to claim if recovered. Thus, Kubaz developed designer strains of insects, declaring distinctive results for specific clans on Kubindi. Then, to increase variety in their meals, the clans began trading individual hives, and capitalistic commerce on Kubindi was soon under way. Kubaz society became dominated by certain clans, which each control millions of insect hives. Today, Kubaz culture, business, finance, and space and computer technology have developed entirely out of the production and sale of insects, along with a very special high-class insect cuisine. Kubaz insect banquets are a highlight of their culture, and the food is considered a delicacy. While Kubaz will not be insulted if a guest does not wish to partake in an insect meal, they would probably conclude that the visitor simply lacks both refinement and good taste.

This singular diet has caused them difficulties interacting in galactic society, as they do not recognize sentient insectoid species as anything other than food. The Old Republic discouraged the Kubaz from developing starship or hyperdrive technology until they acknowledged the rights of intelligent insectoids. The Empire later maintained this policy for no other reason than its overarching attempt to keep other species separated from humans. Kubaz were still eager to explore the galaxy, though, and threw all their scientific efforts into developing hyperdrive technology, but through subterfuge and sabotage, the Empire disrupted their plans. Furthermore, the Empire blamed the destruction of their earlier hyperdrive designs and other scientific developments on the defunct Republic, which encouraged the Kubaz to aid the Empire in various ways—most frequently as spies.

Kubaz are particularly skilled at establishing networks of business associates and information suppliers, often knowing someone who knows someone and using this to their advantage. They are also extremely talented reading intentions through observation, another natural trait that made them very valuable to the Empire. However, not long into the Galactic Civil War, Kubaz discovered the Empire's treachery through their observational prowess, and many left Kubindi to join the Rebellion.

Outside of the spy business, Kubaz are a highly educated people who enjoy the arts, music, literature, and other sophisticated entertainments included with the gentrified ways of society. Espionage cannot be taken as the defining characteristic of Kubaz life or sense of morality. Highly social beings, they are extremely focused on manners and refinement, as well as traditions and history. Decorum and tact are also highly valued.

Kubaz love to dote on their families—raising their children at home until the age of five standard years, then sending them off to the clan crèche, where they are raised by single females. After transferring their offspring to the crèche, the parents maintain a strong presence in the children's lives through daily visitations and shared mealtimes. Academies are maintained on Kubindi for the advanced study of science and the arts, and entry is competitive and highly prestigious. Graduates of these academies either undertake apprenticeships to further their skills or assume positions of societal influence upon completion of their training.

Kubaz are extremely interested in all that occurs around them. They have a love of learning and will ask many questions, almost to the point of creating annoyance. With outsiders they are extremely honorable, forthright, and morally rigid, although they do not view maltreatment of insectoids or the act of spying as morally questionable.

Following the fall of the Empire and rise of the New Republic, the Kubaz had no choice but to join the inestimable ranks of refugees forced to flee their homeworlds when their planet was taken over by the Yuuzhan Vong. Following the Yuuzhan Vong's defeat, the remaining Kubaz, greatly diminished in number, have begun the process of returning to their world to pick up the pieces of their fractured society.

DESIGNATION
Sentient

HOMEWORLD
Kubindi

AVERAGE HEIGHT
1.8 meters

PRONUNCIATION
Kōō′-băz

NOTABLE APPEARANCE
Episode IV: A New Hope

MON CALAMARI

The Mon Calamari are an idealistic, noble people from the Outer Rim planet that commonly bears their name in Basic, although in the Mon Calamari and Quarren languages, the planet and its home star system are properly known as Dac. The Mon Calamari were once considered the soul of the Rebel Alliance, as well as a cornerstone of the New Republic. A positive, forward-thinking species with cultural goals of justice and fairness, they have established themselves as leaders and instigators of galactic harmony.

The Mon Calamari, often called Mon Cals, are an amphibious species with salmon-colored skin, webbed hands, high, domed heads, and huge, fish-like eyes. Similar to other amphibians, they are born in a "tadpole" stage, complete with gills; as they grow into adulthood, they develop lungs. These lungs are quite powerful, and enable them to remain underwater for long periods of time.

Within their water-based society, Mon Cal science grew out of simple fish farming and kelp cultivation on their ocean-covered world. Initially, their scientific and technological advancement progressed at a slow pace because it was difficult to get necessary materials from the planet's core. This problem was later solved with the assistance of their neighbor species, the Quarren, who live at the greatest depths of Mon Calamari's oceans. Thus began their symbiotic relationship with the Quarren, who had the ability to mine minerals found only at those depths.

Soft-spoken and gentle, the Mon Calamari are a peaceful people. They are even-tempered, slow to anger, and possess a remarkable capacity for intense concentration. Mon Cals are also legendary for their determination and for a dedication that can sometimes border on obstinacy. They are naturally heroic and idealistic, taking on causes that would seem hopeless to others simply because they feel it is right to do so, and once they have made a decision, they are not easily swayed from it. One such resolution was their quest to reach "the islands in the galactic ocean"—the stars, a goal they ultimately achieved due to their tenacity.

The Mon Calamari and Quarren live in multileveled cities that float upon the surface of their vast oceans. The Mon Cals dwell on the upper levels of the immense structures, as they prefer more sunlight, while the Quarren reside in the lower levels where there is more comforting darkness. These cities are the centers for civilized culture on their world, and their repertoire of art, music, and literature is impressive.

Mon Calamari technological talents are renowned throughout the galaxy. They can engineer starships or structures for almost any environment. The Mon Cals believe technological or architectural design must be organic, growing and changing with the users.

Mon Cal spaceships are highly complex, and are frequently the vessels of choice for the Gallactic Alliance. Each of these ships is unique in design, and they are constructed specifically for Mon Calamari physiology unless they are built under contract for an offworld client.

When the Mon Cals made their first foray into space, they established contact with peoples from other worlds with great enthusiasm and excitement. Along with the Quarren, they eventually gained representation in the Galactic Senate. But in the days before creation of the Empire, Mon Calamari Senator Meena Tils joined a growing number of Senators who spoke against Palpatine's increasing powers. By the time Palpatine declared himself Emperor, the Mon Cals began to realize their

DESIGNATION
Sentient

HOMEWORLD
Mon Calamari

AVERAGE HEIGHT
1.7 meters

PRONUNCIATION
Mŏn Căl-ä-mär'-ē

fatal mistake. The Emperor viewed the Mon Cals as easy slave labor, and the Empire conquered their world with the assistance of some disgruntled Quarren, who deactivated the planet's protective shield. Both the Quarren and the Mon Cals were put to work as slaves, although the Mon Cals began a movement of passive resistance. In order to squash this opposition, the Empire destroyed three of their floating cities.

It was then that this peaceful species put aside their pacifistic ways and fought back against their taskmasters. Using simple kitchen implements, hand tools, and any other weapons they could find, they and their Quarren counterparts—with the aid of the Rebellion—drove the Empire from their world. Mon Calamari then became the first world to officially throw its full support behind the Alliance.

To this day, there is friction between the Quarren and the Mon Calamari, stemming from both the incident involving the deactivation of the shield, as well as previous tensions over many Quarren siding with the Separatists during the Clone Wars.

Despite this friction, Mon Calamari society continues to function. They have a highly efficient government, organized much like the Republic Senate. Quarren and Mon Cals are equally represented in this body, and because of the Mon Cals' peace-loving nature, they continue to work toward consistent harmony with their Quarren fellows.

The Mon Cals were also largely responsible for freeing the galaxy from the oppression of the Empire. Nowhere was this better represented than by the great Mon Calamari naval commander Admiral Ackbar. A brilliant tactician, Ackbar quickly rose through the ranks to become admiral of the combined Rebel fleet. In addition, through his steady guidance, Ackbar brought Mon Calamari into the Alliance, which aided tremendously in turning the tide of the war. He served as long as he was able, eventually retiring to a quiet life on Mon Calamari. Ackbar passed away from old age toward the conclusion of the war against the Yuuzhan Vong, after briefly coming out of retirement to contribute to the military strategies that defeated the invaders.

NOTABLE APPEARANCE
Episode VI: Return of the Jedi

MUSTAFARIAN

The title *Mustafarian* applies to two subspecies of the same genus native to the planet Mustafar in the Outer Rim, a world of molten lava rivers, active volcanoes, and jagged, rocky landmasses. Both subspecies are hard-shelled arthropods with large, insectoid eyes and long snouts, and evolved in the cooled underground tunnels of their world. Their chitinous exoskeletons lie in plates over their leathery skin, protecting them from the intense heat that they encounter day by day on Mustafar. Unlike most life-forms, Mustafarians have little water in their bodies.

Mustafar's volcanic environment is caused by the gravitational pull of two nearby gas giants, Jestefad and Lefrani. While Mustafar could serve as a moon for either star, it stays in its own orbit, traveling closer to Jestefad while at the same time being pulled on by Lefrani—with all three planetary bodies navigating the star system at a similar rate.

Flourishing in this tumultuous environment, the taller northern Mustafarians are the physically weaker of the two subspecies. Because their bodies are more prone to frailty, the northern Mustafarians who serve as sentries or security forces often have their limbs enhanced with mechanical prosthetics to increase their strength, speed, and endurance. Northern Mustafarians ride insects called Mustafar lava fleas, which they domesticated as mounts in order to move quickly from one cooled lava landmass to another. The lava fleas are large, six-legged insects capable of walking across the cooler surfaces of hardened lava, and they can leap over the flowing lava rivers with ease.

The smaller southern Mustafarians, meanwhile, are more sturdy and hardy. Working in cooperation with their genetic cousins, they handle most of the "heavy lifting," or physically demanding jobs, in Mustafar's expansive lava-mining operations. This shorter subspecies can withstand higher temperatures than the northern Mustafarians, and since they spend more time on the surface than their compatriots do, they wear armor and breath masks to protect themselves from the intense heat. The southerners handle the harvesting platforms, skimming the surface of the lava rivers for metals with large pole-mounted cauldrons.

Mustafarians are a self-involved, egocentric people always bent on improving the limited life on their world. They are technologically savvy, and somewhat creative in that they have managed to find many unique ways to market the products they mine from Mustafar. Even so, their only reason for interacting with outsiders is to trade for new life-improving materials. They care little for any other people besides their own.

While Mustafarians are not naturally aggressive, like most species they have developed weaponry to protect themselves. Since their skin and exoskeletons defend them from heat-producing weapons such as blasters, the weapons that they use fire bolts of kinetic energy. Both vessels and people who are armored to guard themselves against blaster-fire would find themselves vulnerable to such unique armaments.

Mustafarians live and work in saucer-shaped buildings near their mine entrances. The structures are constructed to extend several levels belowground, often utilizing empty mines that no longer produce ore. They also dwell in the cooler hollows of dormant volcanic mountains. The atmosphere on Mustafar is not very hospitable to living beings, and it is a testament to the creatures and animals native to the planet that they have managed to survive. Filled with smoke, ash, and bits of volcanic rock and glass, the air on Mustafar makes drawing every breath a chore for most humanoids.

As mentioned, the Mustafarians had no initial interest in life off their world. But when the Techno Union became fixated on the idea of mining their lava for precious metals, the Mustafarians agreed to help build and manage the operations on Mustafar. This gave them membership in the Confederation of Independent Systems, though their planet was relatively untouched by the Clone Wars.

DESIGNATION
Sentient

HOMEWORLD
Mustafar

AVERAGE HEIGHT
2 meters (northern)
1.5 meters (southern)

PRONUNCIATION
Mōōs-tä-fä'-rē-ăn

Techno Union technology offered the Mustafarians extra protection from the heat, and improved their standard of living drastically. One such item used by workers is a Kubazian skirt equipped with a cooling backpack turbine. And yet, despite some of these helpful devices created by other species, the Mustafarians remain fairly uninterested in larger galactic affairs and are perfectly happy to work on their own world in peace.

The Separatist movement under Count Dooku used Mustafar as one of its main headquarters for operations. As the Clone Wars raged, the Separatist Council enlisted the Mustafarians to build a stronghold on their planet to be used as a protective retreat in the event that the Republic prevailed. The fortress was near impenetrable, bearing the combined protection of Mustafar's dangerous environment with a powerful tractor beam and ray shielding.

The Mustafarians were indifferent to the Separatists' politicking, and helped construct the climate-controlled fortress in the hope that it would someday fall under their control. Their work paid off when Darth Vader slaughtered the Separatists along with the Techno Union leaders on Mustafar, leaving the planet and its people to manage their own affairs.

As the Empire rose to power, however, the Mustafarians had to deal with a new problem. The renegade Geonosian Separatist Gizor Dellso holed himself up in the fortress, refusing to surrender to the Empire. Dellso managed to get a hidden droid factory on Mustafar up and running again, and began generating a series of fresh battle droids that he intended to use as his own army. The 501st Legion of stormtroopers was dispatched to Mustafar, and both Dellso and his battle droids were eradicated. It is believed that both fortress and factory were decimated by Star Destroyers in a subsequent orbital strike.

NOTABLE APPEARANCE
Episode III: Revenge of the Sith

MYNOCK

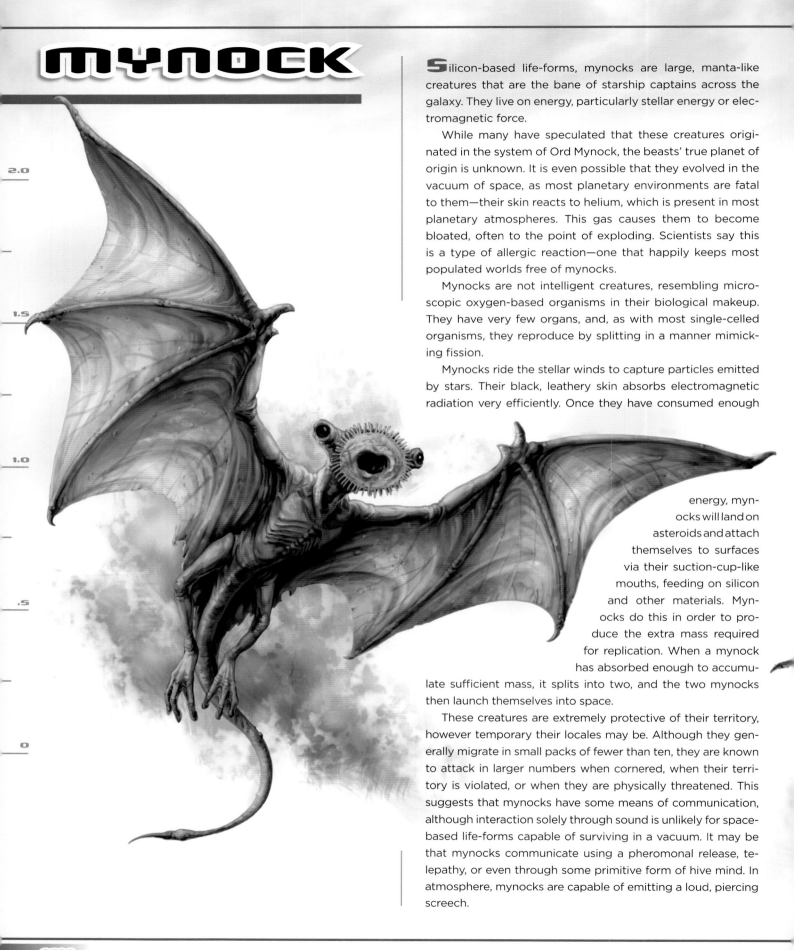

Silicon-based life-forms, mynocks are large, manta-like creatures that are the bane of starship captains across the galaxy. They live on energy, particularly stellar energy or electromagnetic force.

While many have speculated that these creatures originated in the system of Ord Mynock, the beasts' true planet of origin is unknown. It is even possible that they evolved in the vacuum of space, as most planetary environments are fatal to them—their skin reacts to helium, which is present in most planetary atmospheres. This gas causes them to become bloated, often to the point of exploding. Scientists say this is a type of allergic reaction—one that happily keeps most populated worlds free of mynocks.

Mynocks are not intelligent creatures, resembling microscopic oxygen-based organisms in their biological makeup. They have very few organs, and, as with most single-celled organisms, they reproduce by splitting in a manner mimicking fission.

Mynocks ride the stellar winds to capture particles emitted by stars. Their black, leathery skin absorbs electromagnetic radiation very efficiently. Once they have consumed enough energy, mynocks will land on asteroids and attach themselves to surfaces via their suction-cup-like mouths, feeding on silicon and other materials. Mynocks do this in order to produce the extra mass required for replication. When a mynock has absorbed enough to accumulate sufficient mass, it splits into two, and the two mynocks then launch themselves into space.

These creatures are extremely protective of their territory, however temporary their locales may be. Although they generally migrate in small packs of fewer than ten, they are known to attack in larger numbers when cornered, when their territory is violated, or when they are physically threatened. This suggests that mynocks have some means of communication, although interaction solely through sound is unlikely for space-based life-forms capable of surviving in a vacuum. It may be that mynocks communicate using a pheromonal release, telepathy, or even through some primitive form of hive mind. In atmosphere, mynocks are capable of emitting a loud, piercing screech.

This parasite is the main food staple for the giant space slugs that often inhabit asteroid fields. In turn, before being completely digested, mynocks will feed for a time on the space slug's veins and intestinal linings. Due to their sheer size, giant space slugs have been known to be found with large numbers of living mynocks within their bodies. For this reason, some orbital spaceports will try to keep at least one space slug in the vicinity to cut down on the local mynock population.

Constantly thirsting for energy, mynocks often attach themselves to passing starships, chewing on power cables or sucking on ion ports. Mynocks can also absorb matter from a vessel's hull, causing it to slowly dissolve. This is a particular problem that could result in a significant amounts of damage if not discovered and repaired in time, and through the years, there are tales of many ships and lives that have been lost due to hull breaches in open space. The space lanes abound with reports, both anecdotal and verified, of ships launching, only to later discover that a mynock or two had damaged the ship's exterior or, worse, had stowed away and were causing harm while the ship was already in flight. Often, vessels' sensors will detect breaches and the loss of hull integrity, but if sensors are faulty, catastrophic events have sometimes occurred. In addition, if a pack of mynocks infests an orbital shipyard, the economic consequences can be severe and drive a company to near bankruptcy.

In recent years, a new version of sport hunting has emerged called Mynock Puffing, wherein hunters will spacewalk to shoot and kill mynocks with helium-based grenades that attach to the creatures' hides, causing their bodies to balloon

DESIGNATION
Nonsentient

HOMEWORLD
Unknown
(popularly
attributed to
Ord Mynock)

**AVERAGE
LENGTH**
1.6 meters

PRONUNCIATION
Mī'-nŏk

into round balls. The creatures quickly die and immediately float away. Bets are placed on which sharpshooter can "puff out" the most mynocks. Legislation to monitor this activity is being met with resistance from the gambling establishment and the Free Spacers Guild lobby.

Several reports have documented subspecies variants of the mynock. Vynocks, an air-breathing, planetbound subspecies, have been found in the Kalarba system in the Mid Rim and on Corellia in the Core Worlds; apparently, this subspecies does not suffer from the theorized helium allergy. These creatures pose a particular problem for inhabited systems, as not just ships but also buildings, structures, livestock, and even humanoids sleeping outdoors are at risk. Additionally, the pirate Chorssk bred a domesticated version of the mynock, noted for its blue-mottled skin and reproduction methods. Unlike common mynocks, the Chorsskian, or blue, mynock gives birth to live offspring, with the mother sacrificing herself for her child. Chorssk learned to breed mynocks so that he could use them as a weapon; he sought to develop a group of creatures that could attack a ship on command, making his strikes on vessels in the space lanes that much easier. Another variant known as a salt mynock has also been spotted on Lok, but little is presently known about this subspecies due to a lack of corroborating evidence.

In sum, regardless of the variety, mynocks can pose a hazard regardless of their environment. It is a common experience to walk through even the most lightly populated of spaceports and hear cries of "Mynocks on a power cable!"

NOTABLE APPEARANCE
Episode V: The Empire Strikes Back

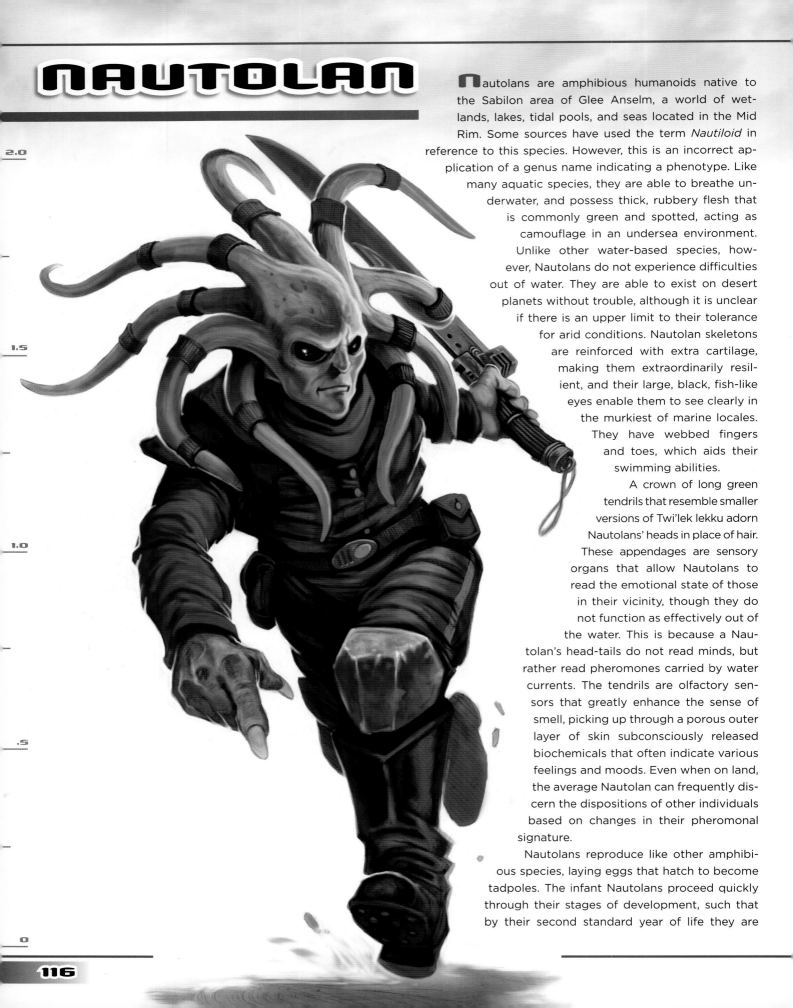

NAUTOLAN

Nautolans are amphibious humanoids native to the Sabilon area of Glee Anselm, a world of wetlands, lakes, tidal pools, and seas located in the Mid Rim. Some sources have used the term *Nautiloid* in reference to this species. However, this is an incorrect application of a genus name indicating a phenotype. Like many aquatic species, they are able to breathe underwater, and possess thick, rubbery flesh that is commonly green and spotted, acting as camouflage in an undersea environment. Unlike other water-based species, however, Nautolans do not experience difficulties out of water. They are able to exist on desert planets without trouble, although it is unclear if there is an upper limit to their tolerance for arid conditions. Nautolan skeletons are reinforced with extra cartilage, making them extraordinarily resilient, and their large, black, fish-like eyes enable them to see clearly in the murkiest of marine locales. They have webbed fingers and toes, which aids their swimming abilities.

A crown of long green tendrils that resemble smaller versions of Twi'lek lekku adorn Nautolans' heads in place of hair. These appendages are sensory organs that allow Nautolans to read the emotional state of those in their vicinity, though they do not function as effectively out of the water. This is because a Nautolan's head-tails do not read minds, but rather read pheromones carried by water currents. The tendrils are olfactory sensors that greatly enhance the sense of smell, picking up through a porous outer layer of skin subconsciously released biochemicals that often indicate various feelings and moods. Even when on land, the average Nautolan can frequently discern the dispositions of other individuals based on changes in their pheromonal signature.

Nautolans reproduce like other amphibious species, laying eggs that hatch to become tadpoles. The infant Nautolans proceed quickly through their stages of development, such that by their second standard year of life they are roughly the same size as a human infant and already possess arms and legs, though their legs are not yet strong enough to support their weight when learning to walk. An infant Nautolan's head-tails begin to develop their extrasensory abilities between their second and third years. This may be a programmed result of evolution, as this is also the time when many Nautolan children begin to speak, and thus their tendrils are able to start aiding in interpreting the potentially confusing input that they are receiving from the world around them.

Because of their empathic abilities, Nautolans' moods often reflect those of nearby individuals. If those around them are feeling joyous, then they are as well, but if others are upset, Nautolans will generally feel the same sadness. If they are attacked in anger, they will respond in kind. As a species, however, Nautolans are a fairly happy people who express joy with abandon, particularly when they are free to use their talents without restraint. For instance, Nautolans have been known to flash a wide, brilliant smile when in the midst of physical combat. While the delight behind the smile is quite genuine, this flash of passion can also be intended to emotionally disarm their opponents, who may perceive it as a sign of the Nautolans' combat superiority.

Other than the fact that their tendrils do not function quite as well out of water, Nautolans prefer aquatic life for another reason—one directly related to their language. Spoken on land, their native tongue, Nautila, is unpronounceable, and loses a good deal of its meaning because much of it is tied to pheromone projections that are released in conjunction with spoken words. As a result, Nautolans will speak Basic with those who use the standard tongue of the galaxy, or Anselmian, the language spoken by the Anselmi, their land-dwelling neighbors on Glee Anselm. The ability to speak Basic has encouraged many Nautolans to take to the stars, chasing a spirit of adventure.

Nautolans are an extremely loyal people, and as such, they will mate for life. Most Nautolans see a happy mating as a necessary requirement of existence, and families are raised with equal input from both parents. Marriage choices are in most cases made through courtship, as is typical in many humanoid societies. Although arranged marriages have declined among the Nautolans in the last few centuries, they do still occur. Those taking part in sociological studies report that they do not feel as if they have surrendered their

choice in mates by participating in such an arrangement, as the parties have the right of refusal upon reaching adulthood. They simply respect the well-considered effort made on their behalf. When an arranged marriage is declined, both parties will go their own way, with no ill will involved.

Nautolan settlements are governed by an elected Council of Elders—although in this case *elders* is a title of respect rather than a sign of age—and the centralized government takes the form of a body of representatives from each settlement. A subcommittee of this body works cooperatively with the overall leadership of Glee Anselm.

One of the best-known Nautolans in history was the Jedi Master Kit Fisto, renowned for his skills with a lightsaber. Fisto's lightsaber, it is said, could operate underwater because of two unique crystals that he used to power it. Also famous for his strength of spirit and his wisdom, Fisto was instrumental in the defeat of the Quarren forces that sympathized with the Confederacy of Independent Systems during a conflict on Mon Calamari. In addition, Master Fisto was unique in that he was one of the few non-Twi'leks able to read Lekku, the Twi'leks' elaborate language of head-tail movements.

Nautolans have coexisted in peace with the Anselmi for thousands of years. Any wars that they have had with each other have been short, though quite passionate and bloody. Some of these conflicts were instigated over underwater developments, as well as fishing rights and the dumping of waste products. The Anselmi, being land dwellers, will often infringe on Nautolan territories to construct new developments when housing is required, sparking the majority of such disagreements. However, the Nautolans are stronger and better fighters, giving them the advantage over their neighbors in such struggles. Many of these conflicts were mediated by representatives of the Old Republic government, though no disagreements between the species are known to have arisen in recent years.

DESIGNATION
Sentient

HOMEWORLD
Glee Anselm

AVERAGE
HEIGHT
1.8 meters

PRONUNCIATION
Nä'-tō-lǎn

NOTABLE APPEARANCE
Episode II: Attack of the Clones

NELVAANIAN

Nelvaanians (also referred to as Nelvaans) are the native inhabitants of the frigid planet Nelvaan in the Koobi system of the Outer Rim. A primitive people, they were easily victimized by the Techno Union and the Separatists during the Clone Wars. Nelvaanians are a canine humanoid species with blue-green fur tipped with a black headcrest, long snouts, black eyes, and sharp teeth. As they age, their hair whitens and their upright, pointed ears begin to fold down and back. During the Clone Wars, many of the species' males were genetically altered by the Techno Union as part of a secret mutant warrior development project, becoming large hulking versions of their former selves. Newer generations of males carry the genetic patterns of their altered forebears, and as a result are much larger than their female counterparts. For whatever reason, the genetic manipulation did not result in mutated females in subsequent generations.

Nelvaanian religious beliefs are central to their simple tribal culture. Life in the tribe is organized around the extended family and other closely related individuals. The strongest male Nelvaanians become warrior scouts, and are responsible for hunting game and providing protection for the tribe from natural predators. Female Nelvaanians, however, have the most important role of all in their society. Not only are females the builders and gatherers among the Nelvaanians, managing the day-to-day life of the tribe, but they also must raise the clan's young. Motherhood is sacred to Nelvaanians, so much so that it forms the basis of their religious beliefs and is revered in all its forms. Regardless of gender, children are a treasured source of joy to all Nelvaanians.

Great respect is paid to the elderly members of the tribe for their experience and wisdom, and typically the tribal chief is one of the eldest members of the group, assuming this role following a long and productive life. The chief leads with the help of his or her bond-mate, and is advised by a tribal shaman. All members of the tribe share communal duties and take part in ceremonies equally, so beyond experience and astuteness, no other special training is required for the role of chief. The responsibility is granted through a show of respect and deference rather than through a trial or other selection process. There is no competition for the position of tribal chief; an individual's ascension to the role is decided by the grace of the "Great Mother," and accepted without question by all members of the tribe.

The responsibility of motherhood in Nelvaanian religious beliefs takes the form of worship of the Great Mother—the planet itself. The Great Mother is the mother of all things, who guides and nurtures the Nelvaanians. Her shaman passes down traditions through stories and tales that are repeated from one generation to the next, and are often recorded in cave paintings. Nelvaanian tribal tales contain one particularly interesting story—one that if studied closely may have helped to predict Anakin Skywalker's eventual transformation into Darth Vader.

While on Nelvaan in pursuit of General Grievous during the last year of the Clone Wars, Obi-Wan Kenobi and Anakin Skywalker encountered the Nelvaanians, who, although initially distrustful of the Jedi—as Skywalker interrupted an important rite of passage for one of the tribe's younger males—did bring them back to their village. The shaman told the Jedi that the Great Mother's inner fires had seemed to go out, as her tears—her rivers—had frozen, and her cries were carried on the wind. Warriors had been dispatched to

discover the cause of the Great Mother's ills, but one by one they disappeared, leaving the women, children, and elderly of the tribe alone. Moreover, their shaman had predicted the dawn of an ice age, but this event came on much too suddenly to be natural.

Old Nelvaanian lore tells the tale of a one-handed warrior known as the holt kazet, or "Ghost Hand," who would fight for the Nelvaanians in their time of greatest need. A fierce warrior, the Ghost Hand would lose his hand in battle but, after taking on a new one, would overcome his limitations and grow to newfound strength. The Ghost Hand is ultimately consumed by his own power, influence that blocks all light and strangles the life from his loved ones. The Nelvaanians believed Anakin Skywalker had the gift of the Ghost Hand.

Given this belief, Skywalker was charged by the Nelvaanian tribal shaman with finding the source of the sickness that was plaguing the Great Mother. He discovered that the disappearances of the warriors and the frozen nature of the land were both due to the work of the Techno Union. Inspired by the cyborg technology used to create General Grievous, the Separatists had created a laboratory in the caverns near the Nelvaanian village. In this facility, they implanted captured male Nelvaanians with cyborg control harnesses, replacing one of each of their arms with a blaster to study how the technology could be applied on a larger scale, in an effort to create advanced fighters that would ultimately replace battle droids. During Skywalker's eventual assault on the facility, the Techno Union released these mutated warriors to attack the Jedi, but one of them, still in the mutation process, retained some of his sensibilities and was able to reach through to his tribesmen by reminding them of who they were. Skywalker was sickened by what the Techno Union's Skakoan scientists had done, as the proud Nelvaanian warriors were now monstrosities, and in a fit of rage, Anakin killed the scientists using the Force. The mutated Nelvaanians helped Anakin Skywalker defeat the remainder of the Techno Union forces and destroy the laboratory. The warriors then returned to their village, and after some initial hesitation were accepted back into their tribe.

DESIGNATION
Sentient

HOMEWORLD
Nelvaan

AVERAGE HEIGHT
1.5 meters (females)
2 meters (males)

PRONUNCIATION
Nĕl-vā'-nē-ăn

NOTABLE APPEARANCE
Clone Wars, volume 2 (animated series)

NERF

Nerfs, once native to the peaceful world of Alderaan, are four-legged, herbivorous ungulates. Since these creatures were and are raised on planets outside Alderaan, the species has survived their homeworld's destruction. Nerf meat is some of the most delicious and expensive in the known galaxy, and nerf steak restaurants are ubiquitous in any medium- or larger-sized Core World city. Nerf meat can also be served in other forms, such as nerfburgers—a favorite of many young people, often served with hubba chips—and nerfspread. In addition, nerfs' fur and hides can be utilized to create excellent wool and leather goods. Although their fur must be treated with strong chemicals to mask its smell before being spun into wool, it is used galaxywide by couturiers and hobbyists alike. Nerf-hide coats are an expensive but common luxury. Given the creatures' utility, nerfs can usually be spotted near most established settlements in the Core and innermost Mid Rim of the galaxy. However, nerfs are not commonly found in great numbers beyond the Mid Rim, as ranchers there tend to raise local favorites such as banthas, which do not pose some of the unique challenges that nerfs do.

Changes in environment and selective breeding have led to the development of several subspecies of nerfs, in addition to the naturally occurring varieties located on several worlds. For example, a particularly rare subspecies has been reported on Grizmallt—a group that appears very dissimilar to common nerfs in that they bear more of a resemblance to eopies with antlers. This change in body shape and neck length could be the result of thousands of years of reaching into trees to eat leaves or berries on high limbs. In addition, before it was destroyed, Alderaan was home to two nerf subspecies: the common, or plains, nerf and the rangier, thinner forest nerf. Another subspecies, the mountain nerf of Fennesa, has adapted to the mountainous terrain of that world and tends to be nimbler than both the plains and flatlands varieties.

In general, these are all herd creatures with dull, curving horns and coarse, curly fur that covers their muscular bodies. They have hard, round hooves and long, furry tails. Nerfs will chew their cuds, and because of this trait, they tend to build up a great deal of saliva in their mouths, making them expectorate a great deal. Nerf spit is black in color, sticky,

and foul smelling; it is impossible to remove from clothing without harsh detergents. In addition, mountain nerf spittle is slightly acidic, and can sting and leave welts if a herder is unlucky enough to be struck on exposed skin. Sadly, all varieties of these creatures are known to spit with great accuracy.

Nerfs are recognized as being some of the smelliest beasts in the galaxy, and those who deal with them regularly tend to reek of the species' aroma. Most nerf herders lose their sense of smell after years of working with the animals. These simple people are eternally patient, living outdoors and traveling with their creatures as they migrate about the grassy plains to feed. They are usually battered, bitten, and bruised by their wards, and their clothes are often covered in black, sticky spittle, giving them a haggard and scruffy appearance. In fact, *scruffy-looking nerf herder* is a common insult throughout the galaxy. Although it is a difficult life, nerf herders are proud, hardworking people, and third- or fourth-generation herders are quite common.

DESIGNATION
Nonsentient

HOMEWORLD
Alderaan

AVERAGE
HEIGHT
1.3 meters

PRONUNCIATION
Nŭrf

Known for being temperamental, nerfs will sit down, spit, or kick when they are in disagreement with their often hapless masters. Generally speaking, if nerf meat weren't one of the staples of diets throughout the galaxy (and perhaps if it weren't so delicious), and if their the pelts weren't so useful, it is doubtful that anyone would take the trouble to domesticate these animals. Moreover, nerf behavior has led some to question their scientific classification as herd animals. Although they exhibit typical herd-like qualities, such as standing in groupings for comfort and safety against predators, nerfs also tend to fight with one another as much as they clash with their keepers.

Nerf ewes are traditionally smaller and less powerful than the domineering rams. With horns that spiral more elaborately, the rams have a tendency to charge, harass, or batter the females and trample over the young. For this reason, they are isolated from the herd during certain times in order to keep the others safe.

On most worlds, nerfs are held in traditional ranch-like settings with enclosed pens and pastures. Fennesa natives differ from this practice by allowing their nerfs to roam free on the mountains, where the creatures often hide in caves or among rocky outcroppings. During mating season, females are allowed to mix with the males, but otherwise males are mostly prevented from grazing within the herd. Young nerfs are born one at a time, and remain with the ewes regardless of gender until they have aged roughly one standard year, at which point the male young are placed with their gender counterparts in order to replace an older ram who is taken to market. Female offspring will go to the field to replace ewe, although sometimes they are taken to market themselves.

Typically, herders take the females and young out into the field for weeks while the males are fed harvested grasses on the ranch. While they are grazing, nerfs can be at risk of attack from predators or rustlers. Herders are therefore frequently armed with slug-throwers—or blasters if they can afford them—to protect their livelihood. Unfortunately, because of the rough nature of their work, these hardworking people are looked down upon by more genteel society.

NOTABLE MENTION
Episode V: The Empire Strikes Back

NEXU

Nexus are fierce, agile feline carnivores native to the planet Cholganna, located near the Perlemian Trade Route in the Outer Rim, specifically the Indona continent. They are quadrupeds, and members of the forest subspecies have four eyes, the second set of which enables them to see in the infrared spectrum of light. Nexus' large mouths, which span the length of their spade-shaped heads, are full of sharp teeth. Tan-brown fur covers their bodies, giving them warmth in cold environments and camouflaging them in their native grassland and forest habitats. Taut, strong muscles can be seen beneath their hides, and sharp, spiny quills adorn nexus' backs to protect them from overhead attacks. These quills will stand erect when a nexu is engaged in a fight. A nexu's forked semi-prehensile tail gives it extra stability, as it can grip inanimate objects for balance. The nexu employs a squat, sprawling stance for even surer footing, and usually strikes with its primary claw, although it can easily attack with either of its front claws. Its shorter secondary claws are often used for gripping tree trunks in the nexu's native habitat.

Several breeds of nexus exist on their native world in different regions, adapting to local conditions, primarily the cool forests of the north and the balmy jungles and rain forests of the south. All nexu breeds will bear litters of ten cubs at a time, which they then protect with the same ferocity that has made them renowned throughout the galaxy. Cubs are pure white at birth, although their fur changes color at about three months. At approximately six months, the mother will abandon her young, as she will soon forget to recognize them as her progeny and be tempted to eat them. As a result, nexus are very solitary, marking their hunting territories with a musky smell they excrete from scent glands in their tails, or by rubbing scent glands located on their heads on trees, rocks, or bushes.

1.0

.5

0

In its home environment, the nexu tends to remain in the forests, using its infrared vision to hunt in the dim light of dusk and evening for the heat signatures of warm-blooded prey, particularly the arboreal octopi and bark rats that make up its primary diet. To kill its prey, the nexu will clamp down on the victim's neck and shake the creature until it dies, often breaking the neck bones in the process.

Most nexus trained as guard animals or arena beasts are taken from their mothers as young cubs. Nexu cubs are not harmless, though: they are born with sharp claws, teeth, and quills. It is crucial that nexus intended for use in patrol or guard duty are taken before they are taught to hunt by their mothers, preferably within an extremely narrow window of three standard months. Otherwise, they will be uncontrollable and unable to be domesticated. During this time, it is also possible to train nexus to not prey on specific creatures, such as their humanoid trainers. In these first three months, the goal is predatorial play, which a trainer will hone so that the nexu respond to specific attack commands. Only after the animal has been thoroughly taught to only strike

on command will it be trained to attack live targets. As can be expected, training nexus is done only by dangerous-animal experts.

Nexus destined for gladiatorial combat are raised differently from domesticated nexus. Gladiatorial animals are allowed to stay with their mothers for longer periods of time—up to six months—before their removal. This is to ensure that the animals know how to hunt and chase prey instinctively. (A longer period of time is not possible, because the young are frequently preyed upon by their mothers, as mentioned above.) These animals are harder to control, of course, but receive no less training once they are brought into captivity. Gladiatorial nexus must be trained to attack without fear, as they may face beasts larger than themselves in the arena.

Known for their speed and agility, nexus are often used to guard the strongholds of major underworld figures, and they can make a quick meal of trespassers. Since they are not easy to train or domesticate, nexus are more often used as executioners, or as gladiatorial foes on Outer Rim worlds such as Geonosis. Nexus have been featured in staged animal-fighting matches on some of the galaxy's more violent worlds, where the grisly blood sport is the subject of intense and high-stakes wagering. On Malastare, nexus are utilized as guard animals on patrol shifts. However, escaped nexus are a menace to the local populace, killing farm animals, destroying crops, and making away with settlers' children. They are rarely kept in zoos or animal preserves because they do not inhabit spaces with other animals well—often killing additional species, as well as members of their own kind.

As some of the most dangerous creatures in the known galaxy, nexus are frequently the targets of big-game hunters. Nexu pelts, and their teeth or bone ivory, are exorbitantly expensive and prized by the upper class of galactic society.

DESIGNATION
Nonsentient

HOMEWORLD
Cholganna

AVERAGE HEIGHT
1 meter
LENGTH WITH TAIL
4.5 meters

PRONUNCIATION
Nĕ'-xōō

NOTABLE APPEARANCE
Episode II: Attack of the Clones

NIKTO

Of all the beings in service to the Hutts, the Nikto are the species most closely identified with their masters. They are fierce people, and probably the most dangerous species to work as the Hutts' enforcers and warriors. They are a fearless and humorless group native to Kintan in the Outer Rim.

The Nikto are a reptilian species consisting of five different subspecies, each displaying unique cosmetic and biological features. These subspecies evolved due to an intense amount of stellar radiation bombarding their planet from a dying star known as M'dweshuu. Although each subspecies exhibits superficial differences, they are genetically compatible and can interbreed. Ninety-three percent of Nikto children born of mixed parentage maintain the characteristics of one of the parents, and carry on those characteristics through their own offspring. The remaining 7 percent—those who show signs of mixed breeding—are

maltreated and abused by the rest of society. They are outcasts, unable to thrive and succeed among their own people. Mixed-breed Nikto usually head offplanet as soon as they reach their adult years, to find work as guards, soldiers, or bounty hunters.

All Nikto have obsidian-black eyes, which are protected by transparent membranes when they are underwater, and also during Kintan's windstorms. They all possess leathery, reptilian skin, and sport various horns or spikes.

The Kajain'sa'Nikto, or Red Nikto, come from the Wannschok, or Endless Wastes—the desert region of Kintan. They have a series of ridges on their foreheads, with eight horns ringing their eyes, and two horns on their chins. Their noses are concealed beneath moving flaps of skin that hang above their mouths. To breathe, they expand this permeable membrane, preventing them from inhaling blowing sand, grit, and other contaminants from their desert environment. They also have a pair of breathing membranes on either side of their necks that are protected by thin breathing pipes. These pipes filter out contaminants and capture exhaled water vapor in order to keep it recycling through their systems, enabling them to go for longer periods of time without water.

The Kajain'sa'Nikto have a particular history of producing some of the strongest fighters in the galaxy, an ancient secret society known as the Morgukai. By the time of the Geonosian crisis, the Morgukai were on the verge of extinction. It is rumored that Morgukai warriors were so fierce with their cortosis ore weapons that they were even a match for the Jedi Knights, and that, through training, they were highly resistant to mind manipulation. Although little is known about the Morgukai, recovered records from that time period indicate that the Morgukai tradition was passed down in the male line only from father to son, in a training system similar to that of the Jedi–Padawan relationship. Of utmost importance to the Morgukai was personal honor, to the degree that they would overlook issues of good and evil as long as honor was maintained.

The Kadas'sa'Nikto, or Green Nikto, originated in the forested and coastal regions of Kintan. This race has green-gray skin with visible scales and small horns surrounding the eyes. Green Nikto have discernible noses that are sensitive enough to allow them to pick up the scent of other creatures in a forest or jungle environment. They also sport long claws that enable them to climb trees.

Mountain Nikto, usually referred to as the Esral'sa'Nikto, are blue-gray in color and have pronounced facial fins that expand from their cheeks. Like the Kajain'sa'Nikto, they have flaps of skin that cover their noses, with permeable membranes above the mouths. Their long fins are lined with small vibrating hairs that enhance their hearing. By fully expanding these fins, they can disperse excess heat, and by flattening them against their skulls, they can insulate themselves against the cold. They also have expanding and contracting neck cavities that diffuse or trap heat and recycle moisture in their systems. Their claws are small and recessed.

The Pale Nikto, or Gluss'sa'Nikto, are white or gray and populate the Gluss'elta Islands, a chain of a dozen islands on Kintan. These Nikto have ridges of small horns surrounding

their eyes, like Kadas'sa'Nikto, but they also possess small fins similar to the larger fins of the Esral'sa'Nikto.

Finally, the M'shento'su'Nikto, or Southern Nikto, have white, yellow, or orange skin. They do not have horns or fins at all, but possess a multitude of breather tubes on the backs of their skulls that tend to be much longer than their cousins' standard breather tubes. These act as primitive ultrasonic sensory tubes, and scientists believe the extermination of natural predators on Kintan slowed the full development of these organs in other Nikto races.

Because the Nikto subspecies frequently banded together to protect themselves from predators, they eventually became a unified people. Stellar radiation over Kintan had caused horrific monsters to evolve on their world, and that constant threat drove the Nikto to develop tools of defense, as well as cities with high protective walls and other military strategies. They literally fought themselves to the top of the food chain, burning down forests and swamps to force the most dangerous creatures into extinction. But by doing so, they turned their planet into a barren wasteland.

Twenty-five thousand standard years before the Battle of Yavin, Nikto astronomers discovered the star M'dweshuu. Inspired by this star, a strange cult arose that initiated blood sacrifices to appease the spirit of the celestial body. The cult spread quickly across the world, killing thousands of Nikto who did not bow to the cult's control.

After this group ruled Kintan for thirty years, Churabba the Hutt and her clan visited and witnessed the cult in action. They were interested in taking the star system for themselves, and had already enlisted the Nikto's neighbors, the Klatooinians and the Vodrans, as servants. Churabba quickly realized that the cult was suppressing a very disgruntled people. To turn the Nikto to her side, she bombarded the cult's stronghold from space, wiping it out completely. The grateful Nikto people, regarding her as a savior, joined the Treaty of Vontor, which required them to serve the Hutts indefinitely.

This cult rose again, about a thousand years before the Battle of Yavin, and temporarily pushed the Hutts off Kintan, but the Hutts in turn sent armies of mercenaries to squash the rebellion. Since then, the Nikto have remained in the service of the Hutts, although not without the occasional incidents of unrest.

DESIGNATION
Sentient

HOMEWORLD
Kintan

AVERAGE HEIGHT
1.8 meters

PRONUNCIATION
Nĭk'-tō

NOTABLE APPEARANCE
Episode VI: Return of the Jedi

NOGHRI

Noghri are hairless, gray-skinned bipeds native to the mostly barren and isolated Outer Rim planet of Honoghr. They are strong and sinewy creatures, with extraordinarily quick reflexes and inherent agility. They are not tall, but their smaller size often belies their ruthlessness and deadly skills.

These people are compact killing machines, built to hunt and destroy. They are predators who sport long talons, teeth-filled jaws, large, quick-moving, deep-set black eyes, and an extremely keen sense of smell. This sense of smell is *so* refined, *so* powerful, that a Noghri can identify beings' bloodlines by their scent. In addition, given their size, speed, and agility, they are particularly stealthy, able to sneak up on many targets unawares. Noghri prefer to use primitive tools and weapons, killing opponents up close. Along with their superior fighting skills, this trait makes them especially deadly assassins.

Noghri society is matriarchal and clan-oriented. Families often cluster together, creating singular villages. Each clan has a maitrakh or clan leader, usually one of the oldest and wisest female clan members, who makes the ultimate decision on all clan affairs as dictated by a tradition stretching back countless generations. Each clan has a dukha, or community building, within which all major events are held. All village life revolves around this one central meeting place. Historically, interclan rivalries were often brutal and bloody, but over time these internecine conflicts took their toll, and having learned that they would drive themselves to extinction, the clans understood that they must settle their differences and coexist. By the time of the Clone Wars, the Noghri were living in peace, ignorant of the galaxy at large.

As a people, the Noghri are brutal, committed fighters who find honor in serving their charges well. Honor is paramount to Noghri culture, and serving poorly brings disgrace upon their clans. The safety of those they assume responsibility for is of utmost importance. They are also smart, honest, flexible, and take great care to learn and understand the rituals and cultural traditions of others.

Noghri speak Basic in addition to their own language, albeit in gravelly, chilling voices. They are not a fun-loving or sociable people, and in fact have very little in the way of a sense of humor.

Honoghr was originally a lush planet teeming with a wide variety of animals and plant life, with a yearly rotation that is only half a standard year. Now it is a barren world barely capable of supporting its inhabitants. Honoghr's environmental problems began with a space battle about twenty years before the Battle of Yavin—a clash between a Republic cruiser and a Separatist science vessel carrying a poisonous defoliant. Unfortunately, the Separatist ship crashed into Honoghr's surface, spilling its toxic chemicals and resulting in an ecological disaster. This incident poisoned Honoghr's soil and atmosphere, destroying much of the planet's life. Shortly after the end of the Clone Wars, the Sith Lord Darth Vader came to Honoghr, prepared to make servants of the Noghri. Vader convinced the Noghri that the Republic was to blame for the damage to their planet, and that only he and the Empire could repair their environment. In return, seeing that they were gifted, effective warriors, he requested they serve him personally as assassins and bodyguards.

The Noghri, who were at the time of Vader's intervention an agrarian people and facing famine, felt they had no choice but to agree to Lord Vader's solution. Bound by their word of honor as given to the Empire, they served Vader and later Admiral Thrawn, who enlisted the Noghri to be his servants when he announced to them that he was Vader's successor.

It was not long after, as the New Republic was struggling to combat Admiral Thrawn's brilliant battle plans, that Thrawn ordered the Noghri to kidnap Princess Leia Organa Solo, who at the time was pregnant with twins Jaina and Jacen. The Noghri tracked Leia to Kashyyyk, where she was under the protection of the Wookiees. Because of her scent, they recognized her immediately as the Mal'ary'ush, or daughter of Vader.

After stopping the Noghri team and turning them to her side, Leia traveled to Honoghr and asked the Noghri to work with her in overthrowing Thrawn. Leia was initially refused by the clan leaders because of their word of honor to Thrawn, but the Noghri finally agreed to betray the Chiss admiral when Leia showed them that the "help" the Empire was giving them was not curing their destroyed world. The kholmgrass planted by the Imperials was not a restorative but a poison that infected the soil even more by preventing other plants from growing. Every effort expanded by the Empire on Honoghr was aimed at keeping the Noghri enslaved.

The Noghri were enraged and vowed revenge on Thrawn and the Empire that had maintained the deception for so long. Because Thrawn still trusted the Noghri, his own Noghri bodyguards were able to get close enough to slay him. Then, having transferred their unwavering dedication to Leia, to their "Lady Vader," for her attempts to truly repair the Honoghr environment, they undertook self-appointed service as her personal bodyguards, and as bodyguards for her children as they grew up. The Noghri's loyalty to Leia and her family is not unlike that of a Wookiee life debt. The Noghri would sooner die than see Leia come to harm. In fact, several have given their lives to protect her.

Before destroying Thrawn, however, some Noghri decided to take their world's environmental woes into their own hands, in an attempt to begin the rebuilding that the Empire had at one time promised. They discovered and cultivated what they named "The Future of the Noghri," a valley under a series of cliff walls near a river visible only from directly above. This place is a small agricultural oasis on a nearly dead world. Unfortunately, the planet may never fully recover. Despite the best efforts of Princess Leia and New Republic scientists, the devastation was simply too severe and too widespread. Meanwhile, with Leia's assistance, the Noghri have established the thriving colony of New Nystao on Wayland. Although the Noghri rarely venture out of their settlements alone, they have continued to increase their presence in the larger galaxy, going so far as to participate in missions against the Yuuzhan Vong during the height of their invasion.

DESIGNATION
Sentient

HOMEWORLD
Honoghr

AVERAGE HEIGHT
1.4 meters

PRONUNCIATION
Nō'-grē

NOTABLE APPEARANCE
Heir to the Empire (novel)

ORTOLAN

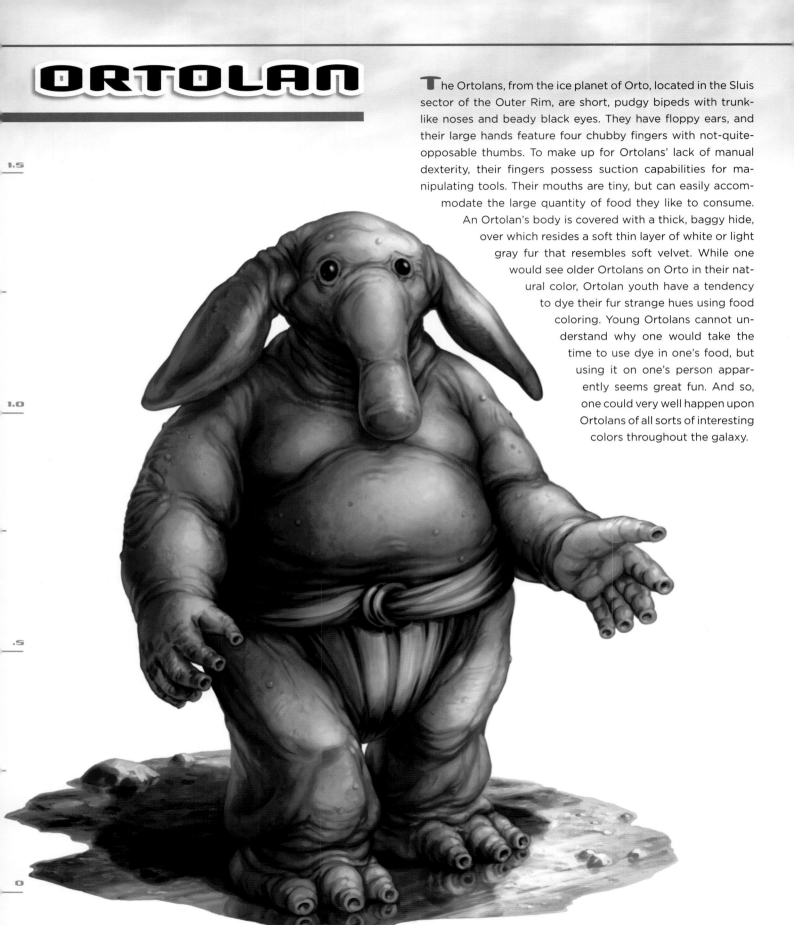

The Ortolans, from the ice planet of Orto, located in the Sluis sector of the Outer Rim, are short, pudgy bipeds with trunk-like noses and beady black eyes. They have floppy ears, and their large hands feature four chubby fingers with not-quite-opposable thumbs. To make up for Ortolans' lack of manual dexterity, their fingers possess suction capabilities for manipulating tools. Their mouths are tiny, but can easily accommodate the large quantity of food they like to consume. An Ortolan's body is covered with a thick, baggy hide, over which resides a soft thin layer of white or light gray fur that resembles soft velvet. While one would see older Ortolans on Orto in their natural color, Ortolan youth have a tendency to dye their fur strange hues using food coloring. Young Ortolans cannot understand why one would take the time to use dye in one's food, but using it on one's person apparently seems great fun. And so, one could very well happen upon Ortolans of all sorts of interesting colors throughout the galaxy.

1.5

1.0

.5

0

Ortolans were originally nocturnal, hence much of their physiology is adapted to night living. Their eyes are almost completely pupil, making them more comfortable in dim lighting while bright illumination hurts their eyes. Ortolans' trunk possesses an incredible smelling ability, allowing them to detect food up to two kilometers away. It also has extremely sensitive tympanic organs that channel low-wavelength sounds up to flexible eustachian tubes in their ears. When this input is added to the sounds registered by the ears, which are also extremely sensitive, Ortolans can pick up the entire range from subsonic to ultrasonic sound waves. Their trunks are also used to generate sound, particularly at the subsonic range. In fact, much of their language is carried out at these extreme frequencies, so that to observers from other species, they seem to be almost mute, save for the rare times they decide to communicate at normal levels.

As would be expected of a species with such highly developed hearing, the Ortolans' favorite form of entertainment is music. Concerts on Orto feature all levels of sound, from subsonic to ultrasonic. Every new performance, live or recorded, of even the most familiar music, is a unique experience for Ortolans, as they can detect nuances in music that other species cannot. These performances are usually held in food bars, and are extremely loud to drown out the sounds of food venders and eating. Furthermore, Ortolans are considered to be some of the finest musicians in the galaxy. When they are found offworld, they are most likely traveling musicians.

Food is the most important thing to an Ortolan because it is so scarce on their world. Ortolans are known to be sociable and pleasant, especially with those who offer them food. Their food fixation has caused other species to think of them as unintelligent—they will often work for food. And yet they are wily enough to use this mistaken perception to sneak food (or other valuables) from their detractors.

The Ortolans' home planet, Orto, is a frozen wasteland. Due to its extreme elliptical orbit around a red sun, its axial tilt, and its thin atmosphere, Orto's growing season is a scant 161 standard days long. This is barely long enough for crops, and most must be grown near the equator for appropriate temperature and water. For this reason, a heavy layer of blubber serves as insulation and provides an auxiliary energy supply for Ortolans in case food becomes scarce, and they eat at every possible opportunity, as periodic famines are not uncommon.

Ortolans have few children. When a child is born, muscles and teeth are fully developed. Parents educate their own children, and when a child shows a gift that the parents are not equipped to address, they participate in a "teaching swap": another Ortolan family teaches their child in exchange for a special service or supplies. At the age of seven, to help conserve the family's supplies, most children are simply thrown out of the house to fend for themselves—unless one exhibits a talent particularly valuable to the family's well-being.

While Ortolan society is industrialized, it is not on a par with much of the galaxy technologically. Their chief trade with other species is in the raw materials and fossil fuels that are plentiful beneath their frozen planet's surface. This trade has introduced the concept of money to Ortolans, but their economy still remains largely barter-based. Ortolans will primarily barter for what they need and save the money they receive to buy foodstuffs they normally cannot obtain at home.

During the Clone Wars, Orto was invaded by the Confederacy of Independent Systems, despite the efforts of Ortolan Jedi Nem Bees. Later, under Imperial rule, Orto was taken over by the Empire as a source for raw materials. The Empire forbade Ortolans to travel offplanet—for their own protection, presumably, although the true reason was to control the Ortolan mining trade, allowing only preselected companies with strong Imperial ties to trade there. As long as this appeared to be the case, the Ortolans were left alone to a large degree. In truth, the Ortolans were trading with the Empire, the Rebellion, and whoever else might provide the best food at the time. However, smugglers managed to kidnap Ortolans to sell into slavery. Many of these ended up serving in the underworld, even if they escaped—they knew of nowhere else to go. After the Battle of Endor, Ortolans were quick to make a break for the stars, drawn by the lure of new and interesting cuisines to savor. They can be found in most active port systems where there is known to be an active nightlife that includes music and all-night buffets.

DESIGNATION
Sentient

HOMEWORLD
Orto

AVERAGE HEIGHT
1.4 meters

PRONUNCIATION
Ôr-tō'-lăn

NOTABLE APPEARANCE
Episode VI: Return of the Jedi

PA'LOWICK

The Pa'lowick are shy, slender-limbed amphibians from the planet Lowick, located in the Outer Rim. They have plump, rounded bodies and long frog-like arms and legs. Their skin is very smooth, and speckled in a pattern of greens, browns, and yellows, causing them to easily blend in with their natural, equatorial rain forest environment. Males tend to have more angular patterns running along their backs and arms than females. The most distinguishing Pa'lowick attribute are their thin, tube-like trunks, which sprout from the center of the face, ending in almost incongruous human-like lips.

Some Pa'lowick possess a second mouth, with tusks resting just beneath the trunk. Youthful Pa'lowick retain this extra mouth through young adulthood, at which time it disappears, absorbed into their facial skin. The second mouth helps the youthful Pa'lowick gain more nutrition during their growing years, as the trunks take in only a limited amount of food at a time. Adults require a smaller amount of food and energy, and so the extra mouth disappears. The tusks, which fall off at the same time the mouth is absorbed, provide young Pa'lowicks with an extra means of defending themselves.

There is a subspecies of Pa'lowick, however, that retains its tusks through adulthood. This subspecies is believed to be older than the species that loses its tusks, though scientists have not been able to determine genetically which species is the progenitor of the other. The tusken variety, however, are localized in a specific area of Lowick where there are more forms of predatory wildlife. This seems to verify the belief that they are the older variety of Pa'lowick, as those subspecies who do not require the extra protection live in other less-hazardous regions. Tusked Pa'lowick tend to be a bit more aggressive than their fellows, but this is only a protective measure. Among their own and outsiders they come to know, they are as gentle as their untusked cousins.

Lowick is a watery world of vast oceans, seas, and mountainous regions. The Pa'lowick developed near the planet's equator, a region of marshes and deep green rain forests. Pa'lowick bodies are therefore made for their marshy home. Their long legs allow them to move easily through the still murky waters of salt marshes searching for fish, reptiles, and waterfowl for nourishment. Their snouts are perfect for eating giant marlello duck eggs, which they puncture with their tongues to suck the yolk through their tube-like mouths.

Their eyes, which rest at the end of two stalks sprouting from their foreheads, allow them to hide underwater while keeping a lookout for predators. Fortunately, Pa'lowick's lungs are well developed, and they are able to hold their breath long enough for most dangerous creatures to pass them by. Pa'lowicks have large air bladders that allow their lungs to expand down into their bellies. These air bladders aid them in swimming as well as singing. In addition, these air bladders make their bodies extremely light and aid their thin legs in supporting their torsos.

Pa'lowick reproduce by laying eggs, and the female will guard the eggs in her home until they hatch. Pa'lowick homes are roofed, hut-like nests made of dried mud, reeds, and grass. Children are raised and educated within their agrarian communities, which are run by noble families in a feudal system. Pa'lowick are omnivorous, eating what they can gather from the salt marshes and also growing a wide variety of foodstuffs. The veejy fruit is a particular delicacy, growing in great quantities all year long in Lowickian rain forests. Characterized by its prickly skin and oblong shape, the yellow flesh of this fruit is sweet tasting, making it a popular export. The veejy fruit is largely responsible for the Pa'lowick's success in the post–Yuuzhan Vong era. When invading Pa'lowick, the Yuuzhan Vong destroyed the planet's mechanical harvesting machines, not the veejy crops themselves. As the Pa'lowickian agricultural base remains intact, their economy is already well on its way to recovery.

Miners looking for valuable Lowickan firegems in the Lowick asteroid belt discovered the species before the Clone Wars. Lowickian firegems are rare but useful, although they are often used for nefarious purposes. Extremely volatile, Lowickan firegems explode when placed near most forms of radiation. For this reason, they are often used as incendiary devices, both in legitimate mining and to cause injury and bring down starships.

Pa'lowick are therefore quite new to galactic society. They are enthusiastic about offworld contact, and enjoy trading food and native items for technology. Pa'lowick are very primitive, and prefer to live a simple life farming and fishing, but they are fascinated by technological items that make their lives easier. Even so, such items have done little to change Pa'lowick culture and life on the whole. While the ruling nobility at times considered joining the New Republic, the New Republic didn't seek them out for membership. Being so new, and offering so little in terms of trade, they tended to be ignored in the shuffle. However, this didn't seem to offend the Pa'lowicks, who really don't pay attention to galactic events anyway.

The Pa'lowicks are a generally patient people, who like to cling to rituals and traditions, rarely changing their ways of doing things. And yet they'll embrace technology that helps them do things the traditional way, only better. Because their heritage is so important, singing and storytelling are valued pursuits. In addition, vocal music is often a religious experi-

DESIGNATION
Sentient

HOMEWORLD
Lowick

AVERAGE
HEIGHT
1.6 meters

PRONUNCIATION
Păl'-ō-wĭk

ence; a great many songs are written with sacred themes. This should not, however, suggest that all Pa'lowick music is religious. Many Pa'lowick sing for the pure enjoyment of it. Written language is a relatively new development in Pa'lowick society, so the need for an oral tradition to pass down history is not surprising. Much Pa'lowick lore is handed down through songs, including family lineages, historical events, and morality tales. Pa'lowick children grow up surrounded by music, and many vie for the few openings as apprentices to community storytellers. Technology is also slowly having an effect on Pa'lowick music.

With the discovery of the planet, some Pa'lowick have begun to learn Basic and adapt the Basic alphabet to spoken Lowickese (to the uneducated, however, it looks like nonsense written in Basic). This, along with the technology to record their songs and music, is allowing Pa'lowick to share their music beyond their own world.

Some ambitious Pa'lowick have taken this long treasured talent of singing to the stars, introducing a whole new, critically acclaimed sound to the galactic music scene. Pa'lowick music has become extremely popular and can be heard in cantinas thoughout the known worlds. Moreover, groups featuring Pa'lowick singers are among the most requested acts on the HoloNet.

While still new to the galaxy, this species was brought to greater public awareness when one female Pa'lowick named Larisselle Chatrunis won the Miss Coruscant beauty contest in the years leading up to the Clone Wars. Lariselle overwhelmed the judges with her singing ability during the talent portion of the contest, then truly impressed them with her knowledge of and sensitivity to the state of the galaxy—unusual for a people who'd only recently learned of the galactic society. Her fame was cut short when the Emperor initiated his anti-alien policies, but Lariselle, being more savvy than many of her fellow Pa'lowick, joined the Rebel Alliance. Using her talent as a singer, she toured the galaxy with a band of musicians, gathering information to pass along to the Alliance. Thought to be in competition with the often-lauded Sy Snootles, a perception she encouraged to deflect attention from her true work, Larisselle's only goal was to make music in order to win freedom from oppression for alien peoples. She survived the civil war and returned home to Lowick where she retired to a quiet life with family and friends.

NOTABLE APPEARANCE
Episode VI: Return of the Jedi

Polis Massans are a humanoid species inhabiting the small asteroid mining colony of Polis Massa in the isolated reaches of the Outer Rim. These short, thin, mute beings originally evolved on a world in the Subterrel sector. No records exist containing details of the species' previous life. After a natural cataclysm broke apart the world known as Polis Massa several centuries ago, they moved their entire society to that world to mine for artifacts from its lost Eellayin civilization, hoping to preserve the memory of these ill-fated people—or to resurrect them through cloning. These alien researchers believe they are descendants of the Eellayin, and because they have been working on this archaeological project for so long, they have become known as Polis Massans themselves, a name they accept with a sense of honor and humility.

These ardent archaeologists and exobiologists are delicate in appearance, with pale faces and gray skin. A Polis Massan's skin is thick and smooth, with some insulating qualities. This suggests that Polis Massans may have evolved from aquatic creatures, possibly within the cetacean genus. Their heads are practically featureless because an osmotic membrane covers the front of their faces. Polis Massans' thin arms end in four long, nimble fingers. They use a form of sign language and technological devices to communicate with others because they do not have vocal cords. In addition, they use a mild form of telepathy to share simple thoughts and feelings. Polis Massans have intensely focused eyes, which help them in their underground and medical research work. Growth rings circle their wiry bodies, although the specific biological reason for this is currently unknown. Most Polis Massans work in a mining capacity, or as medics or exobiologists, and they wear formfitting bodysuits with built-in signaling technology, medical instruments, and utility belts to do their work.

The Polis Massans are an industrious species. Most are seasoned spelunkers, working every day in the deep core of the Polis Massan asteroid field to find artifacts. Other peoples have speculated on the relationship of the present Polis Massans to the original inhabitants—other than their belief that they are their descendants—but the Polis Massans keep such information in solemn secrecy. They are generally known to have an insatiable desire for data on other species, so it might be argued that they have no ulterior motives for their archaeological research other than discovering their own background.

While they interact little with offworlders, Polis Massans are known for their remarkable medical skills and to be compassionate beings who value life and freedom in all forms. If the Polis Massans oppose outside contact, it is to discourage treasure hunters from invading the archaeological dig sites they are uncovering. Piracy is rampant in the Outer Rim, so the Polis Massans are desperate to avoid bringing attention to themselves. Polis Massan medical technicians are trained in cloning techniques, although their cloning technology is not as advanced as that of the Kaminoans who originally taught them. To carry out their cloning research, the Polis Massans built a high-end medical facility in one of their sealed habitats, although it is equipped mainly for the physiology of the Polis Massans.

Luke and Leia Skywalker were born in this very medical center on Polis Massa when Obi-Wan Kenobi and Bail Organa brought in their mother, in critical condition. While the Polis Massans did their best to save Padmé Amidala, she died in childbirth. Known for their honor and secrecy, the Polis Massans revealed nothing of the happenings there, and kept the knowledge of the Skywalker children a close-guarded secret. The Polis Massa asteroid field would play another important role, serving as a Rebel base in the early days of the fight against the Emperor's New Order. Many sorties were launched from Polis Massa during the Rebellion, and in turn the Empire raided Polis Massa. One such raid sought the stolen Death Star plans—which were not found, although the Imperial 501st did find evidence that Leia had them. This discovery led directly to the raid on her ship *Tantive IV,* and to her capture by Darth Vader.

Still, the planet's precious dig sites remained untouched, and the Polis Massans were able to resume their archaeological work. Nor did the site suffer damage during the war against the Yuuzhan Vong; its remote location held little strategic or resource value to the invaders.

DESIGNATION
Sentient

HOMEWORLD
Polis Massa
(by way of the
Subterrel sector)

**AVERAGE
HEIGHT**
1.4 meters

PRONUNCIATION
Pō'-lĕs Mä'-sän

NOTABLE APPEARANCE
Episode III: Revenge of the Sith

QUARREN

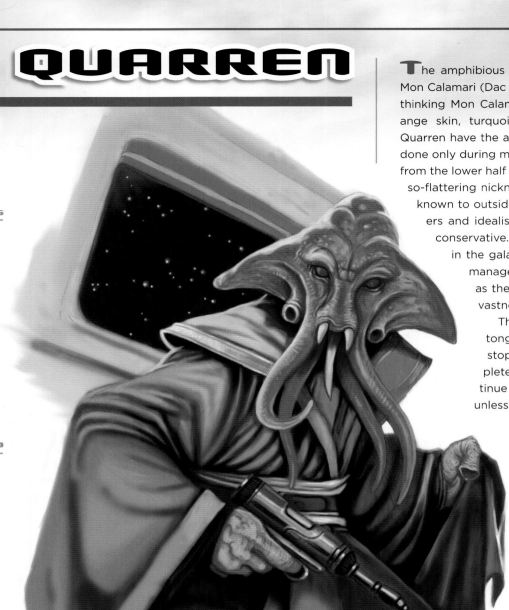

The amphibious Quarren share the Outer Rim world of Mon Calamari (Dac in their native tongue) with the forward-thinking Mon Calamari species. Quarren have leathery orange skin, turquoise eyes, and suction-cupped fingers. Quarren have the ability to alter their skin color, but this is done only during mating rituals. Since four tentacles sprout from the lower half of their faces, they have earned the not-so-flattering nickname of Squid Heads by which they are known to outsiders. While the Mon Calamari are dreamers and idealists, the Quarren are more practical and conservative. They've made a place for themselves in the galaxy acting as accountants and business managers. Despite this, not many leave home, as they prefer their peaceful ocean life to the vastness of the star-studded void.

The two species share a common native tongue, but, because the Mon Calamari have stopped using the language almost completely in favor of Basic, the Quarren continue to speak their own language regularly, unless dealing with outsiders.

Relations between the Quarren and the Mon Calamari have not always been peaceful. Quarren lived at greater depths than the Mon Calamari, and for many generations, they lived in completely separate and isolated communities. When the Quarren started traveling to higher levels of the oceans, they encountered the Mon Calamari and attacked their more technologically advanced neighbors. These battles proved disastrous for the Quarren, who were nearly driven to extinction. As a means of preventing unending wars between their species, the Mon Calamari attempted a daring social experiment aimed at civilizing the Quarren.

During these wars, the Mon Calamari captured nearly one million Quarren. The Mon Calamari were reluctant to release the Quarren, fearing that they would take up arms once more, forcing the Mon Calamari to kill them in battle. Desperate for another solution, the Mon Cals removed a generation of Quarren children from their captured parents and raised them in Mon Calamari cities, educating them in philosophy, mathematics, and science. Otherwise, they made no effort to force their beliefs on the Quarren children or change their hatred of Mon Calamari. After a decade, the children were returned to their families, and the results of the experiment was readily apparent: the children exhibited new respect for the Mon Calamari. Quarren elders felt the children had been brainwashed; the children in turn perceived the elders as primitive savages. The generations no longer had anything in common. Fifteen years later, the children had grown to adulthood and assumed control of Quarren society, and several years after that opened diplomatic relations with their world-mates. While this was a controversial approach on the part of the Mon Calamari, it perhaps saved the Quarren and, in turn, themselves.

After building something of a political friendship, the Mon Calamari encouraged the Quarren to work with them in pursuing dreams of space and advanced science. The Mon Cals provided the ideas, and the Quarren provided the raw materials. Together they built impressive ships for deep space, as well as impressive floating cities that dominate the oceans.

These giant cities extend far below the surface of the water, and serve as centers of learning, culture, and government. In contrast with the Mon Calamari, who prefer more daylight and live in the upper levels of the cities, the Quarren live in the lowest levels of the metropolis in the cool security of the deep. This fits with their cultural identity as a pragmatic people, unwilling to trust or embrace the new idea or lofty concept. Their literature reveals a people who do not dream of brighter tomorrows, but hold fast to remembered yesterdays. Thus, they feel they belong in the sea, not in space.

And yet, many Quarren have followed their neighbors offplanet. Quarren are able to live on land as long as they are able to keep their skin moist. As they benefited from the discoveries and achievements of the Mon Calamari, they have grown dependent upon them. This dependency has caused friction between the two peoples, and may have prompted the Quarren to join Count Dooku and the Confederacy during the Clone Wars. Though an armistice was reached before the end of the wars and the creation of the Empire, it is believed that the Quarren betrayed their ocean compatriots the day that the Imperial fleet arrived. On that day, Mon Calamari's planetary defense systems failed to protect them from invasion. Rumors persist that the Quarren aided the Imperials by sabotaging this protective network.

The Empire enslaved both the Quarren and the Mon Calamari, forcing them to work in labor camps. There, the two species found a unifying cause, and cooperated in a plan of passive resistance. The Empire retaliated by destroying whole cities on Mon Calamari, filling the ocean with the blood of both species. This incited these peaceful peoples to rise up in rage. Using only primitive utensils, hand tools, and sheer will, they forced their Imperial taskmasters to leave their world.

Today Quarren and Mon Calamari live in peace with each other, although there still is some lingering resentment. Persistent elements of Quarren society recall the wars against the Mon Calamari and the Mon Calamari's deceptive "theft" of their children. Some Quarren believe that Mon Cals brought havoc to their world by exploring space in the first place. Similarly, some Quarren believe the adoption of *Mon Calamari* as a name for their planet is one more example of the Mon Calamari species seeking its own glorification at the Quarren's expense. These Quarren do their best to enact revenge against the New Republic and the Mon Cal without bringing harm upon their own. There has been an effort by some Quarren to find another homeworld—one they would not have to share—following the Battle of Mon Calamari during the New Republic era. And yet one sign that healing is occurring between the two peoples is that more interspecies romances are being recorded, one of the better known being the relationship involving two Rogue Squadron pilots: the late Ibtisam, a Mon Calamari, and Nrin Vakil, a Quarren. When Ibtisam was killed in action, their relationship became public knowledge, leading to more openness about the two species interrelating. For many residents of Mon Calamari, this is evidence of hope for their people and their world.

DESIGNATION
Sentient

HOMEWORLD
Mon Calamari

AVERAGE
HEIGHT
1.7 meters

PRONUNCIATION
Kwä'-rĕn

NOTABLE APPEARANCE
Episode VI: Return of the Jedi

RANCOR

Rancors are huge, mostly vicious reptilian creatures found on several worlds throughout the galaxy. There are several different varieties, but all have nearly the same physiology and temperament. How they managed to spread to so many different systems is still a mystery, but most scientists believe that they were taken to some worlds by sentient species who used these massive creatures as battle mounts or beasts of burden.

Standing on two trunk-like legs, more than five meters tall, rancors provide an intimidating sight to those who face

7.0

6.0

5.0

4.0

3.0

2.0

1.0

0

them. Rancor hides are often a combination of gray, green, and brown in color; they have glistening black eyes. Their arms are very long, somewhat slender, and out of proportion when compared with the rest of their muscular bodies. Rancors have huge saliva-dripping fangs, and long, sharp claws on their fingers and toes. These creatures are repto-mammals (part reptile, part mammal), and as such, they lay clutches of two eggs at a time. Rancors care for their young, although they do not suckle. When the creatures are hatched, the parents are gentle with their three-meter-tall offspring—showing a gentle, loving nature that is often incongruous with their fearsome appearance. The mother shares her food with her young, which ride on her back until they are three years of age. At maturity, a rancor leaves its family for the rest of its life.

Carnivorous, rancors prefer fresh, raw meat, particularly large herbivorous creatures. They will eat vegetable matter if nothing else is available, but it is by necessity only. In the wild, rancors have few natural predators, instead being the predators themselves. In addition, some creatures are thought to be subspecies of rancors, such as the terentatek of Korriban, which has larger spines and a more armored head. Another such subspecies is the pygmy rancor, thought to be the result of bioengineering. Although this theory is still in dispute in scientific circles, the pygmy rancor is smaller in stature than the common rancor, but distinctly a rancor according to genetic analysis. Latest theories hypothesize that the pygmy rancor was engineered and released into the wild either by accident or on purpose, to breed. Similar theories have been put forth regarding Dathomiran rancors, which are larger than average.

Rancors are fearsome fighters. Their fists can smash prey flat, while their massive jaws enable them to swallow human-sized morsels whole. Their thick powerful hides make them highly resistant to blasters and other handheld energy weapons. Even melee weapons cannot puncture their tough layers of skin. Rancors' eyes are able to see clearly in dim light, and their sense of smell allows them to track prey over great distances.

The influence of rancors goes beyond their own environments. For example, Rancor Rising is a sequence of movements in the teräs käsi martial arts tradition, based on rancors' hunting characteristics. Also, rancor hide is used in leather consumer goods such as boots. There is also a valuable trade in items carved from rancor teeth. In her days as a Jedi Knight, the Hapan Queen Mother Tenel Ka used a light-saber with a hilt carved of a rancor tooth from her mother's homeworld of Dathomir.

Despite their fierce fighting abilities, rancors are actually inherently benign creatures when they are well fed and allowed to live alongside their own kind. They can be successfully domesticated and trained for riding or to haul goods. In the case of the Witches of Dathomir, rancors have been trained to perform construction labor and serve as transportation. However, training a rancor is not an easy task and should not be attempted without extensive training in zoological behavioral techniques and prior experience with dangerous creatures. Because the Witches of Dathomir are themselves raised with rancors, they come by this training naturally.

Rancors have shown a capacity to bond with other species if given the chance—particularly with those who feed and care for them. This is the case with the breed on Dathomir, whose intelligence makes them extremely useful as battle mounts and protectors. Dathomiri rancors are also very loyal to their owners.

If abused or maltreated, however, these beasts can be driven into an almost perpetual rage that is only temporarily abated by regular feedings. If they are driven to this state, they'll eat anyone or anything that comes within reach out of utter despair and fury. Luke Skywalker reported that he encountered a rancor in this very state on Tatooine. Jabba the Hutt employed a dangerous creature specialist named Malakili from the Circus Horrificus as his rancor keeper. Malakili bonded with the creature, but Jabba would not let him feed the rancor regularly, preferring instead to feed the rancor his enemies and others who displeased him. While this happened frequently, the meat was from beings rather than sustenance animals, and thus did not meet the rancor's basic needs. When Skywalker was tossed into the rancor's pit beneath Jabba's throne room, he had to lure the creature to its death in order to put it out of its misery. Sadly, when a rancor reaches this point, there is little else to do but euthanize it. Even if removed from that environment and placed in one where it can be cared for properly, an abused rancor never seems to forget. It will not get over the distrust, or learn that food and care can be counted on. Zoologists commonly believe that there can be no rehabilitation of a rancor that has been mistreated for a long period of time.

DESIGNATION
Nonsentient

HOMEWORLD
Dathomir/
Ottethan

AVERAGE
HEIGHT
5+ meters

PRONUNCIATION
Răn'-kōr

NOTABLE APPEARANCE
Episode VI: Return of the Jedi

REEK

The reek is a large quadrupedal mammal native to the plains of Ylesia in Hutt space, and often bred on ranches on that world's Codian Moon. Large tusks protrude from their cheeks, which they use for headlocks in contests for dominance among their own kind. One central horn is used to attack an opponent head-on. While they are herbivores by nature, they are often used for exhibition sport as execution animals. When used this way, reeks are fed meat and then starved so they develop the instincts to attack arena gladiators or other animals. Reeks cannot continue to thrive on a meat diet, so arena animals are fed just enough plant matter to keep up their strength and incite their hunger. Heavy and muscular, the reek is a fierce combatant. Its powerful jaw muscles, which usually slice through tough wood-moss chunks with ease, can take off a human limb without much effort. All reeks, even the subspecies, are normally some sort of brown in color with leathery skin, but if fed a diet of meat their skin turns a mottled red.

Reeks tend to reside in small herds in the mossy grasslands and are very protective over their chosen area of wood-moss turf. They use their front claws for digging up wood-moss, which is their primary source of nourishment. Because their cheek horns grow continuously, reeks will rub their horns on trees and rocks to shorten and sharpen them. The horns of male reeks are usually larger than those of females, and they display them to attract a mate. During mating season, male reeks battle each other in ramming contests for the choice females among their herds.

Reeks have been transported to other worlds for various purposes, causing them to adapt to new environments. One subspecies of reek, principally adapted to the world of Ithor, was wiped out in the Yuuzhan Vong invasion. While the Ithorians are very technologically developed, they preferred to use a more natural means of planting and growing. They used reeks as plow animals because they were strong, slow, and naturally gentle. This reek subspecies was, therefore, larger than those found on Ylesia, and stronger for pulling large plows. The animals' horns were also smaller, as they were not as motivated to fight among one another. The Ithorians wisely placed males and females in separate pens and isolated planned pairs for mating, to reduce competition. These reeks were yellow in color because of their consumption of Ithorian flora, with a special affinity for the leaves of bafforr trees.

One other subspecies was developed on the Zabrak world of Iridonia. When the Zabrak first took to the stars, they saw reeks as excellent animals to use for war mounts in that they were naturally armored. Riding reeks into battle, they charge at their opponents, using the animal's horns as an added weapon. Iridonian reeks have tougher skin for resisting blunt or sharp weapon attacks and the harsh Iridonian winds. Zabrak do not feed their mounts meat, preferring them to be strong and fierce with natural vigor. These reeks are more compact in size than the original reek, and gray in color from consuming the native vegetation. Their primary horns are longer and sharper, and they are often decorated with markings mimicking the tattoos the Zabrak adorn themselves with. These tattoos may speak of a reek's personality, its given name, or the family to whom it belongs. Iridonian reeks are encouraged to fight for dominance and for mates as this desensitizes them to violence, making them less likely to bolt or buck in battle. The Zabrak skill of reek riding declined in use as the Zabrak became more technologically advanced, but the skill of riding a war mount is still taught at most schools focusing on the military arts.

While reeks are not terribly fast, they are intelligent. If given patient, gentle training, they can make excellent pack animals. The Codian Moon harbors several reek ranches for this purpose, though diminishing resources and plummeting profits have caused several ranchers to start breeding their reeks for the gladiatorial arenas, feeding them meat and starving them to bring out their wild anger.

In such a situation, reeks are fearsome foes. Snapping their strong jaws, they can bite a humanoid in half, slicing through flesh and crushing bones without effort. Their usual tactic is to gore their opponents with their horns and trample them under their giant, heavy feet.

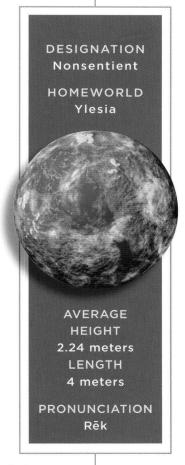

DESIGNATION
Nonsentient

HOMEWORLD
Ylesia

AVERAGE HEIGHT
2.24 meters
LENGTH
4 meters

PRONUNCIATION
Rēk

NOTABLE APPEARANCE
Episode II: Attack of the Clones

RODIAN

Rodians are reptilian beings from Rodia in the Mid Rim's Tyrius system who are renowned as hunters throughout the galaxy. They possess multifaceted eyes that can see heat emanating from quarry hidden in darkness. Rodians have thin, tapering snouts that act as special filters for their finely tuned olfactory senses. Green scales cover their bodies, allowing them to blend with vegetation. Their long, thin fingers have suction cups at the ends, ostensibly for gripping trees and rocky inclines, and their ridged spines crest at the tops of their skulls, both evidence of their unique reptilian ancestry.

Male Rodians are hairless, where females are capable of growing long, flowing, tresses. In addition, females are physically distinguished by their mammary glands. However, in many cases, females when offplanet will shave off their hair and wear clothing to hide their gender, perhaps in an attempt to confuse others or mask their identities if they are hunting prey. Otherwise, female Rodians will proudly display their feminity if it will work to their advantage.

Rodians exude a peculiar scent that most non-Rodians find repugnant. This scent is an oily pheromonal excretion that moisturizes their skin and attracts potential mates. The excretion also communicates to other Rodians family heritage and breeding, distinguishing their identity. While non-Rodians would think all Rodians smell the same, Rodians themselves can tell the difference. One whiff of another Rodian from a clan feuding with his or her own can send a Rodian into a warring frenzy.

Rodian society is clan-based, since they developed as family units huddled together for protection. The rock-climbing lizards who were the Rodians' defenseless ancestors developed tools and weapons in the quest for survival. Over the generations, Rodians concentrated on honing their hunting skills for gathering food, and because they focused on pursuing game, they never developed agricultural skills. The act of hunting became an ingrained part of their culture. Rodians sought honors from society, especially the Grand Protector, the leader of their civilization, for their hunting skills.

After a time, all the predators Rodians hunted on their homeworld became extinct. When this happened, the Rodians began to hunt one another. Manufacturing excuses for wars, they nearly brought themselves to extinction and laid waste to their entire environment. To this day, the Rodian people are obsessed with violence.

Though extinction at one time seemed inevitable, before this could happen, a very wise Grand Protector named Harido Kavila developed one of the Rodians' greatest cultural gifts to the galaxy. He founded Rodian Theater and, with it, helped stop his race from destroying itself.

Since Rodians romanticize violence, drama offers them a catharsis for their violent tendencies without them having to actually bring harm upon one another. Their dramatic efforts developed gradually; the early works were little more than staged fights. But Rodian dramatists quickly realized that the effect of drama was magnified if the fights were presented as elements of an even greater story. Soon the complexity of Rodian stories grew, and they came to be as good as the choreographed violence.

Rodian drama is today highly regarded throughout the galaxy, because although it is violent, it deals with motivations and situations that provoke strong emotional responses in audiences of most species. In addition, these dramas show the realistic effects of violence, so non-Rodians—and even Rodians, if the drama is well written—are struck by the moral impact of each play.

Rodians now import much of their food and many other resources from offplanet, as their own proclivity for hunting and industrial expansion has destroyed Rodia's once lush ecosystem. Meanwhile, they export the weapons they create. Rodians are renowned as brilliant weaponsmiths, and most work in the vast factories that manufacture their famous products. Their main export fits well with their legendary talents as hunters—talents that they also offer for profit. Those who sell their talents often make a great deal of money and gain widespread fame on their homeworld and beyond. Bounty hunting has become an honored profession for Rodians. Prizes are awarded annually for "Best Shot" (for deceased catches), "Longest Trail" (awarded for persistence), "Most Notorious Capture," "Quickest Catch," and "Most Difficult Hunt."

DESIGNATION
Sentient

HOMEWORLD
Rodia

AVERAGE HEIGHT
1.6 meters

PRONUNCIATION
Rō'-dē-ăn

Because hunting is treated as a challenge and a contest on Rodia, when Rodians leave home to participate in bounty hunting, they find it irrelevant that they are participating in law enforcement, not sport. Rodian bounty hunters often "pad" catches, following their quarry and allowing them to commit additional crimes or do more damage, substantially raising the value of the final bounty. While this infuriates their underworld clients, it certainly makes for greater recognition from their own—which they crave.

Despite their hunting prowess, however, Rodians are often viewed as cowards by other species. They are mostly distrusted and reviled. Rodians are generally unwilling to take risks, or put themselves in danger to bring in quarry. For this reason, they often use the biggest and most destructive weaponry available to complete a task. In addition, since Rodians usually receive prizes when returning home with a kill, they will charge less to their employers, especially if they can keep the remains. Rodians demand exorbitant fees for bringing in live prey because it often increases risk, and usually the Rodian will conveniently "forget" that part of a bounty agreement during the hunt.

Rodians are rarely seen in groups on any other world besides Rodia unless they are touring in a dramatic troupe. They hunt alone, believing that life is dangerous enough without getting in the way of or upsetting another of their own kind.

Despite their vicious tendencies, Rodia has participated in galactic events. At the time of the Clone Wars, Rodians were members of the Jedi Order and also represented themselves in the Galactic Senate. However, at the end of the New Republic, Rodia was taken over by the Yuuzhan Vong, who used the Rodians to create a genetically altered slave race called the Vagh Rodiek. In a planetwide project, the Yuuzhan Vong shapers merged Rodian biological material with pieces of other creatures to create a beast with four crab-like legs and arms of half-meter-long bone hooks. In a case of re-creating the Rodians in their own awful image, Yuuzhan Vong transmuted Rodians' headspines to puncturing quills.

NOTABLE APPEARANCE
Episode IV: A New Hope

RYN

The Ryn are a nomadic humanoid species seen in most highly populated cities and settlements throughout the known galaxy. Their skin tone ranges from light purple to dark blue-black, and they have chitinous noses that slope down over their thin-lipped mouths. With their strong prehensile tails, Ryn can grip items or hang from trees, While short, smoke-colored fuzz covers their bodies, the hair on their forearms and tails blends to a dark blue, and is stiff like quills, capable of inflicting sharp wounds in hand-to-hand combat. A Ryn's facial and head hair is snow white, with the males usually wearing snow-white mustaches that they often grow long and shape decoratively. Females wear their hair as crests of slicked-back, luxurious tresses and often adorn themselves in jewelry, dipping their tails in blue paint as an added ornamentation. A Ryn's five-fingered appendages are tipped with sharp claw-like nails. Han Solo once described Ryn as resembling a combination of a manka cat and a woolamander.

Although the massive libraries at Obroa-skai and Woostri have no reports of a Ryn homeworld, some research speculates that such a homeworld is somewhere in the Core Worlds region. Being a nomadic, tribal people, though, the Ryn have no idea which world in the galaxy is their original home; they'd moved from it long before their history was recorded. A Ryn tradition, in fact, forbids them from sleeping in the same place more than once, so they move around quite a bit. Some records indicate that the present generations of Ryn in the galaxy are the descendants of a tribe of ten thousand musicians donated to a nearby world bereft of artists; others suggest that the Ryn's ancestors were warriors deployed against an Inner Rim threat. Either of these theories can be supported, as the Ryn are very talented artists, and also very tenacious and brutal fighters.

In any event, the Ryn are an ever-present part of city life in the galaxy's busy spaceports. They are a hardworking people, making jewelry and serving as itinerant day-employees in a variety of capacities such as spacehands, mechanics, pilots, and construction workers. They also make money at fortune-telling, dancing, playing exhilarating music, and other forms of entertainment. Their native language itself is musical, supporting the theory that the musical arts are at the very root of their culture (though young Ryn also learn to speak Basic, to aid them in navigating galactic society). By blowing air and covering and uncovering the holes in their beak-like noses, Ryn mimic sounds or make music like a wind instrument.

The Ryn are a flamboyant, fun-loving species, and are believed to be the inventors of the gambling game sabacc—they often use sabacc cards for fortune-telling. They wear colorful attire and jewelry and travel in large extended-family or tribal communities, sometimes making their living through con games and theft. These activities have spawned a general galaxywide distrust of the Ryn, who are ostracized and mistreated by society, almost as a rule. Most beings will not even notice Ryn, looking past them as insignificant. While such maltreatment is mostly due to their criminal tendencies and their *do-anything-to-survive* outlook, they are also rejected because of their views on personal hygiene. Their superstitions preclude them from bathing regularly, giving them a rather ripe odor.

Interestingly, although their moving about the galaxy prevents them from training as Jedi, Ryn have demonstrated talents in the Force as spirit adepts. Generally speaking, spirit adepts develop their skills removed from knowledge of Force traditions and often on worlds without a Jedi presence, following local beliefs and superstitions. As Ryn often move from world to world, this path to the Force seems uniquely suited to them. Spirit adepts learn to hear the Force speaking to them as the voices of their ancestors, and the wise listen to their counsel, some never realizing it is the Force at all. Ryn spirit adepts often become clan elders, drawing on the Force to lead their people. It is possible that Ryn fortunetellers could be spirit adepts channeling their skills in this manner, using sabacc cards as a convenient prop.

During the Yuuzhan Vong invasion, Ryn were relegated to the worst part of refugee camps near the latrines because their scent offended the other refugees. In the camps, Ryn were outcasts not worthy of a name, often finding that their species was listed as "other" in camp rosters. However, the Ryn's status as refugees also allowed them to effect some small measure of change in how they were viewed by the galaxy at large. In fact, a Ryn named Droma was responsible for saving the life of Captain Han Solo on the *Jubilee Wheel* when it was attacked by the Yuuzhan Vong. Droma became Solo's companion for a period of time; it is said that, for the

Solos, his company eased the pain of Chewbacca's death earlier in the war.

Throughout their history, the Ryn have been victimized by galactic society. Slavers, in particular, have found them a lucrative commodity, particularly with the Hutts, who place a great deal of value on the species' card-based fortune-telling. On the few worlds where they attempted to establish permanent settlements, Ryn often saw their lands (and often their meager possessions) taken from them in "ethnic relocation" programs, which were no more than rich landowners trying to seize the property of those without the power to refuse. On most of these Ryn settlement worlds, young male Ryn were frequently arrested for theft in community sweeps, at the mere suggestion that thefts had occurred.

As a result of their persecution, the Ryn have grown more secretive, self-sufficient, and suspicious, with an almost defiant will to survive. They do not trust help from outsiders, but have an avid interest in observing them. Information is a moneymaker for them, but also a means to keep them and their people far from danger. They place a tremendous value on secrets, and are very good at keeping them. It was these skills, along with the Ryn's near-total social invisibility, that allowed the Ryn to create what is perhaps their species' greatest achievement— the development and operation of a diverse, pervasive, and very effective spy network that greatly aided later New Republic war efforts against the Yuuzhan Vong.

Although unconfirmed, some Galactic Alliance intelligence sources suggest that the Ryn network may have been in fact sponsored by the known information broker Talon Karrde, to aid the war effort against the Yuuzhan Vong. It has been suggested that by keeping his role and input a secret, Karrde expanded his existing network to include the Ryn. Through these machinations, the Ryn do not suspect they were not independent or that they did not come up with the idea of a spy network themselves. This hypothesis may have merit, as Karrde has countless contacts throughout the galaxy and the Ryn would be only too easy to manipulate, given their prideful and boastful natures. Whatever the source, the Ryn spy network and the courageous efforts of its members contributed greatly to the war effort, often providing conduits for information that could not have been passed along otherwise.

DESIGNATION
Sentient

HOMEWORLD
Unknown

AVERAGE HEIGHT
1.6 meters

PRONUNCIATION
Rĭn

NOTABLE APPEARANCE
Agents of Chaos I: Hero's Trial (novel)

SARLACC

The creature known as the Sarlacc is a mystery to modern zoology, as very few scientists have been able to get close enough to a specimen to study it. One of the largest recorded examples of the species rests in the Great Pit of Carkoon in Tatooine's Dune Sea, although others have been reported on various worlds, including Dathomir and Aargonar. The personal experiences of Luke Skywalker and his fellows on their mission to rescue Han Solo from Jabba the Hutt have been well documented.

What scientists do know is that the Sarlacc is a massive, omnivorous arthropod with plant-like tendencies. While very rare, Sarlaccs are extremely long-lived; estimates place its life span at 20,000 to 50,000 standard years. It has been discovered that the creature reproduces via spores called sarlacci,

which travel through space until they find a suitable world. Just how the sarlacci manage this is a matter of speculation. As is the case with the dianoga, it may be that sarlacci find their way into outbound starships. Due to their estimated age, however, it seems unlikely that this is the only means of transport—Sarlaccs predate space travel on many worlds. Yet biological studies do not seem to indicate whether or not sarlacci can survive in vacuum, as mynocks do. The Sarlacc's initial planet of origin is unknown, but research suggests that it could be Tatooine. The spores are discharged from an oviduct below the Sarlacc's epidermal layer. The sarlacci form male–female pairs, crawl to the surface, and migrate from there. Sarlacci are extremely vulnerable during their immature phase, at risk for either starving to death or being eaten by other creatures. Fortunately very, very few sarlacci take root. When a sarlacci spore implants itself in the ground, it grows downward into the soil or sand like a plant, forming a pit.

From the edge of its sandy pit, the Sarlacc looks like a great hooked beak with a snake-like head coiling from its center, and an enormous, mucus-dripping mouth descending to a trunk-like body surrounded by dozens of writhing,

grasping tentacles. This is only the uppermost part of the creature—the enormous body of the Sarlacc is buried deep beneath the surface, extending out to one hundred meters or more. By burying most of its massive body underground, the Sarlacc protects itself. All its vital organs are inaccessible, rendering the creature nearly impervious to serious or life-threatening damage.

The female Sarlacc is the true danger. Growing to enormous sizes, it is the dominant of the two sexes. Male Sarlaccs are much smaller, and parasitic, attaching themselves to their mates to feed off them. Males do not differ from females other than in size. However, a report from a University of Coruscant anthropological survey team detailed finding the remains of a mutated male Sarlacc that had over the course of many thousands of years grown large enough to consume its mate. No such other remains have been found.

Much of the Sarlacc's anatomy aids it in capturing prey. By hiding the majority of its body underground, it does not betray its inherent danger to its victims. A Sarlacc's teeth are helpful in keeping captured food imprisoned

because they slant inward to prevent a meal from escaping. The Sarlacc uses its tentacles to snag prey and drag it down to its cavernous mouth. These tentacles have been known to reach a full four meters beyond the pit to grab unsuspecting victims. However, the Sarlacc's main means of capturing prey is through scent. The Sarlacc gives off odors that attract herbivores and scavengers, bringing them within reach.

Sarlaccs are completely immobile. Because the Sarlacc cannot hunt for prey and lives in the middle of the desert, it does not feed often; it must wait for prey to come to it. Still, with its extremely slow but highly efficient digestive system, the Sarlacc doesn't need to eat with great frequency. When necessary, the Sarlacc will immediately digest a meal in a primary stomach. During times when sustenance is not critical, the Sarlacc's body can preserve food for incredibly long periods of time, digesting it slowly and storing it in a series of secondary stomachs until nourishment is demanded again. Victims are held in the secondary stomachs by rope-like, meters-long cilia. The Sarlacc's gastric juices in these secondary stomachs are weaker than those in the primary stomach, consisting of specific acids that do not kill victims but slowly decompose them, ensuring fresh meat for the duration of the digestive cycle. Sarlaccs have been rumored to digest their victims over the course of a thousand years.

One of the most prevalent rumors about the Sarlacc is that the creature is mildly telepathic, and over millennia actually gains sentience from victims as it consumes them. Although Sarlaccs do not have advanced neural systems, it is believed that they gain consciousness by assimilating the thoughts of the beings and creatures they consume.

Data that anthropologist Hoole secured from the bounty hunter Boba Fett appears to confirm this. According to Fett's experience in the belly of the beast, not only was the Sarlacc sentient, but it enjoyed torturing those it was digesting. It manipulated the thoughts of its victims, and even kept their intelligence stored in its memories so it could savor their pain at another time. Footage from Fett's helmet recorder revealed a more plant-like physical structure than most scientists had believed, and the secretion of some plant enzyme that might be the cause of the beasts' hallucinogenic power over their victims.

DESIGNATION
Semi-sentient

HOMEWORLD
Tatooine (not confirmed)

AVERAGE DIAMETER
3 meters (mouth only)
LENGTH
100 meters

PRONUNCIATION
Sär'-lăk

NOTABLE APPEARANCE
Episode VI: Return of the Jedi

SHISTAVANEN

Shistavanens, often called Shistavanen Wolfmen, are hairy, canine bipeds from Uvena Prime and their colonized worlds in the Uvena system of the Outer Rim Territories. Like most canine-based species, they have high-set dog-like ears and long muzzles, large, sharp teeth, and sharp claws on their hands and feet. Shistavanens' bodies are covered in thick brown or black fur, and they can walk on four legs as well as upright on two. A particularly notable feature of the species is a Shistavanen's eyes, which glow red. Physically, male Shistavanens tend to be taller and more muscular than their female counterparts.

Because of their canine ancestry, Shistavanens are innately excellent hunters and trackers. They can follow prey with ease, using heightened senses to navigate crowded urban streets and open plains alike. Their sense of sight is so highly developed that they can see in near-absolute darkness with no loss of visual acuity, still able to detect color and detail. They move with great speed and possess remarkable endurance.

Shistavanen society is based on an isolationist ideal. They do not like outsiders visiting Uvena or meddling in their affairs. While they haven't outlawed outsiders from coming to their world, their open prejudice toward non-Shistavanens is made clear by their restrictive laws and trade. Uvena Prime is a self-sufficient world, and the Shistavanens have even colonized all the unpopulated worlds in the Uvena system to prevent strangers from doing so. Most of the population is at hyperspace-level technology, though some pockets of civilization remain at a lower level because of their isolationist ideology.

As a result of their xenophobic societal rules, most Shistavanens are not talkative with beings of other species. While on other worlds, they remain most often by themselves or with others of their own kind. Shistavanens communicate using a language consisting of loud barks and growls, but many also learned Basic after the rise of the Empire. A small minority, however, are actually outgoing. These few are frequently hired as scouts, pilots, bounty hunters, or security guards. While Shistavanens are suspicious of other species, other species are openly afraid of Shistavanens.

At home, Shistavanens are family-focused, raising their offspring (called pups) in family dens. A den, which is a home hewn from natural rock or formed in hard-baked clay, usually houses immediate family and sometimes in-laws, depending on the amount of space available. Pups are homeschooled using a government-approved system of education that utilizes comlinks for grading. After school lessons, all the pups of an area come together to cooperatively learn and practice

"outdoor skills"—hunting, tracking, survival, and martial arts. Adults from the various dens trade off responsibilities in training the youngsters to master these skills. Pups graduate to adulthood once they make their first "kill" hunting alone in the forests of Uvena Prime.

As a largely xenophobic people, Shistavanens do not often travel from home; those who do are usually young and adventurous. Following the rise of the New Republic, more and more Shistavanens took to the stars, hoping to learn new things. This caused some conflict with the older generation, who prefer to remain focused on the affairs of their world. If seen at large, Shistavanens generally serve those who can afford to pay them. Shistavanens take great pride in their work, and they charge high fees.

A primary trait that lends itself to success in pursuits such as bounty hunting is Shistavanens' tendency to be loners. Coupled with their tracking skills, they are very dangerous to those they stalk—and very valuable to those desirous of their abilities. During the height of the Empire, Shistavanens were often employed by Imperial Intelligence, providing a service that was more important to the Imperials than politically oppressing their remote, nonhuman world. As a trade-off, the Empire simply restricted Shistavanens' ability to pursue trade openly. Prior to Palpatine's New Order, Shistavanens also served the Old Republic, including a rare Shistavanen Jedi who took part in the Battle of Geonosis. As fighting troops, Shistavanens are specialists as snipers and at flanking opposing forces, a skill useful to the Rebellion on many occasions. When two Shistavanen hunters work together in this capacity, they are especially deadly and can turn the tide of a battle. Even the New Republic's fabled Rogue Squadron has had a Shistavanen member.

Personality-wise, Shistavanens tend to be belligerent, proud, boastful, and arrogant. Some are able to temper these qualities with a good sense of humor, making them tolerable to others. In addition, while they are very intelligent, they are also very violent and aggressive. But even Shistavanens who are able to negotiate social situations have difficulty working past their cultural prejudices, and few are able to completely rid themselves of them. Usually, Shistavanens are more likely to go out of their way to insult and offend others, simply because they don't like any species but their own.

DESIGNATION
Sentient

HOMEWORLD
Uvena Prime

AVERAGE HEIGHT
1.8 meters

PRONUNCIATION
Shǐst'-ŭ-văn-ĕn

NOTABLE APPEARANCE
Episode IV: A New Hope

SSI-RUU

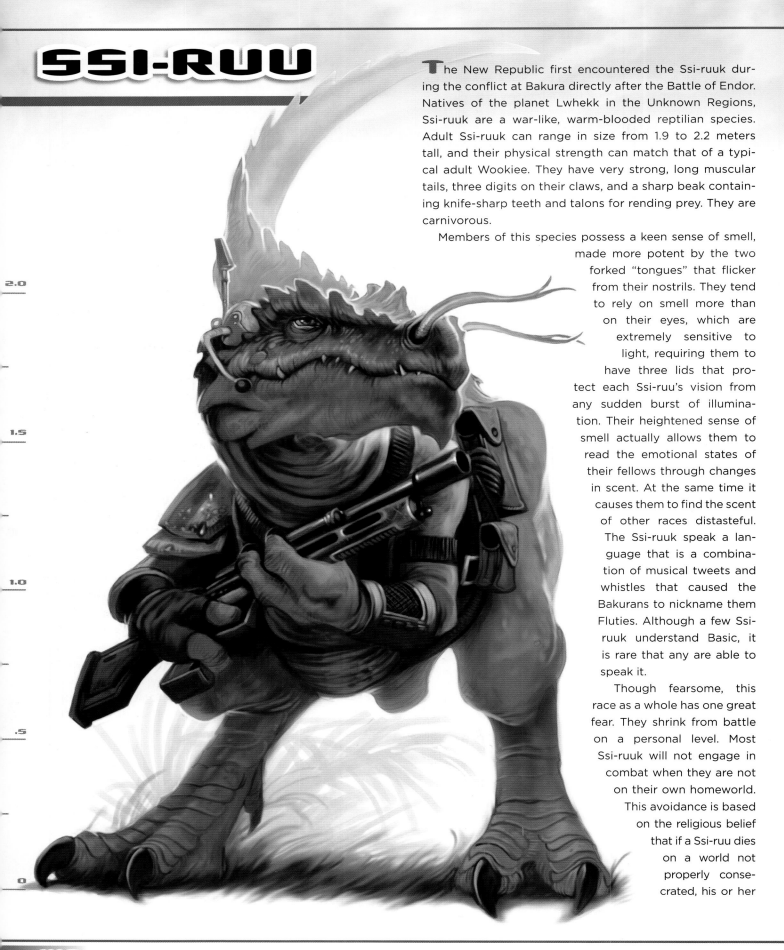

The New Republic first encountered the Ssi-ruuk during the conflict at Bakura directly after the Battle of Endor. Natives of the planet Lwhekk in the Unknown Regions, Ssi-ruuk are a war-like, warm-blooded reptilian species. Adult Ssi-ruuk can range in size from 1.9 to 2.2 meters tall, and their physical strength can match that of a typical adult Wookiee. They have very strong, long muscular tails, three digits on their claws, and a sharp beak containing knife-sharp teeth and talons for rending prey. They are carnivorous.

Members of this species possess a keen sense of smell, made more potent by the two forked "tongues" that flicker from their nostrils. They tend to rely on smell more than on their eyes, which are extremely sensitive to light, requiring them to have three lids that protect each Ssi-ruu's vision from any sudden burst of illumination. Their heightened sense of smell actually allows them to read the emotional states of their fellows through changes in scent. At the same time it causes them to find the scent of other races distasteful. The Ssi-ruuk speak a language that is a combination of musical tweets and whistles that caused the Bakurans to nickname them Fluties. Although a few Ssi-ruuk understand Basic, it is rare that any are able to speak it.

Though fearsome, this race as a whole has one great fear. They shrink from battle on a personal level. Most Ssi-ruuk will not engage in combat when they are not on their own homeworld. This avoidance is based on the religious belief that if a Ssi-ruu dies on a world not properly consecrated, his or her spirit will wander aimlessly throughout the galaxy for all eternity.

Ssi-ruuvi society is dictated by a rigid honor code. Ssi-ruu believe that they are superior to all of ther species, due to an ancient pictograph called the G'nnoch. According to Ssi-ruuk, other races are inferior and are no more than sustenance creatures.

Ssi-ruuvi society is a clan-based hierarchy, and each clan is designated by the color of their scales. The highest-ranking group is the blue-scaled clan. Other clan colors are the gold scales (primarily religious), red-brown scales (military), and the green scales (workers). Most Ssi-ruuk are of the latter caste, which is the lowest caste to still receive esteem and honor. The clans strictly avoid interbreeding with one another, as the products of such unions, determined by their brown scales, are the lowest caste of all. Rare black-scaled Ssi-ruuk are trained as assassins and bodyguards for Ssi-ruuvi leaders. Ssi-ruuk's coloring is obvious as they do not wear clothing, instead carrying belts with pouches for any needed items. They find other species' need to cover themselves humorous.

On their homeworld of Lwhekk, an absolute ruler—called the Shreeftut—controls the Ssi-ruuvi government. Two councils advise this monarch: the Elders' Council and the Conclave. The Elders' Council is made up of the most respected citizens of Lwhekk. Words from an elder are considered as important as those of the monarch himself. The Conclave is a group of spiritual leaders who guide the Shreeftut in setting and enforcing laws that adhere to and complement their religion.

The Ssi-ruuk initially left their home system to search for new energy resources. Since they have not developed fusion technology used by most spacefaring races in this galaxy, they developed instead a process called "entenchment," wherein a living creature's life energy is drawn from the body and transferred into a droid, ship, or other piece of technology to give it power. When offworld, Ssi-ruuk use droid ships in battle to protect themselves, powered by the entenched life forces of captured prisoners. At first, they entenched and enslaved a race called the P'w'eck from their own homeworld. The Ssi-ruuk also use other sentients besides the P'w'eck as slaves, and all of their slaves are brainwashed through a type of mind control that completely subverts their will. This mind control can be broken, but the entenchment process leads to unavoidable death. Entenchment nevertheless is an imperfect process that leaves its victims in perpetual agony;

they do not last long in a ship or other system before needing replacement.

Before the Battle of Endor, the Ssi-ruuk began expanding toward Imperial Space in an attempt to gain captives in sufficient numbers to power their military ships for an escalating war with the Chiss. During this time, Emperor Palpatine made contact with them. Wanting the entenchment technology for himself, Palpatine secretly ceded them a number of Outer Rim systems and allowed Ssi-ruuvi slave raids to go unchecked, blaming the attacks on the Rebels. One of these incursions brought the Ssi-ruuk to the Imperial-controlled world of Bakura. Although the Rebels had destroyed the second Death Star just the day before, they intercepted a drone ship bearing an urgent distress call from Bakura and dispatched a small battle group to assist. Working with the Imperials stationed on Bakura, the nascent Alliance of Free Planets forces turned back the Ssi-ruuk toward their own region of space. It would be years before the Imperial Remnant and the New Republic would sign an armistice, but this joint effort marked the first time the two groups would work together to repel a common enemy.

During this conflict, the Ssi-ruuk discovered that Force-using humans could exceed their expectations as a power source—and could also draw life energy from other creatures to themselves, thereby expanding an entenchment to have a broader area effect. Luke Skywalker foiled a plot to capitalize on this, and afterward set out to find other Force-sensitives to protect them from being exploited in such a way again.

For decades the Ssi-ruuk made no forays into Republic space, but this changed during the war against the Yuuzhan Vong. After the birth and ascension of the mutant, multicolored P'w'eck leader known as the Keeramak, the P'w'ecks approached Bakura with a peace treaty, claiming to have thrown off Ssi-ruuvi domination. Of course, the treaty was a Ssi-ruuvi ruse to take over the planet and gain more slaves, as they had further perfected the entenchment process, allowing for a life force to power a mechanical system indefinitely. With the help of the New Republic, the Ssi-ruuk were defeated again and driven back to Lwhekk, where they came face-to-face with a Yuuzhan Vong armada. The genuine P'w'eck Emancipation Movement did sign a treaty with Bakura, allying themselves for the common good.

DESIGNATION
Sentient

HOMEWORLD
Lwhekk

AVERAGE
HEIGHT
2 meters

PRONUNCIATION
Sē'-rŏŏ

NOTABLE APPEARANCE
Truce at Bakura (novel)

SULLUSTAN

Sullustans are jowled, round-eared humanoids with large, round, black eyes. They inhabit subterranean caverns beneath the surface of Sullust, a volcanic planet with an inhospitable atmosphere that is filled with black clouds of volcanic ash, dust, and toxic fumes.

Sullustans prefer to remain in their cool, humid cave environment, and only go to the surface for short periods of time. Most don environment suits for long excursions. On the surface, besides facing the heavily polluted air, they face the threat of dangerous predators. Many of Sullust's creatures are extremely tough to kill, and Sullustans do their best to avoid them.

Sullustan physiology is well adapted to the underground environment. Their eyes see very well in dim light, and their oversized ears make them extremely sensitive to even the faintest sounds. Due to their skilled hearing, they love music and produce very fine musical compositions. Their language, although it sounds to most species like rapid chatter, includes extremely subtle sound fluctuations that only Sullustans can reproduce and perceive. Any Sullustan born with a hearing impairment has extreme difficulty. Deaf Sullustans do not live long, partially because predators victimize them, but also because they take their own lives out of despair that they cannot truly communicate with their own.

While their unique vision allows them to see in the dark, regular exposure to natural light causes Sullustans to suffer from corneal degeneration. Those who are regularly out in the galaxy will start to see these effects after thirty years of life. Those who start to be affected by this malady choose to wear special visors to protect their eyes from further damage.

While all Sullustans look similar to one another, the truth is that each Sullustan's cranial markings and dew flaps are unique to that individual—as unique as a retinal marker or fingerprint. Some Sullustans take this uniqueness a step further to add ritual tattoos, reinforcing their individualism. Most Sullustans are completely hairless, but those who can grow hair (on their faces only) do so to further announce their uniqueness. Sociologists theorize this emphasis on the individual is prompted by their unique economic system. Most Sullustans work for one corporation, so while variety in what one does is not always possible, diversity in how one looks makes all the difference. In fact, how one looks is so important that Sullustans developed an art of hairstyling and cosmetology. The barbers of Sullust are renowned for their skill, even though most Sullustans have no hair.

All Sullustans also have an enhanced sense of direction, which allows them to find their way through the labyrinthine passages of their cities. Moreover, this ability makes them some of the best navigators and pilots. It has been said that once Sullustans have traveled a path, they never forget it, even when traveling through hyperspace.

The Sullustan people have turned their underground environment into a near paradise. Their passageways lead to beautiful underground cities, where visitors walk cobblestone streets, eat at cafés, and shop for unique items available only in the subterranean markets.

Sullust is home to the SoroSuub Corporation, a leading mineral-processing company that maintains space mining, food-packaging, and technology-producing divisions throughout the galaxy. Important, almost 50 percent of the Sullustan population works for SoroSuub. During the rule of the Empire, SoroSuub proclaimed its loyalty to the New Order. With the Empire's support, the SoroSuub Corporation dissolved the legal government of Sullust and took control of the entire world. Many Sullustans supported the Rebel Alliance because it was actively fighting the Empire. Inspired by the Alliance's just cause, many left Sullust quickly to help in the fight, distinguishing themselves with honor. At the decisive Battle of Endor, Sullustans flew many of the Rebel B-wings; Sullustan hero Nien Nunb flew as Lando Calrissian's copilot in *Millennium Falcon*. Before joining the Rebel Alliance, Nunb had gained renown among his people by raiding SoroSuub Corporation sites and stealing its starships. When the Empire fell, the leadership of SoroSuub tried to escape the wrath of the populace. SoroSuub executives were captured, put on trial, and imprisoned. A new board of directors took control of SoroSuub, and the people returned to their original, democratic form of government. In the ensuing years, Sullustans continued to serve important roles within the New Republic.

A Sullustan core family grouping is called a Warren-clan. Each of these clans is headed by one female, who bears children by several husbands, all of whom live together or in nearby quarters. Females without husbands, called "Fems," are active as leaders and employees of SoroSuub until they are "Ready"—or ready to begin breeding. At this point a Fem seeks out mates to establish a Warren-clan. After

DESIGNATION
Sentient

HOMEWORLD
Sullust

AVERAGE HEIGHT
1.5 meters

PRONUNCIATION
Sŭl'-lŭs-tăn

establishing a Warren-clan, she will no longer work outside the home, considering maintaining her Warren-clan to be her primary job. The husbands, however, work outside the home and some travel offplanet as pilots to supplement their clan's income.

As a people, Sullustans are happy, practical, and fond of playing pranks on their friends. And yet they can be very formal in their social expectations and traditions. All of the elements of their ceremonial traditions bear in mind social status and have specific meaning, as exemplified by their funeral services. Sullustan mourners wear bright-colored tabards to signify their status in society or relation to the deceased. The body is placed in wall crypt and closed in with blocks of transparisteel. All mourners place a block in the wall in order of their social status and relationship to the deceased. The deceased's immediate family goes first, followed by the married males of his clan, other blood relatives, close friends, and representatives of SoroSuub; finally, the one who is considered closest to the deceased (be it friend or spouse) places the last block. Before placing this block, the last person must give a brief statement of as many words as the deceased's age in standard years. The speaker must not eulogize the dead, which would insinuate that others present did not know the deceased as well as the speaker. This comment is to be forward-looking and from the heart. Any deviance from this protocol causes great insult and can lead to some nasty confrontations. Sullustans have similar protocols for all special occasions, be they birthdays, weddings, or holidays.

They enjoy meeting new species and getting to know them. Perpetually curious, they enjoy learning new things, not just about science and technology but also about cultures, traditions, art, and music. Sullustans especially like to learn things through personal experience, making them somewhat reckless. As pilots, they tend to take a lot more chances than the average humanoid, as if testing how much their ships can take. Despite this, they are favorite members of any crew because of knowledge, talents, and wholehearted love of flying.

NOTABLE APPEARANCE
Episode VI: Return of the Jedi

TALZ

The Talz are a tall, physically powerful species from Alzoc III, a frigid world blanketed with fields of snow and ice. They are covered head-to-foot with thick white fur, and their extremely large hands end in sharp-clawed talons that are used for digging through frozen layers of ice and snow. Their fur protects them from the cold, as does an extra layer of blubber beneath their hair. The Talz possess four eyes—two large and two small—and each set can be utilized to accommodate varying degrees of brightness. During the day, their larger eyes are often shut, as the glaring sunlight reflecting off the snow can be almost blinding. At night or in dimly lit environments, Talz will rely on their bigger eyes, which allow them to see better in darker surroundings. In addition, a small, tube-like snout enables them to breathe in sufficient oxygen, something that would normally be a difficult task in exceptionally cold temperatures.

A generally quiet, gentle species, the Talz are also tireless in their work, which is done with simple handmade tools. They are peaceful and curious—perceiving their surroundings with an almost scientific interest. Although the Talz are fairly ignorant of most other species, they will not speak up to ask questions of strangers, instead preferring to learn through observation. Their society is clan-based, keeping supplies plentiful through a sophisticated system that distributes resources for the benefit of all Talz communities.

Because of this largely distributive society, one of their common cultural traits is the Talz's lack of a sense of possession. For instance, while all Talz may have tools to do their work, as well as household implements and the like, they do not feel these items actually belong to them specifically. If Talz possess something that goes unused, they will find someone who does need it and give it away. If they need an item that they do not have, they will often go to a neighbor's living area and simply borrow it without asking, although out of courtesy they will usually let others know in case they need the item themselves. In the midst of other cultures, this can cause some confusion in that the Talz normally do not employ such terms as *hers, his, mine,* or *yours.* Sometimes they give things away that are not currently being used (often items of sentimental value to their non-Talz friends). Species familiar with Talz, particularly those who share company with them on a regular basis, know to keep any materials they value under lock and key, as explaining ownership to a Talz can frequently be a wasted effort. Unfortunately, those ignorant of Talz traditions will sometimes view them as thieves, and as a result they often end up being prosecuted for theft on certain worlds they visit, or, even worse, being hunted by crimelords for unwittingly giving away something of great value.

Although they carry many characteristics of humanoids, the Talz reproduce like insects. A female will lay her eggs, which eventually hatch and produce larvae that are carefully guarded and kept warm by the parents. After a standard year, the larvae cocoon themselves, remaining in a chrysalis state for another year and growing while they slumber, until they crack out of their cocoons as full-sized Talz. However, when the Talz leave their cocoons, they possess little knowledge beyond the language they learned as larvae, and must be educated for several years before becoming full adults. The Talz have no formal schools, and most Talz "children" are home-taught via cooperative family tutelage. Parents who stand out in certain subjects will partner with those who excel in others, so that their offspring will receive as well-rounded an education as possible.

Outside of the Talz Jedi Foul Moudama, who served during the Clone Wars and fell at the hands of General Grievous, the species had little to no interaction with the rest of the galaxy before the Empire rose to power. The Empire essentially discovered the Talz just as the Imperials had crushed the last remnants of the Old Republic, and immediately took advantage of the benign species, seeing them as an easy slave labor force to mine the mineral wealth of

DESIGNATION
Sentient

HOMEWORLD
Alzoc III

AVERAGE
HEIGHT
2.1 meters

PRONUNCIATION
Tălz

Alzoc III. To this day, some primitive Talz continue to tell tales of when "rocks fell from the sky," bringing with them the brutal strangers who forced them to create caves. The Talz suffered through the Rebellion period hoping that the strangers would leave and let them live in peace.

While the Empire greatly benefited from the slave work of the Talz, they never actually recorded the "discovery" of the species, keeping them a secret from the majority of the galaxy. Only a few Talz left their homeworld during this time, and then usually in the presence of Imperials as servants or slaves. If they wandered too far from their masters, they were summarily captured and sent home to the mines. The fall of the Empire spelled freedom for the Talz, and under the New Republic they began to trade and interact more with the galaxy at large, having assumed ownership of their mines. Despite this, they are still wary of their trading partners, and rarely journey off their world to explore the galaxy. They remain rather primitive, preferring to live in obscurity in the cold, uninviting environment of Alzoc III.

Sadly, the suffering of the Talz people did not necessarily end with the fall of the Empire. While they were freed from slavery and allowed to take over their mining operations and trade with other species, Warlord Zsinj captured many Talz for scientific experimentation for his Project Chubar and Dr. Edda Gast's Operation Minefield—the intentions of which were to alter alien races to make them more "human." After these operations were dismantled by Wraith Squadron, the victimized Talz were returned to their homeworld and welcomed with open arms despite their mutations, a sure example of the peaceful acceptance that is at the core of their culture.

NOTABLE APPEARANCE
Episode IV: A New Hope

TAUNTAUN

The frigid planet of Hoth has very few indigenous life-forms, but one of its most numerous is the tauntaun, a bipedal, reptomammal also referred to as a snow lizard. Used as beasts of burden by Rebel Alliance personnel during their stay on Hoth, tauntauns are tall, sturdy ungulates with inherently ornery dispositions. Several different types of tauntauns have been identified in various regions of Hoth, from the glacier tauntaun to the small climbing tauntaun, which uses its muscularity and claws to scale canyons and cliffs. The appearance of these subspecies can also differ from the common fur-covered tauntaun, as they possess a more reptilian appearance with longer forelimbs and thinner frames.

As a result of their native environment, tauntauns have remarkably cold-resistant bodies. Their warm blood is extremely heavy, and their inner organs are close inside their skeletons to keep them safe from cold. A thick layer of fat also acts as insulation under the tauntauns' oily pelts. They have four nostrils: a large pair on the upper portion of their muzzle that helps conduct oxygen to the bloodstream during times of physical exertion, and a smaller pair directly beneath them. When blizzard winds blow, or when tauntauns lie down for the night, their larger nostrils will seal to keep snow out, and the second pair will take over the responsibility of keeping minimal amounts of oxygen flowing to their lungs.

Tauntauns are quick-moving creatures, running on their two rear legs at speeds nearing fifty kilometers per hour. They use their smaller

1.5

1.0

.5

0

forelegs for balance, and also to forage for food, utilizing their dexterous claws to grapple stones or chunks of ice and move them out of their way.

Tauntauns are herbivores, feeding on unique varieties of lichen and fungus that grow beneath the frosty surface of Hoth. They exude waste products and oils through special ducts on their skin, giving them a foul odor. To match their smell, they are irritable creatures, spitting and gurgling in protest when forced to do something they really don't want to do. Their ill temperament may be enhanced by their inhospitable environment, which could be enough to give members of any species a bad temper.

Female tauntauns are more cantankerous, as they outnumber males and are always in competition for mates. They sport curved horns on the sides of their heads with which they battle other females. However, their most effective weapon is their spitting ability, which they can use to disable their opponents, spitting with surprising accuracy and often aiming for the eyes. The gooey saliva is not deadly, but the liquid can freeze instantly in such a frigid environment, and the effect can be lethal, temporarily blinding adversaries and further exposing them to the many hazards of the icy planet Hoth.

While on Hoth, the Rebel Alliance had some initial difficulty training tauntauns as mounts because of their foul tempers. In addition, it was discovered that tauntauns are particularly sensitive to the ultrasonic frequencies emitted by certain droids. When they grew agitated by the droids, the tauntauns were known to sometimes smash them with their tails. General Carlist Rieekan, however, suggested working with the beasts' instincts rather than against them, and to eliminate competition for males, he made sure the only animals trained to be mounts were female. The Alliance then kept the mounts warm, and fed and rewarded them with mook fruit when they performed to standard. Using this method, these intelligent creatures were effectively trained, and served the Alliance well as they adapted various other transport machinery to operate in the cold.

While tauntauns are resilient in extremely bitter temperatures, they are not impervious to them. Like any other warm-blooded creature, they can only take so much cold before they freeze to death. While they can last longer than most species, they often cannot survive for more than three to four standard hours in intense subzero temperatures without finding shelter. In such conditions, they are smart and

dexterous enough to find shelter, or to burrow into a snow-drift in order to create warmth and conserve energy.

Scientists have also identified a subspecies living among the ice caves of Hoth. The animals known as scaly tauntauns are covered with smooth scaly skin over a thick layer of insulating fat and a thin layer of hair. Scaly tauntauns may get their name from their reptilian appearance, but they are indeed reptomammals. For scaly tauntauns, the lack of thick fur mitigates much of the smell associated with common tauntauns, and the males possess smaller horns than their distant cousins, whereas the females lack horns completely. It is thought that the males do not use their horns, which are thus gradually fading with evolution. Otherwise, scaly tauntauns resemble their cousins in size and configuration.

For scaly tauntauns, survival in the frigid environment of Hoth largely means reliance upon hot springs and geothermal vents that heat tunnels below the planet's surface. These caves are several kilometers below ground level, and herds ranging in size from five to ten animals spend most of their lives in these areas. Scaly tauntauns are omnivorous, unlike common tauntauns, and although they eat lichen, they also dine on insects and small vermin found near the hot springs. Herds migrate to follow the availability of a food source. A herd will protect its young, although all varieties of tauntauns would rather run than engage a dangerous predator. Wampas have been known to venture deeper into the Hoth cave systems at night and during blizzards, and even though wampas are exceedingly uncomfortable near the heat of the hot springs, they will ignore their discomfort if hungry enough. When threatened with such an attack, one of the scaly tauntaun herd will frequently sacrifice its life to protect its herd-mates.

As in the case of wampas, tauntaun herds have suffered from hunting. The occasional hunting party, or even a criminal seeking escape, will come to Hoth and often kill indiscriminately. As a result, some scientists have begun a campaign to have tauntauns listed as a protected species.

DESIGNATION
Nonsentient

HOMEWORLD
Hoth

AVERAGE
HEIGHT
1.8 meters

PRONUNCIATION
Tän'-tän

NOTABLE APPEARANCE
Episode V: The Empire Strikes Back

THISSPIASIAN

Thisspiasians are a reptilian species from Thisspias, a world located in the Expansion Region of the galaxy. They can be clearly distinguished from other reptiles because their upper body appears to be humanoid, typically covered in long flowing hair that emanates from their head and face. Their lower half, however, is serpentine, wrapped in scales similar in color to their hair. Their two sets of hands contain five fingers that end in sturdy, elongated claws.

It is believed that Thisspiassians have four hands as a result of their evolution from quadruped reptiles. However, for many Thisspiassians, the smaller, lower set of vestigial arms and hands do not have the strength or dexterity of their larger, upper set. In fact, most upperclass Thisspiassians have taken to wearing voluminous robed garments that hide their second set of limbs completely by omitting a second set of sleeves and incorporating a wide, belt-like sash. In addition, many Thisspiassians go as far as to use hidden apparatuses to bind their lower arms to their bodies. Among this group of Thisspiassians, it is considered unseemly or unsophisticated to publicly show the lower limbs. Physiological studies suggest that over the generations, this may be the cause of the lower limbs' weakness due to continued biological adaptation. It has been demonstrated that among the working classes, lower limbs do not show a similar muscle weakness.

Their prehensile tails give Thisspiasians the capability to carry heavy objects, freeing up their hands to perform other functions. This makes the species even more effective when they are in combat, as well-trained Thisspiasian warriors may strike out with their tails as well as their hands.

There is one particular Thisspiasian trait that other species frequently find a little unnerving, and that is their preference for eating their food live. Like their snake-like ancestors, Thisspiasians principally dine on small, live animals such as rodents, birds, and bugs. While they are omnivorous, consuming their fair share of vegetables, a Thisspiasian feast would not be complete without several cages of tiny species from around the galaxy being placed in the center of the table. After dipping a treat in several sauces containing various seasonings, a Thisspiasian's jaw unhinges at the joint, allowing the mouth to widen and take in the animals whole. As they've come to be in the presence of more and more offworld species who do not share their enthusiasm for squirming meals, many Thisspiasians have taken to eating cooked food for the benefit of companions and guests of other traditions, though they have been known to state with certainty that such food is lacking in zesty flavor.

One other prominent reptilian trait is carried on through the Thisspiasian genes: the tendency to shed their skin every few years. Unlike snakes, however, Thisspiasians will not slip out of their outer layer of skin in one piece. To ease the process of shedding, and to make the progression less noticeable when in the presence of outsiders, they will lubricate their skin with sweet-smelling oils and salves, peeling off the dead membrane in portions during their daily private grooming sessions.

A race of ancient warriors, Thisspiasians have perfected a culture bent on taming their most savage emotions. When the Old Republic was forming, they eagerly joined the fledgling government, aiding it in overcoming threats both internal and external. They are perceived as being calm, wise, and dispassionate, and yet they commonly manage this through several hours a day of intense meditation. Average Thisspiasians meditate for five to six standard hours per day; otherwise, they can become moody and irrational. Because they spend so much time in meditation, they only require about two actual hours of sleep per standard day.

One of the best examples of Thisspiasian mental discipline was displayed by the Old Republic Jedi Master Oppo Rancisis. Combining the natural mental abilities of his species with his Jedi training, Rancisis specialized in Jedi battle meditation. He was able to formulate complex and near-unbeatable battle plans and direct his forces over great distances. His murder at the hands of the fallen Jedi Sora Bulq was a blow to the Republican forces that they were hard pressed to overcome.

The Thisspiasian homeworld is ruled by an absolute leader known as the Blood Monarch. This position is carried on through the bloodline, and it has remained unchanged for thousands of years, although a democratically elected parliament handles much of the legislation on the planet. As with most monarchies, a portion of the populace is of the opinion that the leadership is corrupt, degenerate, and tied to archaic customs that no longer apply to their modern way of life.

During the waning years of the Old Republic, Master Rancisis inherited the role of Blood Monarch over his homeworld, which he rejected in favor of remaining with the Jedi Order. When Count Dooku threatened the Republic with his Separatist movement, Rancisis asked the standing monarch to help in the struggle against the Separatists. Per species tradition, Rancisis had to best the monarch in unarmed combat to have his boon granted. When the Blood Monarch lost to Rancisis, he agreed to lend warriors to several battles.

When the Empire ultimately came to power, Thisspias was bombarded by Imperial warships, and its people were conquered and enslaved. Eager to please the Emperor, an overzealous Imperial governor assassinated the Blood Monarch and imprisoned the crown prince. The outraged Thisspiasians rebelled, but their insurrection was quickly subdued by the Imperials' superior firepower. Not long afterward, Rebel spies infiltrated the Imperial troops' headquarters on Thisspias and freed the prince. Humiliated, the governor threatened the Thisspiasians with annihilation, but he was eliminated by the Emperor's Hand before he could enact his threats. The Hand had been sent to punish the governor for his failure to hold the Thisspiasian heir. The world was then placed under military quarantine, though several Thisspiasians slipped out to join the ranks of the Rebel Alliance.

Following the Battle of Endor, the crown prince of Thisspias returned to reclaim his throne. When he did, he found himself rebuffed, as a vocal portion of his people were declaring their desire for a more democratic government. This confrontation incited a brief yet extremely bloody civil war, wherein the Blood Monarch was returned to power. During the years of the New Republic and the subsequent Galactic Alliance, the people of Thisspias have become convinced that the monarchy has evolved very little, remaining tied to its decadent lifestyle and largely antiquated ancient political traditions.

DESIGNATION
Sentient

HOMEWORLD
Thisspias

AVERAGE
HEIGHT
1.5 meters
(coiled)

PRONUNCIATION
Thĭs-pĭ-ăs'-ē-ăn

NOTABLE APPEARANCE
Episode I: The Phantom Menace

TOGRUTA

Togrutas are a humanoid species native to the temperate planet Shili, positioned in the Expansion Region of the galaxy. All Togrutas have colorful markings on their skin, a genetic trait left over from their predatorial ancestors. Long, striped, curved, hollow horns spiral upward from the top of their skull, and three darker striped head-tails (similar to a Twi'lek's lekku) drape downward, two to the front, falling over their chest, and one thicker tail that is centered at the rear base of their skull. Togrutas' skin is deep red, and their dark eyes and gray lips are embellished by the white markings that adorn their face. Vertical red and white stripes cover the skin of their chest, back, arms, and legs. As Shili is covered in thigh-high turu-grass that is typically a blending of red and white colors, the Togrutas' ancestors (and the Togrutas themselves) blended in with the natural environment, confusing both prey and other predators. When hunting, their head-tails aid them by providing echolocation abilities and a finely tuned spatial sense, which they use to encircle herbivorous prey.

Togrutas are a peaceful, quiet people who are fierce in combat. Loyal to a cause and happy in larger groups, they work well with others and easily fit into teams of mixed cultures. Most do not like to be alone, however, and will tend to follow other members of their group around simply for companionship.

Many outsiders have the misconception that Togrutas are venomous, as they possess prominent incisors that give the impression of a snake's venom-projecting teeth. Togrutas frequently have no idea how this perception originated, but sociologists believe it is because Togrutas prefer to eat their smaller prey while it's still alive, much like Thisspiasians. One of their favorite meals is thimiars, small rodents that hide in the grasslands of Shili. Togrutas will take a living thimiar and bite into it with their incisors, killing the creatures quickly and painlessly, and so observers have been known to mistake the thimiar's death throes for the jolts of an animal dying of poisoning. But even though these convulsions are merely postmortem muscle spasms, most Togrutas will not correct the misconception that they are venomous.

The Togrutas' evolutionary ancestors were predators that lived and hunted in packs, and thus modern Togrutas are also effective hunters who prefer to dwell in dense communal villages camouflaged by the forest canopies and sheltered in hidden valleys. Some vestiges of the Togrutas' beginnings as pack animals remain in their social customs. First, as a habit, Togrutas do not wear shoes whenever possible, feeling that by covering their feet they are cutting themselves off from the land in a spiritual way. Also, every available able-bodied person is expected to take part in the village hunts, and the spoils are shared equally. This is expected even of young children as soon as they are able to effectively hold a weapon, and typically occurs without any specialized training. Togrutas believe that those who are unable to keep pace with the pack should be left to die, and on Shili, those who are unable to fend for themselves often do. Togrutas will not shed any tears over such as loss, a characteristic that can give the impression to outsiders that they are unfeeling beings. This is not the case, though, and the lack of remorse is instead a belief that the death of those unable to defend themselves is simply the course of nature.

In addition, Togrutas wear the results of their hunts proudly, and as a sign of adulthood. It is common to see Togrutas wearing the skins of the animals they've killed, or other trophies of the hunt. For example, the akul is a large, carnivorous animal often hunted on Shili because it is the only native animal that poses a serious threat to the Togrutas. Fierce creatures that emit frightening growls, these orange-furred quadrupeds predominate on the open plains of Shili, attacking settlements and villages. By tradition, akul teeth adornments can only be worn by a Togruta who has slain one without assistance— not an easy task, as akul seem strangely gifted at sensing the presence of other predators, and will begin howling as soon as one is near. The animal's teeth are the common trophy mostly because akul are known for the strength of their jaws, and breaking the hold of an akul is nearly impossible for a normal humanoid. Like a nexu, an akul will use their hold to shake their prey until the victim's neck breaks. The standard jewelry crafted from akul teeth for both males and females is a headdress worn across the forehead and down around the Togruta's eye patches, a combination of indigenous metals, stones, and pearls. Recovered images of the Old Republic Jedi Master Shaak Ti dating back to the time of the Clone Wars have shown her wearing such an akul-tooth headdress, signifying that this is a particularly strong tradition, as she even combined the adornment with her standard Jedi wardrobe.

Akul are not normally native to worlds other than Shili, but they have been exported. When released into the wild on other worlds, they reproduce without the normal ecological safeguards of their native environment and can quickly overwhelm a planet's ecosystem. Inbreeding both on Shili and on other worlds can raise the frequency of naturally occurring mutations, the most common of which is albinism. Akul are often caught for zoos, where they thrive in captivity. However, at great risk to their handlers, both normal and albino akul are trained to perform in lavish stage shows and holonet productions, despite their ferocious natures.

As Togrutas prefer company and normally shun individual in-

dependence, those who live solitary lives away from their people can suffer from acute bouts of depression, putting great pressure on themselves to make up for the life they left behind. Jedi Master Shaak Ti recorded some of her own troubles with this problem even as she proudly espoused the Jedi lifestyle. Some attempt to cling to their non-Togruta friends in order to make up for what they miss in their pack-based life back home. In their culture, individuality is considered somewhat deviant, and yet those who take leadership positions among their people are sometimes forced to achieve their goals through calculated individualism. Sociologists claim this is a sign of the further social evolution of the Togruta people.

With very few exceptions, Togrutas who venture offworld are members of the Jedi Order, and, notably, they tend to be female. Although there is no independent Force tradition on Shili, recovered historical records indicate Togrutas have joined the Jedi as far back as the very beginning of the order, often serving with distinction. As already noted, Shaak Ti was a Jedi Master, one of several Togrutas to earn the rank. In addition, a Togruta female youngling named Ashla was a Padawan at the Jedi Temple on Coruscant during the Clone Wars, and perhaps not coincidentally, her name is an ancient word associated with the light side of the Force. Although reasons for the Togrutas playing such a considerable role in Jedi history are at best speculative due to Emperor Palpatine's destruction of records specifically related to the Jedi and the achievements of non-human species, it appears this species has a special affinity for the Force. How they achieve this heightened Force sense is also a point of speculation, as they have, at best, average midi-chlorian counts in comparison to other species. However, given that Togruta feel a bond with the land (or the planet they happen to be on), as demonstrated by their preference for being barefoot, they may have a unique ability to tap into the life essence of the universe in ways that defy description in terms of the Force or simple midi-chlorian counts. Furthermore, Togrutas are a herding and hunting people, which heightens the detailed spacial sense imparted from their montrails, even for non-Force sensitives. With such an instinctual response to their environment, Togrutas would find feeling the Living Force easier than other species. Unfortunately, there are no current known Togruta members serving the Jedi order, so the source of their affinity for the Force will remain an unknown for the time being.

DESIGNATION
Sentient

HOMEWORLD
Shili

AVERAGE HEIGHT
1.7 meters

PRONUNCIATION
Tō-grōō'-tä

NOTABLE APPEARANCE
Episode II: Attack of the Clones

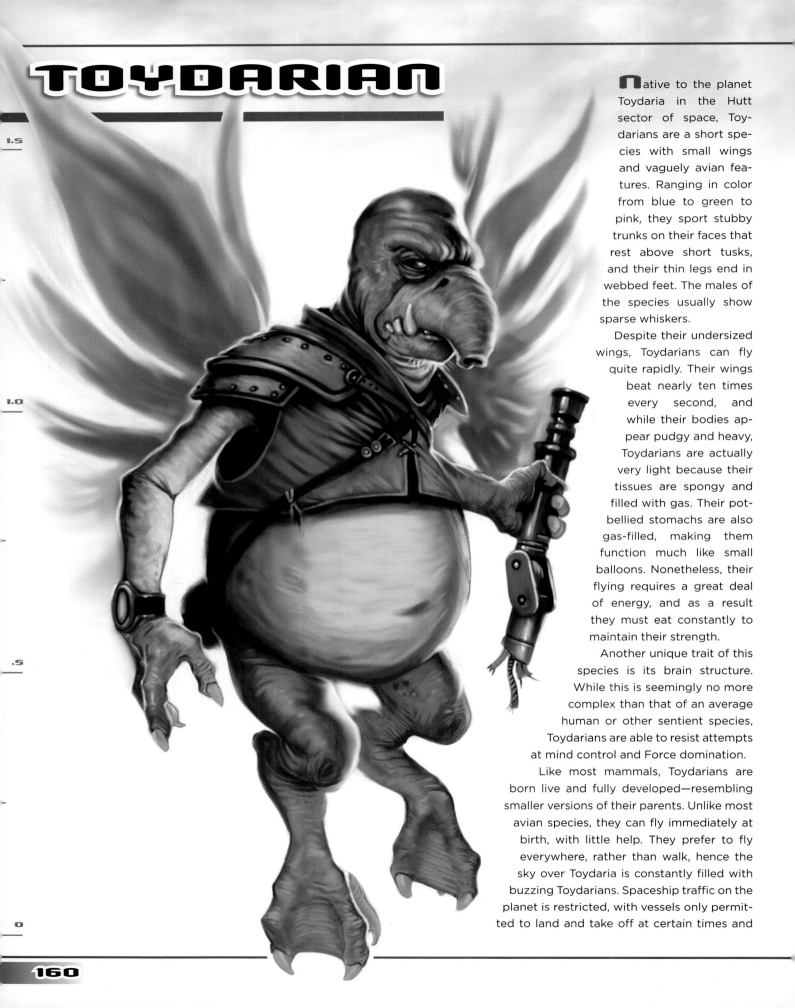

TOYDARIAN

Native to the planet Toydaria in the Hutt sector of space, Toydarians are a short species with small wings and vaguely avian features. Ranging in color from blue to green to pink, they sport stubby trunks on their faces that rest above short tusks, and their thin legs end in webbed feet. The males of the species usually show sparse whiskers.

Despite their undersized wings, Toydarians can fly quite rapidly. Their wings beat nearly ten times every second, and while their bodies appear pudgy and heavy, Toydarians are actually very light because their tissues are spongy and filled with gas. Their pot-bellied stomachs are also gas-filled, making them function much like small balloons. Nonetheless, their flying requires a great deal of energy, and as a result they must eat constantly to maintain their strength.

Another unique trait of this species is its brain structure. While this is seemingly no more complex than that of an average human or other sentient species, Toydarians are able to resist attempts at mind control and Force domination.

Like most mammals, Toydarians are born live and fully developed—resembling smaller versions of their parents. Unlike most avian species, they can fly immediately at birth, with little help. They prefer to fly everywhere, rather than walk, hence the sky over Toydaria is constantly filled with buzzing Toydarians. Spaceship traffic on the planet is restricted, with vessels only permitted to land and take off at certain times and in specified areas to prevent midair collisions. There is little solid ground on the planet, and Toydarians have survived over the centuries by flying virtually everywhere, only landing on the relative safety of algal mats.

Using speeders is prohibited on Toydaria because of all the "air traffic." Consequently, Toydarians have constructed a light-rail system to take offworlders from city to city. Beyond this, they do not have a technologically advanced society, although they have incorporated some offworld technology into their day-to-day lives.

Toydaria is mostly covered with nutrient-rich muck lakes that support a number of predators, including a dangerous species known as grabworms. Toydarians evolved by at first living on the nutrients found in these lakes, and ultimately developed high-end farming techniques to provide food for the populace. But because the amount of sustenance they require is so great, war will often break out between Toydarian confederacies when food supplies are low. During hard times, they feel the simplest way to cope is by stealing provisions from their neighbors, and Toydarians will form armies and fight bitterly, sometimes to the extent of poisoning another group's food supply in the belief that if they can't have it, then no one should. However, when these types of situations eventually improve, the war will immediately end and life will return to normal. This pattern usually recurs roughly every thirty standard years, depending on weather cycles.

Toydarians are talented hagglers. Their economic structure requires constant bartering, and as a result they are very skilled at negotiating prices and striking deals. By nature, they love to gamble and will take a chance on a business deal that looks lucrative, sometimes even despite the odds. Toydarians can be, at their best, professional and business-savvy, but at their worst they are greedy and petty, and will cheat when it serves their purposes. Either way, they are a shrewd and intelligent species—and usually well educated. Toydarians generally speak Basic and Huttese as well as their native language, Toydarian.

Toydaria operates like a sovereign feudal system. There is one ruling king, who is typically good about taking care of his people and is therefore well respected. However, Toydaria is no stranger to violence, as there is always a group of feudal vassals who govern most of the huge system beneath the king—competing and jockeying for positions of power, along with land and natural resources. These vassals are

DESIGNATION
Sentient

HOMEWORLD
Toydaria

AVERAGE HEIGHT
1.4 meters

PRONUNCIATION
Toi-dăr'-ē-ăn

often very rich, and the king will grant favors and orchestrate shifts of power in order to make certain that he always has the allegiance of his vassals by keeping them happy. In turn, the vassals take care of the people and pay their taxes to the system. Oftentimes the king will allow a certain amount of infighting among his vassals, as it weeds out treachery and reveals character and weaknesses among them. In this way, the king is always aware of who is plotting against who, and his vast knowledge of those beneath him keeps the vassals from ever daring to challenge him. By ruling through these methods, the king also promotes the ideas of honesty, loyalty, power, and displays of strength, which, along with wealth, are all important in Toydarian culture.

Members of their species have been found living on worlds beyond Toydaria, but they seem to prefer locales where they can make a profit with little government interference, such as Tatooine. An enterprising species, they will pour all their efforts into a business venture and frequently turn it into a modest success where others could not. One example is the junk shop owned by the Toydarian trader Watto in the city of Mos Espa on Tatooine. Although Watto never made exorbitant numbers of credits on his business, he lived comfortably, if modestly.

Watto's greater role in galactic history was as the onetime slave owner of Shmi and Anakin Skywalker, the young boy who would ultimately become Darth Vader. Although Watto controlled every aspect of their lives, he did at times exhibit a genuine affection for them, going as far as selling Shmi into freedom when the opportunity for her to have some happiness arose, and she became the wife of a moisture farmer. For Watto, slavery was a convenient means to keep Shmi and Anakin around, while also possibly making a profit from the young Anakin's Podracing abilities.

NOTABLE APPEARANCE
Episode I: The Phantom Menace

TRANDOSHAN

Trandoshans, who refer to themselves as T'doshok, are large bipedal reptilians known for their ruthless, warrior culture. Like most reptiles, Trandoshans are cold-blooded and possess scaly skin, which they shed roughly every standard year. Their supersensitive orange eyes can see into the infrared range, and they are able to regenerate lost limbs, at least until they reach Trandoshan middle age. Each of their appendages ends in three digits with sharp claws that are excellent for fighting, although they lack in manual dexterity, causing their finger movements to be rather clumsy. Their oversized, oddly shaped feet also prevent them from wearing any sort of footgear, which is sometimes an impediment when on the hunt or in combat.

As members of a saurian species, female Trandoshans lay clutches of four eggs at a time, and nest them in a warm place in their home. When young Trandoshans hatch, they are already able to walk, and possess a natural instinct for the hunt—usually chasing their clutch brothers or sisters around the home in a type of hiding game. When they reach two standard years of age, the parents take their children out on their first hunt, instructing them on how to track beasts in the wild, and by the age of ten most Trandoshans are proficient in unarmed combat, firearms, and the use of melee weaponry.

This species is extremely violent by nature. Trandoshans' culture is based on the hunting and tracking of beings less powerful than themselves. They worship a female deity known as the Scorekeeper, who awards jagannath points to Trandoshans based on their success or failure in the hunt and mortal combat. Those hunters who earn the most have the highest status in society, and are considered valuable mates by females.

When Trandoshan males have proven themselves successful in the hunt, they return to their homeworld to mate with a convenient clutch mother. These relationships are arranged, and are not considered binding. Once a couple have mated, the female lays her eggs and watches over them until they hatch. As soon as they are old enough, the male children will go out into the galaxy to begin scoring points for their goddess.

The Trandoshans have a particularly adversarial relationship with their insystem neighbors, the Wookiees. Before the birth of the Empire, they attempted to colonize the Wookiee homeworld of Kashyyyk, but were soundly defeated after several bloody battles. When the Wookiees enacted numerous laws to discourage big-game hunting in the system, as well as regulations to protect local ecosystems, the Trandoshans were incensed. They had come to rely on the capital influx from tourism, and they resented the Wookiees' discouragement of the industry in their system. In retribution, they conducted another series of raids on Kashyyyk, this time in an attempt to plunder the natural resources the Wookiees had sought to protect. While bloody conflicts raged on both worlds, the Wookiees appealed to the Senate of the Old Republic, and the governing body intervened, enacting strict trade sanctions against the Trandoshans unless they withdrew from Kashyyyk. They did, once again vowing revenge.

When the Emperor took control of the galaxy, the Trandoshans saw another opportunity to have their vengeance. They aided in the Imperial strikes on Kashyyyk, helping to capture Wookiees in large groups and turning them over to become slaves for the Empire. When the Empire fell, the New Republic demanded that the Trandoshans once more cease their raids on Kashyyyk, under the threat of economic sanctions and military action. They did so with much grumbling, though their previous deeds in support of the Empire have caused them to remain one of the least trusted species in the galaxy.

Making no attempt to disguise their dispositions, Trandoshans continue to enforce the stereotype that they are a violent, egocentric, and malicious people. Aggressive and vindictive, they love competition for its own sake, although it is especially appealing to them as a means of dealing out vengeance. Interclan rivalries have been known to claim numerous lives, and turn son against father. In certain cases, however, they can still show compassion and mercy—particularly if it is a matter of honor. Trandoshans will, like their Wookiee nemeses, pledge their lives to protect another being who has saved them from death—although they would have a difficult time making that pledge to a Wookiee. To this day they despise their Wookiee neighbors, and will never be caught in their company, except in the rarest of circumstances.

And yet, despite their highly aggressive culture, some Trandoshans have been known to show a streak of independence, preferring to keep alternative elements of their society running effectively. These Trandoshans are still considered hunters, although not in a traditional sense. Scientists, for instance, will "hunt" for answers in the study of science, while xenobiologists "hunt" for details on other worlds and their various cultures. Engineers "hunt" for superior weapons or ship designs. Most day-to-day professions can be considered honorable in the sense of the hunt, as long as they produce something that improves or enriches society—though admittedly, Trandoshans would most likely find little value in being an actor or comedian.

DESIGNATION
Sentient

HOMEWORLD
Trandosha
(referred to as Dosha or Hsskor by Trandoshans)

AVERAGE HEIGHT
2 meters

PRONUNCIATION
Trăn-dō'-shăn

NOTABLE APPEARANCE
Episode V: The Empire Strikes Back

TUSKEN RAIDER (SAND PERSON)

Tusken Raiders, also referred to as Sand People, are tall, strong, aggressive, nomadic humanoid warriors who reside in the desert wastelands of Tatooine. From head to toe, every Raider is always covered in strips of cloth-tattered robes that are belted together with dewback-hide leather. They see by using tube-like shields that protect their eyes, and breathe through simple filters that keep them from inhaling the sand particles that constantly swirl through the Tatooine air. Every piece of their attire serves to keep moisture trapped near their bodies, and hygiene is only attended to in complete privacy, for seeing another individual's face, even accidentally, is cause for a blood duel. Only a Tusken's mate is allowed to glimpse his or her face without the bandaging.

Tusken Raiders are ruthless fighters, hardened by their harsh environment to show no mercy to other species. They fear little, although they can be driven away by a substantial display of force. Traveling in bands of up to twenty or thirty, they nearly always ride their bantha mounts in a straight line, journeying one behind the other to hide their numbers from enemies. Their weapon of choice is the gaderffii, or gaffi stick, which is basically a double-edged ax made of cannibalized metal scavenged from abandoned or wrecked vehicles. Some carry blaster rifles, but Tusken blasters are not the most powerful or technologically advanced weapons.

This nomadic people was the dominant sentient species on Tatooine before settlers began to colonize the world during the days of the Old Republic. The Jawas, the only other sentients on the planet, while more intelligent, were not as large or fierce as their brutal neighbors, although there is some scientific evidence that suggests the two groups may both be descended from the same species, an ancient race known as the Kumumgah. The Tusken Raiders received their galaxy-recognized name from an attack they launched on a human settlement called Fort Tusken. While their attempt to force out the offworld settlers failed, this assault became renowned for its brutality. In response, the settlers set about to attempt the utter destruction of the Sand People, eliminating entire tribes at a time—leading to their near extinction before the few remaining tribes retreated to hide in the desert wastes.

As a result of these incidents, Sand People are inherently angered by the presence in their territories of offworld settlers, whom they feel encroach upon their ration of water and food. They will often attack moisture farmers and settlers without provocation—simply for the sake of intimidating those they perceive as enemies.

Despite their bullying natures, Tusken Raiders will typically shy away from massive Jawa sandcrawler fortresses, heavily protected farmsteads, large cities, and even settlements, as well as from the vicious krayt dragons. It is evident that they favor situations where they have the upper hand, and will only take calculated risks.

Since they are a nomadic people, they maintain no permanent shelters and keep few possessions, viewing such belongings as liabilities. Regardless of their willingness to move regularly, they allow no other changes in their society or culture. Tusken Raiders fear machinery, the power of which has decimated their people in the past, and are thus thoroughly resistant to technology, stealing very little of it from hapless patrols, caravans, and moisture farmers. They feel that killing with more primitive weapons brings them the bravest of victories.

To most outsiders, the language of Tusken Raiders is an unintelligible, angry combination of consonants and growls. They have no written language, so they rely on a long and complex oral tradition to keep track of their lineage and legends. Each tribe has a storyteller, whose duty is to preserve and retell the group's history. The storyteller chronicles the coming-of-age tales for each member of the clan, and once he or she gives an account for the first time, not one word is permitted to change from that time forward. At some point, each storyteller will take on an apprentice and begin teaching the clan history, although the learner is not allowed to practice the history aloud, as the words must never be spoken incorrectly. If the apprentice makes a mistake, he or she is killed outright, as it is considered blasphemy. Once an apprentice has learned every tale of each lineage perfectly, he or she becomes the next storyteller, and the teacher will wander into the desert to die.

Because they live such a cruel, war-like existence, the process of coming of age is very important to Tusken Raiders. Children are cared for by adult Tuskens, but they are not considered people until they have endured the actual ceremonies that bring them into maturity. Babies often perish because of the difficult desert life, and Sand People take great pride in knowing that only the strongest survive. To earn the distinction of adulthood, each youth must perform a great feat of skill or prowess, the magnitude of which determines his or her station in the tribe. A solemn ritual is held to prepare Tusken youths for their journey into the wilderness, during which they are given totems, armaments, and some water to carry with them. Saying no words, and showing no fear, they mount their banthas and head off into the desert. If they return with trophies showing that they have been victorious, they are greeted with grand rejoicing. A bonfire is lit, food prepared, and amid great ceremony the storyteller adds the young Tusken's tale of bravery to the tribal history. If they do not return, no word is mentioned of them again.

Sand People make no social distinction between males or females. Only clan leaders keep records on sexes, so that they can arrange marriages, and as soon as a youth becomes a recognized adult, he or she is assigned a mate. Through a ritual that mixes the blood of husband and wife with that of their bantha mounts, they are joined for life.

In extremely rare instances, Tuskens have been known to accept outsiders into their tribes. The Jedi Sharad Hett lived for some time among the Tuskens, and the Jedi Tahiri Veila was raised among the Sand People after her parents died in a Tusken raid.

During the time of the New Republic, fewer Tusken Raiders were reported encroaching on human settlements. A cyclic pattern of harsh sandstorms threatened and destroyed many human settlements, and sociologists believe several of the tribes were affected as well. It is unclear how many Tusken Raider tribes currently reside on Tatooine, as they continue to remain resistant to outsider study.

DESIGNATION
Sentient

HOMEWORLD
Tatooine

AVERAGE
HEIGHT
1.8 meters

PRONUNCIATION
Tŭs'-kĕn Rā'-dĕr
(Sănd Pēr'-sŭn)

NOTABLE APPEARANCE
Episode IV: A New Hope

TWI' LEK

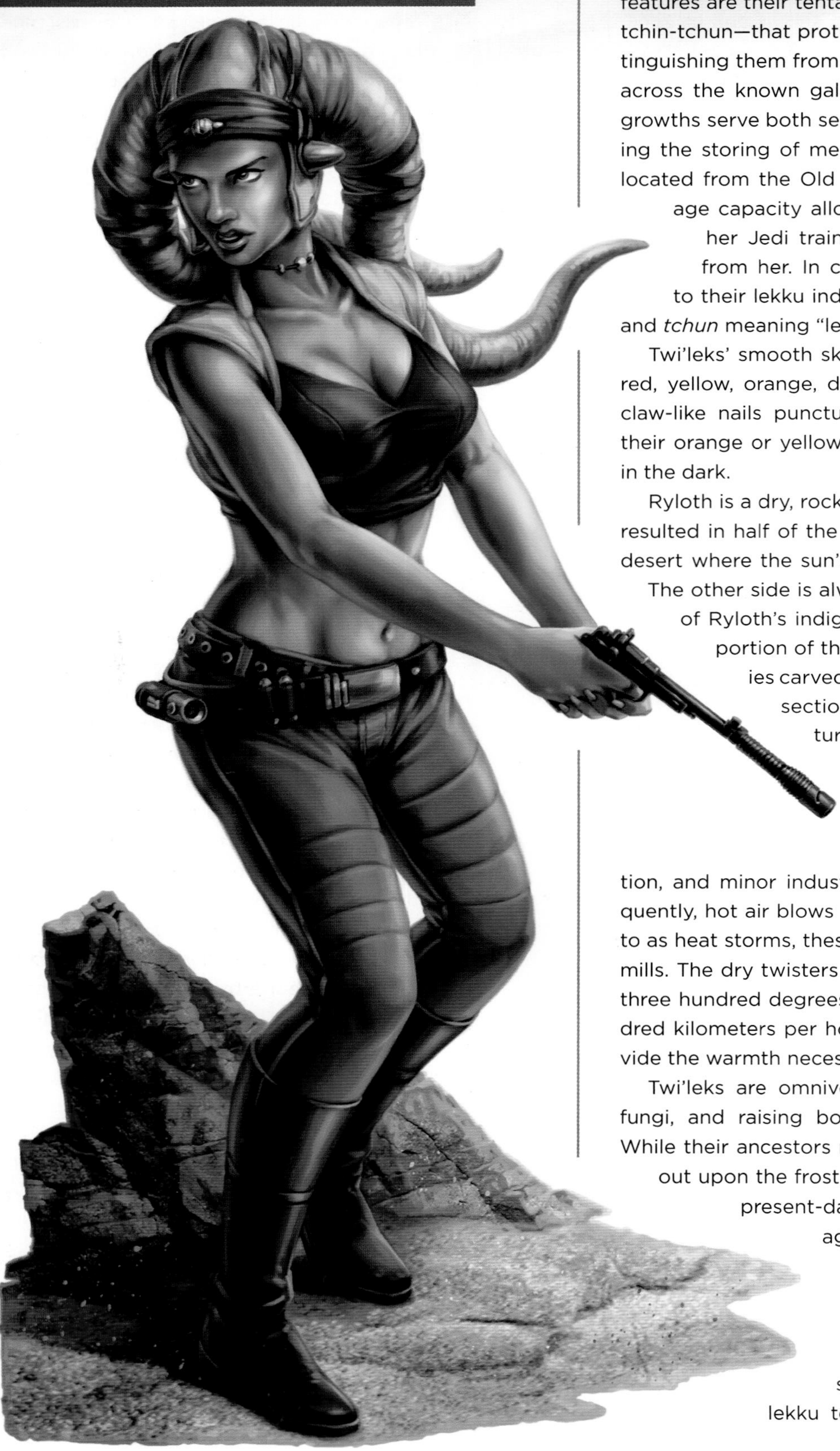

Twi'leks are tall, generally thin humanoids indigenous to the Ryloth star system in the Outer Rim. Their most notable features are their tentacle head-tails—called both lekku and tchin-tchun—that protrude from the back of their skull, distinguishing them from the multitude of other species found across the known galaxy. These fatty, tapered, prehensile growths serve both sensual and cognitive functions, including the storing of memories. In fact, some of the records located from the Old Republic era indicate that this storage capacity allowed the Jedi Aayla Secura to recall her Jedi training after her memories were stolen from her. In conversation, Twi'leks will often refer to their lekku individually: *tchin* meaning "right lekku" and *tchun* meaning "left lekku."

Twi'leks' smooth skin comes in many variations of blue, red, yellow, orange, deep green, and even striped. Sharp, claw-like nails punctuate their long, flexible fingers, and their orange or yellow eyes are especially good for seeing in the dark.

Ryloth is a dry, rocky world with a peculiar orbit that has resulted in half of the planet becoming a barren, unlivable desert where the sun's rays constantly scorch the surface. The other side is always trapped in frigid darkness. Most of Ryloth's indigenous species inhabit the cold, dark portion of the planet, while the Twi'leks live in cities carved out of the mountains in the "twilight" section of the world—where the temperature is somewhat comfortable.

Theirs is a primitive industrial civilization, based on windmills and air-spun turbines that provide power for heat, light, air circulation, and minor industry within their city complexes. Frequently, hot air blows from the sun-based regions; referred to as heat storms, these winds drive the turbines and windmills. The dry twisters can reach temperatures in excess of three hundred degrees Celsius, with gusts hitting five hundred kilometers per hour. While very dangerous, they provide the warmth necessary to sustain life.

Twi'leks are omnivorous, cultivating edible molds and fungi, and raising bovine rycrits for food and clothing. While their ancestors might have been hunters who struck out upon the frosty plains to find game for sustenance, present-day Twi'leks have developed a more agrarian society.

The Twi'lek people are highly intelligent, capable of learning and speaking most galactic languages. Their own dialect combines verbal sounds and subtle movements of their lekku to communicate complete concepts.

1.5

1.0

.5

0

Even the most advanced linguists have difficulty interpreting all the head-tail movements inherent to the Twi'leki language. For this reason, when two Twi'leks converse in public, their discussion often remains completely private, unless it is observed by another Twi'lek or a quality protocol droid.

This linguistic feature has been the cause of much suspicion on the part of many outsiders throughout history, particularly Imperials, who believed that since Twi'leks sent secret signals with their head-tails, they were duplicitous spies. In truth, Twi'leks see their lekku as "spiritual appendages," and in jostling them, they express the movement of inner divinity. While this may indeed be considered extra communication, it is actually contact at a metaphysical level. While the meaning is mostly private between speakers, it is usually not two-faced or deceitful to those outside the communication, unless absolutely necessary. Normally it is merely truthful and real, and cannot go against their verbal expression—not, at least, without extreme concentration. Recent studies done by the Jedi of the New Republic found that Twi'leks are in fact a generally Force-sensitive people, and that their lekku interaction is tied to their inherent Force sensitivity. This may also explain some of their suspect treatment at the hands of the Empire.

Contrary to the paranoia expressed by the Empire, the people of Ryloth are not at all warlike, and remained clear of the Imperial conflict during the Galactic Civil War, although if they had been called upon to spy for either side, they would have been quite good at it. They prefer cunning and slyness over physical confrontation.

Hidden beneath the surface of their world, their city complexes are massive interconnecting networks of catacombs and chambers. Built into rocky outcroppings, they blend right in with the environment of the planet—vivid evidence of this people's subtle nature.

Each of their cities is autonomous and governed by a head clan consisting of five Twi'lek males who collectively direct industry and trade. These leaders are born to their positions, and exercise absolute power. When one member of the head clan dies, the remaining four are driven out to follow their colleague to the "Bright Lands," making room for the next generation. If there is no immediate generation to follow, a set of regents takes over until a new head clan can be selected. Given that a seat within the head clan is handed down within families, intra- and interclan rivalries

abound. Subterfuge within one's own clan is almost to be expected, although Twi'leks who are caught and disgraced among their people are also driven into the Bright Lands.

Because Twi'leks possess no spacefaring capabilities of their own, they have grown dependent on neighboring systems, as well as on pirates, smugglers, and merchants, for much of their galactic interaction. One of their greatest exports is the mineral ryll, which is used in many medicines, but also as an expensive and addictive recreational drug. Ryloth has become very vulnerable to the underbelly of galaxy life: slaving vessels have often combed the planet to stock their thriving ryll stores, while smugglers often raid ryll storehouses. Some head clans have actually given their own people into slavery as a protection payment, feeling threatened by the possibility of widespread pillaging.

Slavery has historically been a serious problem among the Twi'lek clans, particularly for their female members. In traditional Twi'lek society, women are expected to be subservient to men, and are often treated as afterthoughts or accessories. They are not considered particularly intelligent or capable, having value only to the degree that they please others. Twi'lek women were commonly sold into slavery, even by their own clans, to become dancers or companions, as their beauty and grace is favored galaxywide by many different species. Lethan, or red-skinned Twi'lek women, fetch a startlingly high price on the open market.

With the dawn of the New Republic, some head clans on Ryloth banded together to stop the slave trade and protect one another from the retribution of angry smugglers and traders. This has created a much safer environment, and more and more legitimate trading organizations have started to bring business to the world. Following this, Twi'leks began to take on a visible and influential role in the New Republic, often serving as pilots, as advocates, and in other positions. This new prominence was almost jeopardized when the rogue Imperial Warlord Zsinj brainwashed Twi'leks into attempting to assassinate Admiral Ackbar and Republic hero Wedge Antilles. Following this, all Twi'leks were temporarily removed from active military duty until the plot was discovered—thankfully, before it could reach its conclusion. The Twi'lek species was vindicated, and returned to its former level of influence in galactic affairs.

DESIGNATION
Sentient

HOMEWORLD
Ryloth

AVERAGE
HEIGHT
1.7 meters

PRONUNCIATION
Twē'-lĕk

NOTABLE APPEARANCE
Episode VI: Return of the Jedi

UGNAUGHT

Ugnaughts are small, porcine humanoids known for their tireless work ethic. They are especially good mine workers, whether this be gas or mineral mining. Their short, stocky, muscular bodies are able to withstand long periods of work under harsh conditions.

This species is native to the planet Gentes, located in the Anoat system, although very few—if any—remain on that world. Unfortunately, the Ugnaughts suffered the fate of many other primitive species throughout the galaxy, in that entire tribes of the pig-like aliens were gathered by human merchants, smugglers, and traders and taken to new worlds to live and work as indentured servants and slaves.

One of the largest populations of these creatures can be found at Cloud City on Bespin. When the Corellian eccentric Lord Figg decided to build this floating Tibanna gas mine colony high in Bespin's atmosphere, he knew the project would require cheap manual labor. Figg rounded up by force three Ugnaught tribes—the Irden, Botrut, and Isced—and took them to a space station near Bespin to offer them a deal. If they would build his floating city, he would then grant them their freedom. Further, they and their descendants would be allowed to live and work in the colony and share in the company's profits. The Ugnaughts accepted, and went right to work on Figg's project. After the city was finished, they began to reap the profits of their labor.

When Lando Calrissian became the legal administrator of Bespin, he honored the agreement with the Ugnaughts until he lost control of the facility to the Empire. With the onset of Imperial occupation, the Ugnaughts were enslaved once more, and forced to work longer hours under harsh conditions. Many were removed from the facility altogether. Lando eventually returned to Bespin and, with the help of Luke Skywalker, Lando's friend Lobot, and the Ugnaughts, he regained control of the city. He later turned control over to the Ugnaughts' chosen leader of all the tribes, King Ozz. Today they own the city that they helped build.

Although now modernized, the Ugnaught people retain the rich oral tradition they have long maintained. Even after being transplanted to countless new worlds, they have held on to many of the customs and laws they established in the time before their enslavement. Immediately upon their acceptance of Figg's offer, tribes reestablished their ruling councils called Terend, elected officers called ufflor, and chose traditional "blood professions."

Blood professions are vocations passed down from gen-

DESIGNATION
Sentient

HOMEWORLD
Gentes

AVERAGE HEIGHT
1.2 meters

PRONUNCIATION
Ŭg′-nŏt

eration to generation within each family. A miner will teach his children to mine, and a mechanic teaches his children to repair and construct machinery. When Ugnaughts reach the age of twenty, they become candidates for their inherited profession. If the number of new candidates for any given profession exceeds the community's needs, the candidates call a blood duel. Through a series of fights to the death, young Ugnaughts battle for the right to inherit their blood profession.

A similar ritual takes place when a young male Ugnaught wishes to take a bride. All males who wish to be considered for marriage will come together once a year to meet the females who are considered eligible for marriage. If a conflict ensues over one female, the contesting males must compete against each other, with the female choosing the means of competition. Sometimes this is a contest of physical strength, but other times it is a match of wits. Either way, the ruler acts as judge in the single bout to determine who will take the bride home with him.

Despite these arcane traditions, Ugnaughts are a predominantly nonviolent, peaceful species. They tend to shy away from contact with other races, and usually do not learn to speak Basic—though they do understand it—except for the ufflor and members of the Terend. Ugnaughts feel more comfortable when dealing with members of their own tribes.

Ugnaughts are robust, meticulous, skillful, and unpretentious. They are thoroughly committed to their family and their occupations. Ugnaughts who are idle are usually restless and irritable. The best way to keep them happy is to keep them busy.

Of the three tribes on Bespin, the Isced has encountered the most difficulty with outsiders and with the other tribes. This is because they have a vicious sense of humor, and are prone to playing potentially dangerous practical jokes.

During their indentured servant years, a majority of the Ugnaughts lived in the Bespin mining quarters. Once the city was liberated, the Ugnaughts inhabited all portions of the facility. However, council meetings, folk-story telling, dances, and blood duels still take place in various arenas located, by tradition, in the mining quarters area. And while the King of the Tribes meets with the Terends of the tribes in the administrative levels of Cloud City, his coronation and all other special government events are held in this same area, as a reminder of the Ugnaughts' proud tradition as menial laborers.

NOTABLE APPEARANCE
Episode V: The Empire Strikes Back

UTAPAUN (UTAI AND PAU'AN)

PAU'AN

Utapauns is really a name for two species that inhabit the world of Utapau, a barren world of rocks and deep sinkholes located in the remote Tarabba sector of the Outer Rim. The Pau'ans are the upper class of Utapaun society, making up nearly a third of the world's native inhabitants. This species is the taller of the two, with slim builds, gaunt, gray, lined faces, and dark eyes. Dressed in tightly bound, thick clothing, usually only their hands and faces are visible. They serve as governmental administrators, officials, and bureaucrats. Their neighbor species, the Utai, meanwhile, are short and stocky, with round faces and long eyestalks. The Utai serve as the menial laborers, technicians, and ground crew for docking areas. On each foot they have only two toes, and on each hand three fingers and a thumb—but nevertheless they are nimble and dexterous, completing complex manual tasks with ease. Their large, dark eyes allow them to see in the dimmest of light underground.

The Pau'ans are a very long-lived species, and are often called the Ancients because of their longevity. While they originally made their home on the surface of Utapau, climatic changes caused stronger and stronger hyperwind storms, so they were forced to build a new home in the sinkholes, where they first met their native neighbors.

The Utai, in contrast, are often called the Shorts because of their stature—but also because comparatively their lives aren't very long. Utai colonized the walls and crevices of Utapau long before the Pau'ans ever thought of doing so, and while they are not as long-lived, they are the older of the two species. Between the efforts of the two species, entire cities were built beneath the surface of the planet in the tunnels, crevasses, and walls of massive sinkholes. Because of their environment, both species prefer darkness, and Pau'ans in particular prefer to eat meat raw, rather than cooked.

The Pau'ans govern Utapau in a way that allows for a great deal of autonomy among the local cities. Local administrators, called Masters of Port Administration, act as a type of mayor of their city, and they are assisted by an advisory committee. Each of these individual port administrators is a member of the Utapaun Committee, which is managed by the chairman of Utapau, the planetary head of state. As only Pau'ans have these leadership roles, they often serve in them for many years because of their long life span. They receive their positions because of their heritage, with family lines holding on to leadership roles through generations. For example, Tion Medon was an administrator for Pau City, and he was descended from Timon Medon, who first unified the Utapaun peoples.

When the Pau'ans first met their fellow residents, they taught their diminutive cousins how to generate wind power. Over time, the Pau'ans found themselves falling naturally into the leadership role, a role the Utai easily, and readily, relinquished. Although the balance of power is tipped in favor of the Pau'ans, there is no ill will on the part of the Utai. Even though they are relegated to menial or lower-level labor positions, they are not maltreated or underappreciated by their compatriots.

But while there is no conflict between the species, there is some conflict among cities as a whole. Each city on Utapau has its own Pau'an dialect and culture, and rivalry has often been fierce among them. Arguments and competitions have erupted in the politics of the Utapaun Committee on many occasions, though the competing cities always band together to face a worldwide threat.

Such cooperation occurred when the Confederacy of Independent Systems laid siege to the Utapaun homeworld during the Clone Wars. The Utapaun Committee was not at all happy with its plight, and did not like harboring General Grievous, the commander of the Separatists' massive droid army. Committee members quickly and quietly agreed that they would turn him over as soon as the opportunity arose, and when Obi-Wan Kenobi came to Utapau to investigate the situation there, they immediately told him of their situation despite being watched by their overseers. Obi-Wan told them they would be liberated by Republic forces, but sadly Palpatine took control as Emperor and put into play the programming he'd installed in his clone warriors to wipe out the droid army—but take control of Utapau at the same time.

While the Emperor reigned, Utapau remained a dominated world, held in bondage to Imperial forces. When the New Republic came to power, the planet eagerly joined the new government, hoping to take a more active role in galactic society in order to prevent such a political travesty from ever again happening to their world.

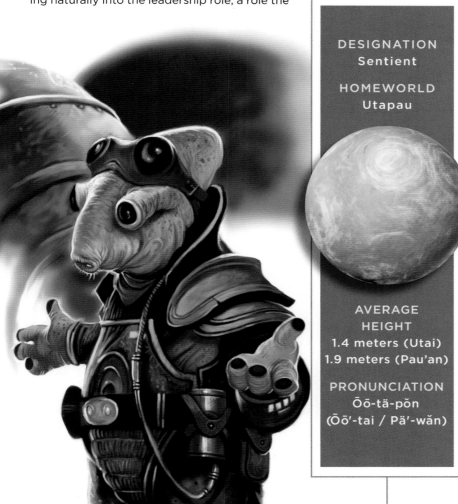

UTAI

DESIGNATION
Sentient

HOMEWORLD
Utapau

AVERAGE HEIGHT
1.4 meters (Utai)
1.9 meters (Pau'an)

PRONUNCIATION
Ōō-tä-pŏn
(Ōō'-tai / Pä'-wăn)

NOTABLE APPEARANCE
Episode III: Revenge of the Sith

VARACTYL

Varactyls are saurian, four-legged herbivores native to the plant Utapau. While they are reptiles, they possess many features of the bird family, such as feathers dotting their scaled skin and long, bird-like tails. A giant, sharp beak of a nose protrudes from the center of varactyls' faces, and two small, dark eyes rest on the sides of their elongated heads. A ring of feathers surrounds the varactyl's neck.

This reptile has an armor-plated skull that protects its brain from blunt injury. Its neck is extremely flexible, and both males and females have crests and a ridge of midbody spines. Some of these defensive quills have developed into feathers, which are used for mating and threat displays. A female varactyl's plumage and overall coloration tend to be more vibrant.

Their large feet have strong claws with five digits, giving them the ability to climb the rocky walls of Utapau's sinkholes at incredible speeds.

Varactyls are cold-blooded lizards, and as such they like to sun themselves on the walls of Utapau's sinkholes. They are most active during daylight hours, crawling up the rocky cliffsides to remain in the sun as it shifts across the sky, avoiding the darkness as it fills the cavernous canyons of the planet surface. They eat the most during the day, feeding on green lichens in the lower, wetter portion of the sinkholes and punching through the dried sandstone in the upper levels to consume arterial roots that weave their way through the soft rock.

Varactyl nests are primarily located in the warmest outcroppings of the sinkhole wall, where during the day they are warmed with the most sunlight. A female varactyl will lay a clutch of about a dozen eggs at a time, and these eggs take nearly two months to hatch. These nests, while they lay where the sun can reach them, are also placed where there is a crag or crevice into which varactyls can hide themselves and the nest to protect their young from predators.

During the night varactyls are more lethargic, and therefore vulnerable to the native predators. One is the dactillion, a distant genetic cousin of varactyls. Dactillions often fly in and attack varactyl nests to eat their eggs or hatched young. For extra security, varactyls will group together for warmth near their nests in the sinkhole walls. While dactillions and varactyls are natural enemies, when domesticated they can be corralled in the same pens.

Varactyls' scaled skin is waterproof, and they are excellent swimmers. They only swim during the middle of the day, however, when sunlight is striking the bottom of the caverns where the water gathers in grottoes. The vicious nos monster is active in the hours of darkness, so they will not attempt the water at night.

While usually calm, imperturbable creatures, varactyls will defend themselves and their young with great ferocity from attack. Females, especially, are more tenacious in this regard. The fan of erect spines along a female's tail would seriously injure an opponent attacking her from the rear. Varactyls are also extremely strong, and their heads, made of strong bone impervious to most blunt attacks, cause a good deal of damage when used in a head-butting maneuver.

The Pau'ans and Utai of Utapau have bred varactyls for centuries as pack animals and mounts because of their pleasant demeanor, strength, and speed. It was the diminutive Utai, though, who learned how to domesticate and train them for their present use. The Utai serve today as the varactyl wranglers for mounts. Dactillions are excellent steed and pack animals. Because of their high-boned backs, both creatures must be fitted with high-backed saddles to give riders appropriate balance.

This is a very intelligent species, loyal to their masters and clever with regard to combat. They are also credited with having long memories. A varactyl will remember all of its riders, and will respond favorably or negatively to them based on past treatment. When they have been treated well by a rider, varactyls respond with loyalty and great affection. If a rider abuses a varactyl mount, the creature will not allow that being to ride them and, in extreme cases, may attack the person. There are reports of many beings having been killed when this happened. One abusive rider reportedly had a varactyl remember him after he had been offplanet for several years.

DESIGNATION
Nonsentient

HOMEWORLD
Utapau

AVERAGE LENGTH
15.24 meters
HEIGHT
3.9 meters

PRONUNCIATION
Vŭ-răk'-tĭl

NOTABLE APPEARANCE
Episode III: Revenge of the Sith

WAMPA

Wampas are burly, vicious primates that inhabit the ice-covered world of Hoth. They stand up to three meters tall, and possess razor-sharp claws and fangs. Wampas that have passed puberty usually have jagged, curving horns on their heads that continue to grow larger and more imposing with age.

Because of their acute sense of smell and the coat of thick white fur that blends perfectly with the landscape of their native planet, wampas make excellent hunters, and are very rarely themselves the victims of predators. They wander the icy wastelands of Hoth preying on tauntauns, antlered mammals called rayboo, and other unwary creatures. After disabling their prey, they drag it to their cavernous, frozen lairs beneath Hoth's surface. Using their saliva, wampas moisten portions of their victims' bodies, then place them against the ceilings of their caves so that the victims will freeze in place, suspended from the ice. Because wampas prefer fresh meat, they often keep their prey alive until they choose to consume it.

Wampas typically hunt alone, but occasionally band together to lash out against a threat to the local wampa population, such as a human settlement. In this, they show a rudimentary form of intelligence and cunning, particularly since they will often scout their enemies' location and strength before formulating an attack.

Luke Skywalker, the renowned Jedi Master, has claimed that these creatures even have long memories. During a routine patrol when the Rebel Alliance had its base established on Hoth, Skywalker was attacked by a wampa, and barely escaped its lair by slicing off its arm with his lightsaber. When he returned on a later visit to Hoth, the same one-armed wampa discovered him, and attacked Luke and his cohort Callista. This time, Luke managed to slay the creature with his lightsaber, allowing them to escape.

During the Alliance encampment on Hoth, wampas repeatedly attacked the Hoth base and its personnel. It was soon discovered that wampas are strangely attracted to the sounds made by astromech droids. After some research, it was revealed that the tweets and whistles emitted by the droids were similar to those made by a female wampa in search of a mate. No doubt some male wampas were disappointed to find a mere piece of machinery waiting for them instead of a new companion, thus further justifying their regular vicious rampages once they had discovered the source of the sounds.

Wampas mate during the warmer months of the Hoth yearly cycle, during which they will gather in regions where game is plentiful, to search for companionship. The males go on the hunt while the females stay together and wait. Once the male succeeds in a kill, he will smear the blood of his victim on his chest and return with the game to show it to the females—demonstrating his ability to effectively care for a mate. Sometimes the males will fight each other for a female's attention, and the victors in these various melees are those who win their preferred female; they are thus treated as the alpha males of the region until the next mating season occurs.

While they are primates, wampas could also be considered marsupials in terms of their reproduction methods. Their cubs are born live, but very underdeveloped—almost resembling a miniature worm that could fit upon a caf spoon. These tiny infants crawl to their mother's pouch, where they nurse, grow, and develop over a period of roughly three months—after which time they leave the pouch with a full set of teeth, small needle-sharp claws, and an innate attitude of invincibility. The mother and father will then teach the children to hunt, to survive in the cold, and to care for game.

Galactic scientists have further discovered that wampas mourn their dead with great intensity. They are protective of their own, and when one is slain, they will fly into a rage directed at the killer. If the death was natural, the grieving wampas will simply take out their anger on their surroundings, smashing walls and ripping apart anything or anyone in their way. Some wampas have been reported to accidentally cause avalanches and underground cave-ins during these fits of hysteria, leading to even more deaths. After expending all their energy, grieving wampas will bury the body in the snow, and keep guard over it for several days—ensuring that the remains are not eaten by other predators.

These intimidating creatures have become popular prey for big-game hunters, and have also been spotted in some of the illegal gladiatorial games that pop up on a number of the Outer Rim worlds. Hunters and poachers are more and more willing to brave the severe cold of Hoth for sport or to make a profit from wampas. While they are not the friendliest of creatures, wampas were included in Galactic Alliance legislation to protect endangered species from extinction.

Some wampa subspecies are found on other worlds, and while it is clear they were transplanted, scientists have been unable to trace how the creatures found their way there from Hoth. One of the more notable subspecies is the swamp wampas of Dromund Kaas. Dark brown in color to blend in with their marshy environment, swamp wampas form cave-like huts of bog moss in which to hide their kill. They are identical to the wampas of Hoth in nearly every other way, prompting scientists to believe that they are indeed descended from their icy cousins. How and when they came to be on Dromund Kaas and developed their present appearance is unknown, but it does speak volumes of the species' adaptability.

The Empire, meanwhile, bioengineered another subspecies of wampa known as the "cliff wampa," after they received reports of how wampas wreaked havoc upon the Rebel base of Hoth. This rock-climbing variety was used to guard Imperial interests on the Outer Rim planet Gall. Gray or light brown in color to blend in with their rocky habitat, the sharp, iron-strong claws of these creatures allows them to dig into solid rock walls to form caves, just as the Hoth variety would dig into ice.

One species that is often mistaken as a wampa relative is the Tatooine Howler, which is sometimes called a "desert wampa." While they do bear a resemblance to the wampa being covered in hair and adorned with tusks, genetic testing has proven that the mysterious, howling desert hunter is no relation at all to the wampa but a separate species altogether.

DESIGNATION
Semi-sentient

HOMEWORLD
Hoth

AVERAGE HEIGHT
2.5 meters

PRONUNCIATION
Wäm'-pä

NOTABLE APPEARANCE
Episode V: The Empire Strikes Back

WEEQUAY

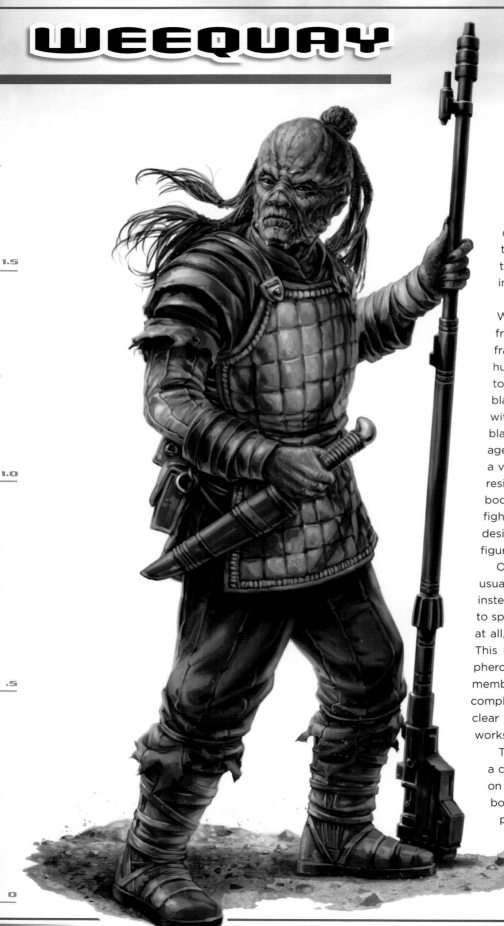

Weequays are a humanoid species from the desert world of Sriluur, located in the system of the same name. They are a strong, rugged people, with countenances weathered by the harsh desert winds. Their skin is coarse and gnarled, and typically black, gray, brown, or tan in color. The males wear topknots drawn to the peak of their otherwise bald heads, while the females usually shave their skulls completely. Male Weequays who are offplanet wear individual topknot braids for each Sriluur year that they are not at home. When they return to Sriluur, they shave off the topknot braids in celebration.

In keeping with their rough appearance, Weequay have a unique resilience to injury from blunt trauma and burns. Their skeletal frames are more dense than those of most humanoid races, and their skin is more like a tough hide. A Weequay's skin can withstand blaster fire and attacks from blunt weapons with little injury—though at close range a blaster will cause their skin to smolder. Average knife attacks are also ineffective, though a vibro-blade can puncture their skin. It is not resistant to lightsabers, however. This natural body armor makes them extremely durable fighters in close quarters and renders them very desirable as personal guards to organized crime figures and the like.

Often seen as threatening, Weequays will not usually speak in the presence of a non-Weequay, instead often hiring a trustworthy non-Weequay to speak for them. In fact, they do not talk much at all, even in the presence of their own people. This is largely because they possess a type of pheromone-based communication that enables members of the same clan to communicate in complete silence. This type of interaction is as clear to the species as the spoken word, but it works only with other clan members.

These people are, indeed, dangerous. Theirs is a complex, impersonal, brutal culture centered on the worship of a multitude of gods that symbolize both natural forces and animals. Their primary deity is Quay, the god of the moon, from whom their people's name is derived. (*Weequay* means, literally, "follower of Quay.") To contact their gods, Weequays use totems that symbolize the sphere of control of each given deity. Their main totem is a spherical object that they utilize for obtaining advice from Quay himself. They address the totem as Quay in an effort to please the god. This totem actually behaves much like a child's toy, and on other worlds it has found use as an amusement device. All Weequays carry one on their person, and will shake it and wait for advice or inspiration to appear, directing them in every important decision they must make. They have a great devotion for the totem, and will grow violently angry if anyone questions the validity of an answer derived from it.

The Quay totem produces its own problems, however, as Weequays may shake the object for hours seeking the answers they wish to receive. But in doing this, they will remain patient, assuming that because all Weequays have totems, the god was probably busy answering the questions posed by others.

The totem also controls Weequay mating. When a male Weequay wishes to take a female as a mate, he questions the totem first as to whether it is a wise idea. If the totem answers in the affirmative, he seeks out the prospective female, who in turn consults her own totem. This process may go around several times until the two have matching answers. In a like manner, Weequays can also end a marriage by consulting the totem. The only part of Weequay life not truly determined by the totem is the producing of children, which the species leaves up to chance, accepting offspring as a special secret present from the gods—though many Weequays still, out of eagerness, ask Quay to tell them the gender and number of children to be born.

While they do take great pride in their offspring, life in a Weequay clan is completely impersonal, and clan members do not even have names, since individuality is not a concept they understand; they will only take a name when they leave their homeworld. Weequays employ limited technology, though they are known as skilled makers of melee weapons such as force pikes.

Weequays were originally a nomadic, desert-dwelling people, but eventually they established large clan cities in coastal areas of Sriluur. At the center of these cities are religious shrines called thal, made of black polished stone, where followers known as sant can leave anonymous offerings. Building thal offplanet is not allowed, although Weequays who are not on Sriluur may sacrifice a strong animal or adversary to the gods. Such traditional religious

sacrifices can often attract unwanted attention from local peoples, as occurred on at least one occasion on Tatooine. Weequay guards and mercenaries in the employ of the crimelord Jabba the Hutt had taken to slaughtering considerable numbers of banthas in their rituals. However, some of these banthas were the bonded mounts of Tusken Raiders, who were angered at the deaths of their beloved animals. Although the Tusken Raiders could not prove the Weequays were to blame, Jabba kept the peace by making it appear as if local humans were behind the deaths.

While it might seem incongruous, there have been Weequay Jedi. Sora Bulq was a well-known Jedi at the time of the Clone Wars, even though his own people would not have been able to identify him by name. While the rest of his species relied on their Quay totems to guide their lives, Sora, raised in the tradition of the Jedi from infancy, saw them as little more than gambling baubles in comparison to the Force. Private notes recorded by Bulq were discovered in Jedi Holocrons in the years following the rise of the new Jedi order. In these, Bulq stated a firm belief that a good number of his people held the potential for Jedi training, but were hopelessly inhibited by their cultural mores. While Bulq might have worked to bring his species to a higher level of development, during the Clone Wars he unfortunately fell under the influence of the dark side before he was ultimately slain by the Jedi Quinlan Vos.

Other Weequay Jedi played an important part during the Clone Wars. Que-Mars Redath-Gom served faithfully during the final years of the Galactic Republic. He was killed in the Battle of Geonosis in the Petranaki Arena. Kossex, a female Weequay, was a Jedi Master who served at the Battle of Kamino as a starpilot. Because they were raised apart from their people, all of these Jedi demonstrated independence from the traditional reliance on the Quay totem that has so engaged their people. Sadly, this has made their memory largely unaccepted by the Weequay populace.

DESIGNATION
Sentient

HOMEWORLD
Sriluur

AVERAGE
HEIGHT
1.8 meters

PRONUNCIATION
Wē'-kwā

NOTABLE APPEARANCE
Episode VI: Return of the Jedi

Whiphids are tall, bulky bipeds with long yellow-white or golden fur. They live on the icy planet known as Toola, and are characterized by their prominent, hairless faces, which boast exaggerated cheekbones and forehead. Two tusks protrude from their lower jaw, and their two massive arms end in three-fingered hands with razor-sharp claws.

The bodies of Whiphids maintain a thick layer of blubber that traps heat in their system, providing protection from their cold environment. Their fur, which is covered with a natural oil, repels water so that they can swim in the frigid seas of their homeworld. In warmer settings, they will shed several centimeters of fur and burn off much of their fat, while their hollow cheeks widen, creating a broader face that serves to dissipate heat.

Whiphids are ferocious, carnivorous predators who have no greater joy than tracking something down to kill it. They have few principles and are motivated by their appetite for wealth and exotic cuisine. However, they exhibit pleasant, easygoing personalities, and when dealing with offworlders, they will take great care to determine who is proper prey and who is not. When encountered offplanet, Whiphids are usually involved in some sort of shady business dealings or are managing underworld operations. Nevertheless, there have been rare Whiphids able to overcome their natural instincts, as demonstrated by those few who traveled offplanet to become Jedi, such as Master K'Kruhk, who served the Republic during the Clone Wars.

On Toola, Whiphids live in nomadic tribes consisting of three to ten families. During the warmer months, these clans build permanent shelters of rocks, skins, and animal bones, to which they return each summer. In winter, the tribes migrate across the snowy steppes, following food and constructing temporary dwellings. They track the native grazing animals known as motmots by sniffing the air, and they are strong enough to slay the large creatures using only their bare hands and tusks. Most Whiphids, however, use spears, crude sabers, and clubs for hunting, carrying their kill on sledges. The most successful hunters, called Spearmasters, become the leaders of these Whiphid tribes, and thus determine where each tribe camps and what quarry it will hunt.

Toola's temperatures are rarely above freezing because of the planet's distance from its sun, as well as its thin atmosphere. The world does, however, have a brief summer when snow melts and plants can grow. If they haven't begun one already, Whiphids will start their families based on these seasonal changes. Most Whiphid children are born to their parents in the summer period, as they are frequently conceived during the cold winter months when more time is spent with loved ones in the protection of their interim shelters. The Whiphid gestation period typically equals the length of their winters, and there is a great celebration when all of the new children are formally introduced to others in the tribe. A grand hunt is conducted; the eating and celebrating can frequently go on for several days at a time.

Whiphid infants have no tusks for their first two years, though they do possess teeth enough to consume meat from the hunts. These children learn quickly to survive under harsh conditions, and require little instruction in order to grasp new concepts. They are shrewd and astute, much like their parents.

Whiphids entered galactic society when advanced species from dry, desert worlds arrived on Toola to harvest its ice in order to fulfill their water needs. Impressed by the technology and other conveniences the strangers brought with them, many Whiphids departed with the water harvesters to find work across the galaxy as mercenaries and bounty hunters. Others established businesses of their own after having learned the ways of offworlders.

One such entrepreneur is Lady Valarian, who made her mark as the owner of the Lucky Despot Hotel and Casino on Tatooine. Crafty and ambitious, not to mention intelligent, Valarian was able to avoid having her name associated with many of her more nefarious endeavors. According to the scant criminal records available, Valarian, the daughter of two gangsters, arrived on Tatooine planning to build her own empire. She ran into competition with Jabba the Hutt, and although the two negotiated a truce, each wanted the other out of the way, not caring much about how that happened. Valarian renovated a grounded ship and turned it into a thriving business, imbuing it with culinary and decorative themes unique to her native culture. Lady Valarian's luck proved better than Jabba's, however, when Luke Skywalker and his comrades disposed of Jabba during their rescue of Han Solo, further opening Tatooine for the Whiphid's exploitation. It is believed that after Jabba's demise, Lady Valarian assumed control of many of his criminal enterprises on Tatooine.

DESIGNATION
Sentient

HOMEWORLD
Toola

AVERAGE
HEIGHT
2 meters

PRONUNCIATION
Hwĭ'-pĭd

NOTABLE APPEARANCE
Episode VI: Return of the Jedi

WOOKIEE

Wookiees are intelligent, arboreal sentients from the jungle world of Kashyyyk. Possessing many natural strengths and abilities from the day they are born, Wookiees are known to be one of the most physically strong sentient species in the galaxy. They are also incredibly bright, with an extraordinary talent for repairing and adapting machines and technology.

Tall, hairy primates, Wookiees possess varying eye colors and fur that ranges in shades from white to light brown and black. Their fur is often a blend of different tones. They have retractable claws on their feet and hands, which they use almost exclusively for climbing. In their culture, employing their claws in hand-to-hand combat is forbidden, and is considered dishonorable or even insane behavior.

Wookiees are especially known for their loyalty and dedication to honor, as well as their capacity for great kindness, sharp wit, and friendship. They are devoted to friends and family, and particularly to those whom they owe a life debt. In the life-debt tradition—which is ironically similar to a tradition of their hated nemeses the reptilian Trandoshans—Wookiees pledge their existence and servitude to an individual who has saved their life, or who has given them another, similarly intense cause for loyalty.

Perhaps the best example in recorded history of the depth of a life debt is that of the one owed to Han Solo by the Wookiee warrior and Clone Wars veteran Chewbacca. While serving in the Imperial Navy, a young Han Solo aided in Chewbacca's escape from slavery, leading to his discharge from the navy. Chewbacca pledged him a life debt. The two became best friends, and over the decades, one was rarely seen without the other, with Chewbacca coming to Solo's rescue more than once. In an act of ultimate sacrifice, Chewbacca gave his life during an early strike by the Yuuzhan Vong, to save Han and Leia Organa Solo's son Anakin.

Wookiees are also known for having short tempers, especially when honor is at stake, and can fly into berserker rages if they, their families, or their "honor families"—those with whom they share a life debt—are threatened. They have a reputation for hostility, and have been known to smash objects and beings when angered.

Theirs is a cultured society, though, and they exist in harmony with the environment of their world, living in well-developed cities on the seventh level of vegetation on Kashyyyk, high in the wroshyr trees. Wookiee cities and homes demonstrate a deep appreciation for their environment. Constructed of native woods with sweeping, gentle lines, the Wookiees' structures seek to bring the outside, inside. Liftcars, held by unbreakable kshyy vines, carry Wookiees from one level to the next, although they can also climb up or down if they are so inclined. Though Wookiees wander the many upper levels of their planet, they rarely ever venture any lower than the fourth, given the many dangers the lower levels hold. Wookiees believe there are nightcrawlers that feast on the blood and spirits of their victims in the darkness of the bottomworld, and that the spirits of those who did not honor their life debts reside there, waiting to trap and kill the unsuspecting. Indeed, no Wookiee who has gone to the lowest level has ever returned. This region of Kashyyyk has yet to be a subject of scientific exploration. Kashyyyk does have several oceans, the beaches of which are the only areas on the planet where the soil is visible and accessible.

When Wookiees reach adulthood, they leave their families to explore the lower levels of the forests, particularly to hunt the dangerous quillarats that live just under the fifth level. These small, brownish-green creatures, standing only half a meter tall, have long needle-sharp quills covering their bodies, and can hurl these quills with deadly accuracy. Hunting on the lower levels represents a rite of passage for Wookiee adolescents known as the hrrtayyk, and is a long-standing and important tradition in Kashyyyk society. The hrrtayyk may be attempted alone, with an older relative, or with friends. For a successful passage, the adolescent seeking adult standing must return with physical proof of bravery: a trophy that may be displayed or worn. Following a successful return from the lower levels, a newly recognized adult Wookiee will often take on a new, more mature name. Under certain circumstances, hrrtayyk may also take place in other forms, sometimes even offplanet, as long as sufficient courage is demonstrated.

Feats of courage extend to Wookiee courtship rituals as well. Male Wookiees will hunt quillarats as an offering that they present when they propose marriage to a female. They must, however, catch the quillarat bare-handed, and kill it without using a weapon. If the female Wookiee accepts the proposal, she will show her approval by biting into the creature's soft underbelly. When they marry, Wookiees become mates for life.

Though Wookiees reside in a very natural environment, they are a mechanically advanced species, and a few thousand standard years before the Battle of Yavin they developed much of their own technology, constructing huge cities in the trees of their homeworld. They also developed high-tech weapons and tools unique to their own culture, the most famous of which is the bowcaster, or laser crossbow. Even the design of Wookiee weaponry captures their love of nature. Often curved and with housings made of wood, weapons such as Wookiee bowcasters can sometimes be mistaken for musical instruments by the uninitiated. They prefer, however, to use simple, homemade implements for accomplishing everyday tasks.

Because Wookiees are very protective of their natural home, they discouraged tourism to their world even as they themselves took to the stars. This greatly upset their Trandoshan neighbors, who had come to depend on tourism as a means of boosting their economy. This, combined with the Trandoshans' historical desire to colonize, soon drove the two peoples into a war that was eventually resolved by the Old Republic Senate.

Their Trandoshan enemies, however, were not impressed and bided their time to enact vengeance. With the emergence of Imperial rule, the Trandoshans suggested that the Empire use the powerful primate people as slave labor. The Clone Wars had barely ended before the Empire quickly overwhelmed the Wookiees, taking them to work in camps located throughout the galaxy. The prisoners helped—under duress—to build the Death Stars. But the Wookiees did not give in easily, and even those remaining on their home planet maintained an undercurrent of rebellion. The Empire made it virtually impossible for those Wookiees to leave their world, and enlisted Trandoshan hunters to capture any Wookiees who did manage to escape. For this reason, there remains quite a bit of animosity between the Wookiees and their Trandoshan neighbors.

Wookiees communicate via a system of grunts, growls, snuffles, barks, and roars, as the structure of their vocal chords and voice boxes won't allow them to speak Basic. For this same reason, humans find their language difficult to reproduce. Their primary dialect, used for trading and dealing with outsiders, is known as Shyriiwook, or "tongue of the tree people." There are various dialects, such as Xaczik, spoken by Wookiees indigenous to the Wartaki Islands. Because the Imperials thought all Wookiees were alike, they did not discover these other dialects, and when the Wookiees were enslaved, they often used Xaczik for delivering secret information to members of their resistance movement.

Today, Wookiees are an active member species of the Galactic Alliance. Now free of Trandoshan and Imperial oppression, they are open to share their innovative talents with the rest of the galactic community.

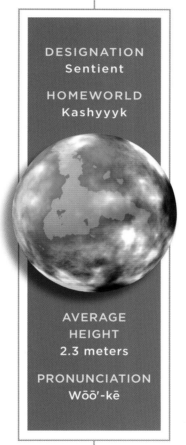

DESIGNATION
Sentient

HOMEWORLD
Kashyyyk

AVERAGE
HEIGHT
2.3 meters

PRONUNCIATION
Wŏŏ'-kē

NOTABLE APPEARANCE
Episode IV: A New Hope

XEXTO/QUERMIAN

Hexto are an arboreal species native to the Outer Rim planet Troiken, where they live in tree-based villages. They are the genetic progenitors of the long-necked Quermians, a resultant subspecies from the Arkanians' genetic experimentation in an illegal research project seventeen thousand standard years before the Battle of Yavin. Fearing legal repercussions for their work, the Arkanians abandoned their new creations to evolve on their own.

Both of these species grew to be technologically advanced by the time the New Republic discovered them. They each joined the Old Republic, rediscovering each other in the process. At first, the Xexto refused to acknowledge their genetic cousins, but when scientific proof of their evolutionary link was produced, they begrudgingly accepted it, though they chafed at the titles the Old Republic gave their races initially: Troiken Xexto and Quermian Xexto. While by and large the Xexto see the Quermians as a shadow of their own greatness, with the dawn of the New Republic, and subsequently working with them in various capacities in the fledgling government, they began to find a sense of common ground with their genetic cousins.

The Xexto have four arms, each with six fingers, and two legs with ten toes. Their skin ranges in color from pasty white to pale yellow. Similar in color, Quermians also have four arms but with fewer fingers. The Xexto and the Quermians have almond-shaped blue eyes and two brains, with one in their chest cavity. The upper brain controls their base emotions and body functions, while the lower controls creative thinking and logic. In their genetic alteration, the Arkanians gave the Quermian creations extra-long necks and moved their olfactory organs to one set of their fingers—the reason why remains a mystery. Quermians' facial expression is much more peaceful; they wear a pleasant smile all the time. Quermians also like to appear more human, keeping their extra set of arms hidden, while their Xexto cousins use their multiple appendages without reservation.

Like most arboreal mammals, the Xexto and their Quermian cousins bear their children live, one at a time. At birth, the children are born with all their limbs, but their necks are only slightly longer than that of a standard human child. As children grow, their necks increase in length, and their spinal columns and bone structure thicken to support the necks. While Xexto and Quermian adults can use their limbs independently, children usually use their hands in tandem for three to four years, unable to move them independently of one another. By the age of five, they fully develop the dexterity and mental capacity to grasp and use objects in their separate limbs. Prior to this, they tend to cling to others or stable objects with all their arms, a trait that xenobiologists believe comes from their arboreal beginnings. Many tree-climbing species cling to tree branches to feed on leaves, and their young hug their parents' necks or tree trunks until they are able to climb and make their way through the trees on their own. While this species left the trees long ago, children still hang on for support while their bodies and minds mature.

Personality-wise, the two species are similar in their calm demeanor, though the Xexto are more enamored of adventure and risk taking because of the harshness and danger of their home environment. The Xexto's lightning-fast reflexes, born of their arboreal ancestors' quickness in pursuing prey and avoiding predators, inspires them to compete in Podraces and games that feed their desire for exhilaration. It has been speculated that this interest in new thrills made them more likely to welcome the Arkanians. One Xexto historian records that mysterious visitors offered members of one community the chance to see a "whole new world," and they jumped at the chance. They vanished not long after and were thought lost. When the Xexto encountered the Quermians in the Old Republic, their conclusion was that their ancestors could not have known that they were to be genetic experiments—while they are adventurous, they are not willing victims. The best way to anger Xexto is to question their bravery.

Even so, both species are levelheaded and cool-tempered. The Quermians are more peaceful and contemplative, influenced, sociologists believe, by the beauty of their garden-like terraformed homeworld, Quermia. Unlike the Xexto, the Quermians did not need to fight to pursue their dinner. Quermians are therefore not as quick as their Xexto cousins and do not seek adventure. They prefer instead to solve problems through reason and logic.

In the Quermian physiology, however, there is a flaw that is not seen in their Xexto cousins. Because their mental abilities have been genetically altered, some Quermians are known to develop sudden psychoses, such as obsessive compulsive disorder, dissociative identity disorder, and the like. The development of the dissociative identity disorder often happens when one of their brains takes on one personality while their second takes on another—causing an internal battle in the individual. Because a Quermian's mental pathways are so complex, it can be a difficult condition to treat, and many of these unfortunate disorder victims commit suicide. Obsessive compulsive disorders, mean-

while, develop when both of a Quermian's brains process input in tandem rather than sequentially. While a Quermian's brain can perform most functions in tandem, input must be processed in order between the two brains. A system of retraining the brains has been useful in treating this genetic condition. In cases where a Quermian suffers from a malady of this sort, the onset of the disorder is usually triggered by a traumatic experience. One example of a Quermian suffering from this latter condition is Dr. Murk Lundi, whose overwhelming obsession with finding a Sith Holocron led to his death. His mental illness was triggered by incarceration.

While most Quermians do not develop such disabling disorders as those mentioned, they will usually have at least one mild phobia or minor compulsion, which will not be debilitating. These sorts of mental conditions seem to be well contained among Quermians who follow the Jedi path, as the training coaches them to deal with fears and habitual behaviors.

Quermians are also telepathic, and communicate by locking eyes with their fellows. Geneticists claim this is a result of their genetic manipulation, though it was a latent trait—one the Xexto could develop in time. When they joined the Old Republic, many Quermians became Jedi, which of course made their world a target during the rise of the Empire. Even non-Jedi Quermians were the victims of violence when Imperials incited mobs by spreading the misinformation that all Quermians were Jedi who could read minds and spread evil thoughts via telepathy. Those who could escape withdrew to their world, remaining in seclusion during Palpatine's reign. With the rise of the New Republic and the subsequent Yuuzhan Vong invasion, Quermians left their solitude to rejoin the galactic community.

Some of the greatest Jedi to come from the Quermian people are Yareal Poof, a member of the Jedi Council at the time of the Battle of Naboo who was greatly skilled in the art of battle meditation. This skill allowed him to give courage to his forces while weakening the resolve of the opposing army. Along with Poof, three other renowned Jedi served the Republic at that time—Loo Raelo, Kindee Ya, and Vinian Ska. All three were known to have great skill in telepathically based Force abilities like Yareal Poof, though little more is known about them. It is obvious to most scientists that Quermian mental abilities make for stronger Jedi—a trait their Xexto forbears have not achieved.

DESIGNATION
Sentient

HOMEWORLD
Troiken/Quermia

AVERAGE
HEIGHT
Xexto: 1.4 meters
Quermian: 2.4
meters

PRONUNCIATION
Zĕx'-tō
Kwer'-mē-ăn

NOTABLE APPEARANCE
Episode I: The Phantom Menace

YARKORA

2.0

1.5

1.0

.5

The Yarkora are rarely seen, appearing in the company of the lowest levels of galactic society, particularly in the Outer Rim Territories. They are tall, bipedal creatures whose huge faces are characterized by two wide-set eyes, a large nose with a pair of unusually large nostrils, and furry whiskers that protrude from each cheek. They have the appearance of an ungulate species, though they do not chew their cud like unintelligent ungulates. They bear thick, heavy black claws on their three-fingered hands, and these indicate an ancestry that can be traced back to hoofed creatures.

Only one Yarkora has ever been examined by scientists (post-mortem) and much was learned of their physiology from that research. As mentioned above, they are an ungulate species, and while they do not chew their cud they have two stomachs. One stomach is always digesting food, while the other stores food to be digested. Yarkora, therefore, like to snack all day to maintain full capacity in both their stomachs. However, because they always have a food store, they can go a good amount of time without eating when necessary.

The Yarkora also have two pancreases, four kidneys, and three livers, and this system redundancy contributes to their longevity. All these organs keep their bloodstream free of corrupting toxins and carcinogens, producing very strong white blood cells. They very rarely die of natural causes, save extreme old age. And even after suffering violence, internal injuries are unlikely to kill them outright, as additional organs take over for any damaged organ. Yarkora also have a remarkably high tolerance for alcohol and other addictive substances. They do not tend to become addicted—as their bodies filter out the chemical that causes the addiction. The only thing that can decrease their long lives is regular smoking, as they do not have additional lungs. But they do not tend to smoke to excess because the addictive qualities of tobacco have no effect on them.

The Yarkora's eyesight is also very unique in that they are able to focus on the tiniest of objects over a distance of 1,600 meters. The inner lenses of the eye are able to focus in and out, almost like a camera zoom. It is believed the Yarkora's keen eyesight is pivotal to discovering some of the information they use for sale, bribery, and manipulation. They also use this ability to cheat at cards and other games of chance.

Their hearing works in a similar manner as they are able to isolate and pinpoint sounds within a morass of noise. Their aural talents allow them to overhear singular conversations within a 10-15 meter radius.

Their powerful senses, of course, tie into the focus of their entire culture. What little scientists have been able to glean about this people indicates that they seem to be obsessed with the gathering and controlling of information for their own gain. They are masterful at extracting information from others without revealing anything about their species, their history, or even their present agenda.

Most of the Yarkora seen in the galaxy are known to be con artists or criminals who prey on the gullibility of others. While members of the species tend to be rather unassuming, sentients who have encountered them have consistently noted that they seem to project an aura that makes others uncomfortable. They exhibit the ability to intimidate others, via either size or demeanor. Some scientists theorize that the Yarkora simply use their ability to observe and exploit a victim's own weaknesses, while recent discoveries of important Yarkoran documents indicate they may actually possess some sort of projected empathy.

While much remains unknown about the Yarkora, an archaeological dig on an as-yet-unnamed world in the Outer Rim yielded a buried settlement that belonged to a Yarkoran community. In this small settlement, collections of written and digital recordings were found, the most useful being the creations of one Yarkora named Saelt-Marae, who filled several journals with information spanning several hundred standard years—proving that these people are long-lived.

Saelt-Marae's journals contained many of his personal observations of the galaxy at large, information he used for bribery and intrigue. They also contained page after page dealing with his traditional courtship with his chosen mate—a courtship that took nearly two hundred years to come to fruition.

According to the journals, all Yarkora woo their intended through extended conversations that can be written or verbal, the topics of which must be examined from every possible angle. Through these conversations, the two come to know each other in a way that they feel is more intimate than simple physical gratification. A conversation on a single topic can take several years, and they are not allowed to start a new topic until the previous one has been exhausted. Saelt-Marae and his beloved continued their discussion as they traveled to different places in the galaxy, sending their discourse in information packets through the HoloNet. In face-to-face conversations, Saelt-Marae wrote of the ability he and his intended had to "read" and "speak" their feelings, not just through glances and body language but also through psychic means—though whether this is a unique latent Force ability or a trait of the species is unclear.

This cultural form of discussion and discovery explains why any Yarkora who have been encountered in the galaxy at large tend to be extremely tenacious about specific subjects, preferring to argue a subject to death over simply winning. It is just one more trait that observers feel make the Yarkora's presence unsettling at best—at worst, positively irritating.

Another characteristic revealed by Saelt-Marae's writings is that Yarkora bear their children live, one at a time. A female Yarkora can only bear children every fifteen standard years, and usually only one at a time, making their race very sparse indeed. Every female, therefore, must become a mother at some time in her lengthy life, to keep the species from going extinct. Because they come so few and far between, all Yarkoran children are treated as firstborns—they are doted upon and acculturated to be rather solitary. As a result, married couples usually do not share the same abode, but build dwellings next to or near the other's so they can have appropriate privacy. Families share meals together at one dwelling or the other, and children usually remain with their mothers—especially during the formative years—but overall, Yarkora prefer to live alone.

Several Yarkora helped the Rebel Alliance in gathering intelligence, but they were given a sizable salary for doing so. A few served the Empire, with some being discovered as double agents, selling information to both sides and making an admirable profit in the meantime. It is clear from his journals that Saelt-Marae is one of the latter. More Yarkora have been seen in the galaxy at large since the rise of the New Republic, the Yuuzhan Vong invasion, and later incursion by the Killiks, but their political interests remain a mystery.

DESIGNATION
Sentient

HOMEWORLD
Unknown

AVERAGE HEIGHT
2 meters

PRONUNCIATION
Yär-kōr'-ä

NOTABLE APPEARANCE
Episode VI: Return of the Jedi

YEVETHA

1.5

1.0

.5

0

The Yevetha were a highly xenophobic, reptilian species from the planet N'zoth in the Koornacht Cluster, an isolated collection of about two thousand stars that has yielded very little intelligent life in its system. This species was wiped out by the Yuuzhan Vong, who saw them as a threat to their planned dominion.

The Yevetha were thin, tall, bony humanoids. Males of the species had scarlet facial crests along their cheeks, jaws, and the tops of their heads. These crests swelled up when a male was spurred to violence, and their primary headcrest engorged when a male was prepared to mate. The females of the species exhibited no such features.

Yevetha had wide-set black eyes and retractable dewclaws, one on the inside of each wrist above six-fingered hands. Yevethan skin incorporated vestigial armor on the back of the neck and down the spine. Their brains were located in their thoraxes behind thick bone brain cages and a line of indentations along their temples contained fine hair cells that controlled auditory sensing.

Yevetha reproduced by laying eggs in "birth casks" or external wombs called mara-nas, often kept in special climate-controlled rooms. If the children remained in these birth casks past birth, the casks were then referred to as nestings. Unborn children were fed blood, which they absorbed through the eggshell. The mother's donated blood was preferable, though the blood of any Yevetha would do. Yevethan leaders often killed underlings and fed their blood to their unborn or nesting children in the casks. The victims considered this a great honor, and would often volunteer for such a death. Most male Yevetha lived day to day with the knowledge that, at any moment, a superior might kill them simply for their blood.

This biological need for blood was the central focus of the Yevethan culture and religious belief system, therefore they were constantly bent on violence to harvest blood. They were a dutiful, attentive, cautious, but fatalistic species shaped by a strictly hierarchical culture. A viceroy—called *darama,* or "the chosen one," because of his dual role as religious and political leader—headed the Yevethan governing body called the Duskhan League. He was at the top of a complex hierarchy, served by military leaders called primates and administrators called proctors. All of these obeyed him without question, and would eagerly have died for him. They were ruthless fighters, unwilling to surrender even in the face of certain defeat.

DESIGNATION
Sentient

HOMEWORLD
N'zoth

AVERAGE HEIGHT
1.9 meters

PRONUNCIATION
Yĕ-vē′-thä

The Yevetha did not fear death. In their legal system, a killing was only considered murder if an inferior killed his or her superior. As mentioned above, dying to feed a superior's children was considered honorable. When Yevetha of lower standing failed in a mission or caused dishonor upon their superiors, they were called *nitakka*—a word meaning "dishonored." The *nitakka* would kneel before their superiors and offer their necks to the superiors' dewclaws, hoping to die as sacrifices to the superiors' children—reestablishing honor upon their own families as well.

Until their contact with the Empire, the Yevetha believed they were the only intelligent creatures in the universe. Initially they submitted to Imperial rule. Then, around the time of the Battle of Endor, the Empire became lax in its control. Without warning, the Yevetha rebelled violently, slaughtering every human stationed on N'zoth, both military and civilian. They spent the next decade mastering Imperial technology, then struck out at neighboring systems to eliminate all non-Yevethan peoples in their sector. Twelve years after the Battle of Endor, the Yevetha began a "cleansing" known as the Great Purge, wiping out all non-Yevetha within the borders of the Koornacht Cluster. The New Republic sought to intervene diplomatically when Yevethan expansion threatened Republic-allied worlds, but the Yevetha attacked instead. The New Republic eventually fought them back, but it cost many thousands of lives and nearly toppled the fledgling government.

As a result of their experience with the Empire, Yevethan ethnocentrism became xenophobia, causing them to consider all other intelligent life morally and physically inferior. They abhorred contact with other species and would go to extreme measures to avoid alien contamination, engaging in intense purification, bathing, and disinfecting procedures if they spent time in close quarters with outsider "vermin." They found the smell of other species distasteful, and claimed that without bathing or purifying themselves, they could still smell the stink of other beings on their own persons.

Yevethan xenophobia was so extreme that even in the shadow of the Yuuzhan Vong, they refused aid from any other galactic species. As a New Republic squadron commander, Jaina Solo reported in her logs that the very last of the Yevetha committed suicide by crashing his starship rather than be aided by her squadron.

NOTABLE APPEARANCE
Shield of Lies (novel)

YUUZHAN VONG

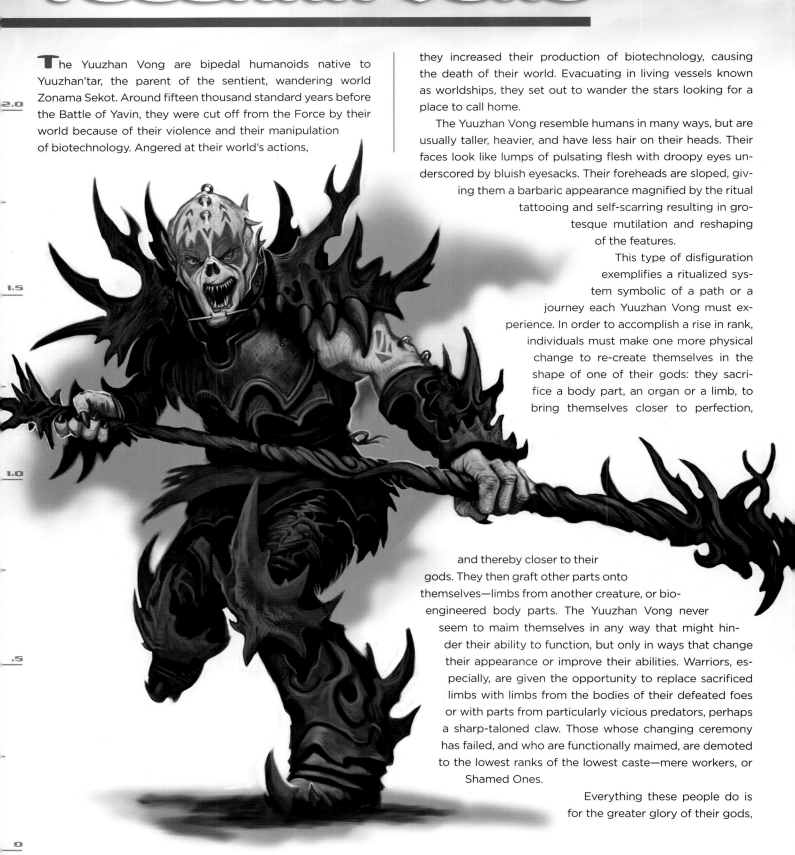

The Yuuzhan Vong are bipedal humanoids native to Yuuzhan'tar, the parent of the sentient, wandering world Zonama Sekot. Around fifteen thousand standard years before the Battle of Yavin, they were cut off from the Force by their world because of their violence and their manipulation of biotechnology. Angered at their world's actions, they increased their production of biotechnology, causing the death of their world. Evacuating in living vessels known as worldships, they set out to wander the stars looking for a place to call home.

The Yuuzhan Vong resemble humans in many ways, but are usually taller, heavier, and have less hair on their heads. Their faces look like lumps of pulsating flesh with droopy eyes underscored by bluish eyesacks. Their foreheads are sloped, giving them a barbaric appearance magnified by the ritual tattooing and self-scarring resulting in grotesque mutilation and reshaping of the features.

This type of disfiguration exemplifies a ritualized system symbolic of a path or a journey each Yuuzhan Vong must experience. In order to accomplish a rise in rank, individuals must make one more physical change to re-create themselves in the shape of one of their gods: they sacrifice a body part, an organ or a limb, to bring themselves closer to perfection, and thereby closer to their gods. They then graft other parts onto themselves—limbs from another creature, or bio-engineered body parts. The Yuuzhan Vong never seem to maim themselves in any way that might hinder their ability to function, but only in ways that change their appearance or improve their abilities. Warriors, especially, are given the opportunity to replace sacrificed limbs with limbs from the bodies of their defeated foes or with parts from particularly vicious predators, perhaps a sharp-taloned claw. Those whose changing ceremony has failed, and who are functionally maimed, are demoted to the lowest ranks of the lowest caste—mere workers, or Shamed Ones.

Everything these people do is for the greater glory of their gods, as they follow their path of conquering and dominating the galaxy, re-creating it—like their own bodies—in the image of their gods.

Yuuzhan Vong warriors will not surrender to an enemy under any circumstances, for fear of insulting their gods. They use bioengineered weapons, tools, and ships to further their cause, and they find the use of actual machinery extraordinarily offensive. They refer to those not of the Yuuzhan Vong as infidels, and take perverse pleasure in their own pain and in the pain of others. An attack on their pride is cause for a death duel, which also can be considered a sacrifice to their gods. To die in battle is among the highest honors they can achieve.

Yuuzhan Vong society is divided into regimented levels or castes, ruled by a supreme overlord. The Yuuzhan Vong people look upon the supreme overlord as a god, for if his victories become legend he will, in their belief, become a god. It is a common belief that the supreme overlord speaks to the gods directly, so his orders are never to be questioned—only obeyed. The other castes include priests, shapers, warriors, intendants, and workers. While a person's caste is usually determined by birth, some have risen out of their assigned caste through marriage. More often, however, priests and warriors fall out of favor and end up a part of the intendant caste, or even as low as the Shamed Ones.

Members of the priest caste are responsible for communicating the will of the gods to the people and act as advisers to the supreme overlord and the warriors. The shapers, meanwhile, create all the weapons and tools the Yuuzhan Vong use in their conquest based upon a very stringent set of religious guidelines. Ignoring even one of these guidelines is heresy, and will engender a swift and brutal penalty. Warriors comprise the caste most frequently encountered in the galaxy. They are vicious fighters who will fight to the death with religious zeal. The highest-ranked warrior is the warmaster, followed by the supreme commander, commander, subcommander, subaltern, and warrior.

Intendants, meanwhile, care for the shapers' creations and maintain supply lines during an invasion. Intendants also work as spies, excelling in subterfuge and deception—tasks below the honor of a warrior.

The lowest caste, the workers, perform the least desirable tasks in a military culture. They also care for the shaped creatures, and harvest the equipment. Workers are made up of those born to that caste, those who have fallen from other castes, enslaved peoples, and Shamed Ones—Yuuzhan Vong whose bodies reject the grafting on of new limbs or organs, or who are deformed.

The Yuuzhan Vong consider all other sentient life-forms to be inferior to themselves, therefore their modus operandi is to enslave or eliminate lesser beings. They consider most species unworthy of slavery, but those who fight back courageously are given a swift, merciful death. In their goal of conquest, the Yuuzhan Vong are inspired by their worship of Yun-Yammka, the Slayer. It was in deference to his commandments that they extended their armies across the galaxy, led by their vanguard force the Praetorite Vong, in the hope of bringing all other beings under their rule or destroying them.

All Yuuzhan Vong weapons, equipment, tools, and clothing are bioengineered organic life-forms. Their ships, for instance, are propelled by dovin basals, living gravity-well projectors, which create warps in space–time to move their ships through hyperspace. Using many dovin basals in concert, the Yuuzhan Vong are able to even move a whole planetary body from its nestled gravitational orbit, as evidenced by the crash of the moon Dobido into its planet, Sernpidal.

The Yuuzhan Vong are unique in that the Jedi cannot sense them through the Force. Luke Skywalker, the Yuuzhan Vong heretic shaper Nen Yim, and a Yuuzhan Vong priest named Harrar discovered that because their homeworld, Yuuzhan'tar, cut the Yuuzhan Vong off from the Force, they are completely devoid of it. As a result, they do not believe it exists, mocking those who do. In fact, Yuuzhan Vong hate Jedi more than any other galactic residents. They receive great honor for killing one.

As the New Republic was beginning to take hold, scout ships reached the known galaxy and set plans in place for invasion. Twenty-five standard years later, the Yuuzhan Vong swept into the galaxy, destroying and conquering everything in their path, eventually claiming Coruscant at the galactic center. With their strange weaponry, brutal tactics, and religious zeal, they took the New Republic completely by surprise, murdering countless thousands of people and demolishing system upon system in the name of their gods. Their conquest ended at Coruscant when Zonama Sekot finally took them as her own, realizing this was the only way to end the bloodshed and teach the Yuuzhan Vong a new way to live—one that transcended pain and violence.

DESIGNATION
Sentient

HOMEWORLD
Yuuzhan'tar

AVERAGE HEIGHT
1.8 meters

PRONUNCIATION
Yōō'-zän Vŏng

NOTABLE APPEARANCE
Vector Prime (novel)

ZABRAK

The Zabrak, also known as Iridonians, are a humanoid species native to the inhospitable world of Iridonia in the Mid Rim—a world of dangerous stalking predators, deep canyons, fierce winds, and acidic seas. Zabrak resemble humans, though their heads are crowned with varying patterns of vestigial horns. For both males and females, horns begin to grow at puberty, and signal the time that their rite of passage is near. Like humans, Zabrak have different skin colors, but these hues are the result of genetic dominance. The variety of colors include a peachy white, tan, brown, and black, with many tonal shadings. Zabrak can also grow hair or be completely bald, depending on subspecies. Horn patterns are often linked with hair growth (or lack thereof). Hair colors are similar to those of humans, although Zabrak do not have eyelashes, eyebrows, or any other facial hair. Zabrak eye colors are also analogous to human, though yellow, purple, red, and orange are also seen on occasion.

Zabrak wear facial tattoos made up of thin lines that they receive during their rite of passage. These tattoos can be symbolic of many things, such as family lineage or where they came from, or a personal design of their own. The Zabrak Sith Lord Darth Maul had black tattoos placed upon his red skin that had special Sith significance.

Zabrak are a self-assured people, confident that they can attain any goal they set out to achieve. To some they seem single-minded, being usually focused on one given idea, concept, or task at a time—with the conviction to accomplish their goal successfully. While with others such confidence might lead to prideful superiority, it isn't within a Zabrak's nature to denigrate other species. All Zabrak demonstrate great pride in their home colony, and while there is some competition among these colonies, intra- or extracultural insults or fights are not common occurrences without extreme provocation. On the contrary, most Zabrak are proud of their species' diaspora, believing that their varied colonies and experiences add to their species' overall value to the galaxy as a whole. The motivation to make a contribution to the greater good is a driving force for many Zabrak.

With instincts developed by tolerating their homeworld's environment, they are renowned

1.5

1.0

.5

0

warriors and explorers. Before colonizing other worlds, Iridonian clans fought continual wars to hone their skills in martial arts, and the Sith made lucrative contacts on the high council of their world, spending exorbitant sums to hire the talents of Iridonian mercenaries. While the Sith as a culture are long gone, the war-like influence remains a part of Zabrak culture, as they are still fierce, proud warriors—particularly those from Iridonia.

Zabrak from Iridonia are culturally distinctive from their fellows from the colonies. They are more war-like overall than their cousins, and more focused on developing and passing on martial art skills to the young. Study in the martial arts is a requirement at every Iridonian school, and those who excel in their training are sent to schools centered on the martial arts for advanced training. Some of the finest hand-to-hand combatants in the known galaxy come from Iridonia. Some speculate that the species' concentration on the martial arts came from its historical connection to the ancient Sith, but the Zabrak maintain it developed from the survival and hunting needs of the people. Wealthy Zabrak from other colonies will often send their children to Iridonia to study the traditional martial arts. Zabrak also ride Iridonian reeks as battle mounts and use quarterstaffs—a skill Darth Maul adapted to accommodate his double-bladed lightsaber.

The traditional Zabrak quarterstaff is known as a zhaboka, which according to Zabrak lore, started as a simple wooden stick with metal blades attached to both ends. The modern zhaboka is 2 meters long with a detachable central grip, and the ends are made from finely tempered durasteel. As befitting a warrior culture, Zabrak have one of the best reputations in the galaxy as weaponsmiths. They are known for producing some of the most reliable and powerful blasters available, along with vibroblades of uncommon quality. Zabrak weapons are valued by collectors and for personal defense, but as they are not mass produced, they are not widely used by military forces except in specialized units, such as snipers and reconnaissance.

Zabrak from other worlds exhibit a drive for excellence similar to that seen among Iridonian Zabrak, but if they do not send their children to Iridonia to study, they encourage their children to succeed in other ways. As a result, Zabrak have become highly successful in many fields, from medicine to entertainment. In addition, several Zabrak have joined the Jedi Order, and two Zabrak Jedi Masters served on the Jedi Council of the Old Republic.

DESIGNATION
Sentient

HOMEWORLD
Iridonia

AVERAGE HEIGHT
1.8 meters

PRONUNCIATION
Ză'-brăk

The Zabrak were an early spacefaring race who colonized many worlds, primarily because the Iridonian environment was so hostile. As a result, most Zabrak identify themselves by their colony world and not by Iridonia itself. They are a strong-willed people who resisted Imperial domination and are known for their incredible willpower. They are able to endure intense physical pain and torture without breaking their resolve. For this reason, Zabraks made terrible slaves, and the Imperial governors who tried to conquer them faced strong, united opposition from underground movements. They are stubborn almost to a fault, though it was this and their resolve that gave them more independence during the dark years of the Empire. Despite being made examples of for other races, having their worlds garrisoned and their industrial base largely destroyed, and being taxed into poverty and denied medical care to the point of genocide, the Zabrak resisted.

The Zabrak drive for self-determination and independence has its basis in a deep respect for life, despite their long and rich martial history or, perhaps, because of it. Zabraks were active in the galactic species rights movement even before their species was targeted by the Empire. During the Clone Wars, Kaysil Verwood was a driving force behind the Refugee Relief Movement, or RRM, and served as its chief spokesbeing. The RRM campaigned strenuously for persons displaced by the hostilities between the Old Republic and the Separatists, encouraging the failing Republic to provide safe havens for those rendered homeless by the war. After Palpatine disbanded the Senate and declared himself Emperor, Verwood recognized that she would become a target of Palpatine's assassins, both for her work on species rights and for her marriage to a human. She and her sister, Elibet Dav, were among the first Zabrak to join the Rebel Alliance, where Verwood used her contacts to create an underground network for the relocation of beings who escaped from forced slavery to the Empire. Verwood later served as the first Zabrak representative to the Galactic Caucus of the New Republic. The Zabrak people quickly joined the fledgling government as a single entity, vowing never again to face the oppression they suffered under the Empire.

NOTABLE APPEARANCE
Episode I: The Phantom Menace

ADDITIONAL SPECIES OF NOTE

ALEENA

Small in stature, the Aleena make up for what they lack in size by sheer courage and spirit. Diminutive reptilians with blue skin that dulls slightly as they age, Aleena have two eyes, flat, broad noses, an almost human mouth that seems up-turned in a perpetual smile, and elongated skulls that sweep backward from their faces. Fiercely devoted to their families, they often travel as a unit when found off their homeworld. Originally from the Inner Rim world of Aleen, they grow up in a harsh and difficult environment that demands quick re-flexes and even quicker reactions. Aleena have evolved a me-tabolism that allows them to process food for energy more quickly than most species. This enables them to escape from extremely fast predators on their homeworld known as sag-catchers. However, the Aleena diet itself is not very enticing, as it is unvaryingly spicy, which over time numbs the taste buds of those who consume it.

The quick reflexes of the Aleena have led several to success on the Podracing circuit—although they are also responsible for Podracing being banned on several worlds. When the Podracer Ratts Tyerell died in the Boonta Eve Classic (the same race that freed young Anakin Skywalker from slavery), his family was there to mourn him, having traveled to Ta-tooine for the race. In the ensuing years, Ratts's son Deland "Pabs" Tyerell began the Ratts Tyerell Foundation, which campaigned for Podracing to be outlawed. Successful on some worlds, it was rumored that the campaign was a cover for the government to crack down on nonhuman activities, but this was denied repeatedly by Old Republic officials speaking on behalf of (then) Chancellor Palpatine.

DESIGNATION: SENTIENT
HOMEWORLD: ALEEN
AVERAGE HEIGHT: 80 CENTIMETERS
PRONUNCIATION: Ä-LĒ'-NÄ

NOTABLE APPEARANCE: EPISODE I: THE PHANTOM MENACE

ANX

A particularly tall species native to the low-gravity planet Gravlex Med in the Mid Rim, the Anx have long necks and equally stretched-out heads, ending at a crest at the top and a pointy chin. The top crests on Anx's heads are actu-ally sinus cavities, which gives them booming low-frequency voices, able to be heard by other Anx even kilometers away. Suffering from extremely poor eyesight, the Anx sense of smell has grown very sensitive through evolution. In addi-tion, the Anx have large, muscular tails, which they need to counterbalance their height.

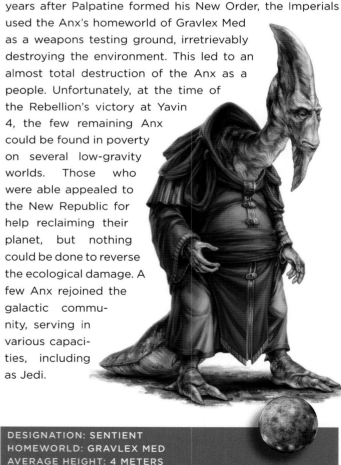

Anx are renowned for their calmness and serenity. They were leaders in the Galactic Senate during the Old Repub-lic, joining the call for peace along with Bail Organa. In the years after Palpatine formed his New Order, the Imperials used the Anx's homeworld of Gravlex Med as a weapons testing ground, irretrievably destroying the environment. This led to an almost total destruction of the Anx as a people. Unfortunately, at the time of the Rebellion's victory at Yavin 4, the few remaining Anx could be found in poverty on several low-gravity worlds. Those who were able appealed to the New Republic for help reclaiming their planet, but nothing could be done to reverse the ecological damage. A few Anx rejoined the galactic commu-nity, serving in various capaci-ties, including as Jedi.

DESIGNATION: SENTIENT
HOMEWORLD: GRAVLEX MED
AVERAGE HEIGHT: 4 METERS
PRONUNCIATION: ĂNKS

NOTABLE APPEARANCE: EPISODE I: THE PHANTOM MENACE

ASKAJIAN

Askajians are a portly humanoid species that seem to be misunderstood by the galactic populace at large. Only recently brought into the galactic arena, they are peaceful and unsophisticated, preferring a life spent at home with their children.

Due to their bulk, they are often dismissed as corpulent, unattractive humans. However, their appearance is due to the ecology of their homeworld, which is an arid desert planet where water is scarce. The Askajian biology, therefore, is specially adapted to hoard water in epidermal sacs that help them survive long periods of time without moisture. When they are in less hostile environments, Askajians can be far slimmer. They can expend up to 60 percent of their stored water without detriment to their health.

The planet Askaj is a desolate world on the Outer Rim, far off the path of the Rimma Trade Route. By and large, Askajians are a primitive people with almost no technology. They live in tribal societies with no central form of political government. Each tribe consists of an extended family community of hunters and gatherers, and is headed by a chieftain whose role is imparted by bloodline. A male typically holds this position, but sometimes a female will rise to this rank in the absence of a male heir. At times, tribes will band together in alliances to war with other tribal groupings, usually over water or hunting rights.

Askajian females give birth to sets of up to six children at a time. They refer to their children as cubs, and each female possesses six breasts with which to nurse her multiple offspring. According to long-standing Askajian tradition, cubs are not given names until their first birthday. When names are conferred, they are chosen with great care, as they are believed to be a harbinger of the cub's future. Names are selected by the parents in consultation with the tribe's shaman or shamaness to reflect the parents' and tribe's hopes for the cub, and to please their primary deity, the Moon Lady.

Dancers maintain a religious role as the keepers of a tribe's history and lore, serving as shaman or shamaness. While all members of the tribe hunt and gather food and handle day-to-day living chores, dancers are considered the spiritual leaders. Their primary functions are to advise the chieftain and to perform and pass on the history of their tribe. As spiritual leaders, they lead the group in worship of the Moon Lady.

Life in these tribal groupings centers on the migration of the tomuon, large woolly herbivores that populate the more habitable regions of Askaj. Askajians use tomuon for everything to benefit their lives—wool for clothing and other fabric essentials, meat, milk, fat for soap, hooves and bones for tools and adhesive, and so forth.

Askaj's main trade and the basis of its economy is the sumptuous and elegant fabric woven by Askajian artisans. This elevates the weaver to a role of prominence within the tribe. Created from wool shorn from namesake animals, tomuon cloth is soft, warm, and wrinkle-resistant, making it highly desirable in the Core Worlds of the galaxy. The weavers' technique is shrouded in secrecy, as master weavers take few apprentices and train them in closely guarded quarters. Weaving skill is so valued that wars have been fought to capture skilled weavers from other tribes. It is even rumored that Emperor Palpatine favored tomuon wool for his personal wardrobe.

DESIGNATION: SENTIENT
HOMEWORLD: ASKAJ
AVERAGE HEIGHT: 1.6 METERS
PRONUNCIATION: ĂS-KĀ'-JĒ-ĂN

NOTABLE APPEARANCE: EPISODE VI: RETURN OF THE JEDI

BARAGWIN

Baragwin are a hunchbacked, saurian humanoid species. They are bipedal, with thick, three-fingered hands, stocky bodies, and heads nearly as wide as their shoulders. There are no obvious differences between males and females. They have thick wrinkled hides in various muted medium to dark green shades. Baragwin are among the species with highly developed senses of smell, able to detect emotions simply from a being's odor. Baragwin are typically treated as less intelligent than other species due to their lumbering gait and ponderous mannerisms, but they are in fact highly intelligent. They generally do not correct these misperceptions, which they use to their own advantage.

Although not particularly numerous, Baragwin are found on many worlds throughout the galaxy. However, their planet of origin has long since been forgotten, even by the Baragwin themselves. Possibly one of the first species to achieve spaceflight, the Baragwin have been travelers so long that no one remembers from where they came. However, the Baragwin have been noted throughout recorded history for their talent as weaponsmiths and armorers. They are particularly renowned for their weapons customizations, creating weaponry for species that may not have the limbs or appendages to use such devices without modification. The Baragwin maintained ties to the Empire and then the Imperial Remnant for many years, even after the Battle of Endor. This relationship continued until Imperial Intelligence Director Ysanne Isard developed and released the Krytos virus on Coruscant, targeting nonhumans. The Baragwin community suffered significant casualties, and the Baragwin switched their allegiance to the New Republic.

DESIGNATION: SENTIENT
HOMEWORLD: UNKNOWN
AVERAGE HEIGHT: 2 METERS
PRONUNCIATION: BÄR'-Ä-GWĬN

NOTABLE APPEARANCE: EPISODE VI: RETURN OF THE JEDI

COLO CLAW FISH

One of the more ferocious predators on Naboo, the colo claw fish is an extremely long sea serpent, with a powerful hinged snout that contains sharp, pointed teeth. Four-legged, the colo claw fish's front set end in claws capable of rending flesh. From its tail, jagged protrusions jut out as potential weapons against prey. Colo claw fish are aquatic carnivores, hiding in underwater tunnels and caves near Naboo's core to hunt. These fish stalk potential prey with great patience, waiting hours for a meal to pass by a hiding spot. Their mottled greenish brown skin helps them blend in with their surroundings, making them invisible to unsuspecting prey.

When it spots its quarry, a colo claw fish will spring from its lair with astonishing speed, capturing its victim in its huge pectoral claws. It then disorients its prey with a hydrosonic shriek produced by structures in its head and throat. Prior to consuming its meal, the claw fish incapacitates its victim with poison emitted through its fangs. Claw fish can dine on creatures of surprisingly large sizes, swallowing them whole—their jaws are hinged, and their luminescent skin expands to allow for large meals. Unfortunately for the victim, a claw fish's stomach acids are not very strong and food is digested very slowly, in a fashion similar to the Sarlacc (although not as long as the Sarlacc's estimated thousand-year digestive cycle).

Colo claw fish have been cloned successfully on Kamino. The saberjowl is a more vicious and adaptable hunter than its progenitor. Otherwise, saberjowl are physically the same as their Naboo cousins, except that the saberjowl's skin tends to be green or greenish blue.

DESIGNATION: NONSENTIENT
HOMEWORLD: NABOO
AVERAGE LENGTH: 40 METERS
PRONUNCIATION: CŌ'-LŌ CLÄW FĬSH

NOTABLE APPEARANCE: EPISODE I: THE PHANTOM MENACE

DACTILLION

Utapau is home to the carnivorous reptavians called dactillions. Domesticated as mounts by native Utapauns, these four-winged creatures are capable of flight. As old a species as the Utapauns (if not older), dactillions are natural predators that in fact once preyed on the Utapauns themselves, during the Utapauns' prehistoric evolutionary period. Dactillions are by nature solitary and nomadic. The Utai first domesticated the genetically related varactyl, but the dactillion was tamed not long after when the Utai discovered that they could gain loyal mounts to take them beyond their sinkholes by providing dactillions with fresh meat.

Dactillions use their limbs to climb the cliff faces of sinkholes to get high enough to soar on rising thermal drafts. They hunt within the sinkhole, diving for grotto fish and other small prey and carrion. If the amount of food within a sinkhole dwindles or dactillions are seeking a mate, they fly to the surface, where they are able to ride the strong winds that buffet the barren Utapaun landscape.

Utapauns gained an understanding of their world's complex weather patterns by observing the flight and migration patterns of dactillions. The Utapauns realized that dactillions fly out of the sinkholes when the prevailing winds are at their weakest. This enabled Utapauns to predict the best times for their people to leave the sinkholes and work on their planet's surface, where they built windmills and other structures, harnessing the limitless wind power available to them.

DESIGNATION: NONSENTIENT
HOMEWORLD: UTAPAU
AVERAGE HEIGHT: 6 METERS
WINGSPAN: 24 METERS
PRONUNCIATION: DĂK-TĬL′-ÉL-ŎN

NOTABLE APPEARANCE: EPISODE III: REVENGE OF THE SITH

DRALL

The Drall are small, furry, bipedal creatures native to the planet Drall in the Corellian system. They have large, black eyes and a gentle countenance, leading many people to perceive them as cuddly pets. In actuality, the Drall are members of an intelligent and highly dignified species who bristle at that perception. They do love learning about others, however, and gossiping about their families—talking to anyone who will listen and asking many questions of their friends both Drall and non-Drall.

Drall society is a combination of matriarchy and meritocracy, in a clan-based organization. There are no elected or hereditary leaders on Drall; instead, each clan follows the dictates of its Duchess, a female appointed for life to lead due to her intelligence, wisdom, and experience. The clan Duchess is the owner of all a family's property, which she keeps until she steps down or appoints an heir. The closest the Drall have to a planetary leader is the most powerful and prosperous Duchess, whose example is followed as a matter of tradition.

Methodical and levelheaded, Drall are perhaps best known as excellent scholars and scientists. They are, by nature, abstract thinkers—preferring to develop new scientific theories rather than put them into practice. Therefore, despite their advanced status in scholarly pursuits, they often trail behind the galaxy in technological achievement. They usually implement technologies developed elsewhere.

Most Drall have positions that involve processing medicinal agriculture—Drall's primary industry. Although they are rarely seen elsewhere in the galaxy, offplanet corporations have hired Drall to serve as scientific researchers.

DESIGNATION: SENTIENT
HOMEWORLD: DRALL
AVERAGE HEIGHT: 1 METER
PRONUNCIATION: DRĂLL

NOTABLE APPEARANCE: AMBUSH AT CORELLIA (NOVEL)

FALUMPASET

Natives of Naboo, falumpasets are large mammalian omnivores that inhabit swamps in small herds of one bull and four to seven cows and their nurslings. They have long, stilt-like legs for wading and are superior swimmers, although they are not able to breathe underwater. Falumpasets eat plants and crustaceans found at the midlevel of Naboo swamplands. Individual falumpasets have unique bellows that allow them to be identified at great distances, and they tend to bellow most at twilight and dawn. The strongest beasts of burden on Naboo, falumpasets are intelligent and trainable, but sometimes ill tempered. Two specially trained handlers are required to properly control a falumpaset.

In addition to their use on many Naboo farms and as personal transports by important Gungan leaders, falumpasets are vital to the Gungan army. They are used in battle to pull war wagons filled with ordnance and to move war machines such as catapults into position.

DESIGNATION: NONSENTIENT
HOMEWORLD: NABOO
AVERAGE HEIGHT: 3 METERS
PRONUNCIATION: FĂL-LŬM′-PŬ-SĔT

NOTABLE APPEARANCE: EPISODE I: THE PHANTOM MENACE

FAMBAA

Like the falumpaset, the fambaa is a domesticated native of the Naboo swamps, and is also used by the Gungan army. Fambaa are the largest herbivores found in the Naboo swamps, and they are slow, clumsy, and not too intelligent, albeit even-tempered. However, they are extraordinarily strong and hardy creatures. Although amphibians, they have thick, scaly hides reminiscent of reptiles; these hides are soft upon hatching, hardening as they mature. Similarly, fambaa are born with gills that are absorbed as they age.

Fambaa are known to knock down trees to get at leaves, fruit, and berries, but they also are able to eat deep thick-stemmed underwater plants without difficulty. In the wild, fambaa will travel in herds of up to twelve creatures, although in captivity, they are corraled in groups of three. Main Gungan breeding herds are often so large that they are pastured in sacred areas of the swamps. The Gungan army uses fambaa to transport particularly heavy or cumbersome war matériel, such as the powerful shield generators and massive projectile weapons used on the battlefield. In addition, a fambaa's hide is used to produce the saddles used on kaadu mounts.

DESIGNATION: NONSENTIENT
HOMEWORLD: NABOO
AVERAGE HEIGHT: 5 METERS
PRONUNCIATION: FĂM'-BÄ

NOTABLE APPEARANCE: EPISODE I: THE PHANTOM MENACE

FLORN LAMPROID

Among the galaxy's most dangerous predators, Florn Lamproids are a warm-blooded snake-like species now known to be native to the planet Florn in the region of the galaxy referred to as Wild Space, although it was once thought they were native to many worlds. Evolved from intestinal parasites, their bodies are masses of gray-skinned, thick, heavily muscled coils with a loosely hinged jaw full of venomous fangs. Like the snakes they resemble, Lamproids' bodies are natural offensive and defensive weapons. Their tongues carry saliva poisonous to most other species, and they are able to use these tongues to smell. In addition, they have a barbed stinger that can be used to attack with astonishing speed. A hunter species, they use their coils to hold and kill captured prey. Lamproids are able to see using light sensors on the ends of eyestalks, often allowing them to escape other predators.

Thought to be animals by much of the galaxy, Lamproids are in fact sentient and quite intelligent. Additionally, there have been Force-sensitive Lamproids, and some do communicate feelings telepathically, although this is not known to be a specieswide trait. Florn Lamproids were Rebel sympathizers during the Galactic Civil War and often worked behind the scenes to recruit new troops.

DESIGNATION: SENTIENT
HOMEWORLD: FLORN
AVERAGE HEIGHT: 1.3 METERS
PRONUNCIATION: FLŌRN LĂM'-PROID

NOTABLE APPEARANCE: EPISODE IV: A NEW HOPE

GEN'DAI

The Gen'Dai are a mysterious and rare species with an extraordinarily long life span; some have reportedly lived for more than four thousand standard years. Their long lives may be attributed in part to unique nervous and circulatory systems that make them highly impervious to injury. The Gen'Dai nervous system consists of millions of nerve clusters spread throughout the body, which gives them extraordinary reflexes. In addition, Gen'Dai do not have a central heart; instead, an extensive vascular system distributes blood. Due to their lack of centralized vital organs, Gen'Dai can withstand multiple injuries that would kill most humanoids. Although it has never been verified, it is rumored that Gen'Dai are able to survive complete dismemberment. They are able to enter into a state of hibernation for long periods of time in which they heal wounds, cure diseases, and slow their aging process.

The Gen'Dai are a nomadic species who have wandered so long, their homeworld is no longer remembered. They are not prolific in terms of numbers, as they have a particularly low birthrate, perhaps a result of their long lives and regenerative abilities. However, this long life also causes their minds to weaken with age, and the Gen'Dai are susceptible to mental disorders such as depression, hysteria, and even forms of psychosis. It is most fortunate for the galaxy that by nature the Gen'Dai are not an aggressive species.

DESIGNATION: SENTIENT
HOMEWORLD: UNKNOWN
AVERAGE HEIGHT: 2.5 METERS
PRONUNCIATION: GĒN'-DĀ

NOTABLE APPEARANCE: STAR WARS REPUBLIC #51 (DARK HORSE COMICS)

GOSSAM

Gossams are a small saurian species native to the planet Castell in the Colonies region of space, not far from the Core Worlds. Known for their intelligence and cunning, Gossams have green scaly skin, wide yellow eyes, and heads that slope back on an incline. Balancing their thin bodies on three-toed feet like dancers on toe point, Gossams also possess three-fingered hands that are long and graceful, and like to wear elaborate clothing with platform shoes in order to appear more impressive when encountering other sentients. Female Gossams take great pride in their hair, molding it with oil-based creams to form sweeping sculptures. The traditional female hairstyle is a wave sweeping up from the back of their heads.

Like most reptiles, Gossams are hatched from eggs, which the female Gossams guard and preen over as status symbols. Being a species that is very appearance-driven, when eggs are about to be laid, Gossam families will construct elaborate nests of fancy warm fabrics and pillows to show off their progeny even before they hatch. They will also throw elaborate parties for "egg viewing"—wherein the eager parents receive gifts from their friends and relatives. Of course, the higher the status of the parents, the more exotic and expensive the gifts. These parties are usually thrown late in the eggs' incubation period in the hope that the eggs will hatch during the event.

Most Gossams are independent-minded, and yet many served as indentured servants to the Commerce Guild on Castell for a portion of their lives. This tradition came about when Castell was embroiled in a devastating economic depression. The depression became so severe, and life so harsh, that Gossams were slaughtering one another for necessities such as food, jobs, and passage offworld. In return for their servitude, the Commerce Guild rescued the world and the Gossams by buying vast tracts of Castell real estate and infusing their economy with large monetary investments. The world soon became a center point to the Commerce Guild's manufacturing operations, and the guild appointed a Gossam whom it had saved, Shu Mai, as chief of property resources after she rose through the corporate ladder. Shu Mai had thus managed to bring this world out of its financial slump through keen business acumen and shrewd negotiation tactics. She later repurchased Castell, but raised rents and demanded tribute from her people, leading to her further advanced standing within the Commerce Guild. Shu Mai was ultimately chosen as the guild's president.

Part of Shu Mai's solution to keep her people employed and fed was to offer contracts for them to serve the guild exclusively for a minimum of ten standard years, in return for food, housing, and a modest income. Once Castell grew out of its depression, the tradition continued, with most young Gossams taking indentured contracts to gain business experience before venturing out into the corporate world on their own. Gossams who were able to amass any amount of wealth largely invested those credits in offplanet banks, not trusting their own. Many Gossams established offworld estates for recreational purposes, with a large contingent choosing to settle on Felucia, and investing in local business ventures as a means of acquiring influence.

Gossams are therefore some of the shrewdest businesspeople in the known galaxy. Their products are often inexpensive to fabricate in mass, and overpriced. Gossams are excellent at bartering and working an angle that benefits them in the end. Their self-centeredness and greed know no limits—scheming to beat others out of every credit they can, and often lying and cheating to obtain what they want. Their word of honor means little, and anyone who does business on a verbal agreement with them is asking for trouble, as the Gossams put no value in it.

Members of this species who are seen throughout the galaxy can be legitimate merchants, or quite the opposite. Due to their industrial relationships with many offworld compa-

nies, most Gossams speak Basic, in addition to their own language. Many are involved in smuggling operations and piracy. Because of their size and calm demeanor, they are frequently underestimated—a perception they will always use to their advantage. However, Gossams generally do not rise to positions of power, with Shu Mai being one well-known exception. Their innate independence and greed seem to prohibit the long-range planning necessary to achieve true influence.

Although the Gossams raised military forces to support the Confederacy of Independent Systems in the Clone Wars, they do not have much of a presence in the galaxy in the post-Imperial era. Having allied themselves with the Commerce Guild and the CIS, the Gossams and their planet were a primary target of Palpatine's reign of terror against nonhuman species. The population was largely enslaved, and Castell's industrial base was repurposed to produce military goods for the Imperial Navy. This total societal takeover left the Gossams mostly unable to join the Rebellion in any substantive numbers. Although the Gossams later gained their freedom through the Rebel victory, their planet has yet to fully recover.

DESIGNATION: SENTIENT
HOMEWORLD: CASTELL
AVERAGE HEIGHT: 1.65 METERS
PRONUNCIATION: GŎSS'-ŬM

NOTABLE APPEARANCE: EPISODE II: ATTACK OF THE CLONES

KAADU

Kaadu are large flightless omnivorous reptavians native to Naboo, where they are the primary mounts used by the Gungans. Two-legged, kaadu have sharp hearing and a well-developed sense of smell. They also have bills containing short, sharp teeth (although they lack incisors) that can inflict a nasty bite if a kaadu is annoyed. Their stubbed tails counterbalance their heads.

Kaadu come in a variety of colors. The majority display a pattern of green shades, but they are also seen in blue, red, or a rusty yellow. Agile creatures, kaadu are extremely fast in even the thickest of Naboo's swamps and possess a great deal of endurance. They are also superior swimmers, and benefit from large compound lungs that allow them to breathe both on land and in water. Being surprisingly intelligent, courageous, and loyal, they make excellent mounts for their riders, whom they seldom abandon.

Their breeding grounds are protected because while adult kaadu are not in danger from natural predators, their eggs are. Kaadu eggs are a favorite of such predators as the peko peko, a flying creature that lives in the Naboo swamps. Kaadu eggs can be easy prey, as female kaadu lay them in elevated nests made of mud on the open ground. Not found on any world other than Naboo, Gungans raise kaadu from hatchlings, forming a lifelong bond with them. A well-trained kaadu is a prized animal, awarded to Gungan soldiers upon their elevation to officer.

DESIGNATION: NONSENTIENT
HOMEWORLD: NABOO
AVERAGE HEIGHT: 2.24 METERS
PRONUNCIATION: KÄ'-DŌŌ

NOTABLE APPEARANCE: EPISODE I: THE PHANTOM MENACE

KOUHUN

Kouhuns are small, silent arthropods from Indoumodo in the part of the galaxy known as Wild Space. They are deadly to almost all mammalian beings and creatures. Kouhuns are commonly seen in two varieties, one with a larger segmented body than the other, which in turn has a less pronounced stinger. Kouhuns have two means of carrying their venom to their prey, by either their tail stinger—which delivers a painful but nonfatal wound—or a fast-acting nerve toxin injected by pincers in their mouths, which kills.

Kouhuns are favored by many assassins and bounty hunters (at least those who don't mind a dead target) because they can by passed through even tight security and are nearly impossible to trace back to the person using them. Assassins often starve their kouhuns before they use them to attack a victim, which causes the kouhuns to head for the nearest warm-blooded life-form when released.

DESIGNATION: NONSENTIENT
HOMEWORLD: INDOUMODO
AVERAGE LENGTH: 30 CENTIMETERS
PRONUNCIATION: KŌ-HŌŌN'

NOTABLE APPEARANCE: EPISODE II: ATTACK OF THE CLONES

KRAYT DRAGON

Krayt dragons, are large, vicious, carnivorous reptiles that inhabit the mountainous regions of Tatooine's Jundland Wastes. They walk on four squat legs, at the ends of which are four-toed claws with sharp nails that can shred steel. Their sense of smell is activated by the flickering of their forked tongues, which, as in most snakes and reptiles, collect the smell for their nostrils. Like most reptiles, they are cold-blooded, and they shed their yellow-brown skin on a yearly basis. Unlike their lizard relatives, however, they continue to grow throughout their lifetimes, and do not weaken with age. An average krayt dragon can grow to be nearly five meters in length and weigh about two thousand kilograms. They can live to be a hundred standard years old.

Despite their ferocity, krayt dragons are often hunted by big-game hunters. Although hunting such creatures may not seem wise, the average krayt dragon's gizzard holds an incredibly valuable and beautiful dragon pearl. One pearl would easily make a person a millionaire; hence many foolhardy hunters try to obtain it. Not many have lived to talk about their experience.

High summer in the Jundland Wastes is the krayt dragon mating season. During this time, the mountains ring with their bellowed cries. Most intelligent beings refuse to venture into the wastes at this time, but those who do are very mindful of the sound, because a dragon in a mating frenzy will kill everything it can reach.

DESIGNATION: NONSENTIENT
HOMEWORLD: TATOOINE
AVERAGE LENGTH: 4.5 METERS
PRONUNCIATION: KRĂT DRĂ'-GŎN

NOTABLE APPEARANCE: EPISODE IV: A NEW HOPE

LANNIK

The Lannik are a small humanoid species native to the violent Mid Rim world with which they share their name. They have long ears that protrude from their skulls and are capable of rotating to register the faintest of sounds. Lannik's skin ranges in color from orange and reddish tones to purple and blue, and while they appear to be hairless, most of their hair normally blends in with the color of their flesh. Hair that is allowed to grow long is often worn in a topknot. Lannik's eyes are also commonly the same color as their skin, although variations have been observed. They are not very expressive, and are usually seen wearing what appears to be a grim scowl on their faces.

A dour expression fits the Lannik culture, for theirs is a long history of combat, with warrior skills honed both by hunting the ferocious predators of their world as well as by engaging in heated battles with one another. Their thin bodies give them a delicate appearance, but Lannik are more strong and agile than they appear. The females are usually thinner than the males, but this makes them no less hardy. Lannik are known to live hundreds of years if they are not killed in a physical confrontation, though early death is an unfortunate possibility for all Lannik. A period of military service is compulsory, and given the factions on their world, combat is an all-too-familiar presence in most Lannik's lives.

The Lannik are a fierce people—quick-minded, clear thinking, and prone to abrupt anger. They have little patience for outsiders who waste their time. Because of their forbidding expressions, non-Lanniks tend to view them as perpetually angry, a misconception that typically affords them a wide berth despite their diminutive presence. Lannik place great value on personal honor, bravery, and defiance in the face of incredible odds. While these traits would make them seem somewhat socially akin to human Corellians, the Lannik's focus on these attributes is the result not of a strictly cultural mind-set or bravado, but of their history as warriors experienced in strenuous and dangerous combat. Wounds suffered in battle are treated so that health may be maintained, but they are not hidden. It is not uncommon to see Lannik fighters with scars crisscrossing their bodies and faces, or perhaps missing a digit or an eye. To the Lannik, the remnants of wounds are a badge signifying personal accomplishment and survival, as opposed to something to be ashamed of.

When the Lannik were discovered by human and Duros explorers from the Old Republic, the arrival of products, technology, and forms of business sent their world into political and economic upheaval. Political factions arose, sharply divided and arguing bitterly regarding how the new technologies would be traded on their planet, creating a social instability that Lannik has never truly recovered from. Underworld organizations, seeing an opportunity to capitalize on the chaos, did just that, establishing contacts that would give them safe haven and encourage their burgeoning black-market businesses. The Core World governments, realizing how the sale of technology in particular had affected the world, tried to limit the sales of certain products on Lannik, but this action only served to make the underworld element more powerful.

Corellian diplomats soon endeavored to broker agreements with the Lannik in order to bolster a legitimate trade in technology with the Core Worlds, but the most powerful of the underworld organizations, terrorists known as the Red Iaro, tangled the process in bureaucratic wrangling within the courts. In the years after the Battle of Naboo, Red Iaro agreed to hold peace negotiations on Malastare with the legal Lannik government. In their most daring move, Red Iaro members actually plotted a complicated ruse to further their cause by killing the Lannik head of state, Prince R'cardo Sooflie IX, along with the Jedi sent to assist in treaty negotiations. Fortunately, the Lannik Jedi Master Even Piell managed to uncover and halt the scheme before it could succeed.

When the Empire rose to power, the flow of trade to Lannik stopped almost completely, throwing the world and its people into near obscurity. In the age of the Galactic Federation of Free Alliances, they are rarely, if ever, seen off their world, and the possibility of the Lannik ever entering into galactic trade or politics again remains remote. Their monarchical government is ruled by a prince whose only interests are to keep his world functioning and to continue the constant rebuilding of the species' economic structure.

DESIGNATION: SENTIENT
HOMEWORLD: LANNIK
AVERAGE HEIGHT: 1.2 METERS
PRONUNCIATION: LĂN'-NĬK

NOTABLE APPEARANCE: EPISODE I: THE PHANTOM MENACE

MASSIFF

Fanged reptiles commonly found in the Outer Rim (particularly on Geonosis and neighboring Tatooine), massiffs are domesticated as pets by Geonosian aristocrats and Tusken Raiders alike. To the Geonosians, massiffs are symbolic of their authority. They give them shelter in return for the massiffs' hunting of sand snakes and other vermin outside their homes. Like most reptiles, massiffs lay eggs in the soft, warm sand of the worlds they inhabit, and females guard their nests with an uncommon ferocity. Males hunt for prey as meals for their young and their mother, and they mate for life. Massiffs howl to other massifs as a form of instinctive communication. With thick hides in shades of brown, massiffs blend in with their environments. When attacking larger creatures, they will attack in packs and will stand on strong hind legs to reach a creature's more sensitive areas.

DESIGNATION: NONSENTIENT
HOMEWORLD: TATOOINE OR GEONOSIS
(UNKNOWN)
AVERAGE HEIGHT: 76 CENTIMETERS
AT THE SHOULDER
PRONUNCIATION: MĂ'-SĬFF

NOTABLE APPEARANCE: EPISODE II: ATTACK OF THE CLONES

MIDI-CHLORIAN

Midi-chlorians are microscopic symbiotic life-forms present in all living beings. When present in sufficient numbers, midi-chlorians allow a being to feel the Force. Furthermore, if that being is able to quiet his or her own mind, a greater level of communion with the Force is possible, in which the individual may know the will of the Force. Jedi have particularly high midi-chlorian counts; it is said that Anakin Skywalker's count was the highest ever recorded. Recovered Jedi journals from the time of the Emperor's rise reveal a suspicion that Anakin Skywalker may have even been conceived by midi-chlorians, and the name of his father was never recorded at the Jedi Temple.

In the years after the end of the Clone Wars, those Jedi who survived, along with the families of children whose parents feared they might have high midi-chlorian counts, took drastic measures to hide this information from Imperial forces. In the Imperials' hunt for the Jedi, mandatory blood tests for midi-chlorians were common on Inner and most Mid Rim worlds. This gave rise to a black-market trade in mostly ineffective blood products and drugs used to fool Imperial examiners, in addition to trade in forged identity documents. Although faulty blood scans and corrupt, bribe-taking examiners allowed many beings to slip through the Empire's grasp, many were also caught, taken into Imperial custody, and never heard from again.

> **DESIGNATION: SENTIENT**
> **HOMEWORLD: NOT APPLICABLE**
> **AVERAGE HEIGHT: NOT APPLICABLE—MICROSCOPIC**
> **PRONUNCIATION: MĬ'-DĒ-KLŌ'-RĒ-ĂN**

NOTABLE APPEARANCE: EPISODE I: THE PHANTOM MENACE

MUSTAFAR LAVA FLEA

Used by Mustafarians as a mount, lava fleas are giant, hard-shelled arthropods found in the northern areas of the volcanic world of Mustafar in the Outer Rim (the term *lava flea* is being used, as the Mustafarian name for this species is unpronounceable). Six-legged, these agile creatures can walk on crusted, cooled lava flows or jump over thirty meters of moving lava in a single bound.

Lava fleas evolved underground, like the Mustafarians themselves. They begin life as half-meter larvae with crystalline exoskeletons. Using acidic enzymes in their digestive tracts, the larvae draw nutrients from mineral-rich rock dust located in inner caverns of the planet. By the end of their first year of life, the larvae have grown to almost a full meter and have encased themselves in pupae for a monthlong period, from which they will emerge with their six legs. Young lava fleas are able to consume soft rocks directly from the cooling lava through an armored feeding tube. To protect their eyespots from the fiery environment, lava fleas have a nictitating eye membrane that closes involuntarily. Older lava fleas shed their protective shells, which were used by early Mustafarians as armor that allowed them to move beyond their caves to the planet surface in safety.

Lava fleas were so entwined in Mustafarian culture that when the Techno Union brought repulsorlift technology to the planet, the natives would not give up the mounts they had learned were worthy of trust. The lava flea is reliable and, unlike technology, does not break down. Attempts to import the lava flea to other worlds have largely been a failure, as the rock dust and lava on Mustafar contain unique nutrients necessary for the lava flea's diet, and these foodstuffs are too costly to ship offplanet or replicate using local materials. Furthermore, the materials cannot be recycled, as the metabolic process renders them useless. However, there are disturbing reports that lava fleas have been used in their acid-filled larval form as a means of torture and corpse disposal by crimelords and in less-than-reputable sectors of the galaxy.

> **DESIGNATION: NONSENTIENT**
> **HOMEWORLD: MUSTAFAR**
> **AVERAGE HEIGHT: 4.3 METERS**
> **PRONUNCIATION: MŌŌ'-STĂ-FĂR LĂ-VĂ' FLĒ**

NOTABLE APPEARANCE: EPISODE III: REVENGE OF THE SITH

MUUN

Tall, thin bipedal humanoids, Muuns are natives of the planet Muunilinst in the Outer Rim. They have elongated, featureless heads without visible nostrils; their skin is grayish. Muuns' circulatory system is unique in that they have three hearts. Extremely intelligent, Muuns tend to be greedy yet cautious when it comes to money. They will favor a calculated risk before a rash action. Muuns are extraordinarily talented at mathematics and statistics; in fact, mathematics is the basis of their written language. Spoken Muun is a series of *eh* and *um* sounds combined in varying pitch patterns similar to Binary Flash Code, a droid language. Muuns will rarely venture off their world, and when they do, it is usually to conduct business. While away, they experience a great deal of homesickness and think only of their return.

During the Old Republic, Muunilinst was the home of the InterGalactic Banking Clan. The Muuns poured their wealth into their largest cities, which were notable for their detailed and opulent architecture. Muuns were later one of the few nonhuman species to escape the oppression of the Emperor's human-centric New Order. This was due to their impressive financial skills, in that no others were deemed better managers of the galactic economy, and the Imperial government did not wish to draw upon itself financial reprisals. Muuns were given Imperial overseers to ensure that they were not directing funds into Rebellion coffers, but there was in fact little need for this—although Muuns are a greedy species, they approach financial matters with great integrity. Muuns served in this capacity well into the era of the New Republic. In recent years, the surface of Muunilinst was unfortunately destroyed in a Yuuzhan Vong planetary bombardment.

DESIGNATION: SENTIENT
HOMEWORLD: MUUNILINST
AVERAGE HEIGHT: 1.9 METERS
PRONUNCIATION: MŌŌN

NOTABLE APPEARANCE: EPISODE II: ATTACK OF THE CLONES

NAGAI

The Nagai are a bipedal, humanoid, warrior people, whose weapons of choice are daggers and knives. Tall, beautiful, and exceedingly thin, with straight black hair and pale, almost white skin, Nagai might fool an unaware observer into thinking they are delicate or weak. This is not the case at all, as Nagai warriors can be formidable. They are intense, focused, and very disciplined. Nagai are known to kill without hesitation if it suits them, particularly if honor demands it, but if there is no honor in killing, or if a foe is weak, they will take no pleasure from the victory.

The Nagai came upon the galactic scene following the truce of Bakura while fleeing their cruel oppressors, the Tofs. After centuries of brutality and oppression at the hands of the Tofs, Nagai are temperamentally ruled by two things: a deep sense of honor and fear of the Tofs. They fear little else. The Nagai have few loyalties other than their immediate families, but will let concern for others override their need for personal freedom. The Nagai once claimed to be from another galaxy, but Nagi, their homeworld, is actually in an uncharted star cluster on the fringe of the Unknown Regions. Many believed the Nagai were on a mission of conquest, when they were actually fleeing. This is because they spread this misinformation to other species to keep their homeworld a secret.

DESIGNATION: SENTIENT
HOMEWORLD: NAGI
AVERAGE HEIGHT: 1.8 METERS
PRONUNCIATION: NÄ-GÄ'-Ē

NOTABLE APPEARANCE: STAR WARS #91 (MARVEL COMICS)

NOSAURIAN

Bipedal reptiles from New Plympto in the Core Worlds, Nosaurians have four-fingered hands and three-toed, bird-like feet. Their heads are crowned by a row of horns, and they have long beaks. They have amazing reflexes, a trait that allowed them to participate in (and live through) many Podraces.

Nosaurians are color-blind, seeing only in black and white. However, they do not find this particularly bothersome and have adapted to it. Nosaurians are able to make the inside linings of their mouths phosphoresce at will. It is believed this is an artifact of evolution, as one theory asserts that Nosaurians descended from insect-eating reptiles who used the ability to lure prey. Nosaurians now use the ability as a signaling device to contact others in the dark forests of New Plympto.

Nosaurians speak their own native language whenever possible, a combination of barks, warbles, and hisses. Their written language relies heavily on metaphors related to nature, weather, and the seasons. Nosaurians are capable of speaking Basic, but prefer not to. One characteristic that distinguishes the personalities of most Nosaurians is that they hate humans, a holdover from their oppression under the

ONGREE

Very little is known about the Ongree, as they are not a prolific species. However, records indicate they are native to the Skustell Cluster in the Outer Rim. Ongree are bipedal, humpbacked, amphibious humanoids easily identified by their unique heads, which appear to most other beings to be upside down. They are sandy brown in color, with variations in shading among members of the species. Their mouths are on top of four nostrils, with their two eyes mounted on eyestalks coming out of the sides of their heads about half-way down their skulls, giving them a somewhat fish-like appearance. Ongree's eyestalks are flexible, and they can see

objects from many angles. Their hands have two thick fingers and opposable thumbs, so although Ongree don't have many digits, they are able to hold even small objects with ease. Surprisingly, given their somewhat awkward appearance, the Ongree are an agile species.

Ongree tend to weigh all possible perspectives before deciding on a course of action. They are accustomed to seeing things visually from all angles; perhaps this is a similar psychological trait. This tendency makes them particularly skilled

Empire. This deep-seated animosity may change, however, due to assistance offered by humans following the Imperial collapse; this is, of course, a slow change. The New Republic gave assistance to New Plympto to help the Nosaurians recover from their long years of occupation, although it could not repair all the damage done to the planet. Later, the Yuuzhan Vong released a life-consuming virus on New Plympto in retaliation for the Nosaurians' resistance. This virus rendered the planet uninhabitable and the subject of an ongoing quarantine. Most Nosaurians were able to flee the planet before the virus struck, and are being resettled on new worlds by the New Republic.

DESIGNATION: SENTIENT
HOMEWORLD: NEW PLYMPTO
AVERAGE HEIGHT: 1.35 METERS
PRONUNCIATION: NŌ-SÄ'-RĒ-ĂN

NOTABLE APPEARANCE: EPISODE I: THE PHANTOM MENACE

diplomats, politicians, and negotiators. Ongree served the Old Republic as best their numbers would allow. At least two Ongree Jedi served during this period, taking part in the Battle of Geonosis. However, their ability to see all sides of an issue also lead many Ongree into less-than-legal activities, consorting with crimelords and gangsters as quickly as they would influential members of mainstream society.

DESIGNATION: SENTIENT
HOMEWORLD: SKUSTELL
AVERAGE HEIGHT: 1.8 METERS
PRONUNCIATION: ÄNG-RĒ

NOTABLE APPEARANCE: EPISODE II: ATTACK OF THE CLONES

OPEE SEA KILLER

Opee sea killers are large, aggressive aquatic monsters native to the deep seas of Naboo, although a specimen is the largest animal on display at the Royal Icqui Aquaria on Coruscant. They are a combination of evolutionary traits of various animals. Growing to an average length of twenty meters, they have the large maw of a fish, but the eight limbs and thick armored body plates of a crustacean. Sightings of dwarf opee have been reported. Extremely territorial, opee sea killers are also very resilient, and on occasion have survived fights with much larger colo claw fish, most likely by using their sharp teeth as weapons. In fact, there are local reports of young opee sea killers even gnawing and clawing their way out of the stomachs of colo claw fish.

Opee sea killers hide among ocean rock formations while hunting, as do colo claw fish. Opees lure in prey, then chase it down, ensnaring it with their long, adhesive tongues. Opees get their great speed by using a propulsion system unseen in other animals. They take in water through their mouths and channel it outward through openings beneath their plates, creating an almost jet-like effect. In addition, opees are mouthbreeders: the female lays her eggs near a male, and the male takes the eggs into his mouth after fertilizing them. The eggs remain in the male's mouth for safekeeping until they hatch three months later.

DESIGNATION: NON-SENTIENT
HOMEWORLD: NABOO
AVERAGE LENGTH: 20 METERS
PRONUNCIATION: Ō'-PĒ SĒ KĬL'-LŮR

NOTABLE APPEARANCE: EPISODE I: THE PHANTOM MENACE

ORRAY

Geonosian beasts of burden capable of hauling heavy loads, orrays are large, tame animals that are also used as mounts by the picadors in the Geonosian arena combats. Omnivorous, with leathery skin, four legs, and great strength, speed, and stamina, they are well suited to the Geonosian environment. In addition, an orray's coloring allows it to blend in with the Geonosian landscape to hide from predators. Prior to their domestication by Geonosians, orrays hunted Geonosian eggs, which had been laid to begin new hives.

The orrays would push their long snouts into egg chambers and consume thousands of larval Geonosians in a single meal. As a holdover from that time, an orray's teeth are blunt enough to crush hard objects such as their eggshells. Orrays have potent tail stingers that they use as defensive weapons, but these are amputated when they are domesticated. The removal of the stinger makes orrays docile and much more manageable for their handlers.

DESIGNATION: NON-SENTIENT
HOMEWORLD: GEONOSIS
AVERAGE HEIGHT: 1.52 METERS
AVERAGE LENGTH: 3 METERS
PRONUNCIATION: Ō'-RĀ

NOTABLE APPEARANCE: EPISODE II: ATTACK OF THE CLONES

PACITHHIP

Natives of Shimia, located in the Outer Rim Territories near the Corellian Run, Pacithhips are plump humanoid pachyderms with wrinkled gray skin, long trunks, and thin, elegant tusks. Pacithhips have two eyes situated on the sides of their head, allowing a full 360 degrees of vision, and the back of their skull is protected by a bony ridge.

Pacithhip society is ruled by a rigid caste system that dictates whether an individual will be a scholar, a warrior, or a farmer. Membership in a given caste is determined by the shape of a Pacithhip's tusks, and because the tusks do not reach their full size and shape until a Pacithhip's adulthood, it is not known until then what caste they will belong to. Education and the law are the responsibility of the scholar caste; warriors enforce the law and defend the populace, and farmers provide food, clothing, and manufactured goods.

Starting with the era of the New Republic, Pacithhips were seen throughout the galaxy in increasing numbers, as their society supports and encourages those who wish to "find their own path." Pacithhips are innately rational and tolerant and enjoy meeting members of other species. In addition to their own language of Shimiese (a combination of snorts, trumpets, and intricate vocalizations), Pacithhips speak Basic easily. Also, they are able to adapt to a variety of climates and customs, making travel to new worlds trouble-free. Encountering Pacithhips on planets as diverse as Tatooine and Coruscant is not uncommon.

DESIGNATION: SENTIENT
HOMEWORLD: SHIMIA
AVERAGE HEIGHT: 1.5 METERS
PRONUNCIATION: PĂ'-SĬTH-ĬP

NOTABLE APPEARANCE: EPISODE IV: A NEW HOPE (SPECIAL EDITION)

RAKATA

Extinct for nearly thirty thousand standard years, the Rakata have a historical significance that warrants mention. As hyperspace travel originated approximately twenty-five thousand years ago, evidence of a species predating such a time period is usually limited to a planet of origin. The Rakata are the exception, as evidence places them on countless worlds. Among the facts being considered are a Rakatan temple found on Honoghr and a strange world steeped in the dark side located far beyond the charted area of the Outer Rim that cannot be examined, as a powerful energy field surrounds it.

That evidence is so scarce suggests a concerted effort was made to purge the Rakata from the galaxy. It is believed that at the height of their power, they formed an empire, and built the Star Forge, a dark side sun generator that was also a potential superweapon. Having gone too far, their subjects rebelled. The Rakatan Civil War ended when the Rakata were struck by a virus that local populations were immune to, and their subjects slew the few Rakata who survived on their worlds. Furthermore, use of the Star Forge on the Rakatan homeworld caused their sun to wither and die. It is possible that to avenge themselves, their former subjects attempted to erase their oppressors from history, destroying all the technology they used to oppress them and leaving them in a primitive state. Left in dwindling numbers, they soon became extinct.

Although the Rakata have disappeared, it is possible their influence is still present in the galaxy. It has been hypothesized that the Rakata may be responsible for altering the orbits of the planets in the Corellian system. Furthermore, Rakata warfare or failed terraforming efforts could be the cause of the cataclysm that turned Tatooine from an ocean planet to a desert world. It has been speculated that such an ancient species was responsible for widespread similarities among beings on far distant planets, as the Rakata would have brought colonists or slaves with them as they expanded their control.

DESIGNATION: SENTIENT
HOMEWORLD: RAKATA
AVERAGE HEIGHT: UNKNOWN
PRONUNCIATION: RÄ-KÄ'-TÄ

NOTABLE APPEARANCE: KNIGHTS OF THE OLD REPUBLIC (VIDEO GAME)

RONTO

Rontos are huge, gentle pack animals commonly used as beasts of burden by Jawas on Tatooine. They are known for their loyalty and their strength, and can carry hundreds of kilograms' worth of equipment. Though large enough to frighten off most attackers, including Tusken Raiders, they are also skittish and easily spooked, especially in more congested urban areas.

Rontos are reptiles, much like the native Tatooine dewbacks that are also used as beasts of burden. Like their dewback cousins, they are easy to train and often become quite fond of their masters. They exhibit a superb sense of smell—they can detect a krayt dragon as much as a kilometer

on a regular basis. Rontos, who are easily motivated to track scent—especially when mating is involved—will immediately be attracted to a Rodian if they encounter one. Needless to say, several ronto heads have garnered prize trophies for Rodian hunters upon their return to Rodia.

DESIGNATION: NONSENTIENT
HOMEWORLD: TATOOINE
AVERAGE HEIGHT: 4.25 METERS
PRONUNCIATION: RŎN'-TŌ

NOTABLE APPEARANCE: EPISODE IV: A NEW HOPE (SPECIAL EDITION)

SANDO AQUA MONSTER

A frightening predator, the sando aqua monster is native to the depths of Naboo's core. It is tremendously strong and has an incredible ability to conceal itself, which for many prevented verification of its existence, until one beached itself. Zoologists hypothesize that the sando evolved on land, later moving to an aquatic environment, due to its unique physiology. The sando has gills and webbed hands as would be expected from a sea animal, but the rest of its body and head does not appear to be optimized for life in water. The sando's tail is the exception, as it allows the creature to swim very effectively. The sando's great speed and aggressive nature make it difficult to study, as it will appear suddenly and attack without warning.

A very successful predator, the sando aqua monster dines on other predators of the oceans such as colo claw fish and opee sea killers. It holds victims in its large hands, until the meal is quickly eaten in the monster's powerful jaws. It would seem that a creature of the sando's size would require a great deal of food, but we can surmise that its success at hunting makes the amount it receives sufficient. Sando aqua monsters have been spotted near Otoh Gunga on occasion, and it is rumored that the Caves of Eleuabad host them on a regular basis. Visitors to the Royal Icqui Aquaria on Coruscant are able to see the tooth of one of these beasts, and are said to be chilled by the very thought of seeing one on a live specimen.

DESIGNATION: NONSENTIENT
HOMEWORLD: NABOO
AVERAGE LENGTH: 160 METERS
PRONUNCIATION: SĂN'-DŌ ÄK'-WÄ MÄNS'-TÛR

NOTABLE APPEARANCE: EPISODE I: THE PHANTOM MENACE

away—but because of their poor vision, sudden movement often takes them by surprise. They will rear, throw off any burdens or riders they are carrying, and run for a distance until they feel the threat has passed. Usually they trample over whatever it was that frightened them in their flight.

Rontos need plenty of water, but their thin, leathery skin easily sheds excess heat, allowing them to function well in desert surroundings. Despite their usefulness, they are rarely exported, because offworlders feel their skittishness makes them unreliable.

Even so, rontos are the favorite pack animals of Jawas, who enjoy working with the kindly animals. Sadly, Jawas are often not strong enough to keep a rearing, frightened Ronto in control. In the towns of Tatooine, rampaging rontos are commonplace, as are injured, cursing Jawas who try to keep them calm.

During mating season, female rontos give off a powerful, musky scent. While attractive to male rontos, it is repulsive to most other species, and females in heat have to be isolated. Many have likened it to the scent that Rodians exude

SARKAN

Sarkans are bipedal saurians native to Sarka in the Mid Rim. Tall creatures, they have thick green-scaled hides, yellow eyes with slit pupils, and thick tails. Sarkans have razor-sharp fangs in tapered snouts. Often, they will decorate their claws with multicolored varnish and clan symbols, and wear brightly colored baggy clothes decorated with gemstones. A Sarkan's tail is used for balance and stability, but it can also be used as a weapon by those trained in traditional Sarkan martial arts.

Sarkans speak Sarkese, an intricate mix of words and body gestures. Sarkan diplomats and explorers will learn Basic, but average Sarkans will not—they are not travelers. On the rare occasions when they do leave their planet, they tend to travel in groups of three, a remnant of the time when Sarka was ruled by a strict caste structure. Solitary Sarkans encountered in the galaxy are often outcasts. Other species who interact with Sarkans often find it a trying experience, as Sarkan culture is based on arcane codes of conduct that outsiders are expected to know. Violators are treated as barbarians and physically removed from the presence of high-ranking Sarkans by well-trained bodyguards.

At the height of the Empire, Sarkans reluctantly allowed humans and those who had the Emperor's favor to insult their strict cultural norms as a matter of necessity. As soon as they learned of the Emperor's death, they stopped the practice. As a result, representatives of such major galactic corporations such as SoroSuub find themselves on the outside of Sarkan trade, as they are unable (or unwilling) to speak Sarkese. Once snubbed, it is difficult to impossible to regain entry to their world.

DESIGNATION: SENTIENT
HOMEWORLD: SARKA
AVERAGE HEIGHT: 2 METERS
PRONUNCIATION: SÄR'-KĂN

NOTABLE APPEARANCE: EPISODE IV: A NEW HOPE (SPECIAL EDITION)

SELONIAN

Selonians are furry, bipedal mammals native to Selonia in the Corellian system. They are taller and thinner than most humans, with slightly shorter arms and legs. They have long bodies and are comfortable walking on two legs or four. Retractable claws at the ends of their paw-like hands give them the ability to dig and climb efficiently, while half-meter tails counterbalance their bodies when they are walking upright. Their bodies are covered with glossy short hair that is usually brown or black, and they have long, pointed faces with bristly whiskers and sharp teeth.

Selonians have a matriarchal society, as their population is largely female due to genetic factors, although the ratio of females to males is currently unknown. They are a thoroughly grounded, serious-minded people, primarily concerned about the safety of their family "dens" and their people as a whole. In their society, the needs of the entire group are more important than those of an individual. Because Selonians believe their actions could affect the entire den, they refuse to lie, considering it as terrible a crime as murder.

Select Selonians are trained to deal with humans and other aliens. While Selonians appear outgoing, friendly, and charitable, most have no interests beyond the den. Selonians have mastered shipbuilding technology, constructing ships that they use within their own solar system. Since they have no desire to travel beyond the boundaries of Corellia, their ships do not have hyperdrive capabilities.

DESIGNATION: SENTIENT
HOMEWORLD: SELONIA
AVERAGE HEIGHT: 2 METERS
PRONUNCIATION: SĔL-Ō'-NĒ'ĂN

NOTABLE APPEARANCE: AMBUSH AT CORELLIA (NOVEL)

SHAAK

Shaaks are large, four-legged herbivores native to the grasslands of Naboo. They usually wander the plains freely, with owned herds usually intermingling with the nondomesticated variety. They have thick woolly coats that are shaved at the beginning of the warm season to weave into warm fabrics. As pachyderms, shaaks have thick, leathery skin, and their bodies are plump with blubber. Shaaks serve as the primary source for meat on Naboo, particularly because of their large rumps, which contain half their weight in extra flesh.

Shaak meat can be stored and prepared easily, and giant cooling warehouses on Naboo serve this purpose.

Given their weight, most shaaks avoid wetland areas—they sink easily. Younger shaaks are light enough to swim, and are often seen dousing themselves with water in the cool lakes or mud banks of Naboo. The fatty ambergris that makes the younger shaaks extremely buoyant is used as a base for expensive perfumes for which Naboo has become famous. In addition, their hides are used to make a variety of excellent leather goods.

Shaaks are gentle and plodding, and while they are sometimes used as pack animals, they do not usually serve as mounts. When they do serve as mounts, they must frequently rest since they are not generally strong enough to carry passengers.

DESIGNATION: NONSENTIENT
HOMEWORLD: NABOO
AVERAGE HEIGHT: 1.5 METERS
PRONUNCIATION: SHĂK

NOTABLE APPEARANCE: EPISODE II: ATTACK OF THE CLONES

SHAWDA UBB

The Shawda Ubb are a squat, green-skinned, potbellied amphibian species native to the planet Manpha, which is located in the Outer Rim. Their spherical bodies are accentuated by twiggy arms and legs, which have three digits apiece. They have small heads, and their faces are topped by heavy brow ridges. A thin row of bumps runs from their foreheads down their necks. Like the Quarren and other water-born species, the Shawda Ubb need to remain moist to keep their skin from drying and cracking, and in extreme heat conditions they become mostly listless. Though small, members of this species have several inborn defenses, the most notable of which is their ability to spit a poison that will immobilize an opponent for a quarter of a standard hour.

One of the better-known Shawda Ubb is Rapotwanalan-tonee (known by his stage name Rappertunie), who played a native instrument called a growdi, a combination of a water-organ and flute.

DESIGNATION: SENTIENT
HOMEWORLD: MANPHA
AVERAGE HEIGHT: 1 METER
PRONUNCIATION: SHĂ'-DA ŬBB'

NOTABLE APPEARANCE: EPISODE VI: RETURN OF THE JEDI (SPECIAL EDITION)

SHI'IDO

Hailing from the Colonies region planet Lao-man (Sh'shuun in Shi'ido, their native language) Shi'ido are a species rarely seen around the galaxy. In natural form, Shi'ido are roughly humanoid, with large craniums, thick limbs, and no hair. Like Clawdites, they are born with the ability to mimic the form of any species that is approximately the same mass as themselves. Younger members of the species can only manage to take the form of other humanoids. Unlike Clawdites, however, this physical limitation disappears when an individual reaches the age of around 150 years, allowing older Shi'ido to shift and enlarge their shape to mimic more complex beings. If Shi'ido attempt a form that is beyond their normal limits, however, they may be forced to stay in that form until their body can recover, which can be several weeks.

Shi'ido physiology is extremely flexible. Their thin bones are very dense, allowing support even in the most awkward mass configurations. Their physiology includes a series of tendons that can release and reattach themselves in different formations. They also have a great deal of hidden fleshy mass that they can access and use to enlarge their shapes. Shi'ido transformations are made complete by the use of telepathic suggestions imposed upon viewers, painting the image of what they want the observers to see in their minds. This helps cover over any inaccuracies in the Shi'ido's transformation, but it is extremely difficult to maintain. Older Shi'ido have more mastery over this talent.

Shi'ido are a long-lived species: some of the oldest members of the race are five hundred standard years old. For this reason, they've developed an acute interest in learning about the universe and all the people in it—learning something new makes traveling from their solitary world worthwhile.

DESIGNATION: SENTIENT
HOMEWORLD: LAO-MAN (SH'SHUUN)
AVERAGE HEIGHT: 1.8 METERS
PRONUNCIATION: SHĒ-Ē'-DŌ

NOTABLE APPEARANCE: GALAXY OF FEAR (NOVEL)

SKAKOAN

Skakoans are mammalian humanoids native to the highly pressurized, methane-atmosphere world of Skako in the Core World region. This world is a teeming metropolis much like Coruscant, though its architecture is not as aesthetically pleasing. Visitors to Skako must wear a special pressure suit

tainment units of the medium- and heavy-pressure suits are not. Methane cells are located within the containment unit, and connect to the faceplate via alloy encased tubing. All the suits are fitted with a vocalizer that allows a Skakoan to be heard, but the result is a very distorted speech pattern. Skakoan pressure suits are known to come with certain dangers, primarily that the suits will explode if punctured. Due to the methane gas the suit contains for the Skakoan to breathe, such an explosion can cause a great deal of damage to the surrounding area and anyone in the vicinity. As a fail-safe, however, all Skakoan pressure suits are self-repairing to prevent ruptures. Skakoan pressure suits are only manufactured on Skako, as the Skakoans will not trust their production to offworlders.

Skakoans rarely leave their homeworld, fearing an accidental death from suit depressurization. When they are seen offworld, it is a demonstration of the strength of their belief in their undertaking. Because Skakoans are usually encountered in their pressure suits, other peoples rarely if ever see physical manifestations of their emotional reactions, such as body language and facial expressions. This leads to the misconception that they are passionless robots. In fact, their emotions are the one thing that truly controls them; in particular, their hatred and xenophobia keep them in virtual isolation from the galaxy at large.

Skakoans are shrewd, manipulative, severe beings bent on self-preservation at all costs. They are supremely logical, expending most of their creative energy on scientific and engineering endeavors. Any other problems they face are met with logical, calculated solutions. They are so engineering-minded that they speak in a formulaic machine language called Skakoverbal, which is similar to Bocce and also contains elements of Binary. Their written language is called Skakoform; it is often mistaken for engineering schematics or circuit diagrams.

The Skakoan people are known for their technological and engineering prowess, though they have not been a part of the galactic trade scene since the time of the Old Republic. During that period, they were the principal members of the Techno Union, a galaxywide association of megacorporations that had representation in the Galactic Senate. The Techno Union met its end when it joined the Separatist movement led by Count Dooku. It was expelled from the Senate at that time, and the Skakoan government decided to leave the Republic as well. Through the Clone Wars, Skakoan technology was pivotal, but when the Empire rose, the Techno Union and its nonhuman leaders were crushed. The Techno Union's member companies were put under Imperial control and the Skakoans returned to their world, angry and spiteful toward the humans who'd spawned the new galactic government. When the Empire fell and the New Republic was born, the Skakoans did lit-

to survive because of the harsh environment there. Likewise, a Skakoan must wear a pressure suit to survive offplanet. Skakoans cannot breathe oxygen or survive in the standard air pressure of most planets, but they are acclimated to most high-pressure worlds. As a result, few outsiders have seen what a Skakoan really looks like. However, some exobiologists have discovered, from obtained research specimens, that under their pressure suits Skakoans look like gaunt humans, with folds of grayish white skin draped over slight skeletons. Their faces are sunken with leering eyes, a flattened nose, and a toothless, scowling mouth.

Skakoans wear three varieties of pressure suits, depending on their work or the outer environment they must visit. Generally, a Skakoan pressure suit consists of two pieces: a full-body membrane layer (including a head carapace), and a durasteel containment unit for the face, neck, and torso. The membrane layer is flexible, but the required durasteel con-

tle to leave their seclusion. Having little trust for humans, they rejected any overtures the New Republic made to encourage them to return to galactic society. They also flatly refused to share any new technological advancements they'd made with the business community.

DESIGNATION: SENTIENT
HOMEWORLD: SKAKO
AVERAGE HEIGHT: 1.75 METERS
PRONUNCIATION: SKĂ-KŌ'-ĂN

NOTABLE APPEARANCE: EPISODE II: ATTACK OF THE CLONES

SKRILLING

Originally nomadic herders, the Skrillings of Agriworld-2079 on the spinward edge of the Mid Rim are stocky humanoids with wrinkled gray skin, stubby fingers, and deep-set eyes. They have multiple rows of needle-like teeth and a bony crest starting at the top of their bald heads, descending to the napes of their necks. Skrillings do not have nostrils, instead breathing through a series of eight tubes that vertically line the fronts of their faces. Skrillings are slow-witted, sulky, greedy scavengers. Most are bright enough, however, to know when they have pestered another being to the point of violence and will at least temporarily leave that person alone.

Skrillings are typically avoided by other sentient species for their unusual habits, most of which violate the galactic norm for civilized beings. They are known, for instance, for stealing battlefield corpses, with an unusual talent for appearing on worlds where battles have been fought and unclaimed bodies can be found. They are regarded as whiners who feed on carrion and uncooked, spoiled meat that would make other beings deathly sick. If Skrillings have decided they want something, they will repeatedly and unceasingly request the item from its owner, even following that individual to other worlds and star systems to obtain the object of their desire. However, this behavior is in fact the result of oppression. When the M'shinni colonized the Skrilling homeworld, they fenced in the Skrilling herds and claimed their lands, leaving Skrillings desperate for a way to survive. They managed to integrate themselves into M'shinni colonies as beggars.

Skrillings now travel the galaxy in starships they piece together from derelicts. They can often be found among criminal organizations and on planets of tyrants—which so often provide reliable supplies of corpses and carrion—although

many were valuable spies for the Rebel Alliance during the Galactic Civil War, passing unnoticed to gather information.

DESIGNATION: SENTIENT
HOMEWORLD: AGRIWORLD-2079
AVERAGE HEIGHT: 1.7 METERS
PRONUNCIATION: SKRĬ'-LĬNG

NOTABLE APPEARANCE: EPISODE VI: RETURN OF THE JEDI

SPACE SLUG

Space slugs are large, toothed, silicon-based gastropods that survive in the cold vacuum of space, feeding on stellar energy emissions, minerals from asteroids, and small vacuum-breathing creatures such as mynocks. They primarily inhabit asteroid fields, where food is plentiful. Most space slugs measure less than ten meters in length, although they have been reputed to grow large enough to swallow small spaceships whole. In cases such as this, the mynocks they swallow are more likely to become internal parasites, rather than nourishment.

These creatures have a highly developed, genetically endowed spatial sense that allows them to calculate the trajectory and speed of every moving body in their area. This primal sense helps them to target food and to move between planetary bodies.

Like most gastropods, space slugs reproduce asexually. They will carry the young for a few months, then give birth. The newborn slug inherently knows how to survive on its own, and will leave the parent to seek out its own life.

Space slugs are prized by sentients for their organs and body parts, which industrial manufacturers use to produce special lubricants and fibers. Some space stations and shipyards also keep space slugs on hand to reduce the mynock population, though their size is carefully regulated.

DESIGNATION: NONSENTIENT
HOMEWORLD: HOTH ASTEROID BELT
AVERAGE LENGTH: 10 METERS
PRONUNCIATION: SPĀS' SLŬG

NOTABLE APPEARANCE: EPISODE V: THE EMPIRE STRIKES BACK

SWAMP SLUG/ NOS MONSTER

The giant swamp slug of the planet Dagobah in the Outer Rim is a gastropod that eats nearly anything it can pull into its wide, lipless mouth, animal or vegetable. Growing to a maximum length of eight meters from head to toe, this beast uses its size as a key natural defense. It has six small legs that enable it to move along the bottom of swamps, rivers, and lakes. Its large, orange eyes can see clearly beneath the murky waters, while two antennae on the top of its head act as sonar, sending signals around the creature's body to determine its distance from the bottom and banks.

These creatures possess a minimal number of vital organs, making it difficult to kill them. As a result, swamp slugs do not fear many predators, and enjoy their position at the top of the Dagobah food chain. Their only two concerns are feeding and reproducing.

Like most gastropods, the swamp slug is a hermaphrodite, and it reproduces without external fertilization. The creature will simply become pregnant and bear a child, which is born completely aware of how to survive. Although it can survive on its own, the baby swamp slug will usually stay with its mother for several months while it gets accustomed to its environment.

Because swamp slugs can eat practically anything, they have no trouble finding food. Anything pulled into a slug's maw is pulverized into digestible pieces by the thousands of tiny grinding teeth that line its throat.

Swamp slugs are closely related to nos monsters, an aquatic monster from the Utapaun depths. These beasts live in low-light to pitch-black grottoes, where their eyes have adapted to the conditions. They are fascinated by any lighted object that passes nearby. Capable swimmers and surprisingly fast on land, they are typically able to catch what interests them.

DESIGNATION: NONSENTIENT
HOMEWORLD: DAGOBAH / UTAPAU
AVERAGE LENGTH: 8 METERS
PRONUNCIATION: NŌS-MŎN'STĔR

NOTABLE APPEARANCE: EPISODE V: THE EMPIRE STRIKES BACK AND EPISODE III: REVENGE OF THE SITH

TIN-TIN DWARF (TINTINNA)

Tin-Tin Dwarfs are actually known formally as the Tintinna, a species from the little-known, rarely visited, primitive Outer Rim world of Rinn. They are a rodent-like species very similar to Ranats, and are considered to be distant relatives.

Unlike their cousins, whose incisors emerge from their bottom jaw, the Tintinna have simple, small, rodent incisors that emerge from the tops of their mouths. They have black, mouse-like eyes, small round ears, and soft brown fur. Small pink paws sport nimble digits, and they look, simply, like giant mice. Because of their environment, they often give off a pleasant, wood-chip smell.

Tintinna live in underground burrows that they dig out without the benefit of tools. They line their earthen homes with wood chips, leaves, and other natural materials that serve to keep them warm and dry. They chew the wood for this purpose, as well as to wear down their teeth, which otherwise may grow to uncomfortable lengths.

Because their planet is remote, Tin-Tin Dwarfs are rarely seen off their homeworld. Traders and smugglers use Rinn as a backwater hiding place, so some Tintinna have been known to befriend spacers and hitch rides offworld. This is an easygoing, pleasant, and curious species, always looking to learn new things about the universe. Tintinna are quick learners, and when exposed to technology, they begin to understand it almost immediately. Spacers have therefore found them useful as teammates and lookouts, because of their highly sensitive rodent hearing and eyesight.

DESIGNATION: SENTIENT
HOMEWORLD: RINN
AVERAGE HEIGHT: 1 METER
PRONUNCIATION: TĬN'-TĬN DWÄRF (TĬN-TĬN'-Ä)

NOTABLE APPEARANCE: STAR WARS EPISODE IV: A NEW HOPE (RADIO DRAMA, BBC)

TROIG

Troigs are a two-headed humanoid species native to Pollillus in the Vannell planetary system beyond the Koornacht Cluster of the Deep Core. Each head is capable of thought and speech, so it is most accurate to consider Troigs as two individuals who share a body. Troigs have four arms, two of which are controlled by each head. They have a primary hand and three off-hands. As such, they lack coordination unless the heads work together. In contrast, the personality and sense of identity of a Troig is a somewhat coordinated effort. The left head and identity is the Saprah (the source of "blood humors," or strong emotions such as love, anger, and passion), while the right head and identity is the Saprin (the source of "breath humors," or loyalty, faith, and cunning). The identities look out for each other, so they are not often caught unawares. Most Troigs have two heads, although when the rare Troig is born with more than two, it is a cause for celebration.

The names of each head of a Troig are said together on Pollillus (*FodesinBeed,* for example), but are commonly split by offworlders (*Fode* and *Beed*).

The concept of two individuals sharing a body has long been the subject of debate in the medical and ethical communities. During the years of the Empire, a Troig named DwuirsinTabb raised a controversy regarding what to do when the health of one threatens the other. Dwuir sought to be separated from Tabb, who was described as mentally disturbed and suicidal. As Troig technology at the time did not permit this, the Troigs appealed for assistance offworld. The ethical implications of the surgery were complex—it would have resulted in the death of one of the heads. There is no record that a surgery was ever performed, and the whereabouts of DwuirsinTabb are unknown.

DESIGNATION: SENTIENT
HOMEWORLD: POLLILLUS
AVERAGE HEIGHT: 2 METERS
PRONUNCIATION: TROIG

NOTABLE APPEARANCE: EPISODE I: THE PHANTOM MENACE

UMBARAN

The Umbarans are quiet, pale humanoids from the world of Umbara in the Ghost Nebula, one of the gloomiest systems tucked away in the farthest reaches of the galaxy. Their pale skin coloration is due to the world's limited sunlight. Their sunken eyes are also sensitive to bright illumination because of their world's eternal twilight.

Umbarans have been a political presence from the earliest years of the Old Republic, and yet they are never seen in great numbers. Their specter-like visages haunted the galactic political scene for generations. They have long been objects of fear and suspicion because of their subtle ability to influence others.

Umbaran society is built on a finely detailed caste system of nearly a hundred levels, and only those of the top ten castes are allowed to leave their world. Umbarans bear and raise their children as humans do for the most part, though from early childhood they are schooled in the ways of politics and intrigue to gain prestige among their class, with the hope of rising into the next class. Moving between caste levels is possible because they are so numerous; it is the ultimate ambition of every Umbaran. Through spying, political maneuvering, blackmail, subterfuge, and cool assassination, they move themselves from level to level. Umbarans of the

highest caste are considered royalty (called Rootai), and they form a council that rules their world.

When a plot to move up in societal rank fails, however, the result can be devastating for individual Umbarans and their families. If, for instance, Umbarans attempt assassination and fail, they are imprisoned, and their family is dropped to one of the lowest caste levels. Depending on the rank of the individual they tried to kill, they may end up with a death sentence for themselves, and perhaps for their entire family.

As harsh as this may sound, assassination is attempted quite often because most Umbarans feel the attempt is worth the risk. Those able to kill and replace a high-ranking Umbaran are well rewarded with prestige for themselves and their families. If they fail and die, it is still better than dropping to the lowest of castes—which, to most Umbarans, is a fate worse than death.

When Umbarans attempt assassination, they prefer to do it through sly, hidden means. Attempting murder with such messy weapons as blasters or vibroblades is considered completely lacking in refinement. Umbarans will use more subtle, elegant means to kill someone, such as microscopic poison darts, nanotechnology, undetectable poisons, and small, stylish stiletto-like knives called vootkar. Umbarans will also wear, when spying or making such attacks, a special garment known as a shadowcloak that uses special sensors allowing wearers to blend in with their surroundings, making them virtually undetectable to those with normal vision.

During the rise of the Empire, Umbarans used their influence to secure favor with the new government. The Emperor found them extremely useful in carrying out his Jedi Purge, for Umbaran spies were skilled in tracking down Jedi in hiding. They were also good at weeding out Imperial officers who were out for their own agendas rather than those of their superiors. The Emperor chose an Umbaran to be one of his own top aides, finding Umbaran secrecy beneficial when hatching his plots. When the Rebellion became a threat, they were excellent at exposing Rebel sympathizers in the Senate and other levels of government.

When the Emperor was killed, Umbarans retreated quickly to their homeworld, fearing reprisals from members of the Alliance and the Imperial Remnant. Since the formation of the New Republic, they have rarely, if ever, made forays into galactic society, and galactic society prefers it that way. They are enigmatic, scheming, and unreadable beings who only desire power and prestige. Masterful at confusing and mystifying others, they never make known to others their agendas. Most Umbarans have a dark, cruel sense of humor—they enjoy seeing their victims bewildered, perplexed, or demoralized.

There is a great deal of debate as to whether Umbarans' ability to influence others is tied to some Force mind control ability, or if they are just really talented communicators. Since they are secretive, shunning any close ties with outsiders, in-depth study of this issue has been impossible.

Rumors abound of Umbarans taking control of, and/or becoming influential in, major underworld crime syndicates including the Black Sun and others. It's been suggested that they have offered their services to smugglers, influential corporations, mercenary organizations, pirates, and other nefarious persons and institutions. Their key motivation, of course, is power. Umbaran spies have also been noticed slinking around the many levels of Coruscant, no doubt keeping a discerning eye on galactic politics. Whether they will attempt a return to the Senate halls is anyone's guess, though they may wait a good long while in the hope that their reputation as conniving backstabbers fades with the passage of time.

DESIGNATION: SENTIENT
HOMEWORLD: UMBARA
AVERAGE HEIGHT: 1.8 METERS
PRONUNCIATION: ŎŎM-BÄR'-ĂN

NOTABLE APPEARANCE: EPISODE II: ATTACK OF THE CLONES

VRATIX

The Vratix are a highly intelligent insectoid species native to the world Thyferra in the Inner Rim. They are the creators of the miraculous healing substance known as bacta. Tall beings with greenish gray skin and black bulbous eyes, they stand upright on four slender legs—two long and two short. Triple-jointed arms extend from their shoulders, ending in long, three-fingered hands. At their elbow joints they have sharp spikes, which are often used in hand-to-hand combat. Two skinny, floppy antennae on their small heads give them very acute hearing. A thin, long neck connects the head to their scaly torsos. Vratix reproduce asexually.

Vratix excrete a chemical called denin that changes the color of their skin as an expression of emotion. This coloration is connected to their language, which is expressed in high-pitched voices, punctuated by clicking sounds. Because of their continuous trade relationship with other races, Vratix can speak and comprehend Basic. They also possess limited telepathic ability, allowing them to share thoughts with fellow Vratix whom they know well.

Bacta is a translucent solution of alazhi and kavam bacterial particles exuded from the skin of the Vratix themselves. Combined with a liquid called ambori, the solution acts like

a body's own vital fluids to heal all but the most serious of wounds. Bacterial particles actually seek out the injuries and promote amazingly quick tissue growth without scarring.

Vratix culture centers on a type of hive mentality, and single Vratix usually refer to themselves with their hive name. They also use the plural when referring to themselves—preferring *we* to *I*, for example.

Like most worker insects, the Vratix are a very practical people. All industry and creative effort goes into producing items for everyday use. The concepts of art, music, and other forms of creative expression elude their understanding. They are very calculating, examining problems from every angle before proceeding toward a solution. They are somewhat detached from their emotions, and while they are natural healers, they see the practice of medicine as a mechanical or biological practice rather than one of compassion.

DESIGNATION: SENTIENT
HOMEWORLD: THYFERRA
AVERAGE HEIGHT: 1.8 METERS
PRONUNCIATION: VRĀ'-TĬX

NOTABLE APPEARANCE: X-WING ROGUE SQUADRON: THE BACTA WAR (NOVEL)

VULPTEREEN

The natives of the Deep Core planet Vultper are thick, barrel-chested, carnivorous reptiles with six tusk-like growths protruding from their long, tapering snouts. At the top of their heads, two pointed ears jut straight upward. They also have yellow-green eyes with snake-like black pupils that enable them to see in low-light conditions, but with poor depth perception. As a result, they use echolocation to sense where they are. Their two arms end in clawed hands, the amputation of which, uniquely, due to their lack of a central brain, will cause aphasia. They are otherwise very dexterous and hardy, considering that they are constantly subject to toxic environmental conditions. These traits give Vulptereens some degree of success at Podracing, a natural endeavor, as the planet is home to one of the galaxy's largest Podracer production facilities.

Although Vulpter was once a beautiful world of grasslands, forests, and other environments, it became a polluted wasteland during the Old Republic, the product of overindustrialization and exploitation at the hands of the Trade Federation. The world was for decades the dumping ground of the Federation, which saw the planet as only a factory and its inhabitants as inferior. One city was inhabitable for every five, there were no surface animals left, and the residents suffered from diseases caused by the toxic air they breathed and water they drank. Instead of leaving, however, Vulptereens held on to the world they called home.

The planet was considered so insignificant it was often left off star charts, first by the Trade Federation and then the Empire. After it came to power, the Empire blockaded the planet, not considering it worthy of even food shipments, causing widespread rioting and famines. However, the Rebel Alliance used the world as a safe haven and, after the Galactic Civil War, began successful reclamation efforts.

DESIGNATION: SENTIENT
HOMEWORLD: VULPTER
AVERAGE HEIGHT: 1 METER
PRONUNCIATION: VŬLP'-TĔ-RĒN

NOTABLE APPEARANCE: EPISODE I: THE PHANTOM MENACE

VURK

Vurks are nomadic, amphibious reptomammals native to the isolated planet Sembla in the Outer Rim, near the Tion Hegemony. Tall bipedal humanoids, they have a large, upswept headcrest that comes to a blunt, thin, tapered end above two deep-set dark eyes. Two arms end in large, three-fingered hands; their skin is a leathery gray-green. As befitting amphibious beings, female Vurks give birth underwater, and midwives are venerated in their culture for the service they provide.

As a planet, Sembla is in transition and has not yet been the subject of much study. Its warm seas are divided by volcanic ridges that are still slowly forming continents. Perhaps because their planet is still evolving, as a species Vurks are seen as doing the same. This world does not have heavy industry, and the species did not develop space travel on its own. Generally, Vurks are considered primitive by the rest of the galaxy, but this is inaccurate. The Vurks are highly intelligent and have a well-developed philosophical tradition that respects individual freedom, places a premium on integrity, and encourages self-reflective honesty about oneself. A Vurk will behave consistently with these beliefs in all matters. Given their calm, compassionate nature, Vurks are thus skilled diplomats and negotiators.

This is not to say they will not defend themselves. Vurks are worthy opponents—they see protecting themselves and their charges as extensions of personal integrity. In fact, a Vurk Jedi served the Old Republic.

And Sembla remains today much as it was during that time. Not receiving much attention on a galactic scale and being off most trade routes, it escaped the invasion of the Yuuzhan Vong. It had not sent sufficient numbers into the galaxy at large to be asked to join the New Republic or the Galactic Federation of Free Alliances.

DESIGNATION: SENTIENT
HOMEWORLD: SEMBLA
AVERAGE HEIGHT: 2.1 METERS
PRONUNCIATION: VŪRK

NOTABLE APPEARANCE: EPISODE II: ATTACK OF THE CLONES

WOMP RAT

Womp rats are a carnivorous, ill-tempered, and plentiful rodent species native to the desert world of Tatooine. There are a couple of different varieties of these creatures, but for the most part they all exhibit the same features. Depending on the breed, womp rats can grow to be upward of three meters long, and they frequently travel in packs to overwhelm their prey—which includes dewbacks and banthas. They primarily live in the caves of Beggar's Canyon and the Jundland Wastes.

Like most rodents, womp rats possess keen eyesight, hearing, and smell. Their fur is usually brown, tan, or gray, and their orange eyes refract sunlight. Womp rats have sharp claws and teeth that can easily slice through flesh, enabling them to kill and eat just about any creature they encounter. Their long, narrow tails are quite strong, and can be used to whip around their prey's legs to drag it off its feet. A ridge of spiky, dark fur forms a line down the length of their spines. They reproduce at an alarming rate in broods of sixteen or more at a time.

The most common womp rat is the variety that lives in the Beggar's Canyon region of Tatooine. These usually grow no larger than two meters, but are well known for attacking Jawas and raiding the storehouses of moisture farmers in the region. Another variety, larger than the Beggar's Canyon type, is sometimes called the mutant womp rat. Mutant womp rats are found in the Jundland Wastes, and are known for the long, wing-like ears growing from their heads. These creatures appeared mysteriously a short time after the Empire came to Tatooine, and rumors persist that they evolved from Beggar's Canyon rats that raided caustic substances in Imperial waste dumps. They are not as numerous, and do not reproduce as often as the regular Beggar's Canyon womp rats.

DESIGNATION: NONSENTIENT
HOMEWORLD: TATOOINE
AVERAGE LENGTH: 2 METERS
PRONUNCIATION: WŎMP' RĂT

NOTABLE APPEARANCE: EPISODE IV: A NEW HOPE

YODA'S SPECIES

Very little is known about this species. Exhaustive research by several groups of investigators has been unable to locate a homeworld for this species, or even more than three individual members. And yet the contributions of those three individuals have earned them mention here. Unfortunately, most of what we know is sketchy at best, leaving much room for conjecture. What we do know is that each of the three was a Jedi Master. While they may not typify their species and there is no firm evidence to indicate that every member of the species is Force-sensitive, it is a considerable fact that must be mentioned.

This unnamed bipedal humanoid species is typified by a short stature, large pointed ears, and mottled green-toned skin. They have three gnarled fingers (one opposing) on each of two hands, as well as five-toed feet, with three toes in front and two in back. Two males and a female have been observed. Although they have hair, it is wispy for the males and thins as they age. Life span is unknown, but records indicate that they are extraordinarily long-lived. Jedi Grand Master Yoda is said to have been nine hundred standard years old at the time of his death, and Master Yaddle lived for more than four hundred years. The first recorded member of this species is Master Vandar, a Jedi Master four thousand years before the Battle of Yavin, but records could not be found confirming his age. This species was well known for its members' wisdom, deliberation, and compassion, as well as their mirthful sense of humor. However, they were also known for their strange tastes in food, often consuming meals that others could not even bear to smell.

DESIGNATION: SENTIENT
HOMEWORLD: UNKNOWN
AVERAGE HEIGHT: 66 CENTIMETERS
PRONUNCIATION: UNKNOWN

NOTABLE APPEARANCE: EPISODE VI: THE EMPIRE STRIKES BACK

YUZZUM

The Yuzzum of Endor, not to be confused with the Yuzzem of Ragna III, are an intelligent yet primitive species with round, fur-covered bodies, long, thin legs, and wide mouths that show protruding teeth. They often travel in groups, hunting down ruggers—the rodents that are their primary source of food.

Yuzzum actually vary widely in appearance. Some have sharp fangs, while others have blunt teeth. Some have thick, woolly coats; others, short fur. Hence, the term *Yuzzum* actually refers to a class of migratory, fur-bearing mammals on Endor. Developmentally they are at the same level as their diminutive Ewok neighbors, defending themselves from predators and outsiders with spears and other primitive weapons. Their livelihood depends upon their large size, which often intimidates predators and even drives them away.

The Yuzzum people communicate in a language made up of musical elements, and it is sung rather than spoken. For this reason, their voices retain a gravelly tone, and many

Yuzzum are hailed as excellent singers. Those Yuzzum who have managed to leave Endor—very few ever really do—often end up singing for their suppers.

DESIGNATION: SENTIENT
HOMEWORLD: MOON OF ENDOR
AVERAGE HEIGHT: 2.5 METERS
PRONUNCIATION: YŬZ'-ZŬM

NOTABLE APPEARANCE: EPISODE VI: RETURN OF THE JEDI (SPECIAL EDITION)

ZELTRON

The extremely attractive Zeltrons are a somewhat near-human species native to the planet Zeltros, located on the edge of the Outer Rim and Unknown Regions. While they share some characteristics with humans, Zeltrons, like the Chiss, are now considered a distinct species from humans due to genetic differences. Their skin is bright pink, a special pigmentation that develops from a reaction to their sun's radiation. The Zeltron people have the ability to project powerful pheromones, much like those emitted by Falleen. These can be activated at will and can affect a specific individual or entire groups at the same time. Zeltrons will go to any length to please guests, and they get pleasure from being hospitable, holding massive celebrations for practically any event. They are extremely promiscuous, and extremely proud of their sexuality.

Zeltrons are also empathic, able to sense the feelings of others as well as project their own. For this reason, love and comfort are extremely important to them. Sharing positive emotions is deemed to be to everyone's benefit, while sharing negative emotions is not. In accordance with this, Zeltros's democratic government will go to great lengths to make sure no one on the planet is unhappy. Zeltros has had few tyrants or despotic rulers, because they cannot commit atrocities without experiencing another's pain. Zeltros has, however, been invaded twelve times in the past six centuries. But most invaders, because of Zeltrons' pheromones, have given up their hostile intentions and joined in the nonstop festivities. Hence, Zeltrons don't worry about such trivial matters as planetary defenses or military forces. They are able fighters, though, and they stay in peak physical condition at all times.

Zeltron technology is on par with that of most spacefaring worlds. They are capable of space travel, use advanced agricultural and industrial methods, and enjoy excellent knowledge of medicine, particularly antibiotics. Because of their popularity, and because they spend their lives pursuing gratification, Zeltrons are quite common in the galaxy, particularly at spaceports, where they can find many prospective mates.

DESIGNATION: SENTIENT
HOMEWORLD: ZELTROS
AVERAGE HEIGHT: 1.7 METERS
PRONUNCIATION: ZĔL'-TRŎN

NOTABLE APPEARANCE: STAR WARS #70 (MARVEL COMICS)

APPENDIX 1: PRONUNCIATION GUIDE

The pronunciation of a species' name will vary depending on the accent inherent to the speaker's home planet. The pronunciation guide below lists some key pronunciation symbols used in most standard dictionaries that will guide you in articulating the names of alien species. Note: an apostrophe (') is used after the emphasized syllable in each name.

Vowel sounds:

ă: short *a* sound as in the word *bat* and *act*.

ā: long *a* sound as in the word *age* or *rate*.

ä: open *a* sound used for words like *part, calm,* or *father*. It duplicates the short *o* sound of the word *hot*.

ĕ: short *e* sound used in *edge* or *set*.

ē: long *e* sound used in *equal* or *seat*.

ēr: this vowel sound before *r* may range from ē through ĭ in different dialects.

ĭ: short *i* sound used in *hit* or *pit*.

ī: long *i* sound used in *bite* or *whine*.

ŏ: short *o* sound used in *hot* and *pot*.

oi: a diphthong vowel sound that is a combination of an ō and an ē, such as in the words *boy* and *toy*.

ō: long *o* sound used in *moan* and *tone*.

ōō: long *o* sound used in *toot* and *hoot*.

ô: relatively long *o* used in *order* and *border*.

ŏŏ: short double *o* sound used in *book* and *tour*.

ŭ: the short *u* sound used in *up* and *sum*.

ûr: the *u* sound used in *turn* and *urge*.

Consonants:

kh: a hard *k* pronounced at the back of the throat, such as *loch* or *ach*.

hw: a soft *w* sound used in the words *who* and *what*.

APPENDIX 2: A TIME LINE OF ALIEN HISTORY

As the varied peoples of the galaxies matured and headed for the stars, they charted trade routes, fought wars, made alliances, and established galactic society as it is presently known. This time line of pivotal events in the history of alien species movement and development demonstrates the formation of the panorama of galactic history and culture.

Circa 5,000,000,000 B.B.Y.

The galaxy is formed, many believe, by the gravitational collapse of an immense cloud of dust and gas spanning 1,000,000 light-years, made up of four hundred billion stars. Around half of these have planets that could support some form of life. Ten percent of those developed life, and one in a thousand of these worlds developed sentient life (about twenty million forms of sentient life).

Circa 3,000,000 B.B.Y.

An asteroid strikes Vinsoth, destroying most life on this planet. Surviving species evolve into the Chevin.

Circa 2,000,000 B.B.Y.

Wookiees begin to evolve on Kashyyyk, establishing dominance as climbers of the wroshyr trees.

Circa 57,000 B.B.Y.

Early humanoid settlements are established on Utapau.

Circa 35,000 B.B.Y.

A species known as the Rakata conquers much of the galaxy at the time, forming the "Infinite Empire." Rakata are credited with building Centerpoint Station, and reputedly turn Tatooine into a desert world through their special manipulations.

The ancient Killiks are driven from their homeworld of Alderaan and their colony on Alsakan (presumably by a species known as the Architects). They witness the creation of the Maw in the Corellian system.

Circa 27,500 B.B.Y.

The first human colonists arrive on Alderaan and its surrounding worlds.

Circa 26,000 B.B.Y.

The ancient Nikto discover the M'dweshuu Nova and form a religion called the Cult of M'dweshuu, which dominates the entire culture.

Circa 25,200 B.B.Y.

The Rakatan Empire falls due to a plague that affects only their people and a subsequent rebellion. The Rakata are driven to near-extinction.

Circa 25,100 B.B.Y.

The Klatooinians, Vodrans, and Niktos sign the Treaty of Vontor, binding them to the Hutts as permanent slaves.

The Hutts defeat Xim the Despot and take over his criminal empire.

Corellian scientists perfect their version of the hyperdrive based on the archaic Rakatan Force-powered device.

Circa 25,000 B.B.Y.

Galactic exploration begins on a wider scale, establishing the Perlemian and the Corellian Run trade routes.

A remnant of the Taungs, a militaristic, near-human, gray-skinned race from Coruscant, relocates to Mandalore and renames the world for their leader Mandalore the First—forming the basis for the present human Mandalorian culture.

Under the rule of benevolent Queen Rana, Duros scientists develop interstellar flight. They begin to explore the galaxy and build space cities. They establish a colony on Neimoidia.

Circa 17,000 B.B.Y.

The Arkanians take a sampling of six-armed Xexto to Quermia and, through experimentation, form a new race known as the Quermians.

Circa 15,000 B.B.Y.

The Aqualish (Aquala and Quara) fight a civil war, and an off-world exploratory vessel lands on their world. The two races unite to kill the visitors while taking their ship intact. After learning the secret of starship engineering, they cobble together an armada that leaves their star system to conquer other systems. They are defeated by the New Republic and are demilitarized.

The Hutts co-opt a planet named Evocar in the Y'Toub system, displace its citizens, and rename it Nal Hutta or "Glorious Jewel." They move their entire civilization to this world, abandoning their home world of Varl.

Circa 15,000 B.B.Y.

The Yuuzhan Vong are expelled from their sentient homeworld of Zonama Sekot and cut off from the Force, sending them on a search for a new homeworld and motivating their goals of conquest.

Circa 10,000 B.B.Y.

The Gran begin their recorded history.

Solar flares destroy most of the plant life on Kubindi, causing the (then) herbivorous Kubaz to feed on insects to survive, and launching their focus on insect farming and cuisine as a species trait.

8,000 B.B.Y.

The Gran found colonies on Hok and Malastare.

Circa 7,000 B.B.Y.

The Devaronians develop star travel.

Circa 4,500 B.B.Y.

The Barabels of Barab I are embroiled in a civil war that nearly destroys their species. An unknown Jedi mediates a truce that is never broken. The Barabels are consequently eternally indebted to, and respectful of, the Jedi.

Circa 4,030 B.B.Y.

Jedi Master Arca Jeth and a band of Jedi destroy the Lorell Raiders, and the women of the Hapes Cluster, freed from the Raiders' dominance, form a matriarchal society on Hapes.

Circa 3,970 B.B.Y.

The Lorrdians are subjugated by the Argazdans, who forbid them to speak with one another. They create a new language of facial tics, expressions, and hand gestures. They also become well versed in reading body language.

3,670 B.B.Y.

Jedi Knights free the Lorrdians from their slavery at the hands of the Argazdans. The Lorrdians later become very vocal critics of slavery.

Circa 3,500 B.B.Y.

The Iktotchi are discovered by the Republic.

Circa 3,000 B.B.Y.

Pioneer Freia Kallea establishes the Hydian Way hyperspace route, opening up new sectors of the galaxy to exploration and colonization.

Circa 1,500 B.B.Y.

As a means of preventing unending wars between their species and the Quarren, the Mon Calamari attempt a daring social experiment to civilize their opponents. They capture a million Quarren, take one generation of their children, and educate them among the Mon Calamari, making that generation more sympathetic to their enemies. While the experiment works, it creates lasting resentment on the part of the Quarren.

600 B.B.Y.

The first recorded domesticated rancors are reported on Dathomir.

Circa 500 B.B.Y.

Archaeological excavation begins at Polis Massa.

490 B.B.Y.

The Corporate Sector is formed, encompassing dozens of unexplored worlds.

350 B.B.Y.

The Trade Federation is established. Neimoidians serve pivotal roles in its formation and administration.

Circa 300 B.B.Y.

The Techno Union discovers Mustafar.

300 B.B.Y.

The Bothans start to master intelligence gathering, exploiting it for political gain.

The Bith engage in a civil war, destroying their planetary environment. Bith change their culture, repressing their emotions to prevent further wars.

200 B.B.Y.

The Dressellians are discovered by the Bothans, who, upon seeing their potential, leave them to evolve without interference.

120 B.B.Y.

Old Republic scouts come to Elom, and encounter the industrialized but not spacefaring Elomin. They subsequently set up trade and mining operations, which leads to the Elomin's first encounter with the other species on their world, the subterranean Elom.

100 B.B.Y.

The Gungans of Naboo fight off unknown invaders of their world, assembling their first Grand Army.

32 B.B.Y.

The Kaminoans of Kamino, at the behest of Chancellor Palpatine (and secretly Count Dooku), start the process of creating a clone army based on the template of Mandalorian Jango Fett. These clones soon make up the Grand Army of the Republic, serving as the basis for the Clone Wars and later becoming the core of the Imperial Army.

25 B.B.Y.

A group of Yuuzhan Vong land on the obscure planet Bimmiel, and begin surveying the surrounding sectors for the coming invasion.

22–19 B.B.Y.

A Separatist faction arises in the Republic, calling itself the Confederacy of Independent Systems. Forming a droid army that threatens the Republic, the conflict escalates to war, causing chaos and uprisings throughout the galaxy.

20 B.B.Y.

A space battle between a Republic cruiser and a Separatist science vessel named *Gahenna* (carrying a poisonous defoliant developed for the war) contaminates the world Honoghr. The native Noghri suffer in silence for several years as the vegetation on their world dies.

19 B.B.Y.

Palpatine declares himself Emperor, bringing about the rise of High Human Culture: the ideology that humans are inherently superior to aliens. Many aliens find their rights and freedoms restricted or revoked and face prejudice encouraged by the New Order.

The Empire enslaves the Wookiees and bombs their cities. The Trandoshans hunt those who escape the beleaguered world.

Caamas, a peaceful and noble world loved throughout the Empire, is completely ravaged by unknown attackers. Caamasi are relocated to refugee camps, one being Alderaan.

Darth Vader offers environmental aid to the Noghri people on Honoghr in return for their servitude. Vader then orders his staff to further contaminate the world to keep them enslaved.

Senior Anthropologist Hoole exiles himself from his homeworld of Sh'shuun, beginning his most famous studies of other species.

11 B.B.Y.

Imperials discover the planet Maridun, home of the Amanin, and establish bases there. They later take the Amanin for slaves.

10 B.B.Y.

Miners looking for valuable Lowickan firegems in the Lowick asteroid belt discover the Pa'lowick species. Not long afterward, their unique vocal talents become legendary.

9 B.B.Y.

A "death wave" (only the fifth recorded in Chadra-Fan history) occurs on Chad as ocean floor quakes create massive tsunamis. Hundreds of thousands of Chadra-Fan are killed.

7 B.B.Y.

On the planet Falleen, scientists under Darth Vader's orders develop a biological weapon that accidentally infects the Falleen populace. To protect the Empire from the virus, Darth Vader orders a bombardment of the planet. More than two hundred thousand Falleen die.

1–0 B.B.Y.

Mon Mothma issues a Declaration of Rebellion, distributed by holo to thousands of galactic worlds, which openly declare their allegiance to the Alliance. These worlds are quickly suppressed, but the event shines a new light of hope for oppressed species in the galaxy.

0 B.B.Y.

The world Alderaan is destroyed by the Death Star.

Firrerre is destroyed by Hethrir, a student of Vader. The Firrerreo people are either killed or enslaved.

4 A.B.Y.

Anakin Skywalker (Darth Vader) kills Emperor Palpatine ending his rule and persecution of all non-humans.

The Ssi-ruuvi Imperium attacks at Bakura, and is repelled.

7.5 A.B.Y.

Remnants of the Empire release a deadly plague, the Krytos virus, which targets nonhumans on Coruscant.

Rogue Squadron liberates Thyferra from rogue Imperial Admiral Ysanne Isard's control, and freeing up bacta production. The Vratix assume control of bacta production.

9 A.B.Y.

The Noghri pledge their service to the Alliance and help defeat Admiral Thrawn.

16–17 A.B.Y.

The Yevetha threaten the New Republic and are defeated.

19 A.B.Y.

The New Republic discovers that Bothans were involved in the destruction of Caamas.

23–24 A.B.Y.

A radical political movement called the Diversity Alliance is formed, which spouts alien superiority and the genocide of the human species. After an attempt to infect worlds with a plague, the Diversity Alliance is disbanded.

25 A.B.Y.

The Yuuzhan Vong begin their conquest of the galaxy.

The Yuuzhan Vong pull the moon Dobido down upon the world of Sernpidal, killing the famed Wookiee Chewbacca.

The Yuuzhan Vong decimate the garden world of Ithor to eliminate the bafforr trees that weaken Yuuzhan Vong vonduun crab armor.

26 A.B.Y.

The Yuuzhan Vong annihilate Nal Hutta, driving the Hutts from the system. In addition they attack Rodia, Druckenwell, Falleen, and Kalarba in an attempt to cut off the Corellian Run. In the end, they terraform Duro to use it as a launching point to attack the Core Worlds.

27 A.B.Y.

The Yuuzhan Vong conquer Coruscant and begin to terraform the world.

28 A.B.Y.

The New Republic wins a critical battle against Yuuzhan Vong at Ebaq 9, causing the invaders to begin stretching their resources.

The New Republic is restructured. Under a new constitution, the Galactic Federation of Free Alliances (or the Galactic Alliance) is formed, allowing a new federalism that clearly defines the balance of power among the judiciary, the Senate, and the planetary governments.

28.2–28.7 A.B.Y.

The Yuuzhan Vong conquer Barab I, Rutan, and Belderone.

29 A.B.Y.

Mandalorian Supercommandos led by Boba Fett drive the Yuuzhan Vong from the Caluula sector. This further defeat causes the Yuuzhan Vong to retreat to Coruscant in desperation.

35–36 A.B.Y.

Stirred from their obscurity by the arrival of three refugees from the Yuuzhan Vong War, the Killiks begin an expansion into territories decimated in the wake of the Yuuzhan Vong. Absorbing entire peoples into its hive mind, corrupted by a dark Jedi, the Colony threatens to succeed in its conquest where the Yuuzhan Vong failed.

The Killik expansion is repelled, when the core of the Dark Nest, Dark Jedi Lomi Plo, is defeated and Raynar Thul is removed from the hive mind.

BIBLIOGRAPHY

Coruscant and the Core Worlds • Wizards of the Coast, 2003

Agents of Chaos I: Hero's Trial • Star Wars: The New Jedi Order, Book 4, James Luceno, Del Rey Books, 2000

Agents of Chaos II: Jedi Eclipse • Star Wars: The New Jedi Order, Book 5, James Luceno, Del Rey Books, 2000

Alien Anthology • Wizards of the Coast, 2001

Alien Encounters: The Star Wars Aliens Compendium • Paul Sudlow et al., West End Games, 1998

Ambush at Corellia • Star Wars: The Corellian Trilogy, Book 1, Roger MacBride Allen, Bantam Books, 1995

Anakin • one-shot comic, Dark Horse Comics, 1999

The Art of Star Wars Episode I: The Phantom Menace • Jonathan Bresman, Del Rey Books, 1999

Assault at Selonia • Star Wars: The Corellian Trilogy, Book 2, Roger MacBride Allen, Bantam Books, 1995

The Bacta War • Star Wars: X-Wing, Book 4, Michael A. Stackpole, Bantam Books, 1997

Balance Point • Star Wars: The New Jedi Order, Book 6, Kathy Tyers, Del Rey Books, 2001

Before the Storm • Star Wars: The Black Fleet Crisis Trilogy, Book 1, Michael P. Kube-McDowell, Bantam Books, 1996

The Cestus Deception • Star Wars: Clone Wars, Steven Barnes, Del Rey Books, 2005

Children of the Jedi • Barbara Hambly, Bantam Books, 1995

Classic Star Wars • twenty-issue series, Archie Goodwin and Al Williamson, Dark Horse Comics, 1992–1994

The Courtship of Princess Leia • Dave Wolverton, Bantam Books, 1994

The Crystal Star, • Vonda McIntyre, Bantam Books, 1995

Dark Apprentice • Star Wars: Jedi Academy, Book 2, Kevin J. Anderson, Bantam Books, 1994

Dark Empire • six-issue series, Tom Veitch, Dark Horse Comics, 1991–1992

Dark Empire Sourcebook • Michael Allen Horne, West End Games, 1993

Dark Force Rising • Star Wars: The Thrawn Trilogy, Book 2, Timothy Zahn, Bantam Books, 1992

Dark Force Rising Sourcebook • Bill Slavicsek, West End Games, 1992

Dark Horse Presents Annual, 1999 • "Luke Skywalker's Walkabout," Phil Norwood, 1999

Dark Journey • Star Wars: The New Jedi Order, Book 10, Elaine Cunningham, Del Rey Books, 2002

Dark Lord: The Rise of Darth Vader • James Luceno, Del Rey Books, 2005

The Dark Rival • Star Wars: Jedi Apprentice, Book 2, Jude Watson, Scholastic, 1999

Dark Tide: Onslaught • Star Wars: The New Jedi Order, Book 2, Mike Stackpole, Del Rey Books, 2000

Dark Tide: Ruin • Star Wars: The New Jedi Order, Book 3, Mike Stackpole, Del Rey Books, 2000

Darksaber • Kevin J. Anderson, Bantam Books, 1995

Destiny's Way • Star Wars: The New Jedi Order, Book 14, Walter Jon Williams, Del Rey Books, 2003

Droids • ongoing series, Dark Horse Comics, 1995

Edge of Victory I: Conquest • Star Wars: The New Jedi Order, Book 7, Greg Keyes, Del Rey Books, 2001

Edge of Victory II: Rebirth • Star Wars: The New Jedi Order, Book 8, Greg Keyes, Del Rey Books, 2001

Empire's End • two-issue series, Tom Veitch, Dark Horse Comics, 1995

Enemy Lines I: Rebel Dream • Star Wars: The New Jedi Order, Book 11, Aaron Allston, Del Rey Books, 2002

Enemy Lines II: Rebel Stand • Star Wars: The New Jedi Order, Book 12, Aaron Allston, Del Rey Books, 2002

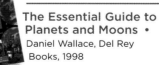

The Essential Guide to Planets and Moons • Daniel Wallace, Del Rey Books, 1998

The Ewok Adventure • "Caravan of Courage," MGM/UA, 1984

The Final Prophecy • Star Wars: The New Jedi Order, Book 18, Greg Keyes, Del Rey Books, 2003

Force Heretic I: Remnant • Star Wars: The New Jedi Order, Book 15, Sean Williams and Shane Dix, Del Rey Books, 2003

Force Heretic II: Refugee • Star Wars: The New Jedi Order, Book 16, Sean Williams and Shane Dix, Del Rey Books, 2003

Force Heretic III: Reunion • Star Wars: The New Jedi Order, Book 17, Sean Williams and Shane Dix, Del Rey Books, 2003

Galaxy Guide 2: Yavin and Bespin • Jonathan Caspian et al., West End Games, 1989

Galaxy Guide 4: Alien Races • Troy Denning, West End Games, 1989

Galaxy Guide 12: Aliens: Enemies and Allies • C. Robert Carey et al., West End Games, 1995

Galaxy of Fear • Books 1–12, John Whitman, Bantam Books, 1997–1999

Geonosis and the Outer Rim Worlds • Wizards of the Coast, 2004

Han Solo and the Corporate Sector Sourcebook • Michael Allen Horne, West End Games, 1993

Han Solo and the Lost Legacy • Star Wars: Han Solo Adventures, Book 3, Brian Daley, Del Rey Books, 1979

Han Solo at Stars' End • Star Wars: Han Solo Adventures, Book 1, Brian Daley, Del Rey Books, 1979

Hard Contact • Star Wars: Republic Commando, Karen Traviss, Del Rey Books, 2004

Hard Merchandise • Star Wars: The Bounty Hunter Wars, Book 2, K. W. Jeter, Bantam Books, 1999

Heir to the Empire • Star Wars: Thrawn Trilogy, Book 1, Timothy Zahn, Bantam Books, 1991; six-issue comics adaptation, Mike Baron, Dark Horse Comics, 1995–1996

Heir to the Empire Sourcebook • Bill Slavicsek, West End Games, 1992

Hero's Guide • Wizards of the Coast, 2003

The Hidden Past • Star Wars: Jedi Apprentice, Book 3, Jude Watson, Scholastic, 1999

The Illustrated Star Wars Universe • Kevin J. Anderson and Ralph McQuarrie, Bantam Books, 1995

The Jedi Academy Sourcebook • Paul Sudlow, West End Games, 1996

Jedi Search • Star Wars: Jedi Academy, Book 1, Kevin J. Anderson, Bantam Books, 1994

Jedi Trial • Star Wars: Clone Wars, David Sherman and Dan Cragg, Del Rey Books, 2004

The Joiner King • Star Wars: Dark Nest, Book 1, Troy Denning Del Rey Books, 2005

The Krytos Trap • Star Wars: X-Wing, Book 3, Michael A. Stackpole, Bantam Books, 1996

Labyrinth of Evil • Star Wars: Episode III Prequel, James Luceno, Del Rey Books, 2005

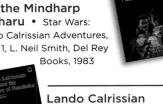

Lando Calrissian and the Mindharp of Sharu • Star Wars: Lando Calrissian Adventures, Book 1, L. Neil Smith, Del Rey Books, 1983

Lando Calrissian and the Starcave of Thonboka • Star Wars: Lando Calrissian Adventures, Book 3, L. Neil Smith, Del Rey Books, 1983

The Last Command • Star Wars: The Thrawn Trilogy, Book 3, Timothy Zahn, Bantam Books, 1993; six-issue comics adaptation, Mike Baron, Dark Horse Comics, 1997–1999

The Last Command Sourcebook • Eric Trautmann, West End Games, 1994

Lightsabers • Star Wars: Young Jedi Knights, Book 4, Kevin J. Anderson and Rebecca Moesta, Berkley Books, 1995

The Joiner King ...

Lyric's World • Star Wars: Junior Jedi Knights, Book 2, Nancy Richardson, Berkley Books, 1995

The Mandalorian Armor • Star Wars: The Bounty Hunter Wars, Book 1, K. W. Jeter, Bantam Books, 1998

Medstar I: Battle Surgeons • Star Wars: Clone Wars, Michael Reaves and Steve Perry, Del Rey Books, 2004

Medstar II: Jedi Healer • Star Wars: Clone Wars, Michael Reaves and Steve Perry, Del Rey Books, 2004

The Movie Trilogy Sourcebook • Greg Farshtey and Bill Smith, West End Games, 1993

The New Essential Chronology • Daniel Wallace, Del Rey Books, 2005

The New Essential Guide to Characters • Daniel Wallace, Del Rey Books, 2002

The New Jedi Order Sourcebook • Wizards of the Coast, 2002

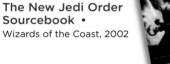

The New Rebellion • Kristine Kathryn Rusch, Bantam Books, 1996

Outbound Flight, • Timothy Zahn, Del Rey Books, 2006

The Paradise Snare • Star Wars: The Han Solo Trilogy, Book 1, A. C. Crispin, Bantam Books, 1997

Planet of Twilight • Barbara Hambly, Bantam Books, 1997

Prophets of the Dark Side • Paul Davids and Hollace Davids, Bantam Books, 1993

Rebel Dawn • Star Wars: The Han Solo Trilogy, Book 3, A. C. Crispin, Bantam Books, 1998

Rogue Planet • Greg Bear, Del Rey Books, 2000

Rogue Squadron • Star Wars: X-Wing, Book 1, Michael A. Stackpole, Bantam Books, 1996

Secrets of Tatooine, • Wizards of the Coast, 2001

Shadows of the Empire • Steve Perry, Bantam Books, 1996; six-issue series, John Wagner et al., Dark Horse Comics, 1996

Shadows of the Empire Sourcebook • Peter Schweighofer, West End Games, 1996

Shatterpoint • Star Wars: Clone Wars, Matthew Woodring Stover, Del Rey Books, 2004

Shield of Lies • Star Wars: The Black Fleet Crisis Trilogy, Book 2, Michael P. Kube-McDowell, Bantam Books, 1996

Showdown at Centerpoint • Star Wars: The Corellian Trilogy, Book 3, Roger MacBride Allen, Bantam Books, 1995

Specter of the Past • Star Wars: Hand of Thrawn, Book 1, Timothy Zahn, Bantam Books, 1997

Splinter of the Mind's Eye • Alan Dean Foster, Del Rey Books, 1978; four-issue series, Terry Austin et al., Dark Horse Comics, 1995–1996

Star by Star • Star Wars: The New Jedi Order, Book 9, Troy Denning, Del Rey Books, 2002

Star Wars • ongoing series, Marvel Comics, 1984–1987

Star Wars • National Public Radio dramatizations, Brian Daley, 1981; published by Del Rey Books, 1994

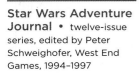

Star Wars Adventure Journal • twelve-issue series, edited by Peter Schweighofer, West End Games, 1994–1997

Star Wars Battlefront • video game, LucasArts Entertainment

Star Wars: Behind the Magic • CD-ROM, LucasArts Entertainment, 1997

Star Wars— Clone Wars • animated, Volume 1, 2003

Star Wars— Clone Wars • animated, Volume 2, 2003

Star Wars Encyclopedia • Steven J. Sansweet, Del Rey Books, 1998

Star Wars Episode I: The Phantom Menace • film, Lucasfilm Ltd., 1999; novelization, Terry Brooks, Del Rey Books, 1999

Star Wars Episode I Insider's Guide • CD-ROM, LucasArts, 1999

Star Wars Episode II: Attack of the Clones • film, Lucasfilm Ltd., 2002; novelization, R. A. Salvatore, Del Rey Books, 2002

Star Wars Episode III: Revenge of the Sith • film, Lucasfilm Ltd., 2005; novelization, Matthew Stover, Del Rey Books, 2005

Star Wars Episode IV: A New Hope • film, Twentieth Century Fox, 1977; novelization, George Lucas, Del Rey Books, 1976

Star Wars Episode V: The Empire Strikes Back • film, Lucasfilm Ltd., 1980; novelization, Donald F. Glut, Del Rey Books, 1980

Star Wars Episode V: The Empire Strikes Back • National Public Radio dramatization, Brian Daley, 1983; published by Del Rey Books, 1985

Star Wars Episode VI: Return of the Jedi • film, Lucasfilm Ltd., 1983; novelization, James Kahn, Del Rey Books, 1983

Star Wars Galaxies • video game, LucasArts Entertainment

Star Wars Jedi Knight: Jedi Academy • video game, LucasArts Entertainment

Star Wars: Knights of the Old Republic • video game, LucasArts Entertainment

Star Wars: Knights of the Old Republic II: The Sith Lords • video game, LucasArts Entertainment

Star Wars Monopoly Game • Parker Brothers, 1996

Star Wars Republic Commando • video game, LucasArts Entertainment

Star Wars: The Roleplaying Game • second edition, Bill Smith, West End Games, 1992

Star Wars Sourcebook • Bill Slavicsek and Curtis Smith, West End Games, 1987

The Swarm War • Star Wars: Dark Nest, Book 3, Troy Denning, Del Rey Books, 2005

Tales from the Mos Eisley Cantina • edited by Kevin J. Anderson, Bantam Books, 1995

Tales of the Bounty Hunters • edited by Kevin J. Anderson, Bantam Books, 1997

Tales of the Jedi • five-issue series, Tom Veitch, Dark Horse Comics, 1993–1994

Tales of the Jedi: Dark Lords of the Sith • six-issue series, Tom Veitch and Kevin J. Anderson, Dark Horse Comics, 1994–1995

Tales of the Jedi: The Freedon Nadd Uprising • two-issue series, Tom Veitch, Dark Horse Comics, 1994–1995

Tales of the Jedi: The Golden Age of the Sith • five-issue series, Kevin J. Anderson, Dark Horse Comics, 1996–1997

Tales of the Jedi: Knights of the Old Republic • five-issue series, Tom Veitch, Dark Horse Comics, 1994

Tales of the Jedi: The Sith War • six-issue series, Kevin J. Anderson, Dark Horse Comics, 1995–1996

Tales of the Jedi Companion • George R. Strayton, West End Games, 1996

Traitor • Star Wars: The New Jedi Order, Book 13, Matthew Woodring Stover, Del Rey Books, 2002

Triple Zero • Star Wars: Republic Commando, Karen Traviss, Del Rey Books, 2006

The Truce at Bakura • Kathy Tyers, Bantam Books, 1993

Tyrant's Test • Star Wars: The Black Fleet Crisis Trilogy, Book 3, Michael P. Kube-McDowell, Bantam Books, 1997

Ultimate Adversaries • Wizards of the Coast, 2004

Ultimate Alien Anthology • Wizards of the Coast, 2003

The Unifying Force • Star Wars: The New Jedi Order, Book 19, James Luceno, Del Rey Books, 2004

The Unseen Queen • Star Wars: Dark Nest, Book 2, Troy Denning, Del Rey Books, 2005

Vader's Fortress • Star Wars: Junior Jedi Knights, Book 5, Rebecca Moesta, Berkley Publishing Group, 1995

Vector Prime • Star Wars: The New Jedi Order, Book 1, R. A. Salvatore, Del Rey Books, 1999

Vision of the Future • Star Wars: Hand of Thrawn, Book 2, Timothy Zahn, Bantam Books, 1998

Wedge's Gamble • Star Wars: X-Wing, Book 2, Michael A. Stackpole, Bantam Books, 1996

The Wildlife of Star Wars: A Field Guide • Terryl Whitlatch and Bob Carrau, Chronicle Books, 2001

X-Wing Rogue Squadron • ongoing series, Dark Horse Comics, 1995–1999

Yoda: Dark Rendezvous • Star Wars: Clone Wars, Sean Stewart, Del Rey Books, 2004

ABOUT THE AUTHORS

PHOTO: © JOSEPH LEWIS

ANN MARGARET LEWIS began her career writing children's stories, comic book stories, and activity books for DC Comics. She has contributed to several media magazines, books, and websites, and is the author of the first *Star Wars: The Essential Guide to Alien Species*. She inhabits a section of our universe known as the Bronx in New York City with her life mate, Joseph Lewis, her toddler offspring, Raymond Allen Lewis, and a member of a feline species whose name is Camille.

PHOTO: © SEAN REISER

HELEN KEIER has had a varied career, including advanced training as a research psychologist and statistician. She currently works as an online learning specialist and technical trainer and writer. Helen has written for several genre and media websites and is a past contributor to *Star Wars Insider,* the official Lucasfilm magazine. She lives in New York City with her son, Vince Skrapits, and two cats, Wedge Antilles and Aurra Sing.

ABOUT THE ILLUSTRATORS

PHOTO: © YUEN HAM

CHRIS TREVAS grew up playing with lightsabers and Wookiees in the suburbs of Detroit, Michigan. He attended the College for Creative Studies before beginning his official *Star Wars* career in 1995. Since then he has created artwork for a multitude of *Star Wars* projects, including books, magazines, games, trading cards, packaging, and toys. Chris is also a writer and illustrator for *Star Wars Insider* magazine. Visit him online at www.christrevas.com.

PHOTO: © WILLIAM O'CONNOR

WILLIAM O'CONNOR was born on Long Island, New York, in 1970. He began studying art formally at the age of ten. After receiving a BFA from Alfred University in 1992, he continued his studies as an illustrator in Manhattan, where he quickly became a familiar face in the gaming and publishing field. Working with clients such as Wizards of the Coast, Hasbro, HarperCollins, AEG, The History Channel, and Doubleday Books, William has created thousands of paintings and drawings for hundreds of projects. The artist now keeps his studio in New Jersey, where he illustrates and paints, and also teaches in his free time. You can visit him at www.wocillo.com.